Alkaline Solutions

a. STOCK 15*N* SODIUM HYDROXIDE NEEDED FOR THE PREPARATION OF 6*N*, 1*N*, AND 0.1*N* SOLUTIONS: Prepare by cautiously dissolving 625 g solid NaOH in 800 ml distilled water to form 1 liter of solution; or 454 g in 650 ml distilled water. Clarify the solution of sodium carbonate precipitate by keeping it at the boiling point for a few hours in a water bath, or by letting the particles settle for at least 48 hr in an alkali-resistant container (wax-lined or polyethylene) protected from atmospheric carbon dioxide with a soda lime tube. Use the supernate for the preparation of the following dilute solutions.

Alternatively, prepare the dilute solutions by dissolving the proper weight of solid NaOH in carbon dioxide-free distilled water and diluting to 1,000 ml.

Table B: Preparation of Uniform Sodium Hydroxide Solutions

Normality of NaOH Solution	Required Weight of NaOH to Prepare 1,000 ml of Solution *g*	Required Volume of 15*N* NaOH to Prepare 1,000 ml of Solution *ml*
6	240	400
1	40	67
0.1	4	6.7

Store the NaOH solutions in polyethylene (rigid, heavy type) bottles with polyethylene screw caps, paraffin-coated bottles with rubber or neoprene stoppers, or pyrex bottles with rubber or neoprene stoppers. Check the solutions periodically to keep abreast of possible carbon dioxide contamination. Protect the solutions by attaching a tube of carbon dioxide-absorbing granular material such as soda lime, Ascarite,* Caroxite,† or equivalent. Use at least 2 ft of rubber tubing to minimize vapor diffusion from the bottle. Replace the absorption tube before it becomes exhausted. Withdraw the solution by a siphon to avoid opening the bottle.

b. AMMONIUM HYDROXIDE CONCENTRATIONS: Prepare 5*N*, 3*N*, and 0.2*N* ammonium hydroxide solutions by diluting 300 ml, 200 ml, and 13 ml, respectively, of the concentrated reagent (sp gr 0.90, 29.0%, 15*N*) to 1 liter with distilled water.

Indicator Solutions

1. *Phenolphthalein indicator solution:* Use either the aqueous *(a)* or alcoholic *(b)* solution.

a) Dissolve 5 g phenolphthalein disodium salt in distilled water and dilute to 1 liter.

b) Dissolve 5 g phenolphthalein in 500 ml 95% ethyl or isopropyl alcohol and add 500 ml distilled water.

If necessary, add 0.02*N* NaOH dropwise until a faint pink color appears in solution *(a)* or *(b)*.

2. *Methyl orange indicator solution:* Dissolve 500 mg methyl orange powder in distilled water and dilute to 1,000 ml.

---

* Fisher Scientific Co.
† A. H. Thomas Co.

STANDARD METHODS

for the Examination of Water and Wastewater

Thirteenth Edition

First Printing, February 1971
Second Printing, August 1971
Third Printing, December 1971

Library of Congress Catalog Card Number: 55–1970

SBN Number: 87553–060–5

Cover design by William J. Fleming

 3

STANDARD METHODS

for the Examination of Water and Wastewater

Thirteenth Edition

Prepared and published jointly by:
American Public Health Association
American Water Works Association
Water Pollution Control Federation

Joint Editorial Board:
Michael J. Taras, AWWA, *Chairman*
Arnold E. Greenberg, APHA
R. D. Hoak and M. C. Rand, WPCF

Publication office:
American Public Health Association
1015 Eighteenth Street, N.W.
Washington, D.C. 20036

PREFACE TO THE THIRTEENTH EDITION

Thirteen editions of *Standard Methods* have been published since 1905. Each effort has enlarged the manual's scope to embrace methods suitable for the examination of many types of water, wastewater, and materials related to the control of sanitation and water quality.

A brief history of *Standard Methods* is of interest because of its contemporary relevance. A movement for "securing the adoption of more uniform and efficient methods of water analysis" led in the 1880's to the organization of a special committee of the Chemical Section of the American Association for the Advancement of Science. A report of this committee, published in 1889, was entitled: A Method, in Part, for the Sanitary Examination of Water, and for the Statement of Results, Offered for General Adoption.* Five topics were covered: (1) "free" and "albuminoid" ammonia; (2) oxygen-consuming capacity; (3) total nitrogen as nitrates and nitrites; (4) nitrogen as nitrites; and (5) statement of results.

In 1895, members of the American Public Health Association, recognizing the need for standard methods in the bacteriologic examination of water, sponsored a convention of bacteriologists to discuss the problem. As a result, an APHA committee was appointed "to draw up procedures for the study of bacteria in a uniform manner and with special references to the differentiation of species." Submitted in 1897,† the procedures found wide acceptance.

In 1899, APHA appointed a Committee on Standard Methods of Water Analysis, charged with the extension of standard procedures to all methods involved in the analysis of water. The report of this committee, published in 1905, constituted the first edition of *Standard Methods* (then entitled *Standard Methods of Water Analysis*). Physical, chemical, microscopic and bacteriologic methods of water examination were included. In its letter of transmittal, the Committee stated:

> The methods of analysis presented in this report as "Standard Methods" are believed to represent the best current practice of American water analysts, and to be generally applicable in connection with the ordinary problems of water purification, sewage disposal and sanitary investigations. Analysts working on widely different problems manifestly cannot use methods which are identical, and special problems obviously require the methods best adapted to them; but, while recognizing these facts, it yet remains true that sound progress in analytical work will advance in proportion to the general adoption of methods which are reliable, uniform and adequate.
>
> It is said by some that standard methods within the field of applied science tend to stifle investigations and that they retard true progress. If such standards are used in the proper spirit, this ought not to be so. The Committee strongly desires that every effort shall be continued to improve the

* *J. Anal. Chem.* 3:398 (1889).

† *Proc. APHA* 23:56 (1897).

techniques of water analysis and especially to compare current methods with those herein recommended, where different, so that the results obtained may be still more accurate and reliable than they are at present.

Revised and enlarged editions were published by APHA under the title *Standard Methods of Water Analysis* in 1912 (second edition), 1917 (third), 1920 (fourth), and 1923 (fifth). In 1925, the American Water Works Association joined APHA in publishing the Sixth Edition, which employed the broader title, *Standard Methods for the Examination of Water and Sewage.* Joint publication was continued in the Seventh Edition, dated 1933.

In 1935, the Water Pollution Control Federation (then the Federation of Sewage Works Associations) issued a committee report, "Standard Methods of Sewage Analysis." * With minor modifications, these methods were incorporated into the Eighth Edition (1936) of *Standard Methods,* which was thus the first to provide methods for the examination of "sewages, effluents, industrial wastes, grossly polluted waters, sludges, and muds." The Ninth Edition, appearing in 1946, likewise contained these methods, and in the following year the Federation became a full-fledged publishing partner. Since 1947, the work of the *Standard Methods* committees of the three associations—APHA, AWWA and WPCF—has been coordinated by a Joint Editorial Board on which all three are represented.

The Tenth Edition, 1955, included specific methods for the examination of waterborne industrial wastes, and this was reflected by the new title: *Standard Methods for the Examination of Water, Sewage and Industrial Wastes.*

In order to describe more accurately and concisely the contents of the Eleventh Edition, the title was compressed to *Standard Methods for the Examination of Water and Wastewater,* which has remained unchanged to this date.

The Thirteenth Edition

In preparing each new edition, the criteria for selecting the analytical procedures to be included have invariably been considered a major topic for discussion. Should *Standard Methods* present only comparatively simple procedures applicable to the control of treatment processes, or should it contain also technics that are useful primarily for special investigations and that may require complex, costly equipment, as well as a high degree of skill and training on the part of the analyst?

An increasing number of larger laboratories have been placing greater reliance on instrumental methods. Concurrent with this trend, recent editions have offered ultraviolet, infrared, and atomic absorption spectrophotometric, spectrographic, gas chromatographic, and selective ion electrode methods. Future editions will doubtless witness an extension of this emphasis.

The need for simple control methods for the operation of treatment facilities has not been overlooked. Accordingly, control procedures are given for each

* *Sewage Works J.* 7:444 (1935).

determination, along with the more complex technics, where available. The distinguishing features, advantages, limitations and applicability of alternative technics for a determination are discussed under the heading "Selection of Method" in each case. Careful study of the introductory material preceding most of the method descriptions will make possible selection of the appropriate technic.

Worthy of note in the Thirteenth Edition has been the reduction from nine to six principal parts, made possible by consolidation of the wastewater methods into a single cohesive entity. The major divisions now comprise:

Part 100—Physical and Chemical Examination of Natural and Treated Waters in the Absence of Gross Pollution
200—Physical, Chemical and Bioassay Examination of Polluted Waters, Wastewaters, Effluents, Bottom Sediments, and Sludges
300—Examination of Water and Wastewater for Radioactivity
400—Bacteriological Examination of Water To Determine Its Sanitary Quality
500—Identification of Iron and Sulfur Bacteria
600—Biological Sampling and Analysis

A new numbering system has been devised for the entire text in order to facilitate cross reference throughout the book. The General Introduction bears three zeroes (Part 000), while the segment concerned with the chemical analysis of water is numbered from 100 to 165, that covering wastewater from 200 to 233, that on radioactivity from 300 to 306, and so on throughout the book. Each major component, such as acidity, alkalinity and aluminum, has been assigned a specific identifying number.

A number of changes occur in Part 100. Colorimetric methods appearing for the first time include the eriochrome cyanine R method for aluminum, the aluminon method for beryllium; the leuco crystal violet method, the methyl orange method, and the stabilized neutral orthotolidine method for residual chlorine; the direct bathocuproine disulfonate method for copper, the phenate method for ammonia, and the gallic acid method for vanadium. The following metals are determinable by the atomic absorption spectrophotometric method: aluminum, barium, beryllium, cadmium, chromium, iron, lead, magnesium, manganese, silver and zinc. Other instrumental methods introduced in this volume are the gas chromatographic method for chlorinated hydrocarbon pesticides, the electrode method for fluoride, the combustion-infrared method for total organic carbon, and the nephelometric method for turbidity. A low-flow carbon adsorption method for organic contaminants has been added to the previous high-flow method. The ferrous diethyl-*p*-phenylenediamine method for residual chlorine displaces the former orthotolidine version. The determination of taste has been divorced from that of odor and is offered as an independent section. The segment entitled "Examination of Industrial Water Supplies" in the Introduction of Part 100 has been extensively revised.

Meriting mention also are an ion-exchange modification for high-hardness and wastewater-effluent samples in the curcumin method for boron; the admissibility of trichlorotrifluoroethane solvent in the oil and grease determination; and the presentation of all current National Bureau of Standards buffer solutions for the determination of pH in both water and wastewater samples. Elevated to standard status is the methylene blue method for surfactants and methylene blue-active substances. Deleted from this edition are the aluminon method for aluminum, the flash orthotolidine qualitative method for residual chlorine, the preliminary steam distillation step for fluoride, the alizarin photometric method for fluoride, the orthotolidine colorimetric method for manganese, the polarographic method for nitrate, the distillation-colored sol method for selenium, and the polarographic method for zinc.

Duplication has been diminished in Parts 100 and 200 by concentrating the principal text for similar procedures in one write-up, with important specific modifications described in the related water and wastewater sections. Prominent in this regard are the chloride, methane, nitrate, ammonia and organic nitrogen, and phosphate write-ups.

The following changes are worthy of notice in Part 200. Consolidation of the formerly separate sections dealing with polluted waters, industrial wastes, and sediments has eliminated considerable duplication of methods. In the combined descriptions of methods, care has been exercised to indicate under the heading, "Selection of Methods," the applications and limitations of each technic so far as these have been established experimentally. New technics of sample pretreatment are presented which permit the determination of fluoride and of the various forms of phosphate in wastewaters and polluted waters, as well as the application of atomic absorption spectrophotometry for determining most of the metals for which the technic can be used in clean water. A gas chromatographic method for phenols appears for the first time, as does a specific method for halogenated phenols. Definitions, and the corresponding details of technic, have been revised in the methods for acidity and alkalinity and for residues.

New colorimetric methods include a cadmium reduction method for nitrate, the chromotropic acid method for nitrate, and the ascorbic acid and vanadophosphomolybdic acid methods for phosphate. The membrane electrode method for dissolved oxygen appears for the first time. The volumetric method for analysis of sludge digester gas appears in addition to the gas chromatographic method.

In the iodometric method for residual chlorine, titration with standard iodate is now permitted as an alternative to the use of standard iodine solution. In the determination of grease, trichlorotrifluoroethane is admissible as the solvent. In the chemical method for dissolved oxygen, the modification for samples containing high concentrations of dissolved oxygen or of organic matter is given, but as an optional variant of the azide modification. In the determination of nonfiltrable residue, the preparation of a filter for each determination from a suspension of asbestos fibers is replaced by the use of prefabricated glass fiber filters. The visual colorimetric method for sulfides is recommended for approximate work only, and a new photometric method is recommended for more exact results. The bioassay method for toxicity of wastewaters has been rewritten, and incorporated in Part 200 rather than appearing as a separate section of the book.

Excluded from the Thirteenth Edition are quiet-pool polarography for heavy metals, the polarographic method for nitrate, the alkali-hypochlorite modification of the method for dissolved oxygen, and the "short" modification for dissolved oxygen.

In Part 300 there have been several significant changes, among them a discussion of equipment for single and multichannel gamma spectrum analysis; alpha and beta scintillation counting; and low-background beta counting. As a result of extensive collaborative testing and evaluation, all the methods of the Twelfth Edition have been refined and accorded standard status. Likewise, a standard test for tritium has been added.

In Part 400, media making has been modified by requiring the use of prepared dehydrated media in which pH may be adjusted only by means of a pH meter. The recommendation for refrigeration of bacteriological samples has been restored. A membrane filter method for fecal coliforms has been added, the earlier procedures for fecal streptococci have been given standard status, and a tentative plate count method for fecal streptococci has been added. A new section is presented on the detection of pathogenic microorganisms, particularly *Salmonella,* and the section on enteric viruses has been rewritten. It is pointed out, however, that procedures for pathogens are not to be treated as routine, and their use, except for special investigations by highly trained microbiologists, is not recommended. Methods specific to swimming pools have been restored. These comprise standard tests for coliforms, fecal coliforms, and fecal streptococci and tentative tests for *Staphylococcus aureus* and *Pseudomonas aeruginosa.*

Part 500 has been entirely rewritten to emphasize microscopic identification of iron and sulfur bacteria rather than cultural procedures for their detection and isolation. It is felt that this change will be more consistent with laboratory practices, which seldom require detailed bacteriological studies of these organisms.

Part 600 also has been completely rewritten. It has been organized into sections dealing with plankton, periphyton, macrophyton, macroinvertebrates, fishes, and the identification of aquatic organisms. In addition to methods for the collection and enumeration of organisms, procedures are given for the measurement of chlorophyll and biological productivity. A large number of new figures and black and white plates illustrating organisms have been prepared.

The Thirteenth Edition retains the General Introduction with its important information concerning proper execution of the procedures described in the various parts of the manual. The section dealing with quality of the required chemical reagents has been expanded. The number of common acid and alkali concentrations has been maintained at a practical minimum. The Joint Editorial Board strongly urges every reader to study carefully the General Introduction, as well as the introduction to the other parts of the manual. Each introduction discusses vital matters of wide application within its specific province in order to minimize repetition throughout the succeeding text. The success of the analysis may well rest on the manner in which the recommendations set forth in the various pertinent introductions are carried out. The same precaution holds true with respect to individual determinations. The complete discussion of each procedure, embracing selection of method, sampling and storage, general discussion, and interference, should be read and fully understood before preparation of the necessary reagents is undertaken.

The methods presented in each edition of this work are the best available and generally accepted procedures for the analysis of water and wastewaters. They therefore offer the recognized basis for control and evaluation.

Obviously, many of the procedures are in need of more intensive investigation of their sensitivity, precision and accuracy, and general applicability. Such research is continually under way, as is evidenced by the improved technics given in the Thirteenth and, in fact, in all previous editions.

Status of Methods

As in its predecessor, all methods in the Thirteenth Edition are "standard" unless designated "tentative"; no other categories are employed. Methods with "standard" status have been extensively studied and accepted as applicable within the limits of sensitivity, precision and accuracy recorded. "Tentative" methods are those still under investigation which have not yet been fully evaluated or are not considered sufficiently specific at present to be designated "standard."

Many of the methods in this manual have been studied and checked through the Analytical Reference Service, U. S. Public Health Service, under the direction of Earl F. McFarren. Statistical evidence has thereby been obtained concerning the reliability and application of these technics.

Technical progress makes advisable the establishment of a program to maintain *Standard Methods* abreast of advances in research and general practice. The Joint Editorial Board has developed the following procedure for effecting interim changes in methods between editions of the manual:

1. Any method given "tentative" status in the current edition may be elevated to "standard" by action of the Joint Editorial Board, based on adequate published data supporting such a change as submitted to the Board by the committee concerned with that part of the manual in which the method is included. Notification of such a change in status shall be accomplished by publication in the official journals of the three associations sponsoring *Standard Methods.*

2. No method having "standard" status may be abandoned or reduced to "tentative" status during the interval between editions.

3. A new method may be adopted as "tentative" or "standard" by the Joint Editorial Board between editions, such action being based on adequate published data as submitted by the committee concerned with that part of the manual in which the method will be included. Upon adoption, the details of the method, together with a résumé of the supporting data, shall be published in the official journal of any one of the three sponsoring associations, and reprints shall be made available at a nominal charge. Notice of such publication and of the availability of reprints shall appear in the official journals of the other two sponsors.

During the six-year period since publication of the Twelfth Edition, several methods have been added and others elevated from "tentative" status to "standard," thus demonstrating continued progress in the study of methods and keeping each edition abreast of scientific advances.

Acknowledgments

For the major portion of the work in preparing and revising the methods in the Thirteenth Edition, the Joint Editorial Board gives full credit to the *Standard Methods* committees of the three association sponsors. A list of the personnel of these committees, and their advisers, follows this preface.

The Joint Editorial Board expresses its appreciation to Berwyn F. Mattison, M.D., and James R. Kimmey, M.D., past and present Executive Director, respectively, American Public Health Association; Raymond J. Faust and Eric F. Johnson, past and present Executive Director, respectively, and James B. Ramsey, Director of Standards, American Water Works Association; and Ralph E. Fuhrman, Dr. Eng., and Robert A. Canham, past and present Executive Secretary, respectively, Water Pollution Control Federation, for their continuous cooperation and helpful advice. George J. Kupchik, Dr. Eng., Deputy Executive Director for Environment, American Public Health Association, has capably handled the administrative details and the myriad other tasks incidental to the preparation of another edition of *Standard Methods*.

Special recognition for her valuable services is due to Helen F. Hough, production editor of the Thirteenth Edition, who worked out a numbering system for the book and who has efficiently carried out the editorial responsibilities upon which a completed volume depends; and to Mary Ann H. Franson, who compiled the index.

The Fourteenth Edition

The American Society for Testing and Materials will join the American Public Health Association, the American Water Works Association, and the Water Pollution Control Federation in the sponsorship and development of the Fourteenth Edition of this Manual.

Joint Editorial Board

Michael J. Taras, *Chairman*
Arnold E. Greenberg
Richard D. Hoak
M. C. Rand

JOINT EDITORIAL BOARD

MICHAEL J. TARAS, *American Water Works Association,* Chairman

ARNOLD E. GREENBERG, *American Public Health Association*

RICHARD D. HOAK and M. C. RAND, *Water Pollution Control Federation*

COMMITTEES FOR THE THIRTEENTH EDITION

American Public Health Association

Subcommittee on *Standard Methods for the Examination of Water and Wastewater* of the Coordinating Committee on Laboratory Methods

ARNOLD E. GREENBERG, *Chairman*
NORMAN A. CLARKE, *Vice-Chairman*
EDWIN E. GELDREICH
PAUL W. KABLER
JAMES B. LACKEY
WARREN LITSKY
C. DAVID MCGUIRE
ORLA E. MCGUIRE
THEODORE A. OLSON
HUGH D. PUTNAM
ELIZABETH D. ROBINTON
WALLACE W. SANDERSON
L. W. SLANETZ

Subcommittee on Radiological Methods for Biological and Environmental Samples

LLOYD R. SETTER, *Chairman*
ABRAHAM S. GOLDIN
PHILLIP GUSTAFSON
JOHN HARLEY
BERND KAHN
WILLIAM LYONS
JULIAN NIELSEN
DAVID E. RUSHING, *Subchairman for Water Analyses*
JAMES A. CORBETT
RICHARD B. HAHN
FRED B. JOHNS
VINCENT SODD
GEORGE S. UYESUGI

American Water Works Association

Committee on *Standard Methods for the Examination of Water and Wastewater*

Michael J. Taras, *Chairman*
Robert A. Baker
Dwight G. Ballinger
Elwood L. Bean
A. P. Black
Russell F. Christman
Jesse M. Cohen
Joseph J. Connors
Daryl W. Ebert
Joseph F. Erdei
Samuel D. Faust
Russell E. Frazier
Roland L. Giusti
Sidney A. Hannah
John D. Hem
Laurel M. Henley
James J. Hickey
Robert S. Ingols
J. Donald Johnson
Ray Kaplan
Harry P. Kramer
Robert C. Kroner
Russell W. Lane
Thurston E. Larson
Henry F. Laughlin
Lester L. Louden
Kenneth M. Mackenthun
Franz J. Maier
DeLoss M. Matheson
Earl F. McFarren
Robert L. Morris
J. W. Murphrey
Remo Navone
M. Starr Nichols
Morris Nussbaum
James E. O'Brien
Harold E. Pearson
Charles I. Pierce
Richard D. Pomeroy
Lloyd R. Robinson, Jr.
Aaron A. Rosen
John R. Rossum
Edward J. Shervin
Kenneth E. Shull
Marvin W. Skougstad
Frank W. Sollo
Werner Stumm
Sidney Sussman
J. F. James Thomas
James C. Vaughn
Paul J. Weaver, Jr.
Foymae K. West
Nicholas S. Zaleiko

Water Pollution Control Federation

Committee on *Standard Methods for the Examination of Water and Wastewater*

Richard D. Hoak, *Chairman*
M. C. Rand, *Vice-Chairman*
Franklin J. Agardy
George J. Alkire
John F. Andrews
Robert A. Baker
Dwight G. Ballinger
Francis B. Birkner
Robert Blumenthal
A. W. Busch
H. J. Caspers
Ralph J. Chamberlain
Leonard L. Ciaccio
Nicholas L. Clesceri
Jesse M. Cohen
C. H. Connell
Richard A. Conway
Michael Dannis
Paul DeFalco, Jr.
Peter Doudoroff
Richard S. Engelbrecht
James E. Etzel
Samuel D. Faust
Tsuah-Hun Fong
K. Fraschina
Peter E. Gaffney
Anthony F. Gaudy, Jr.
Brian L. Goodman
Werner N. Grune
C. Fred Gurnham
N. Bruce Hanes
John D. Hem
Donald J. Hernandez
Kay K. Huffstutler
Joseph V. Hunter
Emmanuel F. Hurwitz
David Jenkins
S. H. Jenkins
J. Donald Johnson
Thaddeus C. Kmieciak
R. E. Kreider
Irwin Jay Kugelman
J. Kushner
James B. Lackey
Alonzo William Lawrence
Gerald W. Lawton
Raymond C. Loehr
Lester L. Louden
F. J. Ludzack
Kenneth M. Mackenthun
Claude Z. Maehler
K. H. Mancy
Perry L. McCarty
Earl F. McFarren
James J. McKeown
J. D. Menzies
Basil W. Mercer, Jr.
E. F. Mohler, Jr.
Alan H. Molof
W. Allen Moore
James J. Morgan
Joe Nagano
John B. Nesbitt
Isadore Nusbaum
Fred E. Nussberger
J. M. Pappenhagen
John D. Parkhurst
Wesley O. Pipes, Jr.
Frederik G. Pohland
John L. Puntenney
Clifford W. Randall
Donald J. Reish
James A. Robertson
Maurice L. Robins
Lloyd R. Robinson, Jr.
Aaron A. Rosen
Wallace W. Sanderson
Milton C. Schroeder
Karl L. Schulze
Lloyd R. Setter

Edward H. Sheers
Marvin W. Skougstad
Peter Skupeko
F. W. Sollo
Paul C. Soltow, Jr.
Robert G. Spicher
Otis J. Sproul
Vernon T. Stack, Jr.
Adib F. Tabri
George R. Tallon
Clarence M. Tarzwell
William W. Ullman
Man Mohan Varma
Donald R. Washington
Cooper H. Wayman
Walter J. Weber, Jr.
Lloyd E. West
Robert E. White
John D. Wolszon
Leon A. Woods
Charles C. Wright
Nicholas S. Zaleiko

ADVISORS

The valued assistance of the following persons, not members of the various committees, is acknowledged by the Joint Editorial Board:

American Public Health Association

Biological Sampling and Analysis:

Herbert W. Jackson, *General Chairman and Subchairman for Introduction, Fishes, and Identification of Types*
J. B. Anderson, *Subchairman for Macroinvertebrates*
Kenneth M. Mackenthun, *Subchairman for Plankton*
C. Mervin Palmer, *Subchairman for Macrophyton*
C. I. Weber, *Subchairman for Periphyton*

W. A. Brungs, Jr.
W. B. Cooke
J. R. Geckler
L. E. Keup
W. T. Mason, Jr.
D. I. Mount
R. S. Safferman
R. M. Sinclair
R. K. Stewart
N. A. Thomas

The black and white plates were produced under the supervision of:

J. B. Anderson—Plates 22–30
S. L. Chang—Plates 13–15, 17 and 18
H. W. Jackson—Plates 7 and 33–37
C. M. Palmer—Plates 1–4 and 8–12
R. M. Sinclair—Plates 16, 31 and 32
C. I. Weber—Plates 5 and 6, 19–21

Iron and Sulfur Bacteria:

R. J. Lewis

Radiological Methods:

Edmond J. Baratta
Herbert A. Bevis
Lial W. Brewer
James C. Daly
Kenneth W. Edwards
Esther S. Ferri
Russell E. Frazier
Richard M. Fry

James M. Hardin
Andrew P. Hull
Victor J. Janzer
Peter Kauffman
Forest E. Knowles
P. K. Kuroda
Lester L. Louden
Alan A. Moghissi
James W. Mullins
Harold E. Pearson
Romola Popper
LeRoy J. Schroder
Jacob Sedlet
S. David Shearer
Ann B. Strong
Richard J. Velten

American Water Works Association

Robert J. Becker
Ervin Bellack
Charles A. Black
Robert C. Black
Karl A. Blum
Bernhard Brauchmann
Theodore E. Brenner
Maxey Brooke
Henry F. Bruner
Charles T. Bryant
Norman C. Bunton
Arnold K. Cherry
N. M. DeJarnette
Albert Dragon
Carleton Duke
Joseph Dvir
Charles A. Goetz
Ben L. Grimes
Gene R. Guthan
John T. Hatcher
Clarence R. Henry
Roy C. Hoather
Barry E. Hunt
Stephen R. Kin
Kenneth F. Knowlton
John W. Krasauskas
William L. Lamar
Laurella Lederer
G. Fred Lee
P. Lefcourt
Maxim Lieber
Raymond J. Lishka
F. J. Ludzack
Anthony G. Macejunas
Victor M. Marcy
John Matthews
D. Mercer
H. A. C. Montgomery
Ragnar Overby
R. F. Packham
A. H. Paessler
Arthur T. Palin
Frank W. Pogge
Thomas M. Riddick
Olsen J. Rogers
F. Fraser Ross
George W. Runyon
C. H. Schmiege
William B. Schworm
Charlotte M. Silva
George Spears
E. Windle Taylor
W. J. Traversy
George A. Uman
Clinton S. Ung
Peter E. Ventura
Phillip W. West
George P. Whittle
Benjamin F. Willey
Donald B. Williams
John A. Winter
W. G. Woxholt

Water Pollution Control Federation

BERTIL G. ANDERSON
WILLIAM A. BRUNGS, JR.
GEORGE BURDICK
PHILIP A. BUTLER
CROSSWELL HENDERSON
DAN L. MCNULTY
EUGENE W. SURBER

Table C: International Relative Atomic Weights, 1969

(Based on the assigned relative atomic mass of $^{12}C = 12$)

The following values apply to elements as they exist in materials of terrestrial origin and to certain artificial elements. When used with the footnotes, they are reliable to ±3 in the last digit.

	Symbol	Atomic number	Atomic weight
Actinium	Ac	89	
Aluminum	Al	13	26.9815[a]
Americium	Am	95	
Antimony	Sb	51	121.75
Argon	Ar	18	39.948[bcdg]
Arsenic	As	33	74.9216[a]
Astatine	At	85	
Barium	Ba	56	137.34
Berkelium	Bk	97	
Beryllium	Be	4	9.01218[a]
Bismuth	Bi	83	208.9806[a]
Boron	B	5	10.81[cde]
Bromine	Br	35	79.904[c]
Cadmium	Cd	48	112.40
Calcium	Ca	20	40.08
Californium	Cf	98	
Carbon	C	6	12.011[bd]
Cerium	Ce	58	140.12
Cesium	Cs	55	132.9055[a]
Chlorine	Cl	17	35.453[c]
Chromium	Cr	24	51.996[c]
Cobalt	Co	27	58.9332[a]
Copper	Cu	29	63.546[cd]
Curium	Cm	96	
Dysprosium	Dy	66	162.50
Einsteinium	Es	99	
Erbium	Er	68	167.26
Europium	Eu	63	151.96
Fermium	Fm	100	
Fluorine	F	9	18.9984[a]
Francium	Fr	87	
Gadolinium	Gd	64	157.25
Gallium	Ga	31	69.72
Germanium	Ge	32	72.59
Gold	Au	79	196.9665[a]
Hafnium	Hf	72	178.49
Helium	He	2	4.00260[be]
Holmium	Ho	67	164.9303[a]
Hydrogen	H	1	1.0080[bd]
Indium	In	49	114.82
Iodine	I	53	126.9045[a]
Iridium	Ir	77	192.22
Iron	Fe	26	55.847
Krypton	Kr	36	83.80
Lanthanium	La	57	138.9055[b]
Lawrencium	Lr	103	
Lead	Pb	82	207.2[dg]
Lithium	Li	3	6.941[cde]
Lutetium	Lu	71	174.97
Magnesium	Mg	12	24.305[c]
Manganese	Mn	25	54.9380[a]
Mendelevium	Md	101	
Mercury	Hg	80	200.59
Molybdenum	Mo	42	95.94

[a] Mononuclidic element.

[b] Element with one predominant isotope (about 99 to 100% abundance).

[c] Element for which the atomic weight is based on calibrated measurements.

[d] Element for which variation in isotopic abundance in terrestrial samples limits the precision of the atomic weight given.

[e] Element for which users are cautioned against the possibility of large variations in atomic weight due to inadvertent or undisclosed artificial isotopic separation in commercially available materials.

[f] Most commonly available long-lived isotope.

[g] In some geological specimens this element has a highly anomalous isotopic composition, corresponding to an atomic weight significantly different from that given.

SOURCE: International Union of Pure and Applied Chemistry.

Table C: International Relative Atomic Weights, 1969

(Based on the assigned relative atomic mass of $^{12}C = 12$)

The following values apply to elements as they exist in materials of terrestrial origin and to certain artificial elements. When used with the footnotes, they are reliable to ±3 in the last digit.

	Symbol	Atomic number	Atomic weight
Neodymium	Nd	60	144.24
Neon	Ne	10	20.179[c]
Neptunium	Np	93	237.0482[b]
Nickel	Ni	28	58.71
Niobium	Nb	41	92.9064[a]
Nitrogen	N	7	14.0067[bc]
Nobelium	No	102	
Osmium	Os	76	190.2
Oxygen	O	8	15.9994[bcd]
Palladium	Pd	46	106.4
Phosphorus	P	15	30.9738[a]
Platinum	Pt	78	195.09
Plutonium	Pu	94	
Polonium	Po	84	
Potassium	K	19	39.102
Praseodymium	Pr	59	140.9077[a]
Promethium	Pm	61	
Protactinium	Pa	91	231.0359[a]
Radium	Ra	88	226.0254[afg]
Radon	Rn	86	
Rhenium	Re	75	186.2
Rhodium	Rh	45	102.9055[a]
Rubidium	Rb	37	85.4678[c]
Ruthenium	Ru	44	101.07
Samarium	Sm	62	150.4
Scandium	Sc	21	44.9559[a]
Selenium	Se	34	78.96
Silicon	Si	14	28.086[d]
Silver	Ag	47	107.868[c]
Sodium	Na	11	22.9898[a]
Strontium	Sr	38	87.62[g]
Sulfur	S	16	32.06[d]
Tantalum	Ta	73	180.9479[b]
Technetium	Tc	43	98.9062[f]
Tellurium	Te	52	127.60
Terbium	Tb	65	158.9254[a]
Thallium	Tl	81	204.37
Thorium	Th	90	232.0381[a]
Thulium	Tm	69	168.9342[a]
Tin	Sn	50	118.69
Titanium	Ti	22	47.90
Tungsten	W	74	183.85
Uranium	U	92	238.029[bce]
Vanadium	V	23	50.9414[bc]
Wolfram	W	74	183.85
Xenon	Xe	54	131.30
Ytterbium	Yb	70	173.04
Yttrium	Y	39	88.9059[a]
Zinc	Zn	30	65.37
Zirconium	Zr	40	91.22

[a] Mononuclidic element.

[b] Element with one predominant isotope (about 99 to 100% abundance).

[c] Element for which the atomic weight is based on calibrated measurements.

[d] Element for which variation in isotopic abundance in terrestrial samples limits the precision of the atomic weight given.

[e] Element for which users are cautioned against the possibility of large variations in atomic weight due to inadvertent or undisclosed artificial isotopic separation in commercially available materials.

[f] Most commonly available long-lived isotope.

[g] In some geological specimens this element has a highly anomalous isotopic composition, corresponding to an atomic weight significantly different from that given.

SOURCE: International Union of Pure and Applied Chemistry.

TABLE OF CONTENTS

TABLES

FIGURES

PLATES

Black and white plates of aquatic organisms

Color plates of blue-green algae (unpaginated special color section)

PART 000

GENERAL INTRODUCTION

000 A. Laboratory Apparatus, Reagents and Technics

1. Containers

For general laboratory use, the most suitable material for containers is resistant borosilicate glass, commonly called "pyrex." * Special glasses are available with such characteristics as high resistance to alkali attack, low boron content, or exclusion of light. Stoppers, caps and plugs should be chosen to resist the attack of material contained in the vessel. Cork stoppers wrapped with a relatively inert metal foil are suitable for many samples. Metal screw caps are a poor choice for any sample that will cause them to corrode readily. Glass stoppers are unsatisfactory for strongly alkaline liquids because of their tendency to stick fast. Rubber stoppers are excellent for alkaline liquids but very poor for organic solvents, in which they swell or disintegrate. Teflon or silver plugs may be obtained for burets, which arc to be used for strongly alkaline liquids. For particular purposes, other materials such as porcelain, nickel, iron, platinum, stainless steel, and Vycor † can be employed to advantage.

It is recommended that samples be collected and stored in bottles made of pyrex, hard rubber, polyethylene or other inert material.

For relatively short storage periods, or for constituents which are not affected by storage in soft glass, such as calcium, magnesium, sulfate, chloride, and perhaps others, the newer type of 2.5-liter acid-bottle "bell closure" is satisfactory. This type of closure holds a glass disk against the ground-glass surface of the bottle lip and insures adequate protection for the sample. If part of the sample is to be analyzed at a later date for silica, sodium or other substances which would be affected by prolonged storage in soft glass, it may be transferred to a small polyethylene bottle, while the remainder of the sample is left in the soft-glass bottle.

Sample bottles must be carefully cleaned before each use. Glass bottles may be rinsed with a chromic acid cleaning mixture made by adding 1 liter of conc H_2SO_4 slowly, with stirring, to 35 ml saturated sodium dichromate solution, or with an alkaline permanganate solution followed by an oxalic acid solution. Rinsing with other concentrated acids may be used to remove inorganic matter. The newer detergents are excellent cleansers for many purposes; either detergents or conc HCl can be used for cleaning hard-rubber and polyethylene bottles. After having been cleaned, bottles must be rinsed thoroughly with tap water and then with distilled water.

For shipment, bottles may be packed in wooden, metal, plastic or heavy fiberboard cases, with a separate compartment for each bottle. Boxes may be lined with corrugated fiber paper, felt or other resilient material, or may be provided with spring-loaded corner strips, to prevent breakage. Lined wicker baskets may also be used. Sam-

* As used in this manual, "pyrex" refers not to a specific brand, but to the general type, such as that manufactured by Corning Glass Works (under the name "Pyrex"), or Kimble Glass Co., Division of Owens-Illinois ("Kimax"), or equivalent.

† A high-silica glass product of Corning Glass Works.

ples stored in polyethylene bottles need no protection against breakage by impact or through freezing.

2. *Distilled Water*

Some of the colorimetric tests described in this manual are sufficiently sensitive to respond to even the minute traces of impurities which may be found in ordinary distilled water. In such cases, the use of double- or triple-distilled water may be required. The material of which the still is constructed may contribute impurities to the distillate. Most commercial stills, for example, are constructed in part of copper, and distilled water from them frequently contains 10 to 50 μg/l Cu. For special purposes, water may be distilled from an all-pyrex apparatus, or from an apparatus in which the condenser is made of glass, fused quartz, silver, or block tin.

Ordinary distillation of water will not remove ammonia or carbon dioxide; in fact, distilled water is often supersaturated with carbon dioxide because of the decomposition of raw-water bicarbonates to carbonates in the boiler. Ammonia can be removed by distillation from acid solution or by passing the water through a column of mixed resins. Carbon dioxide can be removed by distillation from a solution containing an excess of alkali hydroxide, by boiling for a few minutes, by vigorously aerating the water with a stream of inert gas for a sufficient period, or by passing the water through a column of strong anion-exchange resin in the hydroxide form. If ammonia and carbon dioxide are present at the same time, boiling and aerating are not effective.

If kept in glass containers, distilled water will slowly leach the more soluble materials from the glass and will increase in total dissolved solids.

Demineralized water from a mixed-bed ion exchanger is satisfactory for many applications in this manual. However, as ion exchange fails to remove such nonelectrolytes and colloids as plankton, nonionic organic materials, and dissolved air, it is not suitable for determinations where such constituents interfere.

A very high-purity water, with less than 0.1 micromho/cm conductance, can be produced by passing ordinary distilled water through a mixed-bed exchanger and discarding the effluent until the desired quality is obtained. A water prepared in this way is often satisfactory for use in the determination of trace cations and anions.

Three types of special distilled water are specified for various methods in this book. For easy reference, the preparation of these waters is described on the inside front cover.

3. *Reagents*

It is to be understood that only the best quality of chemical reagents must be employed even though this injunction is not repeated in the description of a particular method. Chemicals for which the American Chemical Society has published specifications should always be ordered in the "ACS grade." Other chemicals should be ordered as "analytical reagent grade" or "spectral grade organic solvents." Methods of checking the purity of reagents which are suspect will be found in books of reagent specifications listed in the bibliography under laboratory reagents (Section 000D).

Unfortunately, many commercial

dyes for which the ACS grade has not been established fail to meet exacting analytical requirements owing to variations in the color response of different lots. In such cases, dyes certified by the Biological Stain Commission may be satisfactory for chemical analysis.

Where neither the ACS grade nor the certified Biological Stain Commission dye is available, best results will be obtained by purifying the solid dye through recrystallization.

The following standard substances, each bottle of which is accompanied by a certificate of analysis, are issued by the National Bureau of Standards, Department of Commerce, Washington, D.C., for the purpose of standardizing analytical solutions:

Acidimetric:
- 84h —Acid potassium phthalate
- 350 —Benzoic acid

Oxidimetric:
- 40g —Sodium oxalate
- 83c —Arsenic trioxide
- 136b —Potassium dichromate

Buffer:
- 185d —Acid potassium phthalate
- 186Ic —Potassium dihydrogen phosphate
- 186IIb—Disodium hydrogen phosphate
- 187a —Borax
- 188 —Potassium hydrogen tartrate
- 189 —Potassium tetroxalate
- 190 —Potassium dihydrogen citrate
- 191 —Sodium bicarbonate
- 192 —Sodium carbonate

Many hundreds of other standards issued by NBS are described in its Miscellaneous Publication 260.

A successful dithizone test demands reagents of the highest purity. Chloroform and carbon tetrachloride are now commercially available in a grade declared to be suitable for the dithizone methods. Reagents of this quality should be selected preferentially for the several dithizone methods described in this manual.

The general availability of the water-soluble sodium salts of the common indicators at nominal cost has resulted in their predominant recommendation for indicator preparation in this edition.

When alcohol or ethyl alcohol is specified for the preparation of such solutions as phenolphthalein indicator, 95% ethyl alcohol is the reagent of choice, with a similar grade of isopropyl alcohol a permissible alternate.

Certain organic reagents are somewhat unstable upon exposure to the atmosphere. In the event the stability of a chemical is limited or unknown, the purchase of small lots at frequent intervals is suggested.

Many of the chemical reagents prescribed in this book should be treated with the utmost care, both in their original state and in the form of solutions. Chemical reagents bearing commercial labels with the words POISON, DANGER, CAUTION, FLAMMABLE, or comparable warnings should be handled with special discretion. Continuing investigations are revealing the carcinogenic properties of common reagents such as orthotolidine dihydrochloride, 1-naphthylamine hydrochloride, and 3, 3′-diaminobenzidine hydrochloride, specified in this volume. These aromatic amines and other suspected amines should be handled with a circumspection that will prevent their inhalation, ingestion, absorption or contact through the lungs, mouth or skin. In the interest of personal safety, the analyst will be well repaid by a study of the manual entitled *Safety Practice for Water Utilities* published by the American Water Works Association and of the *Guide for Safety in the Chemical Laboratory* prepared by the Manufacturing Chemists Association and detailing the hazards which may occur in the laboratory.

All anhydrous reagent chemicals required for the preparation of standard calibration solutions and titrants should be dried in an oven at 105 to 110 C for at least 1 to 2 hr and preferably overnight. After cooling to room temperature in an efficient desiccator, the proper amount should promptly be weighed for dissolution. Should a different drying temperature be necessary, a note to this effect is specified for the particular chemical. In the case of hydrated salts, milder drying in an efficient desiccator can be substituted for oven-drying.

4. *Common Acid and Alkali Solutions*

a. Concentration units used: Reagent concentrations are expressed in this manual in terms of normality, molarity and additive volumes.

A *normal solution* contains one gram equivalent weight of solute per liter of solution.

A *molar solution* contains one gram molecular weight of solute per liter of solution.

In additive volumes $(a+b)$, the first number, *a,* refers to the volume of the concentrated reagent; the second number, *b,* refers to the volume of distilled water required for dilution. Thus, "1 + 9 HCl" denotes that 1 volume of concentrated HCl is to be diluted with 9 volumes of distilled water.

In order to make a solution of exact normality from a chemical which cannot be measured as a primary standard, a relatively concentrated stock solution may first be prepared, and then an exact dilution of this may be made to the desired strength. Another method is to make a solution of slightly stronger concentration than that desired, standardize it, and then make suitable adjustments in the concentration. Alternatively, the solution may be used as first standardized, with appropriate modification of the factor used in the calculation. This alternative procedure is especially useful in the case of a solution which slowly changes strength—for example, thiosulfate solution, which must be restandardized at frequent intervals. Often, however, adjustment to the exact normality specified is desirable when a laboratory runs a large number of determinations with one standard solution.

As long as the normality of a standard solution does not result in a titration volume so small as to preclude accurate measurement or so large as to cause abnormal dilution of the reaction mixture, and as long as the solution is properly standardized and the calculations are properly made, the determinations can be considered to be in accord with the instructions in this manual.

b. Preparation and dilution of solutions: If a solution of exact normality is to be prepared by dissolving a weighed amount of a primary standard or by diluting a stronger solution, it must be brought up to exact volume in a volumetric flask.

The stock and standard solutions prescribed for the colorimetric determinations in the chemical sections of this manual should also be accurately prepared in volumetric flasks. Where the concentration does not need to be exact, it is often easier to mix the concentrated solution or the solid with measured amounts of water, using graduated cylinders for these measurements. There is usually a significant change of volume when strong solutions are mixed, so that the total volume is less than the sum of the volumes used. For approximate dilutions, the volume changes are negligible when concentrations of 6*N* or less are diluted.

Very thorough and complete mixing is essential when making dilutions. One of the commonest sources of error in analyses using standard solutions diluted in volumetric flasks is failure to attain complete mixing.

c. *Storage of solutions:* Some standardized solutions alter slowly because of chemical or biologic changes. The practical life, required frequency of standardizations, or storage precautions will be indicated for such standards. Others, such as dilute hydrochloric acid, are nonreactive. Yet they, too, may change in strength as a result of evaporative processes. Such evaporation is not prevented by a glass stopper. Changes in temperature cause a bottle to "breathe," thus allowing some evaporation. Rarely should a standard be considered valid for more than a year unless it is restandardized, and it is valid for that length of time only if conditions are such that evaporation is minimal. If the bottle is often opened or if it is much less than half full, evaporation may be serious in a few months.

Where glass bottles are called for, they must be of chemically resistant glass. For standard solutions which do not react with rubber or neoprene, it is often advantageous to use stoppers of these materials, because they can, if properly fitted, prevent evaporation as long as the bottle is closed. Screw-cap bottles will also be found effective. If the cap has a gasket of a reasonably resistant material, permissible usage will be about the same as that for rubber stoppers.

d. *Hydrochloric and sulfuric acid as alternatives:* Dilute standardized sulfuric and hydrochloric acids are called for in various procedures. Often these solutions are interchangeable. Where one is mentioned, the analyst may use the other if he is certain that the substitution will make no difference.

e. *Preparation:* Instructions in this manual usually describe the preparation of a liter of solution. A laboratory will frequently find it expedient to prepare a smaller or larger volume. The analyst should consider this and not limit the amount to 1 liter just because the instructions are so written. Sometimes instructions call for the preparation of 100 ml; the solutions involved either have a short life or are used in small amounts, so that 1 liter would be an excessive amount for any ordinary laboratory. A safe general rule to follow in the preparation of solutions is to add the more concentrated acid or alkali to the water, with stirring, in a vessel which can withstand thermal shock, and then to dilute to the final volume after cooling to room temperature.

f. *Uniform reagent concentrations:* An attempt has been made in the chemical sections of this manual to establish a uniform number of common acid and base concentrations which will serve for the adjustment of the acid and alkaline reaction of samples prior to color development or final titration. The following acid concentrations are recommended for general desk use: the concentrated reagent of commerce, 6*N*, 1*N*, 0.1*N*, and 0.02*N*. The preparation of these acid concentrations, as well as the required 15*N*, 6*N* and 1*N* sodium hydroxide solutions, and 5*N*, 3*N* and 0.2*N* ammonium hydroxide solutions, are tabulated and described on the inside front cover of this book for easy reference at all times.

5. *Volumetric Glassware*

Volumetric glassware may be calibrated either by the analyst who will use it or by some competent laboratory which can furnish certificates of accuracy. Volumetric glassware is calibrated either "to contain" (TC) or "to deliver" (TD). Glassware which is designed "to deliver" will do so with accuracy only when the inner surface is so scrupulously clean that water wets it immediately and forms a uniform film upon emptying. Whenever possible, pyrex glassware should be used.

Approved quantitative technics will yield the best results in the standard procedures. For this reason, the careful measurement of weights and volumes has been recommended in the preparation of standard solutions and calibration curves. Similar precautions should be observed in the measurement of sample volumes. Resort to volumetric pipets or burets is intended where the volume is designated to two decimal places (X.00 ml) in the text. Volumetric flasks are indicated for those cases where the volume is specified as 1,000 ml rather than 1 liter, as well as where a volumetric flask is actually called for.

6. *Nessler Tubes*

Nessler tubes should be of the "tall" form (except when otherwise indicated), made of resistant glass, and selected from uniformly drawn tubing. The glass should be clear and colorless. The bottoms of the nessler tubes should be plane-parallel. When the tubes are filled with liquid and viewed from the top using a light source beneath the tubes, there should be no dark spots nor any lenslike distortion of the transmitted light. The best quality of tube is manufactured by fusion-sealing a separately prepared, ground and polished circle of glass to the tube to form its bottom. The less expensive tubes are manufactured with integral bottoms, which cannot be made perfectly flat, but which appear to be satisfactory. The tops of the tubes should be flat, preferably fire-polished, and smooth enough to permit cover slips to be cemented on for sealing. Nessler tubes provided with standard-taper clear glass tops are commercially available. The graduation marks should completely encircle the tubes.

The 100-ml tubes should have a total length of approximately 375 mm. The inside diameter of such tubes should approximate 20 mm and the outside diameter 24 mm. The graduation mark on the tube should be as near to 300 mm above the inside of the bottom as possible. Tubes sold in sets should be of such uniformity that this distance does not vary more than 6 mm. (Sets are available commercially in which the maximum difference between tubes is not more than 2 mm.) A graduation mark also at 50 ml is permissible.

The 50-ml tubes should have a total length of about 300 mm. The inside diameter of the tubes should approximate 17 mm and the outside diameter 21 mm. The graduation mark on the tube should be as near 225 mm above the inside of the bottom as possible. Tubes sold in sets should be of such uniformity that this distance does not vary more than 6 mm. (Sets are available commercially in which the maximum difference between tubes is not more than 1.5 mm.) A graduation mark also at 25 ml is permissible.

Tubes for Jackson candle turbidimeters, in addition to conforming precisely to the measurements given in Section 163, Turbidity, should also conform to all the requirements of quality, glass color, and workmanship pertaining to nessler tubes.

7. Colorimetric Equipment and Technic

Many of the procedures in this manual depend upon matching colors, either by eye or with a photometric instrument. In order to obtain the best possible results, the analyst should understand the principles and limitations of these methods, especially as the choice of instrument and of technic must be left to his discretion.

Both visual and photometric methods have their place in water analysis, and each method has advantages.

Tall-form nessler tubes provide a 30-cm light path, which is highly desirable when very faint colors are to be compared. Nessler tubes are inexpensive; their use does not require much training; they are not subject to mechanical or electrical failure; and in general they are entirely satisfactory for much of the routine work. Because they are portable and do not require a source of electric light, they can be used in the field.

Photometric instruments are more versatile than nessler tubes; they are generally capable of superior accuracy if used intelligently; and they do not depend upon external lighting conditions or upon the analyst's eyesight. Therefore, results obtained with photometric instruments are less subject to personal bias and are more reproducible from one operator to another. Their use often allows corrections to be made for interfering color or turbidity. It is not necessary to prepare a complete set of standards for every single determination if a photometric instrument is used, whereas it is necessary to prepare such a set, or to maintain permanent standards, if nessler tubes are used for visual comparison.

Photometric methods are not, however, free from specific limitations. An analyst will recognize that something has gone wrong if he sees an off color or turbidity when making a visual comparison, but such a discrepancy may easily escape detection while making a photometric reading, for the instrument will always yield some sort of reading, whether meaningful or not. Filter photometers or spectrophotometers are subject to electrical and mechanical failure and sometimes to line voltage fluctuations. The photocells are subject to fatigue and to loss of sensitivity. Testing, maintaining and repairing such instruments call for specialized skills.

It must be emphasized that a photometer is not uniformly accurate over its entire scale. At very low transmittances the scale is crowded in terms of concentration, so that a considerable change in the relative concentration of the substance sought will cause only a slight change in the position of the indicator dial or needle. At very high transmittances, slight differences between optical cells, the presence of condensed moisture, dust, bubbles, fingerprints, or a slight lack of reproducibility in positioning the cells can cause as great a change in readings as would a considerable relative change in concentration. The difficulties are minimized if readings fall in the middle range of the scale, and therefore the sample should be diluted or concentrated, or the light path varied, by selecting cells of appropriate size so that the middle range can be used.

Some suggestions as to suitable ranges and light paths are offered under individual methods in this manual, but much reliance must necessarily be placed on the knowledge and judgment of the analyst. Most photometers are capable of their best performance when readings on samples fall in the range from approximately 10% to 80% transmittance (i.e., approximately 1 to 0.1 absorbance) with respect to a blank adjusted to read 100% transmittance or 0 absorbance. The closer the readings approach 0% or 100% transmittance, the less accurate they can be expected to be. If it is impractical to use an optical cell with a sufficiently long light path—as in some commercial instruments—or to concentrate the sample or select a more sensitive color test, then it may actually be more accurate to compare very faint colors in nessler tubes than to attempt photometric readings close to 100% transmittance.

In general, the best wavelength or filter to select is that which produces the largest spread of readings between a standard and a blank. This usually corresponds to a visual color for the light beam which is complementary to that of the solution—for example, a green filter for a red solution, a violet filter for a yellow solution.

Although the employment of a photoelectric instrument makes unnecessary the preparation of a complete set of standards for every single set of samples to be analyzed, it is necessary to prepare a reagent blank and at least one standard in the upper end of the optimum concentration range, along with every group of samples, in order to verify the constancy of the calibration curve. This precaution will reveal any unsuspected changes in the reagents, the instrument, or the technic. At regular intervals, or if at any time results fall under suspicion, a complete set of standards—at least five or six—should be prepared, spaced to cover the optimum concentration range, in order to check the calibration curve. Also valuable in this regard is the absorptivity information given in this manual for a number of new photometric methods.

The utmost care should be exercised in the use of calibration curves supplied by the instrument manufacturer, or in the use of commercial permanent standards of colored liquids or glasses. The analyst must verify for himself at frequent intervals the accuracy of the curves or permanent standards by comparison with standards prepared in the laboratory, using the same set of reagents, the same instrument, and the same procedure as those used for analyzing samples. Even if permanent calibration curves or artificial standards have been accurately prepared by the manufacturer, they may not be valid under conditions of use. Permanent standards may be subject to fading or color alteration, and their validity may also depend upon certain arbitrary lighting conditions. Standards and calibration curves may be incorrect owing to slight differences between reagents, instruments or technics at the manufacturer's laboratory and those at the analyst's laboratory.

If a photometer provides readings in terms of absorbance, it is convenient to plot calibration curves on rectangular graph paper; if readings are in terms of percentage transmittance, it is more convenient to plot calibration curves on semilogarithmic graph paper, with transmittance on the logarithmic scale and concentration on the linear scale. Usually, such graphs will be straight, or nearly straight, lines. Straight lines are easier to draw and read than strongly curved lines, and may be checked by verification of only a few points.

Photometric compensation can be used to correct for the interference caused by color or turbidity present in a sample, and also for impurities in the chemicals and distilled water used in the reagent blank, but not for those interfering substances which react with the color-developing reagents to produce a color. The principle involved is the additivity of absorbances.

If there is a significant reagent blank, but no color or turbidity in the sample, the necessary correction can be made by adding the color-developing reagents to distilled water and nulling the photometer with the resulting solution.

If there is color or turbidity or both in the sample, but a negligible reagent blank, correction can be made by carrying an additional aliquot of the sample through the procedure, with the exception that either: (1) one of the essential color-developing reagents is omitted; or, preferably, (2) the color is bleached out after it has been produced, but in such a way that the interfering color or turbidity is not bleached. The special blank is then used for nulling the photometer. Any significant change in volume produced by the addition or omission of reagents must be taken into account.

If color or turbidity or both are present in the sample, and if, in addition, the reagent blank is significant, then a slightly more complicated procedure is needed to correct for both interferences: The calibration curve should be prepared by setting the photometer to zero absorbance with plain distilled water and reading all the standards, including a zero standard or reagent blank, against the distilled water. If the graph is plotted in the recommended manner, and Beer's law holds, a straight line will be obtained; but if there is a measurable reagent blank, this line will not pass through the point of origin.

For each sample, a special blank must be prepared by either: (a) omitting a reagent, or (b) bleaching out the color as described above. Each special blank is then placed in the photometer in turn, the instrument is adjusted each time to read zero absorbance, and each regularly developed sample is read against its corresponding blank. The observed absorbances are then interpreted from the calibration graph. As before, any significant increase or decrease in volume caused by addition or omission of reagents must be considered in the calculations.

In visual color comparison with some instruments, compensation for color and turbidity can be made by the Walpole technic. The treated sample, after color development, is viewed through distilled water, while the color standard is viewed through an untreated sample. It is inconvenient to use the Walpole technic when viewing tall-form nessler tubes axially, because of their clumsy length.

Sometimes none of the cited expedients will apply. In such an event, several approaches are available for the separation of turbidity from a sample. The nature of the sample, the size of suspended particles, and the reasons for conducting the analysis will all combine to dictate the method for turbidity removal. The turbidity may be coagulated by the addition of zinc sulfate and an alkali, as is done in the direct nesslerization method for ammonia nitrogen. For samples of relatively coarse turbidity, centrifuging may suffice. In some instances, glass fiber filters, filter paper or sintered-glass filters of fine porosity will serve the purpose. For very small particle sizes, the more recently developed cellulose acetate membrane filters may provide the required retentiveness. Used with discretion, each of these methods will yield satisfactory results in a suitable situation. However, it must be emphasized that no single universally ideal method of turbidity removal is available. Moreover, the analyst should be perpetually alert to adsorption losses possible with any flocculating or filtering procedure and an attendant alteration in the sample filtrate.

8. Other Methods of Analysis

The use of an instrumental method of analysis not specifically described in procedures in this manual is permissible, provided that the results so obtained are checked periodically, either against a standard method described in this manual or against a standard sample of undisputed composition. Identification of any such instrumental method used must be included in the laboratory report along with the analytical results.

a. Atomic absorption spectroscopy: Atomic absorption spectrophotometry has been applied to the determination of a growing number of metals in drinking water without the need for prior concentration or extensive sample pretreatment. The use of organic solvents coupled with oxyacetylene, oxyhydrogen or nitrous oxide-acetylene flames enables the determination of metals which form refractory oxides. This manual presents atomic absorption methods for many metals. Although not described in the text, calcium, lithium, potassium, sodium and strontium can also be determined readily by the atomic absorption approach.

b. Flame photometry: Flame photometry is used for the determination of sodium, potassium, lithium and strontium. To some extent it is also useful for the determination of calcium and other ions.

c. Emission spectroscopy: Arc-spark emission spectroscopy is becoming an important analytical tool for water analysis and is proving valuable both for trace analysis and for certain determinations not easily made by any other method. Considerable specialized training and experience with this technic are required to obtain satisfactory results, and frequently it is practical to obtain only semiquantitative results from such methods in water analysis. It should be noted that an arc-spark emission spectrograph is relatively expensive when used exclusively for routine water testing, but its purchase is justified if it can be used as a general laboratory analytical instrument.

Among the advantages of arc-spark spectrographic analyses are: (1) the minute size of sample required; (2) elimination of the necessity for bringing solids, such as precipitates and corrosion products, into solution; (3) detection of all determinable elements present in a sample, whether specifically looked for or not; and (4) their unexcelled sensitivity for some elements. Among the disadvantages of spectrographic analyses are: (1) the high cost of first-class equipment; (2) the need for special training and experience; (3) the possible occurrence of severe interferences which must be taken into account if reasonable accuracy is to be achieved; and (4) the inability to distinguish between different valence states of an element, as, for instance, between chromic and chromate or ferric and ferrous.

Silver is the only element for which a spectrographic method is described in this manual. The following can also be determined spectrographically: aluminum, barium, boron, chromium, copper, iron, lead, lithium, magnesium, manganese, nickel, silicon, strontium and zinc. Among the elements for which there is no standard method in this manual but which are determinable by arc-spark spectrography are cobalt, molybdenum, tin, titanium, vanadium and a number of others.[1, 2]

d. Polarography: Polarography is suggested for scanning industrial wastes for various metal ions, especially where the possible interferences in the precise colorimetric procedures are unknown. The older polarographic method for dissolved oxygen also remains from the past.

Recent developments in polarography include the introduction of pulse polarographs with dual synchronized electrodes capable of differential derivative output. Operation in the pulse mode permits determination of seven or more metals on a single portion of the sample after ashing with nitric acid. If a 100-ml portion of the sample is ashed, determinations may be made in the low microgram-per-liter range.

A method closely allied to polarography is amperometric titration, which is suitable for the determination of residual chlorine and other iodometric methods by titrimetry.

e. Potentiometric titration: Growing in acceptance for titrimetric work are electrical instruments called titrimeters, or electrotitrators. If used discreetly with an understanding of their limitations, these instruments can be applied to many of the titrimetric determinations described, including those for acidity and the alkalinities. In addition, titrimetric precipitation reactions such as those for chloride, as well as titrimetric procedures based on complexometric and oxidation-reduction reactions, can be performed with these instruments. To be suitable for these extensive applications, an instrument must be equipped with all the necessary special electrodes. Some recent electrotitrator models embody automatic features by which a titration is self-executing after the preliminary settings are made. In order to avoid spurious readings, the analyst is urged to check instrument operation against representative known samples in the same concentration range as the water under examination.

f. Specific ion electrodes and probes: The past decade has witnessed the advent of specific ion electrodes and probes for the rapid estimation of certain constituents in water. These electrodes function best in conjunction with the concurrently developed expanded-scale pH meters. For the most part, the new electrodes operate on the ion-exchange principle. The specific ion electrodes available at this time are designed for the measurement of calcium, divalent copper, divalent hardness, potassium, sodium, total monovalent and total divalent cations, and bromide, chloride, cyanide, fluoride, iodide, nitrate, perchlorate and sulfide anions among others. Additional specific ion electrodes can doubtless be anticipated in the future.

These devices are subject to varying

degrees of interference from other ions in the sample and must still receive the thorough study that would warrant their adoption as tentative and standard methods. Nonetheless, their value for monitoring activities is readily apparent. To remove all doubt of variations in reliability, each electrode should be checked in the presence of interferences as well as the ion for which it is intended. This manual details the electrode method for fluoride after a collaborative study established its credibility in the presence of common interferences (Section 121).

The commercial dissolved oxygen probes vary considerably in their dependability and maintenance requirements. Despite these shortcomings, they have been applied to the monitoring of dissolved oxygen levels in a variety of waters and wastewaters. Most probes embody an electrode covered by a thin layer of electrolyte held in place by an oxygen-permeable membrane. The oxygen in solution diffuses through the membrane and electrolyte layer to react at the electrode, inducing a current which is proportional to the activity (and concentration) of the dissolved oxygen. Satisfactory dissolved-oxygen electrodes are also available without a membrane. In either case, the face of the dissolved oxygen sensor should be kept well agitated, and temperature compensation should be provided, in order to insure acceptable results in the laboratory or monitoring application.

g. Gas chromatography: Considerable work is under way in the development of gas chromatographic methods suitable for water and wastewater analysis. Two such methods appear in this manual: one for the determination of chlorinated hydrocarbon pesticides in drinking water; the second for the determination of the components in sludge digester gas. Investigations reveal that gas chromatography may also be useful for the determination of phenols. The skill of the operator and the expense entailed in its purchase will probably limit use of this specialized instrumentation to the larger organization which can afford the sizable financial outlay involved.

h. Automated analytical instrumentation: Automated analytical instruments are now available and in use to run individual samples at rates of 10 to 60 samples per hour. The same instruments can be modified to perform analyses for two to twelve constituents simultaneously from one sample. The instruments are composed of a group of interchangeable modules joined together in series by a tubing system. Each module performs the individual operations of filtering, heating, digesting, time delay, color sensing, etc., that the procedure requires.

The read-out system employs sensing elements with indicators, alarms and/or recorders. For monitoring applications, automatic standardization-compensation, electrical and chemical, is done by a self-adjusting recorder when known chemical standards are sent periodically through the same analytical train. Such instrument systems are presently available.

Appropriate methodology is supplied by the manufacturer for many of the common constituents of water and wastewater. Some methods are based on procedures described in this manual, while others originate from the manufacturer's adaptation of published research. Since a number of methods of varying reliability may be available for a single constituent of water and wastewater, a critical appraisal of the method adopted is obviously mandatory.

Automated methodology is susceptible to the same interferences as the original method from which it derives. For this reason, new methods developed for automated analysis must be subjected to the exacting tests for accuracy and freedom from adverse response already met by the accepted standard methods.

Off color and turbidity produced during the course of an analysis will be visible to an analyst manually performing a given determination, and the result will be properly discarded. Such abnormal effects caused by unsuspected interferences might escape notice in an automated analysis. Calibration of the instrument system at least once each day with standards containing interferences of known concentration could help to expose such difficulties. Routine practice is to check instrument action and guard against questionable results by the insertion of standards and blanks at regular intervals—perhaps after every 10 samples in the train. Another important precaution is proper sample identification by arrangement into convenient groups.

In brief, a fair degree of operator skill and knowledge, together with adequately detailed instructions, is required for successful automated analysis.

i. Other newer methods of analysis: Instrumentation and new methods of analysis are always under development. The analyst will find it to his advantage to keep abreast of current progress. Reviews of each branch of analytical chemistry are published regularly in the periodical, *Analytical Chemistry.*

9. *Interferences*

Many analytical procedures are subject to interference from substances which may be present in the sample. The more common and obvious interferences are known, and information about them has been given in the details of individual procedures. It is inevitable that the analyst will encounter interferences about which he is not forewarned. Such occurrences are unavoidable because of the diverse nature of waters and particularly of wastewaters. Therefore, the analyst must be alert to the fact that hitherto untested ions, new treatment compounds—especially complexing agents—and new industrial wastes constitute an ever-present threat to the accuracy of chemical analyses. He must be on his guard at all times to detect the occurrence of such interferences.

Any sudden change in the apparent composition of a supply which has been rather constant, any off color observed in a colorimetric test or during a titration, any unexpected turbidity, odor or other laboratory finding is cause for suspicion. Such a change may be due to a normal variation in the relative concentrations of the usual constituents, but it may be caused by the introduction of an unforeseen interfering substance.

A few substances—such as chlorine, chlorine dioxide, alum, iron salts, silicates, copper sulfate, ammonium sulfate and polyphosphates—are so widely used in water treatment that they deserve special mention as possible causes of interference. Of these, chlorine is probably the worst offender, in that it bleaches or alters the colors of many of the sensitive organic reagents which serve as titration indicators and as color developers for photometric methods. Among the methods which have proved effective in removing chlorine residuals are: the addition of minimal amounts of sulfite, thiosulfate or arsenite; exposure to sunlight or an artificial ultraviolet source; and prolonged storage.

Whenever interference is encountered or suspected, and no specific recommendations are found in this manual for overcoming it, the analyst must endeavor to determine what technic, if any, suffices to eliminate the interference without adversely affecting the analysis itself. If two or more choices of procedure are offered, often one procedure will be less affected than another by the presence of the interfering substance. If different procedures yield considerably different results, it is likely that interference is present. Some interferences become less severe upon dilution, or upon use of smaller aliquots; any tendency of the results to increase or decrease in a consistent manner with dilution indicates the likelihood of interference effects.

a. Interference may cause the analytical results to be either too high or too low, as a consequence of one of the following processes:

1) An interfering substance may react like the substance sought, and thus produce a high result—for example, bromide will respond to titration as though it were chloride.

2) An interfering substance may react with the substance sought and thus produce a low result—for example, chloride will react with a portion of the nitrate in the presence of the sulfuric acid, using the phenoldisulfonic acid method.

3) An interfering substance may combine with the analytical reagent and thus prevent it from reacting with the substance sought—for example, chlorine will destroy many indicators and color-developing reagents.

Nearly every interference will fit one of these classes. For example, in a photometric method, turbidity may be considered as a "substance" which acts like the one being determined—that is, it reduces the transmission of light. Occasionally, two or more interfering substances, if present simultaneously, may interact in a nonadditive fashion, either canceling or enhancing one another's effects.

b. The best way to minimize interference is to remove the interfering substance or to render it innocuous by one of these methods:

1) Either the substance sought or the interfering substance may be removed physically: For example, fluoride and ammonia may be distilled off, leaving interferences behind; chloride may be converted to silver chloride and filtered off, leaving nitrate behind. The interferences may also be adsorbed on an ion-exchange resin, a process described more fully in Section 100B.

2) The pH may be adjusted so that only the substance sought will react.

3) The sample may be oxidized or reduced to convert the interfering substance to a harmless form—for example, chlorine may be reduced to chloride by adding thiosulfate.

4) The addition of a suitable agent may complex the interfering substance so that it is innocuous although still present: For example, iron may be complexed with pyrophosphate to pre-

vent it from interfering with the copper determination; copper may be complexed with cyanide or sulfide to prevent interference with the titrimetric hardness determination.

5) A combination of the first four technics may be used: For example, phenols are distilled from an acid solution to prevent amines from distilling; thiosulfate is used in the dithizone method for zinc to prevent most of the interfering metals from passing into the carbon tetrachloride layer.

6) Color and turbidity may sometimes be destroyed by wet or dry ashing, or may be removed by use of a flocculating agent. Some types of turbidity may be removed by filtration. These procedures, however, introduce the danger that the desired constituent will also be removed.

c. If none of these technics is practical, several methods of compensation can be used:

1) If the color or turbidity initially present in the sample interferes in a photometric determination, it may be possible to use photometric compensation. The technic is described in Section 000A.7 preceding.

2) The concentration of interfering substances may be determined and then identical amounts may be added to the calibration standards. This involves much labor.

3) If the interference does not continue to increase as the concentration of interfering substance increases, but tends to level off, then a large excess of interfering substance may be added routinely to all samples and to all standards. This is called "swamping." For example, an excess of calcium is added in the photometric magnesium determination.

4) The presence in the chemical reagents of the substance sought may be accounted for by carrying out a blank determination.

10. Recovery

A qualitative estimate of the presence or absence of interfering substances in a particular determination may be made by means of a recovery procedure. Although this method does not enable the analyst to apply any correction factor to the results of an analysis, it does give him some basis for judging the applicability of a particular method of analysis to a particular sample. Furthermore, it enables the analyst to obtain information in this regard without an extensive investigation to determine exactly which substances can interfere in the method used. It also does away with the necessity of making separate determinations on the sample for the interfering substances themselves.

A recovery may be performed at the same time as the determination itself. Of course, recoveries would not be run on a routine basis with samples whose general composition is known or when using a method whose applicability to the sample is well established. Recovery methods are to be regarded as tools to remove doubt about the applicability of a method to a sample. In brief, the recovery procedure involves applying the analytical method to a reagent blank; to a series of known standards covering the expected range of concentration of the sample; to the sample itself, in at least a duplicate run; and to the recovery samples, prepared by adding known quantities of the substance sought to separate portions of the sample itself, each portion equal to the size of sample taken for the run. The substance sought should be added in sufficient quantity to overcome the limits of error of the analytical method, but without causing the total in the sample to exceed the range of the known standards used.

The results are first corrected by subtracting the reagent blank from each of the other determined values. The resulting known standards are then graphically represented. From this graph, the amount of sought substance in the sample alone is determined. This value is then subtracted from each of the determinations consisting of sample plus known added substance. The resulting amount of substance divided by the known amount originally added and multiplied by 100 gives the percentage recovery.

The procedure outlined above may be applied to colorimetric or instrumental methods of analysis. It may also be applied in a more simple form to titrimetric, gravimetric and other types of analyses.

Rigid rules concerning the percentage recoveries required for acceptance of results of analyses for a given sample and method cannot be stipulated. Recoveries of substances in the range of the sensitivity of the method may, of course, be very high or very low and approach a value nearer to 100% recovery as the error of the method becomes small with respect to the magnitude of the amount of substance added. In general, intricate and exacting procedures for trace substances which have inherent errors due to their complexity may give recoveries that would be considered very poor and yet, from the practical viewpoint of usefulness of the result, may be quite acceptable. Poor results may reflect either interferences present in the sample or real inadequacy of the method of analysis in the range in which it is being used.

It must be stressed, however, that the judicious use of recovery methods for the evaluation of analytical procedures and their applicability to particular samples is an invaluable aid to the analyst in both routine and research investigations.

000 B. Expression of Results

1. Units

Analytical results should be expressed in milligrams per liter (mg/l). Assuming that 1 liter of water, sewage or industrial waste weighs 1 kilogram, milligrams per liter is equivalent to parts per million.* Only the significant figures (see Section 000B.2 below) should be recorded.

If the concentrations are generally less than 1 mg/l, it may be more convenient to express the results in micrograms per liter (μg/l). This is equivalent to parts per billion (ppb), where billion is understood to be 10^9. If the concentration is greater than 10,000

* It should be noted that, in water analysis, "parts per million" is *always* understood to imply a weight/weight ratio, even though in practice a volume may be measured instead of a weight. By contrast, "percent" may be either a volume/volume or a weight/weight ratio.

mg/l, the results should be expressed in percent, 1% being equivalent to 10,000 mg/l.

In reporting analyses of stream pollution or evaluating plant operation and efficiencies, it is desirable to express the results on a weighted basis, including both the concentration and the volume of flow in cubic feet per second (cfs) or million gallons daily (mgd). These weighted results may be expressed as *quantity units* (*QU*) according to the practice of the U.S. Public Health Service; as *pounds per 24 hr;* or as *population equivalents* based on biochemical oxygen demand (BOD). Totals of the weighted units may be converted to the weighted average mg/l. The various units are calculated as follows:

$$QU_1 = (\text{mg/l}) \times (1{,}000 \text{ cfs})$$

$$QU_2 = (\text{mg/l}) \times (\text{mgd})$$

$$\text{lb/24 hr} = (\text{mg/l}) \times (\text{mgd}) \times 8.34$$

$$\text{lb/24 hr} = (\text{mg/l}) \times (\text{cfs}) \times 5.39$$

Population equivalent

$$= (\text{mg/l 5-day BOD}) \times (\text{mgd}) \times \frac{8.34}{0.17}$$

Table 000(1) presents the factors which are useful for converting the concentrations of the common ions found in water—from milligrams per liter to milliequivalents per liter, and vice versa. The term milliequivalent used in this table represents 0.001 of an equivalent weight. The equivalent weight, in turn, is defined as the weight of the ion (sum of the atomic weights

TABLE 000(1): CONVERSION FACTORS *

(Milligrams per Liter—Milliequivalents per Liter)

Ion (Cation)	me/l = mg/l ×	mg/l = me/l ×	Ion (Anion)	me/l = mg/l ×	mg/l = me/l ×
Al^{3+}	0.1112	8.994	BO_2^-	0.02336	42.81
B^{3+}	0.2775	3.604	Br^-	0.01251	79.91
Ba^{2+}	0.01456	68.67	Cl^-	0.02821	35.45
Ca^{2+}	0.04990	20.04	CO_3^{2-}	0.03333	30.00
Cr^{3+}	0.05770	17.33	CrO_4^{2-}	0.01724	58.00
			F^-	0.05264	19.00
Cu^{2+}	0.03148	31.77	HCO_3^-	0.01639	61.02
Fe^{2+}	0.03581	27.92	HPO_4^{2-}	0.02084	47.99
Fe^{3+}	0.05372	18.62	$H_2PO_4^-$	0.01031	96.99
H^+	0.9921	1.008	HS^-	0.03024	33.07
K^+	0.02557	39.10	HSO_3^-	0.01233	81.07
Li^+	0.1441	6.939	HSO_4^-	0.01030	97.07
Mg^{2+}	0.08226	12.16	I^-	0.007880	126.9
Mn^{2+}	0.03640	27.47	NO_2^-	0.02174	46.01
Mn^{4+}	0.07281	13.73	NO_3^-	0.01613	62.00
Na^+	0.04350	22.99	OH^-	0.05880	17.01
NH_4^+	0.05544	18.04	PO_4^{3-}	0.03159	31.66
Pb^{2+}	0.009653	103.6	S^{2-}	0.06238	16.03
Sr^{2+}	0.02283	43.81	SiO_3^{2-}	0.02629	38.04
Zn^{2+}	0.03060	32.69	SO_3^{2-}	0.02498	40.03
			SO_4^{2-}	0.02083	48.03

* Factors are based on ion charge and not on redox reactions which may be possible for certain of these ions. Cations and anions are listed separately in alphabetical order.

of the atoms making up the ion) divided by the number of charges normally associated with the particular ion. The factors for converting results from mg/l to me/l were computed by dividing the ion charge by the weight of the ion. Conversely, the factors for converting results from me/l to mg/l were calculated by dividing the weight of the ion by the ion charge. This table is offered for the convenience of laboratories which report results in me/l as well as mg/l.

2. *Significant Figures*

To avoid ambiguity in reporting results or in presenting directions for a procedure, it is the custom to use "significant figures." All the digits in a reported result are expected to be known definitely, except for the last digit, which may be in doubt. Such a number is said to contain only significant figures. If more than a single doubtful digit is carried, the extra digit or digits are not significant. If an analytical result is reported as "75.6 mg/l," the analyst should be quite certain of the "75," but may be uncertain as to whether the ".6" should be .5 or .7, or even .4 or .8, because of unavoidable uncertainty in the analytical procedure. If the standard deviation were known from previous work to be ±2 mg/l, the analyst would have, or at least should have, rounded off the result to "76 mg/l" before reporting it. On the other hand, if the method were so good that a result of "75.61 mg/l" could have been conscientiously reported, then the analyst should not have rounded it off to 75.6.

A report should present only such figures as are justified by the accuracy of the work. The all too common practice of requiring that quantities listed in a column have the same number of figures to the right of the decimal point is justified in bookkeeping, but not in chemistry.

a. Rounding off: Rounding off is accomplished by dropping the digits which are not significant. If the digit 6, 7, 8 or 9 is dropped, then the preceding digit must be increased by one unit; if the digit 0, 1, 2, 3 or 4 is dropped, the preceding digit is not altered. If the digit 5 is dropped, the preceding digit is rounded off to the nearest even number: thus 2.25 becomes 2.2, and 2.35 becomes 2.4.

b. Ambiguous zeros: The digit 0 may record a measured value of zero, or it may serve merely as a spacer to locate the decimal point. If the result of a sulfate determination is reported as 420 mg/l, the recipient of the report may be in doubt whether the zero is significant or not, because the zero cannot be deleted. If an analyst calculates a total residue (total solids) content of 1,146 mg/l, but realizes that the 4 is somewhat doubtful and that therefore the 6 has no significance, he will round off the answer to 1,150 mg/l and so report, but here, too, the recipient of the report will not know whether the zero is significant. Although the number could be expressed as a power of 10 (e.g., 11.5×10^2 or 1.15×10^3), this form is not generally used, as it would not be consistent with the normal expression of results and might also be confusing. In most other cases, there will be no doubt as to the sense in which the digit 0 is used. It is obvious that the zeros are significant in such numbers as 104, 40.08, and 0.0003. In a number written as 5.000, it is understood that all the zeros are significant, or else the number could have been rounded off to 5.00, 5.0, or 5, whichever was appropriate. Whenever the zero is ambiguous, it is advisable to accompany the result with an estimate of its uncertainty.

Sometimes, significant zeros are dropped without good cause. If a buret is read as "23.60 ml," it should be so recorded, and not as "23.6 ml." The first number indicates that the analyst took the trouble to estimate the second decimal place; "23.6 ml" would indicate that he read the buret rather carelessly.

c. The plus-or-minus (±) *notation:* If a calculation yields as a result "1,476 mg/l" with a standard deviation estimated as ±40 mg/l, it should be reported as 1,480 ± 40 mg/l. But if the standard deviation is estimated as ±100 mg/l, the answer should be rounded off still further and reported as 1,500 ± 100 mg/l. By this device, ambiguity is avoided and the recipient of the report can tell that the zeros are only spacers. Even if the problem of ambiguous zeros is not present, showing the standard deviation is helpful in that it provides an estimate of reliability.

d. Calculations: As a practical operating rule, the result of a calculation in which several numbers are multiplied or divided together should be rounded off to as few significant figures as are present in the factor with the fewest significant figures. Suppose that the following calculation must be made in order to obtain the result of an analysis:

$$\frac{56 \times 0.003462 \times 43.22}{1.684}$$

A ten-place desk calculator yields an answer of "4.975740996," but this number must be rounded off to a mere "5.0" because one of the measurements, 56, which entered into the calculation has only two significant figures. It was a waste of time to measure the other three factors to four significant figures because the "56" is "the weakest link in the chain" and limits the accuracy of the answer. If the other factors were measured to only three, instead of four, significant figures, the answer would not suffer and the labor would be less.

When adding or subtracting numbers, that number which has the fewest decimal places, not necessarily the fewest significant figures, puts the limit on the number of places that may justifiably be carried in the sum or difference. Thus the sum

$$\begin{array}{r} 0.0072 \\ 12.02 \\ 4.0078 \\ 25.9 \\ 4{,}886 \\ \hline 4{,}927.9350 \end{array}$$

must be rounded off to a mere "4,928," no decimals, because one of the addends, 4,886, has no decimal places. Notice that another addend, 25.9, has only three significant figures and yet it does not set a limit to the number of significant figures in the answer.

The preceding discussion is necessarily oversimplified, and the reader is referred to the bibliography for a more detailed discussion.

000 C. Precision and Accuracy

A clear distinction should be made between the terms "precision" and "accuracy" when applied to methods of analysis. *Precision* refers to the reproducibility of a method when repeated on a homogeneous sample under controlled conditions, regardless of whether or not the observed values are widely displaced from the true value as a result of systematic or constant errors present throughout the measurements. Precision can be expressed by the standard deviation. *Accuracy* refers to the agreement between the amount of a component measured by the test method and the amount actually present. *Relative error* expresses the difference between the measured and the actual amounts, as a percentage of the actual amount. A method may have very high precision but recover only a part of the element being determined; or an analysis, although precise, may be in error because of poorly standardized solutions, inaccurate dilution technics, inaccurate balance weights, or improperly calibrated equipment. On the other hand, a method may be accurate but lack precision because of low instrument sensitivity, variable rate of biologic activity, or other factors beyond the control of the analyst.

It is possible to determine both the precision and the accuracy of a test method by analyzing samples to which known quantities of standard substances have been added. It is possible to determine the precision, but not the accuracy, of such methods as those for suspended solids, BOD, and numerous physical characteristics because of the unavailability of standard substances that can be added in known quantities on which percentage recovery can be based.

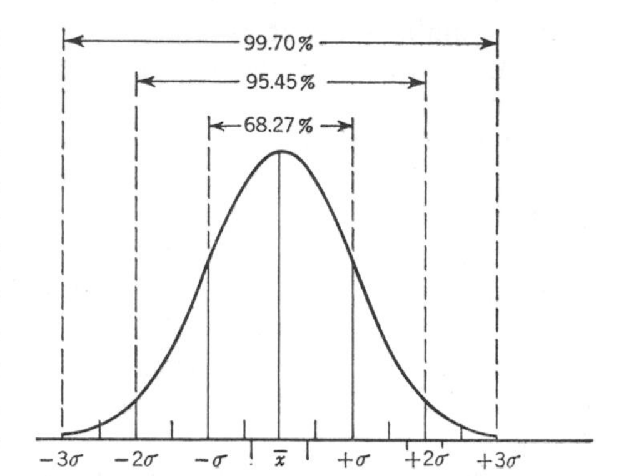

Figure 1. Gaussian or normal curve of frequencies.

1. Statistical Approach

a. Standard deviation (σ): Experience has shown that if a determination is repeated a large number of times under essentially the same conditions, the observed values, *x*, will be distributed at random about an average as a result of uncontrollable or experimental errors. If there are an infinite number of observations from a common universe of causes, a plot of the relative frequency against magnitude will produce a symmetrical bell-shaped curve known as the Gaussian or normal curve (Figure 1). The shape of this curve is completely defined by two statistical parameters: (1) the mean or average, $\bar{x}$, of n observations; and (2) the standard deviation, σ, which fixes the width or spread of the curve on each side of the mean. The formula is:

$$\sigma = \sqrt{\frac{\Sigma (x - \bar{x})^2}{n - 1}}$$

The proportion of the total observations lying within any given range about the mean is related to the standard deviation. For example, 68.27% of the observations lie between $\bar{x} \pm 1\ \sigma$; 95.45%, between $\bar{x} \pm 2\ \sigma$; and 99.70%, between $\bar{x} \pm 3\ \sigma$. These limits do not apply exactly for any finite sample from a normal population; the agreement with them may be expected to be better as the number of observations, n, increases.

b. Application of standard deviation: If the standard deviation, σ, for a particular analytical procedure has been determined from a large number of samples, and a set of n replicates on a sample gives a mean result $\bar{x}$, there is a 95% chance that the true value of the mean for this sample lies within the values $\bar{x} \pm 1.96\ \sigma/\sqrt{n}$. This range is known as the 95% confidence interval. It provides an estimate of the reliability of the mean, and may be used to forecast the number of replicates needed to secure suitable precision.

If the standard deviation is not known and is estimated from a single small * sample, or a few small samples, the 95% confidence interval of the mean of n observations is given by the equation $\bar{x} \pm t\sigma/\sqrt{n}$, where t has the following values:

n	t
2	12.71
3	4.30
4	3.18
5	2.78
10	2.26
∞	1.96

The use of t compensates for the tendency of small samples to underestimate the variability.

* A "small sample" in statistical discussions means a small number of replicate determinations, n, and does not refer to the quantity used for a determination.

c. Range (R): The difference between the smallest and largest of n observations is also closely related to the standard deviation. When the distribution of errors is normal in form, the range, R, of n observations exceeds the standard deviation times a factor d_n only in 5% of the cases. Values for the factor d_n are:

n	d_n
2	2.77
3	3.32
4	3.63
5	3.86
6	4.03

As it is rather general practice to run replicate analyses, use of these limits is very convenient for detecting faulty technic, large sampling errors, or other assignable causes of variation.

d. Rejection of experimental data: Quite often in a series of observations, one or more of the results deviate greatly from the mean, whereas the other values are in close agreement with the mean value. The problem arises at this point as to rejection of the disagreeing values. Theoretically, no results should be rejected, since the presence of disagreeing results shows faulty technics and therefore casts doubt on all the results. Of course the result of any test in which a known error has occurred is rejected immediately. For methods for the rejection of other experimental data, standard texts on analytical chemistry or statistical measurement should be consulted.

e. Presentation of precision and accuracy data: The precision and accuracy data are presented in one of three ways in this volume, depending on when and how the information was originally assembled.

In point of time, the oldest data are given in the wastewater section and present for the most part the precision with which certain determinations can be performed. These data first appeared in the 10th Edition and survive unchanged in the current volume. The complex character of wastewater samples initially dictated this approach.

Beginning with the 11th Edition, a concerted effort was made to offer an idea of the precision and accuracy with which selected methods can be applied on a broad geographic basis in examination of the relatively simpler water samples. The manner of best expressing the resulting data has remained to this day a matter of relentless study. The 11th and 12th Editions presented both precision and accuracy in terms of mg/l. This practice is retained for the time being where such data continue to be cited in this manual. However, experience of the past decade suggests that data can be presented with greater brevity and easier understanding in the form of a percentage. By this system, the standard deviation is expressed as a percentage of the mean and is now termed the relative standard deviation. It measures the precision or reproducibility of a method, independent of the known concentration of the sample constituent. Similarly, the relative error gives the difference between the mean of a series of test results and the true value, expressed as a percentage of the true value. Thus, the relative error represents the measure of the accuracy of a method. The relative standard deviation and relative error are preferred in quoting the precision and accuracy of a method because they are independent of the concentration.

f. Quality control: Quality control may be defined for the purpose of this manual as a statistical system for monitoring the precision (variation), or reproducibility, of analytical procedures in a given laboratory.

The control chart provides an important tool for identifying the causes of variation in the quality of a procedure. Certain variations in chemical procedures occur by chance, about which little or nothing can be done. However, variations can also result from "assignable causes" such as differences in methods, reagents, equipment, and the skill of persons performing the tests. Chance variations behave in a random manner and show no cycles, runs, or similarly recognizable pattern. If, on the other hand, the variations in the data exhibit cycles, runs, or a definite pattern, at least one assignable cause may be at work, and the conditions producing the variations are said to be "out of control."

Two basic types of control charts have proved valuable. The $\bar{x}$-chart is used to monitor the average of a procedure, while the R-chart is used to monitor the variability of a procedure. An $\bar{x}$-chart discloses the variation in the averages of a number of replications of a given procedure. It consists of a central line, $\bar{x}$, and upper and lower control limits, which may range from $+1\sigma$ to $+3\sigma$ and -1σ to -3σ standard deviations from the center line. (The values of $\bar{x}$ and the standard deviation are derived from past data.) Figure 5 in Section 100C.1 illustrates one application of control charts. As long as the sample averages remain inside the control limits and show only random variation within the limits, the procedure is said to be "in control" with respect to its central tendency. If an average falls outside the control limits, or if there is nonrandom variation within the limits, the process is said to be "out of control" with respect to its central tendency. Such a condition should prompt an investigation into the assignable cause or causes of the extreme variation.

The same basic principles which apply to the $\bar{x}$-chart also hold for the R-chart, except that the R-chart is a plotting of the ranges of samples. It reveals variations in the ranges of samples rather than variation in the averages of samples.

One of the most important factors in a quality control program is an adequate supply of a stable known control. This control can be a large sample from a natural source known to contain the constituent of concern or a synthetic sample prepared in the laboratory from chemicals of the highest purity grade. Once the test to be controlled has been selected, 20 or more determinations for the same constituent in the control sample are made under routine daily conditions. The values are then totaled and the average value is obtained. The standard deviation is calculated to ascertain the range of allowable variation that can be expected in routine work for this particular constituent. If this same sample is then treated as a routine daily control sample, it is possible to determine by the use of a control chart constructed from the original 20 determinations whether the daily assays for this constituent are in or out of control. When the control sample is prepared from chemicals of the highest purity, the probable accuracy of the determination can also be estimated.

Duncan's volume on *Quality Control and Industrial Statistics* describes the $\bar{x}$- and R-charts in detail and their relevance to quality control. Youden's book on *Statistical Techniques for Collaborative Tests* offers valuable information on collaborative tests.

2. Graphical Representation of Data

Graphical representation of data is one of the simplest methods for showing the influence of one variable on another. Graphs are frequently desirable and advantageous in colorimetric analysis because they show any variation of one variable with respect to the other within specified limits.

a. General: Ordinary rectangular-coordinate paper is satisfactory for most purposes. Twenty lines per inch is recommended. Semilogarithmic paper is convenient when one of the coordinates is to be the logarithm of an observed variable.

The five rules listed by Worthing and Geffner for choosing the coordinate scales are useful. Although these rules are not inflexible, they are satisfactory. When doubt arises, common sense should prevail. The rules are:

1) The independent and dependent variables should be plotted on abscissa and ordinate in a manner which can be easily comprehended.

2) The scales should be chosen so that the value of either coordinate can be found quickly and easily.

3) The curve should cover as much of the graph paper as possible.

4) The scales should be chosen so that the slope of the curve approaches unity as nearly as possible.

5) Other things being equal, the variables should be chosen to give a plot which will be as nearly a straight line as possible.

The title of a graph should adequately describe what the plot is intended to show. Legends should be presented on the graph to clarify possible ambiguities. Complete information on the conditions under which the data were obtained should be included in the legend.

b. Method of least squares: If sufficient points are available and the functional relationship between the two variables is well defined, a smooth curve can be drawn through the points. If the function is not well defined, as is frequently the case when using experimental data, the method of least squares is used to fit a straight line to the pattern.

Any straight line can be represented by the equation $x = my + b$. The slope of the line is represented by the constant m and the slope intercept (on the x axis) is represented by the constant b. The method of least squares has the advantage of giving a set of values for these constants not dependent upon the judgment of the investigator. Two equations besides the one for a straight line are involved in these calculations:

$$m = \frac{n\Sigma xy - \Sigma x \Sigma y}{n\Sigma y^2 - (\Sigma y)^2}$$

$$b = \frac{\Sigma y^2 \Sigma x - \Sigma y \Sigma xy}{n\Sigma y^2 - (\Sigma y)^2}$$

n being the number of observations (sets of x and y values) to be summed. In order to compute the constants by this method, it is first necessary to calculate Σx, Σy, Σy^2, and Σxy. These operations are carried out to more places than the number of significant figures in the experimental data because the experimental values are assumed to be exact for the purposes of the calculations.

Example: Given the following data to be graphed, find the best line to fit the points:

Absorbance	Solute Concentration *mg/l*
0.10	29.8
0.20	32.6
0.30	38.1
0.40	39.2
0.50	41.3
0.60	44.1
0.70	48.7

Let y equal the absorbance values which are subject to error, and x the accurately known concentration of solute. The first step is to find the summations (Σ) of x, y, y^2, and xy:

x	y	y^2	xy
29.8	0.10	0.01	2.98
32.6	0.20	0.04	6.52
38.1	0.30	0.09	11.43
39.2	0.40	0.16	15.68
41.3	0.50	0.25	20.65
44.1	0.60	0.36	26.46
48.7	0.70	0.49	34.09
Σ = 273.8	2.80	1.40	117.81

The next step is to substitute the summations in the equations for m and b; $n = 7$ as there are seven sets of x and y values:

$$m = \frac{7\,(117.81) - 2.80\,(273.8)}{7\,(1.40) - (2.80)^2} = 29.6$$

$$b = \frac{1.4\,(273.8) - 2.80\,(117.81)}{7\,(1.40) - (2.80)^2} = 27.27$$

To plot the line, three convenient values of y are selected—say, 0, 0.20, 0.60—and corresponding values of x are calculated:

$$x_0 = 29.6(0) + 27.27 = 27.27$$
$$x_1 = 29.6(0.20) + 27.27 = 33.19$$
$$x_2 = 29.6(0.60) + 27.27 = 45.04$$

When the points representing these values are plotted on the graph, they will lie in a straight line (unless an error in calculation has been made), which is the line of best fit for the

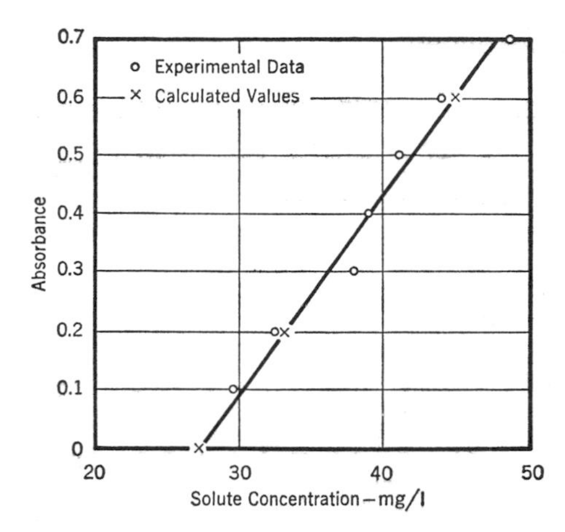

Figure 2. Example of least-squares method.

given data. The points representing the latter are also plotted on the graph, as in Figure 2.

3. *Self-Evaluation (Desirable Philosophy for the Analyst)*

A good analyst continually tempers his confidence with doubt. Such doubt stimulates a search for new and different methods of confirmation for his reassurance. Frequent self-appraisals should embrace every step—from collecting samples to reporting results.

The analyst's first critical scrutiny should be directed at the entire sample collection process in order to guarantee a representative sample for the purpose of the analysis and to avoid any possible losses or contamination during the act of collection. Attention should also be given to the type of container and to the manner of transport and storage, as discussed elsewhere in this volume.

A periodic reassessment should be made of the available analytical methods, with an eye to applicability for the purpose and the situation. In addition, each method selected must be evaluated by the analyst himself for sensitivity, precision and accuracy, because only in this way can he determine whether his technic is satisfactory and whether he has interpreted the directions properly. Self-evaluation on these points can give the analyst confidence in the value and significance of his reported results.

The benefits of less rigid intralaboratory as well as interlaboratory evaluations deserve serious consideration. The analyst can regularly check standard or unknown concentrations with and without interfering elements, and compare results on the same sample with other workers in the laboratory. Such programs can uncover weaknesses in the analytical chain and enable improvements to be instituted without delay. The results can disclose whether the trouble stems from faulty sample treatment, improper elimination of interference, poor calibration practices, sloppy experimental technic, impure or incorrectly standardized reagents, defective instrumentation, or even inadvertent mistakes in arithmetic.

Other checks of a water analysis are described in Section 100C and involve anion-cation balance, specific conductance, ion exchange, and the recovery of added substance in the sample (see also Section 000A.10 preceding).

All these approaches are designed to appraise and upgrade the level of laboratory performance and thus inspire greater faith in the final reported results.

000 D. References

1. W. D. SILVEY. 1961. Concentration method for the spectrochemical determination of minor elements in water. *U. S. Geological Survey Water Supply Paper* No. 1540-B.

2. ———. 1967. Occurrence of selected minor elements in the waters of California. *U. S. Geological Survey Water Supply Paper* No. 1535-L.

000 E. Bibliography

General

WELCH, P. S. 1948. *Limnological Methods.* Blakiston Co., Philadelphia.

HAUCK, C. F. 1949. Gaging and sampling waterborne industrial wastes. ASTM Bull. (Dec.)

BLACK, H. H. 1952. Procedures for sampling and measuring industrial wastes. *Sewage & Ind. Wastes* 24:45.

WELCH, P. S. 1952. *Limnology* (2nd ed.). McGraw-Hill Book Co., New York.

MANUFACTURING CHEMISTS' ASSOCIATION, GENERAL SAFETY COMMITTEE. 1954. *Guide for Safety in the Chemical Laboratory.* D. Van Nostrand Co., Princeton, N. J.

MINISTRY OF HOUSING AND LOCAL GOVERNMENT. 1956. *Methods of Chemical Analysis as Applied to Sewage and Sewage Effluents* (2nd ed.). Her Majesty's Stationery Office, London.

AMERICAN WATER WORKS ASSOCIATION. 1958. *Safety Practice for Water Utilities.* Manual M6, AWWA, New York.

TAYLOR, E. W. 1958. *Examination of Waters and Water Supplies* (7th ed.). Little, Brown & Co., Boston.

WORLD HEALTH ORGANIZATION. 1963. *International Standards for Drinking Water* (2nd ed.). WHO, Geneva.

HEM, J. D. 1959. Study and interpretation of the chemical characteristics of natural water. *U. S. Geological Survey Water Supply Paper* No. 1473.

KLEIN, LOUIS. 1959. *River Pollution. I. Chemical Analysis.* Academic Press, New York.

INSTITUTE OF WATER ENGINEERS. 1960. *Approved Methods for the Physical and Chemical Examination of Water* (3rd ed.). Inst. Water Eng., London.

RAINWATER, F. H. & L. L. THATCHER. 1960. Methods for collection and analysis of water samples. *U. S. Geological Survey Water Supply Paper* No. 1454.

AMERICAN SOCIETY FOR TESTING AND MATERIALS. 1962. *Manual on Industrial Water and Industrial Waste Water* (2nd ed.). Special Technical Pub. 148-I, ASTM, Philadelphia.

U. S. PUBLIC HEALTH SERVICE. 1963. Public Health Service drinking water standards, 1962. *PHS Pub. No.* 956.

CAMP, T. R. 1963. *Water and Its Impurities.* Reinhold Publishing Corp., New York.

CALIFORNIA STATE WATER POLLUTION CONTROL BOARD. 1963. *Water Quality Criteria* (2nd ed.). Calif. State Water Pollution Control Board, Sacramento.

STEERE, N. V., Ed. 1967. *Handbook of Laboratory Safety.* Chemical Rubber Company, Cleveland, Ohio.

SAWYER, C. N. & P. L. MCCARTY. 1967. *Chemistry for Sanitary Engineers* (2nd ed.). McGraw-Hill Book Co., New York.

AMERICAN WATER WORKS ASSOCIATION. 1950. *Water Quality and Treatment* (2nd ed.). AWWA, New York.

Water Supply Data

LOHR, E. W. & S. K. LOVE. 1954. The industrial utility of public water supplies in the United States. 1952. Parts 1 and 2. *U. S. Geological Survey Water Supply Papers* No. 1299 and 1300.

Laboratory Reagents

The Pharmacopoeia of the United States of America (17th rev.). 1965. Mack Printing Co., Easton, Pa., pp. 928–1067.

AMERICAN CHEMICAL SOCIETY. 1968. *Reagent Chemicals—American Chemical Society Specifications* (4th ed.). ACS, Washington, D. C.

ROSIN, J. 1967. *Reagent Chemicals and Standards* (5th ed.). D. Van Nostrand Co., Princeton, N. J.

NATIONAL BUREAU OF STANDARDS. 1968. Standard materials issued by the National Bureau of Standards. *NBS Misc. Pub.* 260.

General Analytical Technics

FOULK, C. W., H. V. MOYER & W. M. MACNEVIN. 1952. *Quantitative Chemical Analysis.* McGraw-Hill Book Co., New York.

WILLARD, H. H., N. H. FURMAN & C. E. BRICKER. 1956. *Elements of Quantitative Analysis* (4th ed.). D. Van Nostrand Co., Princeton, N. J.

HUGHES, J. C. 1959. Testing of glass volumetric apparatus. *NBS Circ. No.* 602.

WILSON, C. L. & D. W. WILSON, Eds. *Comprehensive Analytical Chemistry,* Vol. 1A (1959), Vol. 1B (1960), Vol. 1C (1962). Elsevier Publishing Co., New York.

VOGEL, A. I. 1962. *Textbook of Quantitative Inorganic Analysis, Including Elementary Instrumental Analysis* (3rd ed.). John Wiley & Sons, New York.

WELCHER, F. J., Ed. *Standard Methods of Chemical Analysis* (6th ed.), 1963, Vol. IIA; 1966, Vol. IIIA. D. Van Nostrand Co., Princeton, N. J.

MEITES, L., Ed. 1963. *Handbook of Analytical Chemistry.* McGraw-Hill Book Co., New York.

PECSOK, R. & L. D. SHIELDS. 1968. *Modern Methods of Chemical Analysis.* John Wiley & Sons, New York.

KOLTHOFF, I. M., E. J. MEEHAN, E. B. SANDELL & S. BRUCKENSTEIN. 1969. *Quantitative Chemical Analysis* (4th ed.). Macmillan Co., New York.

Colorimetric Technics

MELLON, M. G. 1947. Colorimetry and photometry in water analysis. *JAWWA* 39:341.

NATIONAL BUREAU OF STANDARDS. 1947. Terminology and symbols for use in ultraviolet, visible, and infrared absorptiometry. *NBS Letter Circ.* LC-857 (May 19).

GIBSON, K. S. & M. BALCOM. 1947. Transmission measurements with the Beckman quartz spectrophotometer. *J. Research NBS* 38:601.

SNELL, F. D. & C. T. SNELL. 1948. *Colorimetric Methods of Analysis* (3rd ed.). D. Van Nostrand Co., Princeton, N. J., Vol. 1.

MELLON, M. G., Ed. 1950. *Analytical Absorption Spectroscopy.* John Wiley & Sons, New York.

DISKANT, E. M. 1952. Photometric methods in water analysis. *JAWWA* 44:625.

BOLTZ, D. F., Ed. 1958. *Colorimetric Determination of Nonmetals.* Interscience Publishers, New York.

SANDELL, E. B. 1959. *Colorimetric Determination of Traces of Metals* (3rd ed.). Interscience Publishers, New York.

Potentiometric Titration

FURMAN, N. H. Potentiometric titrations. *Anal. Chem.* 22:33 (1950); 23:21 (1951); 26:84 (1954).

KOLTHOFF, I. M. & H. A. LAITINEN. 1958. *pH and Electrotitrations.* John Wiley & Sons, New York.

WILLARD, H. H., L. L. MERRITT & J. A. DEAN. 1965. *Instrumental Methods of Analysis* (4th ed.). D. Van Nostrand Co., Princeton, N. J.

Polarography

BUTTS, P. G. & M. G. MELLON. 1951. Polarographic determination of metals in industrial wastes. *Sewage & Ind. Wastes* 23:59.

MULLER, O. H. 1951. *Polarographic Method of Analysis* (2nd ed.). Chemical Education Publishing Co., Easton, Pa.

KOLTHOFF, I. M. & J. J. LINGANE. 1952. *Polarography* (2nd ed.). Interscience Publishers, New York.

Bibliography of Polarographic Literature, 1922–1955. 1956. E. H. Sargent Co., Chicago.

Emission Spectroscopy (See also References 1 and 2 above)

HARRISON, G. R. 1939. *Wavelength Tables.* John Wiley & Sons, New York.

BRODE, W. 1943. *Chemical Spectroscopy* (2nd ed.). John Wiley & Sons, New York.

HARRISON, G. R., R. C. LORD & J. R. LOOFBOUROW. 1948. *Practical Spectroscopy.* Prentice-Hall, New York.

NACHTRIEB, N. H. 1950. *Principles and Practice of Spectrochemical Analysis.* McGraw-Hill Book Co., New York.

HARVEY, C. E. 1950. *Spectrochemical Procedures.* Applied Research Labs., Glendale, Calif.

SAWYER, R. A. 1951. *Experimental Spectroscopy* (2nd ed.). Prentice-Hall, New York.

TWYMAN, F. 1951. *Metal Spectroscopy* (2nd ed.). Charles Griffin & Co., London.

AHERNS, L. A. 1954. *Quantitative Spectrochemical Analysis of Silicates.* Pergamon Press, London.

MEGGERS, W. F. Emission spectroscopy. *Anal. Chem.* 21:29 (1949); 22:18 (1950); 24:23 (1952); 26:54 (1954); 28:616 (1956).

AHRENS, L. H. & S. R. TAYLOR. 1961. *Spectrochemical Analysis* (2nd ed.). Addison-Wesley Publishing Co., Reading, Mass.

AMERICAN SOCIETY FOR TESTING AND MATERIALS. 1961. *Methods for Emission Spectro-chemical Analysis* (3rd ed.). ASTM, Philadelphia.

Other New Methods of Analysis

LOVE, S. K. 1951. Analytical instruments used in the modern water plant laboratory. *JAWWA* 43:725.

BOLTZ, D. F., Ed. 1952. *Selected Topics in Modern Instrumental Analysis.* Prentice-Hall, New York.

OSBORN, G. H. 1953. Bibliography on the analytical applications of ion-exchange resins. *Analyst* 78:221.

EWING, G. W. 1954. *Instrumental Methods of Chemical Analysis.* McGraw-Hill Book Co., New York.

LEDERER, E. & M. LEDERER. 1957. *Chromatography* (2nd ed.). Elsevier Press, Houston, Tex.

BLOCK, R. J., E. L. CURRUM & G. ZWEIG. 1958. *A Manual of Paper Chromatography and Paper Electrophoresis* (2nd ed.). Academic Press, New York.

LINGANE, J. J. 1958. *Electroanalytical Chemistry* (2nd ed.). Interscience Publishers, New York.

SAMUELSON, O. 1963. *Ion Exchangers in Analytical Chemistry.* John Wiley & Sons, New York.

HARLEY, J. H. & S. E. WIBERLEY. 1967. *Instrumental Analysis* (2nd ed.). John Wiley & Sons, New York.

HEFTMANN, E., Ed. 1967. *Chromatography* (2nd ed.). Reinhold Publishing Corp., New York.

General Analytical Reviews and Bibliographies

WEIL, B. H. et al. 1948. *Bibliography on Water and Sewage Analysis.* State Engineering Experiment Station, Georgia Institute of Technology, Atlanta.

Annual reviews of analytical chemistry. *Anal. Chem.* 25:2 (1953); 26:2 (1954); 27:574 (1955); 28:559 (1956); 29:589 (1957); 30:553 (1958); 31:776 (1959); 32:3R (1960); 33.3R (1961); 34:3R (1962); 35:3R (1963); 36:3R (1964); 37:1R (1965); 38:1R (1966); 39:1R (1967); 40:1R (1968); 41:1R (1969).

Annual literature review, analytical methods. *JWPCF* 32:443 (1960); 33:445 (1961); 34:419 (1962); 35:553 (1963); 36:535 (1964); 37:735 (1965); 38:869 (1966); 39:867 (1967); 40:897 (1968); 41:873 (1969).

Statistics

WORTHING, A. G. & J. GEFFNER. 1943. *Treatment of Experimental Data.* John Wiley & Sons, New York.

AMERICAN SOCIETY FOR TESTING AND MATERIALS. 1950. Symposium on application of statistics. *ASTM Spec. Tech. Pub.* 103.

———. 1951. Manual on quality control of materials. *ASTM Spec. Tech. Pub.* 15C.

DEAN, R. B. & W. J. DIXON. 1951. Simplified statistics for small numbers of observations. *Anal. Chem.* 23:636.

YOUDEN, W. J. 1951. *Statistical Methods for Chemists.* John Wiley & Sons, New York.

KOLTHOFF, I. M. & E. B. SANDELL. 1952. *Textbook of Quantitative Inorganic Analysis* (3rd ed.). Macmillan Co., New York, Chapter 15.

GORE, W. L. 1952. *Statistical Methods for Chemical Experimentation.* Interscience Publishers, New York.

DIXON, W. J. & F. J. MASSEY, JR. 1957. *Introduction to Statistical Analysis* (2nd ed.). McGraw-Hill Book Co., New York.

DUNCAN, A. J. 1959. *Quality Contents Industrial Statistics.* Richard R. Irwin, Inc., Homewood, Ill.

Guide for measures of precision and accuracy. 1962. *Anal Chem.* 34:364R.

HOEL, P. G. 1962. *Introduction to Mathematical Statistics.* John Wiley & Sons, New York.

OSTLE, B. 1963. *Statistics in Research.* Iowa State Univ. Press, Ames.

YOUDEN, W. J. 1967. *Statistical Techniques for Collaborative Tests.* Association of Official Analytical Chemists, Washington, D. C.

GREENBERG, A. E., N. MOSKOWITZ, B. R. TAMPLIN & J. THOMAS. 1969. Chemical reference samples in water laboratories. *JAWWA* 61:599.

PART 100

PHYSICAL AND CHEMICAL EXAMINATION OF NATURAL AND TREATED WATERS IN THE ABSENCE OF GROSS POLLUTION

INTRODUCTION

The procedures described in Part 100 of this manual are intended for the physical and chemical examination of natural and treated waters in the absence of gross pollution. Such waters include surface water, ground water, softened water, cooling or circulating water, process water, boiler water, and boiler feedwater. Other parts of this manual are applicable to examination of sewages and industrial wastes. The examination of water as an industrial raw material is described in the ASTM *Manual on Industrial Water and Waste Water*,[1] which is intended to cover only methods of examination and analysis, not standards of quality. For the effects of various constituents, see the 1962 U.S. Public Health Service Drinking Water Standards,[2] *Water Quality and Treatment*,[3] and *Water Quality Criteria*.[4]

The physical and chemical recommendations of the 1962 U.S. Public Health Service Drinking Water Standards [2] are presented in Table 100(1).

TABLE 100(1): U.S. PUBLIC HEALTH SERVICE DRINKING WATER STANDARDS, 1962

Characteristic	Suggested Limit That Should Not Be Exceeded	Cause for Rejection
Physical		
Color	15 units	
Taste	Unobjectionable	
Threshold odor number	3	
Turbidity	5 units	
Chemical	*mg/l*	*mg/l*
Alkyl benzene sulfonate	0.5	
Arsenic	0.01	0.05
Barium		1.0
Cadmium		0.01
Chloride	250	
Chromium (hexavalent)		0.05
Copper	1	
Carbon chloroform extract *	0.2	
Cyanide	0.01	0.2
Fluoride †	0.7–1.2	1.4–2.4
Iron	0.3	
Lead		0.05
Manganese	0.05	
Nitrate	45	
Phenols	0.001	
Selenium		0.01
Silver		0.05
Sulfate	250	
Total dissolved solids	500	
Zinc	5	

* Organic contaminants.

† The concentration of fluoride may be between 0.6 and 1.7 mg/l, depending on the listed annual average maximum daily air temperatures.

The concentrations in the first column should not be present in a water supply in excess of the listed concentrations where, in the judgment of the reporting agency and the certifying authority, other more suitable supplies are or can be made available. The values listed in the second column constitute grounds for the rejection of the drinking water. In the matter of radioactivity the supply shall be approved if the amounts of radium 226 and strontium 90 do not exceed 3 and 10 pCi/l respectively, and, in the known absence of strontium-90 and alpha emitters, gross beta concentrations do not exceed 1,000 pCi/l.

100 A. Collection of Samples

1. Quantity

A 2-liter sample should suffice for most physical and chemical analyses. For certain special determinations, larger samples may be necessary. No attempt should be made to use the same sample for chemical, bacteriologic, and microscopic examinations because the methods of collection and handling are quite different.

2. Time Interval between Collection and Analysis

In general, the shorter the time that elapses between collection of a sample and its analysis, the more reliable will be the analytical results. For certain constituents and physical values, immediate analysis in the field is required in order to obtain dependable results, because the composition of the sample may change before it arrives at the laboratory.

It is impossible to state unequivocally how much time may be allowed to elapse between collection of a sample and its analysis; this depends upon the character of the sample, the particular analyses to be made, and the conditions of storage. Changes caused by the growth of organisms may be greatly retarded by keeping the sample in the dark and at a low temperature until it can be analyzed. The following maximum limits are suggested as reasonable for samples for physical and chemical analysis:

Unpolluted waters	72 hr
Slightly polluted waters	48 hr
Polluted waters	12 hr

The time elapsed between collection and analysis should be recorded on the laboratory report. If the samples are preserved by the addition of acid or other germicide, they may be allowed to stand for longer periods than those just mentioned, but no specific recommendations can be offered. The laboratory report should state which, if any, preservative was added.

Some determinations are more likely to be affected than others by storage of samples prior to analysis. Certain cations are subject to loss by adsorption on or ion exchange with the walls of glass containers. Such cations include aluminum, cadmium, chromium, copper, iron, lead, manganese, silver and zinc, which are best collected in a separate clean bottle and acidified with concentrated hydrochloric or nitric acid to a pH of approximately 3.5 in order to minimize precipitation and adsorption on the walls of the container.

Temperature can change very quickly; pH may change significantly in a matter of minutes; dissolved gases may be lost (oxygen, carbon dioxide, hydrogen sulfide, chlorine) or gained (oxygen, carbon dioxide). For this reason, determinations of temperature, pH, and dissolved gases should always be carried out in the field. With changes in the pH-alkalinity-carbon dioxide balance, calcium carbonate may precipitate and cause a decrease in the values for calcium and for total hardness.

Iron and manganese form readily soluble compounds in their lower (reduced) valence states, and relatively insoluble compounds in their higher (oxidized) valence states; therefore, these cations may precipitate out, or they may dissolve out of a sediment, depending upon the redox potential of the sample. Microbiologic activity may be responsible for changes in the nitrate-nitrite-ammonia balance, for decreases in phenols and in BOD, or for the reduction of sulfate to sulfide. Any residual chlorine is converted to chloride. Sulfide, sulfite, ferrous iron, iodide and cyanide may be lost through oxidation. Color, odor and turbidity may increase, decrease, or change in quality. Sodium, silica and boron may be leached out of the glass container. Hexavalent chromium may be reduced to the trivalent state.

This list is by no means all-inclusive. It is clearly impossible to prescribe absolute rules for the prevention of all possible changes. Some advice will be found in the discussions under individual determinations, but to a large degree the dependability of water analyses must rest upon the experience and good judgment of the analyst.

3. *Representative Samples*

Often much time and trouble can be saved if the analyst and the person for whom the tests are to be made will confer in advance concerning the best technic for collecting and analyzing the sample.

Care should be taken to obtain a sample that is truly representative of existing conditions, and to handle it in such a way that it does not deteriorate or become contaminated before it reaches the laboratory. Before filling, the sample bottle should be rinsed out two or three times with the water to be collected. Representative samples of some supplies can be obtained only by making composites of samples which have been collected over a period of time or at many different sampling points. The details of collection vary so much with local conditions that no specific recommendations would be universally applicable. Sometimes it will be more informative to analyze numerous separate samples instead of one composite.

Care must be exercised to insure that the analyses are representative of the actual composition of the water sample. Important factors affecting the results are the presence of turbidity, the method chosen for its removal, and the physical and chemical changes brought about by storage or aeration. Each sample showing turbidity must be treated individually with regard to the substances to be determined, the amount and nature of the turbidity present, and other conditions which may influence the results.

It is impossible to give directions covering all conditions which will be encountered, and the choice of technic must be left to the analyst's judgment. In general, any significant amount of suspended matter should be separated by decantation, centrifugation, or an appropriate filtration procedure. Often a slight amount of turbidity can be tolerated if experience shows that it will cause no interference in gravimetric or volumetric tests and that it can be corrected for in colorimetric tests, where it has potentially the greatest interfering effect. When pertinent, the analyst should state whether or not the sample has been filtered.

A record should be made of every sample collected, and every bottle should be identified, preferably by attaching an appropriately inscribed tag or label. The record should contain sufficient information to provide positive identification of the sample at a later date, as well as the name of the sample collector, the date, hour, and exact location, the water temperature, and any data which may be needed in the future for correlation, such as weather conditions, water level, stream flow, or the like. Sampling points should be fixed by detailed description, by maps, or with the aid of stakes, buoys or landmarks in such a manner as to permit their identification by other persons without reliance upon memory or personal guidance.

Hot samples collected under pressure should be cooled while under pressure (see Section 100E.3 and Figure 6).

Before samples are collected from distribution systems, the lines should be flushed for a sufficient period to insure that the sample is representative of the supply, taking into account the diameter and length of the pipe to be flushed and the velocity of flow.

Samples from wells should be collected only after the well has been pumped for a sufficient time to insure that the sample will represent the ground water which feeds the well. Sometimes it will be necessary to pump at a specified rate to achieve a characteristic drawdown, if this determines the zones from which the well is supplied. It may be desirable to record the pumping rate and the drawdown as part of the sample record.

When samples are collected from a river or stream, the analytical values may vary with depth, stream flow, and distance from shore and from one shore to the other. If equipment is available, it is best to take an "integrated" sample from top to bottom in the middle of the stream in such a way that the sample is made composite according to the flow. If only a grab sample can be collected, it is best taken in the middle of the stream and at mid-depth.

Lakes and reservoirs are subject to considerable variations from normal causes such as seasonal stratification, rainfall, runoff, and wind. The choice of location, depth and frequency of sampling will depend upon local conditions and upon the purpose of the investigation.

These general directions do not provide enough information for collecting samples in which dissolved gases are to be determined, and specific instructions will be found in the sections which describe these determinations.

100 B. Ion-Exchange Resins

Ion-exchange resins provide the chemist with an important analytical tool. In water analysis, ion exchangers can be applied to: (a) remove interfering ions, (b) determine total ion content, (c) indicate the approximate volume of sample for certain gravimetric determinations, (d) concentrate trace quantities of cations, and (e) separate anions from cations. This manual recommends the use of ion-exchange resins for the removal of interference in the sulfate determination and for the determination of total ion content. Inasmuch as the ion-exchange process can be applied in other determinations, a brief description of typical operations will be given here for convenient use where supplementary applications are warranted.

1. Selection of Method

The batch method of ion exchange is satisfactory for sample volumes below 100 ml, while the column method is recommended for larger sample volumes. In the batch method, the resin is agitated with the sample for a given period, after which the resin is removed by filtration. The column method is more efficient in that it provides continuous contact between the sample and the resin, thereby enabling the exchange reaction to go to completion. In this modification, the solution passes slowly through the resin bed and the given ions are quantitatively removed from the sample. Elution of the resin permits recovery of the adsorbed substances.

2. Procedure

Use resins specifically manufactured for analytical applications. Prepare the ion exchanger by rinsing the resin with several volumes of ion-free water (good-quality distilled water) to remove any coloring matter and other leachable material which might interfere with subsequent colorimetric procedures.

a. BATCH METHOD FOR CATION REMOVAL: Pipet an aliquot containing 0.1 to 0.2 me of cations into a 250-ml erlenmeyer flask or beaker and add enough distilled water to bring the final volume to 75 ml. Add 2.0 g strongly acidic cation-exchange resin and stir the mixture at moderate speed for 15 min. Filter through a plug of glass wool placed in the neck of a 4-in. pyrex funnel. When the filtration is complete, wash the resin with two 10-ml portions of distilled water and make up to 100 ml total volume with distilled water.

Regeneration and storage of resin: Transfer the spent resin from the batch procedure to a flask containing 500 ml 3*N* nitric acid. When sufficient resin has accumulated, wash into a column (Figure 3) and regenerate by passing 3*N* nitric acid through the column at a

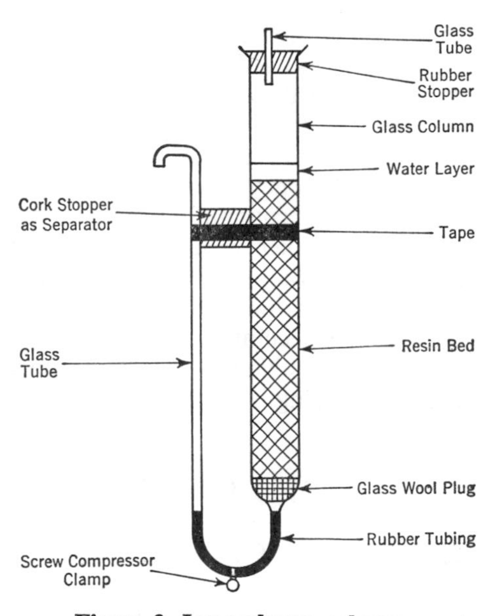

Figure 3. Ion-exchange column.

rate of 0.1 to 0.2 ml of acid per milliliter of resin per minute. Use 50 me of 3*N* nitric acid per milliliter of resin in the column. Finally, wash the resin with sufficient distilled water until the pH of the effluent is 5–7, using the same rate of flow as in the regeneration step. If desired, remove the resin from the column and store under distilled water in a wide-mouth container. Should the water become colored during storage, decant and replace with fresh distilled water. Prior to use, filter the resin through a plug of glass wool placed in the neck of a funnel, wash with distilled water, and allow to drain. The resin is then ready for use.

b. COLUMN METHOD FOR CATION REMOVAL: Prepare the column as depicted in Figure 3 (length of resin bed, 21.5 cm; diameter of column, 1.3 cm; representing approximately 21 ml, or 20 g of resin). Other ion-exchange columns can be used equally well. One of the simplest consists of a buret containing a plug of glass wool immediately above the stopcock. (Whatever type of column is adopted, never allow the liquid level in the column to fall below the upper surface of the resin because the trapped air causes uneven flow rates and poor efficiency of ion exchange.)

Charge the column by stirring the resin in a beaker with distilled water and then carefully washing the suspension into the column through a funnel. Backwash the column immediately by introducing distilled water at the bottom and passing it upward through the column until all air bubbles and channels are removed from the column. Connect a separatory funnel to the top of the column. Allow the sample to flow through the column at the rate of 0.2 ml of solution per milliliter of resin in the column per minute. After all of the sample has passed through the column, wash the resin with distilled water until the effluent pH is 5–7. Use strips of blue litmus paper or other indicating methods to determine when the column has been washed free of acid. When adsorbing cations from such large volumes of sample as one or more liters, conveniently start this operation before the close of a workday and allow the exchange process to proceed overnight. The column will not run dry because of the curved outlet.

Column elution: After the distilled-water wash, elute the adsorbed cations by passing 100 ml 3*N* nitric acid through the column at a rate of 0.2 ml of acid per milliliter of resin per minute. Since a volume of 100 ml 3*N* nitric acid quantitatively removes 3 me of cations, use additional increments of 100 ml 3*N* nitric acid for quantities of adsorbed cations in excess of 3 me. After the elution step, rinse the column free of acid with enough distilled water to produce an effluent pH of 5–7. Conduct the wash at the same flow rate as the acid elution. The acid elution and wash regenerate the column for future use. The combined acid eluates contain the cations originally present in the sample.

100 C. Checking Correctness of Analyses

1. Anion-Cation Balance

Theoretically, the sum of the anions, expressed in me/l, must exactly equal the sum of the cations, in me/l, in any sample. In practice, the sums are seldom equal because of unavoidable vari-

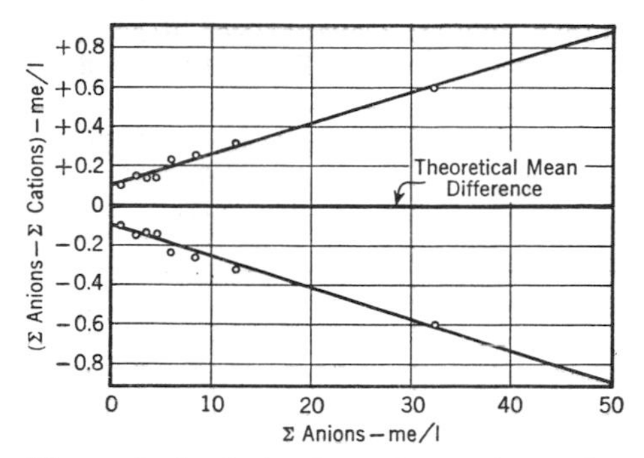

Figure 4. Control chart for anion-cation balances.

ations in the analysis. This inequality increases as the ionic concentration increases. A control chart can be constructed so that it will be immediately evident if the difference between the sum of the anions and cations, in me/l, falls between acceptable limits, which have been taken as ±1 standard deviation. If the difference is plotted against the sum of the anions, the lines showing ±1 standard deviation, that is, the acceptable limits, are given by the equation:

$$\Sigma \text{ anions} - \Sigma \text{ cations} = \pm (0.1065 + 0.0155\ \Sigma \text{ anions})$$

This is shown in Figures 4 and 5, which represent modified control charts. Values of differences of the sums falling outside of the limits set by the equations indicate that at least one of the determinations deserves to be rechecked.

By a fortuitous combination of erroneous analyses which result in the balancing of errors (compensating errors), it is possible for the sum of the anions to agree with the sum of the cations even though two or more individual analytical results are seriously incorrect. The additional methods of checking which follow are useful for detecting such discrepancies.

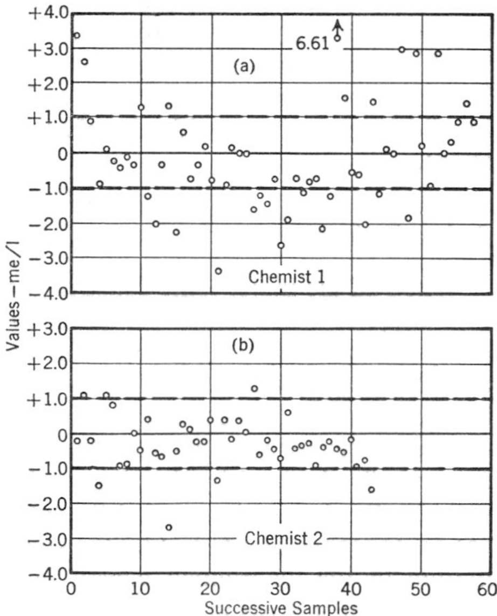

Figure 5. Control chart with transformed limits: The vertical scale is plotted:

$$\frac{\Sigma \textit{ anions} - \Sigma \textit{ cations}}{0.1065 + 0.0155\ \Sigma \textit{ anions}}$$

2. *Specific Conductance*

In using specific conductance to check analyses, two methods of calculation may be employed.

a. *Rough calculation:* In most natural waters it has been found that when specific conductance (in micromhos/cm at 25 C) is multiplied by a factor which ordinarily lies in the range 0.55–0.7, the product is equal to mg/l total filtrable residue. For waters which contain appreciable concentrations of free acid or caustic alkalinity, the factor may be much lower than 0.55, and for highly saline waters it may be much higher than 0.7. An approximate check based on this principle will reveal gross mistakes in analysis.

b. *More refined calculations:* In order to obtain better results based upon electrical conductance, it is necessary to dilute the sample so that its conductance falls within a narrow range and to take into account the contribution of each separate ion to the total measured conductance. Distilled water, boiled and cooled, is used to dilute the sample in a known ratio until the conductance lies between 90 and 120 micromhos/cm. Some trial may be necessary to achieve the proper dilution, because the conductance does not vary in exact ratio to the dilution; if it did, dilution would be unnecessary. The exact dilution ratio, D, must be known:

$$D = \frac{V_s + V_w}{V_s}$$

in which V_s is volume of sample and V_w is volume of distilled water. The conductance of the distilled water must be determined; it should not be greater than 2 micromhos/cm. Conductance is determined in the usual way. The "diluted conductance," K_d, is calculated from the equation:

$$K_d = \frac{AD \times 10^6}{R_d} - (D - 1)\,K_w$$

where A is the cell constant, R_d is the measured resistance, in ohms, of the diluted sample, and K_w is the distilled-water conductance.

Next, the diluted conductance is computed from the chemical analysis by multiplying the concentration found (as either me/l or mg/l) by the appropriate factor in Table 100(2) and summing the products. If this computed diluted conductance is more than 1.5% greater or more than 2% lower than the measured value of the diluted conductance, it is advisable to recheck the chemical analysis.

The diluted-conductance method of checking is not applicable to samples which have conductances initially lower than 90 micromhos/cm or which have pH values less than 6 or greater than 9, or to samples which contain significant quantities of ions not listed in Table 100(2). The conductances due to hydrogen ion and hydroxyl ion are much greater than those due to other ions, and will cause the method to be invalid for samples outside the pH 6–9 range.

TABLE 100(2): CONDUCTANCE FACTORS OF IONS COMMONLY FOUND IN WATER

Ion	Conductance (25 C) *micromhos/cm*	
	Per me/l	Per mg/l
Bicarbonate	43.6	0.715
Calcium	52.0	2.60
Carbonate	84.6	2.82
Chloride	75.9	2.14
Magnesium	46.6	3.82
Nitrate	71.0	1.15
Potassium	72.0	1.84
Sodium	48.9	2.13
Sulfate	73.9	1.54

3. *Ion Exchange*

When all the major ionic constituents of a simple natural water are quantitatively determined, the accuracy of the chemical analysis can also be checked by means of an ion-exchange method. A serious discrepancy between the cations, me/l, obtained by titration of the sample after ion exchange and the total cation concentration found by the summation of the determined constituents can uncover a gross error in the water analysis.

The ion-exchange method is based upon the replacement of the cations in the original sample with hydrogen ions supplied by a strongly acidic cation-exchange resin. The acid produced by mixing the sample with the resin is titrated with standard sodium hydroxide. The total alkalinity of the original sample must also be ascertained in order to complete the calculation.

The apparatus required for the ion-exchange method consists of a pH meter (line- or battery-operated) or methyl orange indicator; a magnetic or mechanical stirrer provided with a speed control; a 10-ml buret graduated in 0.05-ml steps; and glass wool. The reagents comprise 0.02*N* standard acid, 0.02*N* standard sodium hydroxide, a strongly acidic cation-exchange resin like Amberlite IR-120 (H) * of analytical grade, and distilled water.

The procedure is carried out by pipetting a sample of water containing 0.1 to 0.2 me of cations into a 250-ml erlenmeyer flask or beaker and adding enough distilled water to bring the final volume to 100 ml. Then 2.0 g of cation-exchange resin is added and the mixture is stirred at moderate speed for 15 min. The resin is removed by filtration through a plug of glass wool placed in the neck of a 4-in. pyrex funnel and is washed with two 15-ml portions of distilled water. The combined filtrate and washings are titrated to pH 4.5 with 0.02*N* standard sodium hydroxide, using a pH meter or methyl orange as end-point indicator, and stirring the solution during the titration.

The cation exchange can also be performed by the column method described in Section 100B.2b preceding.

The alkalinity present in the water sample, in me/l, is determined by titrating an aliquot of the original water sample to a pH of 4.5 with 0.02*N* standard acid, using a pH meter or methyl orange as end-point indicator.

The total cations in the sample (*E*, me/l) is finally computed by the equation:

$$E = \frac{AB \times 1{,}000}{C} + D \qquad 1$$

in which A is the volume (ml) of the standard sodium hydroxide used in titrating the filtrate from the ion exchange, B is the normality of the standard sodium hydroxide, C is the volume (ml) of water sample taken, and D is the alkalinity (me/l) present in the water sample.

The column method of ion exchange is preferred for checking the results of the gravimetric determinations for filtrable residues because less attention to the total milliequivalents of cations in the sample is required.

The filtrable and fixed filtrable residues are determined by multiplying the quantity $(E - D)$ from the preceding Eq 1 by a factor—usually found to be between 70 and 90, depending on the water tested and the resin used in the column—and adding $50D$. For more accurate determinations, the factors can be derived for the type of water tested routinely by subtracting $50D$ from the filtrable residues and dividing the results by the quantity $(E - D)$, thus:

$$\frac{R_{fg} - 50D}{E - D} = F_1 \qquad 2$$

$$\frac{R_{ffg} - 50D}{E - D} = F_2 \qquad 3$$

where R_{fg} and R_{ffg} are the filtrable and fixed filtrable residues determined gravimetrically and F_1 and F_2 are the resulting factors. The equations for calculating the filtrable residues are then:

$$(E - D)\,F_1 + 50D = R_{fs} \qquad 4$$
$$(E - D)\,F_2 + 50D = R_{ffs} \qquad 5$$

* Rohm and Haas Company.

where R_{fx} and R_{ffx} are the filtrable and fixed filtrable residues determined by ion exchange.

Once these factors are derived for the particular water, the filtrable-residue values can be determined by ion exchange and the gravimetric values obtained less frequently, or only when there is a major change in the water being checked.

For approximation purposes, a factor of 80 may be used in either Eq 4 or Eq 5. If the water tested has an unusually high sulfate or bicarbonate content compared to chloride (mg/l), or has unusually high organic content, the factor in Eq 4 approaches 90. If the water tested has an unusually high chloride content compared to sulfate (mg/l), the factor more nearly approximates 70.

100 D. Evaluation of Methods in Water Section

The precision and accuracy data cited in Part 100 for a number of laboratory determinations are based on results of studies by the Analytical Reference Service * which is conducted by the Public Health Service.

This activity is devoted to the collaborative study of water chemistry methodology. These studies provide a basis for the evaluation of selected analytical methods—both existing standard methods and new methods that offer promise. They supply a factual basis for judgment of what may be expected by practitioners applying such methods. Currently almost 300 agencies—public, private and universities—comprise the membership of the Analytical Reference Service.

* Information brochure available upon request of PHS.

100 E. Examination of Industrial Water Supplies

The following brief paragraphs summarize the reasons for conducting an examination of an industrial water supply. Inasmuch as this section is limited in scope, the reader is urged to refer to comprehensive reference books on industrial water treatment [1, 5–7] for an appreciation of the complexities of the subject.

1. Industrial Needs

Industrial water is that water used directly or indirectly in an industrial process. From a volume standpoint, the most important industrial usage is cooling, either on a once-through basis or with cooling towers. Of almost equal importance is industrial water destined for steam generation.

Many industries, particularly those producing foods and beverages, use water as a raw material. Still others, such as the dye industry, take advantage of water's solvent power. One of the newest uses of water is in the nuclear industries for radiation shielding and reactor modulation. Other industries use water to carry matter, as in hydraulic classifiers, or to carry energy, as in high-pressure sprays for debarking timber or descaling steel.

2. *Industrial Water Treatment*

Water, as found in nature, is seldom suitable for industrial use. Fortunately, technics exist for fitting any water to any job. The only limitation is imposed by economics.

Water treatment may be divided into two phases. Primary, external, or pretreatment is that treatment applied to water before it reaches the point of use. Secondary, internal, or posttreatment takes place after the water reaches the point of use.

Although the number of basic water treatment processes and operations is not large, the combinations and variations of these steps are almost infinite. For example, treatment for a boiler feedwater may consist of sedimentation, chlorination, cold lime soda, filtration, ion exchange, acidizing, aeration, and degassing. A discussion of these treatment processes is beyond the scope of this book.

3. *Analysis of Industrial Water*

The matter of examination assumes great importance during the selection of a proper supply for a specific industrial application or a variety of uses.[2-4]

Diagnosis of existing or potential water problems requires a maximum of information concerning the particular system involved. Thorough and accurate analyses of makeup water and of water from operating systems, analyses and examination of deposits and sections removed from operating systems, plus full information on the size, design characteristics and operating conditions of the water system or water-using equipment are all desirable in helping the water treatment specialist to make a decision regarding the materials that must be removed or added to the water by treatment in order to render it suitable for the intended process. Guidelines are difficult to give in a limited space, except to say that there is no substitute for experience.

Once the most suitable raw water supply has been chosen and a treatment system has been established, a control testing program is inaugurated to insure adequate treatment rather than expensive overtreatment.[5-7] A control testing schedule can vary from a simple color comparison for chromate in a closed cooling system to an elaborate determination of a dozen or more ions in the μg/l range in the case of supercritical boiler operations. The control program must be tailored for each individual case. For example, analysis for only chloride and phosphate concentrations may be necessary for treatment control in one type of system, whereas in the case of a very high-pressure boiler, alkalinity, chloride, copper, hydrazine or sulfite, iron, morpholine, pH, phosphate, sulfate and other analyses may be required.

Table 100(3) lists the determinations most frequently performed to control the quality of water destined for steam generation, heating, cooling and other manufacturing processes. The method of analysis for each particular constituent is set forth under the appropriate heading in the Water Section, and in a few cases in Part 200, the Wastewater Section of this manual. Procedures for chromate,[8] hydrazine,[9] morpholine,[9] nickel,[9] and octadecylamine [9] are described in the references

TABLE 100(3): ROUTINE AND SPECIAL DETERMINATIONS ON INDUSTRIAL WATER SAMPLES

Determination	Applications *
Acidity	B, C, P
Alkalinity:	
Hydroxyl (OH)	B, P
Phenolphthalein (P)	B, C, P
Total, methyl orange or mixed indicator (M)	B, C, P
Ammonia	B, P
Boron	C, P
Calcium	B, C, P
Carbon dioxide	B, P
Chloride	B, C, P
Chlorine, residual	C, P
Chromium, hexavalent	B, C, P
Color	P
Copper	B, C, P
Fluoride	C, P
Hardness	B, C, P
Hydrazine	B
Iron	B, C, P
Lead	P
Magnesium	B, C, P
Manganese	C, P
Morpholine	B
Nickel	B, P
Nitrate	B, C, P
Nitrite	B, C, P
Octadecylamine	B
Oil and grease	B, C, P
Oxygen, dissolved	B, P
pH	B, C, P
Phosphate:	
Ortho	B, C, P
Poly	B, C, P
Residue, total (103 C):	
Filtrable	B, C, P
Nonfiltrable	B, C, P
Silica	B, C, P
Sodium	B, C, P
Specific conductance	B, C, P
Sulfate	B, C, P
Sulfide	C, P
Sulfite	B, C, P
Tannin and lignin	B, C, P
Turbidity	P
Zinc	B, C, P

* Key: B—boiler water, feedwater, or condensate; C—cooling water, recirculating (open and closed systems) or once-through; P—industrial process applications.

(Section 100G) at the end of this section.

a. Collection of Samples: An analysis and the conclusions drawn from it can be no better than the sample on which it is made. Proper sampling technics must be used for each particular case in order to obtain the specificity or representativeness required. Sometimes it is necessary to take a continuous aliquot of a stream. At other times an occasional spot sample will be adequate. In any event, proper attention must be given to flushing sample lines, preventing contamination, and making sure the sample is representative.

Samples not collected under pressure are obtained in the usual manner, observing the precautions outlined in Section A. Boiler waters collected under pressure should be cooled to approximately 20 C while still under pressure. Figure 6 illustrates typical sampling-cooling installations. Certain determinations demand specialized sampling equipment and procedures, and/or analyses conducted immediately after collection of samples. Specific examples include carbon dioxide, dissolved oxygen, dissolved and total iron, hydrogen sulfide, or octadecylamine in condensate. For such determinations, the sampling procedures are generally specified as part of the analytical method.

b. Expression of Results: Results of analyses are usually expressed as milligrams per liter or parts per million (ppm) of the ion tested. The parallel units, micrograms per liter or parts per billion (ppb), are used for extremely low concentrations, as in water for nuclear reactors and extremely high-pressure boilers. They are sometimes calculated as the oxide or as equivalent

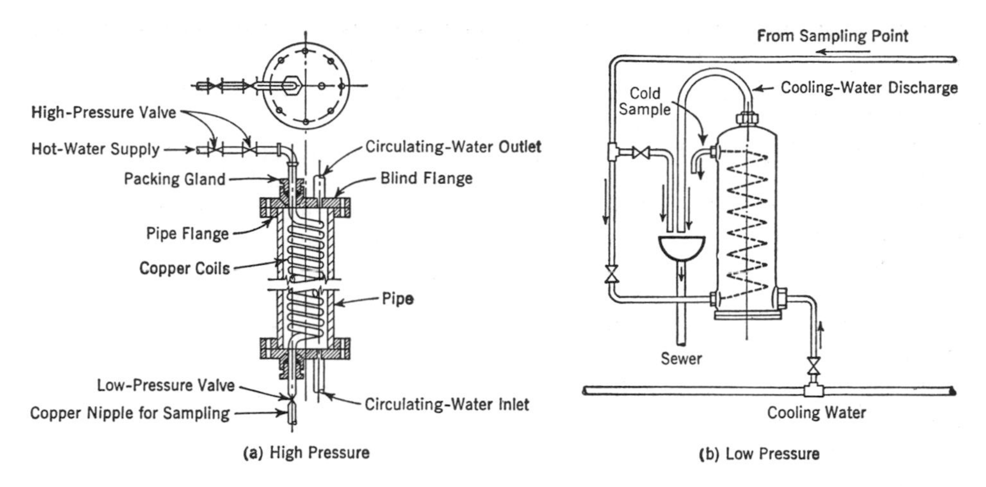

Figure 6. Cooling coils for boiler water sampling: These illustrations do not represent standardized equipment, but exemplify the characteristics of the devices that should be used.

calcium carbonate. The unit, grains per gallon (gpg), is seldom used. The unit, equivalents per million (epm), can be valuable for making treatment calculations and is included in some water analysis reports. Conversion of the results into milliequivalents per liter enables a comparison of the positive and negative ions.

4. Scale

The occurrence of scale or sludge formation in industrial water systems may induce equipment failures, such as boiler tube ruptures or plugged heat-exchanger tubing. Such occurrences frequently result from increased temperature, evaporation or aeration, which cause insolubility of some of the ionic combinations present. Common scale deposits may consist of calcium carbonate, phosphate, silicate, or sulfate, or of magnesium hydroxide, phosphate, and silicate. Others may be from oxides, silica, or related substances.

In distribution systems of 0 – 93 C (32 – 200 F) temperature, the tendency of a water supply to form calcium carbonate scale may be estimated by calculating the Langelier pH of saturation (pH_s) from the alkalinity, calcium, dissolved solids, and temperature of the water (see Saturation and Stability with Respect to Calcium Carbonate, Section 149) and subtracting this pH_s from the actual measured pH of the water. A positive value indicates scale-forming tendency; a negative value indicates scale-dissolving (or probably corrosive) tendency. A balanced or stable water generally has a zero or slightly positive index. Ryznar [10] has used the same pH_s and calculated a value of $2pH_s$—pH which he calls a Stability Index and which correlates well with field experience of increasingly heavy scale as the numerical value of this index decreases from about 6.5, and increasingly serious corrosion as the index increases above this value. The literature also offers methods for calculating indices or solubilities of calcium phosphate,[11] calcium sulfate,[12] and magnesium hydroxide.[13]

Scale prevention in boilers[5, 14] is usually attained by ion exchange or other hardness-reduction or solubilizing methods. The residual hardness is then precipitated inside the boiler by the addition of phosphate or carbonate and organic sludge conditioning chemicals, producing a nonadhering sludge rather than a scale; or is reacted with chelating agents to form soluble complexes.

For sludge removal and maintenance of scale-free conditions, and for the control of steam quality, maximum limits are designated for the total dissolved solids, and control is accomplished by blowdown as necessary.

In cooling towers, the application of acid for alkalinity reduction and scale prevention is generally employed; however, presoftening of makeup water is practiced in some cases. Polyphosphates and other chemicals are also applied to control calcium carbonate, calcium phosphate, and silica deposit formation.[15, 20] Proper and adequate bleedoff is an important part of treatment of cooling water.

5. *Corrosion*

Deterioration of metals caused by corrosion may produce soluble metallic ions in the system, which may redeposit later as oxides. Certain constituents or contaminants in the water, including dissolved oxygen, carbon dioxide, anions (such as chloride and sulfate) and acidity (low pH) increase the corrosive tendency of the water. Microorganisms such as sulfate-reducing or iron bacteria also cause corrosion and/or deposits.

Development of a thin protective layer of calcium carbonate on the metal surfaces is often effective for preventing corrosion of the metal in the water distribution system. The Saturation Index or Ryznar[10] Stability Index may be used to suggest the tendency to dissolve calcium carbonate or the degree of stability or balance.

Another procedure[16] for estimating corrosive tendency is calculation of the

$$\text{ratio } \frac{\text{me per liter } (Cl^- + SO_4^=)}{\text{me per liter alkalinity as } CaCO_3}\,.$$

In the neutral pH range (7 to 8) and in the presence of dissolved oxygen, ratios equal to or below about 0.1 indicate general freedom from corrosion, whereas increasingly higher ratios are generally indicative of more aggressive waters.

Corrosion in boilers is controlled by removal of the oxygen from the feedwater by deaeration, and by the reaction of residual oxygen with sodium sulfite or hydrazine. The corrosion of iron is also effectively reduced by the application of alkaline chemicals such as caustic soda and sodium phosphates to provide boiler water pH in the range of 10–12. At high boiler pressures (about 1,500 psi and above) it may be considered preferable to employ a "low solids" type of treatment (ammonia, amines, hydrazine) so as to avoid localized corrosion associated with high pH. Due to the lack of buffering and softening agents in this treatment, high-quality demineralized water very low in silica is necessary and only minimum condenser leakage can be tolerated.

Carbonate and bicarbonate decompose in the boiler to release carbon dioxide in the steam. This causes formation of carbonic acid in the steam condensate,[17,18] and corrosion by acid results. The presence of dissolved oxygen accelerates the carbonic acid attack.

Steam condensate corrosion can be minimized by maintaining minimum carbonate content in the boiler water, and by the use of low bicarbonate or carbonate makeup waters. Volatile neutralizing amines such as morpholine and cyclohexylamine reduce corrosion in condensate systems by providing higher pH and pH control of condensate. Octadecylamine,[19] which forms a monomolecular film on the walls of the condensate piping to prevent contact with an acidic environment, is also effective in reducing corrosion.

Inhibition of corrosion in cooling towers is provided by the application of corrosion inhibitors such as chromates, phosphates and silicates, applied singly or in various combinations. Open recirculating cooling systems [15,20] in which water is continuously saturated with dissolved oxygen offer more difficult corrosion control problems than do closed recirculating systems. The generally low makeup water requirements of closed systems account for the minimum scale and corrosion problems. In the case of excessive makeup water usage due to poor design or leakage, scale or corrosion problems may be encountered unless corrective treatment is used.

6. Special Problems

Fouling is the deposition of a material, normally in suspension, on a surface in contact with the water. Such deposition may cause reduced flow, inefficiency in heat transfer, and localized corrosion. Fouling may also result from reaction of dissolved minerals and water-conditioning chemicals and from the growth of microorganisms. Control of fouling is possibly one of today's greatest water-conditioning problems.

Sanitation practices to retard the growth of undesirable living organisms may encompass the destruction of pathogenic organisms by heat, as applied in the food industries, or the application of selective biocides to kill slime-forming or sulfate-reducing organisms growing on heat transfer surfaces. Also included is the destruction of algae growing in cooling towers, water plants growing in reservoirs, and mollusks growing in the cooling water pipes of industries using once-through sea water. Since many industries rely on biological methods to treat their wastewater, the applied biocides must be of a nature that will not inhibit the growth of desirable organisms in the disposal treatment system and in the stream effluent.

Taste and odor result from organic or inorganic matter in the water. Taste- and odor-forming bodies may be removed by adsorption on a number of materials, among them activated carbon; or they may also be oxidized by chlorine, chlorine dioxide, oxygen, ozone and permanganate; in some cases they may be rendered nonoffensive by masking.

A problem of disposal may arise when some industries must reuse water to such a degree that high concentrations of solids or impurities develop. The customary methods of disposal are to inject the wastewater into a disposal well, or to run it into a stream, lake or ocean. Wastewater injected into a disposal well must be chemically compatible with the aquifer; otherwise the sands will clog and the well will have a short life. Wastewater must be chemically, biologically and thermally compatible with the receiving stream or lake to avert serious upset of the ecological balance.

Water-conditioning, waste disposal, and corrosion control problems are as varied as the industries seeking to solve them.

100 F. Standard Specifications for Water Treatment Chemicals

Many laboratories perform analyses on the bulk chemicals received at the plant for the treatment of water. The standards usually followed for such analyses are those prepared and issued by a committee of the American Water Works Association. Each separate standard describes the acceptable physical and chemical characteristics of the material and presents methods for collecting the sample and determining the major components in order to ascertain compliance with the specifications. The detailed *Standard Specifications for the Water Treatment Chemicals* [21] are available at nominal cost from the American Water Works Association.

100 G. References

1. AMERICAN SOCIETY FOR TESTING AND MATERIALS. 1969. *Manual on Water and Industrial Waste Water* (3rd ed.). ASTM Special Tech. Pub. 442. Philadelphia, Pa.
2. U. S. PUBLIC HEALTH SERVICE. 1962. Public Health Service drinking water standards, 1962. PHS Pub. No. 956, Washington, D. C.
3. AMERICAN WATER WORKS ASSOCIATION. *Water Quality and Treatment* (3rd ed.). AWWA, New York. In preparation.
4. CALIFORNIA STATE WATER POLLUTION CONTROL BOARD. 1963. *Water Quality Criteria* (2nd ed.). Calif. State Water Pollution Control Board, Sacramento.
5. Boiler water chemistry symposium. 1954. *Ind. Eng. Chem.* 46:953.
6. E. NORDELL. 1961. *Water Treatment for Industrial and Other Uses* (2nd ed.). Reinhold Publishing Corp., New York.
7. P. HAMER, J. JACKSON & E. F. THURSTON. 1961. *Industrial Water Treatment Practice*. Butterworths, London.
8. N. H. FURMAN, Ed. 1962. *Standard Methods of Chemical Analysis* (6th ed.). D. Van Nostrand Co., Princeton, N. J., Vol. I, pp. 354, 360.
9. AMERICAN SOCIETY FOR TESTING AND MATERIALS. 1968. *Book of ASTM Standards,* Part 23, Water; Atmospheric Analysis. ASTM, Philadelphia.
10. J. W. RYZNAR. 1944. A new index for determining amount of calcium carbonate scale formed by a water. *JAWWA* 36:472.
11. J. GREEN & J. A. HOLMES. 1947. Calculation of the pH of saturation of tricalcium phosphate. *JAWWA* 39:1090.
12. W. L. DENMAN. 1961. Maximum re-use of cooling water. *Ind. Eng. Chem.* 53:817.
13. T. E. LARSON et al. 1959. Stabilization of magnesium hydroxides in the solids-contact process. *JAWWA* 51:1551.
14. S. B. APPLEBAUM & R. J. ZUMBRUNNEN. 1956. Selecting water-treating processes

for medium-pressure boilers. *ASME Paper No.* 56–A–191.

15. R. W. LANE & T. E. LARSON. 1963. Role of water treatment in the economic operation of cooling towers. *Amer. Power Conf.* XXV, 687–701.
16. T. E. LARSON & R. V. SKOLD. 1958. Laboratory studies relating mineral quality of water to corrosion of steel and cast iron. *Corrosion* 14:6, 285t.
17. L. F. COLLINS. 1943. More information concerning corrosion in steam heating systems. Fourth Water Conference, Engineers Society of Western Pennsylvania 33.
18. A. A. BERK & J. NIGON. 1948. Amine volatility and alkalinity in relation to corrosion control in steam heating systems. *U. S. Bur. Mines Tech. Paper* 714.
19. J. F. WILKES et al. 1955. Filming amines—Use and misuse in power plant water-steam cycles. *Amer. Power Conf.* XVII, 527.
20. S. B. APPLEBAUM. 1950. Treatment of cooling water. *Combustion* 22:5 (Nov.), 41–48.
21. AMERICAN WATER WORKS ASSOCIATION. Standards for Water Treatment Chemicals. AWWA separates, as follows:
    B200–69 Sodium Chloride
    B201–59 Soda Ash
    B202–65 Quicklime and Hydrated Lime
    B250–51 Cation Exchanger Test Procedures
    B300–64 Hypochlorites
    B301–59 Liquid Chlorine
    B302–64 Ammonium Sulfate
    B303–67 Sodium Chlorite
    B402–68 Ferrous Sulfate
    B403–69 Aluminum Sulfate
    B404–58 Liquid Sodium Silicate
    B405–60 Sodium Aluminate
    B406–64 Ferric Sulfate
    B500–66 Trisodium Phosphate
    B501–64 Caustic Soda
    B502–67 Sodium Hexametaphosphate
    B600–66 Powdered Activated Carbon
    B601–64 Sodium Pyrosulfite
    B602–59 Copper Sulfate
    B603–68 Potassium Permanganate
    B701–60 Sodium Fluoride
    B702–60 Sodium Silicofluoride
    B703–60 Fluosilicic Acid

100 H. Bibliography

General

TAYLOR, F. B. 1963. Significance of trace elements in public finished water supplies. *JAWWA* 55:619.

Collection of Samples

ELLISON, G., H. W. HACKLER & W. A. BUICE. 1932. Effects of age and storage temperatures on growth of bacteria in water samples. *JAWWA* 24:895.

WELCH, P. S. 1948. *Limnological Methods.* Blakiston Co., Philadelphia, Chapter 14.

HAUCK, C. F. 1949. Gaging and sampling waterborne industrial wastes. *ASTM Bull.* (Dec.), pp. 38–43.

BLACK, H. H. 1952. Procedures for sampling and measuring industrial wastes. *Sewage & Ind. Wastes* 24:45.

WELCH, P. S. 1952. *Limnology* (2nd ed.). McGraw-Hill Book Co., New York, Chapter 5.

AMERICAN SOCIETY FOR TESTING AND MATERIALS. 1957. *Standard Methods of Sampling Industrial Water.* ASTM Pub. D510–57, Philadelphia.

TAYLOR, E. W. 1958. *Examination of Waters and Water Supplies* (7th ed.). Little, Brown & Co., Boston, Chapter 11.

RAINWATER, F. H. & L. L. THATCHER. 1960. Methods for collection and analysis of water samples. *U. S. Geological Survey Water Supply Paper No.* 1454.

Ion Exchange

KUNIN, R. et al. Ion exchange. *Anal. Chem.* 21:87 (1949); 22:64 (1950); 23:45 (1951); 24:64 (1952); 26:104 (1954); 28:729 (1956); 30:681 (1958); 32:67R (1960); 34:101R (1962); 38:176R (1966); 40:136R (1968).

SAMUELSON, O. 1963. *Ion Exchange in Analytical Chemistry.* John Wiley & Sons, New York.

Checking Analyses

ROSSUM, J. R. 1949. Conductance method for checking accuracy of water analyses. *Anal. Chem.* 21:631.

ROBERTSON, R. S. & M. F. NIELSEN. 1951. Quick test determines dissolved solids. *Power* 95:87 (Feb.).

NAVONE, R. 1954. Sodium determination with ion-exchange resin. *JAWWA* 46: 479.

GREENBERG, A. E. & R. NAVONE. 1958. Use of the control chart in checking anion-cation balances in water. *JAWWA* 50: 1365.

Evaluation of Methods

KRAMER, H. P. & R. C. KRONER. 1959. Cooperative studies on laboratory methodology. *JAWWA* 51:607.

KRONER, R. C., D. G. BALLINGER & H. P. KRAMER. 1960. Evaluation of laboratory methods for analysis of heavy metals in water. *JAWWA* 52:117.

MULLINS, J. W. et al. 1961. Evaluation of methods for counting gross radioactivity in water. *JAWWA* 53:1466.

LISHKA, R. J., F. S. KELSO & H. P. KRAMER. 1963. Evaluation of methods for determination of minerals in water. *JAWWA* 55:647.

101 ACIDITY

The acidity of a water is the capacity of that water to donate protons. This includes the un-ionized portions of weakly ionizing acids such as carbonic acid and tannic acid, as well as hydrolyzing salts like ferrous and/or aluminum sulfate. Mineral acids contribute to acidity when the sample has a low pH value. The acidity is significant because acids contribute to the corrosiveness of water.

1. General Discussion

a. Principle: An equilibrium between carbonate, bicarbonate, and carbon dioxide exists in many natural waters used for potable purposes. The carbonate and bicarbonate can be estimated by titrating the alkalinity with standard acid to the bicarbonate equivalence point of pH 8.3 and then to the carbonic acid equivalence point in the pH range of 4 to 5. Acid pollutants entering a water supply in sufficient quantity will disturb the carbonate-bicarbonate-carbon dioxide equilibrium. The extent of this disturbance may be estimated by titrating with standard alkali to the end points of pH 4.5 and 8.3.

The titration of the sample at boiling temperature in the presence of phenolphthalein indicator has been found useful for water plant control where the source of supply is polluted with mineral acids and acid salts originating from acid mine drainage and some industrial wastes. Heat speeds the hydrolysis of iron and aluminum sulfate, enabling rapid completion of the titration. This determination provides an estimate of the lime application which may be required to make such water supplies satisfactory for general use.

b. Interference: A fading and impermanent end point characterizes the phenolphthalein acidity titration performed at room temperature on a sample containing iron and aluminum sulfate. Better results are obtained by titrating the sample at boiling temperature. Free available residual chlorine may bleach methyl orange indicator in an acid medium, an effect which can be overcome by dechlorinating the sample with 1 drop of 0.1*N* sodium thiosulfate.

c. Sampling and storage: Samples should be collected in polyethylene or pyrex bottles and stored at a low temperature. Determinations should be performed as soon after sampling as practicable, preferably within 1 day.

2. Apparatus

Refer to Alkalinity, Section 102.2, below. The apparatus described there is also suitable for the acidity titrations.

3. Reagents

Except for standard 0.02*N* sulfuric acid or hydrochloric acid, all the reagents listed for the determination of Alkalinity, Section 102.3, are required, and in addition:

a. Standard sodium hydroxide titrant, 0.02*N:* Dilute 20.0 ml 1*N* NaOH with CO_2-free distilled water to 1 liter. Store in a tightly rubber-stoppered pyrex glass bottle protected from atmospheric CO_2 by a soda lime tube. For best results, prepare weekly. Standardize the solution against 0.0200*N* potassium biphthalate solution which has been prepared by dissolving 4.085 g anhydrous $KHC_8H_4O_4$, and diluting to the mark of a 1-liter volumetric flask with CO_2-free distilled water. Alternatively, the alkali may be standardized against standard 0.02*N* HCl or H_2SO_4 made up for the alkalinity tests (Section 102.3). Perform the standardization exactly as the typical acidity titration, using the identical volumes of final solution, phenolphthalein or methyl orange indicator, and the same time interval for the determination. For best results, take for standardization a volume of 0.0200*N* potassium biphthalate solution which approximates the average acidity of the water samples normally encountered in the given laboratory. Since the response to end-point color changes varies among individuals, each analyst should perform the standardization independently and use the normality factor appropriate for his own technic. A standard NaOH solution, exactly 0.0200*N,* is equivalent to 1.00 mg $CaCO_3$ per 1.00 ml.

4. Procedure

Use sample volumes requiring less than 25 ml of titrant because they yield the sharpest color changes at the end point. If indicator methods are used, remove the free available residual chlorine by adding 0.05 ml (1 drop) 0.1*N* sodium thiosulfate solution.

a. Methyl orange acidity: Add 0.1 ml (2 drops) methyl orange indicator to a sample of suitable size, 50.0 or 100 ml if possible, in a white porcelain casserole or an erlenmeyer flask, over a white surface. Titrate with standard 0.02*N* NaOH until the color changes to the faint orange characteristic of pH 4.5.

b. Phenolphthalein acidity: Add 0.15 ml (3 drops) phenolphthalein indicator to a sample of suitable size, 50.0 or 100 ml if possible, in a white porcelain casserole or an erlenmeyer flask, over a white surface. Titrate with standard 0.02*N* NaOH to the appearance of the faint pink color characteristic of pH 8.3.

c. Phenolphthalein acidity at boiling temperature: Add 0.15–0.5 ml (3–10 drops) phenolphthalein indicator to a sample of suitable size, 50.0 to 100 ml if possible (or an aliquot diluted to these volumes), in a white porcelain casserole or an erlenmeyer flask, over a white surface. Heat the sample to boiling and boil for 2 min. Titrate the hot sample with standard $0.02N$ NaOH to a permanent pink end point.

5. Calculation

$$\text{Acidity as mg/l } CaCO_3 = \frac{A \times N \times 50{,}000}{\text{ml sample}}$$

where A = ml NaOH titrant and N = normality of NaOH.

In reporting results, state the indicator used and the temperature at which the titration was performed.

6. Bibliography

ELLMS, J. & J. C. BENEKER. 1901. The estimation of carbonic acid in water. *J. Amer. Chem. Soc.* 23:405.

JOHNSTON, J. 1916. The determination of carbonic acid, combined and free, in solution, particularly in natural waters. *J. Amer. Chem. Soc.* 38:947.

KOLTHOFF, I. M. 1917. Titration of carbonic acid and its salts. *Chem. Weekblad.* 14:781.

SELVIG, W. A. & W. C. RATLIFF. 1922. The nature of acid water from coal mines and the determination of acidity. *Ind. Eng. Chem.* 14:125.

102 ALKALINITY *

The alkalinity of a water is the capacity of that water to accept protons. Alkalinity is usually imparted by the bicarbonate, carbonate and hydroxide components of a natural or treated water supply. It is determined by titration with a standard solution of a strong mineral acid to the successive bicarbonate and carbonic acid equivalence points, indicated electrometrically or by means of color. Phenolphthalein indicator enables the measurement of that alkalinity fraction contributed by the hydroxide and half of the carbonate. Indicators responding in the pH range 4–5 are used to measure the alkalinity contributed by hydroxide, carbonate and bicarbonate. The phenolphthalein alkalinity and total-alkalinity titrations are useful for the calculation of chemical dosages required in the treatment of natural water supplies. The stoichiometric relationships between hydroxide, carbonate and bicarbonate are valid only in the absence of significant concentrations of weak acid radicals other than hydroxyl, carbonate or bicarbonate.

1. General Discussion

a. Selection of potentiometric or indicator method: A number of advantages make the potentiometric titration the method of choice for accurate determinations. The equivalence point can be identified by the inflection in the titration curve or by the differential method of calculation.† The plot of a potentiometric titration curve also reveals any shift in the equivalence point caused by temperature, ionic strength, and, in the case of the total alkalinity, the effect of the carbon dioxide concentration at the equivalence point. Moreover, the potentiometric method is free from residual-chlorine interference, the influence of color and turbidity, and individual visual idiosyncrasies. Properly performed, however, the more

* See also Carbon Dioxide and the Three Forms of Alkalinity (Section 111A) and Saturation and Stability with Respect to Calcium Carbonate (Section 149).

† For an illustration of this method, see Section 203C.4a and 4b.

rapid and simple indicator method is satisfactory for control and routine applications.

b. Equivalence points: The equivalence point to which the total-alkalinity titration must be carried is determined by the concentration of CO_2 present at the end of the titration. If the sample originally contained relatively little CO_2 or hydroxide, and if the mixing during the titration is not vigorous, then the alkalinity will determine the equivalence point. The following pH values are suggested as the equivalence points for the corresponding alkalinity concentrations as calcium carbonate: pH 5.1 for total alkalinities of about 30 mg/l, pH 4.8 for 150 mg/l, and pH 4.5 for 500 mg/l. Indicators effective in these ranges will give the most reliable results. A mixed indicator prepared from bromcresol green and methyl red is suitable for the higher pH values, while methyl orange can be used for those below 4.6. Since a written description of color shadings can frequently mislead rather than inform—dominant wavelength being a more exact method of defining color—the analyst is urged to prepare buffer solutions of the applicable pH, add the proper volume of indicator, and use these solutions as standards for color comparison until acquaintance with the various indicator color transitions is achieved. The same considerations apply to the phenolphthalein end point. For purposes of ascertaining the faint phenolphthalein end point, it is advisable to employ a buffer solution with a pH value of 8.3, to which the proper volume of indicator is added, as a standard of comparison. (See Carbon Dioxide, Section 111B.3c).

c. Interference: Free available residual chlorine markedly affects the indicator color response in some water supplies through bleaching action. The addition of minimal volumes of sodium thiosulfate eliminates this interference without significant loss of accuracy. Where an error is demonstrated, the appropriate correction should be applied. Ultraviolet irradiation also removes residual chlorine. Another interfering factor is the finely divided calcium carbonate and magnesium hydroxide produced during the lime-soda softening process, which may cause a fading end point. This suspended material should be removed by filtering the sample through fine filter paper before titration. Salts of weak inorganic (phosphoric, silicic) and organic acids may contribute to alkalinity.

d. Sampling and storage: For best results, samples should be collected in polyethylene or pyrex bottles. Because of the instability of samples containing considerable causticity or carbon dioxide, the alkalinity determinations should be performed as soon as practicable, and preferably within 1 day.

2. Apparatus

a. Daylight fluorescent lamps have proved satisfactory for use in identifying the alkalinity end points by virtue of the fact that they enable the maintenance of uniform lighting conditions at all times, and, in particular cases, accentuate certain indicator color changes.

b. Electrically operated titrators, suitably calibrated: Where such devices are available, the alkalinity titrations may be performed using the standard solutions. The alkalinity determinations can also be performed by means of a properly calibrated pH meter, titrating with the standard solutions to the proper equivalence pH.

3. Reagents

a. Carbon dioxide-free distilled water: Prepare all stock and standard solutions, and dilution water for the standardization procedure, with distilled water which has a pH of not less than 6.0. If the water has a lower pH, it should be freshly boiled for 15 min and cooled to room temperature. Deionized water may be substituted for distilled water provided that it has a conductance of less than 2 micromhos/cm and a pH greater than 6.0.

b. Phenolphthalein indicator solution.

c. Standard sulfuric acid or hydrochloric acid titrant, 0.02*N*: Prepare stock solutions approximately 0.1*N* by diluting either 8.3 ml conc HCl or 2.8 ml conc H_2SO_4 to 1 liter. Dilute 200 ml of the 0.1*N* stock solution to 1 liter with CO_2-free distilled water. Standardize the 0.02*N* acid against a 0.0200*N* sodium carbonate solution which has been prepared by dissolving 1.060 g anhydrous Na_2CO_3 (primary standard grade), oven-dried at 140 C, and diluting to the mark of a 1-liter volumetric flask with CO_2-free distilled water. Alternatively, the acid may be standardized against standard 0.02*N* NaOH prepared for the acidity test (Section 101.3). Perform the standardization exactly as the typical alkalinity titration, using the identical volumes of final solution, sodium thiosulfate, phenolphthalein, and total-alkalinity indicator, and the same time interval as for the sample determination. For best results take for standardization a volume of 0.0200*N* sodium carbonate solution which approximates the average alkalinity of the water samples normally encountered in the given laboratory. Since the response to end-point color changes varies among individuals, each analyst should perform the standardization independently and use the normality factor appropriate for his own technic. A standard acid solution, exactly 0.0200*N*, is equivalent to 1.00 mg $CaCO_3$ per 1.00 ml.

d. Mixed bromcresol green-methyl red indicator solution: Use either the aqueous or the alcoholic solution.

1) Dissolve 20 mg of methyl red sodium salt and 100 mg of bromcresol green sodium salt in 100 ml distilled water.

2) Dissolve 20 mg methyl red and 100 mg bromcresol green in 100 ml 95% ethyl alcohol or isopropyl alcohol.

e. Methyl orange indicator solution.

f. Sodium thiosulfate, 0.1*N*: Dissolve 25 g $Na_2S_2O_3 \cdot 5H_2O$ and dilute to 1 liter with distilled water.

4. Procedure

Use sample volumes requiring less than 25 ml of titrant because they yield the sharpest color changes at the end point. If indicator methods are used, remove the free residual chlorine by adding 0.05 ml (1 drop) 0.1*N* sodium thiosulfate solution or by ultraviolet irradiation.

a. Phenolphthalein alkalinity: Add 0.1 ml (2 drops) phenolphthalein indicator to a sample of suitable size, 50.0 or 100 ml if possible, in an erlenmeyer flask. Titrate over a white surface with 0.02*N* standard acid to the coloration corresponding to the proper equivalence point of pH 8.3.

b. Total alkalinity by mixed bromcresol green-methyl red indicator method: Add 0.15 ml (3 drops) indicator to the solution in which the phenolphthalein alkalinity has been determined, or to a sample of suitable size, 50.0 or 100 ml if possible, in an erlenmeyer flask. Titrate over a white surface with 0.02*N* standard acid to the proper equivalence point. The indicator yields the following color responses: above pH 5.2, greenish blue; pH 5.0, light blue with lavender gray; pH 4.8, light pink-gray with a bluish cast; pH 4.6, light pink.

c. Total alkalinity by methyl orange indicator method: Add 0.1 ml (2 drops) indicator to the solution in which the phenolphthalein alkalinity has been determined, or to a sample of suitable size, 50.0 or 100 ml if possible, in an erlenmeyer flask. Titrate over a white surface with 0.02*N* standard acid to the proper equivalence point. The indicator changes to orange at pH 4.6 and to pink at 4.0.

d. Potentiometric titration of low alkalinity: For greatest accuracy, titrate low alkalinities (less than 10 mg/l) potentiometrically rather than by indicator methods. Potentiometric titration avoids the error due to the sliding end point caused by free CO_2 in the sample at completion of the titration.

With a microburet, titrate carefully a sample of suitable size, 100 to 200 ml, and record the volume C (in ml) of standard acid titrant (normality *N*) required to reach a pH of 4.5. Continue the titration to pH 4.2 and record the total volume D (in ml) of acid titrant. (Precise standardization of the pH meter is unnecessary.)

5a. Calculation

1) *Indicator methods:*

$$\text{Phenolphthalein alkalinity as mg/l } CaCO_3 = \frac{A \times N \times 50{,}000}{\text{ml sample}}$$

$$\text{Total alkalinity as mg/l } CaCO_3 = \frac{B \times N \times 50{,}000}{\text{ml sample}}$$

2) *Potentiometric method for low alkalinity:*

$$\text{Total alkalinity as mg/l } CaCO_3 = \frac{(2C - D) \times N \times 50{,}000}{\text{ml sample}}$$

Where A = ml titration for sample to reach the phenolphthalein end point, B = total ml titration for sample to reach the second end point, C = ml titration for sample to reach pH 4.5, D = total ml titration for sample to reach pH 4.2, and *N* = normality of acid.

NOTE: If total alkalinity is determined on the same sample used for phenolphthalein alkalinity, be sure to include the volume of acid required for the phenolphthalein titration, A, in the total milliliters, B, of standard acid.

5b. Calculation of Alkalinity Relationships

The results obtained from the phenolphthalein and total alkalinity determinations offer a means for the stoichiometric classification of the three principal forms of alkalinity present in many water supplies. The classification ascribes the entire alkalinity to bicarbonate, carbonate and hydroxide, and assumes the absence of other (weak) acids of inorganic or organic composition, such as silicic, phosphoric and boric acids. This classification system further presupposes the incompatibility of hydroxide and bicarbonate alkalinities in the same sample. Since the calculations are made on a stoichiometric basis, ion concentrations in the strictest sense are not represented in the results. According to this scheme:

1) Carbonate alkalinity is present when the phenolphthalein alkalinity is not zero but is less than the total alkalinity.

2) Hydroxide alkalinity is present if the phenolphthalein alkalinity is more than half the total alkalinity.

3) Bicarbonate alkalinity is present if the phenolphthalein alkalinity is less than half the total alkalinity.

The mathematical conversion of the results is shown in Table 102(1).

TABLE 102(1): ALKALINITY RELATIONSHIPS *

Result of Titration	Hydroxide Alkalinity as $CaCO_3$	Carbonate Alkalinity as $CaCO_3$	Bicarbonate Alkalinity as $CaCO_3$
$P = 0$	0	0	T
$P < \frac{1}{2}T$	0	2P	$T - 2P$
$P = \frac{1}{2}T$	0	2P	0
$P > \frac{1}{2}T$	$2P - T$	$2(T - P)$	0
$P = T$	T	0	0

* Key: P—phenolphthalein alkalinity; T—total alkalinity.

The various alkalinity relationships may also be computed nomographically (see Carbon Dioxide, Section 111A). If the pH value of the water has been determined accurately by electrometric means, and from this the mg/l OH^- as $CaCO_3$ is calculated, then the mg/l $CO_3^=$ and HCO_3^- may also be calculated as $CaCO_3$ from the mg/l OH^-, and the phenolphthalein and total alkalinities by the following equations:

$$CO_3^= = 2P - 2[OH^-]$$

$$HCO_3^- = T - 2P + OH^-$$

Similarly, if difficulty is experienced with the phenolphthalein end point, or if it is desired to check the phenolphthalein titration, the phenolphthalein alkalinity may be calculated as $CaCO_3$ from the results of the nomographic determinations of the carbonate ($CO_3^=$) and hydroxide (OH^-) ion concentrations, by the use of the relationship:

$$P = \frac{1}{2}[CO_3^=] + OH^-$$

6. Precision and Accuracy

A precision of ± 1 mg/l and an accuracy of ± 3 mg/l, expressed as $CaCO_3$, can be achieved with reasonably good technic in the range between 10 and 500 mg/l.

7. Bibliography

BAYLIS, J. R. 1923. The use of acids with alum in water purification and the importance of hydrogen ion concentration. *JAWWA* 10:365.

STRAUB, F. G. 1932. Determination of alkalinity in boiler waters. *Ind. Eng. Chem.*, Anal. Ed. 4:290.

SCHROEDER, W. C. 1933. Errors in determination of carbonate in boiler waters. *Ind. Eng. Chem.*, Anal. Ed. 5:389.

COOPER, S. S. 1941. The mixed indicator bromcresol green-methyl red for carbonates in water. *Ind. Eng. Chem.*, Anal. Ed. 13:466.

FLEISHER, H. 1943. Sensitive indicator for volumetric determination of boiler feedwater alkalinity. *Ind. Eng. Chem.*, Anal. Ed. 15:742.

TARAS, M. 1948. Two new total alkalinity indicators. *JAWWA* 40:468.

———. 1949. New indicator for carbonate alkalinity. *JAWWA* 41:527.

LARSON, T. E. & L. M. HENLEY. 1955. Determination of low alkalinity or acidity in water. *Anal. Chem.* 27:851.

DONG, G., R. L. GIUSTI & A. E. GREENBERG. 1957. How to make alkalinity measurements in water. *Water & Sewage Works* 104:509.

DYE, J. F. 1958. Correlation of the two principal methods of calculating the three kinds of alkalinity. *JAWWA* 50:800.

THOMAS, J. F. J. & J. J. LYNCH. 1960. Determination of carbonate alkalinity in natural waters. *JAWWA* 52:259.

103 ALUMINUM

Aluminum is the third most abundant element of the earth's crust, occurring in minerals, rocks and clays. This wide distribution accounts for the presence of aluminum in practically all natural water supplies as a soluble salt, a colloid, or an insoluble compound. Soluble, colloidal and insoluble aluminum may appear additionally in treated water as a residual from alum coagulation. There are many conflicting statements in the literature about the amount of this residual, but recent work indicates that filtered water from a modern rapid sand filtration plant should have an aluminum concentration between 20 and 50 μg/l.

Selection of method: The atomic absorption spectrophotometric method is free from such common interferences as fluoride and phosphate, and therefore preferred where the necessary equipment is on hand. The Eriochrome cyanine R colorimetric method provides a means for estimating aluminum with simpler instrumentation.

103 A. Atomic Absorption Spectrophotometric Method

See Metals, Section 129 A.

103 B. Eriochrome Cyanine R Method (TENTATIVE)

1. General Discussion

a. Principle: Dilute aluminum solutions buffered to a pH of 6.0 produce with Eriochrome cyanine R dye a red to pink complex which exhibits maximum absorption at 535 mμ. The intensity of the developed color is influenced by the aluminum concentration, reaction time, temperature, pH, alkalinity, and the concentration of other accompanying ions in the sample. To compensate for color and turbidity, the aluminum in one portion of sample is complexed with EDTA to provide a blank. The interference of iron and manganese, two elements which are often found in water, is eliminated by the addition of ascorbic acid. The optimum aluminum range lies between 20 and 300 μg/l but can be extended upward by sample dilution.

b. Interference: Negative errors are caused by both fluoride and polyphosphates. When the fluoride concentration is constant, the percentage of error decreases with increasing amounts of aluminum. As the fluoride concentration is often known, or can readily be determined, fairly accurate results can be obtained by adding the known amount of fluoride to a set of standards. If less accuracy can be tolerated, a simpler correction can be determined from the family of curves in Figure 7. A

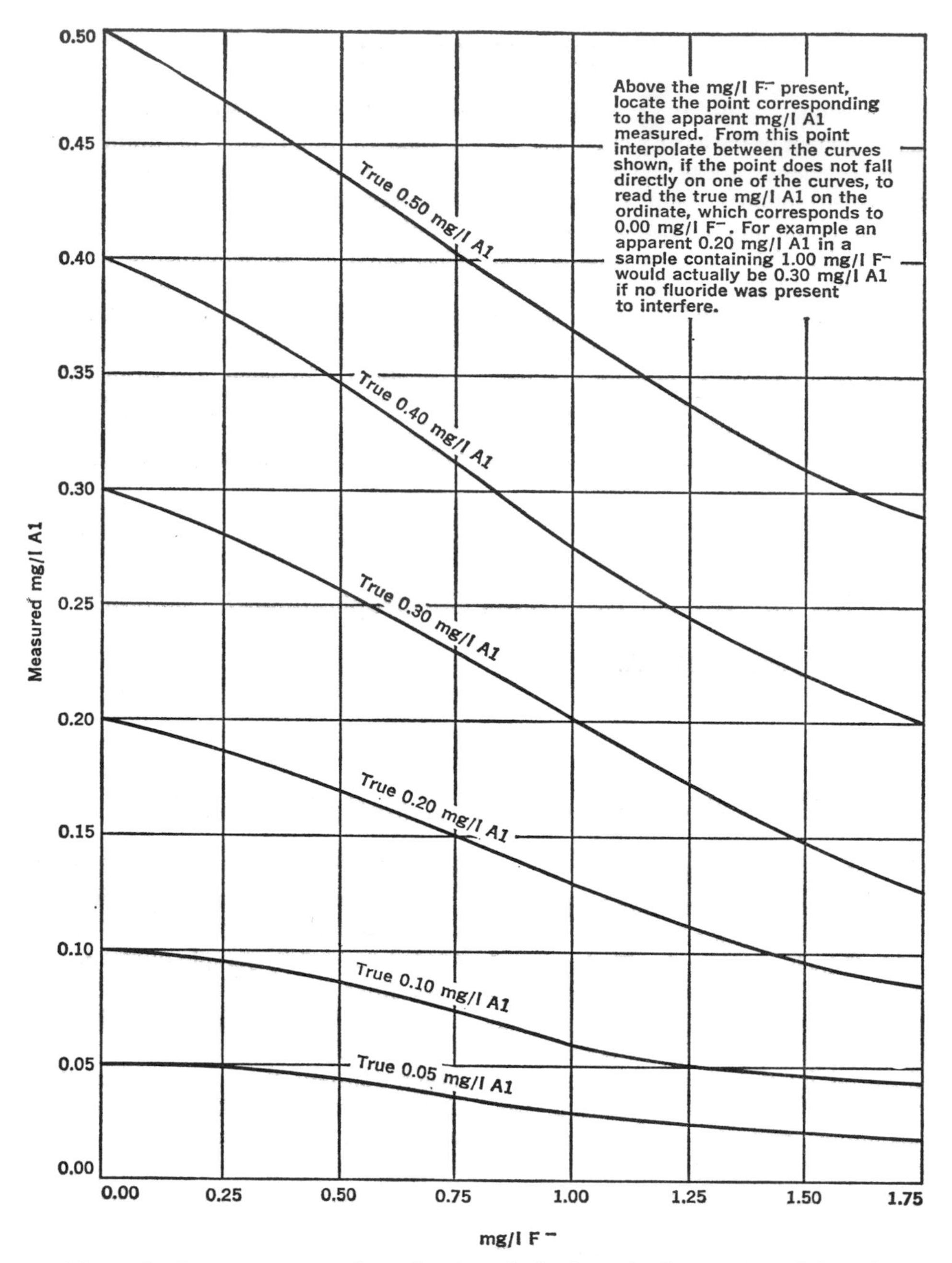

Figure 7. Correction curves for estimation of aluminum in the presence of fluoride.

procedure is given for the removal of complex phosphate interference. Orthophosphate in concentrations under 10 mg/l does not interfere. The interference caused by even small amounts of alkalinity is removed by acidifying the sample just beyond the neutralization point of methyl orange. Sulfate does not interfere up to a concentration of 2,000 mg/l.

c. Minimum detectable concentration: The minimum aluminum concentration detectable by this method in the absence of fluorides and complex phosphates is approximately 6 μg/l.

d. Sample handling: Samples should be collected in clean, acid-rinsed bottles, preferably plastic, and should be examined as soon as possible after collection. If the concentration desired is of soluble aluminum only, a portion of the sample should be filtered through a 0.45-μ membrane filter and the filtrate used for the determination. Filter paper, absorbent cotton and glass wool are completely unsuited for filtering any solution that is to be tested for aluminum, as they will remove most of the soluble aluminum.

2. Apparatus

a. COLORIMETRIC EQUIPMENT—One of the following is required:

1) *Spectrophotometer,* for use at 535 mμ and utilizing a light path of 1 cm or longer.
2) *Filter photometer,* providing a light path of 1 cm or longer and equipped with a green filter showing maximum transmittance between 525 and 535 mμ.
3) *Nessler tubes,* 50-ml, tall form, matched.

b. GLASSWARE—All glassware must be treated with warm 1 + 1 HCl and then rinsed with aluminum-free distilled water to avoid errors due to materials adsorbed on the glass. Rinse sufficiently to remove all acid.

3. Reagents

Use reagents low in aluminum, and aluminum-free distilled water.

a. STOCK ALUMINUM SOLUTION: The metal (1) or the salt (2) may be used for the preparation of the stock solution, which contains 500 μg Al per 1.00 ml:

1) Dissolve 500.0 mg aluminum metal in 10 ml of conc HCl by heating gently. Dilute to 1 liter in a volumetric flask with distilled water.

2) Dissolve 8.792 g aluminum potassium sulfate (also called potassium alum), $AlK(SO_4)_2 \cdot 12H_2O$, in distilled water and dilute to 1 liter in a volumetric flask.

b. STANDARD ALUMINUM SOLUTION: Dilute 10.00 ml of the stock aluminum solution to 1 liter in a volumetric flask with distilled water; 1.00 ml = 5.00 μg Al. Prepare daily.

c. SULFURIC ACID, 0.02*N* and 6*N*.

d. ASCORBIC ACID SOLUTION: Dissolve 0.1 g ascorbic acid in distilled water and make up to 100 ml in a volumetric flask. Prepare fresh daily.

e. BUFFER REAGENT: Dissolve 136 g sodium acetate, $NaC_2H_3O_2 \cdot 3H_2O$, in distilled water, add 40 ml 1*N* acetic acid, and dilute to 1 liter.

f. STOCK DYE SOLUTION: A number of products are available. Any of the following may be used:

1) *Solochrome cyanine R-200* or Eriochrome cyanine†:* Dissolve 100

* A product of Arnold Hoffman & Co., Providence, R. I.

† A product of K & K Laboratories, Plainview, N. Y.

mg of the dye in distilled water and dilute to 100 ml in a volumetric flask. This solution should have a pH value of about 2.9.

2) *Eriochrome cyanine R*‡: Dissolve 300 mg of the dye in about 50 ml distilled water. Adjust the pH value, which will be about 9, to about 2.9 with 1 + 1 acetic acid (approximately 3 ml will be required). Dilute with distilled water to 100 ml.

3) *Eriochrome cyanine R*§: Dissolve 150 mg of the dye in about 50 ml of distilled water. Adjust the pH value, which will be about 9, to about 2.9 with 1 + 1 acetic acid (approximately 2 ml will be required). Dilute with distilled water to 100 ml.

Stock solutions, prepared as described above, have excellent stability. They can be kept for at least a year.

g. WORKING DYE SOLUTION: Dilute 10.0 ml of any one of the stock dye solutions to 100 ml in a volumetric flask with distilled water. Working solutions are stable for at least 6 months.

h. METHYL ORANGE INDICATOR SOLUTION, or the mixed bromcresol green-methyl red indicator solution specified in the total alkalinity determination (Section 102.3d).

i. 0.01*M* EDTA (disodium ethylenediamine tetraacetate): Weigh 3.7 g of the reagent, dissolve in distilled water, and dilute to 1 liter.

j. SODIUM HYDROXIDE, 1*N* and 0.1*N*.

4. Procedure

a. PREPARATION OF CALIBRATION CURVE:

1) Prepare a series of aluminum standards from 0 to 7 μg (0–280 μg/l based on a 25-ml sample) by accurately measuring the calculated volumes of standard aluminum solution into 50-ml volumetric flasks or nessler tubes. Add distilled water to a total volume of approximately 25 ml.

Add 1 ml 0.02*N* sulfuric acid to each standard and mix. Follow with 1 ml ascorbic acid solution and mix.

2) Add 10 ml buffer solution and mix. With a volumetric pipet, add 5 ml of working dye reagent and mix. Immediately make up to a volume of 50 ml with distilled water. Mix and let stand for 5–15 min (the color begins to fade after 15 min).

3) Read the transmittance or absorbance on a spectrophotometer, using a wavelength of 535 mμ or a green filter providing maximum transmittance between 525 and 535 mμ. Adjust the instrument to 100% transmittance or zero absorbance with the standard containing no aluminum.

Plot a calibration curve relating micrograms aluminum to the instrument reading.

b. SAMPLE TREATMENT IN THE ABSENCE OF FLUORIDE AND COMPLEX PHOSPHATES: Place a 25.0-ml sample, or an aliquot diluted to 25 ml, in a porcelain dish or flask, add a few drops of methyl orange indicator, and titrate with 0.02*N* sulfuric acid to a faint pink color. Record reading and discard this sample.

To two similar samples at room temperature add the same amount of 0.02*N* acid used in the titration and 1 ml in excess.

To one of the samples add 1 ml EDTA solution. This one will serve as a blank by complexing any aluminum present and compensating for color and turbidity.

‡ A product of Pfaltz & Bauer, Inc., Flushing, N. Y.

§ A product of Hartman-Leddon Co., Philadelphia, Pa.

Add 1 ml ascorbic acid to the blank and sample, followed by 10 ml buffer reagent and 5.00 ml working dye reagent as prescribed in ¶ (2) above.

Set the instrument to zero absorbance or 100% transmittance using the EDTA blank. After a 5–15 min contact time, read the transmittance or absorbance of the sample and determine the aluminum concentration from the previously prepared calibration curve.

c. VISUAL COMPARISON: If photometric equipment is not available, prepare and treat the standards and a sample, as described above, in 50-ml nessler tubes. Make up to the mark with distilled water and compare the color of the sample with the standards after a 5–15 min contact time. A sample treated with EDTA is not needed when nessler tubes are used. If the sample shows turbidity or color, the use of nessler tubes may result in considerable error.

d. REMOVAL OF PHOSPHATE INTERFERENCE: Add 1.7 ml 6*N* sulfuric acid to 100 ml of sample in a 200 ml erlenmeyer flask.

Heat on a hot plate for at least 90 min, keeping the solution temperature just below the boiling point.

At the end of the heating period, the solution volume should be about 25 ml. Add distilled water whenever necessary to keep it at or above that volume.

After cooling, neutralize the solution to a pH value between 4.3 and 4.5 with sodium hydroxide, using 1*N* hydroxide at the start and 0.1*N* for the final fine adjustment, and a pH meter.

Make up to 100 ml with distilled water, mix, and use a 25-ml aliquot for the aluminum test.

Run a blank in the same manner, using 100 ml of distilled water and 1.7 ml 6*N* sulfuric acid. Subtract blank from the sample or use it to set the instrument to zero absorbance or 100% transmittance before reading the sample.

e. SAMPLE TREATMENT IN THE PRESENCE OF FLUORIDE: Measure the fluoride concentration of the sample by the SPADNS method or electrode method. Perform one of the following:

1) Add the same amount of fluoride as in the sample to each aluminum standard.

2) Determine the fluoride correction from the set of curves in Figure 7. This method may be used when a slight loss in accuracy can be tolerated.

5. Calculation

$$\text{mg/l Al} = \frac{\mu\text{g Al}}{\text{ml sample}}$$

6. Precision and Accuracy

A synthetic unknown sample containing 520 μg/l Al and no interference in distilled water was determined by the Eriochrome cyanine R method, with a relative standard deviation of 34.4% and a relative error of 1.7% in 27 laboratories.

A second synthetic unknown sample containing 50 μg/l Al, 500 μg/l Ba and 5 μg/l Be in distilled water was determined, with a relative standard deviation of 38.5% and a relative error of 22.0% in 35 laboratories.

A third synthetic unknown sample containing 500 μg/l Al, 50 μg/l Cd, 110 μg/l Cr, 1.00 mg/l Cu, 300 μg/l Fe, 70 μg/l Pb, 50 μg/l Mn, 150 μg/l Ag and 650 μg/l Zn in distilled water was determined, with a relative standard deviation of 28.8% and a relative error of 6.2% in 26 laboratories.

A fourth synthetic unknown sample containing 540 μg/l Al and 2.5 mg/l polyphosphate in distilled water was determined, with a relative standard deviation of 44.3% and a relative error of 1.3% in 16 laboratories which hydrolyzed the sample in the prescribed manner. In 12 laboratories which applied no corrective measures, the relative standard deviation was 49.2% and the relative error 8.9%.

A fifth synthetic unknown sample containing 480 μg/l Al and 750 μg/l F in distilled water was determined, with a relative standard deviation of 25.5% and a relative error of 2.3% in 16 laboratories which relied on the curve to correct for the fluoride content. The 17 laboratories which added fluoride to the aluminum standards showed a relative standard deviation of 22.5% and a relative error of 7.1%.

7. Bibliography

SHULL, K. E. & G. R. GUTHAN. 1967. Rapid modified Eriochrome cyanine R method for determination of aluminum in water. *JAWWA* 59:1456.

104 ARSENIC

Severe poisoning can arise from the ingestion of as little as 100 mg arsenic; chronic effects can appear from its accumulation in the body at low intake levels. Carcinogenic properties have also been imputed to arsenic. The arsenic concentration of most potable waters seldom exceeds 10 μg/l, although values as high as 100 μg/l have been reported. Arsenic may occur in water as a result of mineral dissolution, industrial discharges, or the application of insecticides.

Selection of method: The silver diethyldithiocarbamate method should be used when greater precision and accuracy are desired than that possible with the mercuric bromide stain method. Although its minimum detectable concentration is 1 μg As, the mercuric bromide stain method should be confined to qualitative or semiquantitative (±5 μg) determinations. Successful application of both methods often requires considerable practice.

104 A. Silver Diethyldithiocarbamate Method

1. General Discussion

a. Principle: Inorganic arsenic is reduced to arsine, AsH_3, by zinc in acid solution in a Gutzeit generator. The arsine is then passed through a scrubber containing glass wool impregnated with lead acetate solution and into an absorber tube containing silver diethyldithiocarbamate dissolved in pyridine. In the absorber, arsenic reacts with the silver salt, forming a soluble red complex which is suitable for photometric measurement.

b. Interference: Although certain metals—chromium, cobalt, copper, mercury, molybdenum, nickel, platinum and silver—interfere in the generation of arsine, the concentrations of these metals normally present in water samples do not constitute significant interference in the method. Antimony salts in the sample form stibine, which may interfere with color development by yielding a red color with maximum absorbance at 510 mμ.

c. Minimum detectable concentration: 1 μg As.

2. Apparatus

a. ARSINE GENERATOR AND ABSORPTION TUBE: See Figure 8.*

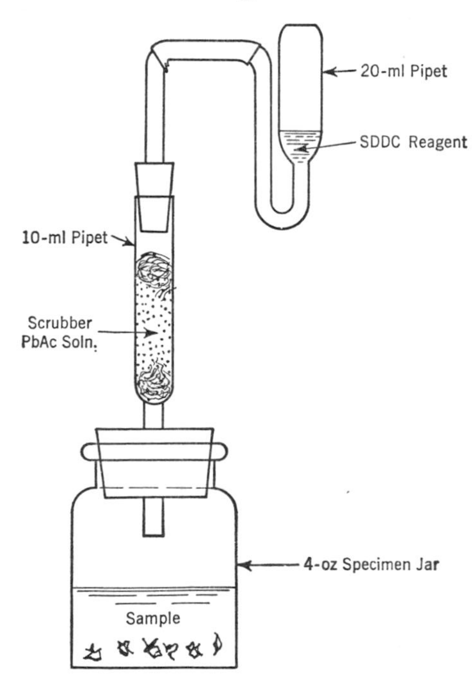

Figure 8. Arsine generator and absorber assembly.

b. PHOTOMETRIC EQUIPMENT:

1) *Spectrophotometer,* for use at 535 mμ with 1-cm cells.

* Fisher Scientific Co., No. 1–405 or equivalent apparatus.

2) *Filter photometer,* with green filter having a maximum transmittance in the range 530–540 mμ, with 1-cm cells.

3. Reagents

a. Hydrochloric acid, conc.

b. Potassium iodide solution: Dissolve 15 g KI in 100 ml distilled water. Store in a brown bottle.

c. Stannous chloride reagent: Dissolve 40 g arsenic-free $SnCl_2 \cdot 2H_2O$ in 100 ml conc hydrochloric acid.

d. Lead acetate solution: Dissolve 10 g $Pb(C_2H_3O_2)_2 \cdot 3H_2O$ in 100 ml distilled water.

e. Silver diethyldithiocarbamate reagent: Dissolve 1 g $AgSCSN(C_2H_5)_2$ in 200 ml pyridine. Store in a brown bottle.

f. Zinc: 20-30 mesh, arsenic-free.

g. Stock arsenic solution: Dissolve 1.320 g arsenic trioxide, As_2O_3, in 10 ml distilled water containing 4 g NaOH, and dilute to 1,000 ml with distilled water; 1.00 ml = 1.00 mg As. (CAUTION: Toxic—take care to avoid ingestion of arsenic solutions.)

h. Intermediate arsenic solution: Dilute 5.00 ml stock solution to 500 ml with distilled water; 1.00 ml = 10.0 μg As.

i. Standard arsenic solution: Dilute 10.00 ml intermediate solution to 100 ml with distilled water; 1.00 ml = 1.00 μg As.

4. Procedure

a. Treatment of sample: Pipet 35.0 ml sample into a clean generator bottle. Add successively, with thorough mixing after each addition, 5 ml conc HCl, 2 ml KI solution, and 8 drops (0.40 ml) $SnCl_2$ reagent. Allow 15 min for reduction of arsenic to the trivalent state.

b. Preparation of scrubber and ab-

sorber: Impregnate the glass wool in the scrubber with lead acetate solution. Do not make too wet because water will be carried over into the reagent solution. Pipet 4.00 ml silver diethyldithiocarbamate reagent into the absorber tube.

c. Arsine generation and measurement: Add 3 g zinc to the generator and connect the scrubber-absorber assembly immediately. Make certain that all connections are tightly fitted.

Allow 30 min for complete evolution of arsine. Warm the generator slightly to make sure that all arsine is released. Pour the solution from the absorber directly into a l-cm cell and measure the absorbance of the solution at 535 $m\mu$, using the reagent blank as the reference.

d. Preparation of standard curve: Treat aliquots of the standard solution containing 0, 1.0, 2.0, 5.0, and 10.0 μg as described in this section, ¶s a through d. Plot absorbance versus concentration of arsenic in the standard.

5. Calculation

$$\text{mg/l As} = \frac{\mu\text{g As}}{\text{ml sample}}$$

6. Precision and Accuracy

A synthetic unknown sample containing 40 $\mu g/l$ As, 250 $\mu g/l$ Be, 240 $\mu g/l$ B, 20 $\mu g/l$ Se, and 6 $\mu g/l$ V in distilled water was determined by the silver diethyldithiocarbamate method, with a relative standard deviation of 13.8% and a relative error of 0% in 46 laboratories.

104 B. Mercuric Bromide Stain Method

1. General Discussion

a. Principle: After concentration of the sample, arsenic is liberated as arsine, AsH_3, by zinc in acid solution in a Gutzeit generator. The generated arsine is then passed through a column containing a roll of cotton moistened with lead acetate solution. The generated arsine is allowed to produce a yellow-brown stain on test paper strips impregnated with mercuric bromide. The length of the stain is roughly proportional to the amount of arsenic present.

b. Interference: Antimony interferes by giving a similar stain if present in quantities greater than 0.10 mg.

c. Minimum detectable concentration: 1 μg As.

2. Apparatus

Arsine generator: See Figure 9.

3. Reagents

a. Sulfuric acid, 1 + 1.

b. Nitric acid, conc.

c. Roll cotton: Cut a roll of dentist's cotton into 25-mm lengths.

d. Lead acetate solution: Prepare as directed in Method A, ¶ 3d.

e. Mercuric bromide paper: Use commercial arsenic papers cut uniformly into strips about 12 cm long and 2.5 mm wide (papers can be obtained already cut and sensitized). Soak strips for at least 1 hr in filtered solution prepared by dissolving 3–6 g $HgBr_2$ in 95% ethyl or isopropyl alco-

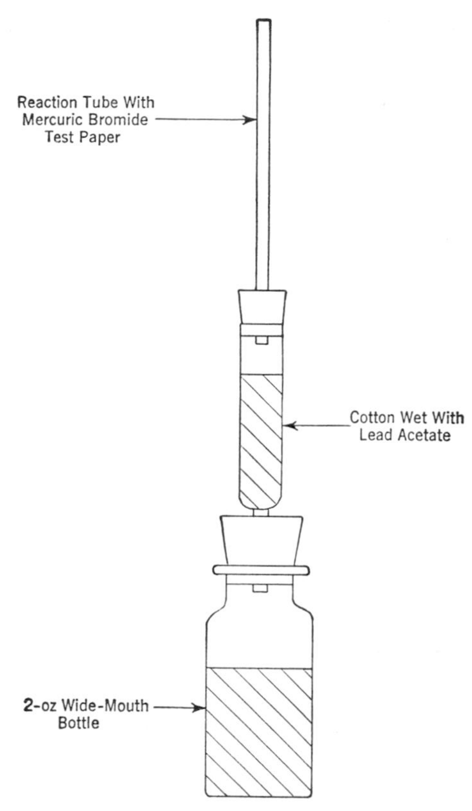

Figure 9. Generator used with mercuric bromide stain method.

hol; dry by waving in air. Store in dry dark place. For best results, make up papers just prior to use.

f. Potassium iodide solution: Prepare as directed in Method A, ¶ 3b.

g. *Stannous chloride reagent:* Prepare as directed in Method A, ¶ 3c.

h. Zinc, 20–30 mesh, arsenic free.

i. Standard arsenic solution: Prepare as directed in Method A, ¶ 3i.

4. Procedure

a. Concentration of sample and oxidation of any organic matter: To a suitable aliquot of sample containing from 2 to 30 μg As, add 7 ml 1 + 1 H_2SO_4 and 5 ml conc HNO_3 and evaporate to SO_3 fumes. Cool; add about 25 ml distilled water; and again evaporate to SO_3 fumes to expel oxides of nitrogen. Maintain an excess of HNO_3 until the organic matter is destroyed. Do not allow the solution to darken while organic matter is being destroyed because arsenic is likely to be reduced and lost.

b. Preparation of guard column and reaction tube: Dip one end of the 2.5-cm length of cotton into the lead acetate solution and introduce into the glass column. Then put the dried narrow glass tube in place and insert the $HgBr_2$ test paper. Make sure the paper strip is straight.

c. Treatment of sample concentrate: To the 25-ml sample concentrate in the generator, add 7 ml 1 + 1 H_2SO_4 and cool. Add 5 ml KI solution, 4 drops $SnCl_2$ reagent, and finally 2 to 5 g zinc. Immediately connect the reaction tube to the generator. Immerse the apparatus to within 2.5 cm of the top of the narrow tube in a water bath kept at 20 to 25 C and allow evolution to proceed for 1.5 hr. Remove the strip and compute the average length of stains on both sides. Using a calibration curve, the preparation of which is described below, estimate the amount of arsenic present.

d. Preparation of calibration curve: Prepare a blank and standards at 3-μg intervals in the 0 to 30 μg As range with 14 ml 1 + 1 H_2SO_4 and bring the total solution volume to 25 ml. Place in the generator and treat in the same manner as described for the sample concentrate. Remove the strip and compute the average length of stains on both sides, in millimeters. Plot the length in millimeters against micrograms of arsenic and use as a standard curve.

5. Precision and Accuracy

A synthetic unknown sample containing 50 μg/l As, 400 μg/l Be, 180 μg/l B, and 50 μg/l Se in distilled water was determined by the mercuric bromide stain method, with a relative standard deviation of 75.0% and a relative error of 60.0% in five laboratories.

104 C. Bibliography

Silver Diethyldithiocarbamate Method

VASAK, V. & V. SEDIVEC. 1952. Colorimetric determination of arsenic. *Chem. Listy* 46:341.

STRATTON, G. & H. C. WHITEHEAD. 1962. Colorimetric determination of arsenic in water with silver diethyldithiocarbamate. *JAWWA* 54:861.

BALLINGER, D. C., R. J. LISHKA & M. E. GALES. 1962. Application of silver diethyldithiocarbamate method to determination of arsenic. *JAWWA* 54:1424.

Mercuric Bromide Stain Method

FURMAN, N. H., Ed. 1962. *Standard Methods of Chemical Analysis* (6th ed.), Vol. I. D. Van Nostrand Co., Princeton, N. J., pp. 118–124.

105 BARIUM

Barium stimulates the heart muscle. However, a barium dose of 550–600 mg is considered fatal to human beings. Afflictions arising from its consumption, inhalation and absorption involve the heart, blood vessels, and nerves.

Despite a relatively abundant prevalence in nature (16th in order of rank), barium occurs in trace amounts in potable water supplies. The barium concentration of U.S. drinking waters ranges between 0.7 and 900 μg/l, with a mean of 49 μg/l. Therefore, an appreciable presence in a water supply signals undesirable industrial waste pollution.

105 A. Atomic Absorption Spectrophotometric Method

See Metals, Section 129A.

106 BERYLLIUM

Beryllium and its compounds are believed to be exceedingly poisonous and capable of causing death in high concentrations. Inhalation of beryllium dust can cause a serious affliction called berylliosis. Beryllium disease can also take the following forms: dermatitis, conjunctivitis (eye disease), acute pneumonitis (lung disease), and chronic pulmonary berylliosis.

In the form of the element, compounds or alloys, beryllium is used in atomic reactors, aircraft, rockets, and missile fuels. Entry into a water supply can result from the discharges of such industries. Beryllium has been reported to occur in U.S. drinking waters in the range of 0.01–0.7 μg/l, with the mean at 0.013 μg/l.

Selection of method: The atomic absorption spectrophotometric method and the colorimetric method are equally suitable for the determination of beryllium. Personal preference and the equipment available can dictate the method to be used.

106 A. Atomic Absorption Spectrophotometric Method

See Metals, Section 129A.

106 B. Aluminon Method (TENTATIVE)

1. General Discussion

a. Principle: The addition of a small amount of an ethylenediamine tetraacetic acid complexing solution prevents interference from moderate quantities of aluminum, cobalt, copper, iron, manganese, nickel, titanium, zinc and zirconium. An aluminon-buffer reagent is then added to form a beryllium lake and the color developed is measured at 515 mμ.

b. Interference: Under the conditions specified in the method, not much more than 10 mg of copper can be tolerated. If more is present, the amount of EDTA reagent will have to be increased. The complexed copper absorbs slightly at 515 mμ, but this interference can be eliminated by adding an equivalent amount of copper to the standards.

c. Minimum detectable concentration: 5 μg/l.

d. Absorptivity: 900.

2. Apparatus

a. Spectrophotometer, for use at 515 mμ, with a light path of 5 cm.

b. Filter photometer, equipped with a light path of 5 cm and a green filter, exhibiting a maximum transmittance near 515 mμ.

3. Reagents

a. Stock beryllium solution: Dissolve 9.82 g beryllium sulfate tetrahydrate, $BeSO_4 \cdot 4H_2O$, in 100 ml distilled water, filter if necessary, and dilute to 500 ml; 1.00 ml = 1.00 mg Be.

b. Standard beryllium solution: Dilute 10.00 ml stock beryllium solution with distilled water to 1,000 ml in a volumetric flask; 1.00 ml = 10.0 μg Be.

c. EDTA reagent: Add 30 ml distilled water and a drop of an alcoholic solution of methyl red (50 mg/100 ml) to 2.5 g ethylenediamine tetraacetic acid, also called (ethylenedinitrilo)-

tetraacetic acid. Neutralize with ammonium hydroxide, cool, and dilute to 100 ml.

d. Aluminon buffer reagent: Transfer 500 g ammonium acetate, $NH_4C_2H_3O_2$, to 1 liter distilled water in a 2-liter beaker. Add 80 ml conc (glacial) acetic acid and stir until completely dissolved. Filter if necessary. Dissolve 1 g aurintricarboxylic acid ammonium salt (aluminon),* in 50 ml distilled water and add to the buffer solution in the 2-liter beaker. Dissolve 3.0 g benzoic acid ($C_7H_6O_2$) in 20 ml methyl alcohol and add to the buffer solution while stirring. Dilute the mixture to 2 liters. Transfer 10 g gelatin to 250 ml distilled water in a 400-ml beaker. Place the beaker in a boiling water bath and stir occasionally until the gelatin has dissolved completely. Pour the warm gelatin into a 1,000-ml volumetric flask containing 500 ml distilled water. Cool to room temperature, dilute to the mark, and mix. Transfer the gelatin solution and buffer solutions to a 4-liter chemical-resistant dark glass bottle. Mix and store in a cool dark place. The reagent is stable for at least a month.

4. Procedure

Dilute 0.50, 1.00, and 2.00 ml standard beryllium solution to 100 ml in volumetric flasks. Dilute a 50-ml sample, or an aliquot containing less than 20 μg Be, to 100 ml in a volumetric flask. Add 2 ml EDTA reagent to each flask and dilute with distilled water to approximately 75 ml. Add 15 ml aluminon buffer reagent, dilute to 100 ml with distilled water, and mix thoroughly. Allow it to stand away from the light for 20 min after the aluminon buffer is added. Filter if necessary. Read the absorbancy of the standard and unknown as compared to the blank in a spectrophotometer or filter photometer at a 515-mμ wavelength using 5-cm cells. Construct a calibration curve by plotting the absorbancy of the standards versus micrograms of beryllium. Determine the amount of beryllium in the unknown by referring to the corresponding absorbance on the calibration curve.

* Eastman No. P4468 or equivalent.

5. Calculation

$$\text{mg/l Be} = \frac{\mu\text{g Be}}{\text{ml sample}}$$

6. Precision and Accuracy

In 32 laboratories a synthetic unknown sample of distilled water containing 250 μg/l Be, 40 μg/l As, 240 μg/l B, 20 μg/l Se, and 6 μg/l V, the beryllium was determined with a relative standard deviation of 7.13% and a relative error of 12%.

7. Bibliography

LUKE, C. L. & M. E. CAMPBELL. 1952. Photometric determination of beryllium in beryllium-copper alloys. *Anal. Chem.* 24:1056.

LUKE, C. L. & K. C. BROWN. 1952. Photometric determination of aluminum in manganese, bronze, zinc die casting alloys, and magnesium alloys. *Anal. Chem.* 24:1120.

107 BORON

Although an essential element for plant growth, boron in excess of 2.0 mg/l in irrigation water is deleterious to certain plants, and there is evidence that some plants are adversely affected by concentrations as low as 1.0 mg/l (or even less in commercial greenhouses). Drinking waters rarely contain more than 1 mg/l boron, and generally less than 0.1 mg/l, concentrations which are considered innocuous for human consumption. Boron may occur naturally in some waters or may find its way into a watercourse by virtue of its presence in some cleaning compounds and industrial waste effluents.

The ingestion of large amounts of boron can affect the central nervous system, and protracted ingestion may result in a clinical syndrome known as borism.

1. *Selection of method:* The curcumin method (A) is applicable in the 0.10–1.0 mg/l range, while the carmine method (B) is suitable for the determination of boron concentrations in the 1–10 mg/l range. The potentiometric titration method (C) is useful for the boron range of 0.10–5 mg/l. The range of all three methods can be extended by dilution or concentration of the original sample. The colorimetric methods offer some advantages over the potentiometric titration method. Smaller aliquots (1–25 ml) are needed, in contrast to the 250-ml volume required for the titrimetric method. In addition, phosphate does not interfere with the colorimetric methods. The curcumin method, however, fails in the presence of nitrate nitrogen exceeding 20 mg/l. The potentiometric method, on the other hand, is especially applicable to waters of high boron concentration where accuracy is important.

2. *Sampling and storage:* Samples should be stored in polyethylene bottles or alkali-resistant, boron-free glassware.

107 A. Curcumin Method

1. General Discussion

a. Principle: When a sample of water containing boron is acidified and evaporated in the presence of curcumin, a red-colored product called rosocyanine is formed. The rosocyanine is taken up in a suitable solvent, and the red color is compared with standards visually or photometrically.

b. Interference: Nitrate nitrogen concentrations above 20 mg/l interfere. Significantly high results are possible when the total of calcium and magnesium hardness exceeds 100 mg/l as $CaCO_3$. Moderate hardness levels can also cause a considerable percentage error in the low boron range. The interference springs from the insolubility of the hardness salts in 95% ethanol, thereby imparting a turbidity to the final solution. Filtration of the final solution is one way of coping with this situation. Passing the original sample through a column of strongly acidic cation-exchange resin in the hydrogen form removes the interfering cations and enables the method to be applied to waters and effluents of high hardness or solids content.

c. Minimum detectable concentration: 0.2 μg B.

2. Apparatus

a. Colorimetric equipment—One of the following is required:

1) SPECTROPHOTOMETER, for use at 540 mμ, with a minimum light path of 1 cm.

2) FILTER PHOTOMETER, equipped with a green filter having a maximum transmittance near 540 mμ, with a minimum light path of 1 cm.

b. Evaporating dishes, 100–150 ml capacity, of Vycor glass,* platinum or other material found suitable through use.

c. Water bath, set at 55 ± 2 C.

d. Glass-stoppered volumetric flasks, 25- and 50-ml capacity.

e. Ion-exchange column, 50 cm long by 1.3 cm in diameter.

3. Reagents

a. Stock boron solution: Dissolve 571.6 mg anhydrous boric acid, H_3BO_3, in distilled water and dilute to 1,000 ml; 1.00 ml = 100 μg B. Because H_3BO_3 loses weight on drying at 105 C, use a reagent meeting ACS specifications and keep the bottle tightly stoppered to prevent the entrance of atmospheric moisture.

b. Standard boron solution: Dilute 10.00 ml stock boron solution to 1,000 ml with distilled water; 1.00 ml = 1.00 μg B.

c. Curcumin reagent: Dissolve 40 mg finely ground curcumin † and 5.0 g oxalic acid in 80 ml of 95% ethyl alcohol. Add 4.2 ml conc HCl and make the solution up to 100 ml with ethyl alcohol in a 100-ml volumetric flask (isopropyl alcohol, 95%, may be used in place of ethyl alcohol). This reagent will be stable for several days if stored in a refrigerator.

d. Ethyl alcohol, 95%.

e. Reagents for removal of high hardness and cation interference:

1) STRONGLY ACIDIC CATION EXCHANGE RESIN.

2) HYDROCHLORIC ACID, 1 + 5.

4. Procedure

a. Precautions: Close control of such variables as volumes and concentrations of reagents, as well as time and temperature of drying, must be exercised for a successful determination. Evaporating dishes must be identical in shape, size and composition to insure equal evaporation time. Increasing the time of evaporation results in intensification of the resulting color.

b. Preparation of calibration curve: Pipet 0 (blank), 0.25, 0.50, 0.75, and 1.00 μg boron into evaporating dishes of the same type, shape and size. Add distilled water to each standard to bring the total volume to 1.0 ml. Add 4.0 ml curcumin reagent to each and swirl the dish gently to mix contents thoroughly. Float the dishes on a water bath set at 55 ± 2 C and evaporate the contents to complete dryness. Remove each dish from the water bath 15 min after the contents appear dry and the odor of HCl is gone. After the dishes cool to room temperature, add 10.0 ml 95% ethyl alcohol to each dish, stirring gently with a polyethylene rod to insure complete dissolution of the red-colored product.

Wash the contents of each dish into

---

* A product of Corning Glass Works.

† Eastman No. 1179 or equivalent.

a 25-ml volumetric flask, using 95% ethyl alcohol. Make up to the mark with 95% ethyl alcohol and mix thoroughly by inverting the flask. Read the transmittance or absorbance of the standards and samples at a wavelength of 540 mμ after setting the reagent blank at 100% transmittance, or zero absorbance. The calibration curve is linear from 0 to 1.00 μg boron. Make the photometric readings within 1 hr of drying the samples.

c. Sample treatment: For waters containing 0.10–1.00 mg/l boron, use 1.00 ml of sample. For waters containing more than 1.00 mg/l boron, make an appropriate dilution with boron-free distilled water, so that a 1.00-ml aliquot contains approximately 0.50 μg boron.

Pipet the 1.00 ml of sample or dilution into an evaporating dish. Unless the calibration curve is being determined at the same time, prepare a blank and a standard containing 0.50 μg boron and run in conjunction with the unknown. Proceed as in ¶ b preceding, beginning with "Add 4.0 ml curcumin reagent. . . ." If the final solution is turbid, filter through filter paper (Whatman No. 30 or equivalent) before reading the absorbance. Obtain the boron content from the calibration curve.

d. Visual comparison: The photometric method may be adapted to visual estimation of low boron concentrations, from 50 to 200 μg/l, as follows: Dilute standard boron solution so that 1.00 ml equals 0.20 μg boron. Pipet 0, 0.05, 0.10, 0.15, and 0.20 μg boron into the evaporating dishes as indicated in ¶ 4b. At the same time add an appropriate volume of sample (1.00 ml or aliquot diluted to 1.00 ml) to an identical evaporating dish. The boron content of the sample taken should be between 0.05 and 0.20 μg. Proceed as in ¶ 4b, beginning with "Add 4.0 ml curcumin reagent. . . ." Compare the color of the unknowns with the standards within 1 hr after dissolution of the red color in the alcohol.

e. Removal of high hardness and cation interference: Prepare an ion-exchange column of the type illustrated in Figure 3 and described in the Introduction, Section 100 B.2b. Charge the column with a strongly acidic cation exchange resin. Backwash the column with distilled water to remove the entrained air bubbles. Henceforth, make certain that the resin remains covered with liquid at all times. Pass 50 ml 1 + 5 hydrochloric acid through the column and then wash it free with distilled water.

Pipet 25 ml sample, or a smaller aliquot of a sample of known high boron content, onto the resin column. Adjust the rate of flow through the column to about 2 drops per sec and collect the effluent in a 50-ml volumetric flask. Wash the column with small portions of distilled water until the flask is full to the mark. Mix the contents of the flask and transfer 2.00 ml into the evaporating dish. Add 4.0 ml curcumin reagent and complete the analysis as described in ¶ 4b preceding.

5. Calculation

The following equation may be used in calculating the boron concentration from the absorbance readings:

$$\text{mg/l B} = \frac{A_2 \times C}{A_1 \times S}$$

in which A_1 = absorbance of the standard taken, A_2 = absorbance of unknown water sample, C = micrograms boron in standard taken, and S = ml unknown water sample used.

6. Precision and Accuracy

A synthetic unknown sample containing 240 μg/l B, 40 μg/l As, 250 μg/l Be, 20 μg/l Se, and 6 μg/l V in distilled water was determined by the curcumin method with a relative standard deviation of 22.8% and a relative error of 0% in 30 laboratories.

107 B. Carmine Method

1. General Discussion

a. Principle: In the presence of boron, a solution of carmine or carminic acid in concentrated sulfuric acid changes from a bright red to a bluish red or blue, depending on the concentration of boron present.

b. Interference: The ions more commonly found in water and sewage do not interfere in this method.

c. Minimum detectable concentration: 2μg B.

2. Apparatus

COLORIMETRIC EQUIPMENT—One of the following is required:

a. Spectrophotometer, for use at 585 mμ, with a minimum light path of 1 cm.

b. Filter photometer, equipped with an orange filter having a maximum transmittance near 585 mμ, with a minimum light path of 1 cm.

3. Reagents

Store all reagents in polyethylene or boron-free containers.

a. Standard boron solution: Prepare as directed in Method A, ¶ 3b.

b. Hydrochloric acid, conc and 1 + 11.

c. Sulfuric acid, conc.

d. Carmine reagent: Dissolve 920 mg carmine N.F. 40, or carminic acid, in 1 liter conc H_2SO_4.

e. Sodium hydroxide, 1*N*.

4. Procedure

a. Preliminary sample treatment: If the sample contains less than 1 mg/l B, pipet an aliquot containing 2–20 μg B into a platinum dish, make alkaline with 1*N* NaOH plus a slight excess, and evaporate to dryness on a steam or hot water bath. If necessary, destroy any organic material at this point by ignition at 500–550 C. Acidify the cooled residue (ignited or not) with 2.5 ml 1 + 11 HCl and triturate with a rubber policeman to dissolve. Centrifuge if need be to obtain a clear solution. Pipet 2.00 ml clear concentrate into a small flask or 30-ml test tube. Subject a reagent blank to the same steps as the sample.

b. Color development: Prepare a series of boron standard solutions (100, 250, 500, 750 and 1,000 μg) in 100-ml volume with distilled water. Pipet 2.00 ml of each standard solution into a small flask or 30-ml test tube.

Treat the blank and calibration standards exactly as the sample throughout the procedure. Add 2 drops (0.1 ml) conc HCl, then carefully introduce 10.0 ml conc H_2SO_4, mix, and allow to cool to room temperature. Add 10.0 ml carmine reagent, mix well, and after 45–60 min measure the absorbance at 585 mμ in a cell of 1-cm or longer light path, using the blank as the reference.

To avoid error, make sure that no bubbles are present in the optical cell while the photometric readings are being made. The bubbles may appear as a result of the incomplete mixing of the reagents. Because the carmine reagent deteriorates, check the calibration curve daily.

5. Calculation

$$\text{mg/l B} = \frac{\mu\text{g B}}{\text{ml sample}}$$

6. Precision and Accuracy

A synthetic unknown sample containing 180 μg/l B, 50 μg/l As, 400 μg/l Be, and 50μg/l Se in distilled water was determined by the carmine method with a relative standard deviation of 35.5% and a relative error of 0.6% in nine laboratories.

107 C. Potentiometric Method

1. General Discussion

a. Principle: When a dilute solution containing boric acid or borate is neutralized and then treated with mannitol, a complex acid is produced which can be titrated with dilute NaOH. The amount of boron is proportional to the amount of NaOH needed to return the pH of the solution to the initial pH.

b. Interference: Phosphate reacts with mannitol but not quantitatively. A phosphate concentration exceeding 10 mg/l should be removed by precipitation with lead nitrate, followed by removal of the excess lead with sodium bicarbonate. Germanium and tetravalent vanadium react like boron but are not normally present in water supplies. Buffer substances, such as ammonia, carbonate or phosphate, may interfere by decreasing the sharpness of the end point. The absorption of acidic or alkaline gases from the laboratory air during the course of the titration may cause a drift of the meter and resultant error.

Hydrochloric acid or ammonia should not be permitted in the room while boron titrations are being carried out. The error from atmospheric carbon dioxide can be minimized by titrating rapidly. Titration of the blanks and standards, if carried out under conditions as closely similar as possible to those of the sample titrations, will nearly compensate for any carbon dioxide error.

2. Apparatus

a. Buret, so calibrated that the volume can be read to 0.01 ml.

b. Glassware: Pyrex beakers can be used, but new beakers should be cleaned by filling with dilute acid and heating on a steam bath.

c. Motor stirrer or magnetic stirrer.

d. Electrical equipment: Either a potentiometer [1] or a pH meter sensitive to 0.01–0.05 pH may be used as an indicating system, set so that at balance the solution under test will have a pH of 7.00. The glass-saturated calomel electrode pair commonly used in pH measurements is satisfactory. The indicator needle of the pH meter should remain steady and unaffected by drift from a reading of pH 7.00 when the initial point of the titration is established as in ¶ 4d following.

3. Reagents

a. Bromthymol blue indicator solution: Dissolve 1.0 g water-soluble bromthymol blue sodium salt in distilled water and dilute to 100 ml.

b. Sulfuric acid, 1*N.*

c. Standard buffer, pH 7.00, commercially prepared for standardizing a pH meter.

d. Sodium hydroxide solution, carbonate free, saturated.

e. Sodium hydroxide, 0.5*N.* Dilute 2.9 ml of the supernate from the saturated NaOH solution to 100 ml with freshly boiled distilled water. Prepare each day.

f. Standard sodium hydroxide titrant, 0.0231*N.* Measure a volume of the supernate from the carbonate-free saturated NaOH solution to give about 1 g NaOH and dilute to 1 liter with CO_2-free distilled water. Standardize against 5.00 ml standard boron solution plus 250 ml distilled water as described in the procedure. Dilute with CO_2-free distilled water so that 1.00 ml = 250 μg B. Store in a boron-free container (low-boron glass, paraffin-lined or polyethylene bottle) protected by a CO_2 trap filled with soda lime or a sodium hydroxide asbestos absorbent.*

g. Mannitol, boron free. The blank titration for 5 g mannitol should not exceed 0.1 ml standard NaOH.

h. Standard boron solution: Prepare as directed in Method A, ¶ 3b.

4. Procedure

a. Preliminary sample treatment: Transfer to a 400-ml tall-form beaker 250 ml of the sample containing not more than 1 mg B. If the sample is high in boron, dilute an aliquot portion to 250 ml.

Add a few drops of bromthymol blue indicator and acidify with 1*N* H_2SO_4, adding 0.5–1 ml in excess. Bring to a boil and stir—cautiously at first, then vigorously—to expel carbon dioxide. Cover and cool to room temperature, preferably in a water bath.

b. Standardization of pH meter: Standardize the pH meter to 7.00 with standard buffer solution. Wash the electrodes thoroughly with distilled water and introduce the electrodes into the solution to be titrated. Add carbonate-free 0.5*N* NaOH to approximately pH 5.0. Gently stir the solution during the titration procedure. Adjust the solution to exactly pH 7.00 with the standard NaOH titrant (¶ 3f). This is the initial point of the titration.

c. Titration of sample: Add 5 g ± 0.1 g mannitol. If boron is present, the indicator will change to the acid color, and the pH meter will show an acid pH. Add standard NaOH titrant until the pH meter indicates 7.00. Note the number of milliliters of standard NaOH titrant required after adding mannitol at the initial point of the titration.

d. Blank and standard determination: Determine a reagent blank by using 250 ml boiled distilled water instead of the sample. Proceed as indicated above, beginning with ¶ 4a. Run a standard boron solution (500 μg boron) in conjunction with the unknown in order to check reagents and technic.

5. Calculation

$$\text{mg/l B} = \frac{(A - C) \times N \times 10{,}820}{\text{ml sample}}$$

where A = ml titration for sample, C = ml titration for blank, N = normality of standard NaOH titrant, and B = boron.

* Ascarite (A. H. Thomas Co.) or equivalent.

6. Precision and Accuracy

A synthetic unknown sample containing 180 μg/l B, 50 μg/l As, 400 μg/l Be, and 50 μg/l Se in distilled water was determined by the potentiometric method with a relative standard deviation of 8.3% and a relative error of 1.1% in two laboratories.

107 D. Reference

1. *Standard Methods for the Examination of Water, Sewage, and Industrial Wastes* (10th ed.), 1955. APHA, AWWA & FSIWA, New York, page 48.

107 E. Bibliography

Curcumin Colorimetric Method

SILVERMAN, L. & K. TREGO. 1953. Colorimetric microdetermination of boron by the curcumin-acetone solution method. *Anal. Chem.* 25:1264.

DIBLE, W. T., E. TRUOG & K. C. BERGER. 1954. Boron determination in soils and plants—Simplified curcumin procedure. *Anal. Chem.* 26:418.

LUKE, C. L. 1955. Determination of traces of boron in silicon, germanium, and germanium dioxide. *Anal. Chem.* 27:1150.

LISHKA, R. J. 1961. Comparison of analytical procedures for boron. *JAWWA* 53:1517.

BUNTON, N. G. & B. H. TAIT. 1969. Determination of boron in waters and effluents using curcumin. *JAWWA* 61:357.

Carmine Colorimetric Method

HATCHER, J. T. & L. V. WILCOX. 1950. Colorimetric determination of boron using carmine. *Anal. Chem.* 22:567.

Potentiometric Titration Method

FOOTE, F. J. 1932. Determination of boron in waters. *Ind. Eng. Chem.*, Anal. Ed. 4:39.

WILCOX, L. V. 1932. Electrometric titration of boric acid. *Ind. Eng. Chem.*, Anal. Ed. 4:38.

———. 1940. Determination of boron in plant material. *Ind. Eng. Chem.*, Anal. Ed. 12:341.

108 BROMIDE

Bromide may occur in varying amounts in well supplies in coastal areas as a result of sea water intrusion. The bromide content of some groundwater supplies has been ascribed to connate water. Industrial discharges may contribute the bromide found in some freshwater streams. Under normal circumstances, the bromide content of most drinking waters is negligible, seldom exceeding 1 mg/l.

1. General Discussion

a. Principle: Phenol red undergoes a color change from yellow to red over the pH range 6.4–8.0. With dilute hypobromite, phenol red forms an indicator of the bromphenol blue type, which changes from yellow to blue-purple over the pH range of 3.2–4.6. The oxidation of the bromide and the bromination of the phenol red take place readily in the presence of chloramine-T (sodium toluene-p-sulfonchloramide). If the color comparison is made at a pH of 5.0–5.4, the brominated compound will be reddish to violet, depending upon its concentration. Thus, a sharp differentiation can be made between varying quantities of bromide. The concentration of chloramine-T and the timing of the reaction before dechlorination are critical.

b. Interference: Materials present in ordinary tap water do not interfere.

c. Minimum detectable concentration: 100 μg/l Br.

2. Apparatus

a. COLORIMETRIC EQUIPMENT—One of the following is required:

1) *Spectrophotometer,* for use at 590 mμ providing a light path of 1 cm.

2) *Filter photometer,* providing a 1-cm light path and equipped with an orange filter having a maximum transmittance near 590 mμ.

3) *Nessler tubes,* matched, 100-ml, tall form.

b. ACID-WASHED GLASSWARE: Wash all glassware with 1 + 6 HNO_3 and rinse with distilled water to remove all trace of adsorbed bromide.

3. Reagents

a. Acetate buffer solution: Dissolve 68 g sodium acetate trihydrate, $NaC_2H_3O_2 \cdot 3H_2O$, in distilled water. Add 30 ml conc (glacial) acetic acid and make up to 1 liter. The pH should be 4.6–4.7.

b. Phenol red indicator solution: Dissolve 21 mg phenolsulfonephthalein sodium salt and dilute to 100 ml with distilled water.

c. Chloramine-T solution: Dissolve 500 mg chloramine-T and dilute to 100 ml with distilled water. Store in a dark bottle and refrigerate.

d. Sodium thiosulfate, 2M. Dissolve 49.6 g $Na_2S_2O_3 \cdot 5H_2O$ or 31.6 g $Na_2S_2O_3$ and dilute to 100 ml with distilled water.

e. Stock bromide solution: Dissolve 744.6 mg anhydrous potassium bromide, KBr, in distilled water and make up to 1,000 ml; 1.00 ml = 500 μg Br.

f. Standard bromide solution: Dilute 10.00 ml stock bromide solution to 1,000 ml with distilled water; 1.00 ml = 5.00 μg Br.

4. Procedure

a. Treatment of sample: To 50.0 ml of sample containing 0.1–1.0 mg/l Br, add 2 ml buffer solution, 2 ml phenol red solution, and 0.5 ml chloramine-T solution. Mix thoroughly. After exactly 20 min following the chloramine-T addition, dechlorinate by adding, with mixing, 0.5 ml sodium thiosulfate solution. Compare visually in nessler tubes against bromide standards prepared simultaneously, or preferably read in a photometer at 590 mμ and determine the bromide values from a calibration curve.

b. Preparation of calibration curve: Prepare standards by diluting aliquots of the standard bromide solution to 50.0 ml; 1.00 ml of the standard solution diluted to 50.0 ml is equivalent to 0.1 mg/l Br.

Construct a calibration curve consisting of 10 to 15 points in the concentration range of 0.1–1.0 mg/l Br. Read standards at 590 mμ on a spectrophotometer or a filter photometer against a distilled-water blank.

5. Calculation

$$\text{mg/l Br} = \frac{\mu\text{g Br}}{\text{ml sample}}$$

6. Bibliography

STENGER, V. A. & I. M. KOLTHOFF. 1935. Detection and colorimetric estimation of microquantities of bromide. *J. Amer. Chem. Soc.* 57:831.

HOUGHTON, G. U. 1946. The bromide content of underground waters. *J. Soc. Chem. Ind.* (London) 65:277.

GOLDMAN, E. & D. BYLES. 1959. Suggested revision of phenol red method for bromide. *JAWWA* 51:1051.

109 CADMIUM

Cadmium has high toxic potential, having been implicated in some cases of poisoning through food. Minute quantities of cadmium are suspected of being responsible for adverse renal arterial changes in human kidneys. A cadmium concentration of 200 μg/l has been found toxic to certain fish. On the other hand, there is an indication that cadmium might possibly be a dietary essential. The cadmium concentration of U.S. drinking waters has been reported to vary between 0.4 and 60 μg/l, with a mean of 8.2 μg/l. Cadmium may enter a water as a result of industrial discharges or the deterioration of galvanized pipe.

Selection of method: The atomic absorption spectrophotometric and dithizone methods are equally satisfactory for the determination of cadmium.

109 A. Atomic Absorption Spectrophotometric Method

See Metals, Section 129A.

109 B. Dithizone Method

1. General Discussion

a. Principle: Cadmium ions under suitable conditions react with dithizone to form a pink to red color which can be extracted with chloroform. The chloroform extracts are measured photometrically and the cadmium concentration is obtained from a calibration curve prepared from a standard cadmium solution treated in the same manner as the sample.

b. Interference: Under the conditions of this method, concentrations of metal ions normally found in water do not interfere. Lead concentrations up to 6 mg, zinc up to 3 mg, and copper up to 1 mg in the aliquot taken for analysis do not interfere. Ordinary room lighting does not affect the cadmium dithizonate color.

c. *Minimum detectable concentration:* 0.5 μg Cd with a 2-cm light path.

2. Apparatus

a. COLORIMETRIC EQUIPMENT: One of the following is required—

1) *Spectrophotometer,* for use at 518 mμ with a minimum light path of 1 cm.

2) *Filter photometer,* equipped with a green filter having a maximum light transmittance near 518 mμ, with a minimum light path of 1 cm.

b. SEPARATORY FUNNELS, 125–150 ml, preferably with teflon stopcocks.

c. GLASSWARE: All glassware, including sample bottles, should be cleaned with 1 + 1 HCl and then rinsed thoroughly with tap water and distilled water.

3. Reagents

a. STOCK CADMIUM SOLUTION: Weigh 100.0 mg pure cadmium metal and dissolve in a solution composed of 20 ml distilled water plus 5 ml conc HCl. Use heat to assist dissolution of the metal. Transfer the solution quantitatively to a 1-liter volumetric flask and dilute to the mark with distilled water: 1.00 ml = 100 μg Cd. Store in a polyethylene container.

b. STANDARD CADMIUM SOLUTION: Pipet 10.00 ml stock cadmium solution into a 1-liter volumetric flask, add 10 ml conc HCl, and dilute to the mark with distilled water. Prepare as needed and use the same day; 1.00 ml = 1.00 μg Cd.

c. SODIUM POTASSIUM TARTRATE SOLUTION: Dissolve 250 g $NaKC_4H_4O_6 \cdot 4H_2O$ in distilled water and make up to 1 liter.

d. SODIUM HYDROXIDE—POTASSIUM CYANIDE SOLUTIONS:

1) *Solution (I):* Dissolve 400 g NaOH and 10 g KCN in distilled water and make up to 1 liter. Store in a polyethylene bottle. This solution is stable for 1–2 months.

2) *Solution (II):* Dissolve 400 g NaOH and 0.5 g KCN in distilled water and make up to 1 liter. Store in a polyethylene bottle. This solution is stable for 1–2 months.

CAUTION—*Potassium cyanide is extremely poisonous and more than customary precautions should be observed in its handling. Never use mouth pipets to deliver volumes of cyanide solutions.*

e. HYDROXYLAMINE HYDROCHLORIDE SOLUTION: Dissolve 20 g $NH_2OH \cdot HCl$ in distilled water and make up to 100 ml.

f. STOCK DITHIZONE SOLUTION: Dissolve 100 mg diphenylthiocarbazone * in 1 liter chloroform, $CHCl_3$. Keep in a brown bottle in the refrigerator until required and use while still cold.

g. CHLOROFORM, ACS grade passed for "suitability for use in dithizone test." Test for a satisfactory chloroform by adding a minute amount of dithizone to a portion of the $CHCl_3$ in a stoppered test tube so that a faint green is produced; the green color should be stable for a day.

h. TARTARIC ACID SOLUTION: Dissolve 20 g $H_2C_4H_4O_6$ in distilled water and make up to 1 liter. Keep the solution in the refrigerator, as it must be cold when used.

i. STANDARD DITHIZONE SOLUTION:

* Eastman No. 3092 or equivalent.

Dilute 100 ml stock dithizone solution to 1 liter with $CHCl_3$. Keep in a brown bottle in the refrigerator and allow to warm to room temperature before using.

j. HYDROCHLORIC ACID, conc.

k. THYMOL BLUE INDICATOR SOLUTION: Dissolve 0.4 g thymolsulfonephthalein sodium salt in 100 ml distilled water.

l. SODIUM HYDROXIDE, 6*N*.

4. Procedure

a. Preparation of standard curve: Pipet 0 (blank), 2.00, 4.00, 6.00, 8.00, and 10.00 μg Cd into a series of separatory funnels. Add sufficient distilled water to make up to a final volume of 25 ml.

b. Color development, extraction, and measurement: Add reagents in the following order, mixing after each addition: 1 ml sodium potassium tartrate solution, 5 ml NaOH-KCN solution (I), 1 ml hydroxylamine hydrochloride solution, and 15 ml stock dithizone solution. Stopper the funnels and shake for 1 min, relieving the vapor pressure in the funnels through the stopper rather than the stopcock. Drain the $CHCl_3$ layer into a second funnel containing 25 ml cold tartaric acid solution. Add 10 ml $CHCl_3$ to the first funnel; shake for 1 min and drain into the second funnel again. Do not permit the aqueous layer to enter the second funnel in these operations. As the time of contact of the $CHCl_3$ with the strong alkali must be kept to a minimum, perform the two extractions without delay after addition of the dithizone (cadmium dithizonate decomposes on prolonged contact with strong alkali saturated with $CHCl_3$).

Shake the second funnel for 2 min and discard the $CHCl_3$ layer. Add 5 ml $CHCl_3$, shake 1 min, and discard the $CHCl_3$ layer, making as close a separation as possible. In the following order, add 0.25 ml hydroxylamine hydrochloride solution and 15.0 ml standard dithizone solution. Add 5 ml NaOH–KCN solution (II), and *immediately* shake for 1 min. Insert a pledget of cotton in the stem of the funnel and filter the $CHCl_3$ layer into a dry photometer tube. Read the absorbance at 518 mμ against the blank. Plot a calibration curve.

c. Treatment of samples: Pipet the appropriate volume of the sample containing 1–10 μg Cd into a separatory funnel and make up to 25 ml with distilled water. In the case of potable water containing 10 μg/l Cd or less, add 0.5 ml conc HCl to 200 ml sample and evaporate to 20 ml. Add a few drops of thymol blue indicator solution and then 6*N* NaOH solution until the indicator just turns yellow at a pH of approximately 2.8. Make up to 25 ml with distilled water. Adjust in a similar fashion the pH of a sample which has been processed by acid digestion. Unless the calibration curve is being prepared at the same time, prepare a blank and a standard containing 6.00 μg Cd in a final volume of 25 ml and run it in conjunction with the unknown. Proceed as in ¶ 4b above. Obtain the Cd concentration from the calibration curve.

5. Calculation

The following equation may be used for calculating the Cd concentration from the absorbance readings:

$$\text{mg/l Cd} = \frac{A_2 \times C}{A_1 \times S}$$

in which A_1 = absorbance of the standard taken, A_2 = absorbance of unknown water sample, C = micrograms Cd in standard taken, and S = milliliters of unknown water sample used.

6. Precision and Accuracy

A synthetic unknown sample containing 50 μg/l Cd, 500 μg/l Al, 110 μg/l Cr, 470 μg/l Cu, 300 μg/l Fe, 70 μg/l Pb, 120 μg/l Mn, 150 μg/l Ag, and 650 μg/l Zn was determined by the dithizone method with a relative standard deviation of 24.6% and a relative error of 6.0% in 44 laboratories.

7. Bibliography

SALTZMAN, B. E. 1953. Colorimetric microdetermination of cadmium with dithizone. *Anal. Chem.* 25:493.

GANOTES, J., E. LARSON & R. NAVONE. 1962. Suggested dithizone method for cadmium determination. *JAWWA* 54:852.

110 CALCIUM

The presence of calcium (5th among the elements in order of abundance) in water supplies results from passage through or over deposits of limestone, dolomite, gypsum, and gypsiferous shale. The calcium content may range from zero to several hundred mg/l, depending on the source and treatment of the water. Small concentrations of calcium carbonate combat corrosion of metallic pipes by laying down a protective coating. Appreciable calcium salts, on the other hand, break down on heating to form harmful scale in boilers, pipes and cooking utensils. The matter of "Saturation and Stability with Respect to Calcium Carbonate" is discussed under that heading in Section 149. Chemical softening treatment or ion exchange is employed to reduce the calcium and the associated hardness to tolerable levels.

Selection of method: Personal preference often dictates whether the classical gravimetric or the permanganate titrimetric method will be used for the accurate determination of calcium. The longer time required for gravimetric manipulations may restrict this method to occasional samples. The permanganate method, on the other hand, is often preferred for the analysis a large number of samples simultaneously. The rapidity and simplicity of the EDTA titrimetric method make it suitable for control and routine applications.

Storage of samples: The customary precautions are sufficient if care is taken to redissolve any calcium carbonate that may precipitate on standing.

110 A. Gravimetric Method

1. General Discussion

a. Principle: Ammonium oxalate precipitates calcium quantitatively as calcium oxalate. An excess of oxalate overcomes the adverse effects of magnesium. Optimum crystal formation and minimum occlusion are obtained only when the pH is brought slowly to the desired value. This is accomplished in two stages, with intervening digestion to promote seed crystal formation. The precipitate is ignited to, and weighed as, calcium oxide.

b. Interference: The sample should be free of interfering amounts of strontium, silica, aluminum, iron, manganese, phosphate, and suspended matter. Strontium may precipitate as the oxalate and cause high results. In such an event, a flame photometric determination should be performed for strontium and the proper correction applied to the gravimetric estimate in order to obtain a reliable calcium result. Silica interference should be disposed of by the classical dehydration procedure. Aluminum, iron and manganese should be precipitated by ammonium hydroxide after treatment with persulfate. Precipitation as the ferric salt is an accepted procedure for eliminating phosphate. Suspended matter can be removed by centrifuging or by filtration through paper, sintered glass or a cellulose acetate membrane (see Residue, Sections 148 B.2 and 3 and 148 C.2 and 3).

2. Reagents

a. Methyl red indicator solution: Dissolve 0.1 g methyl red sodium salt and dilute to 100 ml with distilled water.

b. Hydrochloric acid, 1 + 1.

c. Ammonium oxalate solution: Dissolve 10 g $(NH_4)_2C_2O_4 \cdot H_2O$ in 250 ml distilled water. Filter if necessary.

d. Ammonium hydroxide, 3*N*. Add 240 ml conc NH_4OH to about 700 ml distilled water and dilute to 1 liter. Filter before use to remove suspended silica flakes.

e. Ammonium hydroxide, 1 + 99.

f. Special reagents for removal of aluminum, iron, and manganese interference:

1) AMMONIUM PERSULFATE, solid.

2) AMMONIUM CHLORIDE SOLUTION. Dissolve 20 g NH_4Cl in a liter of distilled water. Filter if necessary.

3. Procedure

a. Removal of silica interference: Remove interfering amounts of silica from the sample by the gravimetric procedure described in Silica, Section 151 A.4. Discard the silica precipitate and save the filtrate for removal of interfering amounts of combined oxides described in ¶ b below. If combined oxides are absent, proceed to ¶ c.

b. Removal of combined oxides interference: Remove interfering amounts of aluminum, iron and manganese by concentrating the filtrate from the gravimetric silica determination to 120–150 ml. Add enough HCl so that the filtrate from the silica removal contains at least 10 ml conc HCl at this point. Add 2–3 drops of methyl red indicator and 3*N* NH_4OH until the indicator color turns yellow. Add 1 g ammonium persulfate; when the solution begins to boil, add 3*N* NH_4OH carefully until the solution becomes slightly alkaline and the steam bears a distinct but not a strong odor of ammonia. Test the solution with litmus paper. Boil the solution a minute or two and let the hot solution stand 10 min, until the hydroxides coagulate, but no longer. Filter the precipitate and wash three or four times with ammonium chloride solution. Treat the filtrate as described in the following.

c. pH adjustment of sample: To 200 ml of the sample, which must not contain more than 250 mg Ca, or to a smaller aliquot diluted to 200 ml, add

2 or 3 drops methyl red indicator solution. Neutralize with 1 + 1 HCl and boil for 1 min. Add 50 ml ammonium oxalate solution and if any precipitate forms, add just enough 1 + 1 HCl to redissolve it.

d. Initial precipitation of calcium oxalate: Keeping the solution just below the boiling point, add 3*N* NH_4OH dropwise from a buret, stirring constantly. Continue the addition until the solution is quite turbid (about 5 ml are required.) Digest for 90 min at 90 C. Complete precipitation by slowly adding 3*N* NH_4OH over a period of several minutes until the solution turns yellow. Digest for 15 min at 90 C; then filter through S&S No. 589 Red Ribbon or equivalent filter paper. Wash with cold 1 + 99 NH_4OH at once. (If magnesium is to be determined gravimetrically, set aside the combined filtrate and washings for this purpose.)

e. Second precipitation of calcium oxalate: Where time is not a factor and interferences are suspected or known to be present in the sample, repeat precipitation in the following manner: Dissolve the precipitate with 50 ml warm 1 + 9 HCl and wash the filter paper thoroughly with hot distilled water. Capture the solution and washings in the beaker in which the first precipitation was performed. Add 2–3 drops methyl red indicator solution. Dilute or concentrate the volume to 150 ml. Add 50 ml ammonium oxalate solution and repeat the precipitation as described in ¶ d above.

f. Ignition and weighing of precipitate: Ignite the precipitate in a covered crucible, preferably platinum, at 1,100–1,200 C for 15-min intervals until constant weight is attained. Because calcium oxide is extremely hygroscopic, take suitable precautions in cooling and weighing the crucible. Weigh immediately after the crucible reaches balance temperature. For best results, use a fresh charge of an efficient desiccant such as anhydrous magnesium perchlorate or activated aluminum oxide in the desiccator.

4. Calculation

$$\text{mg/l Ca} = \frac{\text{mg CaO} \times 714.7}{\text{ml sample}}$$

5. Precision and Accuracy

A synthetic unknown sample containing 108 mg/l Ca, 82 mg/l Mg, 3.1 mg/l K, 19.9 mg/l Na, 241 mg/l chloride, 1.1 mg/l nitrate N, 250 μg/l nitrite N, 259 mg/l sulfate, and 42.5 mg/l total alkalinity (contributed by $NaHCO_3$) in distilled water was determined by the gravimetric method, with a relative standard deviation of 3.7% and a relative error of 1.9% in four laboratories.

110 B. Permanganate Titrimetric Method

1. General Discussion

a. Principle: The titrimetric method differs from the gravimetric in that the precipitated calcium oxalate is redissolved in acid and titrated with permanganate. The amount of permanganate required to oxidize the oxalate is proportional to the amount of calcium.

b. Interference: See Method A, ¶ 1b, above.

2. Apparatus

a. Vacuum pump, or other source of vacuum.

b. Filter flasks.

c. Filter crucibles, 30-ml. Medium-porosity crucibles are recommended. Either glass or porcelain crucibles may be used. Paper filters may be used but are not recommended. Crucibles of all-porous construction are difficult to wash quantitatively.

3. Reagents

All the reagents listed in Section 110A.2 are required, plus the following:

a. Sodium oxalate: Obtain primary standard grade $Na_2C_2O_4$ from the National Bureau of Standards or the Mallinckrodt Chemical Works. Dry it at 105 C overnight and store the dried material in a desiccator.

b. Sulfuric acid, $1+1$.

c. Standard potassium permanganate titrant, $0.05N$. Dissolve 1.6 g $KMnO_4$ in 1 liter distilled water. Keep in a brown glass-stoppered bottle and permit it to age for at least a week. Carefully decant or pipet the supernate without stirring up any sediment. Standardize this solution frequently by the following procedure (standard potassium permanganate solution, exactly $0.0500N$, is equivalent to 1.002 mg Ca per 1.00 ml):

Weigh several samples of anhydrous sodium oxalate, $Na_2C_2O_4$, into 400-ml beakers. Weigh to the nearest 0.1 mg samples between 100 and 200 mg. To each beaker, in turn, add 100 ml distilled water and stir to dissolve. Add 10 ml $1+1$ H_2SO_4 and heat rapidly to $90-95$ C. Titrate rapidly with the permanganate solution to be standardized, while stirring to a slight pink end-point color which persists for at least 1 min. Do not allow the temperature to fall below 85 C. If necessary, warm the beaker contents during the course of titration; 100 mg sodium oxalate will consume about 30 ml permanganate solution. Run a blank on the distilled water and H_2SO_4.

$$\text{Normality of } KMnO_4 = \frac{\text{g } Na_2C_2O_4}{(A-B)\times 0.06701}$$

where A = ml titration for sample and B = ml titration for blank. Average the results of several titrations.

4. Procedure

a. Treatment of sample: Using 200 ml of the sample, containing not more than 50 mg Ca (or a smaller aliquot diluted to 200 ml), follow the procedure described in Method A, ¶s 3a–3d, up to and including the directions, "Digest for 15 min at 90 C." Then filter, preferably through a filter crucible, using suction. Wash at once with $1+99$ NH_4OH. Although it is not necessary to transfer all of the precipitate to the filter crucible, remove all excess ammonium oxalate from the beaker. (If magnesium is to be determined gravimetrically, set aside the combined filtrate and washings for this purpose.)

b. Titration of calcium oxalate: Place the filter crucible on its side in the beaker and cover with distilled water. Add 10 ml H_2SO_4 and, while stirring, heat rapidly to 90–95 C. Titrate rapidly with permanganate titrant to a slightly pink end point which persists for at least 1 min. Do not allow the temperature to fall below 85 C; if necessary, warm the beaker contents during the course of the titration. Agitate the crucible sufficiently to insure reaction of the oxalate it contains. Run a blank, using a clean beaker and crucible, 10 ml H_2SO_4, and about the same volume of distilled water as was used in the actual titration.

5. Calculation

$$\text{mg/l Ca} = \frac{(A - B) \times N \times 20{,}040}{\text{ml sample}}$$

where A = ml titration for sample, B = ml titration for blank, and N = normality of $KMnO_4$.

6. Precision and Accuracy

A synthetic unknown sample containing 108 mg/l Ca, 82 mg/l Mg, 3.1 mg/l K, 19.9 mg/l Na, 241 mg/l chloride, 1.1 mg/l nitrate N, 250 μg/l nitrite N, 259 mg/l sulfate, and 42.5 mg/l total alkalinity (contributed by $NaHCO_3$) in distilled water was determined by the permanganate titrimetric method, with a relative standard deviation of 3.5% and a relative error of 2.8% in six laboratories.

110 C. EDTA Titrimetric Method *

1. General Discussion

a. Principle: When EDTA (ethylenediaminetetraacetic acid or its salts) is added to water containing both calcium and magnesium, it combines first with the calcium that is present. Calcium can be determined directly, using EDTA, when the pH is made sufficiently high that the magnesium is largely precipitated as the hydroxide and an indicator is used which combines with calcium only. Several indicators are available that will give a color change at the point where all of the calcium has been complexed by the EDTA at a pH of 12–13.

b. Interference: Under conditions of this test, the following concentrations of ions cause no interference with the calcium hardness determination: copper, 2 mg/l; ferrous iron, 20 mg/l; ferric iron, 20 mg/l; manganese, 10 mg/l; zinc, 5 mg/l; lead, 5 mg/l; aluminum, 5 mg/l; tin, 5 mg/l. Orthophosphate will precipitate calcium at the pH of the test. Strontium and barium interfere with the calcium determination, and alkalinity in excess of 30 mg/l may cause an indistinct end point with hard waters.

2. Reagents

a. Sodium hydroxide, 1*N.*

b. Indicators: Many indicators are available for the calcium titration. Some are described in the literature (see bibliography, Section 110 D); others are commercial preparations and may also be used. Murexide (ammonium purpurate) was the first indicator available for the detection of the calcium end point, and directions are presented for its use in this procedure. Individuals who have difficulty recognizing the murexide end point may find the indicator Eriochrome Blue Black R (color index number 202) or Solo-

* Two United States patents (Nos. 2,583,890 and 2,583,891) have been issued to G. Schwarzenbach disclosing titration and complexometric methods for quantitative determination of water hardness. Nothing contained in this manual is to be construed as granting any right, by implication or otherwise, for manufacture, sale or use in connection with any method, apparatus or product covered by patent, nor as insuring anyone against liability for infringement of patent.

chrome Dark Blue an improvement because of the color change from red to pure blue. The chemical formula for Eriochrome Blue Black R is sodium-1-(2-hydroxy-1-naphthylazo) - 2 - naphthol-4-sulfonic acid. Other indicators specifically designed for use as end-point detectors in the EDTA titration of calcium may be employed.

MUREXIDE (AMMONIUM PURPURATE) INDICATOR: This indicator changes from pink to purple at the end point. An indicator solution can be prepared by dissolving 150 mg of the dye in 100 g of absolute ethylene glycol. Water solutions of the dye are not stable for longer than a day. A ground mixture of the dye powder and sodium chloride provides a stable form of the indicator. It is prepared by mixing 200 mg of murexide with 100 g of solid NaCl and grinding the mixture to 40–50 mesh. The titration should be performed immediately after addition of the indicator because it is unstable under alkaline conditions. End-point recognition is facilitated by preparation of a color comparison blank containing 2.0 ml NaOH solution, 0.2 g solid indicator mixture (or 1–2 drops if a solution is used) and sufficient standard EDTA titrant (0.05–0.10 ml) to produce an unchanging color.

ERIOCHROME BLUE BLACK R INDICATOR: Prepare a stable form of the indicator by grinding together in a mortar 200 mg powdered dye and 100 g solid NaCl to a 40–50 mesh. Store in a tightly stoppered bottle. Use 0.2 g of the ground mixture for the titration in the same manner as murexide indicator. During the course of titration the color changes from red through purple to bluish purple to a pure blue without any trace of reddish or purple tint. The pH of some (not all) waters must be raised to 14 (rather than 12–13) by the use of 8*N* NaOH in order to get a good color change.

c. Standard EDTA titrant, 0.01*M*: The standard EDTA titrant prepared as described for the EDTA total-hardness method (Hardness, Section 122 B.2d following) may be used. Standard EDTA titrant, exactly 0.0100*M*, is equivalent to 400.8 μg Ca per 1.00 ml.

3. Procedure

a. Sample preparation: Because of the high pH used in this procedure, perform the titration immediately after the addition of the alkali. Use 50.0 ml of sample, or a smaller aliquot diluted to 50 ml so that the calcium content is about 5–10 mg. Analyze hard waters with alkalinity higher than 300 mg/l $CaCO_3$ by taking a smaller aliquot and diluting to 50 ml, or by neutralizing the alkalinity with acid, boiling 1 min, and cooling before beginning the titration.

b. Titration: Add 2.0 ml NaOH solution, or a volume sufficient to produce a pH of 12–13. Stir. Add 0.1–0.2 g of the indicator mixture selected (or 1–2 drops if a solution is used). Add EDTA titrant slowly, with continuous stirring to the proper end point. When using murexide, check the end point by adding 1 or 2 drops of titrant in excess to make certain that no further color change occurs.

4. Calculation

$$\text{mg/l Ca} = \frac{A \times B \times 400.8}{\text{ml sample}}$$

$$\begin{array}{c}\text{Calcium hardness}\\ \text{as mg/l CaCO}_3\end{array} = \frac{A \times B \times 1{,}000}{\text{ml sample}}$$

where A = ml titration for sample, and B = mg $CaCO_3$ equivalent to 1.00 ml

EDTA titrant at the calcium indicator end point.

5. Precision and Accuracy

A synthetic unknown sample containing 108 mg/l Ca, 82 mg/l Mg, 3.1 mg/l K, 19.9 mg/l Na, 241 mg/l chloride, 1.1 mg/l nitrate N, 250 μg/l nitrite N, 259 mg/l sulfate, and 42.5 mg/l total alkalinity (contributed by $NaHCO_3$) in distilled water was determined by the EDTA titrimetric method, with a relative standard deviation of 9.2% and a relative error of 1.9% in 44 laboratories.

110 D. Bibliography

Gravimetric and Permanganate Titrimetric Methods

POPOFF, S., L. WALDBAUER & D. C. MCCANN. 1932. Quantitative spectrographic studies of coprecipitation. I. Magnesium in calcium oxalate. *Ind. Eng. Chem.*, Anal. Ed. 4:43.

INGOLS, R. S. & P. E. MURRAY. 1949. Urea hydrolysis for precipitating calcium oxalate. *Anal. Chem.* 21:525.

HILLEBRAND, W. F. et al. 1953. *Applied Inorganic Analysis* (2nd ed.). John Wiley & Sons, New York, Chapters 31 and 40.

WILLARD, H. H., N. H. FURMAN & C. E. BRICKER. 1956. *Elements of Quantitative Analysis* (4th ed.). D. Van Nostrand Co., Princeton, N. J.

KOLTHOFF, I. M., E. J. MEEHAN, E. B. SANDELL & S. BRUCKENSTEIN. 1969. *Quantitative Chemical Analysis* (4th ed.). Macmillan Co., New York.

EDTA Titrimetric Method

BETZ, J. D. & C. A. NOLL. 1950. Further studies with the direct colorimetric hardness titration. *JAWWA* 42:749.

KNIGHT, A. G. 1951. Estimation of calcium in water. *Chem. & Ind.* (London), No. 49 (Dec. 22), p. 1141.

DIEHL, H. & J. L. ELLINGBOE. 1956. Indicator for titration of calcium in the presence of magnesium using disodium dihydrogen ethylenediamine tetraacetate. *Anal. Chem.* 28:882.

PATTON, J. & W. REEDER. 1956. New indicator for titration of calcium with (ethylenedinitrilo) tetraacetate. *Anal. Chem.* 28:1026.

HILDEBRAND, G. P. & C. N. REILLEY. 1957. New indicator for complexometric titration of calcium in the presence of magnesium. *Anal. Chem.* 29:258.

SCHWARZENBACH, G. 1957. *Complexometric Titrations.* Interscience Publishers, New York.

GOETZ, C. A. & R. C. SMITH. 1959. Evaluation of various methods and reagents for total hardness and calcium hardness in water. *Iowa State J. Sci.* 34:104 (Aug. 15).

KATZ, H. & R. NAVONE. 1964. Method for simultaneous determination of calcium and magnesium. *JAWWA* 56:121.

111 CARBON DIOXIDE

Surface waters normally contain less than 10 mg/l free carbon dioxide, while some ground waters may easily exceed that concentration. The carbon dioxide content of a water may contribute significantly to some corrosive situations. The recarbonation of a supply during the terminal stages of water softening is a recognized treatment process. The subject of saturation with respect to calcium carbonate is discussed in Section 149.

Selection of method: A nomographic and a titrimetric method are described for the estimation of free carbon dioxide in water. The titration may be performed potentiometrically or conventionally in the presence of phenolphthalein indicator. Properly conducted, the more rapid, simple indicator method for the determination of free carbon dioxide is satisfactory for field tests and for control and routine applications if it is understood that the method gives, at best, only an approximation.

The nomographic method (A) usually gives a closer estimation of the total free carbon dioxide when the pH and alkalinity determinations are made immediately and correctly at the time of sampling. The pH measurement should preferably be made with an electrometric pH meter, properly calibrated with standard buffer solutions in the pH range of 7 to 8. The error resulting from inaccurate pH measurements grows with an increase in the total alkalinity. For example, an inaccuracy of 0.1 in the pH determination causes a carbon dioxide error of 2 to 4 mg/l in the pH range of 7.0 to 7.3 and a total alkalinity of 100 mg/l as $CaCO_3$. In the same pH range, the error approaches 10 to 15 mg/l when the total alkalinity is 400 mg/l as $CaCO_3$.

Under favorable conditions, agreement between the titrimetric and nomographic methods is usually reasonably good. When the agreement is not precise and the carbon dioxide determination is of particular importance, the analyst should state which method was used.

The calculation of the total carbon dioxide, free and combined, is given in Method C (Section 111 C).

111 A. Nomographic Determination of Free Carbon Dioxide and the Three Forms of Alkalinity *

1. General Discussion

Diagrams and nomographs enable the rapid calculation of the carbon dioxide, bicarbonate, normal carbonate, and hydroxide content of natural and treated waters. These graphical presentations are based on equations relating the ionization equilibria of the carbonates and water. Knowing the pH, total alkalinity, temperature, and total mineral content, any or all of the alkalinity forms and carbon dioxide can be determined nomographically.

A set of charts, Figures 10 through 13, is presented for use where their accuracy for the individual water supply is confirmed. The nomographs and the equations on which they are based are valid only where the salts of weak acids other than carbonic acid are absent or present in extremely small amounts.

Some treatment processes, such as superchlorination and coagulation, can significantly affect the pH and total-

* See also Alkalinity, Section 102 preceding.

alkalinity values of a poorly buffered water of low alkalinity and low total-dissolved-mineral content. In such instances, the concentration of chloride and sulfate may overshadow the concentration of carbonic acid salts in the sample, thereby invalidating the applicability and accuracy of the nomographs.

Where the variables of temperature, total mineral content and pH, alone or severally, exert an insignificant effect on the final result, the Moore charts [1] may be employed optionally. The limitations of these charts, however, must be completely comprehended and their applicability to the given water supply thoroughly demonstrated.

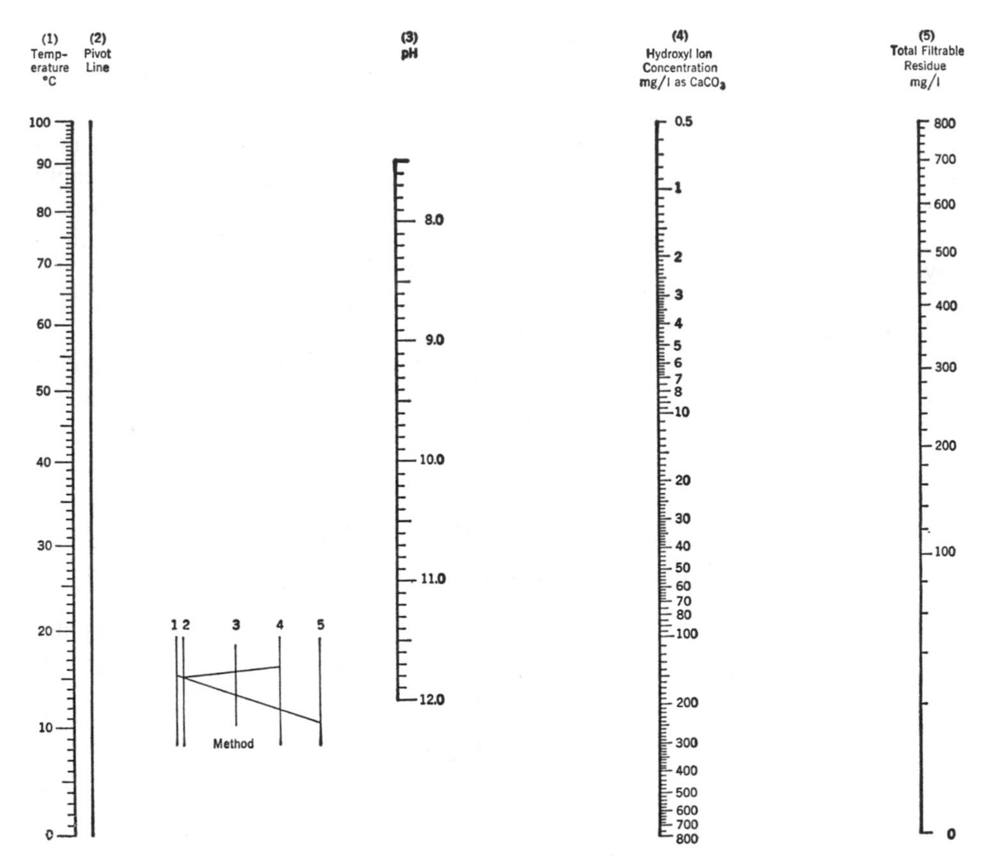

Figure 10. Nomograph for evaluation of hydroxyl ion concentration.† *To use: align temperature (Scale 1) and total filtrable residue (Scale 5); pivot on Line 2 to proper pH (Scale 3); read hydroxyl ion concentration, as mg/l $CaCO_3$, on Scale 4.*

† Copies of the nomographs in Figures 10–13, enlarged to 2.5 times the size shown here, may be obtained from The American Water Works Association, 2 Park Ave., New York, N.Y. 10016 for $1.50 a set.

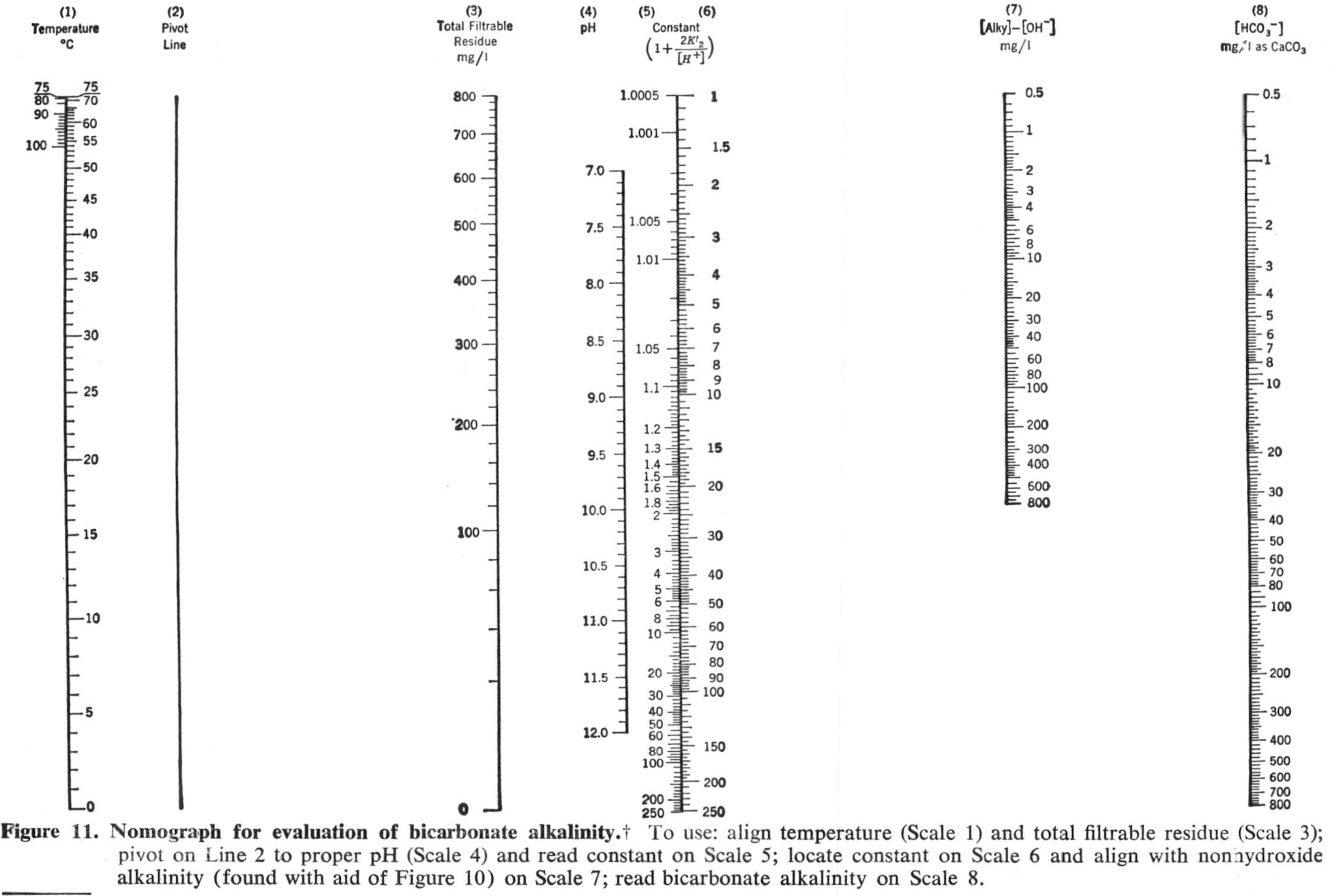

Figure 11. Nomograph for evaluation of bicarbonate alkalinity.† To use: align temperature (Scale 1) and total filtrable residue (Scale 3); pivot on Line 2 to proper pH (Scale 4) and read constant on Scale 5; locate constant on Scale 6 and align with nonhydroxide alkalinity (found with aid of Figure 10) on Scale 7; read bicarbonate alkalinity on Scale 8.

† See note to Figure 10.

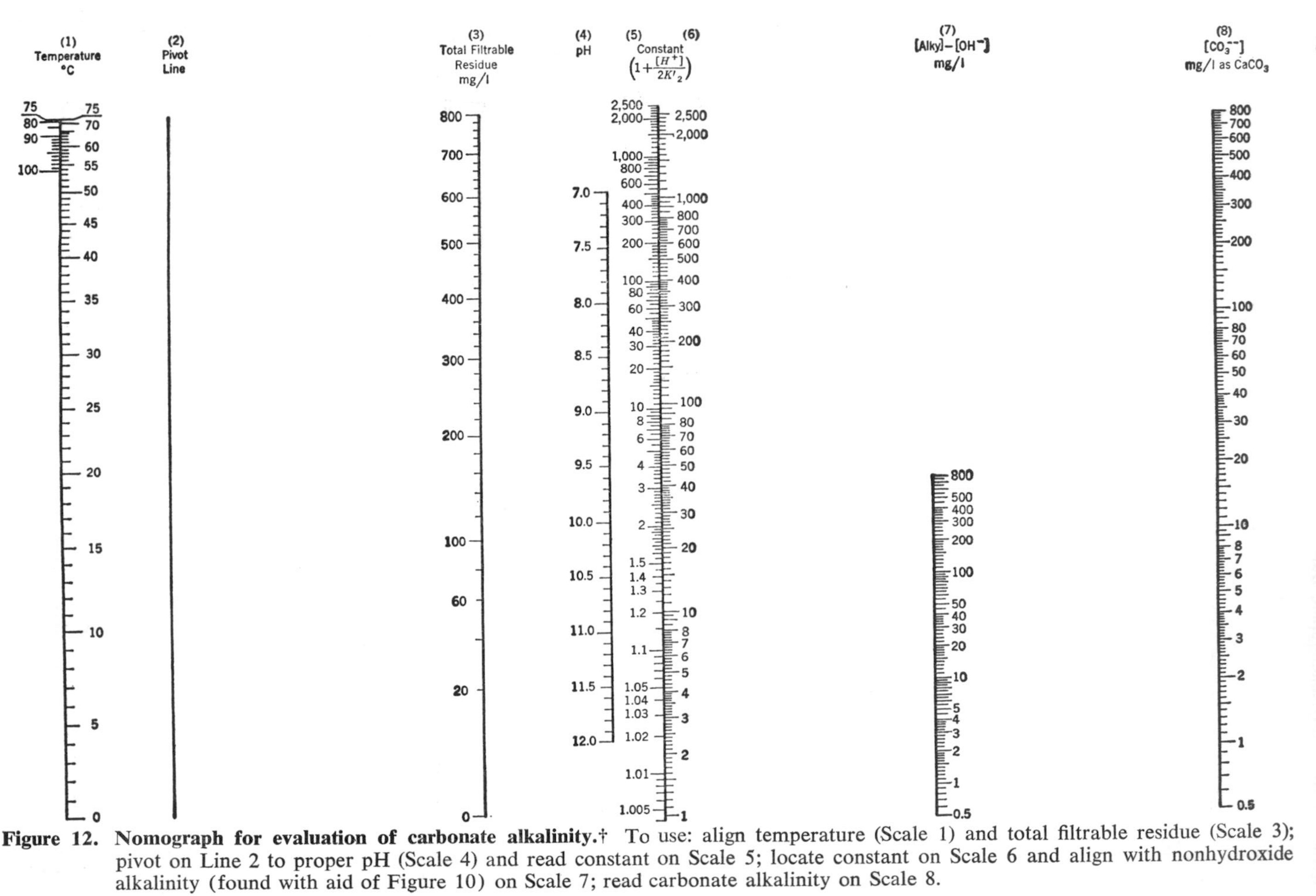

Figure 12. Nomograph for evaluation of carbonate alkalinity.† To use: align temperature (Scale 1) and total filtrable residue (Scale 3); pivot on Line 2 to proper pH (Scale 4) and read constant on Scale 5; locate constant on Scale 6 and align with nonhydroxide alkalinity (found with aid of Figure 10) on Scale 7; read carbonate alkalinity on Scale 8.

† See note to Figure 10.

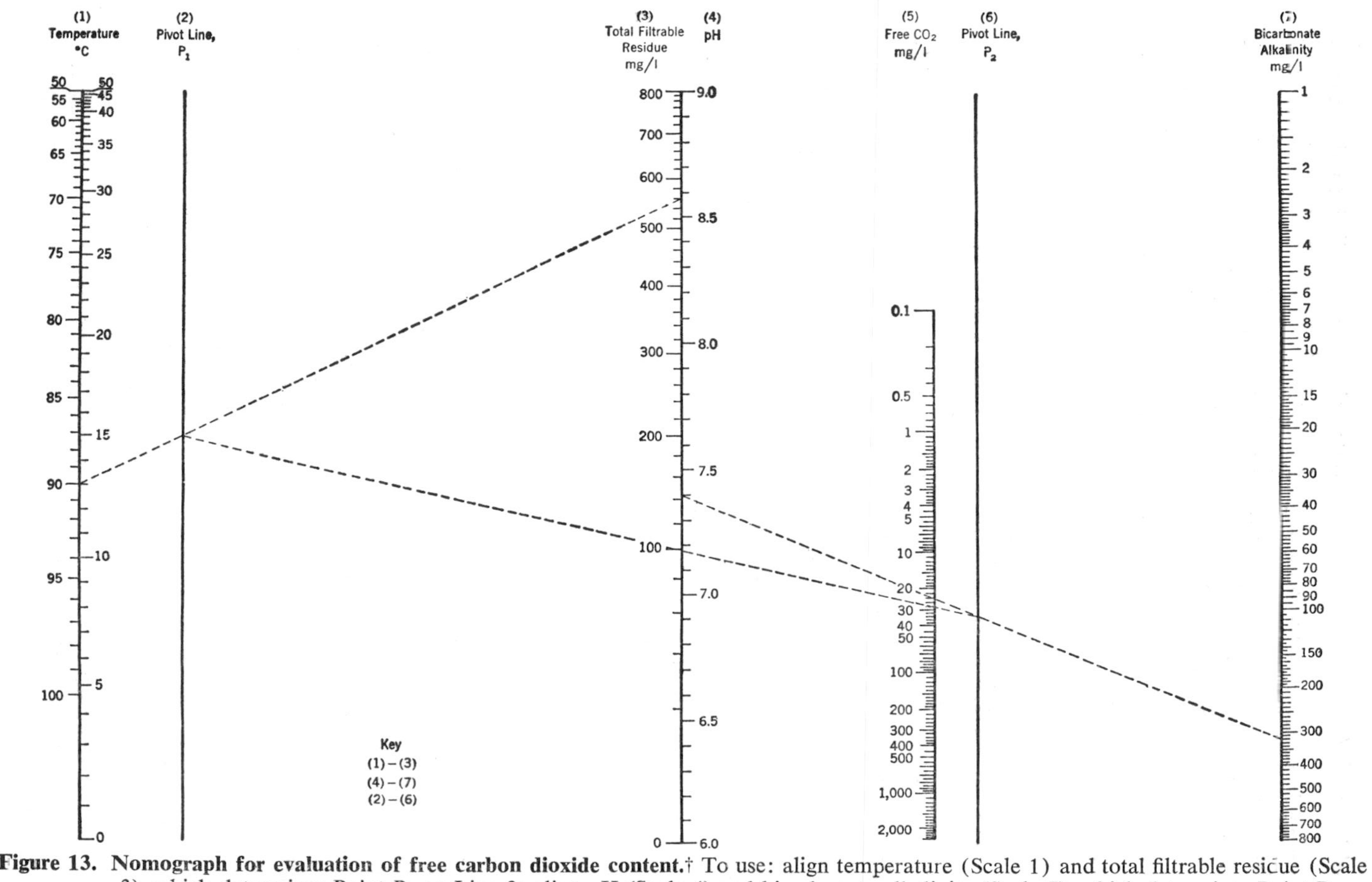

Figure 13. Nomograph for evaluation of free carbon dioxide content.† To use: align temperature (Scale 1) and total filtrable residue (Scale 3), which determines Point P_1 on Line 2; align pH (Scale 4) and bicarbonate alkalinity (Scale 7), which determines Point P_2 on Line 6; align P_1 with P_2 and read free carbon dioxide on Scale 5. (Example: for 13 C temperature, 560 mg/l total filtrable residue, pH 7.4, and 320 mg/l alkalinity, the free carbon dioxide content is found to be 28 mg/l.)

† See note to Figure 10.

2. Precision and Accuracy

The precision possible with the nomographs is contingent upon the size and range of the scales. With practice, the recommended nomographs can be read with a precision of 1%. The overall accuracy of the results is limited, however, by the accuracy of the analytical data which are applied to the nomographs and, additionally, by the validity of the theoretical equations and the numerical constants on which the nomographs are based. An approximate check of the accuracy of the calculations can be made by the summation of the three forms of alkalinity. Their sum should equal the total alkalinity.

III B. Titrimetric Method for Free Carbon Dioxide

1. General Discussion

a. Principle: Free carbon dioxide reacts with sodium carbonate or sodium hydroxide to form sodium bicarbonate. Completion of the reaction is indicated potentiometrically or by the development of the pink color characteristic of phenolphthalein indicator at the equivalence pH of 8.3. An 0.01*N* sodium bicarbonate solution containing the recommended volume of phenolphthalein indicator is a suitable color standard until familiarity is obtained with the color prevalent at the end point.

b. Interference: Cations and anions which quantitatively disturb the normal carbon dioxide-carbonate equilibrium have a detrimental effect on the determination. Aluminum, chromium, copper and iron are examples of metals whose salts contribute to high results. The ferrous-ion level should not exceed 1.0 mg/l. Positive errors are also caused by amines, ammonia, borate, nitrite, phosphate, silicate and sulfide. Mineral acids, and salts of strong acids and weak bases, affect the determination and therefore should be absent. Experience has demonstrated that the titrimetric method for carbon dioxide is inapplicable to samples containing acid mine wastes and effluent from acid-regenerated cation exchangers. Negative errors may be introduced by high total dissolved solids, such as those encountered in sea water, or by adding excess indicator. Fortunately the concentration of these interferences is low in many water supplies used for potable purposes.

c. Sampling and storage: Even with a careful collection technic, some loss in free carbon dioxide can be expected in the storage and transit of the sample. This situation occurs more frequently when the gas is present in large amounts. Occasionally a sample may show an increase in free carbon dioxide content on standing. Consequently, the field determination of free carbon dioxide immediately at the point of sampling is advisable. Where a field determination is impractical, a bottle of sample filled to the top should be collected separately for laboratory examination. The bottled sample should be kept, until tested, at a temperature lower than that at which the water was collected. Moreover, the laboratory examination should be performed as soon as possible in order to minimize the effect of carbon dioxide changes in the sample.

2. Apparatus

a. Daylight fluorescent lamps have proved satisfactory and may be used in identifying the end point, by virtue of the fact that they enable the maintenance of uniform lighting conditions at all times, and, in particular cases, accentuate certain indicator color changes.

b. Electrically operated titrators or pH meters, suitably calibrated: Where such devices are available, the titrations may be performed using the same standard solutions that are given in the indicator method. Gentle agitation with a magnetic stirrer is recommended, as well as insulation of the sample from the heat of the mixer motor by means of a sheet of ⅛-in. asbestos paper. The titration can be made to selected pH values, appropriate for the temperature and total-dissolved-solids content of the samples.[2] The equivalence point may also be identified by inflection of the titration curve or by the differential method of calculation. The potentiometric method is free from residual chlorine interference, the influence of color and turbidity, and individual visual idiosyncrasies.

3. Reagents

a. Phenolphthalein indicator solution: Use carbon dioxide-free distilled water for the preparation of this solution.

b. Standard alkali titrant: Either 0.0454*N* sodium carbonate or 0.0227*N* sodium hydroxide solution may be used. One equivalent of sodium hydroxide or two equivalents of sodium carbonate (1 mol) are required to convert 1 mol of carbon dioxide to the bicarbonate end point. Both titrants are made up so that 1.00 ml = 1.00 mg CO_2.

1) STANDARD SODIUM CARBONATE TITRANT, 0.0454*N:* Dissolve 2.407 g anhydrous Na_2CO_3 (primary standard grade), oven-dried at 140 C, and dilute to the mark of a 1-liter volumetric flask with distilled water which has been freshly boiled for at least 15 min to expel the carbon dioxide and has then been cooled to room temperature. Prepare the solution daily or protect from atmospheric carbon dioxide in a pyrex bottle.

2) STANDARD SODIUM HYDROXIDE TITRANT, 0.0227*N:* Dilute 22.7 ml 1*N* NaOH (prepare as directed in Acidity, Section 101.3a) to 1 liter with distilled water which has been freshly boiled for at least 15 min to expel the carbon dioxide and has then been cooled to room temperature. Prepare the reagent daily and protect from atmospheric carbon dioxide in a pyrex bottle. Standardize as described in Acidity, Section 101.3a preceding.

c. Sodium bicarbonate, 0.01*N:* Dissolve approximately 0.1 g anhydrous sodium hydrogen carbonate, $NaHCO_3$, and dilute to 100 ml with distilled water which has been freshly boiled for at least 15 min to expel the carbon dioxide and has then been cooled to room temperature. Prepare immediately before use.

4. Procedure

a. FIELD DETERMINATION:

1) Collect the sample by means of rubber tubing discharging at the bottom of a 100-ml graduated cylinder or nessler tube. Allow the sample to overflow for a few minutes and withdraw the tubing while the sample is flowing. Flick the cylinder to throw off excess sample above the 100-ml mark.

2) Add 5–10 drops phenolphthalein

indicator (always use the same volume of indicator for the sample as for the standardization procedure). If the sample turns red, free carbon dioxide is absent. If the sample remains colorless, titrate rapidly into the cylinder with standard alkali solution, stirring gently with a stirring rod until a definite pink color persists for 30 sec when viewed through the depth of the sample. This color change is the end point. For best results, use a color comparison standard prepared by adding the identical volume of phenolphthalein indicator to 100 ml sodium bicarbonate solution in a similar graduated cylinder or nessler tube.

3) Where the free carbon dioxide content of the water sample is high, some loss of carbon dioxide to the atmosphere may occur even with this titration technic. Check this possibility by securing a second sample in the recommended manner and immediately run in the full amount of standard alkali solution used in the first titration. Apply 5–10 drops phenolphthalein indicator and, if the sample remains colorless, add sufficient extra alkali solution to titrate to the proper end point. Accept the second result as the more reliable titration.

b. LABORATORY DETERMINATION: Collect the sample in a 500-ml pyrex bottle as described in ¶ 4a(1), completely filling the bottle and leaving no air space. At the laboratory, siphon the sample into a 100-ml graduated cylinder or nessler tube, allowing overflow to occur. Proceed as in ¶ 4a(2).

5. Calculation

If the titrant is Na_2CO_3:

$$\text{mg/l } CO_2 = \frac{A \times N \times 22{,}000}{\text{ml sample}}$$

If the titrant is NaOH:

$$\text{mg/l } CO_2 = \frac{A \times N \times 44{,}000}{\text{ml sample}}$$

where A = ml titration for sample, and N = normality of Na_2CO_3 or NaOH.

6. Precision and Accuracy

Precision and accuracy of the titrimetric method are on the order of ± 10% of the known carbon dioxide concentration.

III C. Total Carbon Dioxide by Calculation

The total carbon dioxide in a water is the sum of the free carbon dioxide and the carbon dioxide existing in the form of bicarbonate and carbonate ions as determined nomographically; or the free carbon dioxide and the carbonate and bicarbonate alkalinities as determined stoichiometrically by titration.

The total carbon dioxide can be calculated from the concentrations of free carbon dioxide, bicarbonate alkalinity, and carbonate alkalinity by the following equation, using alkalinities expressed as $CaCO_3$:

$$\text{mg/l total } CO_2 = \text{mg/l free } CO_2 + 0.88\ (A + B)$$

where A = mg/l bicarbonate alkalinity, and B = ½ (mg/l carbonate alkalinity).

111 D. References

1. E. W. MOORE. 1939. Graphic determination of carbon dioxide and the three forms of alkalinity. *JAWWA* 31:51.

2. J. F. DYE. 1958. Correlation of the two principal methods of calculating the three kinds of alkalinity. *JAWWA* 50:812.

111 E. Bibliography

Nomographic Method

LANGELIER, W. F. 1936. The analytical control of anticorrosion water treatment. *JAWWA* 28:1500.

DEMARTINI, F. E. 1938. Corrosion and the Langelier calcium carbonate saturation index. *JAWWA* 30:85.

LARSON, T. E. & A. M. BUSWELL. 1942. Calcium carbonate saturation index and alkalinity interpretations. *JAWWA* 34:1667.

DYE, J. F. 1944. The calculation of alkalinities and free carbon dioxide in water by the use of nomographs. *JAWWA* 36:895.

———. 1952. Calculation of effect of temperature on pH, free carbon dioxide, and the three forms of alkalinity. *JAWWA* 44:356.

Titrimetric Method

Standard Methods for the Examination of Water and Sewage (8th ed.). 1936. APHA & AWWA, New York, pp. 69, 122.

Approved Methods for the Physical and Chemical Examination of Water (3rd ed.). 1960. Institute of Water Engineers, Royal Institute for Chemistry, and Society of Public Analysts & Other Analytical Chemists, London, p. 40.

NORDELL, E. 1961. *Water Treatment for Industrial and Other Uses* (2nd ed.). Reinhold Publishing Corp., New York, pp. 87–98.

112 CHLORIDE

Chloride is one of the major anions in water and sewage. The salty taste produced by chloride concentrations is variable and dependent on the chemical composition of the water. Some waters containing 250 mg/l chloride may evidence a detectable salty taste with sodium ions. On the other hand, the typical salty taste may be absent in waters containing as much chloride as 1,000 mg/l when there is a predominance of calcium and magnesium ions.

A high chloride content also exerts a deleterious effect on metallic pipes and structures, as well as on agricultural plants.

Selection of method: Two methods are presented for the determination of chloride in potable water. Since the two methods are similar in most respects, selection is largely a matter of preference. Where color offers a problem in the water sample, the determination can be performed potentiometrically, as described in Section 203C, Chloride.

112 A. Argentometric Method

1. General Discussion

a. Principle: In a neutral or slightly alkaline solution, potassium chromate can indicate the end point of the silver nitrate titration of chloride. Silver chloride is quantitatively precipitated before red silver chromate is formed.

b. Interference: Substances in amounts normally found in potable waters will not interfere. Bromide, iodide, and cyanide register as equivalent chloride concentrations. Sulfide, thiosulfate, and sulfite ions interfere. However, sulfite can be removed by treatment with hydrogen peroxide in a neutral solution, while sulfide and thiosulfate can be removed by treatment with hydrogen peroxide in alkaline solution. Orthophosphate in excess of 25 mg/l interferes by precipitation as silver phosphate. Iron in excess of 10 mg/l will interfere by masking the end point.

2. Reagents

a. CHLORIDE-FREE WATER: If necessary, use redistilled or deionized distilled water.

b. POTASSIUM CHROMATE INDICATOR SOLUTION: Dissolve 50 g K_2CrO_4 in a little distilled water. Add silver nitrate solution until a definite red precipitate is formed. Allow to stand 12 hr, filter, and dilute the filtrate to 1 liter with distilled water.

c. STANDARD SILVER NITRATE TITRANT, 0.0141*N:* Dissolve 2.395 g $AgNO_3$ in distilled water and dilute to 1,000 ml. Standardize against 0.0141*N* NaCl by means of the procedure described in ¶ 3b below. Store in a brown bottle. Standard silver nitrate solution, exactly 0.0141*N*, is equivalent to 500 μg Cl per 1.00 ml.

d. STANDARD SODIUM CHLORIDE, 0.0141*N:* Dissolve 824.1 mg NaCl (dried at 140 C) in chloride-free water and dilute to 1,000 ml; 1.00 ml = 500 μg Cl.

e. SPECIAL REAGENTS FOR REMOVAL OF INTERFERENCE:

1) Aluminum hydroxide suspension: Dissolve 125 g aluminum potassium sulfate or aluminum ammonium sulfate, $AlK(SO_4)_2 \cdot 12H_2O$ or $AlNH_4(SO_4)_2 \cdot 12H_2O$, in 1 liter of distilled water. Warm to 60 C and add 55 ml conc NH_4OH slowly with stirring. After allowing it to stand about 1 hr, transfer the mixture to a large bottle and wash the precipitate by successive additions, with thorough mixing, and decantations of distilled water, until free from chloride. When freshly prepared, the suspension occupies a volume of approximately 1 liter.

2) Phenolphthalein indicator solution.

3) Sodium hydroxide, 1*N*.

4) Sulfuric acid, 1*N*.

5) Hydrogen peroxide, 30%.

3. Procedure

a. Sample preparation: Use a 100-ml sample or a suitable aliquot diluted to 100 ml.

If the sample is highly colored, add 3 ml $Al(OH)_3$ suspension, mix, allow to settle, filter, wash, and combine filtrate and washing.

If sulfide, sulfite, or thiosulfate is present, make the water alkaline to phenolphthalein with sodium hydroxide solution. Add 1 ml H_2O_2 and stir. Neutralize with sulfuric acid.

b. Titration: Titrate samples in the pH range 7–10 directly. Adjust samples not in this range with sulfuric acid or sodium hydroxide solution. Add 1.0 ml K_2CrO_4 indicator solution. Titrate with standard silver nitrate titrant to a pinkish yellow end point. The means of consistent end-point detection are left to the individual analyst.

Standardize the silver nitrate titrant and establish the reagent blank value by the titration method outlined above. A blank of 0.2 to 0.3 ml is usual for the method.

4. Calculation

$$\text{mg/l Cl} = \frac{(A - B) \times N \times 35{,}450}{\text{ml sample}}$$

where A = ml titration for sample, B = ml titration for blank, and N = normality of $AgNO_3$.

$$\text{mg/l NaCl} = \text{mg/l Cl} \times 1.65$$

5. Precision and Accuracy

A synthetic unknown sample containing 241 mg/l chloride, 108 mg/l Ca, 82 mg/l Mg, 3.1 mg/l K, 19.9 mg/l Na, 1.1 mg/l nitrate N, 250 µg/l nitrite N, 259 mg/l sulfate, and 42.5 mg/l total alkalinity (contributed by $NaHCO_3$) in distilled water was determined by the argentometric method, with a relative standard deviation of 4.2% and a relative error of 1.7% in 41 laboratories.

112 B. Mercuric Nitrate Method *

1. General Discussion

a. Principle: Chloride can be titrated with mercuric nitrate because of the formation of soluble, slightly dissociated mercuric chloride. In the pH range 2.3–2.8, diphenylcarbazone indicates the end point of this titration by formation of a purple complex with the excess mercuric ions. The error in titration is about 1% of the volume of titrant used per change of 0.1 pH unit in the pH range 2.1–2.8. Since exact pH adjustment is not feasible except by use of a pH meter, it is felt that keeping within a range of ±0.1 pH unit is sufficient for most water analyses. Therefore, in this method, a specific mixture of nitric acid and diphenylcarbazone is added to a water sample, automatically adjusting the pH of most potable waters to pH 2.5 ± 0.1. A third substance in this alcoholic mixture, xylene cyanol FF, is used as a pH indicator and as a background color to facilitate end-point detection. The introduction of 10 mg sodium bicarbonate to both the blank and the standard titration provides a pH of 2.5 ± 0.1 when 1.0 ml indicator-acidifier reagent [¶ 2d(1)] is added. Increasing the strength of the titrant and modifying the indicator mixture enable determination of the higher chloride concentrations common in wastewater.

b. Interference: Bromide and iodide are titrated with mercuric nitrate in the

* United States Patent No. 2,784,064 has been issued to F. E. Clarke, relative to the mercurimetric titration of chloride. Nothing contained in this manual is to be construed as granting any right, by implication or otherwise, for manufacture, sale or use in connection with any method, apparatus or product covered by patent, nor as insuring anyone against liability for infringement of patent.

same manner as chloride. Chromate, ferric, and sulfite ions interfere when present in excess of 10 mg/l.

2. Reagents

a. Standard sodium chloride, 0.0141 *N.* See Method A, ¶ 2d above.

b. Nitric acid, 0.1*N*.

c. Sodium hydroxide, 0.1*N*.

d. Reagents for low-chloride titrations:

1) INDICATOR-ACIDIFIER REAGENT: The nitric acid concentration of this reagent is an important factor in the success of the determination and can be varied as indicated in (1) or (2) to suit the alkalinity range of the sample being titrated. Reagent (1) contains sufficient nitric acid to neutralize a total alkalinity of 150 mg/l as $CaCO_3$ to the proper pH in a 100-ml sample.

Dissolve, in the order named, 250 mg s-diphenylcarbazone, 4.0 ml conc nitric acid, and 30 mg xylene cyanol FF in 100 ml of 95% ethyl alcohol or isopropyl alcohol. Store in a dark bottle in a refrigerator. This reagent is not stable indefinitely. Deterioration causes a slow end point and high results. Inasmuch as pH control plays a critical role in this method, adjust the pH of highly alkaline or acid samples to 2.5 ± 0.1 with 0.1*N* nitric acid or sodium hydroxide, not with sodium bicarbonate. Use a pH meter with a nonchloride type of reference electrode for the pH adjustment. If only the usual chloride-type reference electrode is available for the pH adjustment, determine the amount of acid or alkali required to achieve a pH of 2.5 ± 0.1 and discard this particular sample portion. Then treat a separate sample portion with the determined amount of acid or alkali and continue the analysis to its prescribed end. Under these circumstances, omit the nitric acid from the indicator reagent to maintain the proper sample pH. Alternatively, vary the nitric acid concentration of the indicator-acidifier reagent to accommodate conditions wherein water samples of very high or very low alkalinity are being analyzed.

2) STANDARD MERCURIC NITRATE TITRANT, 0.0141*N:* Dissolve 2.3 g $Hg(NO_3)_2$, or 2.5 g $Hg(NO_3)_2 \cdot H_2O$, in 100 ml distilled water containing 0.25 ml conc HNO_3. Dilute to just under 1 liter. Perform a preliminary standardization by following the procedure described in ¶ 3a. Use replicates containing 5.00 ml standard NaCl solution and 10 mg $NaHCO_3$ diluted to 100 ml with distilled water. Adjust the mercuric nitrate titrant to exactly 0.0141*N* and perform a final standardization. Store away from the light in a dark bottle. Standard mercuric nitrate titrant, exactly 0.0141*N*, is equivalent to 500 μg Cl per 1.00 ml.

e. Reagents for high-chloride titrations:

1) MIXED INDICATOR REAGENT: Dissolve 5 g diphenylcarbazone powder and 0.5 g bromphenol blue powder in 750 ml 95% ethyl or isopropyl alcohol and dilute to 1 liter with ethyl or isopropyl alcohol.

2) STRONG STANDARD MERCURIC NITRATE TITRANT, 0.141*N:* Dissolve 25 g $Hg(NO_3)_2 \cdot H_2O$ in 900 ml distilled water containing 5.0 ml conc HNO_3. Dilute to just under 1 liter, and perform a preliminary standardization by following the procedure described in ¶ 3b. Use replicates containing 25.00 ml standard NaCl solution and 25 ml distilled water. Adjust the titrant to exactly 0.141*N* and perform a final standardization. The chloride equivalence of the titrant is 5.00 mg per 1.00 ml.

3. Procedure

a. Titration of low-chloride concentrations prevailing in drinking water: Use a 100-ml sample or smaller aliquot so that the chloride content is less than 10 mg.

Add 1.0 ml of indicator-acidifier reagent to the sample. (The color of the solution should be green-blue at this point. A light green indicates a pH of less than 2.0; a pure blue indicates a pH of more than 3.8. For most potable waters, the pH after this addition will be 2.5 ± 0.1. When highly alkaline or acid waters are encountered, a preliminary pH adjustment to about pH 8 will be necessary before the indicator-acidifier reagent is added.)

Titrate the treated sample with $0.0141N$ mercuric nitrate titrant to a definite purple end point. The solution will turn from green-blue to a blue a few drops from the end point.

Determine the blank by titration of 100 ml distilled water containing 10 mg $NaHCO_3$.

b. Titration of high-chloride concentrations: Place 50.0 ml sample in a 150-ml beaker (5.00 ml sample may be used when more than 5 ml titrant are needed). Add approximately 0.5 ml mixed indicator reagent and mix well. The color should be purple. Add $0.1N$ HNO_3 dropwise until the color just turns yellow. Titrate with $0.141N$ mercuric nitrate titrant to the first permanent dark purple. Titrate a distilled water blank using the same procedure.

4. Calculation

$$\text{mg/l Cl} = \frac{(A - B) \times N \times 35{,}450}{\text{ml sample}}$$

where A = ml titration for sample, B = ml titration for blank, and N = normality of $Hg(NO_3)_2$.

$$\text{mg/l NaCl} = \text{mg/l Cl} \times 1.65$$

5. Precision and Accuracy

A synthetic unknown sample containing 241 mg/l chloride, 108 mg/l Ca, 82 mg/l Mg, 3.1 mg/l K, 19.9 mg/l Na, 1.1 mg/l nitrate N, 250 μg/l nitrite N, 259 mg/l sulfate, and 42.5 mg/l total alkalinity (contributed by $NaHCO_3$) in distilled water was determined by the mercurimetric method, with a relative standard deviation of 3.3% and a relative error of 2.9% in 10 laboratories.

112 C. Bibliography

Argentometric Method

HAZEN, A. 1889. On the determination of chlorine in water. *Amer. Chem. J.* 11:409.

KOLTHOFF, I. M. & V. A. STENGER. 1947. *Volumetric Analysis* (2nd ed.), Vol. 2. Interscience Publishers, New York, pp. 242–245, 256–258.

Mercuric Nitrate Method

KOLTHOFF & STENGER (above), pp. 334–335.

DOMASK, W. C. & K. A. KOBE. 1952. Mercurimetric determination of chlorides and water-soluble chlorohydrins. *Anal. Chem.* 24:989.

GOLDMAN, E. 1959. New indicator for the mercurimetric chloride determination in potable water. *Anal. Chem.* 31:1127.

113 CHLORINATED HYDROCARBON PESTICIDES

The increasing application of pesticides in large-scale agriculture and in forest areas can contribute to the presence of these toxic materials in a water supply. Contamination can occur through drainage from the surrounding terrain, precipitation from the atmosphere, accidental spills of pesticides in the watershed area, or a cross-connection on a distribution system.

Experimental investigations have demonstrated that conventional water treatment processes (in the absence of carbon) are capable of coping with DDT but are considerably less effective against most of the other chlorinated hydrocarbons.

113 A. Gas Chromatographic Method (TENTATIVE)

1. General Discussion

a. Principle: Gas chromatography is the most useful single technic presently available to the residue analyst. The mobile phase, called the carrier gas, is a permanent gas such as N_2, Ar, He, or H_2. The stationary phase is a liquid that has been impregnated on a granular support. This constitutes the column packing, which is held in a glass or metal tubing. The column is installed in an oven so that the inlet is attached to a heated injector block and the outlet is attached to a detector. Precise and constant temperature control of the injector block, the oven and the detector is critical. Stationary-phase material and concentration, column length and diameter, oven temperature, gas flow and detector type are controllable variables.

Minute volumes of the sample solution are injected through a rubber septum into the injector block, using a microsyringe. The pesticides are vaporized and are moved through the column by the carrier gas. They travel through the column at different rates, depending on differences in their partition coefficients between the mobile and the stationary phase. As each component of the sample passes through the detector a quantitatively proportional electrical signal is sent to a strip-chart recorder. Each component is observed as a peak on a continuous line. The elution time is indicative of the particular pesticide and the peak height is proportional to the quantity that was injected.

Variables may be manipulated to obtain important confirmatory identification data. For example, the detector system is somewhat optional, depending on the specificity and sensitivity needed. The use of specific response detectors can supply valuable data. The detector used in this method is a tritium foil electron-capture detector which is very sensitive to chlorinated compounds. Additional confirmatory identification can be made from retention data of two or more columns where the stationary phases are of different polarities. This method describes a two-column procedure that has been found particularly useful.

b. Interference: There are some substances besides chlorinated compounds that affect responses by the electron-capture detector. Among these are oxygenated and unsaturated compounds. Sometimes plant or animal extractives essentially obscure the pesticide peaks. These interfering substances can often be removed by ancillary "cleanup" technics. This method describes a Florisil column cleanup.

c. Detection limits: The ultimate detection limit of a substance is affected by a number of factors—for example, the detector sensitivity, the extraction and cleanup efficiency, the concentrations, and attenuation setting at an acceptable chromatogram base-line noise level. Lindane can usually be determined at 0.01 μg/l in a sample of relatively unpolluted water; the DDT detection limit will be somewhat higher.

It should be noted that the higher the sensitivity desired, the more the interference, and the greater the number of pesticides investigated, the longer the time required for an analysis.

2. Apparatus

All glassware specified in ¶s 2a through f below should be carefully washed with soap and water, rinsed with tap water, then with distilled water, and finally rinsed thoroughly at least three times with A. R. grade or better acetone. The glassware should be allowed to drain between rinsings. The glass wool should be thoroughly extracted with acetone or other suitable solvent and dried.

a. Sample bottles: 1-gal capacity, glass, with teflon-lined screw cap. Place permanent calibration mark 2 in. below the mouth of the bottle, measure, and record the volume contained.

b. Evaporative concentrator, Kuderna-Danish, 250-ml flask, and 10-ml graduated lower tube, or equivalent.

c. Separatory funnels, 250-ml capacity.

d. Erlenmeyer flasks, 500-ml capacity, glass-stoppered.

e. Chromatographic column, 20-mm diameter × 400-mm length.

f. Miscellaneous glassware: small funnels, glass wool, transfer pipets, miscellaneous volumetric flasks, assorted beakers, etc.

g. Magnetic stirrer, large, with 1⅝-in. teflon-coated bar.

h. Microsyringes, suitable for injecting 1 to 8 μl of solutions.*

i. Steam bath: Operate in a hood to vent solvent fumes.

j. Gas chromatograph system: The many available variations in gas chromatograph instrumentation will necessitate variable operating procedures. Therefore, each chromatographer should familiarize himself with the manufacturer's operating manuals, gas chromatography catalogs, and other references (see Section 7, Bibliography, following).

1) Carrier gas line should have a molecular sieve-drying cartridge. The carrier gas must be dry and there must be no gas leaks throughout the system.
2) Oven temperature must be very stable at the desired setting.
3) Chromatographic columns may be purchased or prepared in the laboratory. It is not appropriate to

---

* Hamilton 701–N or equivalent.

specify rigidly the size or compositions to be used, since experience has shown that some instruments perform better using different columns than do others. Good separations have been attained using 10% DC-200 silicone fluid, 12,500 centistokes * on 80/90 mesh Anakrom ABS * in a ¼-in. O.D. by 6-ft-long column. A good confirmatory column is 4% DC-200 and 6% QF-1 fluorosilicone * with the same support and dimensions. A column is suitable when it effects clean, reproducible separations.

To prepare a 10% DC-200 column, dissolve 2 g DC-200 in 50 ml ethyl acetate in a 250-ml beaker. Slowly add 20 g Anakrom ABS with stirring. Occasionally swirl to mix the solution and the support while evaporating the solvent on the steam bath. When the mixture becomes a thick slurry, gently spread it in a thin layer in a shallow dish and air-dry. Complete the drying in an oven at 100 C for 2 hr and then precondition the material at 230 C for 2 to 4 hr.

Select a tubing prefitted to the chromatograph oven, lightly pack a glass wool plug into one end, apply vacuum to that end, and introduce the prepared packing into the other end. Tap or vibrate the tubing until it is firmly filled, then place a glass wool plug in the end.

Place the column in the normal operating position in the gas chromatograph. As soon as the temperature and gas flow have stabilized, the column is ready for use.

Prepare the second column in the same manner after dissolving 0.8 g DC-200 and 1.2 g QF-1 in 50 ml ethyl acetate.

Some tubing materials catalyze sample component decomposition within the column. The most inactive material is pyrex glass, but due to the breakage hazard, aluminum or some stainless steel tubings may be preferred. Do not use copper.

4) Detector, electron-capture, with DC power supply.
5) Strip-chart recorder must be compatible with the electrometer.
6) Operating parameters should be kept as simple and reproducible as possible. Conditions that have produced satisfactory chromatograms for pesticide analyses are: injector temperature, 230 C; oven temperature, 180 C; detector temperature, 200 C; carrier gas flow rate, 120 ml/min. Adjust the electrometer, input and output attenuations, detector voltage supply, recorder gain, and damping in accordance with operating manual for optimum sensitivity and linearity.

3. Reagents

All reagents specified in ¶s 3a through 3g should be free of interfering peaks when used as in the procedure. Laboratory distillation of solvents in glass may be suitable, but it is usually easier and cheaper to purchase chromatographic-grade solvents.

a. Hexane.

b. Petroleum ether.

c. Diethyl ether.

d. Ethyl acetate.

e. Mixed ethers: Mix one volume diethyl ether with three volumes redistilled petroleum ether.

* Analabs Inc., 9 Hobson Ave., Hamden, Conn., or equivalent.

f. Florisil, activated at 650 C and stored at 130 C.

g. Sodium sulfate, anhydrous granular.

h. Anakrom ABS, 80/90 mesh or equivalent.

i. DC-200 silicone fluid, 12,500 centistokes.

j. QF-1 Fluorosilicone.

k. Nitrogen gas: Purified grade should be moisture- and O_2-free.

l. Pesticide concentrates: Where possible, obtain pure substances from chromatographic equipment suppliers.

m. Stock pesticide solutions: Dissolve 100 mg of the pesticides of interest in ethyl acetate and dilute to 100 ml in a volumetric flask to form a solution containing 1.00 mg per 1.00 ml.

n. Intermediate pesticide solutions: Dilute 1.0 ml stock pesticides solution to 100 ml with ethyl acetate; 1.0 ml = 10 μg.

o. Standard pesticide solutions: Prepare the final standard pesticide solutions to accord with the detector sensitivity and linearity. Normally, select a concentration that causes a peak height of about 10 chart-percent when 1 μl is injected. If 20 pg (picogram) of lindane cause a 10 chart-percent deflection, prepare a working standard solution of 20 pg/μl by diluting 0.2 ml intermediate pesticide solution to 100 ml with hexane.

Conveniently prepare and use mixtures of pesticides; however, avoid mixtures of pesticides that have very similar retention times.

4. Procedure

a. Sample collection: Fill bottle to the calibration mark only.

b. Extraction of pesticides: Insert a magnetic stirring bar, add 10 ml hexane to the sample, and loosely screw on the cap. Place the bottle on the magnetic stirrer somewhat off center in order to cause greater displacement and circulation of the hexane in the form of small drops in the water. Stir the sample fast enough to cause dispersion of the hexane through the sample, but no faster than necessary. After 15 min, allow the phases to separate. Remove the hexane layer to a small separatory funnel, using a transfer pipet. Since it is impossible to remove all the hexane, add a small amount of hexane to the residual solution and again remove this to the separatory funnel. Repeat this step once more, thus minimizing the pesticide left in the sample bottle. Add 10 ml hexane and repeat the extraction procedure, combining the extracts in the separatory funnel.

Separate the water from the hexane and then dry the hexane by transferring to an erlenmeyer flask containing approximately 10 g anhydrous sodium sulfate. Perform all hexane transfers quantitatively, with several rinsings of small amounts of fresh hexane. Transfer the dried solution to an evaporative concentrator (Kuderna-Danish or equivalent) and reduce the volume to about 7 ml. Quantitatively transfer the solution to a 10-ml volumetric flask and dilute to volume.

c. Chromatography: Inject 5 μl extract solution into one of the columns of the gas chromatograph. Always inject the same amount of liquid. Inspect the resulting chromatogram for peaks corresponding to the pesticides of concern, and evaluate for the presence of significant interference. Also ascertain whether the sensitivity is adequate. [See

Figure 14 and Tables 113(1) and 113(2).]

1) If there are presumptive pesticide peaks and no significant interference, then rechromatograph 5.0 μl extract solution over the alternate column. Proceed to ¶ 4e below for the next step.

2) If necessary, concentrate the extract solution for greater sensitivity, or dilute when a peak is too large. Attain similar effects by adjustment of the electrometer attenuator.

3) If significant interference is present, separate the interfering substances from the pesticide materials in the extract by means of the cleanup procedure described in ¶ 4d:

d. Cleanup: Compact a 20 × 100 mm Florisil column by vibrating or tapping, and add a 25-mm layer of sodium sulfate. Wet the column by adding 40 ml petroleum ether. Discard the eluate. When the liquid surface reaches the column surface, add a selected portion of the extract solution to the column. Collect the eluate. When the liquid surface reaches the column surface, add 200 ml mixed-ethers reagent and collect the eluate. Evaporate the solvents as outlined near the end of ¶ 4b preceding and dilute to the appropriate volume.

e. Preparation of standard curves: Inject a series of increasing amounts of a pesticide into one of the columns. Use injections of 1 to 5 μl if the 1 μl volume is backed up with 4 μl solvent,

TABLE 113(1): ELECTRON-CAPTURE GAS CHROMATOGRAPHY USING NONPOLAR COLUMN

(10% DC-200 on Anakrom ABS)

Pesticide	Relative Retention Time *	Pesticide	Relative Retention Time *
Methyl ester of 2, 4–D	0.29	β-Chlordane	1.60
Benzene hexachloride	0.38, *0.47*	Butoxy ethyl ester of 2, 4–D	1.78
Isopropyl ester of 2, 4–D	0.41	DDT (Tech.)	1.81, 2.44, *3.03*
Lindane	0.47	DDE	1.81
Isobutyl ester of 2, 4–D	0.61	Dieldrin	1.83
Isopropyl ester of 2, 4, 5–T	0.66	o, p′–TDE	1.86
n-Butyl ester of 2, 4–D	0.71	Isooctyl ester of 2, 4–D	2.00, *2.37*
Ronnel	0.78	Endrin	*2.05,* 2.20
Heptachlor	0.79	Ethyl hexyl ester of 2, 4–D	2.07
Ethyl parathion	0.98	Perthane	2.11
Chlorthion	0.99	Endosulfan II	2.16
Aldrin	1.00	TDE	2.33
Kelthane	1.01	Chlorobenzilate	2.43
n-Butyl ester of 2, 4, 5–T	1.08	*o, p′*–DDT	2.44
Sulphenone	1.24	Isooctyl ester of 2, 4, 5–T	2.70, *3.10, 3.65*
Heptachlor epoxide	1.24	Carbophenothion	2.83
Chlorbenside	1.36	Dilan	2.83, *3.37*
TDE olefin	1.42	Butoxy ethyl ester of 2, 4, 5–T	2.85
α-Chlordane	1.43	p, p′–DDT	3.03
Perthane olefin	1.47	Methoxychlor	4.5
Propylene glycol butyl ether		Strobane	1.07–3.55
ester of 2, 4–D	1.51	Toxaphene	1.18–4.97
Endosulfan I	1.58	Tetradifon	5.4
Ovex	1.58	Coumaphos	9.5

* Aldrin reference: retention time approximately 4.25 min. When more than one peak is present, the major peak is noted in italics.

and other volumes totaling 5 μl. If necessary, use more than one concentration to extend the series. Measure each peak height from the base line and plot the quantity of pesticide versus peak height. Use mixed pesticide solutions as long as the peaks do not mutually interfere.

f. Determination of extraction efficiency: Add known amounts of pesticides in ethyl acetate solution to 3¾ liters water and carry through the same procedure as the samples. Dilute an equal amount of the intermediate pesti-

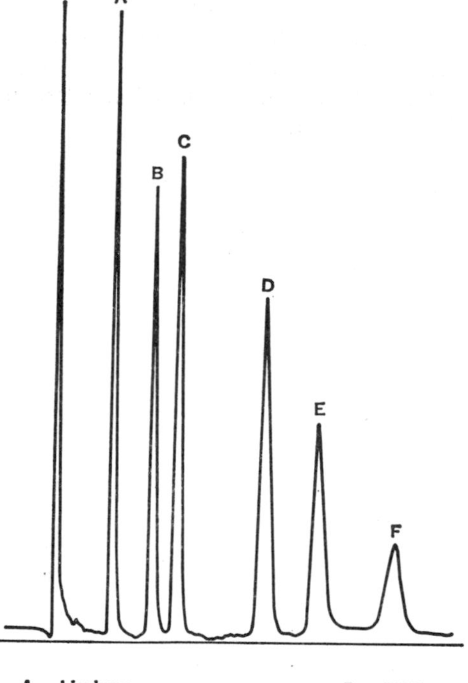

A. Lindane D. DDE

B. Heptachlor E. TDE

C. Aldrin F. p.p'-DDT

Figure 14. Electron-capture gas chromatogram of pesticide standards on nonpolar column.

TABLE 113(2): RELATIVE RETENTION TIMES OF PESTICIDE STANDARDS ON POLAR COLUMN USING ELECTRON-CAPTURE DETECTOR

(4% SE-30 plus 6% QF-1)

Pesticide	Relative Retention Time*
Methyl ester of 2, 4–D	0.44
Benzene hexachloride (Tech.)	0.45, 0.57, 0.68
Methyl ester of silvex	0.46
Isopropyl ester of 2, 4–D	0.57
Lindane	0.57
Diazinon	0.59
Methyl ester of 2, 4, 5–T	0.67
Heptachlor	0.81
Isobutyl ester of 2, 4–D	0.88
Aldrin	1.00
n-Butyl ester of 2, 4–D	1.00
Kelthane	1.38
Heptachlor epoxide	1.50
Methyl parathion	1.53
Malathion	1.71
Endosulfan I	1.92
p, p'–DDE	1.98
Butoxy ethanol ester of 2,4–D	2.08
Ethyl parathion	2.10
Perthane	2.13
Dieldrin	2.31
o, p'–DDT	2.62
Isooctyl ester of 2, 4–D	2.71
TDE	2.89
Carbophenothion	3.04
Endosulfan II	3.07
p, p'–DDT	3.54
Ethion	3.90
Endrin	*4.13*, 6.38
Methoxychlor	5.44
Tetradifon	9.79

* Aldrin reference: retention time approximately 7.2 min. When more than one peak is present, the major peak is noted in italics.

cide solution (¶ 3n above) to the same final volume. Call the peak height from the standard, "a", and the peak height from the spiked sample, "b", whereupon the extraction efficiency, E equals b/a. Have each chromatographer periodically determine the extraction efficiency and a control blank to test the procedure.

5. Calculation

a. Dilution factor: If a portion of the extract solution was concentrated, the dilution factor, C, is a decimal; if it was diluted, the dilution factor exceeds 1.

b. Attenuation factor: Each upward step of the attenuator switch has the same effect as diluting the sample solution. The chromatographer must determine that the linear sample response range is not exceeded when attenuation is used. The attenuation factor, G = the dial setting for the sample peak divided by the dial setting for the standard peak.

c. Computation of pesticide concentration:

$$\mu g/l \text{ pesticide} = \frac{A \times C \times F \times G}{B \times D \times E}$$

where A = ng of pesticide injected into chromatograph (ascertained from the standard curve), B = volume of solution injected in μl, C = volume of extract solution in ml, D = sample volume in liters, E = extraction efficiency, F = dilution factor, and G = attenuation factor.

6. Precision and Accuracy

Three synthetic unknown samples containing varying concentrations of the six specified pesticides in distilled water were analyzed by the gas chromatographic method in 29 to 37 laboratories, with the results indicated in Table 113(3).

TABLE 113(3): PRECISION AND ACCURACY DATA FOR CHLORINATED HYDROCARBON PESTICIDES METHOD

Pesticide	Concentration µg/l	No. of Laboratories	Relative Standard Deviation %	Relative Error %
p,p′-DDT	0.50	36	38.2	5.6
	5.0	31	24.0	2.2
	20	32	24.7	2.6
Dieldrin	0.25	32	35.7	14.0
	5.0	37	42.2	7.2
	15	29	20.2	10.9
Endrin	0.10	31	38.8	16.0
	1.0	34	35.4	24.7
	10	31	16.9	8.5
Heptachlor	1.0	36	67.3	16.3
	7.5	36	41.8	19.5
	15	34	32.3	14.7
Heptachlor epoxide	1.0	33	20.6	7.0
	7.5	35	22.7	1.1
	15	36	25.4	2.5
Lindane	0.50	36	36.6	10.2
	5.0	38	42.6	13.2
	25	29	23.7	12.5

The first sample contained 0.50 μg/l p,p′-DDT, 0.25 μg/l dieldrin, 0.10 μg/l endrin, 1.0 μg/l heptachlor, 1.0 μg/l heptachlor epoxide, and 0.50 μg/l lindane.

The second sample contained 5.0 μg/l p,p′-DDT, 5.0 μg/l dieldrin, 1.0 μg/l endrin, 7.5 μg/l heptachlor, 7.5 μg/l heptachlor epoxide, and 5.0 μg/l lindane.

The third sample contained 20 μg/l p,p′-DDT, 15 μg/l dieldrin, 10 μg/l endrin, 15 μg/l heptachlor, 15 μg/l heptachlor epoxide, and 25 μg/l lindane.

7. Bibliography

TEASLEY, J. I. & W. J. COX. 1963. Determination of pesticides in water by microcoulometric gas chromatography after liquid-liquid extraction. *JAWWA* 55:1093.

BURCHFIELD, H. P., D. C. JOHNSON & E. F. STORRS. 1965. *Guide to the Analysis of Pesticide Residues.* PHS Office of Pesticides, Washington, D.C.

BREIDENBACH, A. W. et al. 1966. Identification and measurement of chlorinated hydrocarbon pesticides in surface waters. FWPCA Pub. WP-22 (2nd ed.), Nov. FWPCA, Washington, D.C.

KAWAHARA, F. K., J. W. EICHELBERGER, B. H. REID & H. STIERLI. 1967. Semiautomatic extraction of organic materials from water. *JWPCF* 39:572.

MENDOZA, C. E., K. A. MCCULLY & P. J. WALES. 1968. Simplified method of preparing column materials for gas-liquid chromatographic separation of some pesticides. *Anal. Chem.* 40:2225.

SCHAFER, M. L., W. S. GARDNER, J. T. PEELER & J. E. CAMPBELL. 1969. Detection and assay for pesticides in finished drinking water. *Environ. Sci. & Tech.* 3:1261.

114. CHLORINE (RESIDUAL)

The chlorination of water supplies accomplishes a number of treatment objectives. The destruction of microorganisms is a primary function. However, overall improvement in the finished water can result from chlorine's reaction with ammonia, iron, manganese, sulfide and protein substances. With some taste- and odor-producing compounds such as phenols, chlorine may intensify the problem or, under careful control, may improve the water quality.

Most methods for the determination of free or combined available chlorine are based on reactions with reducing agents that are not specific for these materials. Definite test conditions under which specificity is attained despite the presence of particular interfering oxidizing agents have been described by a number of investigators, and the results have been considered in compiling this section. Chlorine in water may be present as free available chlorine (in the form of hypochlorous acid or hypochlorite ion, or both); or as combined available chlorine (chloramines and other chloro derivatives). Both free and combined chlorine may be present simultaneously.

Some oxidizing agents, including free halogens other than chlorine, will appear quantitatively as free chlorine; this is also true of chlorine dioxide. A small proportion of nitrogen trichloride (trichloramine) will titrate as free chlorine. These substances rarely appear in sufficient quantity to introduce a significant error; nevertheless, their action should be familiar to the analyst, as they will affect all the chlorine methods described.

The following methods are intended for moderately polluted water, water in the process of purification, water treatment plant effluent, potable water in the distribution system, swimming pool water, and industrial cooling and process water. Highly polluted waters may require other methods for satisfactory analysis as described in Section 204.

1. Selection of Method

The iodometric method is considered the standard against which other methods are judged. It provides the means for standardizing the chlorine water used in preparing temporary standards. It is also suitable for determining high chlorine residuals, which are more frequently encountered nowadays than heretofore. The iodometric method is generally more precise than the colorimetric methods when the residual chlorine concentration exceeds 1 mg/l, but it is not accurate at lower concentrations or in the presence of interferences.

The amperometric titration method rates among the most accurate for the determination of free or combined available chlorine. The method is largely unaffected by the presence of common oxidizing agents, temperature variations, and turbidity and color, which interfere with the accuracy of the other methods. The method is not as simple as the colorimetric methods and requires greater operator skill to obtain the accuracy inherent in the method.

The orthotolidine methods C, D, and E have gained wide acceptance for the routine measurement of residual chlorine in water plant control and in the field because of the simple apparatus developed for this purpose. The orthotolidine-arsenite (OTA) method (Method D) enables the differentiation of free available and combined available chlorine in the presence of color from common interfering substances. The OTA modification is satisfactory for routine control with properly calibrated photometers, visual color disks, and permanent color standards. Erroneous results can occur from negligence in periodically checking color disks and permanent color standards to affirm their validity. The orthotolidine reaction with Halazone, p-(N,N-dichlorosulfamyl)benzoic acid, is incomplete, thereby leading to appreciably low values for combined chlorine produced by that particular disinfectant. However, orthotolidine responds fully with free chlorine and monochloramine formed from ammonia. The drop dilution orthotolidine test (Method E) is provided for field use where approximate results alone are desired. It should not be substituted for the more precise and accurate titrimetric methods.

The ferrous DPD method (Method G) provides a simple and accurate means of differentiating free and combined chlorine fractions. The use of common glassware makes the method suitable for both laboratory and field applications.

The leuco crystal violet, the methyl orange, and the stabilized neutral orthotolidine (SNORT) colorimetric methods (Methods H, I and F, respectively) make possible the differentiation of the free and combined residuals. The SNORT method additionally describes steps for estimating the mono- and dichloramine fractions, as do the amperometric and ferrous DPD methods.

Three solid synthetic unknowns were

TABLE 114(1): PRECISION AND ACCURACY DATA FOR RESIDUAL CHLORINE METHODS

Method	Residual Chlorine Concentration		Number of Laboratories	Relative Standard Deviation %	Relative Error %
	Free μg/l	Total μg/l			
Iodometric		840	32	27.0	23.6
		640	30	32.4	18.5
		1,830	32	23.6	16.7
Amperometric	800		23	42.3	25.0
		640	24	24.8	8.5
		1,830	24	12.5	8.8
Orthotolidine	800		15	64.6	42.5
		640	17	37.3	20.2
		1,830	18	31.9	41.4
Orthotolidine-arsenite	800		20	52.4	42.3
		640	21	28.0	14.2
		1,830	23	35.0	49.6
Stabilized neutral orthotolidine	800		15	34.7	12.8
		640	16	8.0	2.0
		1,830	17	26.1	12.4
Ferrous DPD	800		19	39.8	19.8
		640	19	19.2	8.1
		1,830	19	9.4	4.3
Leuco crystal violet	800		17	32.7	7.1
		640	17	34.4	0.9
		1,830	18	32.4	18.6
Methyl orange	800		26	43.0	22.0
		640	26	30.1	14.2
		1,830	26	19.9	7.2

prepared and distributed for the purpose of evaluating the residual chlorine methods.

One powdered unknown was compounded of 70% calcium hypochlorite * and sodium chloride filler to yield a free available chlorine concentration of 800 μg/l upon dissolution in chlorine demand-free distilled water.

The second powdered unknown was compounded of 70% calcium hypochlorite * and sodium chloride filler to yield a total available chlorine concentration of 640 μg/l upon dissolution and mixing with an aqueous ammonium buffer solution in chlorine demand-free distilled water.

The third powdered unknown was prepared from Halazone,† p-(N,N-dichlorosulfamyl)benzoic acid, to yield a total available chlorine concentration of 1,830 μg/l upon dissolution in chlorine-demand-free distilled water.

The results obtained by the participating laboratories are summarized in Table 114(1).

* Olin Matheson Chemical Corp., HTH (granular).

† Abbott Laboratories.

2. *Sampling and Storage*

Chlorine in aqueous solution is not stable, and the chlorine content of samples or solutions, particularly weak solutions, will rapidly decrease. Exposure to sunlight or other strong light or agitation will accelerate the reduction of chlorine present in such solutions. Therefore, it is recommended that chlorine determinations be started immediately after sampling, avoiding excessive light and agitation. Samples to be analyzed for chlorine cannot be stored.

114 A. Iodometric Method

1. General Discussion

a. Principle: Chlorine will liberate free iodine from potassium iodide solutions when its pH is 8 or less. The liberated iodine is titrated with a standard solution of sodium thiosulfate, using starch as the indicator. The reaction is preferably carried out at pH 3 to 4.

b. Interference: Although the neutral titration minimizes the interfering effect of ferric, manganic and nitrite ions, the acid titration is preferred; it is most accurate for determination of total available residual chlorine. Acetic acid should be used for the acid titration; sulfuric acid may be used only when the analyst has satisfied himself that interfering substances are absent; *but hydrochloric acid should never be used.*

c. Minimum detectable concentration: The minimum detectable concentration approximates 40 μg/l Cl if $0.01N$ sodium thiosulfate is used with a 500-ml sample.

2. Reagents

a. Acetic acid, conc (glacial).

b. Potassium iodide, crystals.

c. Standard sodium thiosulfate, $0.1N$: Dissolve 25 g $Na_2S_2O_3 \cdot 5H_2O$ in 1 liter freshly boiled distilled water and standardize the solution against potassium biniodate or potassium dichromate after at least 2 weeks' storage. Use boiled distilled water and add a few milliliters of chloroform to minimize bacterial decomposition of the thiosulfate solution.

STANDARDIZATION: Standardize the $0.1N$ sodium thiosulfate by one of the following procedures:

1) *Biniodate method:* Dissolve 3.249 g anhydrous potassium biniodate, $KH(IO_3)_2$, of primary standard quality,* in distilled water and dilute to 1,000 ml to yield a $0.1000N$ solution. Store in a glass-stoppered bottle.

To 80 ml distilled water, add, with constant stirring, 1 ml conc H_2SO_4, 10.00 ml $0.1000N$ $KH(IO_3)_2$, and 1 g potassium iodide. Titrate immediately with $0.1N$ $Na_2S_2O_3$ titrant until the yellow color of the liberated iodine is almost discharged. Add 1 ml starch indicator solution and continue titrating until the blue color disappears.

2) *Dichromate method:* Dissolve 4.904 g anhydrous potassium dichromate, $K_2Cr_2O_7$, of primary standard quality, in distilled water and dilute to 1,000 ml to yield a $0.1000N$ solution. Store in a glass-stoppered bottle.

Proceed as in the biniodate method, with the following exceptions: Substi-

* Such as is obtainable from G. F. Smith Chemical Company, Columbus, Ohio.

tute 10.00 ml 0.1000*N* $K_2Cr_2O_7$ for the $KH(IO_3)_2$, and allow the reaction mixture to stand 6 min in the dark before titration with the 0.1*N* $Na_2S_2O_3$ titrant.

Calculation of normality:

$$\text{Normality } Na_2S_2O_3 = \frac{1}{\text{ml } Na_2S_2O_3 \text{ consumed}}$$

d. Standard sodium thiosulfate titrant, 0.01*N* or 0.025*N*: Improve the stability of 0.01*N* or 0.025*N* $Na_2S_2O_3$ by diluting an aged 0.1*N* solution, made as directed above, with freshly boiled distilled water. Avoid trouble by adding a few milliliters of chloroform or 0.4 g sodium borate and 10 mg mercuric iodide per liter of solution. For accurate work, standardize this solution daily in accordance with the directions given above, using 0.01*N* or 0.025*N* $KH(IO_3)_2$ or $K_2Cr_2O_7$. Use an automatic buret of a type in which rubber does not come in contact with the solution, to speed up operations where many samples must be titrated. Standard sodium thiosulfate titrants, exactly 0.0100*N* and 0.0250*N*, are equivalent, respectively, to 354.5 μg and 886.3 μg available Cl per 1.00 ml.

e. Starch indicator solution: To 5 g starch (potato, arrowroot, or soluble), add a little cold water and grind in a mortar to a thin paste. Pour into 1 liter of boiling distilled water, stir, and allow to settle overnight. Use the clear supernate. Preserve with 1.25 g salicylic acid, 4 g zinc chloride, or a combination of 4 g sodium propionate and 2 g sodium azide added to 1 liter of starch solution.

f. Standard iodine, 0.1*N*: Refer to Method B, ¶ 3a(2).

g. Dilute standard iodine, 0.0282*N*: Refer to Method B, ¶ 3a(3).

3. Procedure

a. Volume of sample: Select a sample volume which will require no more than 20 ml 0.01*N* $Na_2S_2O_3$. Thus, for residual chlorine concentrations of 1 mg/l or less, take a 1,000-ml sample; for a chlorine range of 1 to 10 mg/l, a 500-ml sample; and above 10 mg/l, proportionately less sample.

b. Preparation for titration: Place 5 ml acetic acid, or sufficient to reduce the pH to between 3.0 and 4.0, in a flask or white porcelain casserole; add about 1 g potassium iodide estimated on a spatula; pour in the sample and mix with a stirring rod. Add chlorine demand-free distilled water if a larger volume is preferred for titration.

c. Titration: Titrate away from direct sunlight. Add 0.025*N* or 0.01*N* thiosulfate from a buret until the yellow color of the liberated iodine is almost discharged. Add 1 ml starch solution and titrate until the blue color is discharged.

If the titration is made with 0.025*N* thiosulfate instead of 0.01, then, with a 1-liter sample, 1 drop is equivalent to about 50 μg/l. It is not possible to discern the end point with greater accuracy than this. If a 500-ml sample is titrated, 1 drop will correspond to about 100 μg/l, which is within the limit of sensitivity. Hence, use of 0.025*N* solution should be considered acceptable. Many laboratories have this on hand.

d. Blank titration: Correct the result of the sample titration by determining the blank contributed by such reagent impurities as: (a) the free iodine or iodate in the potassium iodide which liberates extra iodine; or (b) the traces of reducing agents that might reduce some of the iodine which is liberated.

Take a volume of distilled water corresponding to the sample used for titration in ¶s 3a–3c, add 5 ml acetic acid, 1 g KI, and 1 ml starch solution. Perform either Blank Titration A or B, whichever applies.

BLANK TITRATION A: If a blue color occurs, titrate with 0.01*N* or 0.025*N* sodium thiosulfate to the disappearance of the blue and record the result.

BLANK TITRATION B: If no blue color occurs, titrate with 0.0282*N* iodine solution until a blue color appears. Back-titrate with 0.01*N* or 0.025*N* sodium thiosulfate and record the difference as Titration B.

Before calculating the chlorine, subtract Blank Titration A from the sample titration; or, if necessary, add the net equivalent value of Blank Titration B.

4. Calculation

For standardizing chlorine solution for temporary standards:

$$\text{mg/ml Cl} = \frac{(A \pm B) \times N \times 35.45}{\text{ml sample}}$$

For the determination of total available residual chlorine in a water sample:

$$\text{mg/l Cl} = \frac{(A \pm B) \times N \times 35{,}450}{\text{ml sample}}$$

where A = ml titration for sample, B = ml titration for blank which may be positive or negative, and N = normality of $Na_2S_2O_3$.

5. Precision and Accuracy

See Table 114(1) preceding and the statement entitled *Selection of Method* (Section 114.1) for pertinent details.

114 B. Amperometric Titration Method

1. General Discussion

Amperometric titration is more practical for the laboratory than for field use, as it requires a source of 110-V current. Amperometric titration also requires a higher degree of skill and care than the orthotolidine method. Chlorine residuals over 2 mg/l are best measured by means of smaller samples, or by dilution. The method can be used to determine total residual chlorine and can also differentiate between free and combined available chlorine. A further differentiation into monochloramine and dichloramine fractions is possible by controlling the potassium iodide concentration and pH.

a. Principle: The amperometric method is a special adaptation of the polarographic principle. Free available chlorine is titrated at a pH between 6.5 and 7.5, a range in which the combined chlorine reacts slowly. The combined chlorine, in turn, is titrated in the presence of the proper amount of potassium iodide in the pH range 3.5–4.5. When determining free chlorine, the pH must not be greater than 7.5, because the reaction becomes sluggish at higher pH values—or less than 6.5, because at lower pH values some combined chlorine may react even in the absence of iodide. When determining combined chlorine, the pH must not be less than 3.5, because substances such as oxidized manganese interfere at lower pH values—nor greater than 4.5, because the reaction is not quantitative at higher pH values. The tendency of monochloramine to react more readily with iodide than does dichloramine provides a means for further differentiation. The addition of a small amount of potassium iodide in the neutral pH range enables the estimation of monochloramine content. Lowering the pH into the acid range and increasing the potassium iodide concentration allows the separate determination of dichloramine.

Stable even in dilute solution, each mole of phenylarsine oxide reacts with two equivalents of halogen. A special galvanic cell is used to detect the end point of the residual chlorine-phenylarsine oxide titration. The cell consists of a nonpolarizable reference electrode which is immersed in a salt solution, and a readily polarizable noble-metal electrode which is in contact both with the salt solution and with the sample that is to be titrated. The electrode circuit is connected to a microammeter. If there is no chlorine residual in the sample, the microammeter reading will be comparatively low because of cell polarization. The greater the residual in the sample, the greater the microammeter reading. The meter acts merely as a null-point indicator—that is, the actual meter reading is not important, but rather the relative readings as the titration proceeds. The gradual addition of phenylarsine oxide causes the cell to become more and more polarized due to the decrease in available chlorine. The end point is recognized when no further decrease in meter reading can be obtained by adding more phenylarsine oxide.

b. Interference: Accurate determinations of free chlorine cannot be made in the presence of nitrogen trichloride or chlorine dioxide, which titrate partly as free chlorine. When present, nitrogen trichloride can titrate partly as free available chlorine and partly as dichloramine, contributing a positive error in both fractions. Organic chloramines can also be titrated in each step. Monochloramine can intrude into the free chlorine fraction and dichloramine can interfere in the monochloramine fraction especially at high temperatures and prolonged titration times. Free halogens other than chlorine will also titrate as free chlorine. Combined chlorine reacts with bromide and iodide ions to produce bromine and iodine. Interference from copper has been noted in samples after heavy copper sulfate treatment of reservoirs, with metallic copper plating out on the electrode. Silver ions also poison the electrode. Interference has also been noted in some highly colored waters, but the interfering substance has not been established. Very low temperatures slow the response of the electrode, and longer time is required for the titration, but the precision is not affected. A reduction in reaction rate is also caused by pH values above 7.5, but this is overcome by buffering all samples to pH 7.0 or less. On the other hand, some substances—such as manganese, nitrite, and iron—that interfere with the orthotolidine method do not interfere with amperometric titration. Stirring can lower chlorine values by volatilization.

2. Apparatus

a. End-point detection apparatus, consisting of a cell unit connected to a microammeter, with the necessary electrical accessories: The cell unit comprises a noble-metal electrode of sufficient surface area, a salt bridge to provide an electrical connection without diffusion of electrolyte, and a reference electrode of silver-silver chloride in a saturated sodium chloride solution which is connected into the circuit by means of the salt bridge.

The noble-metal electrode should be kept free of deposits and similar foreign matter. Vigorous chemical cleaning is fortunately not necessary in ordinary usage. Occasional mechanical cleaning with a suitable abrasive is usually sufficient. The salt bridge should be kept in good operating condition, which means that it should neither become plugged nor permit appreciable flow of electrolyte through it. It is important that the solution surrounding the reference electrode be kept free of contamination and be maintained at constant composition by insuring an adequate supply of undissolved salt at all times. For descriptions of various forms of this device see the bibliography.

b. Agitator, designed to give the greatest possible degree of agitation at the noble-metal electrode surface in order to insure proper sensitivity: The agitator and the exposed electrode system should be thoroughly cleaned to remove all chlorine-consuming contaminants by immersing them in water containing 1 to 2 mg/l free available residual chlorine for a few minutes. Then potassium iodide is added to the same water and the agitator and electrodes are allowed to remain immersed another 5 min. After thorough rinsing with chlorine-demand-free water or the sample to be tested, the sensitized electrodes and agitator are ready for use.

c. Buret: A convenient form is made from a 1-ml pipet with 0.01-ml graduations. This is connected to a delivery tube with a finely drawn tip by means of suitable plastic tubing. Glass beads may be inserted in the plastic tubing to act as valves.

d. All glassware must be exposed to water containing at least 10 mg/l residual chlorine for 3 hr or more before use and then rinsed with chlorine-demand-free water.

3. Reagents

a. STANDARD PHENYLARSINE OXIDE TITRANT: Dissolve approximately 0.8 g phenylarsine oxide powder, C_6H_5AsO, in 150 ml 0.3*N* sodium hydroxide. After settling, decant 110 ml of this solution into 800 ml distilled water and mix thoroughly. Bring the solution to pH 6–7 with 6*N* hydrochloric acid solution and finally dilute almost to 1 liter. Determine the normality of the phenylarsine oxide solution by amperometric titration of standard 0.0282*N* iodine solution. Make the necessary volume adjustments so that the concentration equals the desired 0.00564*N* before completing the final standardization with the amperometric titrator; 1.00 ml of exactly 0.00564*N* phenylarsine oxide titrant = 200 μg available chlorine. Preserve with 1 ml chloroform. (CAUTION: *Toxic—take care to avoid ingestion.*)

1) Standard sodium arsenite, 0.1*N*: Accurately weigh a stoppered weighing bottle containing approximately 4.95 g arsenic trioxide, As_2O_3, primary standard grade. Transfer without loss to a 1-liter volumetric flask and again weigh the bottle. Do not attempt to brush out the adhering oxide. Moisten the As_2O_3 with distilled water and add 15 g NaOH and 100 ml distilled water. Swirl contents of the flask gently until the As_2O_3 is in solution. Dilute to 250 ml with distilled water and saturate the solution with CO_2, thus converting all the NaOH to sodium bicarbonate. Dilute to the mark, stopper the flask, and mix thoroughly. A solution thus prepared will preserve its titer almost indefinitely. (CAUTION: *Toxic—take care to avoid ingestion.*)

$$\text{Normality} = \frac{\text{g } As_2O_3}{49.455}$$

2) Standard iodine, $0.1N$: Dissolve 40 g potassium iodide in 25 ml distilled water and then add 13 g resublimed iodine and stir until dissolved. Transfer to a 1-liter volumetric flask and dilute to the mark.

STANDARDIZATION: Accurately measure 40–50 ml of $0.1N$ sodium arsenite solution into a flask and titrate with $0.1N$ iodine solution, using starch solution as indicator. In order to obtain accurate results, it is absolutely necessary that the solution be saturated with carbon dioxide at the end of the titration. A current of carbon dioxide may be passed through the solution for a few minutes just before the end point is reached, or a few drops of hydrochloric acid may be added to liberate sufficient carbon dioxide to saturate the solution.

3) Dilute standard iodine, $0.0282N$: Dissolve 25 g potassium iodide in a little distilled water in a 1-liter volumetric flask, add the proper amount of $0.1N$ iodine solution exactly standardized to yield a $0.0282N$ solution, and dilute to 1 liter. For accurate work, standardize this solution daily in accordance with directions given in the preceding paragraph, using 5–10 ml of $0.1N$ sodium arsenite solution.

STORAGE: Place in a brown bottle or store in the dark, making certain that the solution is protected from direct sunlight at all times and kept from all contact with rubber.

b. PHOSPHATE BUFFER SOLUTION, pH 7: Dissolve 25.4 g anhydrous potassium dihydrogen phosphate, KH_2PO_4, and 34.1 g anhydrous disodium hydrogen phosphate, Na_2HPO_4, in 800 ml distilled water. Add 2 ml sodium hypochlorite solution containing 1% available chlorine and mix thoroughly. Protect from sunlight for several days and then expose to sunlight until no residual chlorine remains. If necessary, carry out the final dechlorination with a sodium sulfite solution, leaving just a trace of chlorine as shown by a qualitative orthotolidine test. Finally dilute to 1 liter with distilled water and filter if any precipitate is present.

c. POTASSIUM IODIDE SOLUTION: Dissolve 50 g KI and dilute to 1 liter, using freshly boiled and cooled distilled water. Store in a brown glass-stoppered bottle, preferably in the refrigerator. Discard the solution when a yellow color has developed.

d. ACETATE BUFFER SOLUTION, pH 4: Dissolve 480 g conc (glacial) acetic acid and 243 g sodium acetate trihydrate, $NaC_2H_3O_2 \cdot 3H_2O$, in 400 ml distilled water and make up to 1 liter.

4. Procedure

a. Sample volume: Select a sample volume which will require no more than 2 ml phenylarsine oxide titrant. Thus, for residual chlorine concentrations of 2 mg/l or less, take a 200-ml sample; for chlorine levels in excess of 2 mg/l, 100 ml or proportionately less.

b. Free available chlorine: Unless the pH of the sample is definitely known to lie between 6.5 and 7.5, add 1 ml pH 7 phosphate buffer solution to produce a pH of 6.5–7.5. Titrate with standard phenylarsine oxide titrant, observing the current changes on the microammeter. Add the titrant in progressively smaller increments until all needle movement ceases. Make successive buret readings when the needle action becomes sluggish, signaling the approach of the end point. Subtract the last very small increment which causes no needle response due to overtitration.

Continue the titration for combined available chlorine as described in ¶ 4c below or for the separate monochloramine and dichloramine fractions as detailed in ¶s 4e and 4f.

c. Combined available chlorine: To the sample remaining from the free-chlorine titration add exactly 1 ml potassium iodide solution and then 1 ml acetate buffer solution, in that order. Titrate with phenylarsine oxide titrant to an end point, just as above. Do not refill the buret but simply continue the titration after recording the figure for free available chlorine. After concluding the titration, again subtract the last increment which gives the amount of titrant actually used in the reaction with the chlorine. (If the titration was continued without refilling the buret, this figure represents the total residual chlorine. Subtracting the free available chlorine from the total gives the combined residual chlorine.) Wash the apparatus and sample cell thoroughly to remove iodide ion in order to avoid inaccuracies when the titrator is subsequently used for a free available chlorine determination.

d. Separate samples: If desired, determine the total residual chlorine and the free available chlorine on separate samples. If total available chlorine alone is required, treat the sample immediately with 1 ml potassium iodide solution followed by 1 ml acetate buffer solution, and titrate with phenylarsine oxide titrant as described in ¶ 4c preceding.

e. Monochloramine: After the titration for free available chlorine, add 0.2 ml potassium iodide solution to the same sample and, without refilling the buret, continue the titration with phenylarsine oxide titrant to the recognized end point. Subtract the last increment to obtain the net volume of titrant consumed by the monochloramine.

f. Dichloramine: Add 1 ml acetate buffer solution and 1 ml potassium iodide solution to the same sample, and titrate the final dichloramine fraction as described for the previous two chlorine components.

5. Calculation

Convert the individual titrations for free available chlorine, combined available chlorine, total available chlorine, monochloramine, and dichloramine into mg/l by the following equation:

$$\text{mg/l Cl} = \frac{\text{A} \times 200}{\text{ml sample}}$$

where A = ml phenylarsine oxide titration.

6. Precision and Accuracy

See Table 114(1) preceding and the statement entitled *Selection of Method* (Section 114.1) for pertinent details.

114 C. Orthotolidine Method

1. General Discussion

The orthotolidine method measures both free and combined available chlorine. If it is desired to determine whether the chlorine is present in the free or the combined form, the OTA test (Method D) may be used.

a. Principle: To obtain the correct color development with chlorine and orthotolidine, (a) the solution must be at pH 1.3 or lower during the contact period; (b) the ratio by weight of orthotolidine to chlorine must be at least 3:1; and (c) the chlorine concentration must not exceed 10 mg/l.

Commercially available orthotolidine dihydrochloride is considerably purer than the free orthotolidine base. Moreover, the dihydrochloride readily dissolves in water, which makes it easier to prepare the test reagent.

The concentration of the acid in the orthotolidine reagent must be such that it will produce a suitable pH even if the sample has up to 1,000 mg/l of alkalinity.

To insure color development at a pH of 1.3 or lower and a ratio of orthotolidine to chlorine of at least 3:1, the reagent must be placed in the cell, tube, or comparison bottle first, and the sample added to it.

A 6-month stability limit is specified for the orthotolidine reagent as an arbitrary precaution against any discoloration or precipitation due to occasional exposure to high temperatures or direct sunlight. The caution against permitting the reagent to come in contact with rubber is based on observations that significant amounts of reducing substances are extracted from some types of rubber closures by orthotolidine.

The reaction time and the temperature specified were selected to permit measurement of a maximum proportion of the combined available chlorine present, while minimizing loss of color by fading or increase of color due to interfering oxidizing agents such as nitrite, ferric iron and certain compounds formed by chlorine with organic matter.

The method given in ¶ 3a(1) below for preparation of chlorine-demand-free water was selected for convenience; although ammonia-free water is not required, the preference expressed for it is based on difficulties encountered in removing large amounts of ammonia with chlorine alone. Due to the rapidity with which this water may absorb some laboratory fumes, it should be examined for nitrite, chlorine and reducing agents immediately before use when determining very low concentrations of chlorine.

The permanent chromate-dichromate color standards give good visual matches and almost exact spectrophotometric matches when the determination is made at pH 1.3 or less and the orthotolidine-chlorine ratio is at least 3:1. The choice of buffer solutions and their application is based on results of spectrophotometric studies.

Excellent accuracy in determination of residual chlorine with orthotolidine may be obtained by photometric methods. A method for calibration of photometric instruments for residual chlorine testing is referred to in Section 114J (References).[1]

b. Interference: When orthotolidine is used to measure residual chlorine, the analyst must satisfy himself as to the presence and amount of interfering substances in the sample to be tested. Such interferences include ferric, manganic and nitrite compounds, and possibly organic iron compounds, lignocellulose and algae. The effect of these substances is to increase the apparent residual chlorine content of the sample under examination.

Suspended matter interferes and should be removed by centrifuging prior to test; or if the turbidity is not high, a compensating colorimeter, which additionally corrects for existing color and turbidity in the sample, may be used. Compensation of color and turbidity can also be accomplished by adding 1 or 2 drops of a reducing reagent containing an oxidizable sulfur group [see ¶s 3d(1), (2) and (3) below] and stirring until the color disappears. This simple procedure is particularly suited to photometric measurements and for use with samples containing acid-soluble turbidity such as alum floc.

In chlorinated water containing no more than 300 μg/l iron, 10 μg/l manganic manganese, and 100 μg/l nitrite nitrogen, development of the characteristic yellow color with orthotolidine may be accepted as being due to chlorine. If iron and manganese are present in more than the above concentrations, the development of the characteristic yellow color with orthotolidine cannot be accepted as being due to chlorine alone. If nitrite is present in an interfering concentration, color development in total darkness minimizes interference. It should be noted that significant amounts of nitrite will not exist in water containing free available chlorine but may exist in the presence of chloramines.

It is recommended that the orthotolidine-arsenite method be employed to determine the amount of any additional color produced by the above interferences. When such additional color is found, the quantity is deducted to correct the chlorine values and the OTA test should be used as a routine procedure.

c. Minimum detectable concentration: The orthotolidine-chlorine reaction is sensitive to residual chlorine concentrations as low as approximately 10 μg/l.

2. Apparatus

a. ILLUMINATION: All readings should be taken by looking through the samples against an illuminated white surface. The surface may be opaque and illuminated by reflection, or it may be an opal diffusing glass illuminated from behind. Since chlorine determinations are made both day and night in plant control, it is preferable that all comparisons be made with a standard artificial light. The permanent standards give greater accuracy when used with either of the two artificial light sources specified below, both of which are close approximations of average "north" daylight:

1) Filament lamp assembly, consisting of a light source, color filter, and diffuser glass, suitably mounted in a cabinet: It is essential that the diffuser glass be placed in contact with the color filter and on the sample side. The light source should be a 150-W Mazda "C" lamp * with clear envelope. The color filter should be Corning "daylight" No. 5900, having a thickness equivalent to 163 microreciprocal degrees. The diffuser glass should be thin flashed opal glass without color tint.

2) Fluorescent "daylight" lamp as-

* A product of General Electric Company.

sembly: The white reflecting or diffusing surface may be illuminated by a fluorescent "daylight" lamp without the use of a color filter. Those manufactured by General Electric Company or Westinghouse Electric and Manufacturing Company, or equivalent, have proved satisfactory.

If artificial light is not provided, comparisons should be made with good "north" daylight. Under no circumstances should the comparisons be made in sunlight.

b. COLORIMETRIC EQUIPMENT: One of the following is required—

1) Nessler tubes, matched, 100-ml, tall form.

2) Filter photometer, providing a light path of 1 cm or longer and equipped with a violet filter having maximum transmittance in the range of 400 mμ to 450 mμ, and a blue-green filter having maximum transmittance near 490 mμ.

3) Spectrophotometer, for use at 435 mμ and 490 mμ, providing a light path of 1 cm or longer.

3a. Temporary Chlorine Standards

Temporary chlorine standards are not recommended for routine use because extreme care is required in their preparation. These standards are recommended for calibration purposes and for research. The yellow holoquinone color developed obeys Beer's law over a considerable chlorine range when measurements are made with a 1-cm light path. Although the maximum absorption occurs near 435 mμ, filters transmitting in the range between 400 mμ and 450 mμ may be employed for the photometric measurement of low chlorine values. The following information will serve as a guide in the selection of color filters and light paths:

Chlorine Range *mg/l*	Light Path *cm*	Wavelength *mμ*
0.02–0.3	5	400–450
0.1 –1.5	1	400–450
0.5 –7.0	1	490

1) Chlorine-demand-free water: Add sufficient chlorine to distilled water to destroy the ammonia. The amount of chlorine required will be about ten times the amount of ammonia nitrogen present; in no case produce an initial residual of less than 1.0 mg/l free chlorine. Allow the chlorinated distilled water to stand overnight or longer; then expose to direct sunlight until all residual chlorine is discharged. Use distilled water free from ammonia and nitrite to produce the chlorine-demand-free water.

2) Chlorine solution for temporary standards: Chlorine solutions or hypochlorite solutions for research and calibration purposes should be prepared from purified reagents and standardized as described below. Certain commercial solutions of hypochlorite have been found to be of relatively constant composition and of a high degree of stability.* Because of their convenience, their use is preferred for routine purposes.

3) Preparation of temporary standards: Expose all glassware to water containing at least 10 mg/l chlorine for 3 hr or more before use and then rinse with chlorine-demand-free water. Add calculated volumes of chlorine or hypochlorite solution to a series of flasks containing chlorine-demand-free water to cover the range desired. Make up each one to 500 ml and mix

* Of those available at the present time, Zonite (Zonite Products Corporation) and household bleach have been found satisfactory. Zonite contains approximately 1% available chlorine.

gently. Pipet 100 ml from each flask into a series of smaller flasks, each containing 5 ml orthotolidine. Add the chlorine solution slowly, mixing well as it is added. Pour the required amount into the comparator cell or tube. If 100-ml nessler tubes are used, omit the second series of flasks.

4) Titration of chlorine solution: Pour the remaining 400 ml of each temporary standard into a white porcelain casserole and titrate with thiosulfate according to Section 114A.3b and 3c.

5) Calibration of photometer: Construct a calibration curve for the photometer by making dilutions of standardized hypochlorite solution prepared as directed under Chlorine Demand, Section 115A.3a. Take special precautions when diluting to low concentrations because of possible consumption of small amounts of chlorine by trace impurities. Use chlorine-demand-free water [¶ 3a(1) above] in making the dilutions. Expose all glassware to be used in the dilutions to water containing at least 10 mg/l of chlorine, leaving it in contact for a few hours. Then rinse with the chlorine-demand-free water.

Make a suitable series of dilutions; subject these to the analytical procedures described in the orthotolidine method (*C* and *D*); then use the results to construct a calibration curve.

3b. Permanent Chlorine Standards

It cannot be emphasized too strongly that precision in the preparation of the buffer solutions is necessary; therefore, the directions must be followed explicitly.

1) Phosphate buffer stock solution, 0.5*M*: Dry anhydrous disodium hydrogen phosphate, Na_2HPO_4, and anhydrous potassium dihydrogen phosphate, KH_2PO_4, overnight at 105–110 C, and store in a desiccator. Dissolve 22.86 g Na_2HPO_4 together with 46.16 g KH_2PO_4 in distilled water and dilute to 1 liter. Let the solution stand for several days to allow time for any precipitate to form. Filter before using.

2) Phosphate buffer solution, 0.1*M*: This is a standard buffer, pH 6.45. Filter the stock solution as prepared above and dilute 200 ml to 1 liter with distilled water.

3) Strong chromate-dichromate solution: Dissolve 1.55 g potassium dichromate, $K_2Cr_2O_7$, and 4.65 g potassium chromate, K_2CrO_4, in 0.1*M* phosphate buffer and dilute to 1 liter with 0.1*M* phosphate buffer. This solution corresponds to the color produced by 10 mg/l chlorine in the standard orthotolidine procedure when viewed through a depth of 24–30 cm.

4) Dilute chromate-dichromate solution: Dissolve 155 mg potassium dichromate and 465 mg potassium chromate in 0.1*M* phosphate buffer and dilute to 1 liter with 0.1*M* phosphate buffer. Alternatively, prepare the solution by diluting 100 ml of strong chromate-dichromate solution to 1 liter with 0.1*M* phosphate buffer. This solution corresponds to the color produced by 1 mg/l chlorine in the standard orthotolidine procedure when viewed through all cell depths.

5) Low-range permanent chlorine standards, 0.01–1.0 mg/l: Pipet the volumes of dilute chromate-dichromate solution indicated in Table 114(2) for the range of cell depths given into 100-ml tubes of any uniform length and diameter or into 100-ml volumetric flasks. Make the volume up to the

TABLE 114(2): LOW-RANGE CHLORINE STANDARDS—0.01–1.0 MG/L *

Chlorine *mg/l*	Chromate-Dichromate Solution ml/100 ml	Chlorine *mg/l*	Chromate-Dichromate Solution ml/100 ml
0.01	1	0.35	35
0.02	2	0.40	40
0.05	5	0.45	45
0.07	7	0.50	50
0.10	10	0.60	60
0.15	15	0.70	70
0.20	20	0.80	80
0.25	25	0.90	90
0.30	30	1.00	100

* These standards are very close visual matches of the chlorine-orthotolidine color and are preferable to temporary standards, which are difficult to prepare accurately.

TABLE 114(3): HIGH-RANGE CHLORINE STANDARDS—1.0–10.0 MG/L *

Chlorine *mg/l*	Cell Depth—*cm*			
	2.5–5	10	20	24–30
	Chromate-Dichromate Solution—*ml*			
1	10.0	10.0	10.0	10.0
1.5	15.0	15.0	15.0	15.0
2	19.5	19.5	19.7	20.0
3	27.0	27.5	29.0	30.0
4	34.5	35.0	39.0	40.0
5	42.0	43.0	48.0	50.0
6	49.0	51.0	58.0	60.0
7	56.5	59.0	68.0	70.0
8	64.0	67.0	77.5	80.0
9	72.0	75.5	87.0	90.0
10	80.0	84.0	97.0	100.0

* These standards are very close visual matches of the chlorine-orthotolidine color and are preferable to temporary standards, which are difficult to prepare accurately.

100-ml mark with 0.1*M* phosphate buffer solution. These standards can be read at any cell depth up to 30 cm.

6) High-range permanent chlorine standards, 1.0–10.0 mg/l. Pipet the volumes of strong chromate-dichromate solution given in Table 114(3) for the range of cell depths given into 100-ml tubes of any uniform length and diameter or into 100-ml volumetric flasks. Make the volume up to the 100-ml mark with 0.1*M* phosphate buffer solution. Prepare standards for other cell depths or for other concentrations by interpolating between the values in Tables 114(2) and 114(3).

7) Comparison tube specifications: Variations in the viewing depth in any set of color comparison tubes, cells or bottles used in this determination must not be more than ±3%.

8) Protection of standards: Protect the tubes from dust and evaporation by sealing on microcover glasses with collodion, Canada balsam or similar material. Apply the material to the top of the nessler tube by means of a camel's hair brush and put the cover glass into position promptly with forceps. After it is spot-sealed, reinforce the circumference with additional brush-applied sealing material until the joining of the tube and cover glass is complete. Do not use rubber stoppers. If desired, use commercially available nessler tubes with special ground-glass caps that permit optical comparison. Do not store or use the standards in direct sunlight. Prepare new standards whenever turbidity appears.

9) Commercial standards: Commercially prepared permanent standards may be used for routine tests, provided the analyst checks them frequently to satisfy himself of their accuracy.

3c. Orthotolidine Reagent

1) Preparation: Dissolve 1.35 g orthotolidine dihydrochloride in 500 ml distilled water. Add this solution, with constant stirring, to a mixture of 350 ml distilled water and 150 ml conc HCl. Do not use orthotolidine base in the preparation of this reagent.

2) *Storage:* Store the orthotolidine solution in brown bottles or in the dark. Protect at all times from direct sunlight. Use no longer than 6 months. Avoid contact with rubber. Store at room temperature; do not allow the temperature to fall below 0 C because the resulting crystallization of orthotolidine can subsequently lead to deficient color development.

CAUTION—*Handle this reagent with extreme care. Never use a mouth pipet for dispensing this reagent, but rely on an automatic, dropping or safety pipet to measure the necessary volume. Avoid inhalation or exposure to the skin.*

3d. Decolorizing Solution

One of the following reducing reagents with a sulfur group will discharge the yellow holoquinone color formed by the reaction of chlorine and orthotolidine. Mercaptosuccinic acid (thiomalic acid) is preferred because greater quantities of the compound can be tolerated in an acid medium before sulfur begins to precipitate. The use of excess sodium thiosulfate and sodium sulfite leads to the formation of a sulfur colloid. However, 1 or 2 drops of any of these agents can be used with safety:

1) *Mercaptosuccinic acid solution*—Dissolve 10 g mercaptosuccinic acid (also called thiomalic acid), practical grade, and dilute to 100 ml with distilled water. This solution is stable for at least 6 months when stored away from strong light in a glass-stoppered bottle.

2) *Sodium thiosulfate,* 0.1*N*—Dissolve 25 g $Na_2S_2O_3 \cdot 5H_2O$ and dilute to 1 liter with distilled water.

3) *Sodium sulfite solution*—Dissolve 10 g Na_2SO_3 and dilute to 100 ml with distilled water.

4. Procedure

a. Addition of sample to reagent: Use 0.5 ml orthotolidine reagent in 10-ml cells, 0.75 ml in 15-ml cells, 5 ml in 100-ml, and the same ratio for other volumes. Place the orthotolidine reagent in the nessler tube, colorimeter cell or other container; add the sample to the proper mark or volume and mix.

b. Temperature: When the temperature of the sample is less than 20 C, bring it to that temperature quickly after mixing it with orthotolidine. If a comparator cell is used, place it in hot water until the specified temperature is reached. If a nessler tube is used, handle it in the same manner as the cell or transfer the contents to a flask for heating.

c. Color development and comparison: Compare the colors of the sample and standards at the time of maximum color development. (If the potable sample contains predominantly free chlorine, the maximum color appears almost instantly and begins to fade. Samples containing combined chlorine develop their maximum color at a rate that is largely dependent on temperature, although the nitrogenous compounds present may influence this rate. Usually at 20 C maximum color develops in about 3 min; at 25 C, in about 2.5 min; and at 0 C, in about 6 min. About 5 min after maximum color develops, a slight fading begins. Therefore, samples containing combined chlorine should be read within

5 min and should, preferably, be allowed to develop color in the dark.) When color comparison is made against chromate-dichromate standards, use the same cell depth for both samples and standards.

d. Compensation for interference: Compensate for the interference due to the presence of natural color or turbidity in one of two ways: (1) View the sample and standard horizontally after placing an untreated sample of the same thickness behind the standard and the same thickness of clean water behind the sample under comparison; or (2) add 1 or 2 drops (0.05 to 0.1 ml) of decolorizing solution (¶ 3d et seq) to the developed chlorine-orthotolidine color and mix until the yellow color disappears (within a minute). Use the approach in (2) for photometric measurements before and after addition of the decolorizing solution. Read the values from the calibration curve as "apparent chlorine" and "interferences as chlorine" and then subtract. Alternatively, decolorize a portion of the developed sample and use to null the photometer, whereupon the chlorine value is obtained directly from the curve. In the presence of excessive turbidity, centrifuge the sample for a brief period to bring it within nulling range of the photometer.

5. Precision and Accuracy

See Table 114(1) and the statement entitled *Selection of Method* (Section 114.1) for pertinent details.

114 D. Orthotolidine-Arsenite (OTA) Method

1. General Discussion

Within the limitations specified, the orthotolidine-arsenite (OTA) method permits measurement of the relative amounts of free available chlorine, combined available chlorine, and color due to interfering substances. In samples containing a high proportion of combined available chlorine, more free available chlorine may be indicated than is actually present, because temperature plays an important role in the determination of the free-available-chlorine fraction. At room temperature some of the combined available chlorine can react with orthotolidine in the OTA method, yielding a spurious or high free-available-chlorine value. To minimize this interference, the sample should be chilled (as rapidly as circumstances permit) to as near 1 C as possible before addition of the orthotolidine and arsenite reagents [steps described in ¶ 4a(2) below].

Too much emphasis cannot be placed on the fact that the precision of the results depends on strict adherence to (a) the recommended time intervals for the addition of reagents and (b) the temperature of the sample. Since precision is affected by the relative concentrations of free and combined available chlorine in the sample, the temperature of the sample under examination should never exceed 20 C as in ¶ 4a(2) of the procedure. The precision of determination for the free-available-chlorine fraction improves with decreasing temperature.

2. Apparatus

COLORIMETRIC EQUIPMENT—One of the following is required:

a. Spectrophotometer or filter photometer, for use in the wavelength range of 400 to 490 mμ and providing a light path of 1 cm or longer.

b. Comparator, color- and turbidity-compensating.

c. French square bottles, capacity 1 or 2 oz.

3. Reagents

a. Orthotolidine reagent, prepared and stored as directed in Method C (Section 114C. 3c).

b. Sodium arsenite solution: Dissolve 5.0 g $NaAsO_2$ in distilled water and dilute to 1 liter. (CAUTION: *Toxic—take care to avoid ingestion.*)

c. Permanent chlorine standards, prepared commercially or as directed in Section 114C. 3b (to be used in comparator tubes or French square bottles).

4. Procedure

a. VISUAL COMPARISON—

1) Sample and reagent volumes: Label three comparator cells or French square bottles "A," "B," and "C." Use 0.5 ml orthotolidine reagent in 10-ml cells, 0.75 ml in 15-ml cells, and the same ratio for other volumes of sample. Use the same volume of arsenite solution as orthotolidine.

2) Free available chlorine: To Cell A, containing orthotolidine reagent, add a measured volume of water sample. Mix quickly, and immediately (within 5 sec) add arsenite solution. Mix quickly again and compare with color standards as rapidly as possible. Record the result (A) as free available chlorine and interfering colors.

3) Estimation of interference: To Cell B, containing arsenite solution, add a measured volume of water sample. Mix quickly, and immediately add orthotolidine reagent. Mix quickly again and compare with color standards as rapidly as possible. Record the result (B_1). Compare with color standards again in exactly 5 min and record the result (B_2). The values obtained represent the interfering colors present in the immediate reading (B_1) and in the 5-min reading (B_2).

4) Total available chlorine: To Cell C, containing orthotolidine reagent, add a measured volume of water sample. Mix quickly and compare with color standards in exactly 5 min. Record the result (C) as the total amount of residual chlorine present and the total amount of interfering colors.

b. PHOTOMETRIC MEASUREMENT—Measure photometrically the colors developed by following the directions in ¶s 4a(1) to (4) and convert the readings to the proper chlorine values by referring to a calibration curve prepared by treating known chlorine concentrations in the same manner as the unknown samples.

5. Calculation

Total available residual chlorine = $C - B_2$
Free available residual chlorine = $A - B_1$
Combined available residual chlorine
= total available residual Cl − free available residual Cl

6. Precision and Accuracy

See Table 114(1) and the statement entitled *Selection of Method* (Section 114.1) for pertinent details.

114 E. Drop Dilution Method for Field Use

1. General Discussion

The drop dilution method is designed for field measurements of free residual chlorine where concentrations are greater than 10 mg/l and where speed of estimation is of importance. It is particularly useful in connection with the disinfection of mains or tanks where laboratory apparatus is not available. The test is not intended to displace titration methods and should not be used where accuracy is desired. This test must not be made in direct sunlight.

2. Apparatus

a. COLOR COMPARISON EQUIPMENT—One of the following may be used with due consideration being given the amount of chlorine solution taken for the test:

1) Comparator.

2) Nessler tubes, 100 ml.

b. MEDICINE DROPPER—calibrated to deliver 20 drops per milliliter.

3. Reagents

a. Orthotolidine reagent, prepared and stored as directed in Method C (Section 114C.3c).

b. Permanent chlorine standards, prepared as directed in Section 114C. 3b.

4. Procedure

If the comparator cell holds 10 or 15 ml, place 0.5 ml orthotolidine reagent in the cell. If a 100-ml nessler tube is used, place 5.0 ml orthotolidine reagent in the tube. Fill the cell or tube to the mark with distilled water and mix thoroughly. Add to the cell or tube 1 drop of the water under test. Mix thoroughly.

A sample of water with such concentrations of chlorine as may be estimated by this method usually contains only free available chlorine, although traces of combined available chlorine are occasionally found. In view of the rapid color development, compare the color at once against chromate-dichromate standards with the same cell depth for samples and standards.

If the addition of 1 drop of the water under test produces no color, discard the contents of the cell. Refill with orthotolidine and distilled water as before and add 2 drops of the water under test. Continue this procedure with increasing amounts of sample until an easily readable color, equivalent to not less than 0.1 mg/l, is produced.

5. Calculation

Free available residual chlorine:

$$\text{mg/l Cl} = \frac{\text{ml cell volume} \times \text{reading} \times 20}{\text{drops of sample}}$$

114 F. Stabilized Neutral Orthotolidine (SNORT) Method (TENTATIVE)

1. General Discussion

a. Principle: Orthotolidine is quite stable in the reduced form when stored in brown bottles in the presence of hydrochloric acid. The stability of oxidized orthotolidine, however, decreases as the pH increases. For this reason, orthotolidine has classically been used at a pH of 1.3 and lower. As the pH mounts, the rate of reaction of orthotolidine with combined chlorine, iron and nitrite becomes slower and their interference essentially disappears at pH 7. Anionic surface-active agents stabilize the color developed by free chlorine and orthotolidine at pH 7.0. "Aerosol OT," * sodium di(2-ethylhexyl) sulfosuccinate, is the best stabilizing reagent found to date. The concentration of stabilizer required for best stability at high and low temperatures is 40 mg for each 100 ml of sample plus reagents.

The ratio by weight of orthotolidine dihydrochloride to chlorine must be at least 8 to 1. With the concentration of orthotolidine recommended in the procedure, the chlorine concentration must not exceed 6 mg/l.

The pH of the final solution must be between 6.5 and 7.5 to minimize low pH interference and high pH fading. If the pH of the sample is less than 5 or greater than 9, and in addition the alkalinity is greater than 150 or the acidity greater than 200 mg/l, the final pH of the solution should be checked. If the alkalinity is high and the final pH does not lie within the range of 6.5 to 7.5, the sample should be adjusted to this range before analysis.

To insure correct color development, minimum interference, a pH of 6.5 to 7.5, and a ratio of orthotolidine to free chlorine of at least 8 to 1, the sample must be added to the reagents.

The reaction time and temperature are relatively unimportant compared to the usual methods for chlorine determination. Nevertheless, for extremely large combined chlorine to free chlorine ratios, high temperature and long waiting times are undesirable. At 35 C a 1 mg/l monochloramine solution produces a false free chlorine residual of 0.01 mg/l/min. At high temperature and for long waiting times, color fading may become important, especially at levels below 0.1 mg/l of free chlorine. A 1-mg/l solution of free chlorine fades at the rate of 0.005 mg/l/min at 35 C.

Iodide can be added in neutral solution to measure monochloramine, and in acidic solution to measure dichloramine. The reaction of iodide and chloramine yields a concentration of iodine equivalent to the chloramine. In the colorimetric procedure, orthotolidine is present with the chloramine when iodide is added and the iodine produced by the chloramine is immediately reduced back to iodide and acts as a catalyst in generating an amount of blue orthotolidine equivalent to the original chloramine present. Because of this catalytic effect, lesser amounts of iodide are required compared to amperometric titration, which improves the separation of the monochloramine and dichloramine fractions.

The remarks in the orthotolidine

* A trademark of the American Cyanamid Co.

method (Section 114C.1) are applicable to stability and preparation of orthotolidine, the use of chlorine-demand-free water, and precautions for the exclusion of laboratory fumes, reducing agents and oxidizing agents from the reagents.

b. Interference: When orthotolidine or any other chromogenic reagent is used to measure residual chlorine, strong oxidizing agents of any kind form an interference. Such interferences include bromine, chlorine dioxide, iodine, manganic compounds, and ozone. The reduced form of these compounds—bromide, chloride, iodide, manganous ion, and oxygen—do not, however, interfere with the method. Reducing agents such as ferrous compounds, hydrogen sulfide, and oxidizable organic matter do *not* form an interference in the analytical method but may interfere in maintaining chlorine residuals by reducing the chlorine residual by reaction with the chlorine to produce chloride ion, acting simply as chlorine demand.

Turbidity and color also interfere with the method, as with any other colorimetric method, unless the background turbidity or color is compensated for by using a blank. Concentrations of 55 mg/l iron, 92 mg/l nitrite, and 6,000 mg/l chloride do not interfere. The interference of combined chlorine is insignificant in the determination of free chlorine except (as noted before) at high temperature and long waiting times. Manganic compounds produce up to stoichiometric interference but can be compensated for by using a blank. In the presence of more than 10 μg/l manganic manganese, a blank is prepared by adding 5 ml sodium arsenite to a 100-ml sample. This sample is then added to the reagents, as usual, and this blank is used as a reference in measuring the free chlorine present, either by zeroing the photometer with this blank or by using the blank as a reference when making color comparison.

If nitrogen trichloride is present, half reacts as free available chlorine but the remainder does not interfere in the monochloramine and dichloramine measurements. Many different organic chloramines are possible. The extent to which these organic chloramines interfere in the monochloramine or dichloramine steps depends on the nature of the organic compound; they may appear in either or both fractions.

c. Minimum detectable concentration: Approximately 10 μg/l free chlorine.

2. Apparatus

COLORIMETRIC EQUIPMENT—One of the following is required:

a. Filter photometer, providing a light path of 1 cm or longer for 1 mg/l free chlorine residual and below, or a light path from 1 to 10 mm above 1.5 mg/l free chlorine residual; also equipped with a red filter having maximum transmission in the range of 600 to 650 mμ.

b. Spectrophotometer, for use at 625 mμ, providing a light path noted in the paragraph above.

3. Reagents

Prepare *chlorine-demand-free distilled water* as described in the orthotolidine method [Section 114C.3a(1)].

a. Neutral orthotolidine reagent: Add 5 ml conc hydrochloric acid to 100 ml chlorine-demand-free distilled water. Add 10 ml of this acid solution, 20 mg mercuric chloride, $HgCl_2$, 30 mg disodium ethylenediamine tetraacetate dihydrate, also called (ethylenedinitrilo)-tetraacetic acid sodium salt, and 1.5 g orthotolidine dihydrochloride to chlorine-demand-free distilled water and dilute to 1 liter. Store in a brown bottle and observe the other storage precautions in the orthotolidine method, Section 114C.3c(2). (CAUTION: *Handle this chemical with extreme care. Never use a mouth pipet for dispensing this reagent, but rely on an automatic dropping or safety pipet to measure the necessary volumes. Avoid inhalation or exposure to the skin.*)

b. Buffer-stabilizer reagent: Dissolve 34.4 g dipotassium hydrogen phosphate, K_2HPO_4, 12.6 g potassium dihydrogen phosphate, KH_2PO_4, and 8.0 g "Aerosol OT," 100% solid di(2-ethylhexyl)sulfosuccinate, in a solution of 500 ml chlorine-demand-free water and 200 ml diethylene glycol monobutyl ether. Dilute to 1 liter with chlorine-demand-free water.

c. Potassium iodide solution: Dissolve 0.4 g KI in chlorine-demand-free distilled water and dilute to 100 ml. Store in a brown glass-stoppered bottle, preferably in a refrigerator. Discard when a yellow color develops.

d. Sulfuric acid solution: Cautiously add 4 ml conc H_2SO_4 to chlorine-demand-free distilled water and dilute to 100 ml.

e. Sodium carbonate solution: Dissolve 5 g Na_2CO_3 in chlorine-demand-free distilled water and dilute to 100 ml.

f. Sodium arsenite solution: Dissolve 5.0 g $NaAsO_2$ in distilled water and dilute to 1 liter. (CAUTION: *Toxic—take care to avoid ingestion.*)

4. Procedure

a. Calibration of photometer: Construct a calibration curve by making dilutions of standardized hypochlorite solution prepared as directed under chlorine demand, Section 115A.3a. Observe the special precautions listed under orthotolidine method C, ¶ 3a(5). Develop and measure the colors as described below for the sample.

b. Color development of free chlorine: Use 0.5 ml neutral orthotolidine and 0.5 ml stabilizer-buffer reagent with 10-ml samples; 5 ml neutral orthotolidine and 5 ml stabilizer-buffer reagent with 100 ml; and the same ratio for other volumes. Place the neutral orthotolidine and stabilizer-buffer mixture in the photometer tube or a 250-ml beaker on a magnetic stirrer. Mix the reagent slightly and add the sample to the reagents with gentle stirring. Measure the percent transmittance and convert to absorbance at 625 mμ. The value obtained (A) from the calibration curve represents the free chlorine residual. To minimize possible interference from high concentrations of combined chlorine and high-temperature fading, complete mixing of the sample with the reagents and reading on the photometer within approximately 2 min.

c. Monochloramine: Return any aliquot used for measuring free chlorine in ¶ 4b to the sample. Add, with stirring, 0.5 ml potassium iodide solution to each 100-ml sample, or a similar ratio for other sample volumes. Again measure the transmittance of the residual free chlorine plus the monochloramine and obtain the value (B) from the calibration curve.

d. Dichloramine: Return any aliquot used for measuring the monochloramine in ¶ 4c to the sample. Add, with stirring, 1 ml sulfuric acid solution to each 100-ml sample, or a similar ratio for other sample volumes. Allow 30 sec for color development. Add 1 ml sodium carbonate solution slowly with stirring or until a pure blue solution returns. Measure the transmittance of the total residual chlorine—free chlorine, monochloramine and dichloramine—and obtain the value (C) from the calibration curve with a slight dilution correction.

e. Compensation for interferences: Compensate for the presence of natural color or turbidity as well as manganic compounds by adding 5 ml arsenite to 100 ml sample. Add this blank sample to the reagents as above. Use the color of the blank to set 100% transmittance or zero absorbance on the photometer. Measure all samples in relation to this blank. Read from the calibration curve the concentrations of chlorine present in the sample.

5. Calculation

mg/l Free residual chlorine
= A, including ½ trichloramine if present

mg/l Monochloramine = B − A, as mg/l Cl

mg/l Dichloramine = 1.03 C − B, as mg/l Cl

mg/l Total chlorine = 1.03 C, as mg/l Cl

6. Precision and Accuracy

See Table 114(1) and the statement entitled *Selection of Method* (Section 114.1) for pertinent details.

114 G. DPD Ferrous Titrimetric and Colorimetric Methods (TENTATIVE)

1. General Discussion

a. Principle: N,N-diethyl-p-phenylenediamine (DPD) is superior to neutral orthotolidine as an indicator in the ferrous method. The colors produced are more stable, fewer reagents are required, and a full response in neutral solution is obtained from dichloramine. In the titrimetric procedure, decolorization by standard ferrous ammonium sulfate (FAS) titrant is instantaneous, thereby enabling each step to be performed more rapidly. In the colorimetric version of the method, the standard colors are prepared by use of a standard potassium permanganate solution. Where complete differentiation is not required, the procedure may be further simplified to give only free and combined available chlorine or total residual available chlorine.

In the absence of iodide ion, free available chlorine reacts instantly with the N,N-diethyl-p-phenylenediamine (DPD) indicator to produce a red color. Subsequent addition of a small amount of iodide ion acts catalytically to cause monochloramine to produce color. Further addition of iodide ion to excess evokes a rapid response from dichloramine. Unlike the reaction with neutral orthotolidine, any nitrogen trichloride present no longer displays color with free available chlorine but is included with dichloramine. By adding iodide ion before DPD, however, a proportion of the nitrogen trichloride is caused to appear with free available chlorine. A supplementary procedure based upon altering in this way the order of adding the reagents thus permits the estimation of nitrogen trichloride.

Chlorine dioxide appears, to the extent of one-fifth of its total available chlorine content, with free available chlorine. A full response from chlorine dioxide, corresponding to its total available chlorine content, may be obtained if the sample is first acidified in the presence of iodide ion and is subsequently brought back to an approximately neutral pH by the addition of bicarbonate ion. Bromine, bromamine and iodine react with DPD indicator and appear with free available chlorine. DPD procedures for the determination of these halogens and related compounds have been developed.[2, 3]

b. pH Control: For accurate results careful pH control is essential. At the proper pH of 6.2 to 6.5, the red colors produced may be titrated to sharp colorless end points. *The titration must be carried out as soon as the red color is formed in each step.* Too low a pH in the first step will tend to make the monochloramine show in the free-chlorine step and the dichloramine in the monochloramine step. Too high a pH may cause dissolved oxygen to give a color.

c. Temperature control: In all methods for differentiating free chlorine from chloramines, the higher the temperature the greater the tendency for the chloramines to react with the reagents and thus lead to increased apparent free-chlorine results after a fixed-time interval. Exceptions to this are the titration methods, probably due to the speed with which the titration is completed compared with the two to three minutes required for the colorimetric measurement to be made. The DPD methods are among those least affected by temperature.

d. Interference: The only interfering substance likely to be encountered in water is oxidized manganese. To correct for this, place 5 ml buffer solution, one small crystal of potassium iodide, and 0.5 ml sodium arsenite solution (500 mg $NaAsO_2$ plus 100 ml distilled water) in the titration flask. Add 100 ml sample and mix. Then add 5 ml DPD indicator solution, mix, and titrate with standard ferrous ammonium sulfate titrant until any red color is discharged, or measure colorimetrically. Subtract the reading from reading A obtained by the normal procedure as described in ¶ 3a(1) of this method or from the total available chlorine reading obtained in the simplified procedure as given in ¶ 3a(4). If the combined reagent in powder form (see below) is used, add the potassium iodide and arsenite first to the sample and mix, then add the combined buffer-indicator reagent afterwards.

Interference by copper up to approximately 10 mg/l copper is overcome by the EDTA incorporated in the reagents. The presence of EDTA also serves to enhance the stability of the DPD indicator solution by retarding deterioration due to oxidation; and in the test itself provides virtually complete suppression of dissolved oxygen errors by prevention of trace metal catalysis.

2. Reagents

a. Phosphate buffer solution: Dissolve 24 g anhydrous disodium hydrogen phosphate, Na_2HPO_4, and 46 g anhydrous potassium dihydrogen phosphate, KH_2PO_4, in distilled water. Combine this solution with 100 ml distilled water in which 800 mg disodium ethylenediamine tetraacetate dihydrate, also called (ethylenedinitrilo)tetraacetic acid sodium salt, have been dissolved. Dilute to 1 liter with distilled water and add 20 mg mercuric chloride to prevent mold growth, and to prevent interference in the free available chlorine test caused by any trace amounts of iodide in the reagents.

b. N,N-Diethyl-p-phenylenediamine (DPD) indicator solution: Dissolve 1 g DPD Oxalate,* or 1.5 g p-amino-N:N-diethylaniline sulfate,† in chlorine-free distilled water containing 8 ml 1 + 3 sulfuric acid and 200 mg disodium ethylenediamine tetraacetate dihydrate, also called (ethylenedinitrilo)tetraacetic acid sodium salt. Make up to 1 liter, store in a brown glass-stoppered bottle, and discard when discolored. (The buffer and indicator sulfate are commercially available as a combined reagent in stable powder form.) CAUTION: *The oxalate is toxic—take care to avoid ingestion.*

c. Standard ferrous ammonium sulfate (FAS) titrant: Dissolve 1.106 g Mohr's salt, $Fe(NH_4)_2(SO_4)_2 \cdot 6H_2O$ in distilled water containing 1 ml of 1 + 3 sulfuric acid and make up to 1 liter with freshly boiled and cooled distilled water. This primary standard may be used for one month, and the titer checked by potassium dichromate. The FAS titrant is equivalent to 100 μg Cl per 1.00 ml.

d. Potassium iodide, crystals.

e. Potassium iodide solution: Dissolve 500 mg KI and dilute to 100 ml, using freshly boiled and cooled distilled water. Store in a brown glass-stoppered bottle, preferably in a refrigerator. Discard the solution when a yellow color develops.

---

* Eastman chemical No. 7102, or equivalent.

† British Drug House chemical available from Gallard-Schlesinger Chemical Mfg. Corp., 584 Mineola Avenue, Carle Place, N. Y. 11514.

3. Procedure

The quantities given below are suitable for concentrations of total available chlorine up to 4 mg/l. Where the total chlorine exceeds 4 mg/l, use a smaller sample and dilute to a total volume of 100 ml. Mix the usual volumes of buffer reagent and DPD indicator solution, or the usual amount of DPD powder, with distilled water before adding sufficient sample to bring the total volume to 100 ml.

a. FREE AVAILABLE CHLORINE OR CHLORAMINE—Place 5 ml each of buffer reagent and DPD indicator solution in the titration flask and mix (or use about 500 mg of DPD powder). Add 100 ml sample and mix.

1) Free available chlorine: Titrate rapidly with standard FAS titrant until the red color is discharged (reading A).

2) Monochloramine: Add one very small crystal of potassium iodide and mix; or if the dichloramine concentration is expected to be high, add 0.1 ml (2 drops) potassium iodide solution and mix. Continue titration until the red color is again discharged (reading B).

3) Dichloramine: Add several crystals of potassium iodide (about 1 g) and mix to dissolve. Allow to stand for 2 min and then continue titration until the red color is again discharged (reading C). In the case of very high dichloramine concentrations, allow a further 2 min standing if color drift-back indicates slightly incomplete reaction. When dichloramine concentrations are not expected to be high, use half the specified amount of potassium iodide.

4) Simplified procedure for free and combined available chlorine or total available chlorine: Omit stage (2) in order to obtain monochloramine and dichloramine together as combined available chlorine. To obtain total available chlorine in one reading, add the full amount of potassium iodide at the start, with the specified amounts of buffer reagent and DPD indicator, and titrate after 2 min standing.

b. NITROGEN TRICHLORIDE—The absence of color in the first step indicates the absence of nitrogen trichloride (and of chlorine dioxide). Nitrogen trichloride, readily identified by its distinctive odor, may be estimated by the following procedure: Place a small crystal of potassium iodide in a titration flask. Add 100 ml sample and mix. Then add the contents to a second flask containing 5 ml each of buffer reagent and DPD indicator solution (or about 500 mg DPD powder direct to the first flask). Titrate rapidly with standard FAS titrant until the red color is discharged (reading D).

Monochloramine is unlikely to be present with nitrogen trichloride. If high concentrations of dichloramine are present, use potassium iodide solution as in ¶ 3a(2) in place of a potassium iodide crystal.

c. CALIBRATION OF COLORIMETERS—Instead of titrating with standard FAS titrant, measure the developed colors by using either the specified liquid reagents or the solid DPD powder in which the buffer and indicator are combined. To calibrate colorimeters, prepare a standard potassium permanganate solution containing 891 mg $KMnO_4$ per liter. Dilute 10 times for use, whereupon 1 ml made up to 100 ml with distilled water is equivalent to 1 mg/l Cl. Prepare the standard calibration colors by adding the calculated volumes of potassium permanganate solution, thus diluted with distilled water, to the buffer reagent and indicator as detailed in ¶ 3a above. Check for any loss resulting from the permanganate absorption by the distilled water with a titration of the calibration colors against standard FAS titrant. Make the necessary correction in the chlorine equivalent of the standard colors.

4. Calculation

For a 100-ml sample, 1.00 ml standard FAS titrant = 1.00 mg/l available residual chlorine.

Reading	NCl_3 Absent	NCl_3 Present
A	free Cl	free Cl
B − A	NH_2Cl	NH_2Cl
C − B	$NHCl_2$	$NHCl_2$ + ½ NCl_3
D	—	free Cl + ½ NCl_3
2(D − A)	—	NCl_3
C − D	—	$NHCl_2$

Should monochloramine be present with nitrogen trichloride, which is unlikely, it will be included in reading D, in which case NCl_3 is obtained from 2(D − B).

Chlorine dioxide, if present, is included in reading A to the extent of one-fifth of its total available chlorine content.

In the simplified procedure for free and combined available chlorine, only reading A (free Cl) and reading C (total Cl) are required. Combined available chlorine is obtained from C − A.

The result obtained in the simplified total available chlorine procedure corresponds to reading C.

5. Precision and Accuracy

See Table 114(1) and the statement entitled *Selection of Method* (Section 114.1) for pertinent details.

114 H. Leuco Crystal Violet Method (TENTATIVE)

1. General Discussion

The leuco crystal violet method measures separately the free and the total available chlorine. The combined available chlorine may be determined by difference. The residual chlorine in an unknown sample may be determined by visual comparison with chlorine standards or by reference to a standard calibration curve.

a. Principle: The compound 4,4′,4″-methylidynetris(N,N-dimethylaniline), also known by the trivial name of leuco crystal violet, reacts instantaneously with free chlorine to form a bluish color. Interference from combined available chlorine can be avoided by completing the test within a 5-min interval. The correct color development in the free chlorine-leuco crystal violet reaction depends upon the following factors and conditions: (1) The solution must be buffered in the pH range of 3.6 to 4.3; (2) a mercuric chloride solution must be added to the sample either prior to the addition of a leuco crystal violet solution or more conveniently in the form of a mixed indicator; (3) the ratio, by weight, of leuco crystal violet to chlorine must be at least 30 to 1; (4) the free chlorine concentration should not exceed 2.0 mg/l; (5) the mixed indicator solution should be added to the sample in a standardized procedure as described in ¶ 4a(1); (6) the test should be completed within 5 min after the mixed indicator addition; (7) the sample temperature should not exceed 40 C.

The total chlorine determination involves the reaction of the free and combined chlorine with iodide ion to produce hypoiodous acid, which in turn reacts instantaneously with leuco crystal violet to form the dye crystal violet. The color is stable for days and follows Beer's law over a wide range of total chlorine. The extreme sensitivity of the determination may necessitate dilution of the sample with chlorine-demand-free water to bring the chlorine concentration to the desired range of 2.0 mg/l total chlorine. The following factors are important in the total chlorine determination: (1) The solution must be at pH 3.6 to 4.3 during the reaction period; (2) there must be an initial contact of at least 60-sec duration between chlorine and iodide ion; (3) the initial iodide concentration must not exceed 40 mg/l; (4) the total chlorine concentration should not exceed 2.0 mg/l. Semipermanent color standards for the total chlorine determination can be prepared from crystal violet dye for visual matching of samples and standards in nessler tubes or test tubes.

Leuco crystal violet is available commercially in a very pure form which readily dissolves in water acidified with orthophosphoric acid. The concentration of orthophosphoric acid must produce a pH of 1.5 or less in the final indicator reagent. The dissolution of leuco crystal violet with orthophosphoric acid must be carried out in the darkness of brown glass, and the final solution stored in brown glass or opaque plastic containers to minimize reagent deterioration. Both leuco crystal violet and the developed crystal violet dye are relatively inert nontoxic substances, and no special precautions are required other than those normally observed in the handling of any chemical reagent.

The preparation and handling of the saturated mercuric chloride solution require special precautions due to the poisonous and corrosive nature of this chemical. The mixed indicator system, although containing a considerably diluted mercuric chloride solution, should likewise be handled with care.

Improved accuracy in the determination of residual chlorine with leuco crystal violet is possible through photometric measurements.

The importance of using only chlorine-demand-free water and scrupulously cleaned glassware is self-evident because the presence of ammonia in the dilution water or of organic matter on the glassware can consume chlorine and may result in low chlorine values.

b. Interference: No significant interference from combined available chlorine occurs when the free chlorine content is determined within 5 min after indicator addition. Fifteen minutes after indicator addition the apparent error in the free chlorine determination is of the order of 0.04 mg/l at 25 C in a sample containing 5.0 mg/l combined residual chlorine.

The one interference deserving attention in the determination of free residual chlorine is manganic ion, which increases the apparent residual chlorine reading. When manganic ion is known to be present, the arsenite modification outlined in the OTA method (Section 114 D.4) can be applied, substituting the leuco crystal violet indicator system for orthotolidine.

Ferric, nitrate and nitrite compounds do not interfere, while the normal effect of organic compounds is to reduce the free available chlorine. If suspended matter or organic color is present, removal of or compensation for these substances may be accomplished as prescribed in the orthotolidine method, Section 114C.4d.

c. Minimum detectable concentration: 10 μg/l free available chlorine; 5 μg/l total available chlorine.

2. Apparatus

a. ILLUMINATION—The light sources to be used for comparison of samples with standards are described in the orthotolidine method, Section 114C.2a.

b. COLORIMETRIC EQUIPMENT—One of the following is required:

1) Nessler tubes, matched, 50- and 100-ml, tall form.

2) Test tubes, matched, with a capacity of at least 10 ml of sample when the sample surface is near the top of the test tube.

3) Volumetric flasks, 100-ml, with plastic caps or ground-glass stoppers.

4) Filter photometer, providing a light path of 1 cm or longer and equipped with an orange filter having maximum transmittance near 592 mμ.

5) Spectrophotometer, for use at 592 mμ, providing a light path of 1 cm or longer.

c. CLEANING OF GLASSWARE—All glassware or plastic containers, including containers for storage of reagent solutions, must be entirely free of organic matter. This objective can be attained by recourse to either the chlorination or the chromic acid method after the glassware has been thoroughly cleaned with suitable detergent and rinsed with distilled water. The chromic acid method requires less total time, but care is necessary to protect laboratory personnel from contact with the cleaning mixture.

1) Chlorination: Expose all glassware or plastic containers to water containing at least 10 mg/l chlorine for 3 hr or more before use and then rinse with chlorine-demand-free water. After rinsing, oven- or air-dry the glassware in an atmosphere free from organic fumes.

2) Chromic acid: Prepare the chromic acid solution by adding 1 liter conc sulfuric acid to 35 ml saturated sodium dichromate solution contained in a 2-liter beaker. Stir the mixture carefully until all the sodium dichromate has dissolved. When cleaning glassware, carefully heat a suitable volume of chromic acid solution to approximately 50 C. (CAUTION: *Use rubber gloves, safety goggles, and protective clothing in handling this cleaning agent.*) Carefully pour the chromic acid solution into the glassware to be cleaned so that contact is made with the entire inside surface of the container. Allow the cleaning solution to remain in the glassware for 2–3 min or longer. Carefully empty the glassware of chromic acid solution and rinse thoroughly with chlorine-demand-free water. Oven- or air-dry the glassware away from organic or other chlorine-consuming fumes.

3. Reagents

a. CHLORINE-DEMAND-FREE WATER—Chlorine-demand-free water can be made by the chlorination or ion-exchange method. In either case, best results are obtained when distilled water is used as the primary source.

1) Chlorination: Add sufficient chlorine to distilled water to destroy the ammonia. The amount of chlorine required will be about ten times the amount of ammonia nitrogen present; in no event should the initial residual be less than 1.0 mg/l free chlorine. Allow the chlorinated water to stand overnight or longer; then expose to direct sunlight until all residual chlorine is discharged.

2) Ion exchange: Prepare a 3-foot column of approximately 2.5 to 5 cm diameter containing strongly acid cation and strongly basic anion exchange resins. Several commercial mixed-bed resins, analytical grade, are available but the analyst should satisfy himself that ammonia, chloramines, or other compounds that react with chlorine are removed. Pass the distilled water at a relatively slow rate through the resin bed and collect in a scrupulously cleaned receiver that will protect the treated water from undue exposure to the atmosphere.

3) Prepare all *reagent solutions* and dilute all *samples* with the chlorine-demand-free water.

b. STOCK CHLORINE SOLUTION—Prepare the stock chlorine or hypochlorite solution from certain commercial solutions * which contain approximately 1% available chlorine (or household bleach), or by bubbling chlorine gas from a small lecture-size cylinder into distilled water. For convenience, adjust the chlorine concentration to approximately 100 μg per ml of solution. Standardize the stock solution by titrating a suitable aliquot with standard sodium thiosulfate titrant as described in the iodometric method, Section 114A.3b and c, or by the amperometric titration method, Section 114B.4.

c. CHLORINE SOLUTIONS FOR TEMPORARY TOTAL CHLORINE STANDARDS—If measurements of combined residual chlorine are desired, mix an ammonium

* Zonite, a product of Zonite Products Corp.

sulfate solution with chlorine solution in an ammonia-to-chlorine ratio of at least 20 to 1. Dissolve 3.89 g $(NH_4)_2SO_4$ in distilled water and dilute to 1,000 ml to form a solution containing 1.0 mg NH_3 per 1.0 ml. To approximately 800 ml chlorine-demand-free water, add 2.0 ml $(NH_4)_2SO_4$ solution for each 1.0 ml stock chlorine solution which contains 100 μg Cl per 1.0 ml and dilute to 1 liter. Standardize the combined chlorine solution, expressing the concentration as mg/l total Cl, and use immediately for calibration purposes.

d. BUFFER SOLUTION FOR FREE CHLORINE DETERMINATION, pH 4.0—

1) Potassium hydroxide, 4M: Dissolve 224.4 g KOH and dilute to 1 liter with chlorine-demand-free water.

2) Citric acid, 2M: Dissolve 384.3 g $C_6H_8O_7$, or 420.3 g $C_6H_8O_7 \cdot H_2O$, and dilute to 1 liter with chlorine-demand-free water.

3) Potassium citrate solution: To 350 ml 4*M* potassium hydroxide add, with stirring, 700 ml 2*M* citric acid. If desired, prepare smaller volumes in the ratio of 1 volume of potassium hydroxide to 2 volumes of citric acid. Use immediately to prepare final buffer solution *(5)* and discard the remainder of the solution.

4) Acetate solution: Dissolve 161.2 g conc (glacial) acetic acid and 49.5 g sodium acetate, $NaC_2H_3O_2$ or 82.1 g $NaC_2H_3O_2 \cdot 3H_2O$ and dilute to 1 liter with chlorine-demand-free water.

5) Final buffer solution: Mix equal volumes of potassium citrate solution *(3)* with acetate solution *(4)* to make the final pH 4.0 buffer solution for the free chlorine determination. Add 20 mg mercuric chloride to each liter of solution to prevent mold growth.

e. STOCK LEUCO CRYSTAL VIOLET REAGENT: Measure 500 ml chlorine-demand-free water and 14.0 ml 85% orthophosphoric acid into a brown glass container of at least 1-liter capacity. Introduce a magnetic stirring bar into the container and mix the acidified water at moderate speed. Add 3.0 g 4,4′,4″-methylidynetris-(N,N-dimethylaniline),* and with a small amount of water wash down any reagent adhering to the neck or sides of the container.

Continue agitation until dissolution is complete. Finally, add 500 ml chlorine-demand-free water. Store in the brown bottle at room temperature away from direct sunlight. Discard after 6 months. If a rubber stopper must be used, wrap with plastic wrapping material to protect from contact with the reagent.

f. SATURATED MERCURIC CHLORIDE SOLUTION—To 20 g $HgCl_2$ contained in a 300-ml glass-stoppered flask, add 200 ml chlorine-demand-free water. Gently agitate for a few minutes and let stand for 24 hr. (CAUTION: *Label the container with the warning that mercuric chloride is poisonous and corrosive.*)

g. MIXED INDICATOR—To 600 ml stock leuco crystal violet reagent in a brown bottle, add 50 ml saturated mercuric chloride solution and swirl to insure complete mixing. If desired, prepare smaller volumes of mixed indicator in the ratio of 12 volumes stock leuco crystal violet reagent to 1 volume saturated mercuric chloride solution. Follow the storage directions prescribed in ¶ 3e above for the stock leuco crystal violet reagent.

h. BUFFER SOLUTION FOR TOTAL

---

* Eastman chemical No. 3651 or equivalent.

CHLORINE DETERMINATION, pH 4.0—Dissolve 480 g glacial acetic acid and 146 g sodium acetate, $NaC_2H_3O_2$ or 243 g $NaC_2H_3O_2 \cdot 3H_2O$ in 400 ml chlorine-demand-free water and dilute to 1 liter. Transfer the solution to a brown bottle. Add 3.0 g potassium iodide, KI, to the bottle and mix to dissolve the salt. Store the solution in the brown bottle and avoid undue exposure to the air.

i. SOLUTIONS FOR PREPARATION OF SEMIPERMANENT TOTAL CHLORINE STANDARDS—

1) Buffer solution, pH 4.0: Dissolve 480 g conc (glacial) acetic acid and 146 g sodium acetate, $NaC_2H_3O_2$, or 243 g $NaC_2H_3O_2 \cdot 3H_2O$ in 400 ml chlorine-demand-free water and dilute to 1 liter.

2) Crystal violet solution: Dissolve 40.0 mg crystal violet * in 500 ml chlorine-demand-free water containing 20 ml pH 4.0 buffer solution [¶ 3i(1) preceding]. Stir for 30 min or more to effect complete dissolution, then dilute to 1,000 ml with chlorine-demand-free water.

4. Procedure

a. TEMPORARY CHLORINE STANDARDS—Temporary standards are recommended for photometric calibration and research work as well as for visual comparison. Two separate sets of temporary chlorine standards are mandatory because of the divergent colors developed by free and combined residual chlorine. Semipermanent color standards for the total chlorine determination can be prepared from crystal violet dye and have a longevity approaching 3 months. The color system produced with free residual chlorine, on the other hand, differs from the normal crystal violet shade and is stable for only a few days. Commercially prepared standards may be purchased, but it is hoped that a method for preparing standards will be available to all in the future.

1) Preparation of temporary free chlorine standards: Thoroughly clean all glassware as described in ¶ 2c et seq and preferably air- or oven-dry before use. Prepare temporary chlorine standards from a suitable volume of stock chlorine solution added to 2 liters of chlorine-demand-free water contained in a brown glass bottle. Set up a chlorine series in the range of 0.1 to 2.0 mg/l at increments of 0.1 or 0.2 mg/l, for visual comparison studies. Standardize the dilute chlorine solutions by means of the sodium thiosulfate or amperometric titration methods.

After standardization, measure exactly 50 ml dilute chlorine solution into a 100-ml glass-stoppered volumetric flask, taking care to introduce the chlorine solution with a minimum of agitation into the volumetric flask. By means of a Mohr pipet, add 1.0 ml pH 4.0 buffer solution, ¶ 3d(5), and gently swirl the flask to mix. With another measuring pipet, add 1.0 ml mixed indicator, ¶ 3g. Standardize the mixed indicator addition in the following manner: After filling the measuring pipet to the mark, position the pipet tip inside the neck of the volumetric flask so that the tip makes contact with the inside glass surface and allow the mixed indicator to flow down the inside glass surface to the sample, with a minimum of initial agitation of the sample. Remove the pipet from the flask and swirl the contents with a quick firm motion to effect intimate

* Eastman chemical No. C1350 or equivalent.

contact between the mixed indicator and the sample. These steps produce the highest and most consistent absorbance values. *Do not dilute the sample to 100 ml after the addition of mixed indicator* in order to obtain the maximum absorbance values.

Transfer the colored temporary standards to 50-ml nessler tubes for visual comparison or prepare a photometric calibration curve.

VISUAL COMPARISON: If the temporary standards are prepared directly in 50-ml nessler tubes, stopper the tube after addition of the mixed indicator, and mix quickly by inverting the tube several times. If a smaller sample volume is taken, as, for example, 10 ml contained in a test tube, reduce the quantity of pH 4.0 buffer and mixed indicator to 0.2 ml each.

PHOTOMETRIC CALIBRATION: Transfer the colored temporary standards of known free chlorine concentration to cells of 1-cm light path or longer, and read the absorbance in a photometer at a wavelength of 592 mμ against a distilled water reference. Plot the absorbance values versus chlorine concentrations to construct a curve which approximates Beer's law in the lower free chlorine range and exhibits a slight curvature with the higher free chlorine concentrations.

2) Preparation of temporary total chlorine standards: Prepare standardized total chlorine solutions as prescribed in ¶ 3c above in the total chlorine range of 0.1 to 2.0 mg/l. Pipet a 50-ml sample into a 100-ml volumetric flask or 100-ml nessler tube. Add 0.5 ml total chlorine buffer, ¶ 3h, mix, and allow a contact period of at least 60 sec. Add 1.0 ml mixed indicator, mix to develop the color, and dilute to 100 ml. No special precautions are necessary in the addition and mixing of these solutions.

PHOTOMETRIC CALIBRATION: Construct a calibration curve by measuring the absorbance values of the temporary total chlorine standards at 592 mμ, preferably in 1-cm cells.

b. SEMIPERMANENT TOTAL CHLORINE STANDARDS—The variable composition of commercially available crystal violet dye necessitates a reconcilement of the absorbance of the semipermanent standards with the photometric calibration curve. The final semipermanent standards should be adjusted into agreement with the calibration absorbance values obtained on temporary total chlorine standards.

Add the specified volume of crystal violet solution to a 200-ml volumetric flask containing 100 ml distilled water and 4.0 ml pH 4.0 buffer solution, ¶ 3i (1). Dilute to volume with distilled water and compare the absorbance at 592 mμ with the suggested values given in Table 114(4) or with the photometric calibration curve. Protect the standards from direct sunlight and ex-

TABLE 114(4): PREPARATION OF SEMIPERMANENT CRYSTAL VIOLET STANDARDS FOR VISUAL DETERMINATION OF RESIDUAL CHLORINE

Total Chlorine Standard *mg/l*	Crystal Violet Solution *ml*	Absorbance of Final 200-ml Standard *592 mμ in 1-cm cell*
0.1	2.84	0.131
0.2	5.80	0.268
0.3	8.60	0.396
0.4	11.60	0.530
0.5	14.40	0.660
0.6	17.30	0.790
0.7	20.00	0.925
0.8	23.20	1.060
0.9	26.60	1.192
1.0	28.80	1.320

posure to air to maintain stability for approximately 3 months. Seal the standards in glass ampuls for maximum protection.

c. COLOR DEVELOPMENT OF FREE CHLORINE SAMPLE—Measure a 50-ml sample into the same type of flask or tube used to prepare the temporary standards in ¶ 4a(1). Add 1.0 ml pH 4.0 buffer, ¶ 3d(5), and 1.0 ml mixed indicator, ¶ 3g. Apply the mixed indicator to the unknown sample in the same uniform manner prescribed for the temporary standards in ¶ 4a(1). Match the test sample visually with the temporary standards, or read the absorbance photometrically and refer to the standard calibration curve for the free chlorine equivalent. Complete the determination within 5 min of the mixed indicator addition to obviate interference from combined residual chlorine composed of mono-, di-, and trichloramine, and manifested by a slow increase in color. For free chlorine concentrations greater than 2.0 mg/l, dilute the sample with chlorine-demand-free water to contain 2.0 mg/l or less, and proceed with the determination as previously described.

The color development due to combined chlorine residuals is negligible at sample temperatures as high as 40 C, and slightly accelerated at higher temperatures. The color with free chlorine develops instantaneously, and in the absence of combined residual chlorine is stable for several days.

d. COLOR DEVELOPMENT OF TOTAL CHLORINE SAMPLES—

1) Concentrations below 2.0 mg/l: Measure a 50-ml sample into a suitable flask or tube and add 0.5 ml total chlorine buffer, ¶ 3h. Mix and wait at least 60 sec. Add 1.0 ml mixed indicator, ¶ 3g, mix, and dilute to 100 ml. Visually match with standards or read the absorbance photometrically and compare with the calibration curve.

2) Concentrations above 2.0 mg/l: Place approximately 30 ml chlorine-demand-free water in a flask or tube calibrated to contain at least 100 ml. Add 0.5 ml total chlorine buffer, ¶ 3h, followed by a known volume of 20 ml or less of the unknown sample. After mixing, let stand for at least 60 sec. Add 1.0 ml mixed indicator, ¶ 3g, mix, and dilute to the mark with chlorine-demand-free water. Match visually with standards or read the absorbance photometrically and compare with the calibration curve. Select one of the following sample volumes in order to remain within the optimum chlorine range:

Total Chlorine in mg/l	*Sample Volume Required in ml*
2.0–4.0	20.0
4.0–8.0	10.0
8.0–10.0	5.0

The total chlorine color develops instantaneously and remains stable for days. The final color, if too intense for visual matching, may be diluted with chlorine-demand-free water buffered at pH 4.0, matched with standards, and the initial total chlorine estimated by applying the dilution factor.

e. COMPENSATION FOR TURBIDITY AND COLOR—Compensate for the presence of natural color or turbidity as described in the orthotolidine method (Section 114C.4d).

5. Calculation

$$\text{mg/l Total Cl} = \frac{A \times 50}{\text{ml sample}}$$

$$\text{mg/l Combined Cl} = B - C$$

where A = total chlorine in mg/l measured in the diluted sample, B = total chlorine in mg/l in the sample, and C = free chlorine in mg/l.

6. Precision and Accuracy

See Table 114(1) and the statement entitled *Selection of Method* (Section 114.1) for pertinent details.

114 I. Methyl Orange Method (TENTATIVE)

1. General Discussion

a. Principle: Free chlorine bleaches a methyl orange solution quantitatively. In the pH range below 3, methyl orange has a red color with an absorption spectrum which exhibits a maximum at a wavelength of 510 mμ. By measuring the change in absorption at 510 mμ, the concentration of free chlorine in a sample containing a known amount of methyl orange may be established. At pH 2 or greater, the rate of reaction of chloramines with methyl orange is very slow. In the presence of excess bromide ion, chloramines also bleach methyl orange rapidly. Therefore, sodium bromide may be added to the sample after the free chlorine concentration has been determined and the additional decrease in absorption will be due to chloramines.

It is important that there be an excess of methyl orange reagent at all times. If methyl orange is added to the sample, or if the sample is added with insufficient mixing, the chlorine present will not bleach the methyl orange quantitatively. The sample must therefore be added to the reagent with rapid mixing. When the addition of the sample to methyl orange produces a colorless solution, the need for a larger quantity of methyl orange is indicated. The additional methyl orange should not be added to the mixture, but rather the test should be repeated with a new sample and the larger quantity of methyl orange required.

b. pH Control: The final pH of the sample-reagent mixture should be about 2. A higher pH results in incomplete color development and a lower pH increases interference by chlorine-ammonia compounds. Either hydrochloric or chloroacetic acid may be used to adjust the pH. For samples with a limited range of alkalinity, hydrochloric acid is a more convenient reagent. Three drops of 6*N* HCl suffice for a total alkalinity up to 300 mg/l as $CaCO_3$ and 4 drops for a total alkalinity of 300–600 mg/l. The use of 1 ml of chloroacetic acid solution provides the optimum pH in samples containing up to 1,000 mg/l of alkalinity in a 50-ml sample.

c. Interference: Although suspended matter interferes, if the amount of suspended matter is low, a "blank reading" of sample without methyl orange may be used to correct the absorbance. Chloride ion interferes, but the addition of 1 mg/ml chloride ion to the methyl orange reagent eliminates the interference of chloride in concentrations to 1,000 mg/l. In the presence of bromide, chlorine-ammonia compounds will interfere, the extent of interference depending upon the bromide concentration. Bromine and bromine-ammonia compounds also interfere, producing a false chlorine reading equivalent to the active concentration of the bromine compound present. Ferric and nitrite ion in concentrations up to 10 mg/l do not interfere. Manganic ion (0–3 mg/l) bleaches methyl orange quantitatively, but the bleaching due to manganese may be evaluated by treating a sample with sodium arsenite at pH 7 before testing. Sodium arsenite selectively reduces residual chlorine so that the decrease in absorbance in the subsequent test may be assumed to be due to the equivalent manganic ion.

2. Apparatus

COLORIMETRIC EQUIPMENT—One of the following is required:

a. Spectrophotometer, for use at 510 mμ and providing a light path of 1 cm: Since the absorption peak is rather sharp, the specific wavelength of maximum absorption should be used. This may vary slightly with different spectrophotometers due to inaccuracy in the wavelength scales, but it should be approximately 505 to 510 mμ.

b. Filter photometer, providing a light path of 1 cm and equipped with a green color filter exhibiting a maximum transmittance near 510 mμ.

3. Reagents

Prepare all reagents with ammonia-free distilled water.

a. Stock methyl orange solution: Dissolve 500.0 mg $C_{14}H_{14}N_3SO_3Na$ and dilute to 1,000 ml.

b. Standard methyl orange solution: Dilute 100.0 ml stock methyl orange solution to 1,000 ml after adding 1.67 g sodium chloride, NaCl. The reagent is stable indefinitely.

c. Acid solution: Either chloroacetic or hydrochloric acid may be used.

1) CHLOROACETIC ACID SOLUTION—Dissolve 91 g $CH_2ClCOOH$ and dilute to 100 ml.

2) HYDROCHLORIC ACID, 6*N*, 1 + 1.

d. Arsenite buffer: Grind a mixture of 125 mg sodium arsenite, $NaAsO_2$, 375 mg citric acid, $C_6H_8O_7$, 14.5 g sodium citrate dihyrate, $Na_3C_6H_5O_7 \cdot 2H_2O$, together as a dry powder. This buffer produces a final pH of 7 when 100 mg are dissolved in the sample.

e. Sodium bromide solution: Dissolve 2.5 g NaBr in 100 ml.

4. Procedure

The following procedure is suitable for chlorine concentrations to 2 mg/l. Where the total available chlorine concentration exceeds 2 mg/l, dilute the sample with double-distilled ammonia-free water, or extend the standard calibration curve for methyl orange by the use of larger aliquots of methyl orange.

a. Calibration curves: Prepare the standard calibration curves by diluting an iodometrically standardized stock solution of chlorine or hypochlorite and following the procedure given in ¶ 4b below. Plot the absorbance versus free chlorine concentration. For greatest accuracy, perform the calibration at a temperature near that of the samples to be tested, because the absorbance of methyl orange solutions is slightly dependent upon temperature. For routine measurements in the 20–30 C range, the error from this source is negligible.

b. Free available chlorine: To determine free chlorine, combine 5.00 ml standard methyl orange solution and the proper volume of acid solution for pH adjustment. Use 1 ml chloroacetic acid solution or 3–4 drops (0.15–0.20

ml) 6*N* HCl to produce a final pH of 2.0 ± 0.1. Add the 50-ml sample with mixing. After 1–1.5 min, measure the absorbance at 510 mμ, using a 1-cm light path. If the absorbance is greater than 0.10, determine the apparent concentration of free chlorine from the standard calibration curve. If the absorbance is less than 0.10, repeat the test, using 10.00 ml standard methyl orange solution; or dilute the sample with chlorine-demand-free water. (Although the exact chlorine ranges will vary with the wavelength and light path of the photometer on hand, the following volumes of standard methyl orange solution often apply in the indicated chlorine range: 5.00 ml for the chlorine range below 0.75 mg/l, 10.00 ml for the 0.6–1.8 mg/l range, and 15.00 ml for the 1.6–2.75 mg/l range.

If manganese is present, first dissolve 100 mg arsenite buffer reagent in the 50-ml sample to reduce the free chlorine present. Then add the sample to the methyl orange-chloroacetic or hydrochloric acid mixture and measure the absorbance at 510 mμ after 2–2.5 min. Subtract the apparent free chlorine due to manganese from the free chlorine ascertained by the preceding determination.

c. Total available chlorine: To determine total chlorine, add 0.5 ml sodium bromide solution to the sample-reagent mixture after the determination of the free chlorine. Allow 10 min for the reaction of the chlorine-ammonia compounds and again measure the absorbance. If manganese is present, apply the above-mentioned correction to both the free and the total chlorine results.

5. Calculation

In cases where dilution is necessary for either free or total chlorine, the concentration in the sample may be calculated as follows:

$$B = \frac{A \times 50}{\text{ml sample}}$$

where A = mg/l chlorine found in dilution and B = mg/l chlorine in sample. In all instances the combined chlorine may be calculated as the difference between the concentration of free and total chlorine in the sample, the latter always being larger.

6. Precision and Accuracy

See Tables 114(1) and the statement entitled *Selection of Method* (Section 114.1) for pertinent details.

114 J. References

1. M. J. TARAS. 1950. Simplified calibration of photometric instruments for residual chlorine. *Water & Sewage Works* 97:404.
2. A. T. PALIN. 1960. Colorimetric determination of chlorine dioxide in water. *Water & Sewage Works* 107:457.
3. ———. 1967. Methods for the determination in water of free and combined available chlorine, chlorine dioxide and chlorite, bromine, iodine, and ozone, using diethyl-p-phenylene diamine (DPD). *J. Inst. Water Eng.* 21:537.

114 K. Bibliography

Iodometric and Orthotolidine Methods

ELLMS, J. W. & S. J. HAUSER. 1913. Orthotolidine as a reagent for the colorimetric estimation of small quantities of free chlorine. *Ind. Eng. Chem.* 5:915.

THERIAULT, E. J. 1927. The orthotolidine reagent for free chlorine in water. *Pub. Health Rep.* 42:668.

ADAMS, H. W. & A. M. BUSWELL. 1933. Orthotolidine test for chlorine. *JAWWA* 25:1118.

SCOTT, R. D. 1934. Eliminating false chlorine tests. *JAWWA* 26:634.

DAVIS, W. S. & C. B. KELLY. 1934. Photodiscoloration of orthotolidine and artificial standards for free chlorine test in water. *JAWWA* 26:757.

SCOTT, R. D. 1934. Effect of iron in the determination of residual chlorine. *JAWWA* 26:1234.

HULBERT, R. 1934. Chlorine and the orthotolidine test in the presence of nitrite. *JAWWA* 26:1638.

SCOTT, R. D. 1935. Improved standards for the residual chlorine test. *Water Works & Sew.* 82:399.

GRIFFIN, A. E. 1935. Evaluation of residual chlorine. *JAWWA* 27:888.

HALLINAN, F. J. & W. R. THOMPSON. 1939. A critical study of the thiosulfate titration of chlorine. *J. Amer. Chem. Soc.* 61:265.

LAUX, P. C. 1940. Breakpoint chlorination at Anderson. *JAWWA* 32:1027.

GRIFFIN, A. E. & N. S. CHAMBERLIN. 1943. Estimation of high-chlorine residuals. *JAWWA* 35:571.

CHAMBERLIN, N. S. & J. R. GLASS. 1943. Colorimetric determination of chlorine residuals up to 10 ppm with orthotolidine. *JAWWA* 35:1065.

AWWA. 1943. Committee Report: Control of chlorination. *JAWWA* 35:1315.

GILCREAS, F. W. & F. J. HALLINAN. 1944. The practical use of the orthotolidine-arsenite test for residual chlorine. *JAWWA* 36:1343.

Amperometric Titration

FOULK, C. W. & A. T. BAWDEN. 1926. A new type of endpoint in electrometric titration and its application to iodimetry. *J. Amer. Chem. Soc.* 48:2045.

MARKS, H. C. & J. R. GLASS. 1942. A new method of determining residual chlorine. *JAWWA* 34:1227.

HALLER, J. F. & S. S. LISTEK. 1948. Determination of chlorine dioxide and other active chlorine compounds in water. *Anal. Chem.* 20:639.

MAHAN, W. A. 1949. Simplified amperometric titration apparatus for determining residual chlorine in water. *Water Works & Sew.* 96:171.

MARKS, H. C., D. B. WILLIAMS & G. U. GLASGOW. 1951. Determination of residual chlorine compounds. *JAWWA* 43:201.

KOLTHOFF, I. M. & J. J. LINGANE. 1952. *Polarography* (2nd ed.). Interscience Publishers, New York.

Stabilized Neutral Orthotolidine (SNORT) Method

KRUTZSCH, W. 1944. *Wasser Kohle Öl* (4th ed.). Otto Elsner Verlagsgesellschaft, p. 36.

AITKEN, R. W. & D. MERCER. 1951. Photometric measurement of residual chlorine and chloramine in water using neutral orthotolidine. *J. Inst. Water Eng.* 5:321.

PALIN, A. T. 1954. Determining residual chlorine in water by neutral orthotolidine methods—A progress report. *Water & Sewage Works* 101:74.

JOHNSON, J. D., R. OVERBY & D. A. OKUN. 1965. Analysis of chlorine, monochloramine and dichloramine with stabilized neutral orthotolidine. 85th Annual Conference, American Water Works Association, Portland, Oregon, June 28.

JOHNSON, J. D. & R. OVERBY. 1969. Stabilized neutral orthotolidine, SNORT, colorimetric method for chlorine. *Anal. Chem.* 41:1744.

Ferrous DPD Method

PALIN, A. T. 1957. The determination of free and combined chlorine in water by the use of diethyl-p-phenylene diamine. *JAWWA* 49:873.

———. 1961. The determination of free residual bromine in water. *Water & Sewage Works* 108:461.

NICOLSON, N. J. 1965. An evaluation of the methods for determining residual chlorine in water. Part I. Free chlorine. *Analyst* 90:187.

———. Determination of chlorine in water, Parts 1, 2 and 3. *Water Research Association Tech. Papers* Nos. 29 (1963), 47 (1965), and 53 (1966).

Leuco Crystal Violet Method

BLACK, A. P. & G. P. WHITTLE. 1967. New methods for the colorimetric determination of halogen residuals. Part II. Free and total chlorine. *JAWWA* 59:607.

Methyl Orange Method

SOLLO, F. W., JR. & T. E. LARSON. 1965. Determination of free chlorine by methyl orange. *JAWWA* 57:1575.

115 CHLORINE DEMAND

The chlorine demand of a water is caused by such inorganic reductants as ferrous, manganous, nitrite, sulfide and sulfite ions. Ammonia and cyanide consume considerable chlorine during the free residual chlorination process. Chlorine substitutes on phenols and other similar aromatic compounds to form chloro derivative compounds, but may also oxidize the aromatic compounds when larger amounts of chlorine are added. It may also react with ammonia and naturally occurring amino compounds to form chloramines with an active or oxidizing chlorine atom. The destruction of the chloramine compounds can be achieved by the addition of more chlorine and subsequently, with the addition of enough chlorine, a free available residual (hypochlorous acid or hypochlorite) may be attained.

The chlorine demand of water is the difference between the amount of chlorine applied to a treated supply and the amount of free, combined or total available chlorine remaining at the end of the contact period. The chlorine demand of any given water varies with the amount of chlorine applied, time of contact, pH, and temperature. For comparative purposes it is imperative that *all test conditions be stated.* The smallest amount of residual chlorine considered significant is 0.1 mg/l Cl. Presented here are a method for laboratory use and a field procedure which gives less exact results.

115 A. Laboratory Method

1. Discussion

The laboratory method is designed to determine the so-called immediate demand as well as other demands at longer contact periods. Chlorine demand determinations are made to determine the amount of chlorine that must be applied to a water to produce a specific free, combined, or total available chlorine residual after a selected period of contact. If the amount of chlorine applied to waters containing ammonium or organic nitrogen compounds is not sufficient to reach what is termed the "breakpoint," chloramines and certain other chloro derivatives which react as combined available residual chlorine are produced. When sufficient chlorine has been added to reach the breakpoint, which depends on pH, ratio of chlorine to nitrogenous compounds present, and other factors, subsequent additions of chlorine remain in the free available state.

2. Apparatus

COLORIMETRIC EQUIPMENT—One of the following is required:

a. Spectrophotometer or filter photometer, for use in the wavelength range of 400–490 mμ and providing a light path of 1 cm or longer.

b. Comparator, color- and turbidity-compensating.

c. French square bottles, capacity 1 or 2 oz.

3. Reagents

a. Standard chlorine solution: A suitable solution may be obtained from the chlorinator solution hose or by bubbling chlorine gas through distilled or tap water. The stability of the chlorine solution may be improved by storing in the dark or in brown glass-stoppered bottles. Even so, it will lose strength and must be standardized each day that it is used. Alternatively, household hypochlorite solution, which contains about 30,000–50,000 mg/l chlorine equivalent, may be diluted to suitable strength. This is more stable than a chlorine solution, but should not be used more than a week without restandardizing. The solution used for determining chlorine demand should preferably be the same kind of chlorine solution as is actually applied in plant treatment. The preparation of temporary standards for calibrating a photometer entails the fewest problems with hypochlorite. Depending on the intended use, a suitable strength of chlorine solution will usually be between 100 mg/l and 1,000 mg/l. If used for chlorine demand determination, it should be sufficiently strong that the volume of treated portions will not be increased more than 5% by addition of the chlorine solution.

STANDARDIZATION: Place 2 ml acetic acid and 10 to 25 ml distilled water in a flask. Add about 1 g potassium iodide, estimated on a spatula or small spoon, after prior familiarization with the quantity by several weighings. Measure into the flask a suitable volume of the chlorine solution. In choosing a convenient volume, note that 1 ml of 0.025N thiosulfate titrant to be used for titrating is equivalent to about 0.9 mg chlorine.

Titrate with standardized 0.025N sodium thiosulfate titrant until the yellow iodine color is almost gone. Add 1 to 2 ml starch indicator solution and continue the titration to disappearance of the blue color.

Determine the blank by adding identical quantities of acid, KI, and starch indicator to a volume of distilled water corresponding to the sample used for titration.

$$\text{mg/ml Cl} = \frac{(A \pm B) \times N \times 35.45}{\text{ml sample}}$$

where A = ml titration for sample, B = ml titration for blank which may be positive or negative, and N = normality of $Na_2S_2O_3$.

b. Acetic acid, conc (glacial).

c. Potassium iodide crystals.

d. Standard sodium thiosulfate titrant, 0.025N: Prepare as directed in Residual Chlorine, Section 114A.2d preceding.

e. Starch indicator solution: Prepare as directed in Residual Chlorine, Section 114A.2e preceding.

f. Orthotolidine reagent: Prepare as

directed in Residual Chlorine, Section 114C. 3c.

g. Sodium arsenite solution: Prepare as directed in Residual Chlorine, Section 114D. 3b.

4. Procedure

a. Volume of sample: Measure at least 10 equal portions of the sample, preferably into brown glass-stoppered bottles or erlenmeyer flasks of ample capacity to permit mixing. If the object of the test is to determine chlorine demand, measure 200-ml portions; if it is to relate chlorine demand to bacterial removal, the effect on taste and odor, or the chemical constituents of the water, use portions of 500 ml or more. Properly sterilize all glassware for bacteriologic investigation.

b. Addition of chlorine water: Add an amount of chlorine to the first portion which leaves no chlorine residual at the end of the contact period, especially if low demands are being studied. Add increasing amounts of chlorine to the successive portions in the series. Increase the dosage between portions in increments of 0.1 mg/l for determining low demands, and up to 1.0 mg/l or more for higher demands. Mix while the chlorine solution is being added to the sample. Dose the portions of the sample according to a staggered schedule that will permit the determination of chlorine residuals at the predetermined contact time.

c. Contact time: The usual purpose of a chlorine demand test is to determine the amount of chlorine required to produce a specific free, combined or total available chlorine residual after a definite time interval which may vary from a few minutes to many hours. To this end, carry out the test over the desired contact period. If the objective of the test is to duplicate in the laboratory the temperature and the plant contact time, make several preliminary chlorine determinations during different reaction periods, such as 15, 30, and 60 min, in order to ascertain the chlorine consumption with respect to time —information which can be valuable in treatment plant control. Record the contact time. Protect the chlorinated samples from strong daylight throughout the test.

d. Examination of samples: At the end of the contact period, determine the free and the combined available residual chlorine by the OTA test—Section 114D—or other adequate test on a small aliquot from each portion. Plot the residual chlorine or the amount consumed versus the dosage to aid in studying the results. If necessary, remove samples for bacteriologic examination at desired intervals.

e. Taste and odor: Observe the taste and odor of the treated samples at ordinary temperatures with or without dechlorination. For odor observation at elevated temperatures, dechlorinate the samples before heating. Choose the dechlorinating agent with due regard to its effect on the odor in the water under examination. Generally, sodium sulfite is satisfactory if only a slight stoichiometric excess is used.

115 B. Field Method

1. General Discussion

The test below is designed for the measurement of chlorine demand in the plant or field when facilities or personnel are not adequate to employ the more exact method. Results obtained in this test are approximations only.

2. Apparatus

a. Chlorine comparator, color- and turbidity-compensating.

b. Medicine dropper, which will deliver 20 drops per milliliter. When measuring by drops, it is essential that the end of the dropper be well cleaned, so that water adheres all around the periphery, and that the dropper be held in a strictly vertical position, with the drops being formed slowly.

c. Ten 1-qt fruit jars or other suitable containers, marked at the 500-ml level.

d. Ten 2-oz bottles, marked at the 20-ml level.

e. Glass stirring rod.

f. Glass-stemmed thermometer.

3. Reagents

a. Standard chlorine solution: Dilute a 5% household bleaching solution 1 + 4. Standardize as directed in Method A, ¶ 3a, but taking 20 drops of the diluted hypochlorite solution as the sample to be titrated; use the same dropper that will be used in the procedure. For each drop:

$$\text{mg available Cl} = \frac{A \times N \times 35}{20}$$

where A = ml titration for sample, and N = normality of $Na_2S_2O_3$.

Adjust this solution to a strength of 10 mg/ml (0.5 mg chlorine per drop) so that 1 drop added to a 500-ml water sample will represent a dosage of 1 mg/l.

b. Orthotolidine reagent: Prepare as directed in Residual Chlorine, Section 114C. 3c.

c. Sodium arsenite solution: Prepare as directed in Residual Chlorine, Section 114D. 3b.

4. Procedure

a. Measurement of samples: Fill each jar or container to the 500-ml mark with the water under test. Record the temperature at which the samples are held.

b. Addition of chlorine: While stirring constantly, add 1 drop of chlorine solution to the water in the first fruit jar, 2 drops to that in the second jar, 3 drops to that in the third jar, etc.

c. Contact time: Follow directions given in Method A, ¶4c above.

d. Examination of samples: At the end of the contact period, remove a 20-ml portion from each sample, place it in a 2-oz bottle, and proceed with the OTA method as outlined in Residual Chlorine, Section 114D. 4a.

5. Calculation

$$\text{mg/l Cl demand} = \text{mg/l Cl added} - \text{mg/l residual Cl}$$

6. Interpretation of Results

This chlorine demand refers only to the particular dosage, contact time, and temperature used in this test. Plotting the residual chlorine or the amount consumed versus the chlorine added will aid in studying the results.

115 C. Bibliography

GRIFFIN, A. E. & N. S. CHAMBERLIN. 1941. Relation of ammonia-nitrogen to breakpoint chlorination. *AJPH* 31:803.

AMERICAN WATER WORKS ASSOCIATION. 1943. Committee report. Control of chlorination. *JAWWA* 35:1315.

PALIN, A. T. 1950. Chemical aspects of chlorination. *J. Inst. Water Eng.* 4:565.

TARAS, M. J. 1953. Effect of free residual chlorination on nitrogen compounds in water. *JAWWA* 45:47.

116 CHLORINE DIOXIDE

Because the physical and chemical properties of chlorine dioxide resemble those of chlorine in many respects, the entire write-up on Residual Chlorine (Section 114) should be read before a chlorine dioxide determination is attempted.

Chlorine dioxide is applied to water supplies for the purpose of combating tastes and odors due to phenolic-type wastes, Actinomycetes, and algae, as well as for the purpose of oxidizing soluble iron and manganese to a more easily removable form.

Chlorine dioxide is a deep yellow, volatile, and unpleasant-smelling gas which is produced at the site of application by reacting a solution of sodium chlorite with a strong chlorine solution. An excess of chlorine over the theoretical amount is needed so that the final mixture consists of chlorine and chlorine dioxide. When the source of chlorine is a hypochlorite compound, an acid must be added to insure the production of chlorine dioxide.

The reaction between sodium chlorite and chlorine is inhibited at pH values above 4 in dilute solutions. Therefore, chlorine dioxide solutions are prepared for laboratory studies by acidifying a sodium chlorite solution to a pH of 2.5. The evolved chlorine dioxide is scrubbed with sodium chlorite solution to remove free-chlorine impurity and is then passed into distilled water by means of a smooth current of air when a pure chlorine dioxide solution is desired.

1. Selection of Method

The iodometric method (*A*) is designed for standardizing the chlorine dioxide solutions which are needed for the preparation of temporary standards. Temporary standards are valuable for checking the permanent color standards, for the construction of photometric calibration curves required in the OTO method (*B*), and for securing evidence on the accuracy of the amperometric method (*C*). Method *A* cannot be used to check chlorine dioxide residuals after running a chlorine dioxide demand test because of the presence of the chlorite ion.

The orthotolidine-oxalic acid colorimetric method (*B*), generally abbreviated OTO, is a flash test which finds greatest application in the routine determination of chlorine dioxide both in the control laboratory and in the field. The method requires common reagents and the simplest of operations once the visual standards or the photometric calibration curve have been prepared. Reasonable accuracy can be expected when the proper precautions governing orthotolidine reactions are observed.

The amperometric method (*C*) is useful when a knowledge of the various chlorine fractions in a water sample is desired.

2. *Sampling and Storage*

Like residual chlorine, chlorine dioxide determinations should be performed promptly after the sample has been collected. Exposure of the sample to sunlight or strong artificial light, and agitation which excessively aerates the sample, should be avoided. Minimum chlorine dioxide losses will occur when the determination is immediately completed at the site of the sample collection.

116 A. Iodometric Method

1. General Discussion

a. Principle: A pure solution of chlorine dioxide is prepared by slowly adding dilute sulfuric acid to a sodium chlorite solution, removing any contaminants such as chlorine by means of a sodium chlorite scrubber, and passing the gas into distilled water by means of a steady stream of air.

Chlorine dioxide releases free iodine from a potassium iodide solution which has been acidified with acetic or sulfuric acid. The liberated iodine is titrated with a standard solution of sodium thiosulfate, using starch as the indicator.

b. Interference: Little interference is encountered when a pure solution of chlorine dioxide is determined by the iodometric method. However, temperature and strong light affect the stability of the solution. Chlorine dioxide losses can be minimized by storing the stock chlorine dioxide solution in a dark refrigerator and by preparing and titrating the dilute chlorine dioxide solutions for standardization purposes at the lowest practicable temperature and in subdued light.

c. Minimum detectable concentration: One drop (0.05 ml) of 0.01*N* sodium thiosulfate is equivalent to 20 μg/l chlorine dioxide (or 40 μg/l in terms of available chlorine) when a 500-ml sample is titrated.

2. Reagents

All the reagents listed for the determination of residual chlorine in Section 114A.2a-g are required. Also needed are the following:

a. Stock chlorine dioxide solution: Prepare a gas generating and absorbing system similar to the one illustrated in Figure 15. Connect aspirator

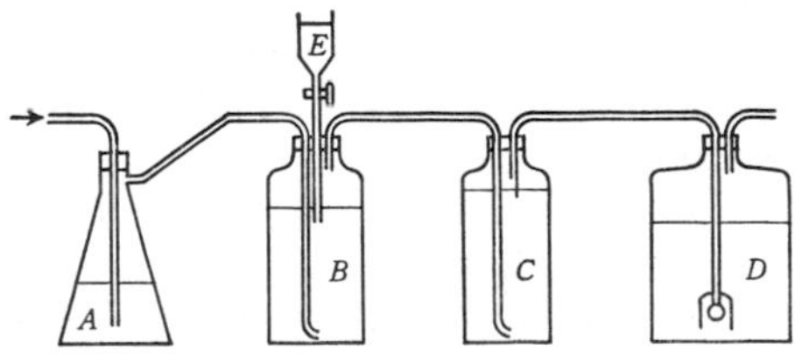

Figure 15. Chlorine dioxide generation and absorption system.

flask A of 500-ml capacity by means of rubber tubing to a source of compressed air. Allow the air to bubble through a layer of 300 ml of distilled water in flask A and then pass over and down through a glass tube to within 5 mm of the bottom of the 1-liter gas generating bottle B. Conduct the evolved gas via glass tubing through a scrubber bottle C containing saturated sodium chlorite solution or a tower packed with flaked sodium chlorite, and finally via glass tubing into a 2-liter pyrex collecting bottle D, where the gas is absorbed in 1,500 ml of distilled water. Provide an air outlet tube on bottle D for escape of the moving air. Select for a gas-generating bottle one which is constructed of strong pyrex glass and has a mouth wide enough to permit the insertion of three separate glass tubes: the first leading almost to the bottom for admission of the air, the second reaching below the liquid surface for the gradual introduction of the sulfuric acid, and the third near the top for exit of the evolved gas and air. Fit to the second tube a graduated cylinder E for containment of the sulfuric acid. If available, locate this entire system in a good fuming hood equipped with an adequate shield.

Dissolve 10 g sodium chlorite ($NaClO_2$), analytical reagent grade, in 750 ml distilled water and place in bottle B.

Carefully add 2 ml conc sulfuric acid to 18 ml distilled water and mix. Transfer to cylinder E.

Connect flask A to bottle B and the latter to bottles C and D. Pass a smooth current of air through the system, as evidenced by the bubbling rate in all bottles.

Introduce 5-ml increments of sulfuric acid from cylinder E into bottle B at 5-min intervals.

Continue the airflow for 30 min after the last portion of acid has been added.

Store the yellow-colored stock solution in a dark refrigerator to minimize loss in strength. The concentration of the chlorine dioxide thus prepared may vary between 250 and 600 mg/l, which corresponds to approximately 600 to 1,600 mg/l when expressed as available chlorine.

b. Standard chlorine dioxide solution: Use this solution for preparing the desired temporary chlorine dioxide standards. Dilute the required volume of stock chlorine dioxide solution to the desired strength with chlorine-demand-free water which has been prepared as described in Residual Chlorine (Section 114), Method C, ¶ 3a(1). Standardize the solution by titrating with standard 0.01*N* or 0.025*N* sodium thiosulfate titrant in the presence of potassium iodide, acid, and starch indicator by following the procedure given in ¶ 3 below. A full or nearly full bottle of chlorine or chlorine dioxide solution retains its titer longer than a bottle which is half full. If repeated withdrawals reduce the volume to a critical level, standardize the solution at the beginning, midway in the series of withdrawals, and at the end of the series. Shake the contents thoroughly before drawing off the needed solution from the middle of the glass-stoppered dark-colored bottle. Prepare this solution frequently.

3. Procedure

Select the volume of sample, prepare the sample for titration, titrate the sample, and conduct the blank titration as described in Residual Chlorine (Section 114), Method A, ¶ 3 et seq. The only exception is the following: *Allow the chlorine dioxide to react in the dark with the acid and the potassium iodide for 5 min before starting the titration.*

4. Calculations

Chlorine dioxide concentrations may be expressed in terms of chlorine dioxide alone or in terms of available chlorine content. The available chlorine is defined as the total oxidizing power of the chlorine dioxide measured by titrating the iodine released by the chlorine dioxide from an acidic solution of potassium iodide and then calculating the result in terms of chlorine itself.

For standardizing chlorine dioxide solution:

$$\text{mg/ml } ClO_2 = \frac{(A \pm B) \times N \times 13.49}{\text{ml sample titrated}}$$

$$\text{mg/ml Cl} = \frac{(A \pm B) \times N \times 35.45}{\text{ml sample titrated}}$$

For determination of chlorine dioxide in temporary standards:

$$\text{mg/l } ClO_2 = \frac{(A \pm B) \times N \times 13{,}490}{\text{ml sample}}$$

$$\text{mg/l Cl} = \frac{(A \pm B) \times N \times 35{,}450}{\text{ml sample}}$$

where A = ml titration for sample, B = ml titration for blank which may be positive or negative, and N = normality of $Na_2S_2O_3$.

116 B. Orthotolidine-Oxalic Acid (OTO) Method

1. General Discussion

a. Principle: After the sample has been treated with oxalic acid to eliminate the residual chlorine, acidic orthotolidine reagent is added for the purpose of producing a yellow color. Sodium arsenite serves to minimize interference and arrest color development. Chlorine dioxide produces less yellow color than residual chlorine, the intensity corresponding to approximately one-half that of a similar concentration of residual chlorine when the result is reported in terms of chlorine dioxide itself. However, the color developed by chlorine dioxide is one-fifth that of the available chlorine content.

The yellow orthotolidine color can be measured by visual or photometric methods. Best results are obtained with photometric instruments which have been carefully calibrated with known chlorine dioxide solutions. Visual comparison is satisfactory for routine determinations in the control laboratory.

b. Precautions: The same attention should be paid to details as in the residual chlorine determinations. Because the amounts of chlorine dioxide normally applied to water supplies are quite small, the following considerations assume conspicuous importance: All glassware used in the determinations should be kept scrupulously clean. An average of two or three determinations may have to be performed on a sample to avoid questionable values. The fact that the readings must be multiplied by 2 or 5 to obtain the final result makes such practices both desirable and prudent.

c. Interferences: The same interferences apply in the case of chlorine dioxide as those described in Chlorine (Residual), Section 114D.1. In addition, the calcium content of hard waters may precipitate following introduction of the saturated oxalic acid solution. Although chlorite ion reacts slowly with orthotolidine, the chlorite ion may react with the oxalic acid solution during the standing period and subsequently with the hydrochloric acid of the orthotolidine reagent to form chlorous acid, which in turn can disproportionate to chlorine dioxide.

d. Minimum detectable concentration: The minimum detectable concentration depends on the terms in which the chlorine dioxide result is reported. If the result is reported as chlorine dioxide, a minimum of 20 μg/l can be detected. When the result is reported in terms of available chlorine content, the minimum becomes 50 μg/l.

2. Apparatus

The same apparatus is required as in Residual Chlorine, Section 114D.2.

3. Reagents

All reagents listed for the determination of residual chlorine by Method D, ¶ 3, are required. Also needed is the following:

a. Oxalic acid saturated solution: Dissolve 110 g $H_2C_2O_4$ in 1 liter distilled water by heating the solution. When the solution has cooled to room temperature, decant the supernatant liquid into the storage bottle. Use only the clear liquid in the test procedure. Dispense with an automatic or safety pipet. (CAUTION: *Toxic—take care to avoid ingestion.*)

4. Procedure

a. VISUAL COMPARISON:

1) Label two comparator cells or French square bottles "D" and "E." Use 0.5 ml orthotolidine reagent in 10-ml cells, 0.75 ml in 15-ml cells, and the same ratio for other volumes of sample. Use the same volume of sodium arsenite solution as orthotolidine reagent.

2) To Cell D, containing a measured volume of water sample, add 1 ml oxalic acid saturated solution. Mix well and allow to stand 10 min in the dark. Depending on the volume of sample used, next add the proper volume of orthotolidine reagent. Mix quickly, and immediately (within 5 sec) add sodium arsenite solution. Mix quickly again and compare with color standards as rapidly as possible. Record the result, *D*, which represents approximately one-half the chlorine dioxide and all of the interfering colors. (If it is desired to report the results in terms of available chlorine, the value *D* represents one-fifth the available chlorine and all of the interfering colors.)

3) To Cell E, containing sodium arsenite solution and 1 ml oxalic acid saturated solution, add a measured volume of water sample. Mix quickly, and immediately add orthotolidine reagent. Mix quickly again and compare with color standards as rapidly as possible. Record the result, B_3, which represents the interfering colors present in the sample.

b. PHOTOMETRIC MEASUREMENT: Measure photometrically the colors developed by following the directions in the preceding paragraphs. Convert the absorbance readings to the proper chlorine dioxide readings by referring to a calibration curve prepared by treating known chlorine dioxide concentrations in the same manner as the unknown samples.

5. Calculations

$$\text{mg/l } ClO_2 \text{ as } ClO_2 = (D - B_3) \times 1.9$$

$$\text{mg/l } ClO_2 \text{ as available chlorine} = (D - B_3) \times 5$$

Inasmuch as chlorine dioxide and residual chlorine coexist in many samples, the residual chlorine determinations can be performed as described in Section 114D.4 and the following calculations then made in terms of available chlorine:

$$\text{Free available residual chlorine} = (A - B_1) - (D - B_3)$$

$$\text{Combined available residual chlorine} = (C - B_2) - (A - B_1)$$

116 C. Amperometric Method

1. General Discussion

a. Principle: The amperometric titration of chlorine dioxide is an extension of the amperometric method for residual chlorine. By performing four titrations with phenylarsine oxide, free chlorine (including hypochlorite and hypochlorous acid), chloramines, chlorite, and chlorine dioxide may be separately determined. In stage one the chlorine dioxide is converted to chlorite and chlorate through the addition of sufficient sodium hydroxide to produce a pH of 12, followed by neutralization to a pH of 7, and the titration of the free chlorine. When potassium iodide is added to a sample which has been similarly treated with alkali and the pH readjusted to 7, the titration yields free chlorine and monochloramine. The third stage involves the addition of potassium iodide and pH adjustment to 7, followed by titration of the free chlorine, monochloramine, and one-fifth of the available chlorine dioxide. The addition of sufficient sulfuric acid to lower the pH to 2 enables all of the available chlorine dioxide and chlorite, as well as the total available chlorine, to liberate an equivalent amount of iodine from the added potassium iodide, and thus be titrated.

b. Precautions: In order to minimize the effects of pH and the time and temperature of reaction, all conditions should be standardized as much as practicable. All samples should be titrated at pH 7. A reaction period of 10 min or longer should be used on the samples which are treated with sodium hydroxide at a pH of 12, as well as those that are treated with sulfuric acid at a pH of 2. A 10-min reaction period is suggested even though the reaction rate is faster in warm samples.

c. Interference: The same interferences apply in the case of chlorine dioxide as those described in Section 114B.1b.

2. Apparatus

The same apparatus is required as in Section 114B.2a through d.

3. Reagents

All reagents listed for the determination of residual chlorine in Section 114B.3 are required. Also needed are the following:

a. Sodium hydroxide, 6*N.*

b. Sulfuric acid, 6*N,* 1 + 5.

4. Procedure

a. Titration of free available chlorine (hypochlorite and hypochlorous acid): Add sufficient 6*N* sodium hydroxide solution to raise the sample pH to 12. After 10 min, add sufficient 6*N* sulfuric acid solution to lower the pH to 7. Titrate with standard phenylarsine oxide titrant to the amperometric end point as given in Section 114B.4. Record the result as *A*.

b. Titration of free available chlorine and chloramine: Add sufficient 6*N* sodium hydroxide solution to raise the sample pH to 12. After 10 min, add sufficient 6*N* sulfuric acid solution to reduce the pH to 7. Add 1 ml potassium iodide solution. Titrate with standard phenylarsine oxide titrant to the amperometric end point. Record the result as *B*.

c. Titration of free available chlorine, chloramine, and one-fifth of the available chlorine dioxide: Add sufficient pH 7 phosphate buffer solution to adjust the sample pH to 7. Add 1 ml potassium iodide solution. Titrate with standard phenylarsine oxide titrant to the amperometric end point. Record the result as *C*.

d. Titration of free available chlorine, chloramines, chlorine dioxide, and chlorite: Add 1 ml potassium iodide solution to the sample. Add sufficient 6*N* sulfuric acid solution to lower the sample pH to 2. After 10 min, add sufficient 6*N* sodium hydroxide solution to raise the pH to 7. Titrate with standard phenylarsine oxide titrant to the amperometric end point. Record the result as *D*.

5. Calculation

Convert the individual titrations (*A*, *B*, *C*, and *D*) into mg/l Cl by the following equation:

$$\text{mg/l chlorine} = \frac{E \times 200}{\text{ml sample}}$$

where E = ml phenylarsine oxide titration for each individual sample *A*, *B*, *C*, or *D*.

Calculate the chlorine dioxide and the individual chlorine fractions as follows:

mg/l ClO_2 as chlorine dioxide $= 1.9\ (C - B)$

mg/l ClO_2 as chlorine $= 5\ (C - B)$

mg/l free available residual chlorine $= A$

mg/l chloramine as chlorine $= B - A$

mg/l chlorite as chlorine $= 4B - 5C + D$

116 D. Bibliography

General

INGOLS, R. S. & G. M. RIDENOUR. 1948. Chemical properties of chlorine dioxide in water treatment. *JAWWA* 40:1207.

HODGDEN, H. W. & R. S. INGOLS. 1954. Direct colorimetric method for determination of chlorine dioxide in water. *Anal. Chem.* 26:1224.

PALIN, A. T. 1960. Colorimetric determination of chlorine dioxide in water. *Water & Sewage Works* 107:457.

FEUSS, J. V. 1964. Problems in determination of chlorine dioxide residuals. *JAWWA* 56:607.

MASSCHELEIN, W. 1966. Spectrophotometric determination of chlorine dioxide with

acid chrome violet K. *Anal. Chem.* 38: 1839.
———. 1969. *Les Oxydes de Chlore et le Chlorite de Sodium.* Dunod, Paris, Chapter XI.

Iodometric Method

POST, M. A. & W. A. MOORE. 1959. Determination of chlorine dioxide in treated surface waters. *Anal. Chem.* 31:1872.

Orthotolidine-Oxalic Acid (OTO) Method

ASTON, R. N. 1950. Developments in the chlorine dioxide process. *JAWWA* 42: 151.

Amperometric Method

HALLER, J. F. & S. S. LISTEK. 1948. Determination of chlorine dioxide and other active chlorine compounds in water. *Anal. Chem.* 20:639.

117 CHROMIUM

The carcinogenic potential of hexavalent chromium is a good reason to protect a potable water supply against its intrusion. The hexavalent chromium concentration of U.S. drinking waters has been reported to vary between 3 and 40 μg/l with a mean of 3.2 μg/l. Chromium salts are used extensively in industrial processes and may enter a water supply through the discharge of wastes. Chromate compounds are frequently added to cooling water for corrosion control. Chromium may exist in water supplies in both the hexavalent and the trivalent state, although the trivalent form rarely occurs in potable water supplies.

1. SELECTION OF METHOD: Method A is applicable for the determination of hexavalent chromium present in a natural or treated water intended for potable uses. The atomic absorption spectrophotometric and permanganate-azide methods are recommended for the determination of total chromium in samples containing organic material. They are the methods of choice for the determination of total chromium in unknown samples. The alkaline hypobromite method is useful as a control method for total chromium in treated waters. It is not designed for samples containing an appreciable amount of organic matter.

2. SAMPLING AND STORAGE: Because chromate ions have a tendency to be adsorbed on the surface of the container, and also may be reduced by various agents, precautions should be observed in sample collection and storage. New bottles rather than old etched containers should be used for sample collection. The sample should be tested during the day of collection if hexavalent chromium is to be determined. Storage for more than 2 or 3 days is not recommended.

117 A. Hexavalent Chromium

1. General Discussion

a. Principle: Hexavalent chromium reacts with diphenylcarbazide to produce a reddish purple color in slightly acid solutions.

b. Interference: In the color development step the following substances may cause interference. Mercury, both mercurous and mercuric, gives a blue or blue-purple color, but the reaction is not very sensitive at the acidity employed. Iron in concentrations greater than 1 mg/l interferes by producing a yellow color with the reagent. Vanadium interferes in the same manner but more strongly. The color produced with vanadium fades fairly rapidly and is negligible 10 min after the addition of the diphenylcarbazide.

c. Minimum detectable concentration: A chromium concentration of 3 μg/l can be detected by visual comparison in 50-ml nessler tubes. The limit is 5 μg/l when a 5-cm light path is used for photometric measurement.

2. Apparatus

COLORIMETRIC EQUIPMENT—One of the following is required:

a. Spectrophotometer, for use at 540 mμ, providing a light path of 1 cm or longer.

b. Filter photometer, providing a light path of 1 cm or longer and equipped with a green filter having maximum transmittance near 540 mμ.

c. Nessler tubes, 50-ml, matched, tall form.

3. Reagents

a. Chromium-free water: Use redistilled or deionized distilled water.

b. s-Diphenylcarbazide reagent: Dissolve 200 mg s-diphenylcarbazide (also called 1,5-diphenylcarbohydrazide) in 100 ml 95% ethyl alcohol or isopropyl alcohol; add, with mixing, an acid solution prepared from 40 ml conc H_2SO_4 and 360 ml distilled water. Refrigerate to maintain stability for about a month. A color change from colorless to tan does not affect the reagent's usefulness.

c. Stock chromium solution: Dissolve 141.4 mg anhydrous potassium dichromate, $K_2Cr_2O_7$, in distilled water and dilute to 1,000 ml; 1.00 ml = 50.0 μg Cr.

d. Standard chromium solution: Dilute 20.00 ml stock chromium solution to 1,000 ml; 1.00 ml = 1.00 μg hexavalent Cr. Prepare daily.

4. Procedure

Use a 50.0-ml sample or an aliquot diluted to 50 ml with chromium-free distilled water. If necessary, clarify by centrifuging. Add 2.5 ml diphenylcarbazide reagent and mix well. Compare visually against standards containing 3 to 200 μg/l Cr. Prepare a calibration curve in the chromium range of 5 to 400 μg/l if photometric measurements are made at 540 mμ with a 5-cm light path. Make comparisons or readings at least 5 min, but not later than 15 min, after the reagent is added.

5. Calculation

$$\text{mg/l hexavalent Cr} = \frac{\mu\text{g hexavalent Cr}}{\text{ml sample}}$$

6. Precision and Accuracy

Photometric measurements in the range below 400 μg/l can be made with a precision of 10 μg/l Cr. Accuracy depends on the promptness with which the determination for hexavalent chromium is undertaken. Storage in glass or polyethylene containers may result in low chromate values.

117 B. Atomic Absorption Spectrophotometric Method for Total Chromium

See Metals, Section 129 A.

117 C. Permanganate-Azide Method for Total Chromium

1. General Discussion

a. Principle: The original hexavalent chromium in the sample is first reduced with sodium sulfite to the trivalent form. The sample is evaporated and fumed with sulfuric acid to destroy the organic matter. The trivalent chromium is oxidized to the hexavalent condition by a slight excess of potassium permanganate. The chromium is reacted with diphenylcarbazide after the excess permanganate has been removed by means of sodium azide.

b. Interference: Same as Method A, ¶ 1b above.

2. Apparatus

a. Colorimetric equipment: Same as Method A, ¶ 2 et seq.

b. Acid-washed glassware: New and unscratched glassware will minimize chromium adsorption on the glass surface during the oxidation procedure. Glassware previously treated with chromic acid, as well as new glassware, should be thoroughly cleaned with hydrochloric or nitric acid for removal of chromium traces.

3. Reagents

All of the reagents listed in Method A, ¶s 3a through d, are required, plus the following:

a. Sulfuric acid, 1 + 1.

b. Sodium sulfite solution: Dissolve 1.26 g Na_2SO_3 in distilled water and dilute to 100 ml. Prepare daily. One milliliter of this solution will reduce approximately 3.4 mg of hexavalent to trivalent chromium.

c. Potassium permanganate, 0.1*N:* Dissolve 3.16 g $KMnO_4$ in distilled water and dilute to 1,000 ml.

d. Sodium azide solution: Dissolve 500 mg NaN_3 in distilled water and dilute to 100 ml.

4. Procedure

a. Preliminary sample treatment: Pipet a sample volume containing 0.3–10 μg Cr into an erlenmeyer flask, and add 5 ml H_2SO_4 and 1 ml Na_2SO_3 solution. Allow to stand 10 min for complete reduction of hexavalent chromium. Add three glass beads or Berl saddles to control bumping. Evaporate to fumes and fume for 15 min or until clear. Cool and carefully dilute to about 50–80 ml. Bring to a boil and add sufficient $KMnO_4$ dropwise, so that a faint pink color persists as the solution continues to boil for 10 min. Then add the NaN_3 solution dropwise and continue boiling until the solution becomes colorless. Boil for about 2 min between azide additions to guard against the use of excess azide. Cool the sample.

If suspended matter and color are absent, transfer to a 50-ml nessler tube or volumetric flask. Remove any suspended matter by filtration through a sintered-glass filter of coarse or medium porosity. Use a filter of coarse porosity for colorless samples. If manganese dioxide precipitate is present, pass the sample through a filter of medium porosity under suction. Wash the filter well. Collect the filtrate in a 100-ml nessler tube or volumetric flask to permit sufficient washing.

b. Color development and measurement: Proceed as in Method A, ¶ 4, for hexavalent chromium and make the reading at least 5 min, but no later than 15 min, after the reagent is added. Prepare the photometric curve from known amounts of chromium handled in the same manner as the unknown sample. Correct the results with a blank carried through all the steps of the procedure.

5. Calculation

$$\text{mg/l total Cr} = \frac{\mu\text{g total Cr}}{\text{ml sample}}$$

6. Precision and Accuracy

A synthetic unknown sample containing 110 μg/l Cr, 500 μg/l Al, 50 μg/l Cd, 470 μg/l Cu, 300 μg/l Fe, 70 μg/l Pb, 120 μg/l Mn, 150 μg/l Ag and 650 μg/l Zn in distilled water was determined by the permanganate-azide method, with a relative standard deviation of 47.8% and a relative error of 27.2% in 31 laboratories.

117 D. Alkaline Hypobromite Method for Total Chromium

1. General Discussion

a. Principle: Total chromium is determined by oxidizing the trivalent form to the hexavalent state with an alkaline hypobromite solution. After removal of the excess bromine with phenol, the color is developed in the normal manner with diphenylcarbazide.

b. Interference: Significant amounts of organic matter or other reducing substances may prevent the complete oxidation of chromic ion, thereby resulting in low chromium values. Other interferences are described in Method A, ¶ 1b above.

2. Apparatus

a. Colorimetric equipment: Same as Method A, ¶ 2 et seq.

b. Acid-washed glassware: Same as Method C, ¶ 2 et seq.

3. Reagents

All of the reagents listed in Method A, ¶ 3 et seq, are required, plus the following:

a. Oxidizing reagent: Add 50 ml 1*N* NaOH to 3 ml saturated bromine water.

b. Sulfuric acid, 6*N*.

c. Phenol solution: Dissolve 1.2 g redistilled phenol in distilled water and dilute to 100 ml. Store in a brown bottle.

d. Sodium hydroxide, 1*N*.

4. Procedure

Determine the sample size by a rough preliminary analysis. To 25.0 ml sample, or an aliquot diluted to 25 ml, in a 125-ml erlenmeyer flask, add 2 ml oxidizing reagent and place the flask on a steam bath for 45 min. Remove any precipitate at this point by filtration through a sintered-glass filter of coarse or medium porosity. Cool the sample, add 0.4 ml 6*N* H_2SO_4, and mix. Add 0.5 ml phenol solution and 2.5 ml 1*N* NaOH, mixing after each addition. Dilute to 50 ml in a nessler tube or volumetric flask and complete the color development and measurement as described in Method A, ¶ 4, for hexavalent chromium. Correct the results with a blank carried through all the steps of the procedure.

5. Calculation

$$\text{mg/l total Cr} = \frac{\mu\text{g total Cr}}{\text{ml sample}}$$

6. Precision and Accuracy

A synthetic unknown sample containing 110 μg/l Cr, 500 μg/l Al, 50 μg/l Cd, 470 μg/l Cu, 300 μg/l Fe, 70 μg/l Pb, 120 μg/l Mn, 150 μg/l Ag and 650 μg/l Zn in distilled water was determined by the alkaline hypobromite method, with a relative standard deviation of 25.9% and a relative error of 27.2% in seven laboratories.

117 E. Bibliography

General

GRAHAM, D. W. 1943. Chromium, a water and sewage problem. *JAWWA* 35:159.

EGE, J. F. JR. & L. SILVERMAN. 1947. Stable colorimetric reagent for chromium. *Anal. Chem.* 19:693.

RUCHHOFT, C. C. et al. 1949. *Tentative Analytical Methods for Cadmium, Chromium, and Cyanide in Water.* U. S. Public Health Service Environmental Health Center, Cincinnati, Ohio.

URONE, P. F. 1955. Stability of colorimetric reagent for chromium, *s*-diphenylcarbazide, in various solvents. *Anal. Chem.* 27:1354.

Permanganate-Azide Method

SALTZMAN, B. E. 1952. Microdetermination of chromium with diphenylcarbazide by permanganate oxidation. *Anal. Chem.* 24:1016.

LIEBER, M. 1956. Permanganate-azide test for total chromium in water. *JAWWA* 48:295.

Alkaline Hypobromite Method

URONE, P. F. & H. K. ANDERS. 1950. Microdetermination of small amounts of chromium in human bloods, tissues, and urine. *Anal. Chem.* 22:1317.

118 COLOR

Color in water may result from the presence of natural metallic ions (iron and manganese), humus and peat materials, plankton, weeds and industrial wastes. Color removal is practiced in order to make a water suitable for general and industrial applications.

The term "color" is used herein to mean true color—that is, the color of the water from which the turbidity has been removed. The term "apparent color" includes not only the color due to substances in solution, but also that due to suspended matter. Apparent color is determined on the original sample without filtration or centrifugation.

The following method for the determination of color is applicable to nearly all samples of potable water. Pollution by certain industrial wastes may produce unusual colors which cannot be matched; such samples may be examined by the procedures for color given in Section 206.

1. General Discussion

a. Principle: Color is determined by visual comparison of the sample with known concentrations of colored solutions. Comparison may also be made with special glass color disks if they have been properly calibrated. The platinum-cobalt method of measuring color is given as the standard method, the unit of color being that produced by 1 mg/l platinum in the form of the chloroplatinate ion. The ratio of cobalt to platinum may be varied to match the hue in special cases; the proportion given below is usually satisfactory to match the color of natural waters.

b. Interference: Even a slight turbidity causes the apparent color to be noticeably higher than the true color; it is therefore necessary to remove turbidity before true color can be approximated by differential reading with different color filters [1] or by differential scattering measurements.[2] Neither of these technics, however, has reached the status of a standard method. The recommended method for the removal of turbidity is centrifugation. Filtration cannot be used because it may remove some of the true color as well as turbidity. If centrifuging will not suffice to remove all of the turbidity, the analyst is referred to the method described by Lamar.[3]

The color value of a water is extremely pH dependent, and invariably increases as the pH of the water is raised. For this reason it is necessary, when reporting a color value, to specify the pH at which the color is determined. For research purposes or when color values are to be compared between laboratories, it is advisable to determine the color response of a given water over a wide range of pH values. This procedure has been described by Black and Christman.[4]

c. Field method: Since the platinum-cobalt standard method is not convenient for field use, the color of water may be compared with that of glass disks held at the end of metallic tubes which contain glass comparator tubes of the sample and colorless distilled water. The color of the sample is matched with the color of the tube of clear water plus the calibrated colored glass when viewed by looking toward a white surface. Every individual disk must be calibrated to correspond with the colors on the platinum-cobalt scale. Experience has shown that the glass disks give results in substantial agreement with those obtained by the platinum-cobalt method, and their use is recognized as a standard field procedure.

d. Nonstandard laboratory methods: The use of glass disks or of liquids other than water as standards for laboratory work is permissible only if these have been individually calibrated against platinum-cobalt standards. Waters of highly unusual color, such as may occur by mixture with certain industrial wastes, may have hues so far removed from those of the platinum-cobalt standards that comparison by the standard method is difficult or impossible. For such waters, the color methods in Section 206 may be employed. The results so obtained are not, however, directly comparable to those obtained with platinum-cobalt standards.

e. Sampling: Samples for the color determination should be representative and must be taken in clean glassware. The color determination should be made within a reasonable period, as biologic or physical changes occurring in storage may affect the color. With naturally colored waters these changes invariably lead to poor results.

2. Apparatus

a. Nessler tubes, matched, 50-ml, tall form.

b. pH meter, for determining the sample pH as described in pH Value (Section 144). The pH may also be determined colorimetrically.

3. Preparation of Standards

a. If a reliable supply of potassium chloroplatinate cannot be purchased, it may be replaced by chloroplatinic acid, which the analyst can prepare from metallic platinum. Commercial chloroplatinic acid should not be used because it is very hygroscopic and therefore may vary in platinum content. Potassium chloroplatinate is not hygroscopic.

b. Dissolve 1.246 g potassium chloroplatinate, K_2PtCl_6 (equivalent to 500 mg metallic platinum) and 1.00 g crystallized cobaltous chloride, $CoCl_2 \cdot 6H_2O$ (equivalent to about 250 mg metallic cobalt) in distilled water with 100 ml conc HCl and dilute to 1,000 ml with distilled water. This stock standard has a color of 500 units.

c. If potassium chloroplatinate is not available, dissolve 500 mg pure metallic platinum in aqua regia with the aid of heat; remove nitric acid by repeated evaporation with fresh portions of conc HCl. Dissolve this product, together with 1.00 g crystallized cobaltous chloride, as directed above.

d. Prepare standards having colors of 5, 10, 15, 20, 25, 30, 35, 40, 45, 50, 60 and 70 by diluting 0.5, 1.0, 1.5, 2.0, 2.5, 3.0, 3.5, 4.0, 4.5, 5.0, 6.0 and 7.0 ml stock color standard with distilled water to 50 ml in nessler tubes. Protect these standards against evaporation and contamination when not in use.

4. Procedure

a. Estimation of intact sample: Observe the color of a sample by filling a matched nessler tube to the 50-ml mark with the water to be examined and comparing it with the standards. Look vertically downward through the tubes toward a white or specular surface placed at such an angle that light is reflected upward through the columns of liquid. If turbidity is present and has not been removed by the procedure given below, report the color as "apparent color." If the color exceeds 70 units, dilute the sample with distilled water in known proportions until the color is within the range of the standards.

b. Estimation of centrifuged sample: To determine true color when turbidity is present, first place the sample in a suitable centrifuge tube or tubes, and centrifuge until the supernate is clear. The time required will depend upon the nature of the sample, the speed of the motor, and the radius of the centrifuge, but rarely will more than 1 hr be necessary. Compare the centrifuged sample in a nessler tube with distilled water to insure that all turbidity has been eliminated. If clear, compare the sample with the standards.

c. Since the color is related to pH, measure the pH of each sample.

5. Calculation

a. Calculate the color units by means of the following equation:

$$\text{Color units} = \frac{A \times 50}{B}$$

where A = estimated color of a diluted sample and B = ml sample taken for dilution.

b. Report the color results in whole numbers and record as follows:

Color Units	Record to Nearest
1–50	1
51–100	5
101–250	10
251–500	20

c. Report the pH of the water sample whose color was determined.

6. References

1. A. G. KNIGHT. 1951. The photometric estimation of color in turbid waters. *J. Inst. Water Eng.* 5:623.
2. I. JULLANDER & K. BRUNE. 1950. Light absorption measurements on turbid solutions. *Acta Chem. Scandinav.* 4:870.
3. W. L. LAMAR. 1949. Determination of color of turbid waters. *Anal. Chem.* 21:726.
4. A. P. BLACK & R. F. CHRISTMAN. 1963. Characteristics of colored surface waters. *JAWWA* 55:753.

7. Bibliography

HAZEN, A. 1892. A new color standard for natural waters. *Amer. Chem. J.* 14:300.

——— 1896. The measurement of the colors of natural waters. *J. Amer. Chem. Soc.* 18:264.

Measurement of Color and Turbidity in Water. 1902. U. S. Geological Survey, Division of Hydrography Circular 8, Washington, D. C.

RUDOLFS, W. & W. D. HANLON. 1951. Color in industrial wastes. *Sewage & Ind. Wastes* 23:1125.

PALIN, A. T. 1955. Photometric determination of the colour and turbidity of water. *Water & Water Eng.* 59:341.

CHRISTMAN, R. F. & M. GHASSEMI. 1966. Chemical nature of organic color in water. *JAWWA* 58:723.

GHASSEMI, M. & R. F. CHRISTMAN. 1968. Properties of the yellow organic acids of natural waters. *Limnol. & Oceanog.* 13:583.

119 COPPER

Copper is an element essential to the human body and the adult daily requirement has been estimated at 2.0 mg. Large oral doses may, however, produce emesis which, if prolonged, may result in liver damage. In amounts above 1.0 mg/l copper can impart a bitter taste to the water. The copper content of drinking waters seldom exceeds 600 μg/l but generally falls below 30μg/l. Copper salts are used in controlling growths in reservoirs, for catalyzing the oxidation of manganese, and for controlling slime in the distribution system. The corrosion of copper, brass and bronze pipe and fittings may result in the introduction of measurable concentrations of copper into a water, as evidenced by blue-green stains on plumbing fixtures.

1. Selection of Method

The cuprethol method is intended for the determination of traces of copper in relatively unpolluted water. It is also intended for those who prefer a nonextraction method. If iron is present in concentrations lower than 0.3 mg/l, the modification suggested in Section 119B.4d offers a simple and highly sensitive procedure ideally adapted to field work. The atomic absorption spectrophotometric and bathocuproine methods are recommended for unknown and polluted waters because of their high degree of freedom from interferences. The neocuproine extraction method for the determination of copper in industrial wastes can also be applied to many water samples; see Heavy Metals, Method for Copper [Section 211 (II) E].

2. Sampling and Storage

Copper ion has a tendency to be adsorbed on the surface of the sample container. Samples should therefore be analyzed as soon as possible after collection. If storage is necessary, 0.5 ml 1 + 1 HCl per 100 ml of sample will prevent "plating out." When such acidified samples are analyzed, a volume correction must be made for the added acid, and the addition of acid called for in the procedure below is not made.

119 A. Atomic Absorption Spectrophotometric Method

See Metals, Section 129A.

119 B. Cuprethol Method

1. General Discussion

a. Principle: Cupric ions form a yellow-colored chelate with the reagent bis(2-hydroxyethyl)dithiocarbamate, whose popular name is cuprethol. The colored compound is soluble and is formed quantitatively. Hydrochloric acid and sodium acetate buffer the solution at a favorable pH, between 5 and 6. Pyrophosphate overcomes the interference of iron up to 20 mg/l as ferric ion and up to 50 mg/l as ferrous ion.

b. Interference: Bismuth, cobalt, mercurous, nickel, and silver ions interfere seriously and must be absent. Other ions which interfere must be limited to the concentration shown in the following tabulation:

Ion	Upper Limit *mg/l*
Aluminum	20
Cadmium	20
Calcium	400
Chromate	2
Chromic	5
Cyanide	20
Dichromate	2
Ferric	20
Ferrous	50
Lead	10
Manganous	10
Mercuric	20
Nitrite	20
Stannic	10
Stannous	20
Sulfite	100
Uranyl	10
Zinc	20

No interference is caused by as much as 1,000 mg/l of ammonium, magnesium, potassium, sodium, borate, carbonate, chloride, fluoride, iodide, nitrate, phosphate or silicate. It is believed that excessive concentrations of interfering ions will seldom be encountered in unpolluted waters; however, certain sewage, industrial and boiler waters may require Methods A and C. Turbidity or color may be corrected by the usual photometric compensation technics or by extraction of the copper chelate with isoamyl alcohol.

c. Minimum detectable concentration: A copper concentration of 20 μg/l can be detected by visual comparison in 100-ml nessler tubes.

2. Apparatus

a. COLORIMETRIC EQUIPMENT: One of the following is required—

1) Spectrophotometer, for use at 435 mμ, providing a light path of 1 cm or longer.

2) Filter photometer, providing a light path of 1 cm or longer and equipped with a violet filter having maximum transmittance near 435 to 440 mμ.

3) Nessler tubes, matched, 100-ml, tall form.

b. ACID-WASHED GLASSWARE: All glassware must be rinsed with conc HCl and then with copper-free water (¶ 3a below).

3. Reagents

a. Copper-free water: Use redistilled or deionized distilled water.

b. Stock copper solution: Weigh 100.0 mg copper metal foil; place it in a 250-ml beaker under a hood; add 3 ml copper-free water and 3 ml conc HNO_3 and cover the beaker with a watch glass. After the metal has all dissolved, add 1 ml conc H_2SO_4 and heat on a hot plate to volatilize the acids. Stop heating just short of complete dryness. Do not bake the residue. Cool and dissolve in copper-free water, washing down the sides of the beaker and the bottom of the watch glass. Transfer quantitatively to a 1-liter volumetric flask and make up to the mark with copper-free water. This stock solution contains 100 μg Cu per 1.00 ml.

c. Standard copper solution: Dilute 50.00 ml stock copper solution to 1,000 ml with copper-free water; 1.00 ml = 5.00 μg Cu.

d. Hydrochloric acid, 1 + 1: Use copper-free water.

e. Sodium pyrophosphate solution: Dissolve 30 g $Na_4P_2O_7 \cdot 10H_2O$ in copper-free water and make up to 1 liter.

f. Sodium acetate solution: Dissolve 400 g $NaC_2H_3O_2 \cdot 3H_2O$ in 600 ml copper-free water. The dissolution of the salt is endothermic and requires heat.

g. Cuprethol reagent mixture:

1) SOLUTION (I)—Dissolve 4.0 g diethanolamine (also called 2,2′-iminodiethanol) in 200 ml methyl alcohol.

2) SOLUTION (II)—Dissolve 3.0 ml carbon disulfide in 200 ml methyl alcohol.

Solutions I and II are quite stable. Prepare the reagent by mixing equal volumes of the two solutions. Tightly stopper the reagent mixture to maintain stability for about 1 week; it slowly decomposes, liberating sulfur, which causes turbidity when added to the sample. (CAUTION: *Keep the reagent away from flame. Dispense it with a safety pipet because of toxicity.*)

h. Isoamyl alcohol.

4. Procedure

a. Preparation of copper standards: Prepare standards for the calibration curve or visual comparison from the standard copper solution according to the following schedule:

Copper μg	Vol. of Std Copper Soln To Be Diluted to 100 ml *ml*
0	0.00
2.50	0.50
5.00	1.00
10.0	2.00
15.0	3.00
20.0	4.00
30.0	6.00
40.0	8.00
50.0	10.00

Treat the standards exactly as described for samples.

b. Color development and measurement: To a 100-ml sample, or an aliquot diluted to 100 ml, add, mixing after each addition, 0.5 ml HCl, 2 ml sodium pyrophosphate solution, and sufficient sodium acetate solution to give a pH between 5 and 6. Let stand for 5 min. Add 1 ml cuprethol reagent mixture. Allow to stand at least 10 min but not more than 30 min. Compare visually in nessler tubes against simultaneously prepared standards in the recommended copper range of 0–50.0 μg, or use a photometer and evaluate on a calibration curve obtained from simultaneously prepared standards.

c. Treatment of turbid or colored samples: Use a photometer if the sample is initially turbid or colored. Add all reagents except cuprethol to a 100-ml sample as directed in ¶ 4b preceding; add 2 ml methyl alcohol in lieu of the cuprethol solution. Correct for the turbidity or color by setting this mixture at 100% transmittance. If turbidity develops upon the addition of cuprethol to a clear solution, it indicates either a stale cuprethol reagent or the presence of an interfering ion in excessive concentration.

Alternatively, overcome the problem of turbidity by extraction with isoamyl alcohol. In visual determinations using nessler tubes, add 5 ml isoamyl alcohol to the samples after the color has been developed as described in ¶ 4b and mix by constantly inverting the tubes for 3 min. The bulk of the color collects in the droplets of isoamyl alcohol which are buoyed up to the surface and there form a layer. Compare the color of the layer, without removal, to standards prepared in a like manner. Break the emulsion by the addition of a few drops of ethyl alcohol to the isoamyl alcohol layer and gently stir this layer with a stirring rod.

d. Modification for field work: When the field sample contains tolerable concentrations of interfering ions (less than 0.3 mg/l ferric ion and 0.6 mg/l ferrous ion, and a pH between 1.5 and 9), add 1 ml cuprethol to a 100-ml sample, mix, and immediately compare the color with simultaneously prepared standards.

5. Calculation

$$\text{mg/l Cu} = \frac{\mu\text{g Cu}}{\text{ml sample}}$$

6. Precision and Accuracy

A synthetic unknown sample containing 470 μg/l Cu, 500 μg/l Al, 50 μg/l Cd, 110 μg/l Cr, 300 μg/l Fe, 70 μg/l Pb, 120 μg/l Mn, 150 μg/l Ag, and 650 μg/l Zn in distilled water was determined by the cuprethol method with a relative standard deviation of 17.5% and a relative error of 8.5% in 25 laboratories.

A second unknown sample containing 1.00 mg/l Cu, 500 μg/l Al, 50 μg/l Cd, 110 μg/l Cr, 300 μg/l Fe, 70 μg/l Pb, 50 μg/l Mn, 150 μg/l Ag and 650 μg/l Zn was determined by the cuprethol method, with a relative standard deviation of 2.7% and a relative error of 1.0% in 17 laboratories.

119 C. Bathocuproine Method

1. General Discussion

a. Principle—Cuprous ions form a water-soluble orange-colored chelate with bathocuproine disulfonate (2,9-dimethyl-4,7-diphenyl-1,10-phenanthrolinedisulfonic acid, disodium salt). Despite the fact that the color forms over the pH range of 3.5 to 11.0, the recommended pH range is between 4 and 5. Hydrochloric acid and citrate buffer the system at a pH of about 4.3, while hydroxylamine hydrochloride serves as a reducing agent. The absorbance is measured at 484 mμ. The method can be applied to copper concentrations up to at least 5 mg/l with a sensitivity of 20 μg/l.

b. Interference—The following ions and substances can be tolerated with an error of less than ±2%:

Ion	*mg/l*
Cations	
Aluminum	100
Beryllium	10
Cadmium	100
Calcium	1000
Chromium (III)	10
Cobalt (II)	5
Iron (II)	100
Iron (III)	100
Lithium	500
Magnesium	100
Manganese (II)	500
Nickel (II)	500
Sodium	1000
Strontium	200
Thorium (IV)	100
Zinc	200
Anions	
Chlorate	1000
Chloride	1000
Fluoride	500
Nitrate	200
Nitrite	200
Orthophosphate	1000
Perchlorate	1000
Sulfate	1000
Compounds	
Residual Chlorine	1
Linear Alkylate Sulfonate (LAS)	40

Cyanide, thiocyanate, persulfate and EDTA can also interfere.

c. Minimum detectable concentration—20 μg/l when a 5-cm cell is used in a spectrophotometer.

d. Absorptivity—164.

2. Apparatus

a. COLORIMETRIC EQUIPMENT—One of the following, equipped with absorption cells and providing light paths of 1 to 5 cm (the latter is recommended), is required:

1) *Spectrophotometer,* for use at 484 mμ.

2) *Filter photometer,* equipped with a blue-green filter exhibiting maximum light transmission near 484 mμ.

3) *Nessler tubes,* matched, 100-ml, tall form.

b. ACID-WASHED GLASSWARE—Rinse all glassware with conc HCl and then with copper-free water.

3. Reagents

a. Copper-free water: Use redistilled or deionized distilled water.

b. Standard copper solution: Prepare as directed in Method B, ¶ 3c preceding; 1.00 ml = 5.00 μg Cu. Prepare daily.

c. Hydrochloric acid, 1 + 1. Use copper-free water.

d. Hydroxylamine hydrochloride solution: Dissolve 100 g $NH_2OH{\cdot}HCl$ in 900 ml copper-free water.

e. Sodium citrate solution: Dissolve 300 g $Na_3C_6H_5O_7{\cdot}2H_2O$ in copper-free water and make up to 1 liter.

f. Disodium bathocuproine disulfonate solution: Dissolve 1.000 g $C_{12}H_4N_2(CH_3)_2(C_6H_4)_2(SO_3Na)_2$ in copper-free water and make up to the mark in a 1-liter volumetric flask.

4. Procedure

Pipet 50.0 ml sample, or a suitable aliquot diluted to 50.0 ml, into a 250-ml erlenmeyer flask. In separate 250-ml erlenmeyer flasks, prepare a 50.0-ml copper-free water blank and a series of 50.0-ml copper standards containing 5.0, 10.0, 15.0, 20.0 and 25.0 μg Cu. To sample, blank and standards add, mixing after each addition, 1.00 ml 1 + 1 HCl, 5.00 ml hydroxylamine hydrochloride solution, 5.00 ml sodium citrate solution, and 5.00 ml disodium bathocuproine disulfonate solution. Transfer to cells and read the absorbance of the sample against the blank at 484 mμ. Plot absorbance against μg

Cu in standards for the calibration curve. Estimate the copper concentration of the sample from the calibration curve.

5. Calculation

$$\text{mg/l Cu} = \frac{\mu\text{g Cu}}{\text{ml sample}}$$

6. Precision and Accuracy

A synthetic unknown sample containing 1.00 mg/l Cu, 500 μg/l Al, 50 μg/l Cd, 110 μg/l Cr, 300 μg/l Fe, 70 μg/l Pb, 50 μg/l Mn, 150 μg/l Ag and 650 μg/l Zn was determined by the bathocuproine method, with a relative standard deviation of 4.1% and a relative error of 0.3% in 33 laboratories.

119 D. Bibliography

Cuprethol Method

WOELFEL, W. C. 1948. Colorimetric determination of copper with carbon disulfide and diethanolamine—An improved dithiocarbamate reagent. *Anal. Chem.* 20: 722.

Bathocuproine Method

SMITH, G. F. & D. H. WILKINS. 1953. New colorimetric reagent specific for copper. *Anal Chem.* 25:510.

BORCHARDT, L. G. & J. P. BUTLER. 1957. Determination of trace amounts of copper. *Anal. Chem.* 29:414.

ZAK, B. 1958. Simple procedure for the single sample determination of serum copper and iron. *Clinica Chim. Acta* 3:328.

BLAIR, D. & H. DIEHL. 1961. Bathophenanthrolinedisulfonic acid and bathocuproinedisulfonic acid, water soluble reagents for iron and copper. *Talanta* 7: 163.

120 CYANIDE

The determination of cyanide in a potable water supply can be performed by the methods described in Section 207.

DETERGENTS: See Surfactants, Section 159.

121 FLUORIDE

A fluoride concentration of approximately 1.0 mg/l is an effective preventive of dental caries without harmful effects on health. Fluoride may occur naturally in water or may be added in controlled amounts. Some fluorosis may occur when the fluoride level exceeds the recommended limits. In rare instances the fluoride concentration naturally occurring may approach 10 mg/l. Such waters should be defluoridated to reduce the fluoride content to the acceptable levels.

The accurate determination of fluoride in water supplies has increased in importance with the growth of the practice of fluoridation of supplies as a public health measure. The maintenance of a constant fluoride concentration is essential in maintaining the effectiveness and safety of the fluoridation procedure.

Among the many methods suggested for the determination of fluoride ion in water, the electrode and colorimetric methods are believed to be the most satisfactory at the present time. The colorimetric methods are based on the reaction between fluoride and a zirconium-dye lake. The fluoride reacts with the dye lake, dissociating a portion of it into a colorless complex anion (ZrF_6^{2-}) and the dye. As the amount of fluoride is increased, the color produced becomes progressively lighter or different in hue, depending on the reagent used.

Because all of the colorimetric methods are subject to errors where interfering ions are present, it may be necessary to distill the sample as directed in the Preliminary Distillation Step prior to making the fluoride determination. When interfering ions are not present in excess of the tolerances of the method, the fluoride determination may be made directly without distillation. The analysis is completed by using one of the two colorimetric methods (B or C).

1. Selection of method

The addition of the citrate buffer frees the electrode method from the interference problems caused by such relatively common ions as aluminum, hexametaphosphate, iron and orthophosphate, which adversely affect the colorimetric methods and necessitate recourse to preliminary distillation. Both colorimetric methods are directly

TABLE 121(1): CONCENTRATION OF INTERFERING SUBSTANCES CAUSING 0.1-MG/L ERROR AT 1.0 MG/L F * IN COLORIMETRIC METHODS

Substance	Method C (SPADNS)		Method D (Alizarin Visual)	
	Conc *mg/l*	Type of Error	Conc *mg/l*	Type of Error
Alkalinity ($CaCO_3$)	5,000	−	400	−
Aluminum (Al^{3+})	0.1 †	−	0.25	−
Chloride (Cl^-)	7,000	+	2,000	−
Iron (Fe^{3+})	10	−	2	+
Hexametaphosphate ($[NaPO_3]_6$)	1.0	+	1.0	+
Phosphate (PO_4^{3-})	16	+	5	+
Sulfate (SO_4^{2-})	200	+	300	+

* Residual chlorine must be completely removed with arsenite reagent. Color and turbidity must be removed or compensated for.

† On immediate reading. Tolerance increases with time: after 2 hr, 3.0; after 4 hr, 30.

applicable to samples in the fluoride range 0.05–1.4 mg/l, while the electrode method can be applied to fluoride concentrations beginning at 0.1 mg/l and extending beyond 5 mg/l. The SPADNS and electrode methods allow measurements to be made at any time after reagent addition. Although the alizarin visual method does not require accurate time control because sample and standards are treated simultaneously under the same conditions, a waiting period of 1 hr after reagent addition is suggested as a satisfactory time lapse for color development. The visual colorimetric method requires inexpensive laboratory glassware, while Methods A and B are instrumental.

Permanent colored standards, commercially or otherwise prepared, may be used if appropriate precautions are taken. These include strict adherence to the manufacturer's directions and careful calibration of the permanent standards against standards prepared by the analyst. (See General Introduction, Section 000A.7, for further discussion of their use.)

2. *Interference in colorimetric methods*

In general, the colorimetric methods are susceptible to the same interfering substances, but to varying degrees. Table 121(1) lists the substances which commonly cause interference with the methods. As these interferences are neither linear in effect nor algebraically additive, mathematical compensation is extremely hazardous. Whenever any one substance is present in sufficient quantity to produce an error of 0.1 mg/l, or whenever the total interfering effect is in doubt, the sample should be distilled. (Distillation is also recommended for colored or turbid samples.) In some instances, sample dilution or addition of the appropriate amounts of interfering substances to the standards may be used to eliminate the interference effect. If alkalinity is the only significant interference, it may be neutralized with either hydrochloric or nitric acid.

Chlorine interferes in all of the colorimetric methods and provision for its removal is made.

In the colorimetric methods, the volume measurement of water sample, and particularly the volume measurement of reagent, are of utmost importance to the accuracy of the determination. Samples and standards must be at the same temperature, at least within 2 C, with constant temperature being maintained throughout the color development period. In the case of the SPADNS method, different calibration curves may be prepared for different temperatures.

3. *Sampling and storage*

Polyethylene bottles are preferred for collecting and storing water samples for fluoride analysis. Glass bottles are satisfactory, provided precautions are taken to prevent the use of containers which previously contained high-fluoride solutions. The usual precaution of rinsing the bottle with a portion of the sample should be observed.

Laboratories which use water samples collected for bacteriologic analysis should be cautioned against an excess of dechlorinating agent in the sample. Sodium thiosulfate in excess of 100 mg/l will interfere by producing a precipitate.

121 A. Preliminary Distillation Step

1. Discussion

Fluoride can be separated from other constituents in water by distillation of fluosilicic (or hydrofluoric) acid from a solution of the sample in an acid with a higher boiling point. Quantitative fluoride recovery is approached by using a relatively large sample volume, and sulfate carry-over is minimized by conducting the distillation over a broad temperature range.

2. Apparatus

Distillation apparatus consisting of a 1-liter round-bottom long-neck pyrex boiling flask, a connecting tube, an efficient condenser, a thermometer adapter, and a thermometer reading to 200 C is illustrated in Figure 16, but any comparable apparatus may be used, provided the essential design features are observed. Figure 18 (Section 132A) shows the general type of distillation apparatus * which is satisfactory for the fluoride, ammonia, albuminoid nitrogen, phenol and selenium distillations. The critical points to observe are those which could affect complete fluoride recovery—such as obstruction in the vapor path and trapping of liquid in the adapter and condenser —and conditions which might enhance sulfate carry-over. In this regard, the use of an asbestos shield or similar device is recommended to protect the upper part of the distilling flask from the burner flame. If desired, this apparatus can be modified so that the heat is automatically shut off when distillation is completed.

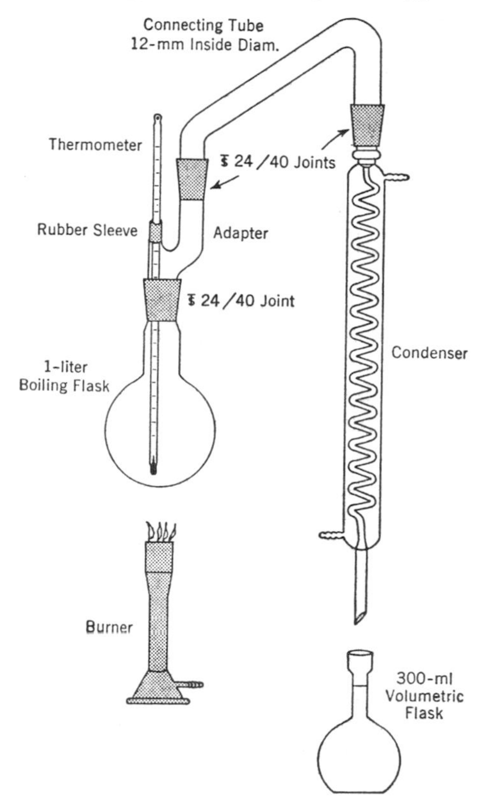

Figure 16. Direct distillation apparatus for fluoride.

3. Reagents

a. Sulfuric acid, conc.

b. Silver sulfate, crystals.

4. Procedure

a. Place 400 ml distilled water in the distilling flask and carefully add 200 ml conc H_2SO_4. Swirl until the flask contents are homogeneous. Add 25–35 glass beads and connect the apparatus as shown in Figure 16, making sure all joints are tight. Begin heating slowly at first, then as rapidly as the efficiency of the condenser will permit (the distillate must be cool) until the

---

* Such as Corning No. 3360 or equivalent.

temperature of the flask contents reaches exactly 180 C. Discard the distillate. This process serves to remove fluoride contamination and to adjust the acid-water ratio for subsequent distillations.

b. After cooling the acid mixture remaining from the steps outlined in ¶ 4a, or previous distillations, to 120 C or below, add 300 ml of sample, mix thoroughly, and distill as before until the temperature reaches 180 C. To prevent sulfate carry-over, do not permit the temperature to exceed 180 C.

c. Add silver sulfate to the distilling flask at the rate of 5 mg per milligram of chloride when high-chloride samples are distilled.

d. Use the sulfuric acid solution in the flask repeatedly until the contaminants from the water samples accumulate to an extent that recovery is affected or interferences appear in the distillate. Check suitability of the acid periodically by distilling standard fluoride samples. After the distillation of high-fluoride samples, flush the still with 300 ml distilled water and combine the two fluoride distillates. If necessary, repeat the flushing operation until the fluoride content of the distillates is at a minimum. Include the additional fluoride recovered with that of the first distillation. After periods of inactivity, similarly flush the still and discard the distillate.

5. Interpretation of Results

The recovery of fluoride is quantitative within the accuracy of the methods used for its measurement.

121 B. Electrode Method

1. General Discussion

a. Principle: The fluoride ion-activity electrode is a specific ion sensor. The electrode is designed to be used with a standard calomel reference electrode and any modern pH meter having an expended millivolt scale. The key element in the fluoride ion-activity electrode is the laser-type doped single lanthanum fluoride crystal across which a potential is established by the presence of fluoride ions. The crystal contacts the sample solution at one face and an internal reference solution at the other. The cell may be represented by

Ag|AgCl, Cl^- (0.3*M*), F^- (0.001 *M*)| LaF_3 |test soln| SCE.

The fluoride ion-activity electrode can be used to measure the activity or the concentration of fluoride in aqueous samples by use of an appropriate calibration curve. The fluoride activity is dependent, however, upon the total ionic strength of the sample, and the electrode does not respond to fluoride which is bound or complexed. These difficulties are largely overcome by the addition of citrate ion to preferentially complex aluminum and by the addition of a buffer solution of high total ionic strength to swamp out variations in sample ionic strength.

b. Interference: Polyvalent cations such as Al(III), Fe(III), and Si(IV) will complex fluoride ion. The extent to which complexing takes place depends on the solution pH and the relative levels of the fluoride and the complexing species. The citrate ion present in the buffer solution, however, will preferentially complex up to 2 mg/l aluminum and releases the fluoride as the free ion. In acid solution, hydrogen ion forms complexes with fluoride ion, but the complexing is negligible if the pH is adjusted to above pH 5. In alkaline solution the hydroxide ion also interferes with the electrode response to fluoride ion whenever the level of hydroxide ion is greater than one-tenth the level of fluoride ion present. However, at pH 8 and below, the hydroxide concentration is 10^{-6} molar or less, and no interference occurs with any measurable fluoride concentration.

2. Apparatus

a. Expanded-scale pH meter, or specific ion meter,† that is provided with a millivolt or other appropriate scale in addition to pH.

b. Sleeve-type reference electrode: * Fiber-tip references are often erratic in very dilute solutions and are not recommended.

c. Fluoride electrode.†

d. Magnetic stirrer, with teflon-coated stirring bar.

e. Stopwatch or clock.

3. Reagents

a. Stock fluoride solution: Dissolve 221.0 mg anhydrous sodium fluoride, NaF, in distilled water and dilute to 1,000 ml; 1.00 ml = 100 μg F.

b. Standard fluoride solution: Dilute 100 ml stock fluoride solution to 1,000 ml with distilled water; 1.00 ml = 10.0 μg F.

c. Total ionic strength adjustment buffer (TISAB): Place approximately 500 ml distilled water in a 1-liter beaker. Add 57 ml conc (glacial) acetic acid, 58 g sodium chloride, NaCl, and 12 g sodium citrate dihydrate, $Na_3C_6H_5O_7 \cdot 2H_2O$. Stir to dissolve. Place the beaker in a water bath (for cooling), insert a calibrated pH electrode and reference electrode into the solution and slowly add approximately 6*N* sodium hydroxide (about 125 ml) until the pH is between 5.0 and 5.5. Cool to room temperature. Put into a 1-liter volumetric flask and add distilled water to the mark.

4. Procedure

a. Instrument calibration: No major adjustment of the pH meter is normally required to use the electrodes in the fluoride range 0.2–2.0 mg/l. For those instruments with zero at center scale (e.g., most Beckman or Leeds & Northrup meters), adjust the calibration control so that the 1.0 mg/l F standard reads at the center zero (100 mV) when the meter is in the expanded scale position. This cannot be done on some meters, such as the Corning model 12, which do not have a mV calibration control. In the case of a specific ion meter, follow instructions of the manufacturer for calibrating the instrument.

b. Preparation of fluoride standards: Measure 0, 1.00, 2.00, 3.00, 4.00, 5.00, 6.00, 8.00, and 10.00 ml standard fluoride solution into a series of 100-ml volumetric flasks to produce fluoride concentrations of 0, 0.20, 0.40, 0.60, 0.80, 1.00, 1.20, 1.60, and 2.00 mg/l. To each flask, add by pipet 50 ml

---

† The precision and accuracy data cited in ¶ 6 were obtained with the Orion fluoride electrode.

* Beckman No. 40463, Corning No. 476-012 or Orion No. 90–01–00 is satisfactory.

TISAB solution and dilute to 100 ml with distilled water. Mix well.

c. Treatment of sample: To a 100-ml volumetric flask, add by pipet 50 ml sample, dilute to the mark with TISAB solution, and mix well. Bring the standards and sample to the same temperature, preferably room temperature (25 C ± 2).

d. Measurement with electrode: Transfer each standard and sample to a series of 150-ml beakers. Immerse the electrodes and measure the developed potential while stirring the test solution on a magnetic stirrer. Avoid stirring the solution before immersion of the electrodes because entrapped air around the crystal can produce erroneous readings or needle fluctuations. Allow the electrodes to remain in the solution 3 min before taking a final millivolt reading (some electrodes yield positive millivolt readings, while others respond negatively). Rinse the electrodes with distilled water and blot dry between each reading.

When using an expanded-scale pH meter, or specific-ion meter, recalibrate the electrode frequently by checking the potential reading of the 1.00 mg/l (50 μg F) standard and adjust the calibration control (if necessary) until the meter reads as before. Confirm the calibration after reading each unknown and also after reading each standard when preparing the standard curve.

Plot the potential measurement in millivolts within the expected range along the arithmetic horizontal axis on 2-cycle semilogarithmic graph paper. Plot mg/l or μg F on the logarithmic axis, with the lowest concentration at the bottom of the page. Using the potential measurement for each unknown sample, read the corresponding fluoride concentration off the standard curve.

5. Calculation

$$\text{mg/l F} = \frac{\mu\text{g F}}{\text{ml sample}}$$

6. Precision and Accuracy

A synthetic unknown sample containing 850 μg/l F in distilled water was determined by the electrode method, with a relative standard deviation of 3.6% and a relative error of 0.7% in 111 laboratories.

A second synthetic unknown sample containing 750 μg/l F, 2.5 mg/l $(NaPO_3)_6$, and 300 mg/l alkalinity added as $NaHCO_3$ was determined by the electrode method, with a relative standard deviation of 4.8% and a relative error of 0.2% in 111 laboratories.

A third synthetic unknown sample containing 900 μg/l F, 500 μg/l Al and 200 mg/l sulfate was determined by the electrode method, with a relative standard deviation of 2.9% and a relative error of 4.9% in 13 laboratories.

121 C. SPADNS Method

1. Discussion

The reaction rate between fluoride and zirconium ions is influenced greatly by the acidity of the reaction mixture. By increasing the proportion of acid in the reagent, the reaction can be made practically instantaneous. Under such conditions, however, the effect of various ions differs from that in the conventional alizarin methods. The selection of dye for this rapid fluoride method is governed largely by the resulting tolerance to these ions.

2. Apparatus

COLORIMETRIC EQUIPMENT—One of the following is required:

a. Spectrophotometer, for use at 570 mμ, providing a light path of at least 1 cm.

b. Filter photometer, providing a light path of at least 1 cm and equipped with a greenish yellow filter having maximum transmittance at 550 to 580 mμ.

3. Reagents

a. Standard fluoride solution: Prepare as directed in the electrode method, Section 121B.3b.

b. SPADNS solution: Dissolve 958 mg SPADNS, sodium 2-(parasulfophenylazo)-1,8-dihydroxy-3,6-naphthalene disulfonate, also called 4,5-dihydroxy-3-(parasulfophenylazo)-2,7-naphthalenedisulfonic acid trisodium salt,* in distilled water and dilute to 500 ml. This solution is stable indefinitely if protected from direct sunlight.

c. Zirconyl-acid reagent: Dissolve 133 mg zirconyl chloride octahydrate, $ZrOCl_2 \cdot 8H_2O$, in about 25 ml distilled water. Add 350 ml conc HCl and dilute to 500 ml with distilled water.

d. Acid zirconyl-SPADNS reagent: Mix equal volumes of SPADNS solution and zirconyl-acid reagent to produce a single reagent, which is stable for at least 2 years.

e. Reference solution: Add 10 ml SPADNS solution to 100 ml distilled water. Dilute 7 ml conc HCl to 10 ml and add to the diluted SPADNS solution. The resulting solution, used for setting the reference point (zero) of the spectrophotometer or photometer, is stable and may be reused indefinitely. This reference solution can be eliminated by using, if desired, one of the prepared standards as a reference.

f. Sodium arsenite solution: Dissolve 5.0 g $NaAsO_2$ and dilute to 1 liter with distilled water. (CAUTION: *Toxic—take care to avoid ingestion.*)

4. Procedure

a. Preparation of standard curve: Prepare fluoride standards in the range of 0 to 1.40 mg/l by diluting appropriate quantities of the standard fluoride solution to 50 ml with distilled water. Pipet 5.00 ml each of SPADNS solution and zirconyl-acid reagent, or 10.00 ml of the mixed acid-zirconyl-SPADNS reagent, to each standard and mix well, exercising care to avoid contamination during the process. Set the photometer to zero absorbance with the reference solution and obtain the absorbance readings of the standards immediately. Plot a curve of the fluoride-absorbance relationships. Prepare a new standard curve whenever a fresh batch of reagent is made up or a different standard temperature is desired. If no reference solution is used, set the photometer at some convenient point established with a prepared fluoride standard.

b. Sample pretreatment: If the sample contains residual chlorine, remove it by adding 1 drop (0.05 ml) of sodium arsenite solution for each 0.1

* Eastman No. 7309 or equivalent.

mg Cl and mix. (Sodium arsenite concentrations of 1,300 mg/l produce an error of 0.1 mg/l at 1.0 mg/l F.)

c. Color development: Use a 50.0-ml sample or an aliquot diluted to 50 ml. Adjust the temperature of the sample to that used for the standard curve. Add 5.00 ml each of the SPADNS solution and zirconyl-acid reagent, or 10.00 ml of the acid-zirconyl-SPADNS reagent; mix well, exercising care to prevent contamination during the process; and read the absorbance immediately or at any subsequent time, first setting the reference point of the photometer as above. If the absorbance falls beyond the range of the standard curve, repeat the procedure, using a smaller sample aliquot.

5. Calculation

$$\text{mg/l F} = \frac{A}{\text{ml sample}} \times \frac{B}{C}$$

where $A = \mu g$ F determined photometrically. The ratio B/C applies only when a sample is diluted to a volume B, and an aliquot C taken from it for color development.

6. Precision and Accuracy

A synthetic unknown sample containing 830 μg/l F and no interference in distilled water was determined by the SPADNS method, with a relative standard deviation of 8.0% and a relative error of 1.2% in 53 laboratories. Following direct distillation of the sample, the relative standard deviation was 11.0% and the relative error 2.4%.

A synthetic unknown sample containing 570 μg/l F, 10 mg/l Al, 200 mg/l sulfate, and 300 mg/l total alkalinity was determined by the SPADNS method, with a relative standard deviation of 16.2% and a relative error of 7.0% in 53 laboratories without resort to distillation. Following direct distillation of the sample, the relative standard deviation was 17.2% and the relative error 5.3%.

A synthetic unknown sample containing 680 μg/l F, 2 mg/l Al, 2.5 mg/l sodium hexametaphosphate, 200 mg/l sulfate, and 300 mg/l total alkalinity was determined, with a relative standard deviation of 12.8% and a relative error of 5.9% in 53 laboratories which followed the direct distillation and SPADNS methods.

121 D. Alizarin Visual Method

1. Apparatus

COLOR COMPARISON EQUIPMENT—One of the following is required:

a. Nessler tubes, matched, 100-ml tall form.

b. Comparator, visual.

2. Reagents

a. Standard fluoride solution: Prepare as directed in Section 121B.3b; 1.00 ml = 10.0 μg F.

b. Zirconyl-alizarin reagent: Dissolve 300 mg zirconyl chloride octahydrate, $ZrOCl_2 \cdot 8H_2O$, in 50 ml distilled water contained in a 1-liter glass-stoppered volumetric flask. Dissolve 70 mg of 3-alizarinsulfonic acid sodium salt (also called alizarin red S) in 50 ml distilled water and pour slowly into the zirconyl solution while stirring. The resulting solution clears on standing for a few minutes.

c. Mixed acid solution: Dilute 101 ml conc HCl to approximately 400 ml with distilled water. Add carefully 33.3 ml conc H_2SO_4 to approximately 400 ml distilled water. After cooling, mix the two acids.

d. Acid-zirconyl-alizarin reagent: To the clear zirconyl-alizarin reagent in the 1-liter volumetric flask, add the mixed acid solution, add distilled water up to the mark, and mix. The reagent changes in color from red to yellow within an hour and is then ready for use. Store away from direct sunlight to extend the reagent stability to 6 months.

e. Sodium arsenite solution: Prepare as directed in Section 121C.3f.

3. Procedure

a. Sample pretreatment: If the sample contains residual chlorine, remove it by adding 1 drop (0.05 ml) of arsenite for each 0.1 mg Cl and mix.

b. Preparation of standards: Prepare a series of standards by diluting various volumes of standard fluoride solution (1.00 ml = 10.0 μg F) to 100 ml in nessler tubes. Choose the standards so that there is at least one with lower and one with higher fluoride concentration than that of the unknown sample. The interval between standards determines the accuracy of the determination. An interval of 50 μg/l is usually sufficient.

c. Color development: Adjust the temperature of samples and standards so that the deviation between them is no more than 2 C. A temperature near that of the room is satisfactory. To 100 ml of the clear sample, or an aliquot diluted to 100 ml, and to the standards in nessler tubes, add 5.00 ml of the acid-zirconyl-alizarin reagent from a volumetric pipet. Mix thoroughly, exercising care to avoid contamination during the process, and compare the samples and standards after 1 hr.

4. Calculation

$$\text{mg/l F} = \frac{A}{\text{ml sample}} \times \frac{B}{C}$$

where A = μg F determined visually. The ratio B/C applies only when a sample is diluted to a volume B, and an aliquot C is taken from it for color development.

5. Precision and Accuracy

A synthetic unknown sample containing 830 μg/l F and no interference in distilled water was determined by the alizarin visual method, with a relative standard deviation of 4.9% and a relative error of 3.6% in 20 laboratories. Following direct distillation of the sample, the relative standard deviation was 6.4% and the relative error 2.4%.

A synthetic unknown sample containing 570 μg/l F, 10 mg/l Al, 200 mg/l sulfate, and 300 mg/l total alkalinity was determined by the alizarin visual method, with a relative standard deviation of 51.8% and a relative error of 29.8% in 20 laboratories without resort to distillation. Following direct distillation of the sample, the relative standard deviation was 11.1% and the relative error 0%.

A synthetic unknown sample containing 680 μg/l F, 2 mg/l Al, 2.5 mg/l sodium hexametaphosphate, 200 mg/l sulfate, and 300 mg/l total alkalinity was determined, with a relative standard deviation of 10.6% and a relative error of 1.5% in 20 laboratories which followed the direct distillation and alizarin visual methods.

121 E. Bibliography

Direct Distillation Step

BELLACK, E. 1958. Simplified fluoride distillation method. *JAWWA* 50:530.

———. 1961. Automatic fluoride distillation. *JAWWA* 53:98.

Electrode Method

FRANT, M. S. & J. W. ROSS, JR. 1966. Electrode for sensing fluoride ion activity in solution. *Science* 154:3756.

LINGANE, J. J. 1967. A study of the lanthanum fluoride membrane electrode for end point detection in titrations of fluoride with thorium, lanthanum and calcium. *Anal. Chem.* 39:881.

FRANT, M. S. & J. W. ROSS, JR. 1968. Use of a total ionic strength adjustment buffer for electrode determination of fluoride in water supplies. *Anal. Chem.* 40:1169.

PATTERSON, S. J., N. G. BUNTON, & N. T. CROSBY. 1969. An evaluation of visual and specific ion electrode methods for the determination of fluoride in potable waters. *J. Soc. Water Treatment & Exam.* 18:182.

SPADNS Method

BELLACK, E. & P. J. SCHOUBOE. 1958. Rapid photometric determination of fluoride with SPADNS-zirconium lake. *Anal. Chem.* 30:2032.

Alizarin Visual Method

SANCHIS, J. M. 1934. Determination of fluorides in natural waters. *Ind. Eng. Chem.*, Anal. Ed. 6:134.

SCOTT, R D. 1941. Modification of fluoride determination. *JAWWA* 33:2018.

TARAS, M. J., H. D. CISCO & M. GARNELL. 1950. Interferences in alizarin method of fluoride determination. *JAWWA* 42:583.

GREASE: See Oil and Grease, Section 137.

122 HARDNESS

Originally, the hardness of a water was understood to be a measure of the capacity of the water for precipitating soap. Soap is precipitated chiefly by the calcium and magnesium ions commonly present in water, but may also be precipitated by ions of other polyvalent metals, such as aluminum, iron, manganese, strontium and zinc, and by hydrogen ions. Because all but the first two are usually present in insignificant concentrations in natural waters, hardness is defined as a characteristic of water which represents the total concentration of just the calcium and magnesium ions expressed as calcium carbonate. However, if present in significant amounts, other hardness-producing metallic ions should be included.

When the hardness is numerically greater than the sum of the carbonate alkalinity and the bicarbonate alkalinity, that amount of hardness which is equivalent to the total alkalinity is called "carbonate hardness"; the amount of hardness in excess of this is called "noncarbonate hardness." When the hardness is numerically equal to or less than the sum of carbonate and bicarbonate alkalinity, all of the hardness is "carbonate hardness," and there is no "noncarbonate hardness." The hardness may range from zero to hundreds of milligrams per liter in terms of calcium carbonate, depending on the source and treatment to which the water has been subjected.

1. SELECTION OF METHOD—Two approaches are presented for the determination of hardness. Approach A, hardness by calculation, is applicable to all waters and is considered to yield the higher accuracy. If a complete mineral analysis is performed, the hardness can be reported by calculation. Method B, the EDTA titration method, which measures the calcium and magnesium ions, may be applied with appropriate modification to any kind of water. The procedure described affords a means of rapid analysis.

2. REPORTING OF RESULTS—When reporting hardness, the analyst should state either the ions determined or the method used, for example, "hardness (Ca, Mg)," "hardness (Ca, Mg, Sr, Fe, Al, etc.)," "hardness (EDTA)."

122 A. Hardness by Calculation

1. Discussion

The accurate method for determining hardness is to compute it from the results of the calcium and the magnesium determinations. If present in significant amounts, other hardness-producing cations must be determined and included in the computation.

2. Procedure

Hardness is computed by multiplying the concentration of each hardness-producing cation by the proper factor to obtain equivalent calcium carbonate concentrations, and by summing these $CaCO_3$ concentrations. To obtain the $CaCO_3$ equivalent (mg/l) of the following cations, multiply the concentration found (mg/l) by the factor shown:

Cation	Factor	Cation	Factor
Ca	2.497	Al	5.564
Mg	4.116	Zn	1.531
Sr	1.142	Mn	1.822
Fe	1.792		

122 B. EDTA Titrimetric Method *

1. General Discussion

a. Principle: Ethylenediamine tetraacetic acid and its sodium salts (abbreviated EDTA) form a chelated soluble complex when added to a solution of certain metal cations. If a small amount of a dye such as Eriochrome Black T is added to an aqueous solution containing calcium and mag-

* Two United States patents (No. 2,583,890 and No. 2,583,891) have been issued to G. Schwarzenbach, disclosing titration and complexometric methods for quantitative determination of water hardness. Nothing contained in this manual is to be construed as granting any right, by implication or otherwise, for manufacture, sale or use in connection with any method, apparatus or product covered by patent, nor as insuring anyone against liability for infringement of patent.

nesium ions at a pH of 10.0 ± 0.1, the solution will become wine red. If EDTA is then added as a titrant, the calcium and magnesium will be complexed. After sufficient EDTA has been added to complex all the magnesium and calcium, the solution will turn from wine red to blue. This is the end point of the titration. Magnesium ion must be present to yield a satisfactory end point in the titration. A small amount of complexometrically neutral magnesium salt of EDTA is therefore added to the buffer, a step which automatically introduces sufficient magnesium and at the same time obviates a blank correction.

The sharpness of the end point increases with increasing pH. The pH, however, cannot be increased indefinitely because of the danger of precipitating $CaCO_3$ or $Mg(OH)_2$, and because the dye changes color at high pH values. The pH value of 10.0 ± 0.1 recommended in this procedure is a satisfactory compromise. A limit of 5 min is set for the duration of the titration in order to minimize the tendency toward $CaCO_3$ precipitation.

b. Interference: Some metal ions interfere with this procedure by causing fading or indistinct end points. This interference is reduced by the addition of certain inhibitors to the water sample before titration with EDTA. The maximum concentrations of interfering substances which may be present in the original sample and still permit titration with EDTA are shown in Table 122(1). The figures are intended as a rough guide only and are based on the use of a 25-ml aliquot diluted to 50 ml.

TABLE 122(1): MAXIMUM CONCENTRATIONS OF INTERFERENCES PERMISSIBLE WITH VARIOUS INHIBITORS *

Interfering Substance	Max. Interference Concentration *mg/l*		
	Inhibitor I	Inhibitor II	Inhibitor III
Aluminum	20	20	20
Barium	†	†	†
Cadmium	†	20	†
Cobalt	over 20	0.3	0 ‡
Copper	over 30	20	0.3
Iron	over 30	5	20
Lead	†	20	†
Manganese (Mn^{++})	†	1	1
Nickel	over 20	0.3	0 ‡
Strontium	†	†	†
Zinc	†	200	†
Polyphosphate		10	

* Based on 25-ml aliquot diluted to 50 ml.
† Titrates as hardness.
‡ Inhibitor fails if substance is present.

Suspended or colloidal organic matter in the sample may also interfere with the end point but may be overcome by evaporating the aliquot to dryness on a steam bath, followed by heating in a muffle furnace at 550 C until the organic matter is completely oxidized. Dissolve the residue in 20 ml 1*N* HCl, neutralize to pH 7 with 1*N* NaOH, and make up to 50 ml with distilled water; cool to room temperature and continue according to the general procedure.

c. Titration precautions: Titrations are best conducted at or near normal room temperatures. The color change becomes impractically slow as the sample approaches freezing temperature. Indicator decomposition presents a problem in hot water.

The pH specified in the recommended procedure may result in an environment conducive to $CaCO_3$ precipitation.

Although the titrant can slowly redissolve such precipitates, a drifting end point will often yield low results. A time limit of 5 min for the overall procedure minimizes the tendency for $CaCO_3$ to precipitate. The following three methods also combat precipitation loss:

1) The sample can be diluted with distilled water to reduce the $CaCO_3$ concentration. The simple expedient of diluting a 25-ml aliquot to 50 ml has been incorporated in the recommended procedure. If precipitation occurs at this dilution, Modification *(2)* or *(3)* can be followed. Reliance upon too small an aliquot contributes a systematic error originating from the buret-reading error.

2) If the approximate hardness of a sample is known or is ascertained by a preliminary titration, 90% or more of the titrant can be added to the sample *before* the pH is adjusted with the buffer.

3) The sample can be acidified and stirred for 2 min to expel CO_2 *before* pH adjustment with the buffer. A prior alkalinity determination can indicate the amount of acid to be added to the sample for this purpose.

2. Reagents

a. BUFFER SOLUTION—

1) Dissolve 16.9 g ammonium chloride, NH_4Cl, in 143 ml conc ammonium hydroxide, NH_4OH; add 1.25 g of magnesium salt of EDTA (this salt is available commercially) and dilute to 250 ml with distilled water.

2) In the absence of the magnesium salt of EDTA, dissolve 1.179 g disodium salt of ethylenediamine tetraacetic acid dihydrate (analytical reagent grade) and 780 mg $MgSO_4 \cdot 7H_2O$ or 644 mg $MgCl_2 \cdot 6H_2O$ in 50 ml distilled water. Add this solution to 16.9 g NH_4Cl and 143 ml conc NH_4OH with mixing and dilute to 250 ml with distilled water. To attain the highest accuracy, adjust to exact equivalence through appropriate addition of a small amount of EDTA or magnesium sulfate or chloride.

Keep the solution *(1)* or *(2)* in a plastic or resistant-glass container, tightly stoppered to prevent loss of NH_3 or pickup of CO_2. Do not store more than a month's supply in a frequently opened container. Dispense the buffer solution by means of a bulb-operated pipet. Discard the buffer when 1 or 2 ml added to the sample fails to produce a pH of 10.0 ± 0.1 at the end point of the titration.

3) Satisfactory alternate "odorless buffers" are described in the literature[1] and are also available commercially. They contain the magnesium salt of EDTA and have the advantage of being relatively odorless and much more stable than the NH_4Cl-NH_4OH buffer. One of these buffers may be prepared by mixing 55 ml conc HCl with 400 ml distilled water and then, slowly and with stirring, adding 310 ml 2-aminoethanol. The magnesium salt of EDTA in the amount of 5.0 g is next added to the solution and the volume diluted to 1 liter with distilled water.

b. INHIBITORS—For most waters there is no need to utilize an inhibitor. However, instances arise where waters contain interfering ions requiring the addition of an appropriate inhibitor to give a clear, sharp change in color at the end point. The following inhibitor reagents have been found satisfactory:

1) Inhibitor I: Add 250 mg sodium

cyanide in powder form to the solution to be titrated. When this inhibitor is used, add sufficient buffer to adjust the pH to 10.0 ± 0.1 in order to offset the additional alkalinity resulting from hydrolysis of the sodium cyanide. (CAUTION: *Sodium cyanide is extremely poisonous and more than customary precautions should be observed in its use.* Flush solutions containing this inhibitor down the drain with large quantities of water provided no acid is present, because acids liberate volatile poisonous HCN.)

2) Inhibitor II: Dissolve 5.0 g $Na_2S \cdot 9H_2O$ or 3.7 g $Na_2S \cdot 5H_2O$ in 100 ml distilled water. Exclude air with a tightly fitting rubber stopper. This inhibitor deteriorates through air oxidation. The inhibitor will give a sulfide precipitate which tends to obscure the end point when appreciable concentrations of heavy metals are present. Use 1 ml of Inhibitor II in ¶ 3a below.

3) Inhibitor III: Dissolve 4.5 g hydroxylamine hydrochloride in 100 ml of 95% ethyl or isopropyl alcohol. Since this inhibitor is added to the dye solution [see ¶ 2c(1)], use the solution both as end-point indicator and as inhibitor for interfering ions indicated in Table 122(1) preceding.

Commercial preparations incorporating the buffer and an inhibitor are available. These products may be used if found satisfactory for the specific needs of the analyst. Mixtures of inhibitors and buffers should maintain a pH of 10.0 ± 0.1 during titration and give a clear sharp end point when added to the sample.

c. INDICATOR—The dye Eriochrome Black T is the sodium salt of 1-(1-hydroxy-2-naphthylazo)-5-nitro-2-naphthol-4-sulfonic acid, No. 203 in the Color Index. Commercial grades are available.* Many types of indicator solutions are advocated in the literature and for the most part are satisfactory. The prime difficulty with indicator solutions is their instability through aging, which gives rise to indistinct end points in the EDTA titration. For example, alkaline solutions of the dye are sensitive to oxidants, and aqueous or alcoholic solutions are stable for only about a week. Dry mixtures of the dye and sodium chloride are stable. Prepared dry mixtures of the indicator and an inert salt are available commercially.

The following formulations have been widely used and are generally satisfactory:

1) Mix 0.5 g dye with 4.5 g hydroxylamine hydrochloride. Dissolve this mixture in 100 ml of 95% ethyl or isopropyl alcohol.

2) Mix 0.5 to 1.0 g dye in 100 g of an appropriate solvent such as 2,2′,2″-nitrilotriethanol (also called triethanolamine) or 2-methoxyethanol (also called ethylene glycol monomethyl ether).

3) Mix together 0.5 g dye and 100 g NaCl to prepare a dry powder mixture.

All indicator formulations tend to deteriorate, especially when exposed to moist air. If the end-point color change is not clear and sharp, it usually means that an appropriate inhibitor is needed. If sodium cyanide inhibitor does not sharpen the end point, the indicator is probably at fault.

d. STANDARD EDTA TITRANT, 0.01 *M*—

---

* Satisfactory commercial grades include "Eriochrome Black T" (Geigy), "Pontachrome Black TA" (Dupont), "Solochrome Black WDFA" (C.I.E.), "Omega Chrome Black S," and "Potting Black C."

1) Analytical reagent grade disodium ethylenediamine tetraacetate dihydrate, also called (ethylenedinitrilo)-tetraacetic acid disodium salt [EDTA], $Na_2H_2C_{10}H_{12}O_8N_2 \cdot 2H_2O$, is commercially available. Weigh 3.723 g of the dry powder, dissolve in distilled water, and dilute to 1,000 ml. Check the titer by standardizing against standard calcium solution (see ¶ 2e) as described in ¶ 3a below.

2) The technical grade of the disodium salt of EDTA dihydrate may also be used if the titrant is allowed to stand for several days and is then filtered. Dissolve 4.0 g of such material in 800 ml distilled water. Standardize against standard calcium solution (see ¶ 2e) as described in ¶ 3a below. Adjust the titrant so that 1.00 ml = 1.00 mg $CaCO_3$.

Because the titrant extracts hardness-producing cations from soft-glass containers, store preferably in polyethylene and secondarily in pyrex bottles. Compensate for gradual deterioration by periodic restandardization and a suitable correction factor.

e. STANDARD CALCIUM SOLUTION—Weigh 1.000 g anhydrous calcium carbonate, $CaCO_3$, powder (primary standard or special reagent low in heavy metals, alkalis and magnesium) into a 500-ml erlenmeyer flask. Place a funnel in the neck of the flask and add, a little at a time, 1 + 1 HCl until all the $CaCO_3$ has dissolved. Add 200 ml distilled water and boil for a few minutes to expel CO_2. Cool, add a few drops of methyl red indicator, and adjust to the intermediate orange color by adding 3*N* NH_4OH or 1 + 1 HCl, as required. Transfer quantitatively to a 1-liter volumetric flask and fill to the mark with distilled water. This standard solution is equivalent to 1.00 mg $CaCO_3$ per 1.00 ml.

3. Procedure

a. Titration of sample: Select a sample volume which requires less than 15 ml EDTA titrant. Do not extend duration of titration beyond 5 min, measured from the time of the buffer addition.

Dilute 25.0 ml sample to about 50 ml with distilled water in a porcelain casserole or other suitable vessel. Add 1–2 ml buffer solution. Usually 1 ml will be sufficient to give a pH of 10.0 to 10.1. The absence of a sharp end-point color change in the titration usually means that an inhibitor must be added at this point in the procedure (¶ 2b et seq) or that the indicator has deteriorated.

Add 1–2 drops indicator solution or an appropriate amount of dry-powder indicator formulation [¶ 2c(3)]. Add the standard EDTA titrant slowly, with continuous stirring, until the last reddish tinge disappears from the solution, adding the last few drops at 3–5 sec-intervals. The color of the solution at the end point is blue under normal conditions. Daylight or a daylight fluorescent lamp is highly recommended; ordinary incandescent lights tend to produce a reddish tinge in the blue at the end point.

If sufficient sample is available and interference is absent, improve the accuracy by increasing the sample size, as described in ¶ 3b below.

b. Low-hardness sample: For ion-exchanger effluent or other softened water and for natural waters of low hardness (less than 5 mg/l), take a larger sample, 100 to 1,000 ml, for titration and add proportionately larger amounts of buffer, inhibitor and indicator. Add the standard EDTA titrant slowly from a microburet and run a blank, using redistilled, distilled or deionized water of the same volume as the sample, to which identical amounts of buffer, inhibitor and indicator have been added.

4. Calculation

$$\text{Hardness (EDTA) as mg/l } CaCO_3 = \frac{A \times B \times 1{,}000}{\text{ml sample}}$$

where A = ml titration for sample, and B = mg $CaCO_3$ equivalent to 1.00 ml EDTA titrant.

5. Precision and Accuracy

A synthetic unknown sample containing 610 mg/l total hardness as $CaCO_3$ contributed by 108 mg/l Ca and 82 mg/l Mg, and the following supplementary substances: 3.1 mg/l K, 19.9 mg/l Na, 241 mg/l chloride, 250 μg/l nitrite N, 1.1 mg/l nitrate N, 259 mg/l sulfate, and 42.5 mg/l total alkalinity (contributed by $NaHCO_3$) in distilled water was determined by the EDTA titrimetric method with a relative standard deviation of 2.9% and a relative error of 0.8% in 56 laboratories.

122 C. Reference

1. J. PATTON & W. REEDER. 1956. New indicator for titration of calcium with (ethylenedinitrilo)tetraacetate. *Anal. Chem.* 28:1026.

122 D. Bibliography

CONNORS, J. J. 1950. Advances in chemical and colorimetric methods. *JAWWA* 42:33.

DIEHL, H., C. A. GOETZ & C. C. HACH. 1950. The versenate titration for total hardness. *JAWWA* 42:40.

BETZ, J. D. & C. A. NOLL. 1950. Total hardness determination by direct colorimetric titration. *JAWWA* 42:49.

GOETZ, C. A., T. C. LOOMIS & H. DIEHL. 1950. Total hardness in water: The stability of standard disodium dihydrogen ethylenediaminetetraacetate solutions. *Anal. Chem.* 22:798.

DISKANT, E. M. 1952. Stable indicator solutions for complexometric determination of total hardness in water. *Anal. Chem.* 24:1856.

BARNARD, A. J., JR., W. C. BROAD & H. FLASCHKA. The EDTA titration. *Chemist Analyst* 45:86 (1956) and 46:46 (1957).

GOETZ, C. A. & R. C. SMITH. 1959. Evaluation of various methods and reagents for total hardness and calcium hardness in water. *Iowa State J. Sci.* 34:81 (Aug. 15).

SCHWARZENBACH, G. & H. FLASCHKA. 1969. *Complexometric Titrations* (2nd ed.). Barnes & Noble, Inc., New York.

123 IODIDE

Only trace quantities of iodide are normally present in natural waters. Increased concentrations are found in natural brines or may be associated with certain industrial wastes. Iodide has been used as one possible indicator of sea water intrusion. Although physiologically important, iodide is now added in common table salt rather than in water supplies.

123 A. Photometric Method (TENTATIVE)

1. General Discussion

a. Principle: Iodide can be determined in water supplies by utilizing its ability to catalyze the reduction of ceric ions by arsenious acid, the effect being proportional, but not linearly, to the amount of iodide present. Photometric determination of the loss of ceric ion color directly is difficult without a recording device, since the color fades rapidly while it is being read in the photometer. If the reaction is stopped after a specific time interval by the addition of ferrous ammonium sulfate, the resulting ferric ions, which are directly proportional to the remaining ceric ions, develop a color complex with potassium thiocyanate that is relatively stable. This method has the advantages of requiring only small untreated water samples, eliminating distillation procedures, minimizing certain interferences, and giving stable colors for spectrophotometric determinations.

Digestion with chromic acid and distillation must be undertaken where an estimate is desired of the organically bound and other nonsusceptible forms of iodine in addition to the usual iodide ion. The pertinent procedures for these special applications may be found in the 10th Edition of this work.

b. Interference: An excess of sodium chloride is added to the sample aliquot to eliminate the interference of chloride already present in the water by attaining a stable maximum chloride concentration which sensitizes the reaction. The formation of noncatalytic forms of iodine and the inhibitory effects of silver and mercury are reduced by this addition.

2. Apparatus

a. Water bath, capable of temperature control to 30 ± 0.5 C.

b. Colorimetric equipment—One of the following is required:

1) SPECTROPHOTOMETER, for use at wavelengths of 510 or 525 mμ, and providing a light path of 1 cm.

2) FILTER PHOTOMETER, providing a light path of 1 cm and equipped with a green filter having maximum transmittance near 525 mμ.

c. Test tubes, 2 × 15 cm.

d. Stopwatch.

3. Reagents

Store all of the following stock solutions in tightly stoppered containers in a dark place.

a. Distilled water, containing less than 0.3 μg/l iodine.

b. Sodium chloride solution: Dissolve 200.0 g NaCl in distilled water and dilute to 1 liter. Recrystallize the NaCl if an interfering amount of iodine is present, using a water-ethanol mixture.

c. Arsenious acid, 0.1*N:* Dissolve 4.946 g arsenious oxide, As_2O_3, in distilled water, add 0.20 ml conc H_2SO_4, and dilute to 1,000 ml.

d. Sulfuric acid, conc.

e. Ceric ammonium sulfate, 0.02*N:* Dissolve 13.38 g $Ce(NH_4)_4(SO_4)_4 \cdot 4H_2O$ in distilled water, add 44 ml conc H_2SO_4, and make up to 1 liter.

f. Ferrous ammonium sulfate reagent: Dissolve 1.50 g $Fe(NH_4)_2(SO_4)_2 \cdot 6H_2O$ in 100 ml distilled water containing 0.6 ml conc H_2SO_4. Prepare daily.

g. Potassium thiocyanate solution: Dissolve 4.00 g KSCN in 100 ml distilled water.

h. Stock iodide solution: Dissolve 261.6 mg anhydrous potassium iodide, KI, in distilled water and dilute to 1,000 ml; 1.00 ml = 200 μg I.

i. Intermediate iodide solution: Dilute 20.00 ml stock iodide solution to 1,000 ml with distilled water; 1.00 ml = 4.00 μg I.

j. Standard iodide solution: Dilute 25.00 ml intermediate iodide solution to 1,000 ml with distilled water; 1.00 ml = 0.100 μg I.

4. Procedure

a. Sample size: Add 10.00 ml water sample, or an aliquot made up to 10.00 ml with iodine-free distilled water, to a 2 × 15 cm test tube. If possible, keep the iodide content of the diluted sample in the range 0.2–0.6 μg. Use scrupulously clean glassware and apparatus.

b. Color measurement: Add reagents to the sample in the following order: 1.00 ml NaCl solution, 0.50 ml arsenious acid solution, and 0.50 ml conc H_2SO_4.

Place the reaction mixture and the ceric ammonium sulfate solution in the 30 C water bath and allow to come to temperature equilibrium. Add 1.00 ml ceric ammonium sulfate solution, mix the contents of the test tube by inversion, and start the stopwatch to time the reaction. Use an inert clean test tube stopper when mixing. After 15 ± 0.1 min remove the sample from the water bath and add immediately 1.00 ml ferrous ammonium sulfate reagent with mixing, whereupon the yellow ceric ion color should disappear. Then add, with mixing, 1.00 ml potassium thiocyanate solution. Replace the sample in the water bath. Within 1 hr after the thiocyanate addition, read the red color as percent transmittance in a photometric instrument. Maintain the temperature of the solution and the cell compartment at 30 ± 0.5 C until the transmittance is determined. If several samples are run, start the reactions at 1-min intervals, to allow time for additions of ferrous ammonium sulfate and thiocyanate. (If temperature control of the cell compartment is not possible, allow the final solution to come to room temperature and measure the transmittance with the cell compartment at room temperature.)

c. Calibration standards: Treat standards containing 0, 0.2, 0.4, 0.6 and 0.8 μg I per 10.00 ml of solution as in ¶ 4b above. Run with each set of samples for the purpose of establishing a calibration curve.

5. Calculation

$$\text{mg/l I} = \frac{\mu\text{g I}}{\text{ml sample}}$$

6. Precision and Accuracy

Results obtained by this tentative method are reproducible on samples of Los Angeles source waters, and have been reported to be accurate to ± 0.3 μg/l I on samples of Yugoslavian water containing from 0 to 14.0 μg/l I.

123 B. Bibliography

ROGINA, B. & M. DUBRAVCIC. 1953. Microdetermination of iodides by arresting the catalytic reduction of ceric ions. *Analyst* 78:594.

Standard Methods for the Examination of Water, Sewage and Industrial Wastes (10th ed.). 1955. APHA, AWWA & FSIWA, New York, pp. 120–124.

DUBRAVCIC, M. 1955. Determination of iodine in natural waters (sodium chloride as a reagent in the catalytic reduction of ceric ions). *Analyst* 80:295.

124 IRON

Iron ranks next to aluminum in abundance of metals in the earth's crust. Despite the wide distribution, natural waters contain variable but minor amounts of iron.

In filtered samples of alkaline surface waters iron concentrations seldom approach a maximum of 1 mg/l. Some ground waters and acid surface waters, on the other hand, may contain considerably more iron. Iron's importance in water derives from the stains imparted to laundry and porcelain, and also the bittersweet astringent taste which may be detectable by some persons at levels above 1 or 2 mg/l.

Under reducing conditions, iron which exists in the ferrous state is relatively soluble in natural waters. In the absence of complex-forming ions, ferric iron is significantly soluble only at pH values less than 5. Upon exposure to air, or on addition of oxidants, the iron is oxidized to the ferric state and may hydrolyze to form insoluble hydrated ferric oxide. This is the predominant form of iron in most laboratory samples unless the samples are collected under specific conditions to avoid oxidation.

The form of iron may also undergo alteration as a result of the growth of bacteria in the sample during storage or shipment (see Section 501). In acid wastes at pH less than 3.5, iron in the ferric state may also be soluble.

Accordingly, iron in water may be either in true solution, in a colloidal state which may be peptized by organic matter, in the form of inorganic or organic iron complexes, or in the form of relatively coarse suspended particles. Furthermore, it may be either ferrous or ferric, or both.

Silt and clay in suspension may contain acid-soluble iron. Iron oxide particles are sometimes collected with a water sample as a result of flaking of rust from pipes. Iron may come from a metal cap used to close the sample bottle.

1. *Selection of method*

For natural and treated waters, the orthophenanthroline method has attained the greatest acceptance for reliability. For low concentrations, the bathophenanthroline reagents have a sensitivity about twice that of orthophenanthroline.[1] The bathophenanthroline disulfonate is reported to be capable of detecting 1 $\mu g/l$ and does not require solvent extraction. In the presence of interfering substances, two alternative methods are available: a method employing tripyridine, with ethylenediamine as a complexing agent for interfering substances; or an extraction method using diisopropyl ether to extract the iron from interfering substances.

Recently, the atomic absorption spectrophotometric method has gained rapid favor because of its relative ease and accuracy. The precision and accuracy data developed by a collaborative study of the atomic absorption method for iron yielded results that were superior to the colorimetric methods.

It is difficult to distinguish analytically between dissolved and suspended iron because, on exposure to air, soluble ferrous iron can be oxidized by dissolved oxygen and hydrolyzed at pH greater than 5 to insoluble ferric iron. Dissolved iron might be determined (¶ 4b following) by subsequent analysis of a portion of the sample which has been membrane-filtered and acidified immediately after collection at the site. This procedure suffers from oxidation of ferrous iron and hydrolysis during filtration and tends to yield low results.

A rigorous quantitative distinction between ferrous and ferric iron may be obtained with a special procedure using bathophenanthroline.[1-2] Both the orthophenanthroline and the tripyridine reagents tend to shift the soluble ferric-ferrous equilibrium to ferrous iron. The suggested procedure (¶ 4c) has limited application and requires a large excess of phenanthroline (mol ratio to ferrous plus ferric greater than 30). The sample is stabilized with hydrochloric acid rather than acetic acid because the latter does not provide a sufficiently low pH to stabilize the ferrous iron.

2. *Sampling and storage*

Methods of collecting, storing and pretreating samples should be planned in advance. The sample container should be cleaned with acid and rinsed with distilled water. The value of the determination is greatly dependent upon the care taken to obtain a representative sample. Iron in well water or tap samples may vary in concentration and form with period and degree of flushing before and during sampling. When taking the portion of the sample for the determination, the sample bottle must be shaken often and vigorously to obtain a uniform suspension of the precipitated iron. Particular care must be taken when colloidal iron adheres to the sample bottle. This problem can be acute with plastic bottles.

For a precise determination of total iron, a separate container should be used for collection of the sample. This sample may be treated with acid—at the time of collection to prevent a deposit on the container wall, or before removal of the portion for analysis of total iron, to dissolve the colloidal deposit on the container wall.

124 A. Phenanthroline Method

1. General Discussion

a. Principle: Iron is brought into solution, is reduced to the ferrous state by boiling with acid and hydroxylamine and treated with 1,10-phenanthroline at pH 3.2–3.3. Three molecules of phenanthroline chelate each atom of ferrous iron to form an orange-red complex. The colored solution obeys Beer's law; its intensity is independent of pH from 3 to 9 and is stable for at least 6 months. A pH between 2.9 and 3.5 insures rapid color development in the presence of an excess of phenanthroline.

b. Interference: Among the interfering substances are strong oxidizing agents, cyanide, nitrite, and phosphates—polyphosphates more so than orthophosphate; chromium; zinc in concentrations exceeding ten times that of iron; cobalt and copper in excess of 5 mg/l, and nickel in excess of 2 mg/l. Bismuth, cadmium, mercury, molybdate, and silver precipitate phenanthroline. The initial boiling with acid reverts polyphosphates to orthophosphate and removes cyanide and nitrite, which would otherwise interfere. The addition of more hydroxylamine will eliminate errors caused by excessive concentrations of strong oxidizing reagents. In the presence of interfering metal ions, a larger excess of phenanthroline is required to replace that which is complexed by these interferences. With excessive concentrations of interfering metal ions, the procedure for iron in Section 211(II)F may be used, or preferably the tripyridine or the extraction method.

If much color or organic matter is present, it may be necessary to evaporate the sample, gently ash the residue, and then redissolve in acid. The ashing may be carried out in silica, porcelain or platinum crucibles which have previously been boiled for several hours in 1 + 1 HCl.

c. Minimum detectable concentration: Total, dissolved or ferrous iron concentrations between 0.02 and 4.0 mg/l can be determined directly, and higher concentrations can be determined by the use of aliquots. The minimum is 3 μg with a spectrophotometer (510 mμ), using a 10-cm cell, or with nessler tubes.

2. Apparatus

a. COLORIMETRIC EQUIPMENT—One of the following is required:

1) Spectrophotometer, for use at 510 mμ, providing a light path of 1 cm or longer.

2) Filter photometer, providing a light path of 1 cm or longer and equipped with a green filter having maximum transmittance near 510 mμ.

3) Nessler tubes, matched, 100-ml, tall form.

b. ACID-WASHED GLASSWARE—All glassware must be washed with conc HCl and rinsed with distilled water prior to use, in order to remove the thin film of adsorbed iron oxide which is frequently present because the glassware has been used for other purposes.

3. Reagents

All reagents must be low in iron. Iron-free distilled water is required. Glass-stoppered bottles are recommended for storage. The hydrochloric acid, the ammonium acetate, and the stock iron solutions are stable indefinitely if tightly stoppered. The hydroxylamine and phenanthroline solutions are stable for several months. The standard iron solutions are not stable and must be prepared freshly as needed by diluting the stock solution. Visual standards in nessler tubes are stable for 3 months if protected from light.

a. Hydrochloric acid, conc.

b. Hydroxylamine solution: Dissolve 10 g $NH_2OH{\cdot}HCl$ in 100 ml distilled water.

c. Ammonium acetate buffer solution: Dissolve 250 g $NH_4C_2H_3O_2$ in 150 ml distilled water. Add 700 ml conc (glacial) acetic acid to form slightly more than 1 liter of solution. Since even a good grade of $NH_4C_2H_3O_2$ contains a significant amount of iron, prepare new reference standards with each buffer preparation.

d. Phenanthroline solution: Dissolve 100 mg 1,10-phenanthroline monohydrate, $C_{12}H_8N_2{\cdot}H_2O$, in 100 ml distilled water by stirring and heating to 80 C; do not boil. Discard the solution if it darkens. Heating is not necessary if 2 drops of conc HCl are added to the distilled water. (Note that 1 ml of this reagent is sufficient for no more than 100 μg Fe.)

e. Stock iron solution: The metal (1) or the salt (2) may be used for the preparation of the stock solution, which contains 200 μg Fe per 1.00 ml.

1) Use electrolytic iron wire, or "iron wire for standardizing," to prepare the solution. If necessary, clean the wire with fine sandpaper to remove any oxide coating and to produce a bright surface. Weigh 200.0 mg wire and place in a 1-liter volumetric flask. Dissolve in 20 ml 6*N* H_2SO_4 and dilute to the mark with iron-free distilled water.

2) If ferrous ammonium sulfate is preferred, add slowly 20 ml conc H_2SO_4 to 50 ml distilled water and dissolve 1.404 g $Fe(NH_4)_2(SO_4)_2{\cdot}6H_2O$. Add dropwise 0.1*N* $KMnO_4$ until a faint pink color persists. Dilute with iron-free distilled water to 1,000 ml and mix.

f. Standard iron solutions: These should be prepared the day they are used.

1) Pipet 50.00 ml stock solution into a 1-liter volumetric flask and dilute to the mark with iron-free distilled water; 1.00 ml = 10.0 μg Fe.

2) Pipet 5.00 ml stock solution into a 1-liter volumetric flask and dilute to the mark with iron-free distilled water; 1.00 ml = 1.00 μg Fe.

4. Procedure

a. Total iron: Mix the sample thoroughly and measure 50.0 ml into a 125-ml erlenmeyer flask. (If the sample contains more than 2 mg/l Fe, dilute an accurately measured aliquot containing not more than 100 μg to 50 ml; or use more phenanthroline and a 1- or 2-cm light path.) Add 2 ml conc HCl and 1 ml hydroxylamine solution. Add a few glass beads and heat to boiling. To insure dissolution of all the iron, continue boiling until the volume is reduced to 15–20 ml. (If the sample is ashed as described in ¶ 1b, take up the residue in 2 ml conc HCl and 5 ml distilled water.) Cool to room temperature and transfer to a 50- or 100-ml volumetric flask or nessler tube. Add 10 ml ammonium acetate buffer solution and 2 ml phenanthroline solution, and dilute to the mark with distilled water. Mix thoroughly and allow at least 10–15 min for maximum color development.

b. Filtrable iron: Filter the sample immediately upon collection through a 0.45-μ membrane filter into a vacuum flask containing 1 ml conc HCl per 100 ml of sample. Analyze the filtrate for total filtrable iron (¶ 4a) and/or filtrable ferrous iron (¶ 4c below). (This procedure can also be used on laboratory samples, with the understanding that normal exposure of the sample to air will alter the reduced form of iron during shipment.)

c. Ferrous iron: To determine the ferrous iron concentration, acidify a separate sample with mineral acid at the time of collection to prevent oxidation of ferrous iron. Place 2 ml conc HCl in a 100-ml stoppered sampling bottle. Fill the bottle directly from the sampling source and stopper until facilities for color development and measurement become available. Immediately before analysis, withdraw a 50-ml portion of the acidified sample and add 20 ml phenanthroline solution and 10 ml ammonium acetate solution with vigorous stirring. Dilute to 100 ml and measure the color intensity within 5 to 10 min after addition of the reagents. Do not expose to sunlight. (The color development is rapid in the presence of excess phenanthroline. The phenanthroline volume given is for less than 50 μg total iron; if larger amounts are present, use a correspondingly larger volume of phenanthroline or a more concentrated reagent.)

d. Color measurement: Prepare a series of standards by accurately pipetting calculated volumes of standard iron solutions (use the weaker solution to measure the 1–10 μg portions) into 125-ml erlenmeyer flasks, diluting to 50 ml, and carrying out the steps in ¶ 4a.

For visual comparison, prepare a set of at least ten standards, ranging from 1 to 100 μg Fe in the final 100-ml volume. Compare the colors in 100-ml tall-form nessler tubes.

For photometric measurement, use Table 124(1) as a rough guide for the selection of the proper light path. Read the standards against distilled water set at 100% transmittance (zero absorbance) and plot a calibration curve, including a blank (see ¶ 3c and General Introduction, Section 000A.7).

If the samples are colored or turbid, carry a second set of identical aliquots of the samples through all the steps of the procedure, except that no phenanthroline is added. Then, instead of distilled water, use the prepared blanks to set the photometer to 100% transmittance, and read each developed sample, with phenanthroline, against the corresponding blank without phenanthroline. Translate the observed photometer readings into iron values by means of the calibration curve. This procedure does *not* compensate for the presence of interfering ions. If color and turbidity are absent, it is quicker and just as satisfactory to read the developed samples, as well as the standards, against distilled water.

TABLE 124(1): SELECTION OF LIGHT PATH LENGTH FOR VARIOUS IRON CONCENTRATIONS

50-ml Final Volume	100-ml Final Volume	Light Path *cm*
Fe—μg		
50–200	100–400	1
25–100	50–200	2
10– 40	20– 80	5
5– 20	10– 40	10

5. Calculation

$$\text{mg/l Fe} = \frac{\mu\text{g Fe}}{\text{ml sample}}$$

Details of sample collection, storage and pretreatment should be reported, together with the iron value obtained, if they are pertinent to the interpretation.

6. Precision and Accuracy

a. The precision and accuracy will depend upon the method of sample collection and storage, the method of color measurement, the iron concentration, and the presence of interfering color, turbidity and foreign ions. In general, optimum reliability of visual comparison in nessler tubes is not better than 5% and often only 10%, whereas, under optimum conditions, photometric measurement may be reliable to 3% or 3 μg, whichever is the greater. The sensitivity limit for visual observation in nessler tubes is approximately 1 μg Fe. The variability and instability of the sample may limit the precision and accuracy of this determination more than will the errors of the analysis itself. In the past, serious divergences have been found in reports of different laboratories because of variations in methods of collecting and treating the samples.

b. A synthetic unknown sample containing 300 μg/l Fe, 500 μg/l Al, 50 μg/l Cd, 110 μg/l Cr, 470 μg/l Cu, 70 μg/l Pb, 120 μg/l Mn, 150 μg/l Ag and 650 μg/l Zn in distilled water was determined by the phenanthroline method, with a relative standard deviation of 25.5% and a relative error of 13.3% in 44 laboratories.

124 B. Tripyridine Method

1. General Discussion

a. Principle: Iron is brought into solution by boiling with acid, is reduced to the ferrous state by hydroxylamine, and is then treated with 2,2′,2″-tripyridine. Two molecules of tripyridine chelate each atom of ferrous iron to form a reddish purple complex. The color system obeys Beer's law, is independent of pH over the range 1.5 to 12, and is stable for at least 3 months. Ethylenediamine is used to buffer the mixture at pH 9.6 and to complex heavy metals which might otherwise interfere.

b. Interference: This method is subject to the same type of interference from strong oxidizing agents, color, turbidity, cyanide and nitrite as the phenanthroline method, and the treatment applied for correction is similar. However, phosphates and heavy metals, in concentrations which might be expected as a result of the pollution of a water supply, do not interfere. If much color or organic matter is present, it may be necessary to evaporate the sample, gently ash the residue, and then redissolve it in acid. The ashing should be carried out in silica, porcelain or platinum crucibles which have been cleaned by boiling for several hours in 1 + 1 HCl.

c. Minimum detectable concentration: See Section 124A.1c above.

2. Apparatus

The same apparatus is required as for Method A, except that the spectrophotometer must be used at 555 mμ and the filter photometer provided with a green or greenish yellow filter having maximum transmittance near 555 mμ.

3. Reagents

All reagents must be low in iron. Iron-free distilled water is required. Glass-stoppered reagent bottles are recommended. The hydrochloric acid, ethylenediamine, and stock iron solutions are stable indefinitely if tightly stoppered. The hydroxylamine and tripyridine solutions are stable for several months, but not indefinitely. The standard iron solutions are not stable and must be prepared freshly as needed by diluting the stock solution.

a. Hydrochloric acid, conc.

b. Ethylenediamine, full strength.* (CAUTION—*Do not pipet this liquid by mouth.*)

c. Hydroxylamine solution: See Section 124A.3b above.

d. Tripyridine reagent: With gentle warming, dissolve 100 mg 2,2′,2″-tripyridine † in 100 ml 0.1*N* HCl.

e. Standard iron solutions: See Section 124A.3e and f above.

4. Procedure

a. Treatment of sample: Into a 125-ml erlenmeyer flask, pipet a 50.0-ml portion of the sample. If the iron concentration is high, accurately pipet a smaller aliquot—to contain less than 400 μg Fe for photometric measurement or less than 200 μg Fe for visual comparison—and add enough distilled water to bring the volume up to approximately 50 ml. Add 2 ml conc HCl and boil to insure dissolution of all the iron. Cool to room temperature and add 1 ml hydroxylamine solution, 5 ml ethylenediamine and 5 ml tripyridine solution, in that order. Dilute to 100 ml in a volumetric flask or nessler tube, mix thoroughly, and compare visually or instrumentally with standards after 1 min.

b. Color measurement: Prepare a series of standards by accurately pipetting the calculated volumes of standard iron solution into 125-ml erlenmeyer flasks and carrying out the above steps. For visual comparison, prepare a set of at least 12 standards ranging from 1 to 200 μg Fe in the final 100-ml volume. Carry out the visual comparison in matched nessler tubes. For photometric measurement, use the light paths specified in Table 124(1) as a rough guide. Read the standards against distilled water set at 100% transmittance (zero absorbance) and plot a calibration curve. If the samples are colored or turbid, carry a second set of identical aliquots of the samples through all the steps of the procedure, except that no tripyridine is added. Then, instead of distilled water, use the prepared blanks to set the photometer to 100% transmittance and read each developed sample containing tripyridine against the corresponding prepared blank without tripyridine. Translate the observed photometer readings into iron values by means of the calibration curve. If color and turbidity are absent, it is quicker and just as satisfactory to read the developed samples, as well as the standards, against distilled water.

5. Calculation

See Section 124A.5.

---

* Eastman practical grade, No. P1915, or equivalent.

† Obtainable from G. F. Smith Chemical Company, Columbus, Ohio, under the name "2,2′,2″-terpyridine."

6. Precision and Accuracy

a. See Section 124A.6a and 6b.

b. A synthetic unknown sample containing 300 μg/l Fe, 500 μg/l Al, 50 μg/l Cd, 110 μg/l Cr, 470 μg/l Cu, 70 μg/l Pb, 120 μg/l Mn, 150 μg/l Ag and 650 μg/l Zn in distilled water was determined by the tripyridine method, with a relative standard deviation of 62.4% and a relative error of 13.3% in six laboratories.

124 C. Extraction Method

1. General Discussion

a. Principle: This is a modification of the phenanthroline method (*A*). If interference caused by the presence of metal ions or of anions that may complex iron is suspected, iron can be separated by extraction from 7*N*–8*N* HCl solution with diisopropyl ether. The colorimetric determination is made on a subsequent aqueous extract of the iron from the ether by the phenanthroline method.

b. Interference: This method may be subject to the same type of nonionic interference as the phenanthroline method (*A*) and treatment is similar.

c. Minimum detectable concentration: A 10.0-ml aliquot of the sample provides a concentration range between 0.1 and 20 mg/l with a possible sensitivity of 1 μg with a spectrophotometer (510 mμ) using a 10-cm cell or nessler tubes.

2. Apparatus

The same apparatus as indicated in Section 124A.2 is required. In addition, separatory funnels, 125-ml, Squibb form, with ground-glass or inert teflon stoppers, should be used in performing the extraction.

3. Reagents

The same reagents as indicated in Section 124A.3 are required, as well as diisopropyl ether.

4. Procedure

a. Extraction to ether phase: Select an aliquot of the sample and, if smaller or larger than 10 ml, dilute or concentrate it to that volume. Transfer to a 125-ml separatory funnel and add 15 ml conc HCl. Cool the solution and then extract the iron with 25 ml diisopropyl ether, shaking for 30 sec.

Draw off the lower acidic layer into a second separatory funnel and extract twice with two 10-ml portions of ether. Combine the ether extracts in the original funnel and discard the acidic layer. Failure to decolorize the HCl solution should not be taken as evidence of incomplete extraction of iron. Copper, which is not extracted, has a similar yellow color. Carry a blank with all reagents through the procedure for a zero instrument setting for photometric measurement.

b. Extraction to water phase: Extract the iron to the aqueous phase with 25 ml iron-free distilled water, shaking for 30 sec. Draw off the lower aqueous layer into a 50-ml volumetric flask. Repeat the extraction with 10 ml iron-free distilled water; add the aqueous extract to the first one in the volumetric flask and dilute to the mark with distilled water. Discard the ether layer.

c. Color development: See Method A, ¶ 4a.

d. Color measurement: See Method A, ¶ 4d.

5. Calculation

See Section 124A.5.

6. Precision and Accuracy

See Section 124A.6.

124 D. Atomic Absorption Spectrophotometric Method

See Metals, Section 129 A.

124 E. References

1. G. F. LEE & W. STUMM. 1960. Determination of ferrous iron in the presence of ferric iron using bathophenanthroline. *JAWWA* 52:1567.
2. M. M. GHOSH, J. T. O'CONNOR & R. S. ENGELBRECHT. 1967. Bathophenanthroline method for the determination of ferrous iron. *JAWWA* 59:878.

124 F. Bibliography

Phenanthroline Method

FORTUNE, W. B. & M. G. MELLON. 1938. Determination of iron with *o*-phenanthroline: A spectrophotometric study. *Ind. Eng. Chem.*, Anal. Ed. 10:60.

MEHLIG, R. P. & R. H. HULETT. 1942. Spectrophotometric determination of iron with *o*-phenanthroline and with nitro-*o*-phenanthroline. *Ind. Eng. Chem.*, Anal. Ed. 14:869.

MOSS, M. L. & M. G. MELLON. 1942. Color reactions of 1,10-phenanthroline derivatives. *Ind. Eng. Chem.*, Anal. Ed. 14: 931.

CRONHEIM, G. & W. WINK. 1942. Determination of divalent iron (by *o*-nitrosophenol). *Ind. Eng. Chem.*, Anal. Ed. 14:447.

HALLINAN, F. J. 1943. Determination of iron in water. *Ind. Eng. Chem.*, Anal. Ed. 15:510.

CALDWELL, D. H. & R. B. ADAMS. 1946. Colorimetric determination of iron in water with *o*-phenanthroline. *JAWWA* 38:727.

Standard Methods for the Examination of Water and Sewage (9th ed.), 1946. APHA and AWWA, New York, pp. 51–52.

WELCHER, F. J. 1947. *Organic Analytical Reagents.* D. Van Nostrand Co., Princeton, N. J., Vol. 3, pp. 85–98.

KOLTHOFF, I. M., T. S. LEE & D. L. LEUSSING. 1948. Equilibrium and kinetic studies on the formation and dissociation of ferroin and ferriin. *Anal. Chem.* 20:985.

RYAN, J. A. & G. H. BOTHAM. 1949. Iron in aluminum alloys: Colorimetric determination using 1,10-phenanthroline. *Anal. Chem.* 21:1521.

REITZ, L. K., A. S. O'BRIEN & T. L. DAVIS. 1950. Evaluation of three iron methods using a factorial experiment. *Anal. Chem.* 22:1470.

SANDELL, E. B. 1959. *Colorimetric Deter-*

mination of Traces of Metals (3rd ed.). Interscience Publishers, New York, Chapter 22.

RAINWATER, F. H. & L. L. THATCHER. 1960. Methods of collection and analysis of water samples. *U. S. Geol. Survey Water Supply Paper* No. 1454.

Tripyridine Method

MOSS, M. L. & M. G. MELLON. 1942. Colorimetric determination of iron with 2,2′-bipyridine and with 2,2′,2″-tripyridine. *Ind. Eng. Chem.*, Anal. Ed. 14:862.

WELCHER, F. J. 1947. *Organic Analytical Reagents*. D. Van Nostrand Co., Princeton, N. J., Vol. 3, pp. 100–104.

MORRIS, R. L. 1952. Determination of iron in water in the presence of heavy metals. *Anal. Chem.* 25:1376.

125 LEAD

Lead is a serious cumulative body poison and is to be avoided. Natural waters seldom contain more than 20 μg/l, although values as high as 400 μg/l have been reported. The presence of lead in a water supply may arise from industrial, mine and smelter discharges, or from the dissolution of old lead plumbing. Tap waters which are soft, acid, and not suitably treated may contain lead resulting from an attack on the lead service pipes.

For normal drinking waters low in organic matter and tin, the brief method given here should prove adequate. The method for lead described in Section 211(II)G is recommended for waters high in organic matter, such as sewage and industrial wastes.

Selection of method: The atomic absorption spectrophotometric method entails fewer operations on the sample and is therefore adaptable for multiple screening determinations. The dithizone method yields satisfactory results and is suitable for laboratories equipped with generally available apparatus.

125 A. Dithizone Method

1. General Discussion

a. Principle: Dithizone dissolved in carbon tetrachloride will extract lead from a slightly basic solution. Lead and dithizone form a metal complex, lead dithizonate, which is soluble in carbon tetrachloride, with the formation of a red color. Measurement of the amount of red color formed yields an estimation of the lead present.

b. Interference: Before attempting this method, the analyst is urged to acquaint himself thoroughly with the theory and practice of dithizone procedures. The use of careful technic in this method is of the utmost importance. The necessity of checking and preventing contamination by lead and other metals cannot be overemphasized. The procedure is extremely sensitive, and measurable amounts of lead may be picked up from glassware and reagents. Samples should be collected in bottles made of lead-free glass or plastic containers. If possible, separatory funnels used in the lead determination should be reserved for this purpose only. Reagents should be extracted with a dithizone solution to remove all traces of lead. A reagent blank should be carried through the procedure to compensate for the lead which may be introduced from glassware and reagents.

Interference by most metals which form dithizonates is eliminated by double extraction at controlled pH. In the first extraction, ammonium citrate and cyanide will complex many heavy metals. Hydroxylamine inhibits dithizone oxidation by ferricyanide produced by iron. Tin in large amounts can be removed by volatilization as $SnBr_4$.

Organic material, if present, must be removed by acid digestion or, less satisfactorily, by ignition. The analysis should be carried out in diffused light, since bright sunlight tends to oxidize dithizone and dithizonate.

c. *Minimum detectable concentration:* Approximately 2 μg Pb.

2. Apparatus

a. COLORIMETRIC EQUIPMENT—One of the following is required:

1) Spectrophotometer, for use at 510 mμ with a light path of 1 cm or longer.

2) Filter photometer, equipped with a green filter having a maximum transmittance near 510 mμ and a light path of 1 cm or longer.

b. SEPARATORY FUNNELS—125–150 ml, preferably with inert teflon stopcocks.

c. GLASSWARE—All glassware, including sample bottles, should be cleaned with 1 + 1 HNO_3 and then rinsed thoroughly with lead-free water. A finishing rinse with a dithizone solution may also be advisable.

3. Reagents

a. *Lead-free water:* Prepare by redistilling distilled water in an all-pyrex apparatus, or by passing distilled water through a mixed bed of ion-exchange resins. Use lead-free water for the preparation of all reagents and dilutions.

b. *Stock lead solution:* Dissolve 1.599 g anhydrous lead nitrate, $Pb(NO_3)_2$, in lead-free water to which has been added 1 ml conc HNO_3. Dilute to 1,000 ml. This solution contains 1.00 mg Pb per 1.00 ml.

c. *Intermediate lead solution:* Dilute 10.00 ml stock solution to 200 ml with lead-free water; 1.00 ml = 50.0 μg Pb. Prepare the intermediate solution immediately before use.

d. *Standard lead solution:* Dilute 10.00 ml intermediate lead solution to 250 ml with lead-free water; 1.00 ml = 2.00 μg Pb. Prepare the standard solution immediately before use.

e. *Ammonium citrate reagent:* Dissolve 50 g $(NH_4)_3C_6H_5O_7$ in 100 ml lead-free water. Add lead-free NH_4OH to adjust the pH to between 8.5 and 9.0. Extract with 10-ml portions dithizone solution until the last portion remains green. Wash with carbon tetrachloride to remove excess dithizone.

f. *Hydroxylamine hydrochloride reagent:* Dissolve 20 g $NH_2OH \cdot HCl$ in 65 ml lead-free water. Add conc NH_4OH to make the solution alkaline to thymol blue. Extract with 10-ml portions dithizone solution until the last portion remains green. Wash with carbon tetrachloride to remove excess dithizone. Make the solution just acid with HCl and dilute to 100 ml.

g. *Thymol blue indicator solution:* Dissolve 100 mg thymolsulfonephthalein sodium salt in 100 ml lead-free water.

h. Ammonium hydroxide, conc.

i. Potassium cyanide solution: Dissolve 5.0 g KCN in lead-free water and dilute to about 50 ml. Extract with 10-ml portions dithizone solution until the last portion remains green. Wash with carbon tetrachloride to remove excess dithizone.

CAUTION: *Potassium cyanide is extremely poisonous and more than customary precautions should be observed in its handling. Never use mouth pipets to deliver volumes of cyanide solutions.*

j. Nitric acid, conc, and 1 + 99.

k. Dithizone solution: Dissolve 50 mg diphenylthiocarbazone in 1 liter carbon tetrachloride, CCl_4. Refrigerate this solution to preserve its stability for several weeks.

l. Ammoniacal cyanide-citrate reagent: Dissolve 10 g KCN in 500 ml conc NH_4OH. Add 10 g citric acid, $H_3C_6H_5O_7 \cdot H_2O$, and dilute to 1 liter with lead-free water. *Handle with the same caution as in* ¶ i above.

m. Carbon tetrachloride, CCl_4.

n. Methyl orange indicator solution.

4. Procedure

a. Preparation of calibration curve: Prepare a series of standards containing 0, 2.00, 5.00, 10.0, 15.0 and 20.0 μg Pb per 25.0 ml. Use lead-free water for diluting the standard lead solution. Transfer 25 ml into a separatory funnel. Add 10 ml ammonium citrate reagent, 2 ml hydroxylamine hydrochloride reagent, and 5 drops thymol blue indicator solution. Make alkaline with conc NH_4OH. Carefully add 4 ml KCN solution and adjust the pH to 8.5–9 (green color) with 1 + 99 HNO_3. Immediately extract by shaking vigorously for 30 sec with 5-ml portions dithizone solution until the color in the last portion remains unchanged. To the combined extracts in a second separatory funnel, add 20 ml 1 + 99 HNO_3. Shake for 1 min and discard the CCl_4 layer. Dilute the acid extract with 1 + 99 HNO_3 to 50.0 ml. Add 4.0 ml ammoniacal cyanide-citrate reagent and 5.0 ml dithizone solution and immediately shake for 1 min. After allowing the layers to separate, transfer the CCl_4 extract into a dry absorption cell. Set the blank at 100% transmittance or zero absorbance and determine the transmittance or absorbance of the standards at 510 mμ. Plot a calibration curve, which should be linear.

b. Sample treatment: Pipet a suitable volume of sample containing not more than 15 μg Pb in 25 ml of the sample into a separatory funnel. (If the sample contains less than 50 μg/l Pb, concentrate the sample by measuring 100 ml sample into a beaker, acidifying to methyl orange indicator with conc HNO_3, and adding 1 ml excess conc HNO_3. Cover with a watch glass and evaporate to about 10 ml on a steam bath. Adjust the volume to 25.0 ml with lead-free water.) Prepare a comparison blank, using lead-free water, and treat in the same manner as the sample. Unless the calibration is being determined simultaneously, prepare at least one standard containing 15.0 μg Pb and run it in conjunction with the sample. Proceed as in ¶ 4a above. Read the lead content from the calibration curve.

5. Calculation

$$\text{mg/l Pb} = \frac{\mu\text{g Pb}}{\text{ml sample}}$$

6. Precision and Accuracy

A synthetic unknown sample containing 70 μg/l Pb, 500 μg/l Al, 50 μg/l Cd, 110 μg/l Cr, 470 μg/l Cu, 300 μg/l Fe, 120 μg/l Mn, 150 μg/l Ag and 650 μg/l Zn in distilled water was determined by the dithizone method, with a relative standard deviation of 42.1% and a relative error of 8.5% in 43 laboratories.

7. Bibliography

SANDELL, E. B. 1959. *Colorimetric Determination of Traces of Metals* (3rd ed.). Interscience Publishers, New York, Chapter 23 and pp. 144–176.

RAINWATER, F. H. & L. L. THATCHER. 1960. Methods for collection and analysis of water samples. *U. S. Geol. Survey Water Supply Paper* No. 1454, Chapter D:20.

125 B. Atomic Absorption Spectrophotometric Method

See Metals, Section 129A.

LIGNIN: See Tannin and Lignin, Section 160, following.

126 LITHIUM

A minor constituent of minerals, lithium is present in fresh waters in concentrations below 10 mg/l. Brines and thermal waters may contain higher lithium levels. The use of lithium or its salts in dehumidifying units, medicinal waters, metallurgical processes, and the manufacture of some types of glass and storage batteries may contribute to its presence in wastes. Lithium hypochlorite is available commercially as a source of chlorine and may be used in swimming pools.

126 A. Flame Photometric Method (TENTATIVE)

1. General Discussion

a. Principle: Like its sister elements, sodium and potassium, lithium can be determined in trace amounts by flame photometric methods. The measurement can be performed at a wavelength of 671 mμ.

b. Interference: Barium, strontium and calcium interfere in the flame photometric determination of lithium and can be removed by the addition of a sodium sulfate-sodium carbonate solution which precipitates $BaSO_4$, $SrCO_3$ and $CaCO_3$. The content of either sodium or magnesium individually must not exceed 10 mg in the aliquot taken for analysis.

c. Minimum detectable concentration: The minimum lithium concentration detectable by the flame photometric method is of the order of 0.1 mg/l.

d. Sampling and storage: Collect the sample in a pyrex bottle. Polyethylene bottles are not recommended because of the contamination which may result from the occasional use of lithium chloride as a catalyst in the manufacture of polyethylene.

2. Apparatus

a. Flame photometer: a Perkin-Elmer Model 52-C flame photometer; or a Beckman Model DU spectrophotometer equipped with photomultiplier tube and flame accessory; or the equivalent.

3. Reagents

a. Sodium sulfate and sodium carbonate reagent: Dissolve 5 g Na_2SO_4 and 10 g Na_2CO_3 in distilled water and dilute to 1 liter.

b. Stock lithium solution: Dissolve 610.9 mg anhydrous lithium chloride, LiCl, in distilled water and dilute to 1,000 ml; 1.00 ml = 100 μg Li. Weigh the LiCl very rapidly because the salt is highly deliquescent. Dry the salt overnight in an oven at 105 C.

c. Standard lithium solution: Dilute 20.00 ml stock lithium chloride solution to 1,000 ml with distilled water. This solution contains 2.0 μg Li per ml.

4. Procedure

a. Removal of interference from sample: Take a sample of 50.0 ml or less, so that the concentrations in the aliquot do not exceed the following: Na, 10 mg; Mg, 10 mg. Add 5.0 ml $Na_2SO_4 - Na_2CO_3$ reagent. Bring the solution to a boil to coagulate the precipitate of $BaSO_4$, $SrCO_3$, $CaCO_3$, and possibly $MgCO_3$. Allow enough time for complete precipitation; otherwise a feathery precipitate of $BaSO_4$ will appear after filtration. Pass the sample through Whatman No. 42 filter paper, wash with distilled water, and dilute the filtrate to 50.0 ml for the flame photometric measurement.

b. Treatment of standard solution: Add 5.0 ml $Na_2SO_4 - Na_2CO^3$ reagent to 50.0 ml of the standard lithium solution. (Boiling is unnecessary because no precipitation occurs in the standard. When boiling is avoided, the treated standard contains 1.8 μg Li per ml.)

c. Flame photometric measurement: Determine the unknown lithium concentration by direct intensity measurements at a wavelength of 671 mμ. (The bracketing method can be used with some instruments, while the construction of a calibration curve is necessary with other photometric instruments.) Run the sample, distilled water (0 mg/l Li), and the lithium standard as nearly simultaneously as possible. For best results, take the average of several readings on each solution. In many cases, the calibration readings on distilled water and the lithium standard will suffice. Follow the manufacturer's instructions for operation of the instrument used in the determination.

5. Calculation

$$\text{mg/l Li} = \frac{\mu\text{g Li}}{\text{ml sample}}$$

6. Accuracy

The lithium concentration can be determined with an accuracy of ±0.1–0.2 mg/l in the lithium range of 0.7 to 1.2 mg/l.

7. Bibliography

KUEMMEL, D. F. & H. L. KARL. 1954. Flame photometric determination of alkali and alkaline earth elements in cast iron. *Anal. Chem.* 26:386.

BRUMBAUGH, R. J. & W. E. FANUS. 1954. Determination of lithium in spodumene by flame photometry. *Anal. Chem.* 26:463.

ELLESTAD, R. B. & E. L. HORSTMAN. 1955. Flame photometric determination of lithium in silicate rocks. *Anal. Chem.* 27:1229.

WHISMAN, M. & B. H. ECCLESTON. 1955. Flame spectra of twenty metals using a recording flame spectrophotometer. *Anal. Chem.* 27:1861.

HORSTMAN, E. L. 1956. Flame photometric determination of lithium, rubidium, and cesium in silicate rocks. *Anal. Chem.* 28:1417.

127 MAGNESIUM

Magnesium ranks eighth among the elements in order of abundance and is a common constituent of natural water supplies. Important contributors to the hardness of a water, magnesium salts break down on heating to form deleterious scale in boilers. Concentrations in excess of 125 mg/l can also exert a cathartic and diuretic action. Chemical softening treatment or ion exchange is employed to reduce the magnesium and associated hardness to tolerable levels. The magnesium concentration may vary from zero to several hundred mg/l, depending on the source and the treatment of the water.

Selection of method: The three methods presented for the determination of magnesium are applicable to all natural waters. Magnesium can be determined by the gravimetric method (*A*) only after prior removal of calcium salts and is generally determined by this method on the filtrate and washings from the gravimetric and permanganate calcium determination (see Sections 110A and B). The atomic absorption spectrophotometric (*B*) and photometric (*C*) methods following enable direct determinations on the water sample. The three methods can be applied to all concentrations by the selection of suitable aliquots. Choice of method is largely a matter of personal preference.

127 A. Gravimetric Method

1. General Discussion

a. Principle: Diammonium hydrogen phosphate precipitates magnesium quantitatively in ammoniacal solution as magnesium ammonium phosphate. The precipitate is ignited to, and weighed as, magnesium pyrophosphate. A choice is presented between: (a) destruction of ammonium salts and oxalate, followed by single precipitation of magnesium ammonium phosphate; and (b) double precipitation without pretreatment. Where time is not a factor, double precipitation is preferable. Pretreatment is faster but requires close attention to avoid mechanical loss.

b. Interference: The solution should be reasonably free from aluminum, calcium, iron, manganese, silica, strontium, and suspended matter. The solution should not contain more than about 3.5 g NH_4Cl.

2. Reagents

a. Nitric acid, conc.

b. Hydrochloric acid, conc; also 1 + 1; 1 + 9; and 1 + 99.

c. Methyl red indicator solution: Dissolve 100 mg methyl red sodium salt in distilled water and dilute to 100 ml.

d. Diammonium hydrogen phosphate solution: Dissolve 30 g $(NH_4)_2$-HPO_4 in distilled water and make up to 100 ml.

e. Ammonium hydroxide, conc; also 1 + 19.

3. Procedure

a. By removal of oxalate and ammonium salts: To the combined filtrate and washings from the calcium determination, which should not contain more than 60 mg Mg, or to an aliquot containing less than this amount in a 600- or 800-ml beaker, add 50 ml conc HNO_3 and evaporate carefully to dryness on a hot plate. Take care that the reaction does not become too violent during the latter part of the evaporation; the analyst should be in constant attendance to avoid losses through spattering. Moisten the residue with 2–3 ml conc HCl; add 20 ml distilled water, warm, filter, and wash. To the filtrate add 3 ml conc HCl, 2–3 drops methyl red solution, and 10 ml $(NH_4)_2HPO_4$ solution. Cool and add conc NH_4OH, drop by drop, stirring constantly, until the color changes to yellow. Stir for 5 min; add 5 ml conc NH_4OH and stir vigorously for 10 min more. Allow to stand overnight and then filter through S&S * No. 589 White Ribbon or equivalent filter paper. Wash with 1 + 19 NH_4OH. Transfer to a crucible which has been ignited, cooled and weighed. Dry the precipitate thoroughly in the crucible and then burn the paper off *slowly,* allowing circulation of air. Heat at about 500 C until the residue is white. Then ignite for 30-min periods at 1,100 C to constant weight.

b. By double precipitation: To the combined filtrate and washings from the calcium determination, which should not contain more than 60 mg Mg, or to an aliquot containing less than this amount, add 2–3 drops methyl red solution; adjust the volume to 150 ml and acidify with 1 + 1 HCl. Add 10 ml $(NH_4)_2HPO_4$ solution. Cool the solution. Then add conc NH_4OH, drop by drop, stirring constantly, until the color changes to yellow. Stir for 5 min, add 5 ml conc NH_4OH, and stir vigorously for 10 min more. Allow to stand overnight and then filter through S&S No. 589 White Ribbon or equivalent filter paper. Wash with 1 + 19 NH_4OH. Discard the filtrate and washings. Dissolve the precipitate with 50 ml warm 1 + 9 HCl and wash the paper well with hot 1 + 99 HCl. Add 2–3 drops methyl red solution, 1–2 ml $(NH_4)_2HPO_4$ solution, and precipitate as before, after adjusting the volume to 100–150 ml. Allow the solution to stand in a cool place for at least 4 hr or preferably overnight. Filter through S&S No. 589 White Ribbon or equivalent filter paper and wash with 1 + 19 NH_4OH. Transfer to a cruci-

* Carl Schleicher and Schuell Co.

ble which has been ignited, cooled and weighed. Dry the precipitate thoroughly in the crucible and then burn the paper off *slowly,* allowing circulation of air. Heat at about 500 C until the residue is white. Then ignite for 30-min periods at 1,100 C to constant weight.

4. Calculation

$$\text{mg/l Mg} = \frac{\text{mg } Mg_2P_2O_7 \times 218.5}{\text{ml sample}}$$

5. Precision and Accuracy

A synthetic unknown sample containing 82 mg/l Mg, 108 mg/l Ca, 3.1 mg/l K, 19.9 mg/l Na, 241 mg/l chloride, 1.1 mg/l nitrate N, 250 μg/l nitrite N, 259 mg/l sulfate, and 42.5 mg/l total alkalinity (contributed by $NaHCO_3$) was determined by the gravimetric method, with a relative standard deviation of 6.3% and a relative error of 4.9% in eight laboratories.

127 B. Atomic Absorption Spectrophotometric Method

See Metals, Section 129A.

127 C. Photometric Method

1. General Discussion

a. Principle: When magnesium hydroxide is precipitated in the presence of brilliant yellow, the dye is adsorbed on the precipitate and its color changes from orange to red. A stabilizer is added to maintain the $Mg(OH)_2$ in colloidal suspension.

b. Interference: Interference from calcium and aluminum is avoided by raising the concentrations of these ions to a level where their influence is constant and predictable. Iron is without effect in amounts below 2.5 mg/l, but in excess of that concentration it contributes to the magnesium color. Tolerable limits for other ions are: 250 mg/l chloride, 5 mg/l fluoride, 5 mg/l orthophosphate. Manganic and zinc ions must be absent. Samples containing more than 0.5 mg/l chlorine must be dechlorinated.

c. Minimum detectable concentration: 100 μg Mg.

2. Apparatus

COLORIMETRIC EQUIPMENT—One of the following is required (visual comparison is difficult due to the intensity of color):

a. Spectrophotometer, for use at 525 mμ, providing a light path of 2 cm or longer.

b. Filter photometer, providing a light path of 2 cm or longer and equipped with a green filter having maximum transmittance near 525 mμ.

c. Glassware: All glassware should be cleaned with concentrated hydrochloric acid or nitric acid, followed by thorough rinsing with distilled water.

3. Reagents

All solutions are stable except the dechlorinating, brilliant yellow, and stabilizer solutions.

a. Sulfuric acid, 0.02*N*.

b. Saturated calcium sulfate solution, approximately 20 g/l $CaSO_4$: Add a large excess of $CaSO_4$ to distilled water; let stand as long as possible (preferably overnight); then filter through a filter paper sufficiently retentive for fine particles.

c. Aluminum sulfate reagent: Dissolve 310 mg $Al_2(SO_4)_3 \cdot 18H_2O$ in distilled water, add 0.3 ml conc H_2SO_4, and dilute to 1 liter.

d. Stabilizer solution: Place 1.0 g Methocel type-MC Premium, 25 cps viscosity,* in a glass-stoppered bottle containing 100 ml distilled water and shake a few times. Store in a refrigerator. Allow it to reach the temperature of other reagents before use. Prepare a new solution when mold growth or sediment appears.

e. Brilliant yellow solution: Dissolve 500 mg solid dye † in 1 liter distilled water. Prepare every 2 or 3 days.

f. Sodium hydroxide, 6*N*.

g. Stock magnesium solution: Use either the metal *(1)* or the salt *(2)* for the preparation of the stock solution, which contains 1.00 mg Mg per 1.00 ml.

1) Weigh out 1.000 g rough turnings of pure magnesium metal, not less than 99.9% Mg. Transfer quantitatively to a 500-ml erlenmeyer flask. Place a funnel in the neck of the flask and add about 150 ml distilled water. Add, 1 ml at a time, 5.0 ml 1 + 1 H_2SO_4. Mix well after each addition and allow the reaction to subside before making the next addition of acid. When all the acid has been added and the reaction becomes quiet, bring to a gentle boil and continue boiling for about 10 min to insure complete dissolution. Cool, transfer quantitatively to a 1-liter volumetric flask, and make up to the mark. The solution should be water white and crystal clear.

2) Dissolve 10.136 g magnesium sulfate heptahydrate, $MgSO_4 \cdot 7H_2O$, in distilled water and dilute to 1,000 ml. Determine the exact magnesium concentration in this solution by Method A.

h. Standard magnesium solution: Dilute 100.0 ml magnesium stock solution to 1,000 ml with distilled water; 1.00 ml = 100 μg Mg.

i. Reagent for removal of chlorine interference—sodium sulfite solution: Dissolve 1.0 g anhydrous Na_2SO_3 in 100 ml distilled water. Prepare daily.

4. Procedure

Measure into a 100-ml volumetric flask a sample aliquot containing between 100 and 600 μg Mg. If necessary, add 1 ml sodium sulfite solution to dechlorinate. Add, in order, 1 ml sulfuric acid solution (or sufficient acid to prevent precipitation of succeeding calcium and aluminum additions), 20 ml calcium sulfate solution and 5.0 ml aluminum sulfate reagent. Bring volume to about 80 ml with distilled water and mix. Add 5.0 ml stabilizer solution, 2.0 ml brilliant yellow solution, and 3.5 ml NaOH solution. Dilute to

* Methocel MC Premium 25 (Dow Chemical Co.) is a commercial product for which no specifications can be given. It will be necessary for the analyst to confirm product quality for this application.

† National Aniline Co., Color Index No. 364, or equivalent.

the mark, shake vigorously, and wait 5 min for full color development. Measure photometrically within 1 hr against a blank prepared from distilled water and all of the reagents. Use a light path of 2 cm or longer. Prepare a standard curve, from 0, 100, 200, 400 and 600 μg/Mg. Check at least two points with each set of determinations.

5. Calculation

$$\text{mg/l Mg} = \frac{\mu\text{g Mg}}{\text{ml sample}}$$

6. Precision and Accuracy

A precision of ±1 mg/l and an accuracy of ±2 mg/l can be achieved in the magnesium range 2–75 mg/l.

127 D. Bibliography

Gravimetric Method

EPPERSON, A. W. 1928. The pyrophosphate method for the determination of magnesium and phosphoric anhydride. *J. Amer. Chem. Soc.* 50:321.

KOLTHOFF, I. M. & E. B. SANDELL. 1952. *Textbook of Quantitative Inorganic Analysis* (3rd ed.). Macmillan Co., New York, Chapter 22.

HILLEBRAND, W. F. et al. 1953. *Applied Inorganic Analysis* (2nd ed.). John Wiley & Sons, New York, Chapter 41 and pp. 133–134.

Photometric Method

TARAS, M. 1948. Photometric determination of magnesium in water with brilliant yellow. *Anal. Chem.* 20:1156.

128 MANGANESE

Although manganese in ground water is generally present in the soluble divalent ionic form because of the complete absence of oxygen, there are times when part or all of the manganese in a water treatment plant may occur in a higher valence state. The total manganese determination does not differentiate the various manganese valence states. At present, the permanganate ion in the heptavalent state is used as a treatment procedure for removal of manganese and/or organic matter causing taste. The presence of excess permanganate, complexed trivalent manganese, or a suspension of quadrivalent manganese must be detected with great sensitivity to control the treatment to prevent their discharge into the distribution system. There is evidence to indicate that manganese occurs in surface waters both in suspension in the quadrivalent state as well as in the trivalent state in a relatively stable, soluble complex. Although rarely present in excess of 1 mg/l, manganese imparts objectionable and tenacious stains to laundry and plumbing fixtures. The low manganese limits imposed on an acceptable water stem from these practical considerations rather than for toxicological reasons. Special means of removal are often necessary, such as chemical precipitation, pH adjustment, aeration, superchlorination, and the use of special ion-exchange materials.

1. Selection of method: The atomic absorption spectrophotometric method enables the direct determination of water samples with acceptable accuracy and is the method of choice. Of the two colorimetric methods described, the persulfate method is preferred for unknown samples on two counts: The use of mercuric ion can control the interference from a limited chloride ion concentration, and also the method is more rapid in the presence of low manganese concentrations. The periodate method is suitable for samples which contain more than 10 μg manganese and in which chloride and organic matter are absent.

2. Sampling and storage: Manganese may exist in a soluble form in a neutral water when first collected, but it oxidizes readily to a higher oxidation state and precipitates from solution or becomes adsorbed on the walls of the container. Manganese should be determined very soon after sample collection. When delay is unavoidable, a total manganese can be determined if the sample is acidified at the time of collection.

128 A. Atomic Absorption Spectrophotometric Method

See Metals, Section 129A.

128 B. Persulfate Method

1. General Discussion

a. Principle: Persulfate oxidation of soluble manganous compounds to form permanganate is carried out in the presence of silver nitrate under the conditions shown by Nydahl (1949, see Bibliography, Section 128D, below) to be most effective. The resulting color is stable for at least 24 hr if excess persulfate is present and organic matter is absent.

b. Interference: As much as 0.1 g sodium chloride is prevented from interfering by the addition of mercuric sulfate to form slightly dissociated complexes. Only minute amounts of bromide and iodide may be present. Reasonable amounts of organic matter may be present if the period of heating is increased and more persulfate is added.

c. Minimum detectable concentration: 5 μg Mn.

2. Apparatus

COLORIMETRIC EQUIPMENT—One of the following is required:

a. Spectrophotometer, for use at 525 mμ, providing a light path of 1 cm or longer.

b. Filter photometer, providing a light path of 1 cm or longer and equipped with a green filter having maximum transmittance near 525 mμ.

c. Nessler tubes, matched, 100-ml, tall form.

Visual comparison is recommended only in the range of 5–100 μg Mn (in the 100-ml final solution). For photometric measurement, the following tabulation shows the length of light path appropriate for various concentrations of manganese in the 100-ml final solution:

Mn Range µg	Light Path cm
5–200	15
20–400	5
50–1,000	2
100–1,500	1

3. Reagents

a. Special reagent: Dissolve 75 g mercuric sulfate, $HgSO_4$, in 400 ml conc HNO_3 and 200 ml distilled water. Add 200 ml 85% phosphoric acid, H_3PO_4, and 35 mg silver nitrate, $AgNO_3$, and dilute the cooled solution to 1 liter.

b. Ammonium persulfate, $(NH_4)_2S_2O_8$, solid.

c. Standard manganese solution: Prepare a 0.1*N* $KMnO_4$ solution in the usual manner by dissolving 3.2 g $KMnO_4$ in distilled water and making up to 1 liter. Age this solution for several weeks in sunlight or heat for several hours near the boiling point, then filter through a fritted-glass filter crucible and carefully standardize against sodium oxalate. [The standard $KMnO_4$ solution prepared for the titrimetric calcium determination (Section 110B. 3c above) may be conveniently used.] Calculate the volume of this solution necessary to prepare 1 liter of solution of such strength that 1.00 ml = 50.0 µg Mn, as follows:

$$\text{ml } KMnO_4 = \frac{4.55}{\text{normality } KMnO_4}$$

To this volume add 2 to 3 ml conc H_2SO_4 and then sodium bisulfite solution (10 g $NaHSO_3$ plus 100 ml distilled water) dropwise, with stirring, until the permanganate color disappears. Boil to remove excess SO_2, cool, and dilute to 1,000 ml with distilled water. Dilute this solution further in order to measure small amounts of manganese.

d. Hydrogen peroxide, 30%.

4. Procedure

a. Treatment of sample: To a suitable aliquot of the sample, add 5 ml special reagent. Concentrate to 90 ml by boiling or dilute to 90 ml. Add 1 g ammonium persulfate, bring to boiling, and boil for 1 min. Do not heat on a water bath. Remove from the heat source, allow to stand for 1 min, then cool under the tap. (Too long a boiling time results in decomposition of excess persulfate and subsequent loss of permanganate color; too slow cooling has the same effect.) Dilute to 100 ml with distilled water free from reducing substances, and mix. Compare visually or measure photometrically, using standards containing 0, 5.00, etc., to 1,500 µg Mn, prepared by treating various amounts of the standard Mn solution in the same way. Make the photometric measurements against a distilled-water blank. (See ¶ 2 et seq for information concerning the appropriate wavelength and the proper optical cells to use with different amounts of Mn.)

b. Correction for turbidity or interfering color: Avoid filtration because of possible retention of some permanganate on the filter paper. If visual comparison is used, the effect of turbidity can only be estimated and no correction can be made for the effect of interfering colored ions. When photometric measurements are made, use the following "bleaching" method, which also corrects for interfering color: As soon as the photometer reading has been made, add 0.05 ml hydrogen peroxide solution directly to the sample in the optical cell. Mix the solution and, as soon as the permanganate color has completely faded and no bubbles are left, take the reading again. Convert the readings to absorbances and make the proper deduction. Alternatively, read the values from the calibration curve as "apparent" manganese and interferences as manganese, and make the proper deduction.

5. Calculation

$$\text{mg/l Mn} = \frac{\mu\text{g Mn}}{\text{ml sample}}$$

6. Precision and Accuracy

A synthetic unknown sample containing 120 μg/l Mn, 500 μg/l Al, 50 μg/l Cd, 110 μg/l Cr, 470 μg/l Cu, 300 μg/l Fe, 70 μg/l Pb, 150 μg/l Ag and 650 μg/l Zn in distilled water was determined by the persulfate method, with a relative standard deviation of 26.3% and a relative error of 0% in 33 laboratories.

A second synthetic unknown sample, similar in all respects except for 50 μg/l Mn and 1,000 μg/l Cu, was determined by the persulfate method, with a relative standard deviation of 50.3% and a relative error of 7.2% in 17 laboratories.

128 C. Periodate Method

1. General Discussion

a. Principle: With periodate as the oxidizing agent acting upon soluble manganous compounds to form permanganate, Beer's law holds closely up to 15 mg. The intensity of the color is not affected by variation in acid or periodate concentration and the color is stable for many months. To obtain complete oxidation of small amounts of manganese (10 μg or less), silver nitrate is added and the heating time increased.

b. Interference: Reducing substances capable of reacting with periodate or permanganate must be removed or destroyed before the periodate oxidation is attempted. Although chloride in small amounts can be oxidized by periodate, removal by evaporation with sulfuric acid is preferred, especially when the sample contains only a small amount of manganese. This treatment, however, usually results in the dehydration of silica and the production of turbidity. Interference from other oxidizable substances, including organic materials, is eliminated by boiling the sample with nitric acid. Phosphoric acid is added to decolorize ferric iron by complex formation and prevent possible precipitation of periodates or iodates of manganese. Foreign metals, with a few exceptions, do not interfere, except those whose ions are colored; for these a method of correction is described.

c. Minimum detectable concentration: 5 μg Mn.

2. Apparatus

See Section 128B.2a-c above.

3. Reagents

a. Sulfuric acid, conc.

b. Nitric acid, conc.

c. Phosphoric acid, syrupy, 85%.

d. Periodate: Use either (1) the potassium or (2) the sodium salt.

1) POTASSIUM METAPERIODATE, KIO_4, solid.

2) SODIUM PARAPERIODATE, $Na_3H_2IO_6$ (also called trisodium periodate [para]), solid.

e. Silver nitrate.

f. Standard manganese solution: Prepare as described in Section 128B.3c preceding.

g. Hydrogen peroxide, 30%.

4. Procedure

a. Pretreatment of samples: To remove chloride or other oxidizable substances such as organic matter, take a suitable aliquot of sample and add 5 ml conc H_2SO_4 and 5 ml conc HNO_3, mixing between additions. Evaporate to SO_3 fumes. Cool, add 85 ml distilled water, and cool again. Add 5 ml HNO_3 and 5 ml H_3PO_4, and mix. Treat as described in ¶ b below, beginning with ". . . add 0.3 g KIO_4."

b. Oxidation: To a suitable aliquot of the sample, add 5 ml conc H_2SO_4, mix, and cool. Add 5 ml HNO_3 and 5 ml H_3PO_4, and mix. Concentrate to about 90 ml by boiling. Cool; add 0.3 g KIO_4 or 0.5 g $Na_3H_2IO_6$. If the amount of Mn is 10 μg or less, also add 20 mg $AgNO_3$. Heat to boiling, with stirring, and keep at or slightly below the boiling point for 10 min (or at least 1 hr for very small amounts of Mn). Cool, dilute to 100 ml with distilled water free from reducing substances, and mix. Compare visually or measure photometrically, using standards containing 0, 5.00, etc., to 1,500 μg Mn, prepared by treating the various amounts of standard Mn solution in the same way. Make the photometric measurements against a distilled-water blank. (Refer to Section 128B.2 preceding for information concerning the appropriate wavelength and the proper optical cells to be used with different amounts of Mn.)

c. Correction for turbidity or interfering color: Follow the procedure described in Section 128B.4b above.

5. Calculation

$$\text{mg/l Mn} = \frac{\mu\text{g Mn}}{\text{ml sample}}$$

6. Precision and Accuracy

A synthetic unknown sample containing 120 μg/l Mn, 500 μg/l Al, 50 μg/l Cd, 110 μg/l Cr, 470 μg/l Cu, 300 μg/l Fe, 70 μg/l Pb, 150 μg/l Ag, and 650 μg/l Zn in distilled water was determined by the periodate method, with a relative standard deviation of 36.0% and a relative error of 25.0% in 14 laboratories.

128 D. Bibliography

Persulfate Method

RICHARDS, M. B. 1930. Colorimetric determination of manganese in biological material. *Analyst* 55:554.

NYDAHL, F. 1949. Determination of manganese by the persulfate method. *Anal. Chem. Acta* 3:144.

MILLS, S. M. 1950. Elusive manganese. *Water & Sewage Works* 97:92.

SANDELL, E. B. 1959. *Colormetric Deter-*

mination of Traces of Metals (3rd ed.). Interscience Publishers, New York, Chapter 26.

Periodate Method

MEHLIG, J. P. 1939. Colorimetric determination of manganese with periodate. *Ind. Eng. Chem.*, Anal. Ed. 11:274.

ROWLAND, G. P., JR. 1939. Photoelectric colorimetry: An optical study of permanganate ion and of the chromium-diphenyl carbazide system. *Ind. Eng. Chem.*, Anal. Ed. 11:442.

COOPER, M. D. 1953. Periodate method for manganese and effect of band width. *Anal. Chem.* 25:411.

129 METALS

Such metals as copper, iron, magnesium and zinc can be determined by atomic absorption spectroscopy at concentrations equal to or lower than established drinking water standards. These metals can be determined by directly aspirating the aqueous solution into the flame. Chromium, manganese and silver can be determined in a similar fashion, although the precision and accuracy may not be quite as good. The determination of cadmium and lead by direct aspiration into the flame at the concentration set for drinking water is difficult. Low concentrations of these metals, however, can be determined by complexing with a chelating compound, extracting the chelate into an organic solvent, and aspirating the organic phase into the flame. Aluminum, barium and beryllium, on the other hand, require intervention of the

TABLE 129(1): STOCK SOLUTION, FUEL AND OXIDANT COMBINATIONS, AND WAVELENGTH SETTINGS NEEDED FOR METAL DETERMINATIONS

Metal	Stock Solution Section Reference[b]	Fuel and Oxidant Combination	Wavelength mμ	Sensitivity[a] μg/l per 1%
Aluminum	103B.3a	Nitrous oxide-acetylene	309.3	1,000 μg/l[c]
Barium	129A.3fII(1)	" " "	553.6	200
Beryllium	129A.3fI(4)	" " "	234.8	100[d]
Cadmium	109B.3a	Air-acetylene	228.8	40
Chromium	117A.3c	" "	357.9	150
Copper	119B.3b	" "	324.7	200
Iron	124A.3e	" "	248.3	300
Lead	125A.3b	" "	283.3	500
Magnesium[e]	127C.3g	" "	285.2	15
Manganese[f]	128B.3c	" "	279.4	150
Silver	152B.3l	" "	328.1	100
Zinc	165B.3b	" "	213.8	40

[a] μg/l of metal for 1% absorption in an aqueous solution.
[b] Section number and ¶ in text.
[c] 50 μg/l if extracted.
[d] 5 μg/l if extracted.
[e] Add lanthanum to overcome phosphate interference in magnesium determination.
[f] Add calcium to overcome silica interference in manganese determination.

higher-temperature nitrous oxide-acetylene burner to dissociate the molecules. Barium can be determined by aspiration of the aqueous solution directly into the flame. Aluminum and beryllium at the concentrations of interest in water plant treatment must be concentrated by complexing with a chelating compound and extracting with an organic solvent. Other metals not listed in Table 129(1) (see page 210) can also be determined by atomic absorption spectroscopy after proper pretreatment of the sample.

129 A. Atomic Absorption Spectrophotometric Method

1. General Discussion

a. Principle: Atomic absorption spectroscopy resembles emission flame photometry in that a sample is aspirated into a flame and atomized. The major difference rests in the fact that flame photometry measures the amount of light emitted, whereas in atomic absorption spectroscopy, a light beam is directed through the flame into a monochromator, and onto a detector that measures the amount of light absorbed. Absorption is more sensitive because it depends upon the presence of free unexcited atoms. In the usual flames, the ratio of unexcited to excited atoms at a given moment is very high. Because each metallic element has its own characteristic absorption wavelength, a source lamp composed of that element is employed, making the method relatively free of spectral or radiation interferences. The amount absorbed in the flame is proportional to the concentration of the element in the sample.

b. Interference: The most troublesome type of interference is usually termed "chemical," and it results from the lack of absorption of atoms bound in molecular combination in the flame. This phenomenon can occur when the flame is not sufficiently hot to dissociate the molecule (in the case of phosphate interference with magnesium) or because the dissociated atom is immediately oxidized to a compound that will not dissociate further at the temperature of the flame. The interference of phosphate in the magnesium determination can be overcome by the addition of lanthanum. The introduction of calcium similarly eliminates silica interference in the determination of manganese. The situation wherein barium may undergo ionization in the flame and the ground state (potentially absorbing) population is thereby reduced can be overcome by the addition of an excess of a cation having a similar or lower ionization potential.

2. Apparatus

a. Atomic absorption spectrophotometer.

b. Burner: A Boling burner is recommended for aqueous solutions and a premix burner for solutions in organic solvents. Mandatory for the determination of aluminum, barium and beryllium is a nitrous oxide burner head with a 2-in. slot which reduces the overheating frequently encountered with a 3-in. slot. Clean the burner slot frequently with a razor blade or equivalent before ignition in order to dislodge the carbon crust which forms along the slit surface approximately every 20 min.

c. Autoclave.

d. Separatory funnels, 250-ml, preferably with teflon stopcocks, for extractions with organic solvents.

e. Centrifuge (optional).

f. Glassware: All glassware, including sample bottles, should be rinsed with 1 + 1 HNO_3, followed by deionized distilled water to avoid errors due to contamination. Polyethylene containers are also suitable for storage because of their low metallic content and the nonpolar nature of their surfaces.

3. Reagents

a. Deionized distilled water: Use deionized distilled water for the preparation of all reagents and calibration standards, and as dilution water.

b. Nitric acid, conc.

c. Stock metal solution: Prepare as directed in Table 129(1) or in ¶ 3fI (4) or 3fII(1) following.

d. Standard metal solutions: Prepare a series of standard metal solutions containing 5 to 1,000 μg/l by appropriate dilution of the stock metal solution.

e. Fuel and oxidant: Use an air-acetylene flame for all the metals cited in Table 129(1) except the first three. Use a nitrous oxide-acetylene flame for aluminum, barium and beryllium (¶ 2b above).

f. Special reagents for specified metals:

I—ALUMINUM & BERYLLIUM

1) 8-Quinolinol reagent: Dissolve 20 g 8-quinolinol, also called 8-hydroxyquinoline, in 1*N* acetic acid [60 ml conc (glacial) acetic acid per liter] and make up to a volume of 1 liter with the 1*N* acid.

2) Buffer reagent: Dissolve 200 g ammonium acetate, $NH_4C_2H_3O_2$, and 70 ml conc ammonium hydroxide in distilled water and dilute to 1 liter.

3) Chloroform.

4) Stock beryllium solution: Dissolve 20.7574 g beryllium nitrate trihydrate, $Be(NO_3)_2 \cdot 3H_2O$, in distilled water and dilute to 1,000 ml to obtain a solution containing 1.0 mg/ml Be.

II—BARIUM

1) Stock barium solution: Dissolve 1.7787 g barium chloride, $BaCl_2 \cdot 2H_2O$, in distilled water and dilute to 1,000 ml; 1.00 ml = 1.00 mg Ba.

2) Sodium chloride solution: Dissolve 250 g NaCl in distilled water and dilute to 1,000 ml. To overcome ionization interference in the flame, add 2 ml to 100 ml of sample and standards before aspiration into the flame.

III—CADMIUM & LEAD

1) Hydrochloric acid, 1 or 6*N*.

2) Ammonium pyrrolidine dithiocarbamate solution: Dissolve 4 g ammonium pyrrolidine dithiocarbamate in 100 ml distilled water.*

3) Methyl isobutyl ketone: Check for contamination by burning in the flame. If contaminated, wash 1 volume of methyl isobutyl ketone with 5 volumes of 1 + 99 hydrochloric acid solution. Remove the excess acid by washing with deionized distilled water.

IV—MAGNESIUM

1) Stock lanthanum reagent: Dissolve 58.65 g lanthanum oxide, La_2O_3,

* Ammonium pyrrolidine dithiocarbamate powder can be obtained from K and K Laboratories, Inc., Plainview, N. Y.

in 250 ml conc HCl. Dilute to 1,000 ml with distilled water to obtain a solution containing 5 g La/100 ml. Add the acid slowly until the material is dissolved. Add sufficient amounts of this solution to the magnesium standards and unknowns in order to obtain a final working concentration of 1 g La/100 ml volume.

V—MANGANESE

1) Stock calcium reagent: Dissolve 2.4752 g calcium carbonate, $CaCO_3$, in the minimum volume of hydrochloric acid and dilute to 1,000 ml to obtain a solution containing 1,000 mg/l Ca. Add sufficient amounts of this solution to manganese standards and unknowns to produce a final working concentration of 50 mg Ca/l.

4. Procedure

a. Pretreatment of directly determined sample: Acidify all water samples with 1 ml conc nitric acid per 100 ml sample and autoclave at 121 C (250 F) for 1 hr to solubilize the particulate matter. Readjust the volume if necessary.

b. Precautions: Install the spectrophotometer on a level bench or table, with the burner under a vent.

c. Instrument operation: Because the differences between makes and models of satisfactory atomic absorption spectrophotometers render impossible the formulation of detailed instructions applicable to every instrument, follow the manufacturer's operating instructions. As a rule, choose the correct hollow cathode lamp, install, and align in the instrument; position the monochromator at the correct wavelength indicated in Table 129(1); select the proper monochromator slit width; set the light source current according to the manufacturer's recommendation; light the flame and regulate the flow of fuel and oxidant; adjust the burner for maximum absorption and stability; and balance the photometer. Then run the standards needed for the working curves and plot the concentrations of the standards against absorbance. If necessary on some instruments, convert percentage absorption to absorbance (the calibration curves are nearly linear for most elements). Next, run the samples and read the concentration of each sample from the calibration curve. Overcome instrumental drift by conducting the absorbance measurements of blank, calibration standards, and samples frequently and without undue delay. Record multiple readings (three or more) for averaging, or resort to the bracketing technic in performing the absorbance measurements. (See Sodium, Section 153A.4e.) Check for drift of the zero point resulting from possible burner clogging, especially when dealing with samples of low absorbance.

d. Special procedural steps for low concentrations of specified metals:

I—ALUMINUM & BERYLLIUM: To 100 ml sample add 2 ml 8-quinolinol reagent and 3 ml buffer reagent. Adjust the mixture, if necessary, to a pH of 8.0 ± 0.5 and extract with 5 ml chloroform. Repeat the extraction with a second 5 ml chloroform and combine the two extracts. Determine the amount of metal in the organic phase by comparison with standards which have been similarly extracted.

II—CADMIUM & LEAD: Acidify 200 ml water sample to a pH of 2.2–2.8

by adding hydrochloric acid. Add 1 ml ammonium pyrrolidine dithiocarbamate solution and 5 ml methyl isobutyl ketone, and shake manually for 2 min. If an emulsion forms at the interface of the two layers, centrifuge for 10 min. Repeat the extraction with a second 5 ml methyl isobutyl ketone and combine the two extracts. If a precipitate forms in the solvent phase during the first extraction, add an additional 5 ml methyl isobutyl ketone and repeat the extraction with a second 10 ml. Since the extra solvent reduces the concentration factor and sensitivity of the method, do not apply unless necessary. Determine the metal in the organic phase of the sample as well as the standards that have similarly been extracted.

e. Aspiration of organic solvent into flame: When working with organic solvents, reduce the fuel-to-air ratio because the burning of the organic solvent contributes to the fuel supply, and, in addition to lifting the flame off the burner, may produce an undesirable luminescent flame. In setting the fuel-to-air ratio of the gas mixture at the burner, start with the settings recommended by the manufacturer for the analysis and gradually reduce the fuel flow (while the solvent is being aspirated) until the flame is similar to the flame before aspiration of the organic solvent. In the case of air-acetylene, produce as blue, rather than white, a flame as possible. Adjust the acetylene flow of the nitrous oxide burner until the flame is rose-red, approximately double that for an air-acetylene burner.

5. Calculation

a. Direct determination:

1) When the metal values are plotted in terms of micrograms on the calibration curve, calculate the sample concentration by the following equations:

$$\text{mg/l Metal} = \mu\text{g metal} \times D$$

in which the dilution ratio

$$D = \frac{\text{ml sample} + \text{ml water} + 1\ \text{ml acid}}{\text{ml sample}}$$

2) When the metal values are plotted in terms of μg/l on the calibration curve, calculate the sample concentration by the following equations:

$$\text{mg/l Metal} = \mu\text{g/l metal} \times \frac{D}{1{,}000}$$

in which the dilution ratio

$$D = \frac{\text{total final volume in ml}}{\text{ml sample}}$$

b. Extracted samples:

1) Read the metal value in μg from the extracted standard calibration curve.

$$\text{mg/l Metal} = \frac{\mu\text{g metal}}{\text{ml sample}} \times A$$

in which A = total ml solvent used to extract the metal for the final absorption measurement.

2) Alternatively, read the metal value in μg/l from the extracted standard calibration curve.

$$\text{mg/l Metal} = \mu\text{g/l metal} \times \frac{1}{1{,}000}$$

6. Precision and Accuracy

Three synthetic unknown samples containing varying concentrations of cadmium, chromium, copper, iron, lead, magnesium, manganese, silver and zinc were analyzed in 59 laboratories.

Another set of three synthetic unknown samples containing aluminum, barium and beryllium was analyzed in 17 laboratories for aluminum, 13 laboratories for barium, and 10 laboratories for beryllium. The results for both sets of samples are recorded in Table 129(2).

Regardless of the atomic absorption spectrophotometer or type of burner used, copper and iron were satisfactorily determined at concentrations accepted as meeting the drinking water standards. Direct determination of magnesium and zinc was also possible at low concentrations.

Good results in the chromium, manganese and silver determinations required a Boling burner.

Chelation with ammonium pyrrolidine dithiocarbamate and extraction into methyl isobutyl ketone before aspiration into a premix burner was necessary in the lead and cadmium determinations. The excellent accuracy in the case of cadmium was accompanied by very poor precision following chelation and extraction. Although insufficiently sensitive at the 10 μg/l level, direct cadmium measurements can be made at 50 μg/l.

TABLE 129(2): PRECISION AND ACCURACY DATA FOR ATOMIC ABSORPTION METHODS

Metal	Metal Concentration μg/l	Relative Standard Deviation %	Relative Error %
Direct determination:			
Barium	500	10.0	8.6
	1,000	8.9	2.7
	5,000	3.7	1.4
Cadmium	50	21.6	8.2
Chromium	50	26.4	2.3
Copper	1,000	11.2	3.4
Iron	300	16.5	0.6
Magnesium	200	10.5	6.3
Manganese	50	13.5	6.0
Silver	50	17.5	10.6
Zinc	500	8.2	0.4
Extracted samples:			
Aluminum	50	76.2	26.0
	300	22.2	0.7
	750	16.5	7.9
Beryllium	5	34.0	20.0
	50	39.2	2.0
	100	35.0	3.0
Cadmium	10	72.8	3.0
Lead	50	23.5	19.0

129 B. Bibliography

GOON, E. et al. 1953. Fluorometric determination of aluminum by use of 8-quinolinol. *Anal. Chem.* 25:608.

ALLAN, J. E. 1961. The use of organic solvents in atomic absorption spectrophotometry. *Spectrochim. Acta* 17:467.

WILLIS, J. B. 1961. Determination of calcium and magnesium in urine by atomic absorption spectroscopy. *Anal. Chem.* 33:556.

———. 1962. Determination of lead and other heavy metals in urine by atomic absorption spectroscopy. *Anal. Chem.* 34:614.

SLAVIN, W. 1968. *Atomic Absorption Spectroscopy.* John Wiley & Sons, New York.

RAMIREZ-MUNOZ, J. 1968. *Atomic Absorption Spectroscopy and Analysis by Atomic Absorption Flame Photometry.* American Elsevier Publishing Co., New York.

130 METHANE

Methane is a colorless, odorless, tasteless combustible gas occasionally found in ground waters. The escape of this gas from water may develop an explosive atmosphere not only in the utility's facilities, such as tanks and pumphouses, but also on the consumer's property, particularly where water is sprayed through poorly ventilated spaces like public showers.

The explosive limits of methane in air are 5–15% by volume. At sea level, a 5% methane concentration in air could theoretically be reached in a poorly ventilated space sprayed with hot (68 C) water having a methane concentration of only 0.7 mg/l. At higher water temperatures, the vapor pressure of water is so great that no explosive mixture can form. At lower barometric pressures, the theoretical hazardous concentration of methane in water will be reduced proportionately. In an atmosphere of nitrogen or other inert gas, oxygen must be present at least to the extent of 12.8%.

A qualitative test for high methane concentration can be made as follows: Invert a 1-qt bottle of water and immerse the neck in a pan or trough of water. Insert a tube or hose from a tap upward through the mouth of the bottle and allow the tap water to flow into the bottle, displacing the original water and permitting "gas" to accumulate at the top of the inverted bottle. After approximately ⅛–¼ of the bottle is filled with "gas," remove the hose, place a hand over the mouth of the bottle, and again invert to an upright position, holding the hand in place. When a lighted match is brought to the mouth of the bottle immediately on removing the hand, a brief wisp of blue flame will be apparent in the neck of the bottle if the "gas" is methane in high concentration. The blue flame is best observed in a darkened room. This is not a quantitative test but may indicate as low as 2 mg/l methane (1 cu ft per 1,000 gal). A positive result warrants precautionary measures. A negative result would require a quantitative analysis for certainty. The qualitative test should be performed with the utmost care. Every safeguard should be taken against bodily injury which might result from shattering of the glass container during the flaming operation. Adequate shielding of the container and the wearing of goggles or a face shield are among the elementary precautions to be observed.

Selection of method: The combustible-gas indicator method (*A*) offers the advantages of simplicity, speed, and great sensitivity. The volumetric method (*B*) can be made more accurate for concentrations of 4–5 mg/l and higher, but will not be satisfactory for very low concentrations. The volumetric method is also applicable in a situation demanding differentiation between methane and other gases. Such a situation might arise when a water supply is contaminated by a liquid petroleum gas or other volatile combustible materials.

Methane may also be determined with the gas chromatograph as described in Sludge Digester Gas, Section 225B. The gas chromatograph enables a differentiation to be made between hydrogen, methane and/or the higher homologs.

130 A. Combustible-Gas Indicator Method

1. General Discussion

a. Principle: An equilibrium according to Henry's law is established between methane (CH_4) in solution and the partial pressure of methane in the gas phase above the solution. The partial pressure of methane may be determined with a combustible-gas indicator. The operation of the instrument is based upon the catalytic oxidation of a combustible gas on a heated platinum filament which is made a part of a Wheatstone bridge. The heat generated by the oxidation of the gas increases the electrical resistance of the filament. The resulting imbalance of the electrical circuit causes deflection of a milliammeter. The milliammeter may be calibrated in terms of the percentage of methane or the percentage of the lower explosive limit of the gas sampled.

b. Interference: Small amounts of ethane are usually associated with methane in natural gas and presumably would be present in water that contains methane. Hydrogen gas has been observed in well waters and would behave similarly to methane in this procedure. Hydrogen sulfide may interfere if the pH of the water is low enough for an appreciable fraction of the total sulfide to exist in the un-ionized form. The vapors of combustible oils may also interfere. In general, these interferences are of no practical importance, as the analyst is primarily interested in calculating the explosion hazard to which all combustible gases and vapors contribute.

Interference due to hydrogen sulfide can be reduced by the addition of solid sodium hydroxide to the container before sampling.

c. Minimum detectable concentration: The limit of sensitivity of the test is approximately 0.2 mg/l.

d. Sampling: If the water is supersaturated with methane, a representative sample cannot be obtained unless the water is under sufficient pressure to keep all of the gas dissolved. Wells should be operated for a sufficient period to insure that water coming directly from the aquifer is being sampled. Representative samples can be expected only when the well is equipped with a pump operating at sufficient submergence to assure that no gas escapes from the water.

2. Apparatus

a. Combustible-gas indicator: * A three-way stopcock should be connected to the inlet so that the instrument may be zeroed on atmospheric air immediately before obtaining the sample reading. For laboratory use, the suction bulb may be replaced with a filter pump throttled so as to draw gas through the instrument at a rate of approximately 600 ml/min. A diagrammatic view of the apparatus is shown in Figure 17.

b. Laboratory filter pump.

c. Glass bottle, 1-gal, fitted with a two-hole rubber stopper. The inlet tube should extend to within 1 cm of the bottom and the outlet tube should terminate approximately 1 cm from

---

* Marketed under the following trade names: "Explosimeter," "Methane Gas Detector," and "Methane Tester," all manufactured by Mine Safety Appliance Company, Pittsburgh, Pa.; "J-W Combustible Gas Indicator," manufactured by Johnson-Williams, Inc., Palo Alto, Calif.; and "Vapotester" manufactured by Davis Emergency Equipment Company, Newark, N. J.

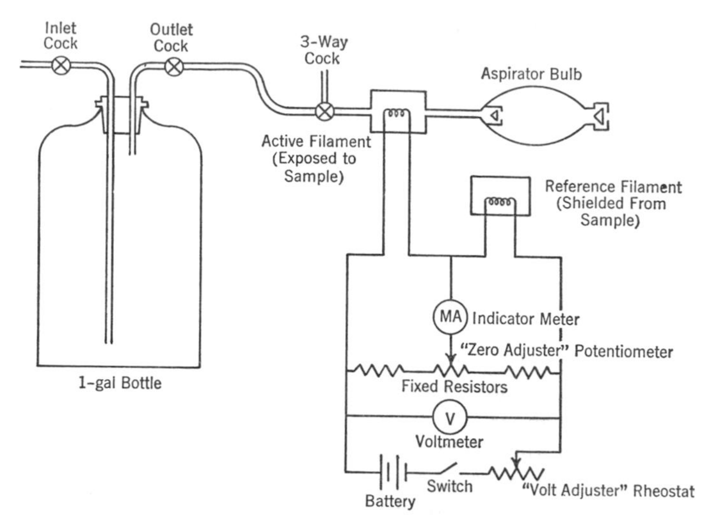

Figure 17. Combustible-gas indicator circuit and flow diagram.

the stopper. The tubes may be metal or glass. Each should be fitted with stopcocks or with short (approximately 5 cm) lengths of rubber tubing and pinchcocks. The entire assembly should be capable of holding a low vacuum for several hours. The volume of the assembly should be determined by filling with water and measuring the volume, or weight, of the water contained.

3. Reagents

a. Sodium hydroxide, pellets.

4. Procedure

a. Rough estimation of methane concentration: Fill the bottle about half full of water, using a rubber tube connecting the sampling tap and the inlet tube, with the outlet tube open. With both the inlet and outlet tubes closed, shake the bottle vigorously for approximately 15 sec and allow the water to stand for approximately 1 min. Sample the gas phase by withdrawing gas from the outlet, leaving the inlet open to admit air. If the needle swings rapidly to a high level on the meter and then drops to zero, the methane-air mixture is too rich to burn, and a smaller volume of water should be taken for the final test; if the needle deflection is too small to read accurately, a larger volume of water should be taken.

b. Accurate determination: If the water contains hydrogen sulfide, add approximately 0.5 g NaOH pellets to the empty bottle to suppress interference from this gas. Evacuate the bottle, using the filter pump. Fill the bottle not more than three-quarters full by connecting the inlet tube to the sampling cock, with the outlet tube closed. After the desired volume of water has been collected, allow the bottle to fill with air through the inlet tube. Close the inlet cock, shake the bottle vigorously for 60 sec, and let stand for at least 2 hr. Sample the gas phase through the outlet tube with the inlet cock open, taking the reading as rapidly as possible before the entering air has appreciably diluted the sample. Measure the volume of water sampled.

5. Calculation

The weight of methane (w), in milligrams, in the sample is given by the equation:

$$w = P\left(\frac{0.257V_g}{T} + \frac{890V_1}{H}\right)$$

where P is the partial pressure of methane, in millimeters of mercury; T is the temperature, in degrees Kelvin; V_g is the volume of the gas phase, in milliliters; V_1 is the volume of the liquid phase, in milliliters; and H is the Henry's law constant, in millimeters of mercury per mole of CH_4 per mole of water. The values for Henry's constant are as follows:

Temperature °C	Henry's Constant $10^6 H$	Temperature °C	Henry's Constant $10^6 H$
0	16.99	40	39.46
5	19.69	45	41.83
10	22.58	50	43.85
15	25.60	60	47.57
20	28.53	70	50.62
25	31.36	80	51.84
30	34.08	90	52.60
35	36.95	100	53.30

For most determinations, it may be assumed that atmospheric pressure is 760 mm and that the temperature is 20 C. The concentration of methane in the sample is then given by:

$$\text{mg/l } CH_4 = Rf\left(6.7\,\frac{V_0 - V_1}{V_1} + 0.24\right)$$

where R is the scale reading, V_0 the total volume of the sample bottle, V_1 the volume of water sampled, and f a factor depending upon the instrument used. If the instrument reads directly in percentage of methane, $f = 1.00$. If the instrument reads in percentage of the lower explosive limit of methane, the factor is 0.05. For instruments which require additional factors, the manufacturer should be consulted. For example, one commercial instrument with a scale that reads in percentage of the lower explosive limit of combustible gases requires an additional factor of 0.77 for methane. Hence, the value of f in the above equation would be 0.77×0.05, or 0.0385.

For more accurate work, or in locations where the normal barometric pressure is significantly lower than 760 mm, the following equation should be used:

$$\text{mg/l } CH_4 = RBf\left(2.57\,\frac{V_0 - V_1}{TV_1} + \frac{8{,}900}{H}\right)$$

where B is the barometric pressure in millimeters of mercury, and the other symbols are the same as above.

6. Precision and Accuracy

The accuracy of the determination is limited by the accuracy of the instrument used. Errors of approximately 10% may be expected. Calibration of the instrument on known methane-air mixtures will improve the accuracy.

130 B. Volumetric Method

1. General Discussion

a. Principle: If methane is slowly mixed with an excess of oxygen in the presence of a platinum coil heated to yellow incandescence, most of the methane will be converted to carbon dioxide and water in a smooth reaction. Several subsequent passes of the mixed gases over the hot coil will serve to burn substantially all of the methane present in the sample. Oxygen and carbon dioxide must be removed from the original sample before the slow combustion is started; and the concentration of methane in the sample should not exceed 20%, the remainder being an inert gas such as nitrogen.

Methane may also be converted to carbon dioxide and water in a catalytic oxidation assembly. If this procedure is followed, an excess of oxygen is mixed with the sample prior to passage through the assembly.

b. Interference: Low-boiling hydrocarbons other than ethane, and vapors from combustible oils, could interfere in this analysis. These substances, however, are not likely to be present in water in sufficiently high concentration to affect the results significantly.

c. Minimum detectable concentration: This method is not satisfactory for determining methane in water where the concentration is less than 2 mg/l.

d. Sampling: The sample may be collected in the same way as for analysis by the combustible-gas indicator method, and the same precautions are necessary to obtain representative samples (see Section 130A.1d). The sodium hydroxide pellets may be omitted, however, and the sample bottle may be filled with water up to 90% of its capacity.

Consult Sludge Digester Gas, Section 225A.2–6, for a description of the apparatus, reagents, procedure, calculation, and precision and accuracy pertaining to the volumetric method.

The percentage of methane found by this method may be applied with Henry's law, to obtain the methane concentration in the original water sample, by substituting the methane percentage for R (scale reading) and $f = 1$ in the calculation given under the Combustible-Gas Indicator Method (Section 130A.5 preceding).

130 C. Bibliography

Combustible-Gas Indicator Method

ROSSUM, J. R., P. A. VILLARRUZ & J. A. WADE. 1950. A new method for determining methane in water. *JAWWA* 42:413.

Volumetric Method

DENNIS, L. M. & M. L. NICHOLS. 1929. *Gas Analysis*. Macmillan Co., New York.

HALDANE, J. S. & J. I. GRAHAM. 1935. *Methods of Air Analysis*. Charles Griffin & Co., London.

BUSWELL, A. M. & T. E. LARSON. 1937. Methane in ground waters. *JAWWA* 29:1978.

BERGER, L. B. & H. H. SCHRENK. 1938. Bureau of Mines Haldane gas analysis apparatus. U. S. Bureau of Mines Information Circular No. 7017.

LARSON, T. E. 1938. Properties and determination of methane in ground waters. *JAWWA* 30:1828.

METHYLENE BLUE-ACTIVE SUBSTANCES: See Anionic Surfactants, Methylene Blue Method, Section 159A.

131 NITROGEN (ALBUMINOID)

The albuminoid-nitrogen determination gives an approximate indication of the quantity of proteinaceous nitrogen present in water. This largely derives from the animal and plant life normal to the aquatic environment.

Following the distillation of free ammonia nitrogen, the addition of a strongly alkaline potassium permanganate solution to a water sample often causes an additional evolution of ammonia. This supplementary release of ammonia represents the albuminoid nitrogen and results largely from the action of potassium permanganate on the unsubstituted amino groups of many amino acids, polypeptides and proteins in an alkaline medium. These nitrogenous materials are important constituents of organic pollution in a water supply. Like free ammonia nitrogen, albuminoid nitrogen frequently exerts a significant influence on the chlorine demand in treatment plants practicing free residual chlorination.

1. General Discussion

a. Principle: After conversion of unsubstituted amino groups by alkaline potassium permanganate to ammonia, the ammonia is distilled and is determined by colorimetry. The determination can also be completed by titration with a standard solution of a strong mineral acid as described in Organic Nitrogen, Section 135 below.

b. Storage of sample: Samples should be stored as directed under Nitrogen (Ammonia), Section 132 following.

2. Apparatus

The same type of apparatus (Figure 18) is required as in Nitrogen (Ammonia), Preliminary Distillation Step, Section 132A.2 following.

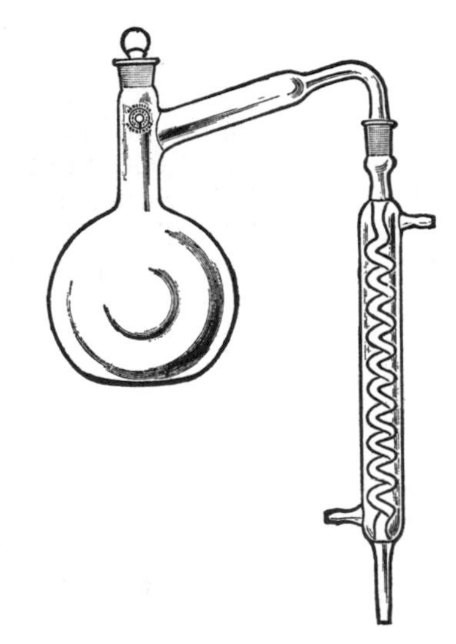

Figure 18. Distillation apparatus for ammonia, albuminoid nitrogen, phenol, selenium, and fluoride determinations.

3. Reagents

All the reagents listed for the determination of ammonia nitrogen by Method A (Section 132A.3) are required. Also needed is:

a. Alkaline potassium permanganate

reagent: In a 3-liter pyrex beaker, dissolve 16 g $KMnO_4$ in sufficient ammonia-free distilled water to effect dissolution. Add 288 g sodium hydroxide, NaOH, or 404 g potassium hydroxide, KOH, and enough ammonia-free water to make up to 2.5 liters. Concentrate to 2 liters on an electric hot plate. Determine the ammonia blank in 50 ml of the reagent and use the results as a basis for correction in subsequent determinations.

4. Procedure

Perform the albuminoid nitrogen determination immediately following the ammonia nitrogen determination on the same sample—see Nitrogen (Ammonia), Preliminary Distillation Step, Section 132A.4c, for preparation of the distillation apparatus and the sample. Measure 700 to 1,000 ml of the neutralized and dechlorinated sample into a 2-liter distilling flask. Add 10 ml phosphate buffer solution together with several glass beads or boiling chips and collect 50 to 300 ml of the ammonia nitrogen distillate. Add 50 ml alkaline potassium permanganate reagent and continue distillation. Collect 200 or 250 ml of distillate. Complete the determination by the nesslerization method, Section 132B.4, or the phenate method, Section 132C.4.

5. Calculation

Calculate the albuminoid nitrogen as for ammonia nitrogen (Section 132-B.5), correcting for the blank on the alkaline permanganate reagent, instead of for the phosphate buffer solution. Report as mg/l albuminoid N.

$$\text{mg/l albuminoid N} = \frac{A}{\text{ml sample}} \times \frac{B}{C}$$

where A = μg N found colorimetrically, B = ml total distillate collected including the H_3BO_3, and C = ml distillate taken for nesslerization.

6. Precision and Accuracy

The recovery of unsubstituted amino nitrogen in the albuminoid nitrogen determination is estimated at approximately 80%. The results can be reproduced within ± 5% of the concentration determined.

7. Bibliography

PHELPS, E. B. 1903 and 1904. A critical study of the methods in current use for the determination of free and albuminoid ammonia in sewage. *APHA Pub. Health Papers & Reports* 29:354; *J. Infect. Dis.* 1:327.

TARAS, M. J. 1950. Preliminary studies on the chlorine demand of specific chemical compounds. *JAWWA* 42:462.

———. 1953. Effect of free residual chlorination on nitrogen compounds in water. *JAWWA* 45:47.

BOLTZ, D. F., Ed. 1958. *Colorimetric Determination of Nonmetals.* Interscience Publishers, New York, pp. 75–97.

132 NITROGEN (AMMONIA)

Ammonia nitrogen is present in many surface and ground waters. A product of microbiological activity, ammonia nitrogen is sometimes accepted as chemical evidence of sanitary pollution when encountered in raw surface supplies. Its occurrence in ground supplies is quite general as a result of natural reduction processes.

At some water treatment plants ammonia is added in the combined residual chlorination of water. Where the free residual chlorination process is employed, ammonia nitrogen will react with chlorine in ratios which vary with the nitrogen concentration. At low ammonia concentrations (0.1 mg/l N) the ratio approximates 1 to 10, while at higher ammonia concentrations the ratio approaches 1 part of ammonia nitrogen to 7.59 parts of chlorine. If a sample contains residual chlorine, then monochloramine, dichloramine or trichloramine (nitrogen trichloride) may be present. Dechlorination prior to analysis will convert these substances to ammonia.

1. *Selection of Method*

Preliminary distillation is required when interferences are present or when it is desired to make a subsequent determination of the albuminoid or organic nitrogen.

The older nessler method is sensitive to 20 μg/l ammonia nitrogen under optimum conditions. However, the sensitivity approximates 200 μg/l ammonia nitrogen and may be used up to 5 mg/l ammonia nitrogen for direct nesslerization measurements. Substances precipitated by hydroxyl ion, such as magnesium and calcium bicarbonate, interfere and may be removed by preliminary distillation or, less satisfactorily, may be precipitated by treatment with zinc sulfate and alkali.

The phenate method for estimating ammonia has a sensitivity of 10 μg/l ammonia nitrogen and is useful for values up to 500 μg/l ammonia nitrogen. Preliminary distillation is required if the alkalinity exceeds 500 mg/l or if there is color or turbidity.

The distillation and titration procedure described in Organic Nitrogen (Section 135) is especially useful for ammonia nitrogen concentrations greater than 5 mg/l, but is equally applicable in the lower ammonia ranges.

Distillation into sulfuric acid absorbent is mandatory for the phenate method when interferences are present. Either sulfuric or boric acid is acceptable as the ammonia absorbent for the nessler method. Boric acid is preferred for a titrimetric finish. Proper color development in the nessler method requires the presence of an adequate alkali and mercuric iodide reserve. These conditions may be satisfied by applying an additional milliliter of nessler reagent. However, the same extra amounts of all reagents used should also be added to the photometric standards.

2. *Interference*

Ammonia recovery from preliminary distillation will be low on water samples containing more than 250 mg/l calcium unless the pH is properly adjusted before distillation is undertaken. The calcium and the phosphate buffer react to precipitate calcium phosphate, releasing hydrogen ions and lowering the pH.

A number of aliphatic and aromatic amines, organic chloramines, acetone, aldehydes and alcohols, among other undefined organic compounds, cause trouble in direct nesslerization. Compounds of this type have been found to yield a yellowish or greenish off color or a turbidity following the addition of nessler reagent to distillates collected from dechlorinated polluted samples. The titrimetric procedure is also subject to amine interference because the standard acid can react with such alkaline bodies. However, the titration procedure is free of interference from neutral organic compounds.

Sulfide has also been reported to cause turbidity following nesslerization. This may be avoided by adding lead carbonate to the flask before distillation. Volatile substances such as formaldehyde can be removed by boiling at low pH, after which the sample can be distilled and nesslerized in the normal manner.

Alkalinity or acidity in excess of 500 mg/l interferes with the phenate method, as do color and turbidity. Samples preserved by acid treatment should be distilled prior to determination by the phenate method.

3. *Storage of Sample*

The most reliable results are obtained on fresh samples. Residual chlorine should be destroyed immediately after the sample is collected in order to prevent its reaction with ammonia. In the event that a prompt analysis is impossible, the addition of 40 mg mercuric ion or 0.8 ml conc sulfuric acid to each 1 liter of sample and storage at 4 C may preserve the ammonia concentration. If acid preservation is practiced, the sample acidity should be neutralized with sodium or potassium hydroxide immediately before the determination is undertaken.

132 A. Preliminary Distillation Step

1. General Discussion

a. Principle: Free ammonia nitrogen can be recovered when the distillation mixture is kept near pH 7.4. Since natural waters exhibit varying pH values and buffering properties, a phosphate buffer is applied for the purpose of maintaining the required pH during the distillation process. When the pH is too high, certain organic compounds of nitrogen are converted to ammonia and when the pH is too low, the recovery of ammonia is incomplete. The value of 7.4 effects a compromise between these conditions. The ammonia distillate is absorbed in sulfuric or boric acid. Each milligram of ammonia nitrogen requires the use of an added increment of 50 ml of boric acid solution for effective ammonia absorption. The isolated ammonia can be determined colorimetrically or by titration with a standard solution of a strong mineral acid as described in Nitrogen (Organic), Section 135. An indicator which responds at the pH (approximately 5.0) of the dilute boric acid absorbent solution is suitable for the titration of the ammonia.

2. Apparatus

a. Distillation apparatus: A pyrex flask of 800–2,000 ml capacity attached to a vertical condenser is so arranged that the outlet tip may be submerged in an acid solution. An all-pyrex apparatus (Figure 18) or one with condensing units constructed of block tin or aluminum tubes may be employed.

b. pH meter.

3. Reagents

a. Ammonia-free water: Prepare by ion-exchange or distillation methods. Since it is virtually impossible to store ammonia-free water in the laboratory without contamination from ammonia fumes, for best results prepare fresh for each batch of samples.

1) ION EXCHANGE—Use deionized distilled water or remove the ammonia with a cation exchanger. Shake 4 liters distilled water with 10 g of a strong cation exchanger,* or pass the distilled water through a column of such an ion exchanger to obtain a satisfactory water for most work. Although the resins may be used repeatedly, run regular blanks to guard against unsuspected exhaustion and the attendant release of ammonia to the ammonia-free water.

2) DISTILLATION—Eliminate traces of ammonia in distilled water by adding 0.1 ml conc sulfuric acid to 1 liter distilled water and redistilling. Alternatively, treat distilled water with sufficient bromine or chlorine water to produce a free halogen residual of 2–5 mg/l and redistill after standing at least 1 hr. Discard the first 100 ml distillate. Check the redistilled water for the possibility of a high blank.

b. Phosphate buffer solution, pH 7.4: Dissolve 14.3 g potassium dihydrogen phosphate, KH_2PO_4, and 68.8 g dipotassium hydrogen phosphate, K_2HPO_4, then dilute to 1 liter with ammonia-free water. Determine the ammonia nitrogen blank on the buffer solution.

c. Dechlorinating agent, N/70: Use 1 ml of any of the following reagents to remove 1 mg/l of residual chlorine in 500 ml sample. Prepare the unstable thiosulfate and sulfite solutions fresh.

1) PHENYLARSINE OXIDE—Dissolve 1.2 g C_6H_5AsO in 200 ml 0.3*N* sodium hydroxide solution, filter if necessary, and dilute to 1 liter with ammonia-free water. (CAUTION: *Toxic—take care to avoid ingestion.*)

2) SODIUM ARSENITE—Dissolve 1.0 g $NaAsO_2$ in ammonia-free water and dilute to 1 liter. (CAUTION: *Toxic—take care to avoid ingestion.*)

3) SODIUM SULFITE—Dissolve 0.9 g Na_2SO_3 in ammonia-free water and dilute to 1 liter.

4) SODIUM THIOSULFATE—Dissolve 3.5 g $Na_2S_2O_3 \cdot 5H_2O$ in ammonia-free water and dilute to 1 liter.

d. Neutralization agent: Prepare with ammonia-free water.

1) SODIUM HYDROXIDE, 1*N*.

2) SULFURIC ACID, 1*N*.

e. Absorbent solution: Use either boric acid or 0.02*N* sulfuric acid.

1) BORIC ACID SOLUTION—Dissolve 20 g H_3BO_3 in ammonia-free water and dilute to 1 liter.

2) SULFURIC ACID, 0.02*N*—Dilute 20 ml approximately 1*N* H_2SO_4 to 1 liter with ammonia-free water.

4. Procedure

a. Sample preparation: Use a 500-ml sample or an aliquot diluted to 500 ml with ammonia-free water. When the ammonia nitrogen content is less than 100 μg/l, or when an albuminoid nitrogen determination is to be made

* Available under the names of Decalso Folin, Folin Permutit, or Ionac C-101, products of Ionac Chemical Co., Birmingham, N. J.

following the ammonia determination, use a sample volume of 1,000 ml. Remove the residual chlorine in the sample by adding dechlorinating agent equivalent to the chlorine residual. If necessary, neutralize the sample to approximately pH 7 with the dilute acid or base, using a pH meter. Add 10 ml phosphate buffer solution. For most water samples this volume is sufficient to maintain a pH of 7.4 ± 0.2 during distillation. For samples containing more than 250 mg Ca, add an additional 10 ml buffer solution for each 250 mg Ca in the sample and adjust to pH 7.4 with acid or base.

Carry out the following steps without any intervening delay.

b. Preparation of equipment: Add 500 ml distilled water, 10 ml phosphate buffer solution, and a few glass beads or boiling chips to a flask of appropriate capacity; steam out the entire distillation apparatus until the distillate shows no trace of ammonia.

c. Distillation: In order to minimize contamination, leave the entire distillation apparatus assembled after the steaming-out process until just before the actual sample distillation is to be started. Empty the distilling flask, taking care to leave the glass beads or boiling chips in it. Pour in the dechlorinated, neutralized and buffered sample. Distill at a rate of 6–10 ml/min with the tip of the delivery tube submerged, collecting the distillate in a 500-ml erlenmeyer flask containing 50 ml 0.02*N* sulfuric acid or boric acid absorbent. (Provide sufficient acid to absorb the ammonia. In the case of boric acid, use additional 50-ml increments of boric acid for each mg of ammonia nitrogen distilled.) Collect at least 300 ml distillate. Lower the collected distillate, free of contact with the delivery tube, and continue distillation during the last minute or two to cleanse the condenser and delivery tube. Dilute to 500 ml with ammonia-free water.

d. Ammonia determination: Determine the ammonia content of the well-mixed distillate by the nesslerization method (Section 132B), the phenate method (Section 132C), or titrimetrically as described under Organic Nitrogen, Section 135 following.

132 B. Nesslerization Method

1. General Discussion

a. Principle: With samples that have a relatively high ammonia content, the distillation step is sometimes omitted and the sample is nesslerized directly. Pretreatment with zinc sulfate and alkali precipitates calcium, iron, magnesium and sulfide, which form turbidity when treated with nessler reagent. The floc also removes suspended matter and sometimes colored matter. The addition of EDTA or Rochelle salt solution inhibits the precipitation of residual calcium and magnesium ions in the presence of the alkaline nessler reagent. However, the use of EDTA demands an extra amount of nessler reagent to insure a sufficient nessler excess for reaction with the ammonia.

The graduated series of yellow to brown colors produced by the nessler-ammonia reaction absorb strongly over a wide wavelength range. The yellow color characteristic of low ammonia nitrogen strengths (20–250 μg per 50 ml of solution) can be measured with acceptable sensitivity in the wavelength region from 400 to 425 mμ when a 1-cm light path is available. A light path of 5 cm extends measurements into the nitrogen range of 5 to 60 μg. The reddish brown hues typical of ammonia nitrogen levels approaching 500 μg may be measured in the wavelength region of 450 to 500 mμ. A judicious selection of light path and wavelength thus enables the photometric determination of ammonia nitrogen concentrations over a considerable range.

Departures from Beer's law may be experienced using photometers equipped with broad-band color filters. For this reason, the calibration curve should be prepared under conditions identical with those adopted for the samples.

b. Minimum detectable concentration: A carefully prepared nessler reagent may respond under optimum conditions to as little as 1 μg ammonia nitrogen. In direct nesslerization, this represents 20 μg/l. However, reproducibility below 5 μg may be erratic.

2. Apparatus

a. Colorimetric equipment—One of the following is required:

1) SPECTROPHOTOMETER, for use at 400 to 500 mμ and providing a light path of 1 cm or longer.

2) FILTER PHOTOMETER, providing a light path of 1 cm or longer and equipped with a violet filter having maximum transmittance at 400 to 425 mμ. A blue filter can be used for higher ammonia nitrogen concentrations.

3) NESSLER TUBES, matched, 50-ml, tall form.

b. pH meter, equipped with a high pH electrode.

3. Reagents

All the reagents listed in the Preliminary Distillation, Section 132A.3, except the phosphate buffer and absorbent solution, are required, plus the following. (Prepare all reagents with ammonia-free water.)

a. Zinc sulfate solution: Dissolve 100 g $ZnSO_4 \cdot 7H_2O$ and dilute to 1 liter.

b. Sodium hydroxide, 6N.

c. Stabilizer reagent: Either EDTA or Rochelle salt may be used to prevent calcium or magnesium precipitation in undistilled samples following the addition of the alkaline nessler reagent.

1) EDTA REAGENT—Dissolve 50 g disodium ethylenediamine tetraacetate dihydrate, also called (ethylenedinitrilo)tetraacetic acid disodium salt, in 60 ml water containing 10 g sodium hydroxide. If necessary, apply gentle heat to complete dissolution. Cool to room temperature and dilute to 100 ml.

2) ROCHELLE SALT SOLUTION—Dissolve 50 g potassium sodium tartrate tetrahydrate, $KNaC_4H_4O_6 \cdot 4H_2O$, in 100 ml water. Remove ammonia usually present in the salt by boiling off 30 ml of solution. After cooling, dilute to 100 ml.

d. Nessler reagent: Dissolve 100 g mercuric iodide, HgI_2, and 70 g potassium iodide, KI, in a small quantity of water, and add this mixture slowly, with stirring, to a cool solution of 160 g NaOH in 500 ml water. Dilute to 1 liter. Store in rubber-stoppered pyrex glassware and out of sunlight to maintain reagent stability for periods up to a year under normal laboratory conditions. Check the reagent to make sure that it yields the characteristic color with 100 $\mu g/l$ ammonia nitrogen within 10 min after addition and does not produce a precipitate with small amounts of ammonia within 2 hr. (CAUTION: *Toxic—take care to avoid ingestion.*)

e. Stock ammonium solution: Dissolve 3.819 g anhydrous ammonium chloride, NH_4Cl, dried at 100 C, in water, and dilute to 1,000 ml; 1.00 ml = 1.00 mg N = 1.22 mg NH_3.

f. Standard ammonium solution: Dilute 10.00 ml stock ammonium solution to 1,000 ml with water; 1.00 ml = 10.0 μg N = 12.2 μg NH_3.

g. Permanent color solutions:

1) POTASSIUM CHLOROPLATINATE SOLUTION—Dissolve 2.0 g K_2PtCl_6 in 300–400 ml distilled water; add 100 ml conc HCl and dilute to 1 liter.

2) COBALTOUS CHLORIDE SOLUTION—Dissolve 12.0 g $CoCl_2 \cdot 6H_2O$ in 200 ml distilled water; add 100 ml conc HCl and dilute to 1 liter.

4. Procedure

a. Treatment of undistilled samples: If necessary, remove the residual chlorine of the sample with an equivalent amount of $N/70$ dechlorinating agent. Add 1 ml zinc sulfate solution to 100 ml sample and mix thoroughly. Add 0.4–0.5 ml sodium hydroxide solution to obtain a pH of 10.5, as determined with a pH meter and a high-pH glass electrode; again mix thoroughly. Allow the treated sample to stand for a few minutes, whereupon a heavy flocculent precipitate should fall, leaving a clear and colorless supernate. Clarify by centrifuging or filtering. Pretest any filter paper used to be sure no ammonia is present as a contaminant. Do this by running ammonia-free water through and testing the filtrate by nesslerization. Filter the sample, discarding the first 25 ml filtrate.

b. Color development:

1) UNDISTILLED SAMPLES—Take 50.0 ml sample, or an aliquot portion diluted to 50.0 ml with ammonia-free water. If the undistilled aliquot contains calcium, magnesium or other ions which produce a turbidity or precipitate with nessler reagent, add 1 drop (0.05 ml) EDTA reagent or 1–2 drops (0.05–0.1 ml) Rochelle salt solution. Mix well. Add 2.0 ml nessler reagent if EDTA reagent is used, or 1.0 ml nessler reagent if Rochelle salt is used.

2) DISTILLED SAMPLES—Neutralize the boric acid used for absorbing the ammonia distillate in one of two ways. Add 2 ml nessler reagent, an excess which raises the alkalinity to the desired high level. Alternatively, neutralize the boric acid with sodium hydroxide before the addition of 1 ml nessler reagent.

3) MIX THE SAMPLES by capping the nessler tubes with clean rubber stoppers (which have been thoroughly washed with ammonia-free water) and then inverting the tubes at least six times. Keep such experimental conditions as temperature and reaction time the same in the blank, samples and standards. Allow the reaction to proceed for at least 10 min after addition of the nessler reagent; then read the color in the sample and the standards. Use a 30-min contact time if the ammonia nitrogen is very low, but in this event run the blank and standards for the same length of time. Measure the

color either photometrically or visually as directed in ¶ c or d below:

c. Photometric measurement: Measure the absorbance or transmittance in a spectrophotometer or a filter photometer. Prepare the calibration curve under the same conditions of temperature and reaction time prevailing for the samples. Make the transmittance readings against a reagent blank and run parallel checks frequently against known ammonium standards, preferably in the nitrogen range of the samples. Redetermine the complete calibration curve following the preparation of each new batch of nessler reagent.

d. Visual comparison: Compare the colors produced in the sample against those of the ammonia standards. Prepare temporary or permanent standards as directed below:

1) TEMPORARY STANDARDS—Prepare a series of visual standards in nessler tubes by adding the following volumes of standard ammonium chloride solution and diluting to 50 ml with ammonia-free water: 0, 0.2, 0.4, 0.7, 1.0, 1.4, 1.7, 2.0, 2.5, 3.0, 3.5, 4.0, 4.5, 5.0 and 6.0 ml. Nesslerize the standards and the portions of distillate by adding 1.0 ml nessler reagent to each tube and mixing well.

2) PERMANENT STANDARDS—Measure into 50-ml nessler tubes the volumes of potassium chloroplatinate and cobaltous chloride solutions indicated in Table 132(1), dilute to the mark, and mix thoroughly. The values given in the table are *approximate;* actual equivalents of the ammonium standards thus prepared will differ with the quality of the nessler reagent, the kind of illumination used, and the color sensitiveness of the analyst's eye. Therefore, compare the color standards with the nesslerized temporary ammonia standards and modify the tints as necessary. Make such comparisons for each newly prepared nessler reagent and have each analyst satisfy himself as to the aptness of the color match. Protect the standards from dust to extend their usefulness for several months. Perform the comparison either 10 or 30 min after nesslerization, depending upon the reaction time used in the preparation of the nesslerized ammonium standards against which they were matched.

TABLE 132(1): PREPARATION OF PERMANENT COLOR STANDARDS FOR VISUAL DETERMINATION OF AMMONIA NITROGEN

Value in Ammonia Nitrogen *µg*	Approximate Volume of Platinum Solution *ml*	Approximate Volume of Cobalt Solution *ml*
0	1.2	0.0
2	2.8	0.0
4	4.7	0.1
7	5.9	0.2
10	7.7	0.5
14	9.9	1.1
17	11.4	1.7
20	12.7	2.2
25	15.0	3.3
30	17.3	4.5
35	19.0	5.7
40	19.7	7.1
45	19.9	8.7
50	20.0	10.4
60	20.0	15.0

e. Preparation of standard curve for distilled samples: Prepare the standard curve under the same conditions as the samples. Distill the reagent blank and appropriate standards—each diluted to 500 ml—in the same manner as the samples. Bring the 300 ml distillate and 50 ml 0.02*N* sulfuric acid or boric acid absorbent to 500 ml before taking a 50-ml portion for nesslerization. Use the same volumes of phosphate buffer, stabilizer reagent and nessler reagent applied to the samples.

5. Calculation

a. Deduct the amount of nitrogen in the volume of ammonia-free water which has been used for diluting the original sample before computing the final nitrogen value.

b. Deduct also the reagent blank for the volume of phosphate buffer solution used with the sample.

c. Compute the total ammonia nitrogen by the following equation:

$$\text{mg/l Ammonia N} = \frac{A}{\text{ml sample}} \times \frac{B}{C}$$

where A = μg N found colorimetrically, B = total distillate collected, including the acid absorbent, and C = ml distillate taken for nesslerization. The ratio B/C applies only to the distilled samples and should be ignored in direct nesslerization.

d. Calculate the free NH_3 and NH_4 values by multiplying the ammonia nitrogen results by the factors 1.216 and 1.288, respectively.

6. Precision and Accuracy

Six synthetic unknown samples containing ammonia and other constituents dissolved in distilled water were analyzed by five procedures. The first three samples were subjected to direct nesslerization alone, distillation followed by a nessler finish, and distillation coupled with a titrimetric finish. Samples 4 through 6 were analyzed by direct nesslerization, by distillation followed by a nessler finish, by the phenate method alone, and by distillation followed by a phenate finish. The results of the participating laboratories are summarized in Table 132(2).

SAMPLE 1 contained the following additional constituents: 10 mg/l chloride, 1.0 mg/l nitrate nitrogen, 1.5 mg/l organic nitrogen, 10.0 mg/l phosphate, and 5.0 mg/l silica.

SAMPLE 2 contained the following additional constituents: 200 mg/l chloride, 1.0 mg/l nitrate nitrogen, 800 μg/l organic nitrogen, 5.0 mg/l phosphate, and 15.0 mg/l silica.

SAMPLE 3 contained the following additional constituents: 400 mg/l chloride, 1.0 mg/l nitrate nitrogen, 200 μg/l organic nitrogen, 500 μg/l phosphate, and 30.0 mg/l silica.

SAMPLE 4 contained the following additional constituents: 400 mg/l chloride, 50 μg/l nitrate nitrogen, 230 μg/l organic phosphorus added in the form of adenylic acid, 7.00 mg/l orthophosphate phosphorus, and 3.00 mg/l polyphosphate phosphorus added as sodium hexametaphosphate.

SAMPLE 5 contained the following additional constituents: 400 mg/l chloride, 5.00 mg/l nitrate nitrogen, 90 μg/l organic phosphorus added in the form of adenylic acid, 600 μg/l orthophosphate phosphorus, and 300 μg/l polyphosphate phosphorus added as sodium hexametaphosphate.

SAMPLE 6 contained the following additional constituents: 400 mg/l chloride, 500 μg/l nitrate nitrogen, 30 μg/l organic phosphorus added in the form of adenylic acid, 100 μg/l orthophosphate phosphorus, and 80 μg/l polyphosphate phosphorus added as sodium hexametaphosphate.

TABLE 132(2): PRECISION AND ACCURACY DATA FOR AMMONIA METHODS

Sample	Number of Laboratories	Ammonia Nitrogen Concentration µg/l	Relative Standard Deviation					Relative Error				
					Distillation Plus					Distillation Plus		
			Direct Nesslerization %	Direct Phenate Method %	Nessler Finish %	Phenate Finish %	Titrimetric Finish %	Direct Nesslerization %	Direct Phenate Method %	Nessler Finish %	Phenate Finish %	Titrimetric Finish %
1	20	200	38.1					0				
	44				46.3					10.0		
	21						69.8					20.0
2	20	800	11.2					0				
	42				21.2					8.7		
	20						28.6					5.0
3	21	1,500	11.6					0.6				
	42				18.0					4.0		
	21						21.6					2.6
4	70	200		39.2					2.4			
	3					15.1					16.7	
	9		22.0					8.3				
	5				15.7					2.0		
5	66	800		15.8					1.5			
	3					16.6					1.7	
	9		16.1					0.3				
	6				16.3					3.1		
6	71	1,500		26.0					10.0			
	3					7.3					0.4	
	8		5.3					1.2				
	6				7.5					3.6		

132 C. Phenate Method (TENTATIVE)

1. General Discussion

a. Principle: An intensely blue compound, indophenol, is formed by the reaction of ammonia, hypochlorite and phenol catalyzed by a manganous salt.

b. Interference: Over 500 mg/l alkalinity, over 100 mg/l acidity; color and turbidity interfere. These interferences may be removed by preliminary distillation.

2. Apparatus

a. COLORIMETRIC EQUIPMENT—One of the following is required:

1) Spectrophotometer, for use at 630 mμ with a light path of approximately 1 cm.

2) Filter photometer, equipped with a red-orange filter having a maximum transmittance near 630 mμ and providing a light path of approximately 1 cm.

b. MAGNETIC STIRRER.

3. Reagents

a. Ammonia-free water: Prepare as directed in Preliminary Distillation Step, Section 132A.3a.

b. Hypochlorous acid reagent: To 40 ml distilled water add 10 ml of a 5% commercial bleach. Adjust pH to 6.5–7.0 with HCl. Prepare this unstable reagent weekly.

c. Manganous sulfate solution, 0.003 *M:* Dissolve 50 mg $MnSO_4 \cdot H_2O$ in 100 ml distilled water.

d. Phenate reagent: Dissolve 2.5 g sodium hydroxide, NaOH, and 10 g phenol, C_6H_5OH, in 100 ml ammonia-free water. Since this reagent darkens on standing, prepare weekly.

e. Stock ammonium solution: Dissolve 381.9 mg anhydrous ammonium chloride, NH_4Cl, dried at 100 C, in ammonia-free water, and dilute to 1,000 ml; 1.00 ml = 100 μg N = 122 μg NH_3.

f. Standard ammonium solution: Dilute 5.00 ml stock ammonium solution to 1,000 ml with ammonia-free water; 1.00 ml = 0.500 μg N = 0.610 μg NH_3.

4. Procedure

To a 10.00-ml sample in a 50-ml beaker, add 1 drop (0.05 ml) manganous sulfate solution. Place on a magnetic stirrer and add 0.5 ml hypochlorous acid solution, followed immediately by the addition, a drop at a time, of 0.6 ml phenate reagent. Avoid erratically low results by adding the phenate reagent without appreciable delay and yet not too rapidly. Use bulb pipets for convenient delivery of the reagents. Mark the pipet for hypochlorous acid at the 0.5-ml level and deliver the phenate reagent from a pipet which has been calibrated by counting the number of drops previously found to be equivalent to 0.6 ml. Stir vigorously during addition of the reagents. Since the color intensity is affected somewhat by the age of the reagents, carry a blank and a standard through the procedure along with each batch of unknowns. Measure the color after zeroing the photometer on the blank. (Color formation is complete in 10 min and is stable for at least 24 hr. Although the blue color has a maximum absorbance at 630 mμ, satisfactory measurements can be made in the 600–660 mμ region.) Prepare a calibration curve in the ammonia nitrogen range of 0.1–5 μg, treating the standards exactly as the sample throughout the procedure.

5. Calculation

Beer's law governs. Calculate the ammonia concentration as follows:

$$\text{mg/l Ammonia N} = \frac{A \times B}{C \times S} \times \frac{D}{E}$$

where A = absorbance of sample, B = μg ammonia nitrogen in standard taken, C = absorbance of standard, and S = ml unknown water sample used, D = total distillate collected, including the acid absorbent, and E = ml distillate used for color development. The ratio D/E applies only to the distilled samples, and should be ignored when the color is developed on undistilled samples.

6. Precision and Accuracy

See Section 132B.6 and Table 132 (2).

132 D. Bibliography

Distillation & Nesslerization Methods

JACKSON, D. D. 1900. Permanent standards for use in the analysis of water. *Massachusetts Inst. Technol. Quart.* 13:314.

NICHOLS, M. S. & M. E. FOOTE. 1931. Distillation of free ammonia from buffered solutions. *Ind. Eng. Chem.* Anal. Ed. 3:311.

GRIFFIN, A. E. & N. S. CHAMBERLIN. 1941. Relation of ammonia nitrogen to breakpoint chlorination. *AJPH* 31:803.

PALIN, A. T. 1950. Symposium on the sterilization of water: Chemical aspects of chlorination. *J. Inst. Water Eng.* 4:565.

SAWYER, C. N. 1953. pH adjustment for determination of ammonia nitrogen. *Anal. Chem.* 25:816.

TARAS, M. J. 1953. Effect of free residual chlorination of nitrogen compounds in water. *JAWWA* 45:47.

BOLTZ, D. F., Ed. 1958. *Colorimetric Determination of Nonmetals.* Interscience Publishers, New York, pp. 75–97.

JENKINS, D. 1967. The differentiation, analysis and preservation of nitrogen and phosphorus forms in natural waters. In *Trace Inorganics in Water.* American Chemical Society, Washington, D. C.

Phenate Method

ROSSUM, J. R. & P. A. VILLARRUZ. 1963. Determination of ammonia by the indophenol method. *JAWWA* 55:657.

WEATHERBURN, M. W. 1967. Phenol-hypochlorite reaction for determination of ammonia. *Anal. Chem.* 39:971.

133 NITROGEN (NITRATE)

Nitrate represents the most highly oxidized phase in the nitrogen cycle and normally reaches important concentrations in the final stages of biologic oxidation. It generally occurs in trace quantities in surface water supplies but may attain high levels in some ground waters. In excessive amounts, it contributes to the illness known as infant methemoglobinemia. A limit of 45 mg/l nitrate has accordingly been imposed on drinking waters as a means of averting this condition. The nitrate concentration of most drinking waters usually falls below 10 mg/l.

1. Selection of Method

Although the phenoldisulfonic acid and ultraviolet spectrophotometric methods alone are presented in this chapter, the brucine, cadmium and zinc reduction, and chromotropic acid methods given in Section 213 are equally satisfactory for the determination of nitrate in water. They have been omitted only to avoid duplication. For this reason, the corresponding paragraph, *Selection of Method,* in Section 213 should be consulted as an integral part of this discussion. Nitrate is a difficult determination in the presence of interfering ions. The phenoldisulfonic acid method is subject to severe chloride interference, necessitating complete chloride removal for a correct result. Nitrite responds like nitrate, but this interference is relatively minor because of the low nitrite concentrations prevalent in potable water supplies. Nitrate nitrogen levels down to 10 μg/l may be estimated by the method.

The ultraviolet spectrophotometric method is useful in screening a large number of drinking water samples for public health acceptability. It makes possible identification of those samples which yield high uncorrected nitrate values. The nitrate results of such samples should then be checked by alternative methods to ascertain the correct nitrate values.

2. Storage of Sample

To prevent any change in the nitrogen balance through biologic activity, the nitrate determinations should be started promptly after sampling. If such a step is impractical, storage near freezing either in the presence of preservatives such as 0.8 ml conc sulfuric acid or 40 mg of mercuric ion added as $HgCl_2$ to each 1 liter of sample is advisable. If acid preservation is employed, sample acidity should be neutralized to at least pH 7 immediately before the analysis is undertaken.

$HgCl_2$ interferes with NH_3 detn - Forms strong complex!

133 A. Phenoldisulfonic Acid Method

1. General Discussion

a. Principle: The yellow color produced by the reaction between nitrate and phenoldisulfonic acid obeys Beer's law up to at least 12 mg/l N at a wavelength of 480 mμ when a light path of 1 cm is used. At a wavelength of 410 mμ, the point of maximum absorption, determinations may be made up to 2 mg/l with the same cell path.

b. Interference: As even small concentrations of chloride result in nitrate losses using this method, it is important that the chloride content be reduced to a minimum, preferably below 10 mg/l. However, the silver sulfate used for this purpose presents problems with some water samples owing to the incomplete precipitation of silver ion, which produces an off color or turbidity when the final color is developed. The preferred alkali for color development in the final stage of the determination is ammonium hydroxide, particularly where chloride removal must be practiced on the sample. Potassium hydroxide should be used only if ammonia fumes must be reduced to a minimum in the laboratory atmosphere (for example, when trace amounts of ammonia nitrogen are being determined concurrently). A faint tinge of brown is imparted by potassium hydroxide to the final color when a silver compound has been previously applied for chloride precipitation. Nitrite levels in excess of 0.2 mg/l N erratically increase the apparent nitrate concentration. Colored ions and materials physically modifying the color system should be absent.

c. Minimum detectable concentration: In the absence of interference, the phenoldisulfonic acid method is sensitive to 1 μg of nitrate nitrogen, which represents 10 μg/l in a 100-ml sample.

2. Apparatus

COLORIMETRIC EQUIPMENT—One of the following is required:

a. Spectrophotometer, for use at 410 mμ, providing a light path of 1 cm or longer.

b. Filter photometer, providing a light path of 1 cm or longer and equipped with a violet filter having maximum transmittance near 410 mμ.

c. Nessler tubes, matched, 50- or 100-ml.

3. Reagents

Prepare all reagents from chemicals which are white in color and store all solutions in pyrex containers.

a. Standard silver sulfate solution: Dissolve 4.40 g Ag_2SO_4, free from nitrate, in distilled water and dilute to 1.0 liter; 1.00 ml is equivalent to 1.00 mg Cl.

b. Phenoldisulfonic acid reagent: Dissolve 25 g pure white phenol in 150 ml conc H_2SO_4. Add 75 ml fuming H_2SO_4 (15% free SO_3), stir well, and heat for 2 hr on a hot water bath.

c. Ammonium hydroxide, conc: If this cannot be used, prepare 12*N* potassium hydroxide solution by dissolving 673 g KOH in distilled water and diluting to 1 liter.

d. EDTA reagent: Rub 50 g disodium ethylenediamine tetraacetate dihydrate, also called (ethylenedinitrilo)-tetraacetic acid sodium salt, with 20 ml distilled water to form a thoroughly wetted paste. Add 60 ml conc NH_4OH and mix well to dissolve the paste. [The EDTA solution described under Ammonia Nitrogen, Method B, Section 132B.3c(1), can also be used.]

e. Stock nitrate solution: Dissolve 721.8 mg anhydrous potassium nitrate, KNO_3, and dilute to 1,000 ml with distilled water. This solution contains 100 mg/l N.

f. Standard nitrate solution: Evaporate 50.0 ml stock nitrate solution to dryness on a steam or hot water bath; dissolve the residue by rubbing with 2.0 ml phenoldisulfonic acid reagent, and dilute to 500 ml with distilled water; 1.00 ml = 10.0 μg N = 44.3 μg NO_3.

g. Reagents for treatment of unusual interference:

1) ALUMINUM HYDROXIDE SUSPENSION—Dissolve 125 g aluminum potassium or ammonium sulfate, $AlK(SO_4)_2 \cdot 12H_2O$ or $AlNH_4(SO_4)_2 \cdot 12H_2O$ in 1 liter distilled water. Warm to 60 C and add 55 ml conc NH_4OH slowly, with stirring. After permitting the mixture to stand about 1 hr, transfer to a large bottle and wash the precipitate by successive additions (with thorough mixing) and decantations of distilled water, until free from ammonia, chloride, nitrate and nitrite. Finally, after

settling, decant off as much clear liquid as possible, leaving only the concentrated suspension.

2) SULFURIC ACID, 1*N*.

3) POTASSIUM PERMANGANATE, 0.1 *N*—Dissolve 316 mg $KMnO_4$ in distilled water and dilute to 100 ml.

4) DILUTE HYDROGEN PEROXIDE SOLUTION—Dilute 10 ml of 30% hydrogen peroxide (low in nitrate) to 100 ml with distilled water.

5) SODIUM HYDROXIDE, 1*N*.

4. Procedure

a. Color removal: If the sample has a color of more than 10, decolorize by adding 3 ml aluminum hydroxide suspension to 150 ml of sample, stir very thoroughly, allow to stand for a few minutes, then filter, discarding the first portion of the filtrate.

b. Nitrite conversion: To 100 ml of sample add 1 ml of H_2SO_4 and stir. Add dropwise, with stirring, either $KMnO_4$ or H_2O_2 solution. Let the treated sample stand for 15 min to complete the conversion of nitrite to nitrate. (A faint pink color persists for at least 15 min when sufficient $KMnO_4$ is used.) Make the proper deduction at the end of the nitrate determination for the nitrite concentration as determined by the method described in Nitrogen (Nitrite), Section 134 following.

c. Chloride removal: Determine the chloride content of the water (see Section 112) and treat 100 ml of sample with an equivalent amount of standard silver sulfate solution. Remove the precipitated chloride either by centrifugation or by filtration, coagulating the silver chloride by heat if necessary. (Excellent removal of silver chloride can be achieved by allowing the treated sample to stand overnight at laboratory temperature away from strong light. This approach is applicable to samples free of contamination by nitrifying organisms.)

d. Evaporation and color development: Neutralize the clarified sample to approximately pH 7, transfer to a casserole, and evaporate to dryness over a hot water bath. Using a glass rod, rub the residue thoroughly with 2.0 ml phenoldisulfonic acid reagent to insure dissolution of all solids. If need be, heat mildly on the hot water bath a short time to dissolve the entire residue. Dilute with 20 ml distilled water and add, with stirring, about 6 to 7 ml NH_4OH or about 5 to 6 ml KOH until maximum color is developed. Remove any resulting flocculent hydroxides by passing through a filter paper or filtering crucible, or add the EDTA reagent dropwise, with stirring, until the turbidity redissolves. Transfer the filtrate or clear solution to a 50- or 100-ml volumetric flask or nessler tube, dilute to the mark, and mix.

e. Photometric measurement: Make photometric readings in cells with a 1-cm or longer light path at a wavelength of 410 mμ, or with violet filters exhibiting maximum transmittance in the range from 400 to 425 mμ. If available, use a 5-cm light path for measurements in the nitrogen interval from 5 to 50 μg, and a 1-cm light path in a proportionate range. Make readings against a blank prepared from the same volumes of phenoldisulfonic acid reagent and NH_4OH or KOH as used for the samples.

f. Visual comparison: In the case of 50-ml nessler tubes, use the following volumes of standard nitrate solution: 0, 0.1, 0.3, 0.5, 0.7, 1.0, 1.5, 2.0, 3.5, 6.0, 10, 15, 20 and 30 ml. Where it is more convenient to use a total volume of 100 ml, double the volumes of standard solution. To each of these standards add 2.0 ml phenoldisulfonic acid reagent and the same volume of the same alkali as is used in preparation of the sample. These standards may be kept several weeks without deterioration.

5. Calculation

$$\text{mg/l nitrate N} = \frac{\mu\text{g nitrate N}}{\text{ml sample}}$$

$$\text{mg/l } NO_3 = \text{mg/l nitrate N} \times 4.43$$

6. Precision and Accuracy

Accuracy of the order of ±0.1 mg/l nitrate N can be obtained only by the proper treatment of the chloride and nitrite interference. Many laboratories appear to have difficulty in coping with these interferences.

A synthetic unknown sample containing 1.0 mg/l nitrate N, 10 mg/l chloride, 200 μg/l ammonia N, 1.5 mg/l organic N, 10.0 mg/l phosphate, and 5.0 mg/l silica in distilled water was determined by the phenoldisulfonic acid method, with a relative standard deviation of 74.4% and a relative error of 38.0% in 46 laboratories.

A second synthetic unknown sample containing 1.0 mg/l nitrate N, 200 mg/l chloride, 800 μg/l ammonia N, 800 μg/l organic N, 5.0 mg/l phosphate, and 15.0 mg/l silica in distilled water was determined by the phenoldisulfonic acid method, with a relative standard deviation of 57.9% and a relative error of 31.0% in 46 laboratories.

133 B. Ultraviolet Spectrophotometric Method (TENTATIVE)

1. General Discussion

a. Principle: Measurement of the ultraviolet absorption at 220 mμ enables a rapid means of determining nitrate. The nitrate calibration curve follows Beer's law up to 11 mg/l N. Because dissolved organic matter may also absorb at 220 mμ and nitrate does not absorb at 275 mμ, a second measurement is made at 275 mμ for the purpose of correcting the nitrate value. The extent of this empirical correction is related to the nature and concentration of the organic matter and consequently may vary from one water sample to another. Filtration of the sample is intended to remove possible interference from suspended particles. Acidification with 1*N* hydrochloric acid is designed to prevent interference from hydroxide or carbonate concentrations up to 1,000 mg/l as $CaCO_3$. Chloride is without effect on the determination.

b. Interference: Dissolved organic matter, nitrite, hexavalent chromium, and surfactants interfere. The latter three substances may be compensated for by the preparation of individual correction curves.

Organic matter can cause a positive but variable interference, the degree depending on the nature and concentration of the organic material. For this reason, sufficient data must be accumulated in order to obtain a factor which can be used for a given water. This factor may not apply to another water containing organic matter of a different chemical structure.

In this connection, organic contaminants determined by the carbon chloroform extract method or chemical oxygen demand values in excess of 50 μg/l or 5 mg/l, respectively, are significant indicators of organic pollution. Dilution of the sample represents one way of minimizing organic interference.

Occasionally high-quality well waters and river waters give ultraviolet nitrate values which are at first higher than those obtained by the usual determinations of nitrite and nitrate. When such samples are kept for several weeks, the nitrate values obtained by the customary colorimetric methods eventually rise to those found by the ultraviolet method.

All glassware must be thoroughly cleaned and rinsed in order to reduce the error which might result from streaks or particles on the outside of the cuvets, as well as traces of surfactants or dichromate cleaning solution which might adhere on the interior glass surfaces.

The ultraviolet method yields best results in the presence of very low color interference and appreciable nitrate content. Colored samples should accordingly be treated with aluminum hydroxide suspension, or diluted to minimize color interference.

Sulfate, ammonium, bicarbonate, phosphate and fluoride in the concentrations normally present in drinking water offer negligible interference.

c. Minimum detectable concentration: 40 μg/l nitrate N.

2. Apparatus

a. Spectrophotometer, for use at 220 mμ and 275 mμ with matched silica cells of 1-cm or longer light path. A Beckman Model DU spectrophotometer with a photomultiplier attachment and hydrogen lamp source, or equivalent, is satisfactory.

b. Filter—One of the following is required:

1) MEMBRANE FILTER—A Millipore filter, type HA, and appropriate filter assembly, or equivalent, is satisfactory.

2) PAPER—Acid-washed, ashless hard-finish filter paper sufficiently retentive for fine precipitates.

c. Nessler tubes, 50-ml, short form.

3. Reagents

a. Redistilled water: Use the redistilled water for the preparation of all solutions and dilutions.

b. Stock nitrate solution: Prepare as described in Section 133A.3e; 1.00 ml = 100 μg N = 443 μg NO_3.

c. Standard nitrate solution: Dilute 100.0 ml stock nitrate solution to 1,000 ml with distilled water; 1.00 ml = 10.0 μg N = 44.3 μg NO_3.

d. Hydrochloric acid solution, 1*N*: 1 + 11.

e. Aluminum hydroxide suspension: Prepare as directed in Method A, Section 133A.3g(1), preceding.

4. Procedure

a. Color removal: If the sample has a high color or is known to contain organic interference, add 4 ml aluminum hydroxide suspension to each 100 ml of sample in an erlenmeyer flask. Swirl to mix and let settle for 5 min. Filter through a 0.45-μ membrane filter previously washed with about 200 ml distilled water.

b. Treatment of sample: To 50 ml clear sample, membrane-filtered if necessary, or to 50 ml sample filtered after color removal, add 1 ml 1*N* HCl and mix thoroughly.

c. Preparation of standard curve: Prepare nitrate calibration standards in the range 0–350 μg N by diluting to 50 ml the following volumes of the standard nitrate solution: 0, 1.00, 2.00, 4.00, 7.00 . . . 35.0 ml. Treat the nitrate standards in the same manner as the samples.

d. Spectrophotometric measurement: Read the absorbance or transmittance against redistilled water set at zero absorbance or 100% transmittance. Use a wavelength of 220 mμ to obtain the nitrate reading and a wavelength of 275 mμ to obtain the interference due to dissolved organic matter.

e. Preparation of correction curves for nitrite, hexavalent chromium, and surfactants: When nitrite, hexavalent chromium, and anionic surfactants are known to be present in the sample, prepare correction curves for each of these substances at 2-mg/l intervals up to 10 mg/l. Use potassium nitrite, KNO_2, potassium dichromate, $K_2Cr_2O_7$, and linear alkylate sulfonate, with redistilled water for this purpose. Measure the absorbances given by each substance at a wavelength of 220 mμ against redistilled water and plot a separate curve for each of these interfering materials.

5. Calculation

a. Correction for dissolved organic matter: Subtract 2 times the reading at 275 mμ from the reading at 220 mμ to obtain the absorbance due to nitrate. Convert this absorbance value into equivalent nitrate by reading the nitrate value from a standard calibration curve obtained at 220 mμ.

b. Correction for nitrite, hexavalent chromium, or surfactants: Deduct the equivalent nitrate values for each of these interfering substances from the gross nitrate result.

c. Perform the calculation as follows:

$$\text{mg/l nitrate N} = \frac{\text{net } \mu\text{g nitrate N}}{\text{ml sample}}$$

$$\text{mg/l } NO_3 = \text{mg/l nitrate N} \times 4.43$$

133 C. Bibliography

Phenoldisulfonic Acid Method

CHAMOT, E. M., D. S. PRATT & H. W. REDFIELD. 1909, 1910 and 1911. A study on the phenoldisulfonic acid method for the determination of nitrates in water. *J. Amer. Chem. Soc.* 31:922; 32:630; 33:366.

TARAS, M. J. 1950. Phenoldisulfonic acid method of determining nitrate in water: Photometric study. *Anal. Chem.* 22:1020.

BOLTZ, D. F., Ed. 1958. *Colorimetric Determination of Nonmetals.* Interscience Publishers, New York, pp. 135–147.

Ultraviolet Spectrophotometric Method

HOATHER, R. C. 1953. Applications of spectrophotometry in the examination of waters. *Proc. Soc. Water Treatment & Exam.* 2:9.

BASTIAN, R. et al. 1957. Ultraviolet spectrophotometric determination of nitrate. *Anal. Chem.* 29:1795.

HOATHER, R. C. & R. F. RACKHAM. 1959. Oxidized nitrogen and sewage effluents observed by ultraviolet spectrophotometry. *Analyst* 84:549.

GOLDMAN, E. & R. JACOBS. 1961. Determination of nitrates by ultraviolet absorption. *JAWWA* 53:187.

ARMSTRONG, F. A. J. 1963. Determination of nitrate in water by ultraviolet spectrophotometry. *Anal. Chem.* 35:1292.

NAVONE, R. 1964. Proposed method for nitrate in potable waters. *JAWWA* 56:781.

134 NITROGEN (NITRITE)

Nitrite, an intermediate stage in the nitrogen cycle, may occur in water as a result of the biological decomposition of proteinaceous materials. When correlated with the concentration of other nitrogen forms, trace amounts of nitrite may indicate organic pollution. Nitrite may also be produced in water treatment plants or in the distribution system through the action of bacteria or other organisms on ammonia nitrogen fed at elevated temperatures in the combined residual chlorination of water. Nitrite can likewise enter a water supply through its use as a corrosion inhibitor in industrial process water. The nitrite concentration of a drinking water rarely exceeds 0.1 mg/l.

1. General Discussion

a. Principle: The nitrite concentration is determined through the formation of a reddish purple azo dye produced at pH 2.0 to 2.5 by the coupling of diazotized sulfanilic acid with naphthylamine hydrochloride. The diazotization method is suitable for the visual determination of nitrite nitrogen in the range 1–25 μg/l N. Photometric measurements can be performed in the range 5–50 μg/l if a 5-cm light path and a green color filter are available. The color system obeys Beer's law up to 180 μg/l N or 600 μg/l NO_2, with a 1-cm light path at 520 mμ.

b. Interference: Chemical incompatibility makes it unlikely that nitrite, free available chlorine, and nitrogen trichloride will coexist in a sample. Nitrogen trichloride imparts a false red color when the normal order of reagent addition is followed. Although this effect may be minimized somewhat by adding the naphthylamine hydrochloride reagent first and then the sulfanilic acid reagent, an orange color may still result when a substantial nitrogen trichloride concentration is present. A check for a free available chlorine and nitrogen trichloride residual is advisable under such circumstances. The following ions interfere due to precipitation under the conditions of the test and therefore should be absent: antimonous, auric, bismuth, ferric, lead, mercurous, silver, chloroplatinate and metavanadate. Cupric ion may cause low results by catalyzing the decomposition of the diazonium salt. Colored ions which alter the color system should likewise be absent.

When small amounts of suspended solids seriously impair nitrite recovery, a sample may be passed through a membrane filter (0.45-μ pore size) to achieve the necessary clarification before color development is undertaken.

c. Minimum detectable concentration: In the absence of interference, the minimum nitrite nitrogen concentration detectable in a 50-ml nessler tube is 1 μg/l.

d. Storage of sample: The determination should be made promptly on fresh samples to prevent bacterial conversion of the nitrite to nitrate or ammonia.

In no case should acid preservation be used for samples to be analyzed for nitrite. Short-term preservation for 1 to 2 days is possible by deep-freezing (−20 C), or by the addition of 40 mg mercuric ion (as $HgCl_2$) with storage at 4 C.

2. Apparatus

COLORIMETRIC EQUIPMENT—One of the following is required:

a. Spectrophotometer, for use at 520 mμ, providing a light path of 1 cm or longer.

b. Filter photometer, providing a light path of 1 cm or longer and equipped with a green color filter having maximum transmittance near 520 mμ.

c. Nessler tubes, matched, 50-ml, tall form.

3. Reagents

Prepare all reagents from chemicals which are white in color.

a. Nitrite-free water: Prepare nitrite-free water by either of the following methods—

1) Add to 1 liter distilled water one small crystal each of potassium permanganate and an alkali such as barium or calcium hydroxide (1 or 2 drops of the alkaline permanganate reagent used for the albuminoid nitrogen determination, Section 131.3a, is also satisfactory; add to 1 liter of distilled water). Redistill in an all-pyrex apparatus, discarding the initial 50 ml of distillate. Collect that fraction of the distillate which is free of permanganate. [A yellow color with the orthotolidine reagent, used for the residual chlorine determination, Section 114C. 3c(1), indicates the presence of permanganate.]

2) Add 1 ml conc H_2SO_4 and 0.2 ml manganese sulfate solution (36.4 g $MnSO_4 \cdot H_2O$ per 100 ml aqueous solution) to each 1 liter distilled water, and make pink with 1 to 3 ml potassium permanganate solution (400 mg $KMnO_4$ per liter aqueous solution). After 15 min, decolorize with ammonium oxalate solution [900 mg $(NH_4)_2C_2O_4 \cdot H_2O$ per liter aqueous solution].

b. EDTA solution: Dissolve 500 mg disodium ethylenediamine tetraacetate dihydrate, also called (ethylenedinitrilo)tetraacetic acid sodium salt, in nitrite-free water and dilute to 100 ml.

c. Sulfanilic acid reagent: Completely dissolve 600 mg sulfanilic acid in 70 ml hot distilled water, cool, add 20 ml conc HCl, dilute to 100 ml with distilled water, and mix thoroughly.

d. Naphthylamine hydrochloride reagent: Dissolve 600 mg of 1-naphthylamine hydrochloride in distilled water to which 1.0 ml conc HCl has been added. Dilute to 100 ml with distilled water and mix thoroughly. The reagent becomes discolored and a precipitate may form after 1 week, but it is still usable. Discard when sensitivity or reproducibility is affected. Store in a refrigerator to prolong the useful life of the reagent. Filter before using. (CAUTION: *Handle this chemical with extreme care. Never use a mouth pipet for dispensing this reagent but rely on an automatic, dropping or safety pipet to measure the necessary volumes. Avoid inhalation or exposure to the skin.*)

e. Sodium acetate buffer solution, 2M: Dissolve 16.4 g $NaC_2H_3O_2$ or 27.2 g $NaC_2H_3O_2 \cdot 3H_2O$ in nitrite-free water and dilute to 100 ml. Filter if necessary.

f. Stock nitrite solution: The reagent grade of sodium nitrite available commercially assays at less than 99%. Since nitrite is readily oxidized in the presence of moisture, fresh bottles of reagent are desirable for the preparation of the stock solution. The preferred approach is to determine the sodium nitrite content immediately before preparation of the stock solution and to keep bottles tightly stoppered against the free access of air when not in use. The sodium nitrite content may be determined by adding an excess of standard potassium permanganate solution, discharging the permanganate color with a standard reductant such as sodium oxalate or ferrous ammonium sulfate solution, and finally back-titrating with standard permanganate solution.

1) PREPARATION OF STOCK SOLUTION—Dissolve 1.232 g sodium nitrite, $NaNO_2$, in nitrite-free water and dilute to 1,000 ml; 1.00 ml = 250 μg N. Preserve with 1 ml chloroform.

2) STANDARDIZATION OF STOCK SOLUTION [1, 2]—Pipet, in order, 50.00 ml standard 0.05*N* $KMnO_4$ (prepared and standardized as described under Calcium, Section 110B.3c), 5 ml conc sulfuric acid, and 50.00 ml stock nitrite solution into a glass-stoppered flask or bottle. Submerge the tip of the nitrite pipet well below the surface of the permanganate acid solution. Shake the stoppered flask gently. Warm the flask contents to 70–80 C on a hot plate. Discharge the permanganate color by adding sufficient standard 0.05*N* sodium oxalate (3.350 g $Na_2C_2O_4$, primary standard grade, per 1,000 ml solution) in 10.00-ml portions. Titrate the excess sodium oxalate with standard 0.05*N* $KMnO_4$ to the faint pink end point. Carry a nitrite-free water blank through the entire procedure and make the necessary corrections in the final calculation.

When standard 0.05*N* ferrous ammonium sulfate solution is substituted for sodium oxalate, omit the heating to 70–80 C and instead extend the reaction period between the permanganate and ferrous ions to 5 min before the final $KMnO_4$ titration is undertaken. This standard 0.05*N* ferrous solution contains 19.607 g $Fe(NH_4)_2(SO_4)_2 \cdot 6H_2O$ and 20 ml conc H_2SO_4 per 1,000 ml solution and may be standardized as described under Oxygen Demand (Chemical), Section 220.3c.

Calculate the nitrite nitrogen content of the stock solution by the following equation:

$$A = \frac{[(B \times C) - (D \times E)] \times 7}{F}$$

where A = mg/ml nitrite nitrogen in stock nitrite solution, B = total ml standard $KMnO_4$ used, C = normality of standard $KMnO_4$, D = total ml standard reductant added, E = normality of standard reductant, and F = ml stock $NaNO_2$ solution taken for titration. Each 1.00 ml 0.05*N* $KMnO_4$ consumed by the nitrite corresponds to 1,725 μg $NaNO_2$, or 350 μg N.

3) TITRATION OF HIGH-NITRITE SAMPLES—The standardization procedure can also be used for the titration of water samples containing nitrite nitrogen concentrations in excess of 2 mg/l. In such a case, the water sample volume is substituted for F in the previous equation and the factor 7 is increased to 7,000 for the purpose of calculating the nitrite nitrogen value in terms of mg/l.

g. Intermediate nitrite solution: Calculate the volume, G, of stock nitrite solution required for the intermediate nitrite solution by means of the following equation: $G = 12.5/A$. Dilute to 250 ml the calculated volume, G (approximately 50 ml), of the stock nitrite solution with nitrite-free water; 1.00 ml = 50.0 μg N. Prepare daily.

h. Standard nitrite solution: Dilute 10.00 ml intermediate nitrite solution to 1,000 ml with nitrite-free water; 1.00 ml = 0.500 μg N. Prepare daily.

i. Aluminum hydroxide suspension: Prepare as directed in Nitrogen (Nitrate), Section 133A.3g(1).

4. Procedure

a. Removal of turbidity and color: If the sample contains suspended solids and color, add 2 ml aluminum hydroxide suspension to 100 ml sample, stir thoroughly, allow to stand for a few minutes, and filter, discarding the first portion of the filtrate. Alternatively, coagulate the sample with zinc sulfate and hydroxide as described under Nitrogen (Ammonia), Section 132B.4a.

b. Color development: To 50.0 ml clear sample which has been neutralized to pH 7, or to an aliquot diluted to 50.0 ml, add 1.0 ml EDTA solution and 1.0 ml sulfanilic acid reagent. Mix thoroughly. At this point, the pH of the solution should be about 1.4. After the reaction has proceeded for 3 to 10 min, add 1.0 ml naphthylamine hydrochloride reagent and 1.0 ml sodium acetate buffer solution; mix well. At this point, the pH of the solution should be 2.0 to 2.5. Measure the reddish purple color after 10 to 30 min.

c. Photometric measurement: Measure the absorbance at or near 520 mμ against a reagent blank and run parallel checks frequently against known nitrite standards, preferably in the nitrogen range of the samples. Redetermine complete calibration curves following the preparation of new reagents.

d. Color standards for visual comparison: Prepare a suitably spaced series of visual color standards in nessler tubes by adding the following volumes of standard sodium nitrite solution and diluting to 50 ml with nitrite-free water: 0, 0.1, 0.2, 0.4, 0.7, 1.0, 1.4, 1.7, 2.0 and 2.5 ml.

5. Calculation

$$\text{mg/l nitrite N} = \frac{\mu\text{g nitrite N}}{\text{ml sample}}$$

$$\text{mg/l } NO_2 = \text{mg/l nitrite N} \times 3.29$$

6. Precision and Accuracy

A synthetic unknown sample containing 250 μg/l nitrite N, 108 mg/l Ca, 82 mg/l Mg, 3.1 mg/l K, 19.9 mg/l Na, 241 mg/l chloride, 1.1 mg/l nitrate N, 259 mg/l sulfate, and 42.5 mg/l total alkalinity (contributed by $NaHCO_3$) was determined by the diazotization method, with a relative standard deviation of 21.4% and a relative error of 12.0% in 49 laboratories.

7. References

1. AMERICAN CHEMICAL SOCIETY. 1961. *Reagent Chemicals—American Chemical Society Specifications, 1960.* ACS, Washington, D. C., p. 474.
2. N. H. FURMAN, Ed. 1962. *Standard Methods of Chemical Analysis* (6th ed.). D. Van Nostrand Co., Princeton, N. J., Vol. I, pp. 746–747.

8. Bibliography

RIDER, B. F. & M. G. MELLON. 1946. Colorimetric determination of nitrates. *Ind. Eng. Chem.,* Anal. Ed. 18:96.

BARNES, H. & A. R. FOLKARD. 1951. The determination of nitrites. *Analyst* 76: 599.

BOLTZ, D. F., Ed. 1958. *Colorimetric Determination of Nonmetals.* Interscience Publishers, New York, pp. 124–132.

135. NITROGEN (ORGANIC)

The classical kjeldahl method determines organically bound nitrogen in the trinegative state. The organic nitrogen content of a water is contributed in various degrees by amino acids, polypeptides and proteins—all products of biologic processes—and thus includes albuminoid nitrogen. A rise in the organic nitrogen content may often be related to the sewage or industrial-waste pollution of a given water supply.

The method offered in this manual fails to account for the nitrogen in azides, azines, azo, hydrazones, nitrate, nitrite, nitrile, nitro, nitroso, oximes and semicarbazones. If ammonia nitrogen is not removed as described in the initial phase (¶ 4b below) of the organic nitrogen procedure, the term "total kjeldahl nitrogen" is applied to the result. Should the total kjeldahl nitrogen and ammonia nitrogen be determined individually, the "organic nitrogen" can then be obtained by difference.

1. General Discussion

a. Principle: In the presence of sulfuric acid, potassium sulfate, and mercuric sulfate catalyst, the amino nitrogen of many organic materials is converted to ammonium bisulfate. After the mercury ammonium complex in the digestate has been decomposed by sodium thiosulfate, the ammonia is distilled from an alkaline medium and absorbed in boric acid. The ammonia is determined colorimetrically, or, if preferred, by titration with a standard mineral acid.

b. Selection of modification: The sensitivity of the colorimetric methods makes them useful for the determination of organic nitrogen levels below 1 mg/l. The titrimetric method of measuring the ammonia in the distillate is suitable for the determination of a wide range of organic nitrogen concentrations, depending on the volume of boric acid absorbent used and the concentration of the standard acid titrant.

c. Storage of sample: The most reliable results are obtained on fresh samples. If a prompt analysis of a relatively unpolluted water is impossible, every precaution should be taken to retard biologic activity by storing the sample at a low temperature, preferably just above freezing. Where such a measure is impractical, the addition of 0.8 ml conc H_2SO_4 per liter of sample may serve to maintain the nitrogen balance.

Because organic nitrogen in unsterilized sewage, wastewaters and polluted waters is continually ammonified, the determination must be made on a freshly collected sample. If the analysis cannot be made at once, the sample must be preserved with sufficient sulfuric acid to produce a concentration of 1,500 mg/l H_2SO_4 or greater.

2. Apparatus

a. Digestion apparatus: Kjeldahl flasks with a total capacity of 800 ml yield the best results. Digestions should be conducted over a heating device adjusted in such a manner that 250 ml of distilled water at an initial temperature of 25 C can be heated to a rolling boil in approximately 5 min. A heating device meeting this specification will usually provide the temperature range of 344–371 C which is desirable for an effective digestion.

b. Distillation apparatus: The entire assembly (Figure 19) consists of a

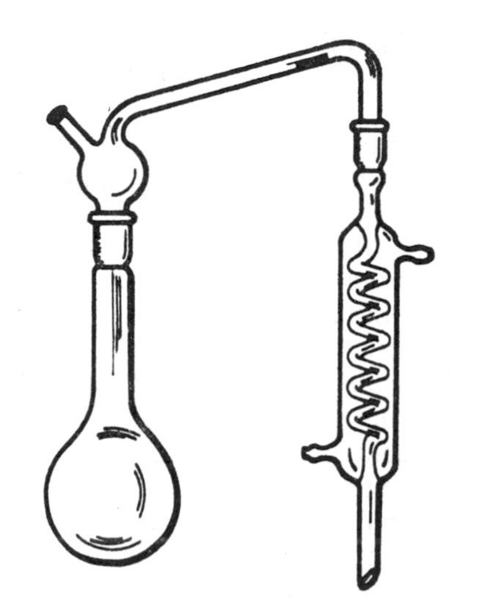

Figure 19. Distillation apparatus for organic nitrogen determination.*

kjeldahl flask, an efficient bulb or trap, and a vertical condenser. Connections between these units can be made with short lengths of rubber tubing. Although gas-heated distillation apparatus may be used, electrically heated units often offer smoother operation and less bumping. The entire apparatus should be steamed out before use, by distilling 500 ml of distilled water (low in ammonia) until the distillate becomes free of ammonia.

c. Colorimetric equipment: One of the following is required—

1) SPECTROPHOTOMETER, for use at 400 to 425 mμ, providing a light path of 1 cm or longer.

2) FILTER PHOTOMETER, providing a light path of 1 cm or longer and equipped with a violet filter having maximum transmittance at 400 to 425 mμ.

3) NESSLER TUBES, matched, 50-ml, tall form.

* Corning No. 3340 or equivalent.

3. Reagents

All of the reagents listed for the determination of Nitrogen (Ammonia), Sections 132A.3 and 132B.3, are required, plus the following:

a. Digestion reagent: Dissolve 134 g potassium sulfate, K_2SO_4, in 650 ml ammonia-free distilled water and 200 ml conc H_2SO_4. Add, with stirring, a solution prepared by dissolving 2 g red mercuric oxide, HgO, in 25 ml 6*N* H_2SO_4. Dilute the combined solution to 1 liter. Keep this solution at a temperature above 14 C to prevent crystallization.

b. Phenolphthalein indicator solution.

c. Sodium hydroxide-sodium thiosulfate reagent: Dissolve 500 g NaOH and 25 g $Na_2S_2O_3 \cdot 5H_2O$ in ammonia-free distilled water and dilute to 1 liter.

d. Mixed indicator solution: Dissolve 200 mg methyl red indicator in 100 ml 95% ethyl or isopropyl alcohol. Dissolve 100 mg methylene blue in 50 ml 95% ethyl or isopropyl alcohol. Combine the two solutions. Prepare monthly.

e. Indicating boric acid solution: Dissolve 20 g H_3BO_3 in ammonia-free distilled water, add 10 ml mixed indicator solution, and dilute to 1 liter. Prepare monthly.

f. Standard sulfuric acid titrant, 0.02 *N:* Prepare and standardize as directed in Alkalinity, Section 102.3c. For greatest accuracy, standardize the titrant against an amount of sodium carbonate which has been incorporated in the indicating boric acid solution to reproduce the actual conditions of the sample titration. A standard acid solution, exactly 0.0200*N*, is equivalent to 280 μg N per 1.00 ml.

4. Procedure

a. Selection of sample volume: Place a measured sample into an 800-ml kjeldahl flask. Determine the sample size from the following tabulation:

Organic Nitrogen in Sample, mg/l	Sample Size, ml
0–1	500
1–10	250
10–20	100
20–50	50.0
50–100	25.0

If necessary, dilute the sample to 300 ml and neutralize to pH 7.

b. Ammonia removal: Add 10 ml phosphate buffer solution to a sample of drinking water quality and 25 ml to wastewater samples. Add a few glass beads or boiling chips and boil off 300 ml. If desired, distill this fraction and determine the ammonia nitrogen. Alternatively, if ammonia has been determined by the distillation method, use the residue in the distilling flask for the organic nitrogen determination.

c. Digestion: Cool and add carefully 50 ml digestion reagent (or substitute 10 ml conc H_2SO_4, 6.7 g K_2SO_4, and 1.5 ml mercuric sulfate solution). If large quantities of nitrogen-free organic matter are present, add an additional 50 ml digestion reagent for each gram of solid matter in the sample. After mixing, heat under a hood, or with suitable ejection equipment, to fumes of SO_3 and continue to boil briskly until the solution clears (becomes colorless or a pale straw color). Then digest for an additional 30 min. Allow flask and contents to cool; dilute to 300 ml with ammonia-free water and add 0.5 ml phenolphthalein indicator solution and mix. Tilt the flask and add, carefully, sufficient (approximately 50 ml for every 50 ml digestion reagent used) hydroxide-thiosulfate reagent to form an alkaline layer at the bottom of the flask.

Connect the flask to the steamed-out distillation apparatus and shake the flask to insure complete mixing. Add more hydroxide-thiosulfate reagent in the prescribed manner if a red phenolphthalein color fails to appear at this stage.

d. Distillation: Distill and collect 200 ml distillate below the surface of 50 ml boric acid solution. Use plain boric acid solution when the ammonia is to be determined by nesslerization and use indicating boric acid for a titrimetric finish. Extend the tip of the condenser well below the level of boric acid solution and do not allow the temperature in the condenser to rise above 29 C. Lower the collected distillate free of contact with the delivery tube and continue distillation during the last minute or two to cleanse the condenser.

e. Final ammonia measurement: Determine the ammonia by (1) nesslerization or (2) titration.

1) NESSLERIZATION—Mix the distillate thoroughly and measure a 50.0-ml portion or less. Complete the determination as described in Nitrogen (Ammonia), Section 132B.4b through e.

2) TITRATION—Titrate the ammonia in the distillate with standard 0.02*N* sulfuric acid titrant until the indicator turns a pale lavender.

f. Blank: Carry a blank through all the steps of the procedure and apply the necessary correction to the results.

5. Calculation

a. Nesslerization finish:

$$\text{mg/l organic N} = \frac{A \times 1{,}000}{\text{ml sample}} \times \frac{B}{C}$$

where A = mg N found colorimetrically, B = ml total distillate collected including the H_3BO_3, and C = ml distillate taken for nesslerization.

b. Titrimetric finish:

$$\text{mg/l organic N} = \frac{(D - E) \times 280}{\text{ml sample}}$$

where D = ml H_2SO_4 titration for sample and E = ml H_2SO_4 titration for blank.

6. Precision and Accuracy

Three synthetic unknown samples containing varying organic nitrogen concentrations and other constituents were analyzed by three procedural modifications: kjeldahl-nessler finish, kjeldahl-titrimetric finish, and calculation of the difference between the total kjeldahl nitrogen and ammonia nitrogen, both determined by a nessler finish. The results of the participating laboratories are summarized in Table 135(1).

Sample 1 contained the following additional constituents: 400 mg/l chloride, 1.50 mg/l ammonia nitrogen, 1.0 mg/l nitrate nitrogen, 500 μg/l phosphate and 30.0 mg/l silica.

Sample 2 contained the following additional constituents: 200 mg/l chloride, 800 μg/l ammonia nitrogen, 1.0 mg/l nitrate nitrogen, 5.0 mg/l phosphate and 15.0 mg/l silica.

Sample 3 contained the following additional constituents: 10 mg/l chloride, 200 μg/l ammonia nitrogen, 1.0 mg/l nitrate nitrogen, 10.0 mg/l phosphate and 5.0 mg/l silica.

7. Bibliography

KJELDAHL, J. 1883. A new method for the determination of nitrogen in organic matter. *Z. Anal. Chem.* 22:366.

PHELPS, E. B. 1905. The determination of

TABLE 135(1): PRECISION AND ACCURACY DATA FOR ORGANIC NITROGEN

Sample	No. of Laboratories	Organic Nitrogen Concentration μg/l	Relative Standard Deviation			Relative Error		
			Nessler Finish %	Titrimetric Finish %	Calculation of Total Kjeldahl N Minus Ammonia N %	Nessler Finish %	Titrimetric Finish %	Calculation of Total Kjeldahl N Minus Ammonia N %
1	26	200	94.8			55.0		
	29			104.4			70.0	
	15				68.8			70.0
2	26	800	52.1			12.5		
	31			44.8			3.7	
	16				52.6			8.7
3	26	1,500	43.1			9.3		
	30			54.7			22.6	
	16				45.9			4.0

organic nitrogen in sewage by the Kjeldahl process. *J. Infect. Dis.* (Suppl.) 1:225.

MEEKER, E. W. & E. C. WAGNER. 1933. Titration of ammonia in the presence of boric acid. *Ind. Eng. Chem.*, Anal. Ed. 5:396.

WAGNER, E. C. 1940. Titration of ammonia in the presence of boric acid. *Ind. Eng. Chem.*, Anal. Ed. 12:771.

MACKENZIE, H. A. & H. S. WALLACE. 1954. The Kjeldahl determination of nitrogen: A critical study of digestion conditions. *Austral. J. Chem.* 7:55.

MORGAN, G. B., J. B. LACKEY & F. W. GILCREAS. 1957. Quantitative determination of organic nitrogen in water, sewage, and industrial wastes. *Anal. Chem.* 29:833.

BOLTZ, D. F., Ed. 1958. *Colorimetric Determination of Nonmetals.* Interscience Publishers, New York, pp. 75–97.

136 ODOR

Increased reuse of available water supplies has led to greater emphasis on the subjective quality criteria of water. Domestic consumers and process industries such as food, beverage and pharmaceutical manufacturers require water essentially free of taste and odors. Most organic and some inorganic chemicals contribute taste or odor. These may originate from municipal and industrial waste discharges, natural sources (such as decomposition of vegetable matter), or from associated microbiological activity. Because odorous materials are detectable when present in only a few micrograms per liter and are often complex, it is usually impractical and often impossible to isolate and identify the odor-producing chemical. Evaluation of odors and tastes is thus dependent on the chemical senses of smell and taste.

According to psychologists, there are only four true taste sensations: sour, sweet, salty and bitter. Dissolved inorganic salts of copper, iron, manganese, potassium, sodium and zinc can be detected by taste. Concentrations producing taste range from a few tenths to several hundred milligrams per liter. As these tastes are not accompanied by odor, the taste test must be used where they are involved.

All other sensations ascribed to the sense of taste are actually odors, even though the sensation is not noticed until the material is taken into the mouth. The ultimate odor-testing device is the human nose. Odor tests are performed to arrive at qualitative descriptions and approximate quantitative measurements of odor intensity. Odor tests are less fatiguing than taste tests; hence, an operator can conduct odor tests for a longer period. Higher temperatures can be used for odor evaluations than for the taste test, with a resultant increase in sensitivity on some samples.

Taste and odor tests are useful as a check on the quality of raw and finished water; for control of odor through the plant and the determination of treatment dosages; as a test of the effectiveness of different kinds of treatment; and as a means of tracing the source of contamination.

1. General Discussion

a. Principle: The sample of water is diluted with odor-free water until a dilution that is of the least definitely perceptible odor to each tester is found. People vary widely as to odor sensitivity, and even the same person will not be consistent in the concentrations he can detect from day to day. Panels of not less than five persons, and preferably 10 or more, are recommended to overcome the variability of using one observer.[1] Some investigators have sought to overcome the problems involved in using one or two observers, or to compare the sensitivity of different individuals, by using a calibrating standard odor substance such as *n*-butyl alcohol. When large numbers of observers are testing the same sample at one location, panel procedures eliminate the necessity for a calibrating standard.

b. Application: This threshold method is applicable to samples ranging from nearly odorless natural waters to industrial wastes with threshold numbers in the thousands. There are no intrinsic difficulties with the highly odorous samples, since they are reduced in concentration proportionately before being presented to the test observers.

c. Qualitative descriptions: A satisfactory system for characterizing odor has not been developed despite efforts over more than a century. Previous editions of this book contained a table of odor descriptions proposed as a guide in expressing odor quality. The reader may continue to encounter the obsolete standard abbreviations of that table. He is referred to the 12th Edition for an explanation of such terms.

d. Sampling and storage: Collect samples for odor testing in glass bottles with glass or teflon-lined closures. Tests should be completed as soon as possible after collection of the sample. If storage is necessary, collect at least 500 ml of sample in a bottle filled to the top; refrigerate, making sure that no extraneous odors can be drawn into this sample when the water cools. Plastic containers are not reliable for odor samples.

e. Dechlorination: Most tap waters and some wastewaters are chlorinated. It is often desirable to determine the odor of the chlorinated sample as well as that of the same sample after removal of chlorine. Dechlorination is achieved using arsenite or thiosulfate in exact stoichiometric quantity as described under Nitrogen (Ammonia), Section 132A.3c(2) and (4). CAUTION—*Arsenic compounds should not be used as dechlorinating agents on samples to be tasted.*

f. Temperature: Threshold values will vary with temperature. For most tap waters and raw water sources, a sample temperature of 60 C will permit the detection of odors that might otherwise be missed; 60 C is the standard temperature for hot threshold tests. For some purposes—because the odor is too fleeting or there is excessive heat sensation—the hot odor test may not be applicable; where experience shows that a lower temperature is needed, a standard test temperature of 40 C should be used. For special purposes, other temperatures are sometimes used. *Always report the temperature at which observations are made.*

2. Apparatus

To assure reliable threshold measurements, it is necessary that all glassware be odor-free. Glassware must be freshly cleaned shortly before use, with nonodorous soap and acid cleaning solution followed by rinsing with odor-free water. Glassware used in threshold testing should be reserved for that purpose only. Rubber, cork or plastic stoppers should not be used. Narrow-mouth vessels are not suitable for running odor tests.

a. Sample bottles, glass-stoppered or with teflon-lined closures, to hold the original samples.

b. Constant temperature bath: A water bath or electric hot plate capable of temperature control of ± 1 C for odor tests at elevated temperatures. The temperature bath must not contribute any odor to the odor flasks.

c. Odor flasks: Glass-stoppered, 500-ml (₮ 32) erlenmeyer flasks, to hold sample dilutions during testing.

d. Pipets:

1) TRANSFER AND VOLUMETRIC PIPETS OR GRADUATED CYLINDERS—200-, 100-, 50- and 25-ml.

2) MEASURING—10-ml, graduated in tenths.

e. Thermometer: Zero to 110 C, chemical or metal-stem dial type.

3. Odor-Free Water

Odor-free dilution water must be prepared as needed by filtration through a bed of activated carbon. Most tap waters are suitable for the preparation of odor-free water, except that it is necessary to check the filtered water for residual chlorine, unusual salt concentrations, or unusually high or low pH. All these may affect some odorous samples. Where supplies are adequate, the use of distilled water obviates these problems as a source of odor-free water. A convenient odor-free water generator may be made as shown in Figure 20. The carbon cartridge described in Section 139A.2a under the Carbon Adsorption Method (CAM) for Organic Contaminants is also suitable. Pass tap or distilled water through the odor-free water generator at a rate of 0.1 liter/min. When the generator is first started, flush to remove the carbon fines before the odor-free water is used.

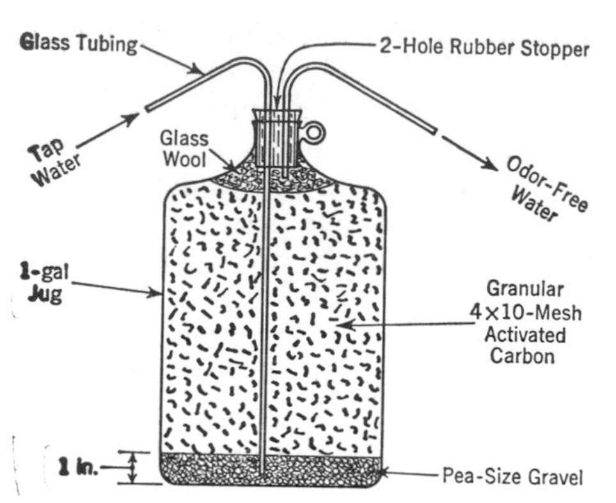

Figure 20. Odor-free water generator.

The quality of water obtained from the odor-free water generator should be checked daily at 40 C and 60 C before use. The life of the carbon will vary with the condition and amount of the water filtered. Subtle odors of biological origin are often found if moist carbon filters are permitted to stand idle between test periods. Detection of odor in the water coming through the carbon indicates that a change of carbon is needed.

4. Procedure

a. Precautions: Carefully select the persons to make taste or odor tests. Although extreme sensitivity is not required, exclude insensitive persons and concentrate on observers who have a sincere interest in the test. Avoid extraneous odor stimuli such as those caused by smoking and eating prior to the test or those contributed by scented soaps, perfumes and shaving lotions. Make sure that the tester is free from colds or allergies that affect odor response. Limit the frequency of tests to a number below the fatigue level by frequent rests in an odor-free atmosphere. Keep the room in which the tests are conducted free from distractions, drafts, and other odor. If necessary in certain industrial atmospheres, set aside a special odor-free room ventilated by air which is filtered through activated carbon and maintained at a constant comfortable temperature and humidity.[2]

For precise work use a panel of five or more testers. Do not allow the persons making the odor measurements to prepare the samples or to know the dilution concentrations being evaluated. Familiarize such persons with the procedure before they participate in a panel test. Start with the most dilute sample to avoid tiring the senses with the concentrated sample. Keep the temperature of the samples during testing within 1 C of the temperature specified for the test.

Since many raw and waste waters are colored or have a decided turbidity which will bias the odor-testing results, use opaque or darkly colored odor flasks, such as red actinic erlenmeyer flasks, to conceal these variations.

b. Characterization: As part of the threshold test or as a separate test, direct each observer to describe in his own words the characteristic odor of the sample tested. Compile the consensus which may appear among the panel members and which affords a clue to the origin of the odorous pollutant. The value of the characterization test increases as the observers become more experienced with a particular category of odor, such as algae, chlorophenol or mustiness.

c. Threshold measurement: * The ratio by which the odor-bearing sample has to be diluted with odor-free water for the odor to be just detectable by the odor test is the "threshold odor number," designated by the abbreviation T. O. Bring the total volume of sample and odor-free water to 200 ml in each test. Follow the dilutions and record the corresponding threshold numbers presented in Table 136(1).

TABLE 136(1): THRESHOLD ODOR NUMBERS CORRESPONDING TO VARIOUS DILUTIONS

Sample Volume Diluted to 200 ml *ml*	Threshold Odor No.	Sample Volume Diluted to 200 ml *ml*	Threshold Odor No.
200	1	12	17
140	1.4	8.3	24
100	2	5.7	35
70	3	4	50
50	4	2.8	70
35	6	2	100
25	8	1.4	140
17	12	1.0	200

If a total volume other than the 200 ml specified is used, compute the threshold number thus:

$$T.O. = \frac{A + B}{A}$$

* There are numerous methods of arranging and presenting samples for odor determinations. The methods offered here are believed to be practical and economical of time and personnel, and are adequate for the problems encountered at most water plants. If extensive tests are planned and statistical analysis of data is required, the experimenter should become familiar with the triangle test and the methods that have been used extensively by flavor and allied industries.[3]

where A = ml sample and B = ml odor-free water. Place the proper volume of odor-free water in the flask first; then pipet the sample into the water, mix by swirling flask, and proceed as follows:

1) Determine the approximate range of the threshold number by adding 200 ml, 50 ml, 12 ml and 2.8 ml sample to separate 500-ml glass-stoppered erlenmeyer flasks containing odor-free water to make a total volume of 200 ml. Use a separate flask containing only odor-free water as the reference for comparison. Heat the dilutions and the reference to the temperature desired for running the test.

2) Shake the flask containing the odor-free water, remove the stopper, and sniff the vapors. Test the sample containing the least amount of odor-bearing water in the same way. If odor can be detected in this dilution, prepare more dilute samples as described in ¶ 5 below. If odor cannot be detected in the first dilution, repeat the above procedure, using the sample containing the next higher concentration of the odor-bearing water, and continue this process until odor is clearly detected.

3) Based on the results obtained in the preliminary test, prepare a set of dilutions using Table 136(2) as a guide. Insert two or more blanks in the series, frequently in the vicinity of the expected threshold but avoiding any repeated pattern. Do not let the observer know which dilutions are odorous and which are blanks. Instruct him to smell each flask in sequence, beginning with the least concentrated sample, until odor is detected with certainty.

TABLE 136(2): DILUTIONS FOR VARIOUS ODOR INTENSITIES

Sample Volume in Which Odor First Noted			
200 ml	50 ml	12 ml	2.8 ml
Volume (ml) of Sample to be Diluted to 200 ml			
200	50	12	(Intermediate dilution)
140	35	8.3	
100	25	5.7	
70	17	4.0	
50	12	2.8	

4) Record the observations by indicating whether odor is noted in each test flask. For example:

ml Sample Diluted to 200 ml	12	0	17	25	0	35	50
Response	–	–	–	+	–	+	+

5) If the sample being tested requires more extensive dilution than is provided by Table 136(2), prepare an intermediate dilution consisting of 20 ml sample diluted to 200 ml with odor-free water. Use this dilution for the threshold determination. Multiply the T. O. obtained by 10 to correct for the intermediate dilution. In rare cases more than one tenfold intermediate dilution step may be required.

5. Calculation

The threshold number is the dilution ratio at which taste or odor is just detectable. In the example above (¶ 4 preceding), the first detectable odor occurred when 25 ml sample was diluted to 200 ml. Thus, the threshold is 200 divided by 25, yielding a result of 8. Table 136(1) lists the threshold numbers that correspond to common dilutions.

Anomalous responses sometimes occur; a low concentration may be called positive and a higher concentration in the series may be called negative. In such a case, the threshold may properly be designated as that point of detection after which no further anomalies occur. For instance:

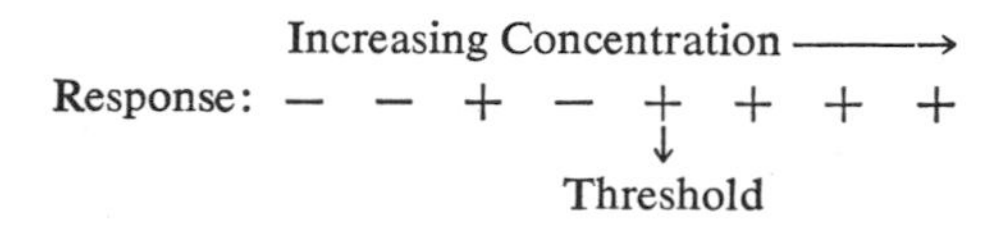

Calculations from large numbers of panel results to find the most probable average threshold are best accomplished by appropriate statistical methods. For most purposes, the threshold of a group can be expressed as the geometric mean of the individual thresholds.

6. Interpretation of Results

A threshold number is not a precise value. In the case of the single observer, it represents a judgment at the time of testing. Panel results are more meaningful because individual differences have less influence on the result. One or two observers can develop useful data if comparison with larger panels has been made to check their sensitivity. Comparisons of data from time to time or place to place should not be attempted unless all test conditions have been carefully standardized and some basis for comparison of observer intensities exists.

7. References

1. American Society for Testing and Materials, Committee E-18. 1968. STP 433, Basic principles of sensory evaluation; STP 434, Manual on sensory testing methods; STP 440, Correlation of subjective-objective methods in the study of odors and taste. ASTM, Philadelphia.
2. R. A. Baker. 1962. Critical evaluation of olfactory measurement. *JWPCF* 34: 582.
3. *Flavor Research and Food Acceptance.* 1958. Reinhold Publishing Corp., New York.

8. Bibliography

Hulbert, R. & D. Feben. 1941. Studies on accuracy of threshold odor value. *JAWWA* 33:1945.

Spaulding, C. H. 1942. Accuracy and application of threshold odor test. *JAWWA* 34:877.

Thomas, H. A., Jr. 1943. Calculation of threshold odor. *JAWWA* 35:751.

Moncrieff, R. W. 1946. *The Chemical Senses.* John Wiley & Sons, New York.

Cartwright, L. C., C. T. Snell & P. H. Kelly. 1952. Organoleptic panel testing as a research tool. *Anal. Chem.* 24: 503.

Geldard, F. A. 1953. *The Human Senses.* John Wiley & Sons, New York.

Laughlin, H. F. 1954. Palatable level with the threshold odor test. *Taste & Odor Control J.* 20: No. 8 (Aug.).

Sechenov, I. M. 1956 and 1958. Problem of hygenic standards for waters simultaneously polluted with harmful substances. *Gigiyena i Sanitariya* (Russian) Nos. 10 and 8.

Shellenberger, R. D. 1958. Procedures for determining threshold odor concentrations in aqueous solutions. *Taste & Odor Control J.* 24: No. 5 (May).

Taste and Odor Control in Water Purification (2nd ed.). 1959. West Virginia Pulp & Paper Co. Industrial Chemical Sales Division, New York. Contains 1,063 classified references.

Cohen, J. M. et al. 1960. Taste threshold concentrations of metals in drinking water. *JAWWA* 52:660.

Baker, R. A. 1961. Problems of tastes and odors. *JWPCF* 33:1099.

Rosen, A. A., J. B. Peter & F. M. Middleton. 1962. Odor thresholds of mixed organic chemicals. *JWPCF* 34:7.

Laughlin, H. F. 1962. Influence of temperature in threshold odor evaluation. *Taste & Odor Control J.* 28: No. 10 (Oct.).

Baker, R. A. 1963. Odor effects of aqueous mixtures of organic chemicals. *JWPCF* 35:728.

Rosen, A. A., R. T. Skeel & M. B. Ettinger. 1963. Relationship of river water odor to specific organic contaminants. *JWPCF* 35:777.

STAFF REPORT. 1963. The threshold odor test. *Taste & Odor Control J.* 29: Nos. 6, 7, 8 (June, July, Aug.).

WRIGHT, R. H. 1964. *The Science of Smell.* Basic Books, New York.

AMERINE, M. A., R. M. PANGBORN & E. B. ROESSLER. 1965. *Principles of Sensory Evaluation of Food.* Academic Press, New York.

BRUVOLD, W. H., H. J. ONGERTH & R. J. DILLEHAY. 1967. Consumer attitudes toward mineral taste in domestic water. *JAWWA* 59:547.

AMERICAN SOCIETY FOR TESTING AND MATERIALS. 1967. *1967 Book of ASTM Standards,* Part 23, D-1292-65, pp. 280–288. ASTM, Philadelphia.

ROSEN, A. A. 1968. Report of Research Committee on Tastes and Odors, presented at AWWA Annual Conference.

137 OIL AND GREASE

Oil or grease may be present in water as an emulsion from industrial wastes or similar sources, or a light petroleum fraction may be in solution. Some oils in natural waters may derive from the decomposition of plankton or higher forms of aquatic life. Most heavy oils and greases are insoluble in water but may be emulsified or saponified by detergents, alkalis or other chemicals. Low-boiling fractions are lost in ordinary oil and grease analysis, and special technics for their determination have been developed.[1–5] Even lubricating oil fractions evaporate at a significant rate at the temperature which is necessary for removal of the last traces of the extraction solvent. Kerosene is still more volatile, and gasoline cannot be determined with any reliability by the organic solvent extraction method, which is designed for waters that may contain small amounts of oil or grease in solution or suspension. For heavily polluted water or wastes, use the methods described under Grease in Section 209.

1. General Discussion

a. Principle: Dissolved or emulsified oil or grease is extracted from water by intimate contact with various organic solvents. Some extractables, especially unsaturated fats and fatty acids, oxidize readily; hence, special precautions regarding temperature and solvent vapor displacement are included to minimize this effect.

b. Interference: Solvents vary considerably in their ability to dissolve not only oil and grease, but other organic substances as well. No solvent is known that will selectively dissolve only oil and grease. On standing, most solvents tend to form oxidation products which leave a gummy residue on evaporation. Saponified oil or grease tends to remain as an emulsion, but acidification of the sample to about pH 1 and saturation with sodium chloride aids in breaking this emulsion. Directions for breaking stubborn emulsions have been described in the literature.[6, 7]

c. Sampling: Care should be taken that the sample is representative. Samples of oil films recovered from the surface of a stream or other body of water will be almost impossible to evaluate in relation to the total volume of water, the total film area, and the thickness involved. Samples should be taken in clean glass-stoppered bottles previously washed with solvent and air-dried before use. The bottle should not be completely filled, as a loss of floating oil may occur in stoppering. It is advisable to collect the desired quantity of sample in an oversized bottle that has previously been marked on the outside at the desired volume.

d. Storage of sample: Stored samples should be acidified with 5 ml of 1 + 1 H_2SO_4 per liter to inhibit bacterial activity. Since many oils and hydrocarbons are utilized by bacteria, storage is obviously detrimental.

2. Apparatus

a. Separatory funnel: In the absence of the preferred inert teflon stopcock, all greasy lubricants should be removed from the ground-glass surfaces. A stopcock lubricant that is insoluble in organic solvents may be prepared by making a paste of bentonite and glycerol. This lubricant dissolves very slowly in water and is not affected by petroleum ether. After using apparatus greased with this lubricant, clean the stopcock thoroughly, as the lubricant tends to harden over a period of time. Other suitable lubricants are listed in handbooks or are available commercially.

b. Electric heating mantle.

3. Reagents

a. Sulfuric acid, 1 + 1.

b. Organic solvent: Use either trichlorotrifluoroethane or petroleum ether. Both extract oil and grease to the same extent. However, trichlorotrifluoroethane is nonflammable and is preferable from the standpoint of laboratory safety. The solvent used should leave no measurable (less than 0.1 mg per 100 ml) residue on evaporation.

1) TRICHLOROTRIFLUOROETHANE *—boiling point, 47 C.

2) PETROLEUM ETHER—boiling point 35–60 C: Distill at least twice in all-glass apparatus, discarding the last 10% remaining in the flask at each distillation. Observe all safety precautions when using petroleum ether because of its potential fire and explosion hazard.

4. Procedure

a. Preparation of sample: Place the sample, usually 1,000 ml, in a separatory funnel of sufficient size to allow the addition of acid and solvent while still leaving space for proper agitation. Acidify the sample with 5 ml sulfuric acid per liter of sample.

b. Extraction with organic solvent: Rinse the sample bottle carefully with 15 ml organic solvent and add the solvent washings to the separatory funnel. Add an additional 25 ml solvent to the separatory funnel, shaking vigorously for 2 min. Allow the organic layer to separate. Withdraw the aqueous portion of the sample into a clean container and transfer the solvent layer into a clean, tared distilling flask capable of holding at least three volumes of solvent. If a clear solvent layer cannot be obtained, filter the solvent layer into the tared distilling flask through a funnel containing a solvent-moistened Whatman No. 40 (or equivalent) filter paper. Use as small a funnel and filter

* Dupont Freon precision cleaning agent or equivalent.

paper as practical. After all the solvent from the two extractions and the final rinsing have been added, wash down funnel and filter paper twice with fresh 5-ml increments of solvent. Return the sample to the separatory funnel, rinsing the container with 15 ml solvent. Add the solvent washings and an additional 25 ml solvent to the separatory funnel, and agitate for another 2 min. Allow the solvent layer to separate and discard the aqueous phase. Add the organic extract to the tared distilling flask and rinse the separatory funnel with 20 ml solvent. Add the solvent washings to the tared distilling flask.

c. Solvent removal: Distill off all but approximately 10 ml of the solvent extract by means of a water bath or an electric heating mantle, observing all necessary safety precautions and keeping the heat source at the proper boiling point. Disconnect the condenser and boil off the remaining solvent from the tared flask at the same temperature. Dry on a water or steam bath. When dry, lay the flask on its side to facilitate the removal of solvent vapor. Introduce approximately three volumes of dry illuminating gas into the flask to displace the solvent vapor. Cool in a desiccator for 30 min and weigh.

5. Calculation

If the organic solvent used is known to be free of residue, the gain in weight of the tared distilling flask is mainly due to oil and grease. The total gain in weight, A, of the tared flask less the calculated residue, B, from the solvent, as determined by the distillation or evaporation of a measured quantity, indicates the amount of oil or grease in the water sample:

$$\text{mg/l oil or grease} = \frac{(A - B) \times 1{,}000}{\text{ml sample}}$$

6. Interpretation of Results

This method attempts to avoid most errors that can affect the determination of oil and grease and should produce satisfactory results when small amounts of oil or grease are present. If the quantity of oil or grease is extremely small, the technical skill of the analyst may be the most important factor in the accuracy of the analysis.

7. References

1. L. A. WEBBER & C. E. BURKS. 1952. The determination of light hydrocarbons in water. *Anal. Chem.* 24:1086.
2. F. M. MIDDLETON et al. 1952. Fundamental studies of taste and odor in water supplies. *JAWWA* 44:538.
3. A. A. ROSEN & F. M. MIDDLETON. 1955. Identification of petroleum refinery wastes in surface water. *Anal. Chem.* 27:790.
4. F. J. LUDZACK & C. E. WHITFIELD. 1956. Determination of high-boiling paraffin hydrocarbons in polluted water. *Anal. Chem.* 28:157.
5. C. LINDGREN. 1957. Measurement of small quantities of hydrocarbons in water. *JAWWA* 49:55.
6. R. POMEROY & C. M. WAKEMAN. 1941. Determination of grease in sewage, sludge, and industrial wastes. *Ind. Eng. Chem.,* Anal. Ed. 13:795.
7. M. J. TARAS & K. A. BLUM. 1968. Determination of emulsifying oil in industrial wastewater. *JWPCF* (Res. Suppl.) 40:R404.

8. Bibliography

KIRSCHMAN, H. D. & R. POMEROY. 1949. Determination of oil in oil field waste waters. *Anal. Chem.* 21:793.

138 ORGANIC CARBON (TOTAL)

The total organic carbon value generally falls below the true concentration of organic contaminants because other constituent elements are excluded. When an empirical relationship can be established between the total organic carbon, the biochemical oxygen demand, and the chemical oxygen demand, the total organic carbon (TOC) provides a speedy and convenient way of estimating the other parameters that express the degree of organic contamination.

*138 A. Combustion-Infrared Method (TENTATIVE)**

1. General Discussion

The carbon analyzer offers a means of measuring total organic carbon in the range of 1–150 mg/l in water and wastewater. Appropriate dilution of the sample enables the determination of greater carbon concentrations as well as the analysis of those water samples bearing a high salt, acid or base content. Smaller carbon concentrations can be estimated by suitable concentration of the sample or through the use of larger aliquots. The procedure yields the best results with homogeneous samples which are reproducibly (± 1.0 mg/l carbon) injectable into the apparatus by a microliter-type syringe. The needle opening of the syringe restricts the maximum size of particles which may be included in the samples.

SAMPLING AND STORAGE—Samples should be collected and stored in bottles made of glass, preferably brown in color. Plastic containers are acceptable after tests have demonstrated the absence of extractable carbonaceous substances. A Kemmerer or similar type sampler is recommended for the collection of samples from a depth exceeding 5 ft. Samples which cannot be examined promptly should be protected from decomposition or oxidation by preservation at ice temperatures, minimal exposure to light and atmosphere, or acidification with hydrochloric acid to a pH not over 2.

a. Principle: The water sample is homogenized or diluted as necessary and a micro aliquot is injected into a heated, packed tube in a stream of oxygen or purified air. The water is vaporized and the organic matter is oxidized to carbon dioxide, which is measured by means of a nondispersive type of infrared analyzer. Since the carbon analyzer measures all of the carbon in a sample after injection into the combustion tube, procedural modifications are needed to limit the determination to organic carbon. Inorganic carbonates may be decomposed with acid and volatilized in the form of carbon dioxide before the organic carbon is determined. Alternatively, the total organic and inorganic carbon determination can be followed by a separate determination for the inorganic carbon. The difference between the total and the inorganic carbon then yields the organic carbon.

b. Interference: The removal of car-

* This method is identical in substance to ASTM D2579-67T.

bonate and bicarbonate by means of acidification and purging with nitrogen gas can result in the loss of very volatile organic substances. Another important loss can occur from the failure of large carbon-containing particles in the sample to enter the hypodermic needle used for injection.

c. Minimum detectable concentration, 1 mg/l carbon: This concentration may be lowered by sample concentration or by increasing the aliquot taken for analysis.

2. Apparatus

a. Sample blender or homogenizer of the Waring type.

b. Magnetic stirrer.

c. Hypodermic syringe, 0–50 or 0–500 μl capacity.*

d. Total organic carbon analyzer.†

3. Reagents

a. Redistilled water: Prepare the blank and standard solutions with redistilled water.

b. Hydrochloric acid, conc.

c. Standard carbon solution: Dissolve 5.571 g anhydrous sodium oxalate, $Na_2C_2O_4$, in redistilled water, and dilute to 1,000 ml; 1.00 ml = 1.00 mg carbon.

d. Packing for oxidation tube: Follow the directions supplied with the total organic carbon analyzer.

e. Oxygen gas, carbon dioxide-free.

f. Nitrogen gas, carbon dioxide-free.

4. Procedure

a. Instrument operation: The differences between satisfactory analyzers render impossible the formulation of detailed instructions applicable to every instrument. Therefore, follow the manufacturer's instructions for assembly, testing, calibration and operation of the analyzer on hand. Vary the injected sample size from the normally recommended 20 μl to 100–200 μl when an enlarged combustion tube is available.

b. Sample treatment: If the sample contains gross particulate matter and/or floating oily material, place about 250 ml in a blender and homogenize for 10 min.

If the sample must be freed of inorganic carbon before analysis, transfer a representative aliquot of 10–15 ml to a 30-ml beaker, add 2 drops (0.1 ml) conc HCl to reduce the pH to 2 or less, and purge with carbon dioxide-free nitrogen gas for 10 min. Do not use plastic tubing. While stirring on a magnetic stirrer, withdraw the sample from the beaker by means of a hypodermic needle with a 150-μ opening. Inject the sample into the analyzer and obtain the peak-height reading. Repeat the injection twice more or until three consecutive peaks are obtained that are reproducible to within ± 5%.

If the instrument on hand provides for a separate determination of the carbonate-plus-bicarbonate carbon, omit the decarbonation step with conc HCl and proceed according to the manufacturer's directions.

c. Preparation of standard curve: Prepare a standard carbon series of 10, 20, 30, 40, 50, 60, 80 and 100 mg/l with redistilled water by diluting 10, 20, 30, 40 and 50 ml standard carbon solution to 1,000 ml, and 30, 40 and 50 ml standard carbon solution to 500 ml. Inject and record the peak heights of these standards.

---

* Hamilton No. 705 N or 750 N, or equivalent.

† Beckman Instruments, Inc., or equivalent.

Plot the carbon concentrations of the standards in mg/l versus the corrected peak height in millimeters on rectangular coordinate paper. Ascertain the sample concentrations from the corrected peak heights of the samples by reference to this calibration curve.

5. Calculation

a. Calculate the corrected peak height in millimeters by deducting the blank correction in the standards and samples as follows:

$$\text{Corrected peak height in mm} = A - B$$

where A = peak height in mm of the standards or sample, and B = peak height in mm of the blank.

b. Apply the appropriate dilution factor when necessary.

6. Precision

The difficulty of sampling particulate matter on unfiltered samples limits the precision of the method to approximately 5–10%. On clear samples or on those that have been filtered prior to analysis, the precision approaches 1–2% or 1–2 mg/l carbon, whichever is greater.

138 B. Bibliography

VAN HALL, C. E., J. SAFRANKO & V. A. STENGER. 1963. Rapid combustion method for the determination of organic substances in aqueous solutions. *Anal. Chem.* 35:315.

VAN HALL, C. E., D. BARTH & V. A. STENGER. 1965. Elimination of carbonates from aqueous solutions prior to organic carbon determinations. *Anal. Chem.* 37:769.

SCHAFFER, R. B. et al. 1965. Application of a carbon analyzer in waste treatment. *JWPCF* 37:1545.

BUSCH, A. W. 1966. Energy, total carbon, and oxygen demand. *Water Res. Research* 2:59.

WILLIAMS, R. T. 1967. Water-pollution instrumentation—Analyzer looks for organic carbon. *Instrumentation Technol.* 14:63.

BLACKMORE, R. H. & D. VOSHEL. 1967. Rapid determination of total organic carbon (TOC) in sewage. *Water & Sewage Works* 114:398.

VAN HALL, C. E. & V. A. STENGER. 1967. An instrumental method for rapid determination of carbonate and total carbon in solutions. *Anal. Chem.* 39:503.

139 ORGANIC CONTAMINANTS

Organic contaminants—in natural substances, insecticides, herbicides and other agricultural chemicals—enter water supplies from runoff of precipitation. Domestic sewage and industrial waste, depending upon the degree of treatment, contribute contaminants in various amounts. As a result of accidental spills and leaks, industrial organic wastes also enter streams. Some of the contaminants, extremely persistent and only partially removed by treatment, reach the consumer in drinking water.

Contaminants, both natural and man-made, can conceivably have undesirable effects on health. Some of these materials interfere with water quality and kill fish. A few micrograms per liter may be significant. The isolation and recovery of chlorinated insecticides, nitriles, orthonitrochlorobenzene, aromatic ethers, waste hydrocarbons, and many other synthetic chemicals suggest that a method for assessing these materials in water is desirable.

The approaches in use for the determination of total organic contaminants fall into two general classes. The first class consists of methods based on direct determination of contaminating components in the water. The Carbon Adsorption Method (CAM) is the most appropriate one in principle because it is based on the direct recovery and weighing of organic contaminants. However, the method is time-consuming and is not yet sufficiently quantitative. In this same class, the Total Organic Carbon (TOC) Method was developed to circumvent these defects of the CAM method. The determination of TOC (Section 138) can be carried out in a few minutes and gives a quantitative measurement of the carbon contained in the organic contaminants of the water. It is therefore related to the weight of organic contaminants.

The second class of methods for measuring organic contaminants is based on determinations of the equivalence of oxidizing agents which can react with the organic substances. The two common procedures are Oxygen Demand (Biochemical) and Oxygen Demand (Chemical). These latter methods, while not direct measures of organic contaminants, are widely used, and a rationale for interpretation of the data has been extensively developed.

SELECTION OF METHOD—Two carbon adsorption methods are described for the estimation of organic contaminants. The high-flow method is applicable to drinking waters, but not limited to them. The high-flow method cannot be applied to most river waters because the carbon filter would be clogged by the amount of suspended matter carried in the prescribed volume of water to be sampled. The recently developed low-flow method is intended for use with all classes of surface waters except drinking water in a public distribution system.

139 A. High-Flow Method (CAM) (TENTATIVE)

1. General Discussion

a. Principle: Activated carbon is a remarkable adsorption medium for many types of organic materials. As used in a carbon adsorption unit (Figure 21), it aids in the detection of low but significant quantities of organic contaminants in large volumes of water.

When a sufficient quantity of water has been run through the unit, the carbon containing the adsorbed sample is removed, dried, and extracted with chloroform. The removal of the chloroform by distillation leaves a weighable residue of contaminants. Other solvents, such as ethyl alcohol, will remove additional organics, but for monitoring and control purposes the chloroform extraction is considered adequate.

This method does not determine the total organic content of water. Although it is very effective, the carbon does not adsorb all the organics, and the solvent does not recover all of the materials adsorbed. Synthetic deter-

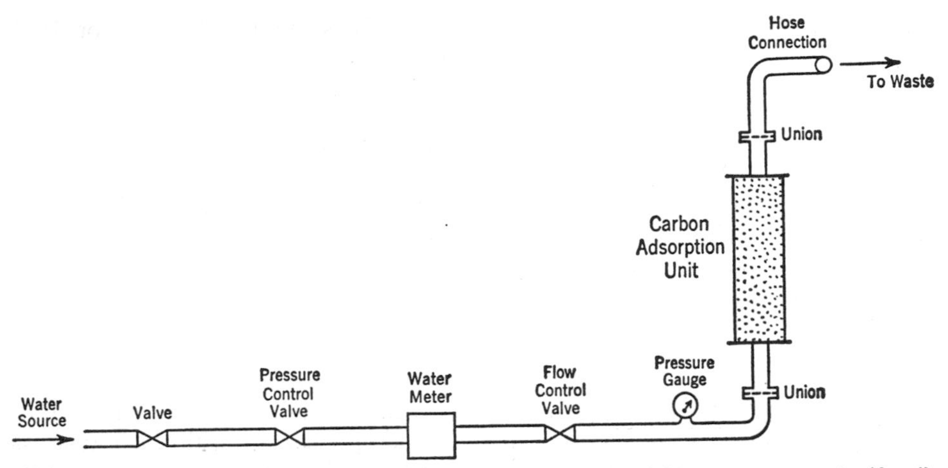

Figure 21. Installation of carbon adsorption unit (*flow rate is 0.25 gpm; pressure is 40 psi*).

gents are not measured by this procedure.

Using known amounts of easily adsorbed materials, recoveries may range from 50 to 90%. Replicate samples agree within ± 10%. The technic provides a relative measure of pollution load not obtainable by other technics. It reveals undue stress on a water from most industrial contaminants, particularly synthetic chemicals, and it furnishes materials that can be subjected to physical, chemical and physiological tests. The residues can be analyzed in a variety of ways, and constant collection of such data constitutes a valuable index of water quality.

b. Application: This method is applicable to drinking waters but is not limited to them.

2. Apparatus *

i—CARBON ADSORPTION ASSEMBLY † (Figures 21 and 22).

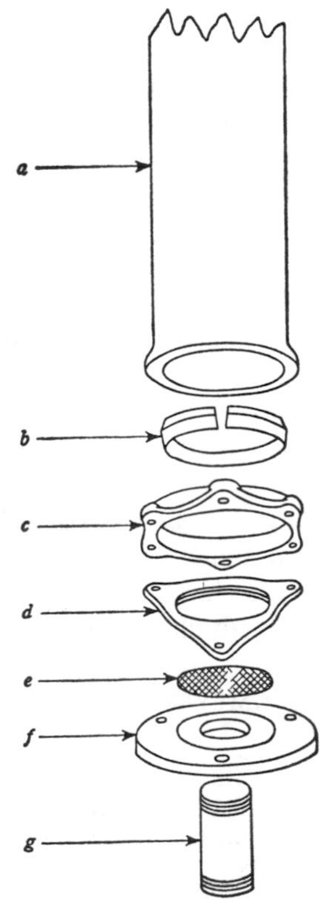

Figure 22. End assembly of carbon adsorption unit (*for complete dimensions and explanations see ¶s under Section 139A.2*).

---

* Complete sampling assemblies are available from General Metal Works, 8368 Bridgetown Road, Cleves, Ohio.

† The assembly is acceptable as in F. B. Taylor et al, *JAWWA* 56:774 (1964).

a. Pyrex pipe, 3-in. diameter, 18-in. length.

b. Asbestos inserts (two), for 3-in. pipe.

c. Flange sets (two), for 3-in. pipe.

d. Neoprene gaskets ‡ (two), ¼-in. thickness, with 3-in. hole slotted to ⅜-in. depth to take screen. Drill 3 holes, $\frac{5}{16}$-in. diameter, to match flange.

e. Stainless-steel screens ‡ (two), 40-mesh, 3¾-in. diameter.

f. Brass plates (two), $\frac{3}{16}$-in. thickness × 6¼-in. diameter. Tap hole in center for ¾-in. nipple. Score a circular groove ($\frac{1}{16}$-in. depth × $\frac{1}{16}$-in. width and 3⅜-in. diameter) into the plate to prevent leakage. Drill 3 holes, $\frac{5}{16}$-in. diameter, to coincide with the flange.

g. Galvanized nipples (two), ¾-in. × 3 in. Thread nipple into brass plate and weld in place.

h. Aluminum bolts and nuts (six), $\frac{5}{16}$-in. × 2 in., for holding assembly together.

ii—EXTRACTION APPARATUS:

a. Large-capacity Soxhlet extractor.§

b. Heating mantle, 3-liter.*

iii—VARIABLE TRANSFORMER,† 0–135 V, 7.5 amp.

iv—GLASS WOOL: Extract before use to remove organic coating. Pack about ¼ lb into the large-capacity extractor and extract with chloroform for several cycles.

v—ERLENMEYER FLASK, 300 ml.

vi—GLASS VIALS, 5 drams or 18.5 ml.

vii—PRESSURE CONTROL VALVE, 40 psi.

viii—FLOW CONTROL VALVE, 0.25 gpm.

ix—WATER METER, ⅝-in. household type.

3. Reagents

a. Activated carbon: Upon receipt of each shipment of 4 × 10-mesh carbon ** and 30-mesh carbon, § test for impurities. Fill the extractors [see ¶ *ii*(a) preceding] with each type of carbon and extract with chloroform. Recover the residues, which should be less than 40 mg for the 4 × 10 mesh and 20 mg for 30 mesh (volume that fits extractor). If larger recoveries are obtained, look for possible sources of contamination. Store the carbon in areas free from paint fumes and other organic vapors. Deduct one-half of the value found on blanks from the sample results.

b. Chloroform: If possible, distill all chloroform used. If this cannot be done, check the impurities by distilling 1 liter of solvent and evaporating to dryness. Use the chloroform if the residue is less than 5 mg and deduct the blank found from the results of the sample extraction.

4. Procedure

a. Assembly of carbon adsorption unit: Attach the end fittings of the adsorption unit to the glass pipe. Draw up the bolts evenly, holding the brass plate to the glass pipe in order to get a good seal on the gasket. Add

‡ Such as can be obtained from Netherland Rubber Co., Cincinnati, Ohio.

§ Corning No. 3885 (Corning Glass Works, Corning, N. Y.), or equivalent.

* Glas-Col Series M (Apparatus Co., Terre Haute, Ind.), or equivalent.

† Powerstat, Type 116 (Superior Electric Co., Bristol, Conn.), or equivalent.

** Cliff Char 4 × 10 mesh (Cliffs Dow Chemical Co., Marquette, Mich.), or equivalent.

§ Nuchar C-190 (Westvaco, New York, N.Y.), or equivalent.

4 × 10-mesh carbon to a depth of 4.5 in.; add 30-mesh carbon to a depth of 9 in. Complete filling the glass pipe with 4 × 10-mesh carbon (4.5 in.). Be sure the unit is full. Tap the cylinder gently but do not tamp the carbon. Attach the end fittings on the adsorption unit and install on the water source as shown in Figure 21.

Avoid organic contaminants in making pipe joints or other plumbing. Use Teflon-type tape or a paste made by mixing red lead powder and water. Clean all new fittings with kerosene and follow with a detergent wash. Rinse thoroughly with clean water.

b. Sample collection: Start the unit by passing water through slowly, because fine carbon washes out at first. Turn on the full flow after a few minutes. Check the operation of the meter and the rate of flow (0.25 gpm). Slight variations from the rate of flow can be tolerated. Measure the total volume accurately. Continue operation until 5,000 gal of water have passed through the unit. Record the meter readings daily.

c. Handling the carbon after use: Immediately after the necessary amount of water has passed through the unit, take the unit apart and remove the carbon for drying. Spread the carbon out in a thin layer on a tray of impervious material such as copper or glass.

Do not use aluminum and galvanized metals for trays because wet carbon reacts with these metals.

Dry the carbon in clean surroundings. Otherwise, paint fumes, spraying-operation, or other organic vapors will be taken up by the carbon and false results will be obtained. To speed drying, pass heated air (35–40 C) over the trays. Avoid high heat. Regard the carbon as dry when it is free flowing and appears like fresh unused carbon. Some moisture that is left will disappear in later processing. The dried carbon is now ready for extraction with chloroform. If the dried carbon must be held, place in a tight vessel for storage. A crimped-lid paint can is a satisfactory storage container.

d. Carbon extraction: Remove the glass plate from the bottom of the Soxhlet extractor. Pack the previously extracted glass wool (¶ 2–*iv*) lightly into the bottom of the extractor in order to keep the fine carbon from passing into the boiling flask. Charge the extractor with the carbon to be extracted. The amount of carbon in a sampling unit fits the extractor. Pour chloroform over the carbon fairly rapidly to help absorb the heat evolved. Continue adding chloroform until siphon action is started. When the chloroform has siphoned into the boiling flask, refill the extraction chamber with chloroform. Add glass beads or porous chips to the boiling flask to prevent bumping and then begin passing water through the condensers. Turn on the heating mantles. A voltage setting of 80 on the variable transformer is usually sufficient. When first starting the extractors, or after the siphon cycle during the run, the solvent in the boiling flask may superheat and bump. Tap the flask or vibrate the apparatus just at the boiling point of the solvent to prevent superheating. Extraction units do not always siphon automatically. Although regular siphoning is not necessary, application of air pressure to the vent of the extractor with a rubber bulb will start the siphon action. Extract the carbon with chloroform for 35 hr. Discard the carbon if no additional work with the carbon is planned.

The carbon retains a substantial amount of solvent even after draining. Burning generates hydrochloric acid and storage releases fumes. If a good hood is available, pass warm air over the carbon for 4 or 5 hr to dry it while still in the extractor. Dispose of the carbon by broadcasting on the ground.

When the extraction is completed, siphon all chloroform into the boiling flask. Remove the flask from the extraction system and distill to about 250 ml (avoid overheating). Filter into a 300-ml erlenmeyer flask and evaporate to about 15–20 ml on a steam bath. Blow a stream of clean air into the flask to hasten evaporation. Transfer to a tared vial and evaporate to dryness by allowing to stand in an open hood (without heat) overnight or longer. Judge completeness of solvent removal by odor. It is better to leave traces of solvent rather than to risk loss of sample by prolonged heating and evaporation.

Weigh the sample and record the weight. Deduct the amount due to the carbon blank (¶ 3a) and the solvent blank (¶ 3b above).

5. Calculation

Record the CCE (carbon chloroform extract) in micrograms per liter:

$$\mu g/l = \frac{g\ CCE \times 10^6}{gal\ sample \times 3.785}$$

6. Interpretation of Results

According to the 1962 USPHS Drinking Water Standards,[1] a concentration of 200 μg/l of CCE should not be exceeded. Waters containing more than this amount are likely to be of poor quality (judged by taste and odor) and may exhibit some of the damaging effects noted in the introduction. The source and kind of contaminants should be investigated if waters consistently exceed 200 μg/l of CCE. Clean surface and ground waters will usually contain only 25 to 50 μg/l of CCE; highly colored waters may exceed this level.

139 B. Low-Flow Method (CAM) (TENTATIVE)

1. General Discussion

a. Principle: Subsequent to the development of the high-flow method, described above, studies have shown that the carbon adsorption of organic contaminants in streams is most efficient at flow rates and throughput volumes substantially less than those which had been employed previously.[2] Furthermore, this method provides a means to gather organic contaminants adsorbed on the suspended solids of surface waters, as well as those in solution. The increased yields per unit volume of water from the low-flow equipment used in this method are primarily due to the longer contact time and smaller sample.

This method yields data approaching the true organic content of the water sampled much more closely than does the high-flow method. The increased recovery is due not only to the improved adsorption conditions described above, but also to the fact that this method includes the recovery of an additional class of adsorbed materials, the carbon alcohol extract (CAE).

2. Apparatus

a. Low-flow organics sampler: * Raw water is passed directly through a carbon column filled entirely with fine carbon at the rate of approximately 120 ml/min for a 1-week sampling period. The flow rate is regulated by a metering pump on the downstream end of the carbon column and the water passed through is automatically measured volumetrically in 1-liter increments and registered on a digital counter. Because the metering pump is pressure sensitive, a way of regulating the pressure on that component is provided by means of a constant-head tank.[3] A sampler of this type is widely used by federal and state agencies.[4, 5]

Since a 1-week sampling run involves only about 1,200 liters of water, a 1-gpm flow control valve is used to assure fresh water at the sampler at all times. Water that does not pass through the carbon column is bypassed and returned to the river. A schematic diagram of the organics sampler is shown in Figure 23.

* Complete sampling assemblies are available from General Metal Works, 8368 Bridgetown Road, Cleves, Ohio.

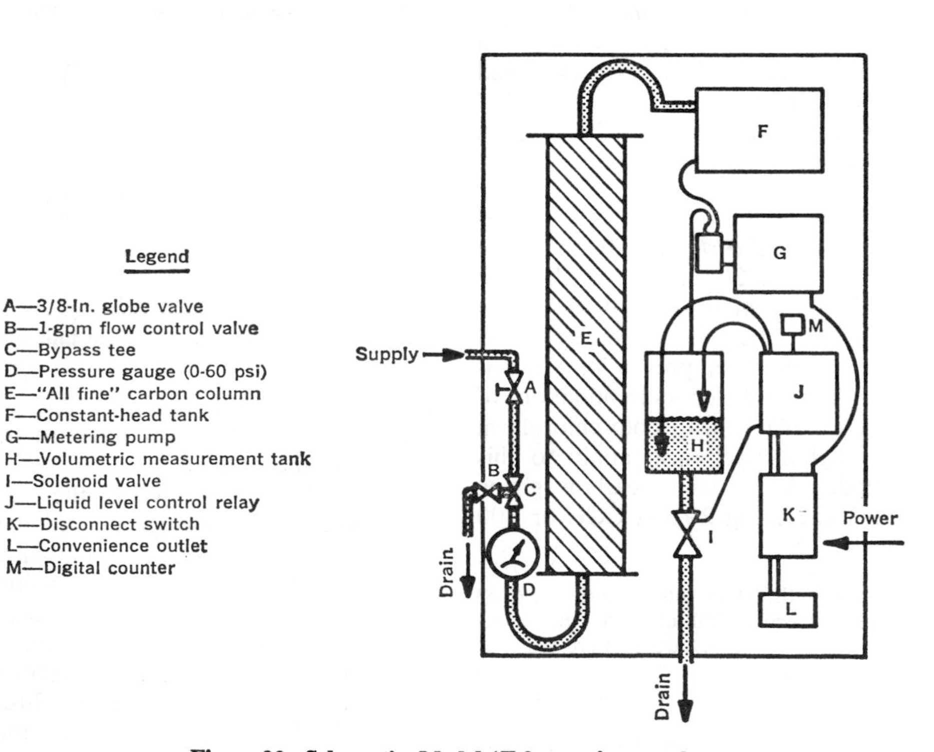

Figure 23. Schematic, Model 1F-2 organics sampler.

The sampler is mounted on a panel 36 in. high and 30 in. wide that can be shipped in a crate about 8 in. deep. The approximate shipping weight of the complete unit is 75 lb.

Operation of the equipment requires a 115-V single-phase 60-cycle electric supply. Two circuits are controlled by a two-pole single-throw disconnect switch. All electrical components of the panel operate from one circuit fused for 15 amp. The second circuit is a duplex outlet with ASA grounding-type sockets for use with auxiliary equipment and is also fused for 15 amp.

b. Carbon adsorption assembly: The carbon adsorption cartridge is identical to that described for use in the high-flow method, Section 139A.2a et seq.

c. Extraction apparatus: The apparatus for extraction, consisting of a large-capacity Soxhlet extractor and auxiliary equipment, is the same as that described in Section 139A.2b through f of the high-flow method.

3. Reagents

a. Activated carbon: Only one grade of carbon, the 30-mesh prescribed for the high-flow method, is used in this procedure. The precautions described in that method for prevention of contamination and for determination of extraction blank, with both chloroform and ethyl alcohol, also apply to this method. Avoid using carbon giving blanks exceeding 20 mg CCE or 100 mg CAE.†

† Some satisfactory lots of carbon exceed the recommended 100 mg CAE blank because of water-soluble salts that are removed during sampling. Such carbons can be recognized by the acceptable CAE blank value obtained when the sample for blank determination is prewashed with distilled water, dried, and extracted.

b. Chloroform: See the high-flow method.

c. Ethyl alcohol: Pure industrial alcohol from a reliable supplier is used for the ethanol extraction. Laboratories not having access to ethanol may substitute a reagent grade of methanol. The solvent should be checked for impurity by distilling 1 liter and evaporating to dryness. If the residue is less than 5 mg, the solvent may be used.

4. Procedure

a. Installation: Samplers may be installed in various locations; installations are of two general types—water plant installations and field installations. Although the arrangement of piping may vary widely with conditions at the site, in general it will resemble the schematic diagram shown in Figure 24 for water plant installations and Figure 25 for field installations where water must be pumped to the sampler.

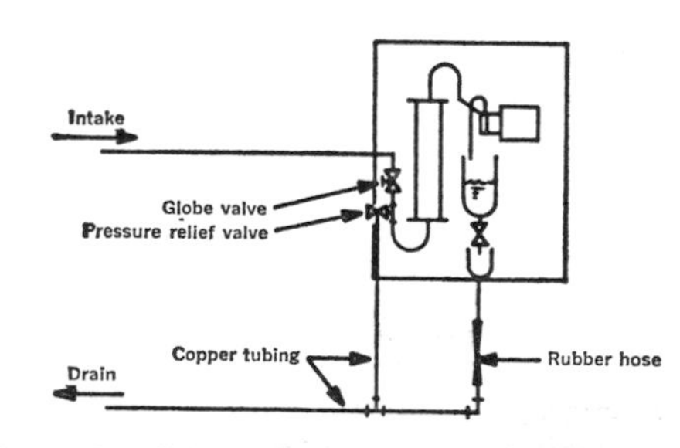

Figure 24. Schematic, water plant installation.

To avoid contamination of the cartridge, take the following precautions:

1) Do not use ordinary organic pipe joint compounds. Instead, use teflon tape or red lead (lead oxide) mixed to a paste with water for this purpose.

2) Avoid plastic hose. If rubber hose is used in any connections, flush thoroughly before connecting to the carbon adsorption cartridge. Copper tubing is ideal for connections. Polyethylene pipe and polyvinyl chloride pipe meeting National Sanitation Foundation standards for drinking water are acceptable.

Install the sampling apparatus rigidly in a vertical position in a location free from outside vibrations for accurate operation of the volumetric measuring system. Proper mounting eliminates almost entirely the vibration of the equipment panel caused by the metering pump and solenoid valve.

Secure a cup drain immediately below the solenoid valve and connect the cup drain to a drain line through a section of ⅜-in. I.D. rubber hose.

By means of copper tubing (½-in. O.D.), connect the water supply to a compression-type fitting in the globe valve.

Connect the discharge side of the flow control assembly (B in Figure 23) to the drain line with copper tubing.

Make the electrical connections for 115-V, single-phase, 60-cycle operation by knocking out one of the holes near the upper right-hand corner of the disconnect switch (K in Figure 23) and introduce a three-wire cable.

b. Calibration: Before the sampler is put into operation, calibrate the volumetric measuring system by adjusting the electrodes of the liquid-level control system so that incremental volumes of 1 liter are measured for each count on the digital counter.

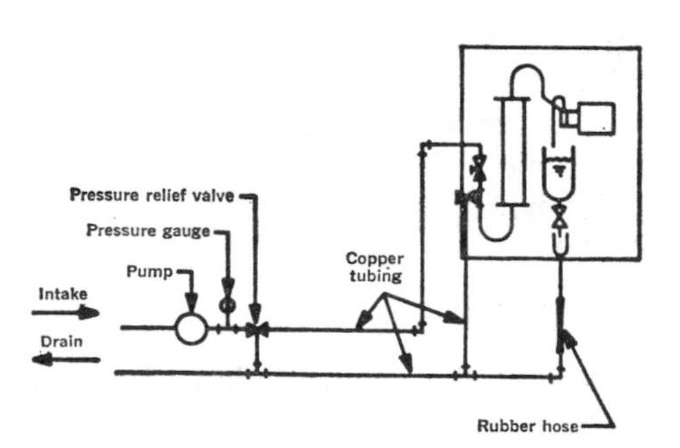

Figure 25. Schematic, field installation.

Calibrate the volumetric measuring system by the following procedure:

1) Throw the electrical switch to "On" to start the metering pump and supply power to the liquid-level control system.

2) Open the globe valve in the water supply system slowly until the constant-head tank has reached its full level.

3) When the metering pump begins to pump water into the volumetric measuring tank, disconnect the lower end of the rubber hose from the drain line and direct it into a 1,000-ml graduated cylinder.

4) When the first incremental volume is discharged into the graduated cylinder, check the volume. If the volume is within 10 ml of 1,000 ml, the counter will give a reading in liters within 1%, which is acceptable. If, however, the volume is off by more than 10 ml, adjust the electrodes in order to correct this error.

5) Correct the volume error as follows: Loosen the bolt that holds the low-level electrode in position. If the volume measure was too small, lower the electrode slightly. Raise the low-level electrode if the volume was too large.

6) After each adjustment, wait until two volumes have been measured by use of the graduated cylinder. If the average of the reading is still more than 10 ml off, repeat the adjustment until an acceptable volume is reached.

7) Be sure to secure the electrode firmly before the sampler is allowed to operate unattended.

c. Assembly of carbon adsorption cartridge: Follow the directions in Section 139A.4a of the high-flow procedure. However, use only the 30-mesh carbon to fill the cartridge.

d. Sample collection: Under most conditions, the sampler will operate properly without attention during a 1-week sampling period.

Install the cartridge in the sampler with teflon hose through hose couplings. Tighten these connections by hand only. Fasten the column in position on the board by a web strap.

Before the sampling run is started, lubricate the metering pump and inspect the pump tubing for soundness. Determine the soundness of the metering pump tubing by removing the tubing from the pump and checking it visually. In addition, ascertain the presence of leaks by removing the tubing from the Swagelock fitting and attempting to blow air through the tube after closing one end.

Start operation by throwing the power supply switch to the "On" position. Next, open the globe valve in the water supply line slowly until the volumetric measuring tank begins to fill. As soon as the constant-head tank has reached its full level, open the valve completely.

Check the calibration of the volumetric measuring system once during each run.

If leaks occur at the ends of the carbon column, stop by tightening the hose coupling by hand. Stop leaks at connections of copper tubing by tightening the brass nut with an adjustable wrench.

Consult reference 5 (Section 139C following) for the correction of problems that may arise in the operation of equipment through malfunction of the volumetric measuring system or because unusual amounts of silt and other suspended matter in the water sample may tend to clog the carbon column.

A complete sampling operation consists of 1,200 liters of water at the rate of 120 ml/min.

e. Handling the carbon after use: Follow the directions in Section 139A.4c of the high-flow method.

f. Chloroform extraction: Follow the instructions in Section 139A.4d of the high-flow method.

g. Ethanol extraction: Remove the residual chloroform from the carbon by blowing precleaned warm air through the carbon (in place in the Soxhlet) and exhausting chloroform vapors through the hood. In order to do this, remove the Soxhlet from the hood and shake the carbon loose to facilitate movement of air through it. Return the Soxhlet, still containing the carbon, to the hood with the glass plate cover removed. Attach a hose from a heated air manifold (approximately 60 C) to the bottom of the siphon tube and blow air up through the carbon for 3–4 hr or until it is dry. Add 95% ethyl alcohol to the dried carbon and perform the extraction in the manner described for the chloroform step. Continue the extraction for 24 hr.

Begin the concentration of the carbon alcohol extract (CAE) as described for the chloroform extract. However, start the drying on a steam bath with a jet of air, then continue in an oven at 75 C until the weight change of successive weighings at 72-hr intervals is less than 1%. (Waters high in inorganic substances sometimes yield CAE having significant inorganic content.)

5. Calculation

Report the concentration of carbon chloroform extract (CCE) in $\mu g/l$ according to the equation in Section 139A.5 of the high-flow method. Use the same equation, substituting CAE for CCE, to record the concentration of CAE.

Calculate the total recovered organic contaminants as the sum of CCE and CAE.

6. Application of Results

The data for total organic contaminants, CCE and CAE, as calculated, constitute a general indication of the level of organic contamination of the water sample. These results are not directly related to the criteria in the high-flow method, because of the higher recovery efficiency of this procedure. However, the results of the low-flow method are more appropriate indications of the quality of raw surface waters. As such, the method is in general use as a tool for the surveillance of stream pollution.

The low-flow procedure yields two extracts, CCE and CAE, consisting of samples of the two major classes of organic contaminants in the water sampled. These extracts can be used for a variety of further chemical analyses. Furthermore, the extract samples are conveniently stored and thus available for comparison with samples obtained by the same procedure from the same water source at times separated by several years. A noteworthy example of the use of such extracts is in the monitoring of insecticides in surface waters.[6]

139 C. References

1. U. S. Public Health Service. 1962. Public Health Service Drinking Water Standards, 1962. PHS Pub. 956. Govt. Ptg. Off., Washington, D.C.
2. R. L. Booth. 1963. *Optimum Sampling Rate and Sample Volume for Quantitative Measurement of Organics by the Present Carbon Adsorption Method.* Division of Water Supply & Pollution Control, PHS. Robert A. Taft Engineering Center, Cincinnati, Ohio (Aug. 26).
3. J. A. Castelli & R. L. Booth. 1964. Low-flow liquid meter. *JAWWA* 56: 1243.
4. B. H. Reid et al. 1965. Preliminary field evaluation of low flow rate carbon adsorption equipment and methods for organic sampling of surface waters. PHS Water Pollution Surveillance System Application & Development Report No. 14. Division of Water Supply & Pollution Control, PHS (Basic Data Branch, Water Quality Section), Cincinnati, Ohio (Mar.).
5. Federal Water Pollution Control Administration. 1967. *Installation, Operation, Maintenance, Organics Samplers for Water.* FWPCA, U. S. Dept. Interior, Washington, D. C. (Dec.).
6. A. W. Breidenbach et al. 1966. Identification and measurement of chlorinated hydrocarbon pesticides in surface waters. U. S. Dept. Interior Pub. WP-22 (Nov.).

139 D. Bibliography

Middleton, F. M., W. Grant & A. A. Rosen. 1956. Drinking water taste and odor, correlation with organic content. *Ind. Eng. Chem.* 48:268.

Middleton, F. M., A. A. Rosen & R. H. Burttschell. 1958. Taste and odor research tools for water utilities. *JAWWA* 50:21.

———. 1959. *Manual for Recovery and Identification of Organic Chemicals in Water.* Robert A. Taft Sanitary Engineering Center, Cincinnati, Ohio.

Middleton, F. M. & J. J. Lichtenberg. 1960. Measurement of organic contaminants in the nation's rivers. *Ind. Eng. Chem.* 52:99A.

ETTINGER, M. B. 1960. Proposed toxicity screening procedure for use in protecting drinking-water quality. *JAWWA* 52:689.

BOOTH, R. L. 1963. Reproducibility of carbon adsorption method (CAM). Memo to Sub-Committee on Applicability of Carbon Adsorption Technique to the Mission of the National Water Quality Network (Jan. 31).

140 OXYGEN (DISSOLVED)

Adequate dissolved oxygen (DO) is necessary for the life of fish and other aquatic organisms. The DO concentration may also be associated with corrosivity of water, photosynthetic activity, and septicity. The DO test is used in the biochemical oxygen demand (BOD) determination in Section 219.

The azide modification of the iodometric method is recommended for most unpolluted waters. [See Oxygen (Dissolved), Section 218B.] Depending on the type of interference present, other modifications may be necessary. Membrane electrodes may also be used and are particularly suitable for field measurements. For a detailed discussion see Section 218F.

141 OXYGEN DEMAND (BIOCHEMICAL)

Biochemical oxygen demand (BOD) in water is determined as described in Section 219. Seeding with sewage organisms, only if necessary (as in the case of chlorinated samples), and elimination of interferences from residual chlorine and other bactericidal substances should be carried out as indicated there. The amount of pollution in the sample will govern the need for and the degree of dilution.

Samples with low DO values can be aerated to increase the initial DO content above that required by the BOD. Air is bubbled through a diffusion tube into the sample for 5 min, or until the DO is at least 7 mg/l. On one portion of the aerated sample the DO is determined; another portion is seeded only if necessary, and is incubated for the BOD determination.

142 OXYGEN DEMAND (CHEMICAL)

The chemical oxygen demand (COD) test indicates the quantity of oxidizable materials present in a water and varies with water composition, concentration of reagent, temperature, period of contact, and other factors. For this reason, the standard method specifies exact control of all analytical conditions. In some instances, a rough correlation between BOD, COD and TOC (total organic carbon) has been established. Since chemical oxidation and biologic oxidation are different processes, the results may differ to a large degree. Methods for determining COD values will be found in Section 220.

143 OZONE (RESIDUAL)

Ozone, a potent germicide, is also employed as an oxidizing agent for the destruction of organic compounds producing taste and odor in water, as well as for the destruction of organic coloring matter and the oxidation of reduced iron or manganese salts to insoluble oxides, which can then be precipitated or filtered from the water. Waters containing such oxidizable minerals must necessarily be filtered after ozonation. The presence of ozone residuals of even less than 0.1 mg/l at the outlet of the ozonation chamber is generally effective for disinfection; therefore, the demonstration of an ozone residual in the water is generally sufficient. For other purposes, perhaps as much as 0.2 mg/l may be necessary.

1) Selection of method: Three methods are described for the determination of ozone in water. The iodometric method (*A*) is quantitative, subject to the fewest interferences, and capable of good precision. The method can also be used for the determination of ozone in air by absorption of the ozone in iodide solution.

The orthotolidine-manganese sulfate method (*B*), generally abbreviated OTM, is semiquantitative. It is subject to relatively slight interference from other common oxidants.

The orthotolidine-arsenite method (*C*), usually designated OTA, is largely qualitative because of its liability to interference. However, it is useful for such control purposes as determination at the outlet of the ozonation chamber.

The ozone concentration in water or air can also be determined continuously by photometric instruments, which can measure the strong absorption ozone exerts at the wavelength of 253.7 mμ.

2) Sampling and storage: A determination for ozone must be performed immediately because samples cannot be preserved or stored owing to the instability of the residual. The stability of residual ozone is markedly improved at low temperatures and low pH values. Samples should be collected in a manner to minimize aeration. Frequency of sampling should be dictated by the variations in the quality of the supply and by the demands of plant operation.

143 A. Iodometric Method

1. General Discussion

a. Principle: Ozone liberates free iodine from a potassium iodide solution. For accurate results the solution should be alkaline during the absorption of ozone. In practice, solutions of potassium iodide quickly become alkaline during the process. After acidification, the liberated iodine is titrated with standard 0.005*N* sodium thiosulfate using starch indicator.

b. Interference: Because ozonated water may contain manganese dioxide, ferric ion, nitrite, possibly peroxide, and other oxidation products, these interferences are avoided by passing the ozone through the gaseous phase into a potassium iodide solution for titration. The stability of ozone solutions decreases progressively at each increment in temperature above freezing and with each increment in pH above 3.0.

c. Minimum detectable concentration: Approximately 30 μg/l ozone.

2. Apparatus

The following are required for sample collection:

a. Standard gas-washing bottles and absorbers, 1-liter and 500-ml capacities, with medium-permeability porous-plate diffusers at bottom.

b. Pure air or pure nitrogen gas supply, 0.2–1.0-liter/min capacity.

c. Glass, stainless steel, or aluminum piping, for carrying ozonized air. Good-quality Tygon * tubing may also be used for short runs, but not rubber.

3. Reagents

a. Potassium iodide solution: Dissolve 20 g KI, free from iodine, iodate and reducing agents, in 1 liter of freshly boiled and cooled distilled water. Store in a brown bottle.

b. Sulfuric acid, 1*N*.

c. Standard sodium thiosulfate, 0.1*N*: Dissolve 25 g $Na_2S_2O_3 \cdot 5H_2O$ in 1 liter of freshly boiled distilled water. Standardize against potassium biniodate (also called potassium hydrogen iodate) or potassium dichromate according to the procedure described in Chlorine (Residual), Section 114A.-2c.

d. Standard sodium thiosulfate titrant, 0.005*N*: Dilute the proper volume (approximately 50 ml) of 0.1*N* sodium thiosulfate to 1,000 ml. For accurate work, standardize this solution daily, using either 0.005*N* potassium biniodate or potassium dichromate solution for the purpose. Perform the standardization in exactly the same manner as the procedure described in ¶ 4c below. Standard sodium thiosulfate titrant, exactly 0.0050*N*, is equivalent to 120 μg ozone per 1.00 ml.

e. Starch indicator solution: To 5 g potato, arrowroot or soluble starch in a mortar, add a little cold distilled water and grind to a thin paste. Pour into 1 liter boiling distilled water, stir, and allow to settle overnight. Use the clear supernate. Preserve with 1.25 g salicylic acid, 4 g zinc chloride, or a combination of 4 g sodium propionate and 2 g sodium azide added to 1 liter of starch solution.

f. Standard iodine, 0.1*N*: Dissolve 40 g KI in 25 ml distilled water; then add 13 g resublimed iodine and stir until dissolved. Dilute to 1 liter and standardize against sodium arsenite, primary standard grade, as described in Chlorine (Residual), Section 114B.-3a(2).

g. Standard iodine, 0.005*N*: Dissolve 16 g KI in a little distilled water in a 1-liter volumetric flask, add the proper volume (approximately 50 ml) of 0.1*N* iodine solution, and dilute to the mark. For accurate work, standardize this solution daily. Store the solution in a brown bottle or in the dark. Protect from direct sunlight at all times and keep from all contact with rubber.

4. Procedure

a. Sample collection: Collect an 800-ml sample in a 1-liter washing bottle with a porous diffuser at the bottom. (Some prefer to add 8 ml 1*N* H_2SO_4 before proceeding to ¶ 4b below; others think this may result in increased interference from the acid itself or from breakdown of substances in the sample.)

b. Ozone absorption: Pass a stream of pure air or nitrogen through the sample and then through an absorber

* US Stoneware Company.

containing 400 ml potassium iodide solution. Continue for not less than 5 min at a rate of 0.2–1.0 liter/min to insure that all ozone is swept from the sample and absorbed in the potassium iodide solution.

c. Titration: Transfer the potassium iodide solution to a 1-liter beaker, rinse the absorber, and add 20 ml H_2SO_4 to produce a pH below 2.0. Titrate with 0.005*N* sodium thiosulfate titrant until the yellow color of the liberated iodine is almost discharged. Add 4 ml starch indicator solution to impart a blue color and continue the titration carefully but rapidly to the end point at which the blue color just disappears. Long contact of iodine and starch develops a blue compound which is difficult to decolorize. (The end point may be determined amperometrically as described in Residual Chlorine, Section 114B.4c, except that sodium thiosulfate can be used as the titrant.)

d. Blank test: Correct the result of the sample titration by determining the blank contributed by such reagent impurities as (a) the free iodine or iodate in the potassium iodide, which liberates extra iodine, or (b) the traces of reducing agents that might reduce some of the iodine which is liberated.

Take 400 ml potassium iodide solution, 20 ml H_2SO_4, and 4 ml starch indicator solution. Perform whichever one of the blank titrations below applies:

1) If a blue color occurs, titrate with 0.005*N* sodium thiosulfate to the disappearance of the blue, and record the result.

2) If no blue color occurs, titrate with 0.005*N* iodine solution until a blue color appears. Back-titrate with 0.005*N* sodium thiosulfate and record the difference.

Before calculating the ozone, subtract the result of the blank titration in ¶ 4d(1) from the sample titration, or add the result of ¶ 4d(2) above.

5. Calculation

$$\text{mg/l } O_3 = \frac{(A \pm B) \times N \times 24{,}000}{\text{ml sample}}$$

where A = ml titration for sample, B = ml titration for blank which may be positive or negative, and N = normality of $Na_2S_2O_3$.

6. Interpretation of Results

The precision of the actual test is within ±1%. However, rapid deterioration of the residual occurs in the time elapsing between sampling and performance of the test. Temperature is also an important factor in the deterioration.

143 B. Orthotolidine-Manganese Sulfate (OTM) Method

1. General Discussion

a. Principle: Residual ozone oxidizes manganous ion to the manganic state, which in turn reacts with the acidic orthotolidine reagent. The final yellow color can be measured visually with a comparator suitable for residual chlorine estimations, or photometrically in the wavelength range of 400–450 mμ.

b. Interference: This method may be affected by the presence of a high oxide of manganese in the original sample but not by such slow-acting interfering agents as nitrite or oxidized iron. The correction for interferences can be determined by thoroughly aerating a second portion of the sample and then following the procedure described in ¶ 4 following.

c. Minimum detectable concentration: Approximately 20 μg/l ozone.

2. Apparatus

COLOR COMPARISON EQUIPMENT—One of the following is required:

a. Comparator, color- and turbidity-compensating, equipped with permanent glass standards suitable for the estimation of residual chlorine by the orthotolidine method.

b. Filter photometer, providing a light path of 1 cm or longer and equipped with a violet filter exhibiting maximum transmittance in the wavelength range of 400–450 mμ.

c. Spectrophotometer, for use at 435 mμ and providing a light path of 1 cm or longer.

3. Reagents

a. Manganese sulfate reagent: Dissolve 3.1 g $MnSO_4 \cdot H_2O$ in distilled water containing 3 ml conc H_2SO_4, and dilute to 1 liter. This solution contains approximately 1 g/l Mn and may be used for many months.

b. Orthotolidine reagent: Dissolve 1.35 g orthotolidine dihydrochloride in 500 ml distilled water. Add this solution, with constant stirring, to a mixture of 350 ml distilled water and 150 ml conc HCl. Store the reagent in brown bottles, or in the dark, and observe the precautions prescribed for its storage in Chlorine (Residual), Section 114C.3c(2). (CAUTION: *Handle this chemical with extreme care. Never use a mouth pipet for dispensing this reagent, but rely on an automatic, dropping or safety pipet to measure the necessary volumes. Avoid inhalation or exposure to the skin.*)

4. Procedure

Place 5 ml manganese sulfate reagent in a 250-ml flask. Add 95 ml of sample and mix quickly. Add 5 ml orthotolidine reagent and mix quickly. Measure the developed yellow color in a comparator fitted with a chlorine color disk, or photometrically in the wavelength range of 400–450 mμ.

5. Calculation

$$\text{mg/l } O_3 = \frac{\text{mg/l apparent "chlorine"}}{1.45}$$

6. Interpretation of Results

The yellow color developed by ozone in this method is theoretically equal to 1.45 times the amount produced by an equal quantity of chlorine. Interfering compounds and uncertainties in reading a color disk comparator may cause appreciable variations in this theoretical factor. Photometric measurement of the color density improves the test accuracy.

143 C. Orthotolidine-Arsenite (OTA) Method

1. General Discussion

a. Principle: Ozone produces an instantaneous yellow color with the acid orthotolidine reagent. This addition of arsenite reagent minimizes interference from such slower-acting ions as nitrite or oxidized iron.

b. Interference: This method is affected by colloidal manganese dioxide, which rapidly reacts with the acid orthotolidine reagent.

c. Minimum detectable concentration: Approximately 20 μg/l ozone.

2. Apparatus

COLOR COMPARISON EQUIPMENT—One of the following is required:

a. Comparator, color- and turbidity-compensating, equipped with permanent glass standards for the estimation of residual chlorine by the orthotolidine method.

b. French square bottles, capacity 1 or 2 oz.

3. Reagents

a. Orthotolidine reagent: Prepare and store as directed in Method B, ¶ 3b preceding.

b. Sodium arsenite solution: Dissolve 5 g $NaAsO_2$ in distilled water and dilute to 1 liter. The solution may be used for several months. (CAUTION: *Toxic—take care to avoid ingestion.*)

4. Procedure

a. Sample and reagent volumes: Label two comparator cells or two French square bottles "A" and "B." Add 0.5 ml orthotolidine reagent to 10-ml cells, 0.75 ml to 15-ml cells, and the same ratio for other volumes of sample. Use the same volume of arsenite solution after color development in ¶ 4b and also for the determination of the interference correction in ¶ 4c below.

b. Color development: To Cell A, containing orthotolidine reagent, add a measured volume of water sample. Mix quickly and thoroughly, and within 5 sec add the sodium arsenite solution. Mix quickly and compare with color standards in the comparator as rapidly as possible. Record the result as *A*.

c. Estimation of interference: To Cell B, containing arsenite solution, add a measured volume of water sample. Mix quickly and thoroughly, and add orthotolidine reagent. Again mix quickly and compare with color standards in the comparator as rapidly as possible. Record the result as *B*, which represents the interfering substances in the water.

5. Calculation

$$\text{mg/l } O_3 = A - B$$

6. Interpretation of Results

The color developed in this test by a given amount of ozone varies greatly in different waters. On the average it approximates the color produced by an equal quantity of chlorine. The method is qualitative only.

143 D. Bibliography

FOULK, C. W. & A. T. BAWDEN. 1926. A new type of endpoint in electrometric titration and its application of iodimetry. *J. Amer. Chem. Soc.* 48:2045.

HANN, V. A. & T. C. MANLEY. 1952. Ozone. In *Encyclopedia of Chemical Technology.* Interscience Publishers, New York, Vol. 9, pp. 735–753.

BIRDSALL, C. M., A. C. JENKINS & E. SPADINGER. 1952. The iodometric determination of ozone. *Anal. Chem.* 24:662.

ZEHENDER, F. & W. STUMM. 1953. Determination of ozone in drinking water (in German). *Mitt Gebiete Lebensm. Hyg.* 44:206.

INGOLS, R. S. & R. H. FETNER. 1956. Sterilization of water by ozone under arctic conditions. Report PB 124786, Office of Technical Services, U. S. Department of Commerce, Washington, D. C.

INGOLS, R. S., R. H. FETNER & W. H. EBERHARDT. 1956. Determination of ozone in solution. *Proc. Int. Ozone Conf.*

HANN, V. A. 1956. Disinfection of drinking water with ozone. *JAWWA* 48:1316.

INGOLS, R. S. & R. H. FETNER. 1957. Some studies of ozone for use in water treatment. *Proc. Soc. Water Treatment & Exam.* 6:8.

PESTICIDES: See Chlorinated Hydrocarbon Pesticides, Section 113 preceding.

144 pH VALUE

The pH of most natural waters falls within the range 4 to 9. The majority of waters are slightly basic due to the presence of carbonate and bicarbonate. A departure from the norm for a given water could be caused by the entry of strongly acidic or basic industrial wastes. A relatively common practice is the pH adjustment of the treatment plant effluent for the purpose of controlling corrosion in the distribution system.

pH is the logarithm of the reciprocal of the hydrogen ion concentration —more precisely, of the hydrogen ion activity—in moles per liter. pH enters into the calculation of carbonate, bicarbonate, and carbon dioxide, as well as of the corrosion or stability index; and into the control of water treatment processes. The practical pH scale extends from 0, very acidic, to 14, very alkaline, with the middle value (pH 7) corresponding to exact neutrality at 25 C. Whereas "alkalinity" and "acidity" express the total reserve or buffering capacity of a sample, the pH value represents the instantaneous hydrogen ion activity.

pH can be measured either colorimetrically or electrometrically. The colorimetric method requires a less expensive investment in equipment but suffers from severe interference contributed by color, turbidity, high saline content, colloidal matter, free chlorine, and various oxidants and reductants. The indicators are subject to deterioration, as are the color standards with which they are compared. Moreover, no single indicator encompasses the pH range of interest in water. In poorly buffered liquids, a description applicable to some waters, the indicators themselves may alter the pH of the sample which they are expected to measure unless they are preadjusted to nearly the same pH as the sample. For these reasons, the colorimetric method is suitable only for rough estimation and is not described in this book. (For details on the colorimetric method, see Clark,[1] Kolthoff[2] and AWWA.[3]) The electrometric method below is considered standard.

144 A. Glass Electrode Method

1. General Discussion

a. Principle: Several types of electrodes have been suggested for the electrometric determination of pH. Although the hydrogen gas electrode is recognized as the primary standard, the glass electrode in combination with the reference potential provided by a saturated calomel electrode is most generally used. The glass electrode system is based on the fact that a change of 1 pH unit produces an electrical change of 59.1 mV at 25 C.

b. Interference: The glass electrode is relatively immune to interference from color, turbidity, colloidal matter, free chlorine, oxidants, or reductants, as well as from high saline content, except for a sodium error at high pH. The error caused by high sodium ion concentrations at a pH above 10 may be reduced by using special "low sodium error" electrodes. When employing ordinary glass electrodes, approximate corrections for the sodium error may be made by consulting a chart which the manufacturer can furnish for the particular make and catalog number of electrode. Temperature exerts two significant effects on pH measurements: The electrodes themselves vary in potential, and ionization in the sample varies.* The first effect can be compensated for by an adjustment which is provided on the better commercial instruments. The second effect is inherent in the sample and is taken into consideration by recording both temperature and pH of each sample.

* This ionization, dependent upon the values of K_1 and K_2 for H_2CO_3 as well as on K_w for H_2O at the various temperatures, is to a significant extent related to the alkalinity of the sample. Increasing alkalinity reduces the effect of temperature change on the pH. This effect of alkalinity is not a direct relationship but it can be quite pronounced even at very low concentrations of alkalinity.

The temperature dial on pH meters is designed only to correct for the temperature characteristics of the electrodes. Instruments without a temperature dial are often provided with data from which this correction for the characteristics of the electrodes may be calculated.

Data for calculating, by interpolation, the pH of natural waters at other temperatures than that of the measurement are provided by Langelier.[4]

2. Apparatus

Where flow-type electrodes are unavailable—or where stirring may be inadequate, as in the ordinary immersion-(dipping) type electrodes—the best procedure is to wash the glass electrode 6–8 times with portions of the sample, particularly when an unbuffered measurement follows one on a buffered solution. Flow-type electrodes are recommended for the accurate measurement of relatively unbuffered waters such as condensates. Measurements on buffered waters can be obtained on open samples. Equilibrium, as shown by the absence of drift, should be established between the sample and the electrode system before readings are accepted as final. If the water is hot or if the pH is over 10, special glass electrodes should be used and the assembly should be standardized under conditions of temperature and concentration as close as possible to those of the sample, taking into account the manufacturer's recommendations. The analyst should constantly be on the alert for possible erratic results arising from mechanical or electrical failures—weak batteries, cracked glass electrodes, plugged liquid junction, and fouling of the electrodes with oily or precipitated materials.

3. Standard Solutions

a. General preparation: Calibrate the electrode system against standard buffer solutions of known pH value. Inasmuch as buffer solutions may deteriorate because of mold growth or contamination, prepare them fresh as needed for accurate work by weighing the amounts of chemicals specified in Table 144(1), dissolving in distilled water at 25 C and diluting to 1,000 ml. Use distilled water having a specific conductance of less than 2 micromhos at 25 C and a pH 5.6 to 6.0 for the preparation of all standard solutions. Freshly boil and cool this distilled water to expel the carbon dioxide and to produce a pH of 6.7 to 7.3, for the preparation of the borax and phosphate solutions. Dry the potassium dihydrogen phosphate and the disodium hydrogen phosphate at 110–130 C for 2 hr in a drying oven before weighing. Do not heat the unstable hydrated potassium tetroxalate above 60 C or dry the other specified buffer salts. Although ACS-grade chemicals are generally satisfactory for the preparation of buffer solutions, use certified materials available as NBS standard samples from the National Bureau of Standards where the greatest accuracy is required (for routine work, commercially available buffer tablets or powders of tested quality are also permissible). In making up buffer solutions from solid salts, dissolve all the material; otherwise the pH may be incorrect. Prepare and calibrate the electrode system with buffer solutions whose pH approximates that of the samples, so as to minimize any error resulting from nonlinear response of the electrode. As a rule, select and prepare the buffer solutions classed as primary standards. Reserve the secondary

TABLE 144(1): PREPARATION OF pH STANDARD SOLUTIONS

Standard Solution (molality)	pH at 25 C	Weight of Chemicals Needed per 1,000 ml of Aqueous Solution at 25 C
Primary standards		
Potassium hydrogen tartrate (saturated at 25 C)	3.557	6.4 g $KHC_4H_4O_6$*
0.05 potassium dihydrogen citrate	3.776	11.41 g $KH_2C_6H_5O_7$
0.05 potassium hydrogen phthalate	4.008	10.12 g $KHC_8H_4O_4$
0.025 potassium dihydrogen phosphate + 0.025 disodium hydrogen phosphate	6.865	3.388 g KH_2PO_4† + 3.533 g Na_2HPO_4†‡
0.008695 potassium dihydrogen phosphate + 0.03043 disodium hydrogen phosphate	7.413	1.179 g KH_2PO_4† + 4.302 g Na_2HPO_4†‡
0.01 sodium borate decahydrate (borax)	9.180	3.80 g $Na_2B_4O_7 \cdot 10H_2O$ ‡
0.025 sodium bicarbonate + 0.025 sodium carbonate	10.012	2.092 g $NaHCO_3$ + 2.640 g Na_2CO_3
Secondary standards		
0.05 potassium tetroxalate dihydrate	1.679	12.61 g $KH_3C_4O_8 \cdot 2H_2O$
Calcium hydroxide (saturated at 25 C)	12.454	1.5 g $Ca(OH)_2$*

* Approximate solubility.
† Dry chemical at 110–130 C for 2 hr.
‡ Prepare with freshly boiled and cooled distilled water (carbon dioxide-free).

standards, potassium tetroxalate and calcium hydroxide solutions, listed at the bottom of Table 144(1), for the extreme situations encountered in wastewater measurements. Consult Table 144(2) for the accepted pH of the standard buffer solutions at temperatures other than 25 C. Where the intent is to apply them for routine control, store the buffer solutions and samples preferentially in polyethylene bottles, and secondarily in pyrex glassware. Even in such circumstances, replace buffer solutions every 4 weeks.

b. Saturated potassium hydrogen tartrate solution: Shake vigorously an excess (5–10 g) of finely crystalline $KHC_4H_4O_6$ with 100–300 ml distilled water at 25 C in a glass-stoppered bottle. Separate the clear solution from the undissolved material by decantation or filtration. If this solution is to be used for routine control, preserve for 2 months or more by the addition of a thymol crystal 8 mm in diameter for each 200 ml of solution.

c. Saturated calcium hydroxide solution: Place the well-washed calcium carbonate, $CaCO_3$, of low-alkali grade, in a platinum dish and ignite for 1 hr at 1,000 C. Hydrate the cooled calcium oxide by adding slowly, with stirring, to distilled water and heating to boiling. Filter the cooled suspension and collect the solid calcium hydroxide on a fritted glass filter of medium porosity. Dry the collected calcium hydroxide in an oven at 110 C, cool, and pulverize to uniformly fine granules. Vigorously shake a considerable excess of the fine granules with distilled water of temperature 25 C in a stoppered polyethylene bottle. Filter the supernate under suction through a sintered-glass filter of medium porosity and use the filtrate as the buffer solution. Discard the buffer solution when atmospheric carbon dioxide causes turbidity to appear.

4. Procedure

Because of the differences between the many makes and models of pH meters which are available commercially, it is impossible to provide detailed instructions for the correct operation of every instrument. In each case, follow the manufacturer's instructions. Thoroughly wet the glass electrode and the calomel electrode and prepare for use in accordance with the instructions given. Standardize the instrument against a buffer solution with a pH approaching that of the sample, and then check the linearity of electrode response against at least one additional buffer of a different pH. The readings with the additional buffers will afford a rough idea of the limits of accuracy to be expected of the instrument and the technic of operation.

5. Precision and Accuracy

The precision and accuracy attainable with a given pH meter will depend upon the type and condition of the instrument employed and the technic of standardization and operation. With the proper care, a precision of ±0.02 pH unit and an accuracy of ±0.05 pH unit can be achieved with many of the new and improved models. However, ±0.1 pH unit represents the limit of accuracy under normal conditions. For this reason, pH values generally should be reported to the nearest 0.1 pH unit. A synthetic unknown sample consisting of a Clark and Lubs buffer solution of pH 7.3 was determined electrometrically with a standard deviation of ±0.13 pH unit in 30 laboratories.

TABLE 144(2): STANDARD pH VALUES ASSIGNED BY THE NATIONAL BUREAU OF STANDARDS

Degrees Centigrade	Primary Standards							Secondary Standards	
	Tartrate (Saturated)	Citrate (0.05 m)	Phthalate (0.05 m)	Phosphate (1:1)	Phosphate (1:3.5)	Borax (0.01 m)	Carbonate (0.025 m)	Tetroxalate (0.05 m)	Calcium Hydroxide (Saturated)
0		3.863	4.003	6.984	7.534	9.464	10.317	1.666	13.423
5		3.840	3.999	6.951	7.500	9.395	10.245	1.668	13.207
10		3.820	3.998	6.923	7.472	9.332	10.179	1.670	13.003
15		3.802	3.999	6.900	7.448	9.276	10.118	1.672	12.810
20		3.788	4.002	6.881	7.429	9.225	10.062	1.675	12.627
25	3.557	3.776	4.008	6.865	7.413	9.180	10.012	1.679	12.454
30	3.552	3.766	4.015	6.853	7.400	9.139	9.966	1.683	12.289
35	3.549	3.759	4.024	6.844	7.389	9.102	9.925	1.688	12.133
38	3.548		4.030	6.840	7.384	9.081		1.691	12.043
40	3.547	3.753	4.035	6.838	7.380	9.068	9.889	1.694	11.984
45	3.547	3.750	4.047	6.834	7.373	9.038	9.856	1.700	11.841
50	3.549	3.749	4.060	6.833	7.367	9.011	9.828	1.707	11.705
55	3.554		4.075	6.834		8.985		1.715	11.574
60	3.560		4.091	6.836		8.962		1.723	11.449
70	3.580		4.126	6.845		8.921		1.743	
80	3.609		4.164	6.859		8.885		1.766	
90	3.650		4.205	6.877		8.850		1.792	
95	3.674		4.227	6.886		8.833		1.806	

144 B. References

1. W. M. CLARK. 1928. *The Determination of Hydrogen Ions* (3rd ed.). Williams & Wilkins Co., Baltimore.
2. I. M. KOLTHOFF. 1937. *Acid-Base Indicators* (4th ed.). Macmillan Co., New York.
3. AMERICAN WATER WORKS ASSOCIATION. 1964. *Simplified Procedures for Water Examination.* Manual M12, AWWA, New York, pp. 52–54.
4. W. F. LANGELIER. 1946. Effect of temperature on the pH of natural waters. *JAWWA* 38:179.

144 C. Bibliography

DOLE, M. 1941. *The Glass Electrode.* John Wiley & Sons, New York.

BATES, R. G. & S. F. ACREE. 1945. pH of aqueous mixtures of potassium dihydrogen phosphate and disodium hydrogen phosphate at 0 to 60 C. *J. Res. Nat. Bureau Standards* 34:373.

BATES, R. G. 1954. *Electrometric pH determinations.* John Wiley & Sons, New York.

FELDMAN, I. 1956. Use and abuse of pH measurements. *Anal. Chem.* 28:1859.

BRITTON, H. T. S. 1956. *Hydrogen Ions* (4th ed.). D. Van Nostrand Co., Princeton, N. J.

KOLTHOFF, I. M. & H. A. LAITINEN. 1958. *pH and Electrotitrations.* John Wiley & Sons, New York.

BATES, R. G. 1962. Revised standard values for pH measurements from 0 to 95 C. *J. Res. Nat. Bureau Standards* 66A:179.

———. 1964. *Determination of pH.* John Wiley & Sons, New York.

STAPLES, B. R. & R. G. BATES. 1969. Two new standards for the pH scale. *J. Res. Nat. Bureau Standards* 73A:37.

145 PHENOLS

Phenols are waste products of oil refineries, coke plants and some chemical-producing facilities. Concentrations of the order of 10 to 100 μg/l are detectable by the taste and odor test. Trace amounts approaching 1 μg/l can impart an objectionable taste to a water following marginal chlorination. The removal of phenolic tastes from a water supply offers a serious challenge at the treatment plant. Among the processes used for coping with the phenol problem are superchlorination, chlorine dioxide or chlorine-ammonia treatment, ozonation, and activated-carbon adsorption.

The term "phenols" as used in this manual includes those hydroxy derivatives of benzene which can be determined under specified conditions by the methods presented in Section 222.

In a water supply containing phenol itself, there will usually be associated with it other phenolic compounds whose sensitivity to the reagents used in these methods may not necessarily be the same. As a general rule, the introduction of substituent groups in the benzene nucleus lowers the sensitivity of the particular compound to color formation with the indicator.

The percentage composition of the various phenolic compounds present in a given sample is unpredictable. It is obvious, therefore, that a standard containing a mixture of phenols cannot be made applicable to all samples. For this reason, phenol itself has been selected as a standard, and any color produced by the reaction of other phenolic compounds is reported as phenol. This value will represent the minimum concentration of phenolic compounds present in the sample.

The same methods are used for the determination of phenols in water as in wastewater, although the preliminary distillation steps may be somewhat different. Section 222 also presents a method for the determination of chlorophenols. Directions for the distillation procedure for water samples are given below.

Storage of samples: For best results, the samples should be stored in accordance with directions given in Section 222A.3, Preservation and Storage of Samples.

145 A. Preliminary Distillation Step

1. Apparatus

a. Distillation apparatus, all glass. A suitable assembly consists of a 1-liter pyrex distilling apparatus with Graham condenser * (see Figure 18, Section 132A.2 preceding).

2. Reagents

All reagents must be prepared with distilled water free of both phenols and chlorine.

a. Copper sulfate solution: Dissolve 100 g $CuSO_4 \cdot 5H_2O$ in distilled water and dilute to 1 liter.

b. Phosphoric acid solution: Dilute 10 ml 85% H_3PO_4 to 100 ml with distilled water.

3. Procedure

To a 500-ml sample of water, add 5.0 ml copper sulfate solution unless it has previously been added as a preservative. Lower the pH of the mixture to below 4.0 with phosphoric acid solution; 0.7 ml is sufficient for most samples. Place the mixture in the all-glass distillation apparatus and distill over 450 ml. Stop the distillation and, when boiling ceases, add 50 ml distilled water to the distilling flask. Continue the distillation until a total of 500 ml has been collected.

If at this point a distinct odor of other organic compounds is noted in the distillate, or if an oily layer is noticeable, then follow the complete procedure given in Sections 222A.1c and 222B.4d for coping with this situation.

* Corning No. 3360 or equivalent.

145 B. Colorimetric Determination

The phenol in the above distillate can be determined by the aminoantipyrine method outlined under Phenols, Section 222C.

1. Precision and Accuracy

A synthetic unknown sample containing 2.0 μg/l phenol in distilled water was determined by the distillation and chloroform-extraction methods, with a relative standard deviation of 81.3% and a relative error of 45.2% in 65 laboratories.

A second synthetic unknown sample containing 50 μg/l phenol in distilled water was determined by the distillation and chloroform-extraction methods, with a relative standard deviation of 20.8% and a relative error of 7.2% in 69 laboratories.

146 PHOSPHATE

Phosphate is frequently added at the water treatment plant in the ortho, poly or condensed form to condition the effluent for subsequent domestic and industrial use. In such case, phosphate determinations serve a control function. The methods described in Section 223 are satisfactory for this purpose.

147 POTASSIUM

Potassium ranks seventh among the elements in order of abundance, yet its concentration in most drinking waters is trivial, seldom reaching 20 mg/l. However, occasional brines may contain in excess of 100 mg/l potassium.

a. Selection of method: Two methods for the determination of potassium are given. The flame photometric method (*A*) is more rapid, sensitive and accurate but requires a special instrument and much preliminary work before samples can be run routinely. The colorimetric method (*B*) is usually inadvisable for potassium levels below 10 mg/l because the determination would then entail more than a tenfold concentration of the sample by evaporation.

b. Storage of sample: Samples should not be stored in soft-glass bottles because of the possibility of contamination from leaching of the glass. Polyethylene or pyrex bottles are preferable.

147 A. Flame Photometric Method

1. General Discussion

a. Principle: Trace amounts of potassium can be determined in either a direct-reading or internal-standard type of flame photometer at a wavelength of 768 mμ. The principles, applications and interferences of the flame photometric method are described under Sodium (Section 153A). Because much of the information pertaining to sodium applies equally to the potassium determination, the entire discussion dealing with the flame photometric determination of sodium (Section 153A) should be studied carefully in advance of the potassium determination.

b. Interference: Burner - clogging particulate matter should be removed from the sample by filtration through a quantitative filter paper of medium retentiveness. Inclusion of a nonionic detergent into the lithium standard may assure proper aspirator function. Interference in the internal-standard method has been reported at sodium-to-potassium ratios of 5:1 or greater. Calcium may interfere if the calcium-to-potassium ratio is 10:1 or more. Magnesium begins to interfere when the magnesium-to-potassium ratio exceeds 100.

c. Minimum detectable concentration: With expert technic, potassium levels approximating 0.1 mg/l can be determined in the better flame photometers.

2. Apparatus

See Sodium, Section 153A.2.

3. Reagents

In order to minimize potassium pickup, all solutions should preferably be stored in plastic bottles. The use of small containers reduces the amount of dry element which may be picked up from the bottle walls when the solution is poured. Each container should be thoroughly shaken to wash the accumulated salts from the walls before the solution is poured.

a. Deionized distilled water: Use this water for the preparation of all reagents, calibration standards, and as dilution water.

b. Stock potassium solution: Dissolve 1.907 g potassium chloride, KCl, dried at 110 C and dilute to 1,000 ml with deionized distilled water to form a solution containing 1.00 mg K per 1.00 ml.

c. Intermediate potassium solution: Dilute 10.00 ml stock potassium solution with deionized distilled water to 100 ml to make a solution containing 100 μg K per 1.00 ml. Use this intermediate solution for preparing the calibration curve in the potassium range of 1–10 mg/l.

d. Standard potassium solution: Dilute 10.00 ml intermediate potassium solution with deionized distilled water to 100 ml to form a solution containing 10.0 μg K per 1.00 ml. Use this solution for preparing the calibration curve in the potassium range of 0.1–1.0 mg/l.

e. Standard lithium solution: See Sodium, Section 153A.3e.

4. Procedure

Perform the determination as described under Sodium, Section 153A.4, but measure the emission intensity at 768 mμ.

5. Calculation

See Sodium, Section 153A.5 et seq.

6. Precision and Accuracy

A synthetic unknown sample containing 3.1 mg/l K, 108 mg/l Ca, 82 mg/l Mg, 19.9 mg/l Na, 241 mg/l chloride, 250 μg/l nitrite N, 1.1 mg/l nitrate N, 259 mg/l sulfate, and 42.5 mg/l total alkalinity (contributed by $NaHCO_3$) was determined by the flame photometric method, with a relative standard deviation of 15.5% and a relative error of 2.3% in 33 laboratories.

147 B. Colorimetric Method

1. General Discussion

a. Principle: Potassium is determined colorimetrically by precipitating it with sodium cobaltinitrite, oxidizing the dipotassium sodium cobaltinitrite with standard potassium dichromate solution in the presence of sulfuric acid, and measuring the excess dichromate colorimetrically. A series of solutions of known potassium concentration must be carried through the procedure together with each set of samples, because the temperature and the time of precipitation affect the results markedly.

b. Interference: Ammonium ion interferes and should not be present. Silica causes no difficulty unless a silica gel is formed, either during evaporation or when the sample becomes acid upon addition of the reagent. If this occurs, as evidenced by turbidity in the final colored solution, filtration will be necessary. Other substances normally present in water do not interfere.

c. Minimum detectable concentration: 0.5 mg potassium can be detected by the photometric method when a 15-cm light path is used. This represents a potassium concentration of 5 mg/l when a 100-ml sample is taken for analysis.

2. Apparatus

a. COLORIMETRIC EQUIPMENT—One of the following is required:

1) Spectrophotometer, for use at 425 mμ, providing a light path of 1 cm or longer.

2) Filter photometer, providing a light path of 1 cm or longer and equipped with a violet filter having maximum transmittance near 425 mμ. Longer light paths are desirable for concentrations below 20 mg/l K.

3) Nessler tubes, matched, 100-ml tall form.

b. CENTRIFUGE.

c. CENTRIFUGE TUBES, 25-ml.

d. SMALL-DIAMETER STIRRING RODS, 2–3 mm, to stir the precipitate in the centrifuge tube.

3. Reagents

a. Nitric acid, 1N.

b. Trisodium cobaltinitrite solution: Dissolve 10 g $Na_3Co(NO_2)_6$ in 50 ml distilled water. Filter before use. Prepare the solution daily.

c. Nitric acid, 0.01*N*. Dilute 10 ml 1*N* HNO_3 to 1 liter with distilled water.

d. Standard potassium dichromate, 0.1000*N*. Dissolve 4.904 g anhydrous $K_2Cr_2O_7$ in distilled water, and make up to 1,000 ml. This solution is stable for long periods.

e. Sulfuric acid, conc.

f. Standard potassium solution: Prepare as directed in Section 147A.3b; 1.00 ml = 1.00 mg K.

4. Procedure

a. Sample volume: If the sample contains from 100 to 700 mg/l K, take a 10.00-ml portion for analysis. If it contains less than this amount, concentrate a larger portion by evaporation to about 5 ml, transfer to a 25-ml centrifuge tube, and make up to 10.00 ml.

b. Color production: At room temperature add, with mixing, 1 ml 1*N* HNO_3 and 5 ml trisodium cobaltinitrite solution. Allow to stand for 2 hr. Inasmuch as the composition of the precipitate is dependent on the time allowed for precipitation as well as on the temperature, keep the time constant (± 15 min) for all samples. A variation of 10 C in either direction will give an error of 2%. Centrifuge for 10 min. Decant and wash the precipitate with 15 ml 0.01*N* HNO_3, using a small-diameter stirring rod; mix to insure complete contact between precipitate and wash solution. Centrifuge again, decant, and add, with mixing, 10.00 ml standard potassium dichromate solution and 5 ml conc sulfuric acid. Cool to room temperature. Make up to 100 ml with distilled water. Filter if the solution is turbid.

c. Preparation of standards: Pipet 1, 2, 3, 4, 5, 6 and 7 ml standard potassium solution into 25-ml centrifuge tubes, dilute each to 10.00 ml, and treat in the same manner as the sample to produce standards containing 1.00 to 7.00 mg K.

d. Color measurement: Measure the color either photometrically or visually.

1) PHOTOMETRIC MEASUREMENT—Use the longest light path available with the instrument to measure the absorbance or transmittance of the sample and standards. For a spectrophotometer with a 2-cm light path, prepare the calibration graph in the range of 2 to 7 mg K. For a filter photometer with a 15-cm light path, prepare the calibration curve in the 0.5 to 7 mg K range.

2) VISUAL COLOR COMPARISON—Compare the sample against the standards in the range from 2 to 7 mg K. Protect from dust and strong light to preserve stability of the solutions for at least 1 week.

5. Calculation

$$\text{mg/l K} = \frac{\text{mg K} \times 1{,}000}{\text{ml sample}}$$

6. Precision and Accuracy

Both visual and spectrophotometric readings using a 2-cm light path can be made with an estimated accuracy of ± 0.5 mg K.

147 C. Bibliography

Flame Photometric Method

All the references cited in the bibliography for the flame photometric method of sodium (Section 153 C following) apply equally well to potassium. The following reference also deserves attention:

MEHLICH, A. & R. J. MONROE. 1952. Report on potassium analyses by means of flame photometer methods. *J. Assoc. Official Agric. Chemists* 35:588.

Colorimetric Method

WANDER, I. W. 1942. Photometric determination of potassium. *Ind. Eng. Chem.*, Anal. Ed. 14:471.

148 RESIDUE

Waters yielding considerable residue are generally inferior with respect to palatability, or they may induce an unfavorable physiological reaction in the transient consumer. Highly mineralized waters are also unsuitable for many industrial applications. For these reasons, a limit of 500 mg/l residue is desirable for drinking waters.

"Total residue" is the term applied to the material left in the vessel after evaporation of a sample of water and its subsequent drying in an oven at a definite temperature. Total residue includes "nonfiltrable residue"—that is, the portion of the total residue retained by a filter—and "filtrable residue," that portion of the total residue which passes through the filter.

In the past, the terms "suspended" and "dissolved" (residue) corresponded to nonfiltrable and filtrable residue, respectively. The latter are more precise designations, however, because these residues are still somewhat indistinct entities whose separation is dependent on a number of variables, some of which can be controlled only with difficulty. The chemical and physical nature of the material in suspension, the pore size of the filter, the area and thickness of the filter mat, and the amount and physical state of the materials deposited on it are the principal factors involved. A method designed to control all the variables affecting filtration would be too cumbersome for practical use. It must be recognized, therefore, that residue determinations are not subject to the usual criteria of accuracy. The various types of residue are defined arbitrarily by the methods used for their determination, and these in turn represent practical approaches to what would otherwise be exceedingly complex operations.

The temperature at which the residue is dried has an important bearing on the results, since weight losses due to volatilization of organic matter, mechanically occluded water, water of crystallization, and gases from heat-induced chemical decomposition, as well as weight gains due to oxidation, are dependent on the temperature and the period of heating. Provision is made for a choice of drying temperatures and the analyst should be familiar with the probable effects of each.

"Fixed residues"—the residue remaining after ignition for 1 hr at 550 C—does not distinguish precisely between organic and inorganic residue because the loss on ignition is not confined to organic matter but includes losses due to decomposition or volatilization of certain mineral salts. A better approximation of the organic matter in water is available by the total organic carbon, biochemical oxygen demand, or chemical oxygen demand methods described in Sections 138, 219 and 220, respectively.

Specific conductance measurements are roughly proportional to the filtrable residue and may be used to advantage in selecting the proper size of sample for residue determinations. Close correlation of results of the two tests should not, however, be expected in every instance.

An additional possibility for checking fixed filtrable residue is the utilization of ion-exchange procedures described in the Introduction, Section 100C.3.

1) Selection of drying temperature: The methods described are gravimetric and permit freedom of choice with respect to the temperature of drying.

Residues dried at 103–105 C may be expected to retain not only water of crystallization but also some mechanically occluded water. Loss of carbon dioxide will result in the conversion of bicarbonate to carbonate. Loss of organic matter by volatilization will be very slight at this temperature if it occurs at all. Because the expulsion of occluded water is marginal at 105 C, attainment of constant weight is very slow.

Residues dried at 179–181 C will lose almost all the mechanically occluded water, but some water of crystallization may remain, especially if sulfates are present. Organic matter is reduced by volatilization but is not completely destroyed. Bicarbonate is converted to carbonate and carbonate may be partially decomposed to oxide or basic salts. Some chloride and nitrate salts may be lost. In general, evaporating and drying water samples at 179–181 C yield values for total residue which conform more closely to those obtained through summation of individually determined mineral salts than do the values for total residue secured through drying at a lower temperature.

The analyst must select the drying temperature best suited to the type of water under examination. Waters that are low in organic matter and total mineral content and are intended for human consumption may be examined under either temperature, but waters containing considerable organic matter or those with pH over 9.0 should be dried at the higher temperature. In any case, the report should indicate the drying temperature.

2) Selection of method for nonfiltrable residue: The amount and type of suspended matter in the sample, the purpose of the water analysis, and the relative ease of making the determination will dictate whether the nonfiltrable residue is obtained by a direct determination or by calculation of the difference between the total residue and the filtrable residue.

3) Sampling and storage: Water has considerable solvent action on glass, and the mineral content of a sample will increase when the water is stored in a bottle made of nonresistant glass. This effect is especially pronounced with alkaline waters. Resistant-glass bottles are therefore desirable. Plastic bottles are satisfactory provided that the material in suspension in the sample does not adhere to the walls of the container. Store samples likely to contain iron or manganese so that oxygen will not come into contact with the water. Analyze these samples promptly to minimize the possibility of chemical or physical change during storage.

148 A. Total Residue

1. General Discussion

a. Principle: The sample is evaporated in a weighed dish on a steam bath and then is dried to constant weight in an oven at either 103–105 C or 179–181 C. The increase in weight over that of the empty dish represents the total residue.

2. Apparatus

a. Evaporating dishes: Dishes of 150–200 ml capacity made of the following materials may be used as indicated:

1) PLATINUM—Generally satisfactory for all tests.

2) NICKEL—Satisfactory if the residue is not to be ignited.

3) PORCELAIN, SILICA, VYCOR,* OR PYREX—Satisfactory for samples having a pH below 9.0.

* A product of Corning Glass Works.

Nickel oxidizes slightly at 600 C, and fixed residues may be difficult to remove. Porcelain, silica, Vycor and pyrex glass are corroded by high-pH waters, and pyrex glass will soften at the ignition temperature. Platinum is the most satisfactory because it is relatively unattacked by mineral salts and suffers comparatively insignificant weight change during heating operations.

b. Steam bath.

c. Drying oven, equipped with a thermostatic control capable of maintaining the temperature within a 2-C range.

d. Desiccator, provided with a desiccant containing a color indicator of moisture concentration.

e. Analytical balance, 200-g capacity, capable of weighing to 0.1 mg.

3. Procedure

a. Preparation of evaporating dish: Subject the dish to be used in the determination of total residue to a preliminary drying in an oven at the same temperature intended for the residue. If ignition of the residue is to be carried out for determination of fixed total residue, ignite the dish in a furnace for 30 min at 550 C.

b. Sample treatment:

1) Choose a volume of sample which will yield a residue between 25 and 250 mg, and preferably between 100 and 250 mg. Estimate the volume to be evaporated from the specific conductance value.

2) Pour a measured portion of the well-mixed sample into a weighed evaporating dish on a steam bath. After complete evaporation of the water from the residue, transfer the dish to an oven maintained at either 103–105 C or 179–181 C. Dry to constant weight. Consider constant weight to be attained when not more than a 0.5-mg weight change occurs between two successive series of operations consisting of heating, cooling in a desiccator, and weighing. Dry for a long period to eliminate the necessity of checking for constant weight. Either dry the dish overnight or determine by trial the minimum time required to attain constant weight with a given type of sample when a number of samples of the same kind are involved. Allow the dish to cool briefly in air before placing it, while still warm, in a desiccator to complete cooling in a dry atmosphere. Do not overload the desiccator. Provide sufficient room so that all dishes may remain flat on the desiccator shelf, and no part of a dish touches another dish or the side of the desiccator.

3) Weigh the dish as soon as it has completely cooled. Do not allow the residue to remain overly long in a desiccator because some residues, especially those dried at 180 C, are very hygroscopic and may remove water from a desiccant that is not thoroughly dry. Report the increase in weight over the empty dish as "total residue on drying at ____ C" in terms of mg/l and to the nearest whole number. For results exceeding 1,000 mg/l report only three significant figures.

4. Calculation

$$\text{mg/l total residue} = \frac{\text{mg total residue} \times 1{,}000}{\text{ml sample}}$$

5. Precision and Accuracy

The precision of the method is about ± 4 mg or $\pm 5\%$. Accuracy cannot be estimated, for residue as determined by this method is an arbitrary quantity essentially defined by the procedure followed. The determined values, therefore, may not check with the theoretical value for solids calculated from the chemical analysis. The Sokoloff reference (Section 148E) should be consulted for approximate methods by which to correlate the chemical analysis with the residue determinations.

148 B. Filtrable Residue

1. General Discussion

a. Principle: The sample is filtered and the filtrate evaporated in a weighed dish on a steam bath. The residue left after evaporation is dried to constant weight in an oven at either 103–105 C or 179–181 C. The increase in weight over that of the empty dish represents filtrable residue and includes all materials, liquid or solid, in solution or otherwise, which pass through the filter and are not volatilized during the drying process.

2. Apparatus

All of the apparatus listed under Section 148A.2 is required and in addition:

a. Filter—One of the following is required:

1) GLASS FIBER FILTER DISK,* 5.5 cm, or 2.1 or 2.4 cm in diameter.

2) MEMBRANE FILTER—The pore size should be chosen on the basis of the size of the critical item (like soil, algae and bacteria) to be removed, but large enough to filter a reasonable volume in an hour's time or less.

3) PAPER—Acid-washed, ashless hard-finish filter paper sufficiently retentive for fine precipitates.

4) CRUCIBLE—Porous-bottom silica, fritted-glass, porcelain, stainless steel or alundum crucible with a maximum pore size of 5 microns.

5) DIATOMACEOUS FILTER CANDLES—with a maximum pore size of 5 microns.

6) GOOCH CRUCIBLE—30-ml capacity, with 2.1- or 2.4-cm glass fiber filter disk.*

b. Filtering apparatus appropriate to the type of filter selected.

* Whatman GF/C, or equivalent.

3. Procedure

Filter a portion of the sample through one of the filters listed in ¶ 2 above and carry out the procedure outlined in Section 148A.3 on an appropriate portion of the filtrate. Report the increase in weight over the empty dish as "filtrable residue on drying at __ C" in terms of mg/l and to the nearest whole number. For results exceeding 1,000 mg/l report only three significant figures. Report the type of filter used.

4. Calculation

$$\text{mg/l filtrable residue} = \frac{A \times 1{,}000}{\text{ml sample}}$$

where A = mg filtrable residue.

5. Precision and Accuracy

Refer to Section 148A.5. A synthetic unknown sample containing 134 mg/l filtrable residue was determined gravimetrically, with a standard deviation of ± 13 mg/l in 18 laboratories, using a drying temperature of 103–105 C.

148 C. Nonfiltrable Residue

1. General Discussion

a. Principle: The sample is filtered and the nonfiltrable residue is determined either directly or by difference between the total residue and the filtrable residue. If the determination is made directly, an appropriate portion of sample is passed through a weighed filter, and the filter with its contents is oven-dried at either 103–105 C or 179–181 C. The increase in weight over that of the empty filter represents nonfiltrable residue.

b. Interference: Occasionally the physical nature of the suspended material may clog the filter and retard the passage of the water. If the time required for filtration in such instances is unduly long, determination by difference is recommended.

2. Apparatus

a. Filters—One of the following is required:

1) CRUCIBLE—Porous-bottom silica, fritted-glass, porcelain, stainless-steel or alundum crucible with a maximum pore size of 5 microns.

2) GOOCH CRUCIBLE—30-ml capacity, with 2.1- or 2.4-cm glass fiber filter disk.†

b. Filtering apparatus, appropriate to the type of filter selected.

c. Drying oven, equipped with a thermostatic control capable of maintaining the temperature within ± 1 C.

d. Desiccator, provided with a desiccant containing a color indicator of moisture content.

e. Analytical balance, capable of weighing to 0.1 mg.

3. Procedure

a. Preparation of filter: If the determination is to be made directly by weighing the residue, subject the filter to a preliminary drying in an oven at the same temperature intended for the sample. If the fixed nonfiltrable residue is to be determined subsequently, heat the filter in a furnace for at least 30 min at 550 C. Because stainless steel and glass filters should not be subjected to ignition temperatures, use a porcelain, silica or alundum filter.

b. Sample treatment: As the amount of nonfiltrable residue in potable waters is usually very small, pass a relatively large volume of sample through the filter to secure a weighable residue. Consider 2.5 mg as the minimum amount of residue to be significant in a direct weighing. Use the turbidity estimation as a reasonable criterion of sample size.

If the sample has a turbidity of 50 units or less, filter 1 liter for nonfiltrable residue; if the turbidity is over 50 units, filter sufficient sample to yield from 50 to 100 mg of nonfiltrable residue. When the amount of residue left on the filter is greater than 100 mg,

† Whatman GF/C, or equivalent.

estimate the nonfiltrable residue by difference between total residue and filtrable residue.

c. After filtration transfer the filter with its contents to an oven maintained at a temperature of either 103–105 C or 179–181 C and dry until constant weight is attained [see Section 148A.-3b(2) for criterion on constant weight]. Dry for a long period to eliminate the necessity of checking for constant weight. Either dry the filter overnight or determine by trial the minimum time required to attain constant weight with a given type of sample when a number of the same kind of samples are involved. Cool briefly in air and transfer to a desiccator to complete the cooling in a dry atmosphere. Report the increase in weight over that of the empty filter as "nonfiltrable residue on drying at __ C" in terms of mg/l and to the nearest whole number. Also report the type of filter used.

4. Calculation

$$\text{mg/l nonfiltrable residue} = \frac{A \times 1{,}000}{\text{ml sample}}$$

where A = mg nonfiltrable residue.

5. Precision and Accuracy

Refer to Section 148A.5.

148 D. Fixed Residue (Total, Filtrable, Nonfiltrable)

1. General Discussion

The dishes with the residue retained after completion of the tests for total residue and filtrable residue, or the filter with its residue retained after completion of the test for nonfiltrable residue, are subjected to heat for 1 hr in a furnace held at 550 C. The increase in weight over that of the ignited empty vessel represents fixed residue in each instance.

2. Apparatus

The apparatus cited in Methods A, B or C, ¶ 2, is required; as well as an electric muffle furnace for operation at 550 C.

3. Procedure

Take the residue produced in Methods A, B or C, and ignite in the dish or filter in a muffle furnace at a temperature of 550 C for 1 hr in order to insure reproducibility. Have the furnace up to temperature before inserting the sample.

After ignition, allow the vessels to partially cool in air until most of the heat has dissipated, then transfer to a desiccator for final cooling in a dry atmosphere. Do not overload the desiccator. Weigh the vessel as soon as it has completely cooled [see Section 148A.3b(3)]. Report the increase in weight over the empty ignited vessel as "fixed total residue," "fixed filtrable residue" or "fixed nonfiltrable residue," whichever is appropriate to the sample, in terms of mg/l and to the nearest whole number. For results exceeding 1,000 mg/l report only three significant figures.

4. Calculation

$$\text{mg/l fixed residue} = \frac{\text{mg fixed residue} \times 1{,}000}{\text{ml sample}}$$

5. Precision and Accuracy

Refer to Section 148A.5.

148 E. Bibliography

HOWARD, C. S. 1933. Determination of total dissolved solids in water analysis. *Ind. Eng. Chem.*, Anal. Ed. 5:4.

SOKOLOFF, V. P. 1933. Water of crystallization in total solids of water analysis. *Ind. Eng. Chem.*, Anal. Ed. 5:336.

149 SATURATION AND STABILITY WITH RESPECT TO CALCIUM CARBONATE

1. General Discussion

Theoretical and practical studies of the scale-forming and corrosive properties of water have been and are being made. An important value upon which theory and application have been built is the theoretical pH_s, the calculated pH at which, without change in total alkalinity and calcium content, a water would be in equilibrium with solid calcium carbonate. Another definition of pH_s is the calculated pH at which, by the addition or removal of carbon dioxide, a water would be brought into equilibrium with solid calcium carbonate.

The calculation of pH_s at a given temperature involves three variables—total alkalinity, calcium and dissolved solids. (An average value applicable to most ordinary fresh waters is often used for the last, thereby reducing the number of variables to two.) The value for pH_s for a given water can be obtained directly by the use of one of the following aids: Langelier stability diagram,[1, 2] Riehl's nomogram,[3, 4] Hirsch's slide rule,[5, 6] and the Caldwell-Lawrence water-conditioning diagram.[7] The values of the various constants used in calculating pH_s are also available.[8–11]

Saturation index and stability index are each calculated from the pH_s and the actual pH of the water. The most important determination is that of the actual pH in the field; a pH determination on a sample which has been exposed to temperature change, storage, agitation or other conditions that can cause pH change is of negligible value. A change in temperature will cause a change in the value of either index, the direction of the change being determined both by the direction of the temperature change and by the alkalinity concentration.[1, 10–13]

The formula[14] for *saturation index* is $pH_{actual} - pH_s$. This value is an indication of the degree of instability with respect to calcium carbonate deposition and solution. A positive value indicates a tendency to deposit calcium carbonate and a negative value indicates a tendency to dissolve calcium carbonate.

The equation[15] for *stability index* is $2\ pH_s - pH_{actual}$. It has been proposed as a more quantitative measure of the $CaCO_3$ scale-forming tendency. The stability index for all waters will be positive. A water having a stability index of about 6.0 or less is considered definitely scale forming, provided the pH_s is not more than 7.5, whereas an index above 7.0 may not give a protective coating of carbonate scale. Scale deposition will decrease, and corrosion will increase, as the index rises above 7.5 or 8.0.

This discussion is necessarily brief and oversimplified. The reader is referred to the bibliography for detailed information regarding the derivation of the basic equations, their application, their limitations when applied to special types of waters, and comparisons between indicated and observed scale formation.

Another means of determining the stability of a water with respect to calcium carbonate is the "marble test," the procedure for which has been outlined by Hoover.[3] This test simply determines whether a water is supersaturated, just saturated, or unsaturated with calcium carbonate, by determining the change in total alkalinity or pH after contact with an excess of pure powdered calcium carbonate.[16] The Enslow stability indicator[17] provides for a continuous flow of the water to be tested through powdered and granular calcium carbonate. Testing the influent to, and the effluent from, this apparatus should give the same results as the marble test. If the results of either test are expressed as a change in pH value, this change must not be confused with, or reported as, the Langelier saturation index, because the change in the pH value in the marble test is caused by a change in total alkalinity, which is assumed to be constant when calculating the pH_s for Langelier's saturation index. If these results are expressed as a change in mg/l total alkalinity, the tests give a quantitative measure of the tendency of the water to dissolve or deposit calcium carbonate scales. These tests are subject to the influence of contact time and temperature change during the test.

2. References

1. W. F. LANGELIER. 1946. Chemical equilibria in water treatment. *JAWWA* 38:169.
2. AMERICAN WATER WORKS ASSOCIATION. 1950. *Water Quality and Treatment* (2nd ed.). AWWA, New York, page 297.
3. C. P. HOOVER. 1938. Practical application of the Langelier method. *JAWWA* 30:1802.
4. A. P. BLACK. 1948. The chemistry of water treatment. *Water & Sewage Works* 95:369.
5. A. A. HIRSCH. 1942. A special slide rule for calcium carbonate equilibrium problems. *Ind. Eng. Chem.*, Anal. Ed. 14:178.
6. ———. 1942. A slide rule for carbonate equilibria and alkalinity in water supplies. *Ind. Eng. Chem.*, Anal. Ed. 14:943.
7. D. H. CALDWELL & W. B. LAWRENCE. 1953. Water softening and conditioning problems. *Ind. Eng. Chem.* 45:535.
8. E. W. MOORE. 1938. Calculation of chemical dosages required for the prevention of corrosion. *J. New England W.W.A.* 52:311.
9. T. E. LARSON & A. M. BUSWELL. 1942. Calcium carbonate saturation index and alkalinity interpretations. *JAWWA* 34:1667.
10. W. F. LANGELIER. 1946. Effect of temperature on the pH of natural waters. *JAWWA* 38:179.
11. T. E. LARSON. 1951. The ideal lime-softened water. *JAWWA* 43:649.
12. S. T. POWELL, H. E. BACON & J. R. LILL.

1945. Corrosion prevention by controlled calcium carbonate scale. *Ind. Eng. Chem.* 37:842.
13. ———. 1946. Recent developments in corrosion control. *JAWWA* 38:808.
14. W. F. Langelier. 1936. The analytical control of anticorrosion water treatment. *JAWWA* 28:1500.
15. J. W. Ryznar. 1944. A new index for determining amount of calcium carbonate scale formed by water. *JAWWA* 36:472.
16. American Water Works Association. 1964. *Simplified Procedures for Water Examination.* Manual M12, AWWA, New York, pp. 21–22.
17. L. H. Enslow. 1939. The continuous stability indicator. *Water Works & Sew.* 86:107.

3. Bibliography

General

See references 2, 4, 7, 11 and 12 in the section preceding (Section 149.2 above); plus the following additional recommended source:

Dye, J. F. 1958. Correlation of the two principal methods of calculating the three kinds of alkalinity. *JAWWA* 50:800.

Theory and Theoretical Calculations

See references 1, 2, 10, 11 and 14 in the section preceding (149.2 above).

Rapid Calculation of pH

See references 1–9, 11 and 12 in the section preceding (149.2 above).

Comparisons of Scale Formation

See reference 13 above and the following additional recommended source:

DeMartini, F. E. 1938. Corrosion and the Langelier calcium carbonate saturation index. *JAWWA* 30:85.

Laboratory Tests for Measurement of Calcium Carbonate Saturation

See references 2, 3 and 17 in the section preceding (149.2 above) and the following additional recommended sources:

McLaughlin, P. L. 1936. Determining the necessary treatment to prevent corrosion. *Water Works & Sew.* 83:81.

Amorosi, A. M. & J. R. McDermet. 1939. Calculation of the distribution of carbon dioxide between water and steam. *Proc. ASTM* 39:1204.

Hartung, H. O. 1948. Stabilization of lime-softened water. *Water & Sewage Works* 95:128.

150 SELENIUM

Selenium has a toxic effect upon man and animals comparable with that of arsenic, giving rise to similar symptoms. Selenium has also been suspected of causing dental caries in man, and has been cited as a potential carcinogenic agent.

The selenium concentration of most drinking waters falls below 10 μg/l. Concentrations exceeding 500 μg/l are rare and limited to seepage from seleniferous soils. The sudden appearance of selenium in a water supply might indicate industrial pollution. Little is known regarding the valence state of selenium in natural waters, but because selenate and selenite are both found in soils, it is reasonable to expect that both may be present in seleniferous water. Water contaminated with wastes may contain selenium in any of its four valence states. Many organic compounds of selenium are known.

Selection of method: Method A involves the least time and is preferred in the absence of large amounts of iodide. Method B can be reserved for those instances where such interferences as iodide and bromide are present in the sample.

150 A. Diaminobenzidine Method

1. General Discussion

a. Principle: Oxidation by acid permanganate converts all selenium compounds to selenate. Many carbon compounds are not completely oxidized by acid permanganate, but it is improbable that the selenium-carbon bond will remain intact through this treatment. Experiments demonstrate that inorganic forms of selenium are oxidized by acid permanganate in the presence of much greater concentrations of organic matter than would be anticipated in water supplies.

There is substantial loss of selenium when solutions of sodium selenate are evaporated to complete dryness, but in the presence of calcium all the selenium is recovered. An excess of calcium over the sulfate is not necessary.

Selenate is reduced to selenite in warm 4*N* HCl. Temperature, time, and acid concentrations are specified to obtain quantitative reduction without loss of selenium. The optimum pH for the formation of piazselenol is approximately 1.5. Above pH 2, the rate of formation of the colored compound is critically dependent on the pH. When indicators are used to adjust the pH, the results are frequently erratic. Extraction of piazselenol is not quantitative, but equilibrium is attained rapidly. Above pH 6, the partition ratio of piazselenol between water and toluene is almost independent of the hydrogen ion concentration.

b. Interference: No inorganic compounds give a positive interference. It is possible that colored organic compounds exist that are extracted by toluene but it seems improbable that interference of this nature will resist the initial acid permanganate oxidation. Negative interference results from compounds that lower the concentration of diaminobenzidine by oxidizing this reagent. The addition of EDTA eliminates negative interference from at least 2.5 mg ferric iron. Manganese has no effect in any reasonable concentration, probably because it is reduced along with the selenate. Iodide, and to a lesser extent bromide, causes low results. The recovery of selenium from a standard containing 25 μg Se in the presence of varying amounts of iodide and bromide is shown in Table 150(1).

TABLE 150(1): SELENIUM RECOVERY IN THE PRESENCE OF BROMIDE AND IODIDE INTERFERENCE

Iodide *mg*	Selenium Recovered—%		
	Br 0 mg	Br 1.25 mg	Br 2.50 mg
0	100	100	96
0.5	95	94	95
1.25	84	80	
2.50	75		70

The percentage recovery improves slightly as the amount of selenium is decreased.

c. Minimum detectable concentration: 1 μg Se with a 4-cm light path.

2. Apparatus

a. COLORIMETRIC EQUIPMENT—One of the following is required:

1) Spectrophotometer, for use at 420 mμ, providing a light path of 1 cm or longer.

2) Filter photometer, providing a light path of 1 cm or longer and equipped with a violet filter having a maximum transmittance near 420 mμ.

b. SEPARATORY FUNNEL—250 ml.

c. CENTRIFUGE—for 12- or 15-ml tubes (optional).

3. Reagents

a. Stock selenium solution: Place an accurately weighed pellet of ACS-grade metallic selenium into a small beaker. Add 5 ml conc HNO_3. Warm until the reaction is complete and cautiously evaporate just to dryness. Dilute to 1,000 ml with distilled water.

b. Standard selenium solution: Dilute an appropriate volume of stock selenium solution with distilled water so that 1.00 ml = 1.00 μg Se.

c. Methyl orange indicator solution.

d. Hydrochloric acid, 0.1*N*.

e. Calcium chloride solution: Dissolve 30 g $CaCl_2 \cdot 2H_2O$ in distilled water and dilute to 1 liter.

f. Potassium permanganate, 0.1*N*: Dissolve 3.2 g $KMnO_4$ in 1,000 ml distilled water.

g. Sodium hydroxide, 0.1*N*.

h. Hydrochloric acid, conc.

i. Ammonium chloride solution: Dissolve 250 g NH_4Cl in 1 liter distilled water.

j. EDTA-sulfate reagent: Dissolve 100 g disodium ethylenediamine tetraacetate dihydrate, also called (ethylenedinitrilo)tetraacetic acid disodium salt, and 200 g sodium sulfate in 1 liter distilled water. Add conc ammonium hydroxide dropwise while stirring until the dissolution is complete.

k. Ammonium hydroxide, 5N: 1 + 2.

l. Diaminobenzidine solution: Dissolve 100 mg 3,3′-diaminobenzidine hydrochloride in 10 ml distilled water. Prepare no more than 8 hr prior to use because this solution is unstable. (CAUTION—*Handle this reagent with extreme care.*)

m. Toluene.

n. Sodium sulfate, anhydrous: Required if no centrifuge is available.

4. Procedure

a. Oxidation to selenate: Prepare standards containing 0, 10.0, 25.0 and 50.0 μg Se in 500-ml erlenmeyer flasks. Dilute to approximately 250 ml, add 10 drops methyl orange indicator solution, 2 ml 0.1*N* HCl, 5 ml $CaCl_2$ solution, 3 drops 0.1*N* $KMnO_4$, and a 5-ml measure of glass beads to prevent bumping. Boil vigorously for approximately 5 min.

To a 1,000-ml sample in a 2-liter beaker add 10 drops methyl orange indicator solution. Titrate to the methyl orange end point with 0.1*N* HCl and add 2 ml excess. Add 3 drops $KMnO_4$, 5 ml $CaCl_2$ solution, and a 5-ml measure of glass beads to prevent bumping. Heat to boiling, adding $KMnO_4$ as required to maintain a purple tint. Ignore a precipitate of MnO_2 because it will have no adverse effect. After the volume has been reduced to approximately 250 ml, quantitatively transfer the solution to a 500-ml erlenmeyer flask.

b. Evaporation: Add 5 ml 0.1*N* NaOH to each flask and evaporate to dryness. Avoid prolonged heating of the residue.

c. Reduction to selenite: Cool the flask, add 5 ml conc HCl and 10 ml NH_4Cl solution. Heat in a boiling water bath or steam bath for 10 ± 0.5 min.

d. Formation of piazselenol: Transfer the warm solution and ammonium chloride precipitate, if present, from the flask to a beaker suitable for pH adjustment, washing the flask with 5 ml EDTA-sulfate reagent and 5 ml 5*N* NH_4OH. Adjust the pH to 1.5 ± 0.3 with NH_4OH, using a pH meter. The precipitate of EDTA will not interfere. Add 1 ml diaminobenzidine solution and heat in a boiling water bath or steam bath for approximately 5 min.

e. Extraction of piazselenol: Cool and then add NH_4OH to adjust the pH to 8 ± 1; the precipitate of EDTA will dissolve. Pour the sample into a 50-ml graduate and adjust the volume to 50 ± 1 ml with washings from the beaker.

Pour the contents of the graduate into a 250-ml separatory funnel. Add 10 ml toluene and shake for 30 ± 5 sec. Discard the aqueous layer and transfer the organic phase to a 12- or 15-ml centrifuge tube. Centrifuge briefly to clear the toluene from water droplets. If a centrifuge is not available, filter the organic phase through a dry filter paper to which has been added approximately 0.1 g anhydrous Na_2SO_4.

f. Determination of absorbance: Read the absorbance at approximately 420 mμ, using toluene to establish zero absorbance. The piazselenol color is stable, but evaporation of toluene concentrates the color to a marked degree in a few hours. Beer's law is obeyed up to 50 μg.

5. Calculation

$$\text{mg/l Se} = \frac{\mu\text{g Se}}{\text{ml sample}}$$

6. Precision and Accuracy

A synthetic unknown sample containing 20 μg/l Se, 40 μg/l As, 250 μg/l Be, 240 μg/l B, and 6 μg/l V in distilled water was determined by the diaminobenzidine method, with a relative standard deviation of 21.2% and a relative error of 5.0% in 35 laboratories.

150 B. Distillation and Diaminobenzidine Method

1. General Discussion

a. Principle: Selenium is quantitatively separated from most other elements by distillation of the volatile tetrabromide from an acid solution containing bromine. The bromine is generated by the reaction of bromide with hydrogen peroxide in order to avoid the inconvenience of handling the element. Selenium tetrabromide, along with a minimum of excess bromine, is absorbed in water. The excess bromine is removed by precipitation as tribromophenol, and the quadrivalent selenium is determined with diaminobenzidine as in Method A.

b. Interference: No substances are known to interfere. The time-honored bromine distillation is satisfactory because recovery of selenium added to tap water is essentially complete.

c. Minimum detectable concentration: 1 μg Se with a 4-cm light path.

2. Apparatus

All of the apparatus in Section 150A. 2a-c plus:

a. Distillation assembly, all-pyrex, for

use with 500-ml erlenmeyer flasks with interchangeable ground-glass necks. See Figure 18 (Section 132A.2) for another suitable apparatus.

3. Reagents

All the reagents described in Section 150A.3 are needed except reagents *h* through *k*. The following are also required:

a. Potassium bromide-acid reagent: Dissolve 10 g KBr in 25 ml distilled water. Cautiously add 25 ml conc H_2SO_4, mixing and cooling under tap water as each increment of acid is added. Prepare immediately before it is to be used, because $KHSO_4$ will precipitate on cooling, and reheating to dissolve this salt will drive off some of the HBr.

b. Hydrogen peroxide, 30%.

c. Phenol solution: Dissolve 5 g phenol in 100 ml distilled water.

d. Ammonium hydroxide, conc.

e. Hydrochloric acid, 1 + 1.

4. Procedure

a. Oxidation to selenate: Same as Section 150A.4a, except that glass-stoppered erlenmeyer flasks are used.

b. Evaporation: Add 5 ml 0.1*N* NaOH to each flask and evaporate to dryness. Avoid prolonged heating of the residue.

c. Distillation: Add 50 ml KBr-H_2SO_4 reagent to the cool flask. Add 1 ml 30% H_2O_2 and fit the flask to the condenser without delay. Distill under the fume hood until the color of bromine is gone from the flask. Use as a receiver a beaker which is suitable for the subsequent pH adjustment and contains just enough water to immerse the tip of the condenser. Wash the small amount of distillate remaining in the condenser into the beaker with 5 ml distilled water.

d. Formation of piazselenol: Add phenol solution dropwise until the color of bromine is discharged. A white precipitate of tribromophenol will form, but a small proportion of the yellow tetrabromophenol causes no trouble. Adjust the pH to 1.5 ± 0.3 using conc NH_4OH and 1 + 1 HCl. Add 1 ml diaminobenzidine solution and heat in a boiling water bath or steam bath for approximately 5 min.

e. Extraction of piazselenol: Cool and then add conc NH_4OH to adjust the pH to 8 ± 1. Pour the sample into a 50-ml graduate, and adjust the volume to 50 ± 1 ml with washings from the beaker. Pour the contents of the graduate into a 250-ml separatory funnel. Add 10 ml toluene and shake for 30 ± 5 sec. Discard the aqueous layer and transfer the organic phase to a 12- or 15-ml centrifuge tube. Centrifuge briefly to clear the toluene of water droplets. If a centrifuge is not available, filter the organic phase through a dry filter paper to which have been added approximately 100 mg anhydrous Na_2SO_4

f. Determination of absorbance: Read the absorbance at approximately 420 mμ, using toluene to establish zero absorbance. Make the absorbance readings within 2 hr after extraction because the phenol used in ¶ 4d above causes the yellow piazselenol color slowly to acquire a greenish tint.

5. Calculation

Refer to Section 150A.5.

6. Precision and Accuracy

Refer to Section 150A.6.

150 C. Bibliography

HOSTE, J. & J. GILLIS. 1955. Spectrophotometric determination of traces of selenium with 3,3′-diaminobenzidine. *Anal. Chem. Acta* 12:158.

CHENG, K. 1956. Determination of traces of selenium. *Anal. Chem.* 28:1738.

MAGIN, G. B. et al. 1960. Suggested modified method for colorimetric determination of selenium in natural water. *JAWWA* 52:1199.

ROSSUM, J. R. & P. A. VILLARRUZ. 1962. Suggested methods for determining selenium in water. *JAWWA* 54:746.

151 SILICA

Silicon ranks next to oxygen in abundance and is a common constituent of igneous rocks, quartz and sand. Many natural waters contain less than 10 mg/l silica, although some may approach 60 mg/l. The formation of a hard coating on the steam-turbine blades of high-pressure boilers necessitates the removal of silica from such boiler feedwaters. Among the methods employed for silica removal are ion exchange, distillation, the hot and cold lime soda-magnesia processes, the ferric hydroxide process and the fluosilicate process.

Silica is present in natural waters in soluble and colloidal forms. Volcanic waters often contain an abundance of silica. A silica cycle occurs in many bodies of water containing organisms, such as diatoms, that utilize silica in their skeletal structure. The silica removed from the water may be slowly returned by re-solution of the dead organisms.

Three methods applicable to natural waters, each subject to certain limitations discussed below, are provided: the gravimetric method (*A*); a colorimetric method with formation of yellow molybdosilicate (*B*); and a colorimetric method with formation of heteropoly blue (*C*). An optional alkali treatment step is provided in Methods B and C.

1. Selection of Methods

Method A must be used to standardize the sodium silicate solutions which are used as standards for Methods B and C. It is the preferred method for water samples which contain at least 20 mg/l silica, but is not recommended for determining lower concentrations. Method B is recommended for relatively pure waters containing from 0.4 to 25 mg/l silica. As with most colorimetric methods, the range can be extended, if necessary, by taking aliquots, by concentrating, or by varying the light path. The interferences due to tannin, color and turbidity are more severe with this method than with Method C. Moreover, the yellow color produced by Method B has a limited stability and some attention to timing is necessary. When applicable, however, it offers greater speed and simplicity than Method C. One less reagent is used; one timing step is eliminated; and many natural waters can be analyzed without dilution, which is not often the case with Method C. Method C is recommended for the low range, from 0.04 to 2 mg/l silica. This range can also be extended if necessary. Such extension may be desirable if interference is expected from tannin, color or turbidity. A combination of factors renders Method C less susceptible than Method B to those interferences; also the blue color of Method C is more stable than the yellow color of Method B. Many samples, however, will require dilution because of the high sensitivity. Permanent artificial color standards are not available for the blue color developed in Method C.

2. *Sampling and Storage*

Samples should be collected in bottles of polyethylene, other plastic, or hard rubber, especially if a delay between collection and analysis is unavoidable. Pyrex glass is a less desirable choice.

151 A. Gravimetric Method

1. General Discussion

a. Principle: Hydrochloric acid decomposes silicates and dissolved silica, forming silicic acids which are precipitated as partially dehydrated silica during evaporation and baking. Ignition completes dehydration of the silica, which is weighed and then volatilized as silicon tetrafluoride, leaving any impurities behind as nonvolatile residue. The residue is weighed and silica is determined as loss on volatilization. Perchloric acid may be used instead of hydrochloric acid to dehydrate the silica. A single fuming with perchloric acid will recover more silica than one with hydrochloric acid, although for complete silica recovery it is necessary to carry out two dehydrations with either acid. The use of perchloric acid lessens the tendency to spatter, yields a silica precipitate that is easier to filter, and shortens the time required for the determination. Because perchloric acid is explosive, a shield must be used.

b. Interference: As glassware may contribute silica, its use should be avoided as much as possible. The reagents and the distilled water should be low in silica. A blank determination should be carried out to correct for silica introduced by the reagents and apparatus.

2. Apparatus

a. Platinum crucibles, with covers.

b. Platinum evaporating dishes, 200-ml. In the dehydration steps, acid-leached glazed porcelain evaporating dishes free from etching may be substituted for platinum.

3. Reagents

For maximum accuracy, batches of chemicals low in silica should be set aside for this method. It is advisable to store all reagents in plastic containers and to run blanks.

a. Hydrochloric acid, 1 + 1 and 1 + 50.

b. Sulfuric acid, 1 + 1.

c. Hydrofluoric acid, 48%.

d. Perchloric acid, 72%.

4. Procedure

Before performing silica determinations, test the sulfuric acid and hydrofluoric acid for interfering nonvolatile matter by carrying out the procedure of ¶ a(5) below. Use a clean, empty platinum crucible. If any increase in weight is observed, make a correction in the silica determinations.

a. HYDROCHLORIC ACID DEHYDRATION:

1) Sample evaporation—To a clear sample containing at least 10 mg silica, add 5 ml 1 + 1 HCl. Evaporate the mixture to dryness in a 200-ml platinum evaporating dish, in several portions if necessary, on a water bath or suspended on an asbestos ring over a hot plate. Protect the contents against contamination by atmospheric dust. During the evaporation, add a total of 15 ml 1 + 1 HCl in several portions. After the dish is dry, place it in a 110 C oven or over a hot plate to bake for ½ hr.

2) First filtration—To the residue in the dish, add 5 ml 1 + 1 HCl, warm, and add 50 ml hot distilled water. While hot, filter the suspension through an ashless medium-texture filter paper, decanting as much of the liquid as possible. Wash the dish and the residue with hot 1 + 50 HCl and then with a minimum volume of distilled water until the washings are chloride free. Save all the washings. Set aside the filter paper with its residue.

3) Second filtration—Evaporate the filtrate and washings from the above operation to dryness in the original platinum dish and then bake the residue in a 110 C oven or over a hot plate for ½ hr. Repeat the steps in ¶ (2) above. Use a separate filter paper and a rubber policeman to aid in transferring all the residue from the dish to the filter.

4) Ignition—Transfer the two filter papers and residues to a covered platinum crucible, dry at 110 C, and ignite at 1,200 C to constant weight. Exercise caution to avoid mechanical loss of residue when first charring and burning off the paper. Cool the crucible in a desiccator, weigh it, and repeat the ignition and weighing until constant weight is attained. Record the weight of the crucible and the contents.

5) Volatilization with hydrofluoric acid—Thoroughly moisten the weighed residue in the crucible with distilled water. Add 4 drops 1 + 1 H_2SO_4, followed by 10 ml HF (measure the latter in a plastic graduated cylinder or pour an estimated 10 ml directly from the reagent bottle). Slowly evaporate the mixture to dryness over an air bath or hot plate in a hood and take precautions to avoid loss by spattering. Ignite the crucible to constant weight at 1,200 C. Record the weight of the crucible and contents.

b. PERCHLORIC ACID DEHYDRATION: Review ¶ 1a, preceding. Follow the procedure in ¶ 4a(1) above until all but 50 ml of the sample has been evaporated. Add 5 ml perchloric acid and evaporate until dense white fumes appear. (CAUTION: *Explosive—place a shield between personnel and the fuming dish.*)

Continue the dehydration for 10 min. Cool; add 5 ml 1 + 1 HCl and then 50 ml hot distilled water. Bring to a boil and filter through an ashless quantitative filter paper. Wash thoroughly ten times with hot distilled water and proceed as directed in ¶s 4a(4) and (5) preceding, with the single-filter paper. For routine work, the silica precipitate is often sufficiently pure for the purpose intended and may be weighed directly, omitting the HF volatilization. Make an initial check against the longer procedure, however, to be sure that the result is within the limits of accuracy required.

5. Calculation

Subtract the weight of crucible and contents after the HF treatment from the corresponding weight before HF treatment. The difference, *A*, in milligrams, is "loss on volatilization" and represents silica:

$$mg/l\ SiO_2 = \frac{A \times 1{,}000}{ml\ sample}$$

6. Precision and Accuracy

The accuracy is limited both by the finite solubility of silica in water under the conditions of the analysis and by the sensitivity of the analytical balance. If all the precautions are observed and if the analyst's quantitative technic is satisfactory, the precision will be approximately ± 0.2 mg SiO_2. If a 1-liter sample is taken for analysis, this will represent a precision of ± 0.2 mg/l

151 B. Molybdosilicate Method

1. General Discussion

a. Principle: Ammonium molybdate at approximately pH 1.2 reacts with silica, and also with any phosphate present, to produce heteropoly acids. Oxalic acid is added to destroy the molybdophosphoric acid but not the molybdosilicic acid. Even if phosphate is known to be absent, the addition of oxalic acid has been found highly desirable and is a mandatory step in both this method and Method C. The intensity of the yellow color is proportional to the concentration of "molybdate-reactive" silica. In at least one of its forms, silica does not react with molybdate even though it is capable of passing through filter paper and does not display noticeable turbidity. It is not known to what extent such "unreactive" silica occurs in waters, and the literature on the subject is contradictory. In the past, terms such as "colloidal," "crystalloidal" and "ionic" have been employed to distinguish between various forms of silica in waters, but such terminology cannot be substantiated. An optional step is included in the procedure to convert any "molybdate-unreactive" silica into the "molybdate-reactive" form. It must be clearly understood that these terms do not imply reactivity, or lack of it, toward *other* reagents or processes.

b. Interference: As apparatus and reagents may both contribute silica, care should be taken to avoid the use of glassware as much as possible and to use reagents low in silica. Also, a blank determination should be carried out to correct for silica so introduced. In both this method and Method C, tannin, large amounts of iron, color, turbidity, sulfide and phosphate are potential sources of interference. The treatment with oxalic acid eliminates interference from phosphate and decreases interference from tannin. If necessary, photometric compensation may be used to cancel interference from color or turbidity in the sample.

c. Minimum detectable concentration: Approximately 1 mg/l SiO_2 can be detected in 50-ml nessler tubes.

2. Apparatus

a. PLATINUM DISHES—100-ml.

b. COLORIMETRIC EQUIPMENT—One of the following is required:

1) Spectrophotometer, for use at 410 mμ, providing a light path of 1 cm or longer.

2) Filter photometer, providing a light path of 1 cm or longer and equipped with a violet filter having maximum transmittance near 410 mμ.

3) Nessler tubes, matched, 50-ml, tall form.

3. Reagents

For best results, set aside and use batches of chemicals low in silica. Store all reagents in plastic containers to guard against high blanks.

a. Sodium bicarbonate (also called sodium hydrogen carbonate), powder.

b. Sulfuric acid, 1N.

c. Hydrochloric acid, 1 + 1.

d. Ammonium molybdate reagent: Dissolve 10 g $(NH_4)_6Mo_7O_{24} \cdot 4H_2O$ in distilled water, with stirring and gentle warming, and dilute to 100 ml. Filter if necessary. Adjust to pH 7–8 with silica-free ammonium or sodium hydroxide and store in a polyethylene bottle to stabilize the reagent. (If the pH is not adjusted, a precipitate gradually forms. If the solution is stored in glass, silica may leach out and cause high blanks.) If necessary, prepare silica-free ammonium hydroxide by passing gaseous ammonia into distilled water contained in a plastic bottle.

e. Oxalic acid solution: Dissolve 10 g $H_2C_2O_4 \cdot 2H_2O$ in distilled water and dilute to 100 ml.

f. Stock silica solution: Dissolve 4.73 g sodium metasilicate nonahydrate, $Na_2SiO_3 \cdot 9H_2O$, in recently boiled and cooled distilled water and dilute to approximately 900 ml. Analyze 100.0-ml aliquots of this solution by Method A and adjust the remainder of the solution to contain exactly 1,000 mg/l SiO_2. Store this stock solution in a tightly stoppered plastic bottle.

g. Standard silica solution: Dilute 10.00 ml stock solution to 1,000 ml with freshly boiled and cooled distilled water; this solution contains 10.0 mg/l SiO_2, or 1.00 ml = 10.0 μg SiO_2. Store in a tightly stoppered plastic bottle.

h. Permanent color solutions:

1) POTASSIUM CHROMATE SOLUTION—Dissolve 630 mg K_2CrO_4 in distilled water and dilute to 1 liter.

2) BORAX SOLUTION—Dissolve 10 g sodium borate decahydrate, $Na_2B_4O_7 \cdot 10H_2O$, in distilled water and dilute to 1 liter.

4. Procedure

Convert any molybdate-unreactive silica to the reactive form or state by digesting the sample with sodium bicarbonate. Omit the digestion if all the silica in the sample is known to react with molybdate.

a. Digestion with sodium bicarbonate: Prepare a clear sample by filtration if necessary. Place a 50.0-ml portion, or a smaller aliquot diluted to 50 ml, in a 100-ml platinum dish. Add 200 mg silica-free sodium bicarbonate and digest on a steam bath for 1 hr. Cool and add slowly, with stirring, 2.4 ml H_2SO_4. Do not interrupt the analysis at this point but proceed *at once* with the remaining steps. Transfer the solution quantitatively to a 50-ml nessler tube and make up to the mark with distilled water. (Tall-form 50-ml nessler tubes are convenient for mixing even if the solution is subsequently transferred to an absorption cell for photometric measurement.)

b. Color development: To the prepared sample, or to 50.0 ml of an untreated sample if the conversion step is omitted, add in rapid succession 1.0 ml 1 + 1 HCl and 2.0 ml ammonium molybdate reagent; mix by inverting at least six times and allow the solution to stand for 5 to 10 min. Add 1.5 ml oxalic acid solution and mix thoroughly. Read the color after 2 min but before 15 min, measuring time from the addition of oxalic acid. Since the yellow color obeys Beer's law, measure photometrically or visually.

c. Preparation of standards: If sodium bicarbonate pretreatment is used for the samples, add to the standards 200 mg $NaHCO_3$ and 2.4 ml H_2SO_4, to compensate both for the slight amount of silica which may be introduced by the reagents and for the effect of the salt upon the intensity of the color.

d. Photometric measurement: Prepare a calibration curve from a series of approximately six standards to cover the optimum ranges cited in Table 151(1). Carry out the steps delineated in ¶ 4b above upon suitable aliquots of standard silica solution diluted to 50.0 ml in nessler tubes. Set the photometer at 100% transmittance (zero absorbance) with distilled water and read all standards, including a reagent blank, against the distilled water. Plot micrograms of silica in the final (54.5 ml) developed solution against photometer readings. Run a reagent blank and at least one standard with each group of samples to confirm that the calibration curve previously established has not shifted.

e. Visual comparison: Make up a set of permanent artificial color standards, using potassium chromate and borax solutions. Mix the volumes of liquids specified in Table 151(2) and

TABLE 151(1): SELECTION OF LIGHT PATH LENGTH FOR VARIOUS SILICA CONCENTRATIONS

Light Path *cm*	Method B	Method C	
	Silica in 54.5-ml Final Volume *μg*	Silica in 56.5-ml Final Volume—*μg*	
		650 mμ Wavelength	815 mμ Wavelength
1	200–1,300	40–300	20–100
2	100–700	20–150	10–50
5	40–250	7–50	4–20
10	20–130	4–30	2–10

TABLE 151(2): PREPARATION OF PERMANENT COLOR STANDARDS FOR VISUAL DETERMINATION OF SILICA

Value in Silica *mg*	Potassium Chromate Solution *ml*	Borax Solution *ml*	Water *ml*
0.00	0.0	25	30
0.10	1.0	25	29
0.20	2.0	25	28
0.40	4.0	25	26
0.50	5.0	25	25
0.75	7.5	25	22
1.0	10.0	25	20

place them in well-stoppered, appropriately labeled 50-ml nessler tubes. Verify the correctness of these permanent artificial standards by comparing them visually against standards prepared by carrying out determinations upon aliquots of the standard silica solution. Use the permanent artificial color standards only for visual comparison, never to calibrate a photometer.

f. Correction for color or turbidity: Prepare a special blank for every sample that needs such correction. Carry two identical aliquots of each such sample through the procedure, including sodium bicarbonate treatment if this is elected. To one aliquot add all reagents as directed in ¶ 4b preceding. To the blank aliquot, add hydrochloric and oxalic acids but no molybdate. Null the photometer with the aliquot blank containing no molybdate before reading the absorbance or transmittance of the molybdate-treated sample.

5. Calculation

$$\text{mg/l } SiO_2 = \frac{\mu g\ SiO_2}{\text{ml sample}}$$

Report whether or not sodium bicarbonate digestion was involved in the colorimetric determination.

6. Precision and Accuracy

A synthetic unknown sample containing 5.0 mg/l SiO_2, 10 mg/l chloride, 200 μg/l ammonia N, 1.0 mg/l nitrate N, 1.5 mg/l organic N, and 10.0 mg/l phosphate in distilled water was determined by the molybdosilicate method, with a relative standard deviation of 14.3% and a relative error of 7.8% in 19 laboratories.

Another synthetic unknown sample containing 15.0 mg/l SiO_2, 200 mg/l chloride, 800 μg/l ammonia N, 1.0 mg/l nitrate N, 800 μg/l organic N, and 5.0 mg/l phosphate in distilled water was determined by the molybdosilicate method, with a relative standard deviation of 8.4% and a relative error of 4.2% in 19 laboratories.

A third synthetic unknown sample containing 30.0 mg/l SiO_2, 400 mg/l chloride, 1.50 mg/l ammonia N, 1.0 mg/l nitrate N, 200 μg/l organic N, and 500 μg/l phosphate in distilled water was determined by the molybdosilicate method, with a relative standard deviation of 7.7% and a relative error of 9.8% in 20 laboratories.

All results were obtained following the digestion of the sample with sodium bicarbonate.

151 C. Heteropoly Blue Method

1. General Discussion

a. Principle: The principles outlined under Method B, ¶ 1a, also apply to this method. The yellow molybdosilicic acid is reduced by means of aminonaphtholsulfonic acid to heteropoly blue. The blue color is more intense than the yellow color of Method B and provides increased sensitivity.

b. Interference: The problems of interference discussed under Method B, ¶ 1b, apply to this method.

c. Minimum detectable concentration: Approximately 20 μg/l SiO_2 can be detected in 50-ml nessler tubes.

2. Apparatus

a. PLATINUM DISHES—100-ml.

b. COLORIMETRIC EQUIPMENT—One of the following is required:

1) Spectrophotometer, for use at approximately 815 mμ. The color system also obeys Beer's law at 650 mμ, with appreciably reduced sensitivity, in the event the instrument available cannot be operated at the optimum wavelength. A light path of 1 cm or longer yields satisfactory results.

2) Filter photometer, provided with a red filter exhibiting maximum transmittance in the wavelength range of 600–815 mμ. Sensitivity improves with increasing wavelength. A light path of 1 cm or longer yields satisfactory results.

3) Nessler tubes, matched, 50-ml, tall form.

3. Reagents

For best results, set aside and use batches of chemicals low in silica. Because of the sensitivity of the method, store all reagents in plastic containers to guard against high blanks. Be on the alert for distilled water which may contain detectable silica after storage in glass.

All of the reagents listed in Section 151B.3 are required, and in addition:

a. Reducing agent: Dissolve 500 mg 1-amino-2-naphthol-4-sulfonic acid and 1 g sodium sulfite, Na_2SO_3, in 50 ml distilled water, with gentle warming if necessary; add this to a solution of 30 g sodium bisulfite, $NaHSO_3$, in 150 ml distilled water. Filter into a plastic bottle. Discard the solution when it becomes dark. Prolong reagent life by storing in a refrigerator and away from light. Avoid aminonaphtholsulfonic acid that is incompletely soluble or that produces reagents which are dark even when freshly prepared; such material is not suitable for silica determinations.*

4. Procedure

a. Color development: Proceed as in Section 151B.4a and b up to and including the words, "Add 1.5 ml oxalic acid solution and mix thoroughly." Measuring time from the moment of addition of oxalic acid, wait for at least 2 min, but not more than 15 min; then add 2.0 ml reducing agent and mix thoroughly. After 5 min, measure the blue color, which is stable for 12 hr and conforms to Beer's law, photometrically or visually. If sodium bicarbonate pretreatment is used, follow Section 151B.4c.

b. Photometric measurement: Prepare a calibration curve from a series of approximately six standards to cover the optimum range indicated in Table 151(1). Carry out the steps described above upon suitable aliquots of standard silica solution diluted to the mark of 50-ml nessler tubes. Null the photometer with distilled water and read all the standards, including a reagent blank, against the distilled water. If it is necessary to correct for color or turbidity in a sample, consult Section 151B.4f. To the special blank add hydrochloric and oxalic acids, but no molybdate or reducing agent. Plot micrograms of silica in the final 56.5-ml developed solution against photometer readings. Run a reagent blank and at least one standard with each group of samples to check the calibration curve.

c. Visual comparison: Prepare a

* Eastman No. 360 has been found satisfactory.

series of not less than twelve standards, covering the range 0 to 120 $\mu g\ SiO_2$ by placing the calculated volumes of standard silica solution in 50-ml nessler tubes, diluting to the mark with distilled water, and developing the color as described in ¶ a preceding.

5. Calculation

$$mg/l\ SiO_2 = \frac{\mu g\ SiO_2}{ml\ sample}$$

Report whether or not sodium bicarbonate digestion was involved in the colorimetric determination.

6. Precision and Accuracy

A synthetic unknown sample containing 5.0 mg/l SiO_2, 10 mg/l chloride, 200 μg/l ammonia N, 1.0 mg/l nitrate N, 1.5 mg/l organic N, and 10.0 mg/l phosphate in distilled water was determined by the heteropoly blue method, with a relative standard deviation of 27.2% and a relative error of 3.0% in 11 laboratories.

A second synthetic unknown sample containing 15.0 mg/l SiO_2, 200 mg/l chloride, 800 μg/l ammonia N, 1.0 mg/l nitrate N, 800 μg/l organic N, and 5.0 mg/l phosphate in distilled water was determined by the heteropoly blue method, with a relative standard deviation of 18.0% and a relative error of 2.9% in 11 laboratories.

A third synthetic unknown sample containing 30.0 mg/l SiO_2, 400 mg/l chloride, 1.50 mg/l ammonia N, 1.0 mg/l nitrate N, 200 μg/l organic N, and 500 μg/l phosphate in distilled water was determined by the heteropoly blue method, with a relative standard deviation of 4.9% and a relative error of 5.1% in 10 laboratories.

All results were obtained following the digestion of the sample with sodium bicarbonate.

151 D. Bibliography

General

ROY, C. J. 1945. Silica in natural waters. *Amer. J. Sci.* 243:393.

VAIL, J. G. 1952. *The Soluble Silicates, Their Properties and Uses.* Reinhold Publishing Corp., New York, Vol. 1, pp. 95–97, 160–161.

Gravimetric Method

HILLEBRAND, W. F. et al. 1953. *Applied Inorganic Analysis* (2nd ed.). John Wiley & Sons, New York, Chapter 43.

KOLTHOFF, I. M., E. J. MEEHAN, E. B. SANDELL & S. BRUCKENSTEIN. 1969. *Quantitative Chemical Analysis* (4th ed.). Macmillan Co., New York.

Colorimetric Methods

DIENERT, F. & F. WANDENBULCKE. 1923. On the determination of silica in waters. *Bull. Soc. Chim. France* 33:1131; *Compt. Rend.* 176:1478.

———. 1924. A study of colloidal silica. *Compt. Rend.* 178:564.

SWANK, H. W. & M. G. MELLON. 1934. Colorimetric standards for silica. *Ind. Eng. Chem.,* Anal. Ed. 6:348.

TOURKY, A. R. & D. H. BANGHAM. 1936. Colloidal silica in natural waters and the "silicomolybdate" colour test. *Nature* 138:587.

BIRNBAUM, N. & G. H. WALDEN. 1938. Coprecipitation of ammonium silicomolybdate and ammonium phosphomolybdate. *J. Amer. Chem. Soc.* 60:66.

KAHLER, H. L. 1941. Determination of soluble silica in water: A photometric method. *Ind. Eng. Chem.,* Anal. Ed. 13:536.

NOLL, C. A. & J. J. MAGUIRE. 1942. Effect

of container on soluble silica content of water samples. *Ind. Eng. Chem.*, Anal. Ed. 14:569.

SCHWARTZ, M. C. 1942. Photometric determination of silica in the presence of phosphates. *Ind. Eng. Chem.*, Anal. Ed. 14:893.

BUNTING, W. E. 1944. Determination of soluble silica in very low concentrations. *Ind. Eng. Chem.*, Anal. Ed. 16: 612.

STRAUB, F. G. & H. GRABOWSKI. 1944. Photometric determination of silica in condensed steam in the presence of phosphates. *Ind. Eng. Chem.*, Anal. Ed. 16:574.

GUITER, H. 1945. Influence of pH on the composition and physical aspects of the ammonium molybdates. *Compt. Rend.* 220:146.

BOLTZ, D. F. & M. G. MELLON. 1947. Determination of phosphorus, germanium, silicon, and arsenic by the heteropoly blue method. *Ind. Eng. Chem.*, Anal. Ed. 19:873.

MILTON, R. F. 1951. Formation of silicomolybdate. *Analyst* 76:431.

———. 1951. Estimation of silica in water. *J. Applied Chem.* (London) 1: (Suppl. No. 2) 126.

CARLSON, A. B. & C. V. BANKS. 1952. Spectrophotometric determination of silicon. *Anal. Chem.* 24:472.

KILLEFFER, D. H. & A. LINZ. 1952. *Molybdenum Compounds, Their Chemistry and Technology*. Interscience Publishers, New York, pp. 1–2, 42–45, 67–82, 87–92.

STRICKLAND, J. D. H. 1952. The preparation and properties of silicomolybdic acid. *J. Amer. Chem. Soc.* 74:862, 868, 872.

CHOW, D. T. W. & R. J. ROBINSON. 1953. The forms of silicate available for colorimetric determination. *Anal. Chem.* 25:646.

152 SILVER

Silver can cause argyria, a permanent, blue-gray discoloration of the skin and eyes which presents a ghostly appearance. Concentrations in the range of 0.4 to 1 mg/l have caused pathologic changes in the kidneys, liver, and spleen of rats. The silver concentration of U.S. drinking waters has been reported to vary between 0 and 2 μg/l with a mean of 0.13 μg/l. Relatively small quantities of silver are bactericidal or bacteriostatic and find limited use for the disinfection of swimming pool waters.

1) Selection of method: The atomic absorption spectrophotometric method is generally preferred for the silver determination. The dithizone method is useful in the absence of sophisticated instrumentation. The spectrographic method may be employed where the necessary equipment is available.

2) Sampling and storage: Samples should be examined as soon as possible after collection because of the silver loss which may occur through adsorption on the container walls. The addition of a small volume of nitric acid of known purity is advisable when sample storage time is excessive. Sample containers should be washed with 1 + 1 nitric acid and rinsed with silver-free water before use.

152 A. Atomic Absorption Spectrophotometric Method

See Metals, Section 129A.

152 B. Dithizone Method (TENTATIVE)

1. General Discussion

a. Principle: Twenty metals are capable of reacting with dithizone to produce colored coordination compounds. Under the proper conditions or upon the removal of all interferences, the reaction can be made selective for a desired substance. In this mixed-color method, a separation of the two colors is not attempted; either the green color of the dithizone or the yellow color of the silver dithizonate can be measured. In view of the sensitivity of the reaction and the numerous interferences among the common metals, the method is somewhat empirical and demands careful adherence to the procedure. The final color evaluation can be made visually or photometrically. The visual finish has been found as accurate as and more efficient than the photometric measurement because it circumvents the extra handling involved with a photometer. The use of cells having a volume greater than 1 ml requires final dilution with carbon tetrachloride or the selection of a larger sample.

b. Interference: Ferric ion, residual chlorine and other oxidizing agents convert dithizone to a yellow-brown color. However, extraction of the silver along with other metals in a carbon tetrachloride solution of dithizone overcomes such oxidation interference from the contaminants which might be present in the water sample. The silver is then removed selectively from the other carry-over metals by the use of an ammonium thiocyanate solution. The extreme sensitivity, as well as silver's affinity for being adsorbed, makes it desirable to prepare and segregate glassware, especially for this determination, and to take unusual precautions at every step in the procedure. The necessity for checking and preventing contamination at all points cannot be overemphasized. Dithizone and the silver dithizonate both decompose rapidly in strong light; therefore, they should not be left in the light beam of the photometer for a longer period than is necessary. Direct sunlight should also be avoided at all times.

c. Minimum detectable concentration: 0.2 μg Ag.

2. Apparatus

a. Colorimetric equipment: One of the following is required—

1) SPECTROPHOTOMETER—for measurements at either 620 mμ or 462 mμ, and providing a light path of 1 cm.

2) FILTER PHOTOMETER—providing a light path of 1 cm and equipped with a red filter having maximum transmittance at or near 620 mμ or a blue filter having maximum transmittance at or near 460 mμ.

3) MICRO TEST TUBES—10-ml capacity, 1 × 7.5-cm size.

b. Separatory funnels, with a capacity of 500 ml or larger, and also funnels with a capacity of 60 ml, preferably with inert teflon stopcocks.

c. Glassware: All glassware, dishes and crucibles should first be treated with a sulfuric-chromic acid mixture and then washed in 1 + 1 HNO_3 to dissolve any trace of chromium or silver adsorbed on the glassware. After thorough rinsing with silver-free water, "Desicote" * or a similar silicone coat-

* Beckman Instruments, Inc.

ing fluid should be applied to establish a repellent surface. Omission of these extremely important steps will result in serious errors. If desired, glassware can be dried in an oven, but acetone rinses should be avoided because this solvent frequently contains enough interferences to affect the determination.

d. Vycor dishes or silica crucibles.

3. Reagents

a. Silver-free water: Use redistilled or deionized distilled water for the preparation of all reagents and dilutions.

b. Sulfuric acid, conc.

c. Carbon tetrachloride: Store in a glass container and do not allow contact with any metals before use. If this reagent is found to contain traces of an interfering metal, redistill in an all-pyrex apparatus.

d. Stock dithizone solution: Dissolve without heating 100 mg diphenylthiocarbazone † in 100 ml carbon tetrachloride, CCl_4, in a separatory funnel. Free the solution from copper as follows. To the solution contained in the separatory funnel, add 100 ml silver-free water and 5 ml conc ammonium hydroxide, and shake the mixture vigorously. Discard the CCl_4 layer and wash the alkaline liquid with two 5-ml portions CCl_4. Add 200 ml CCl_4 and then 1 + 1 hydrochloric acid in small portions until the aqueous layer is colorless on shaking. Run off the CCl_4 layer and store in the dark in a brown glass bottle. This solution contains 0.5 mg dithizone per ml.

e. Dithizone solution (I): Dilute 50 ml stock dithizone solution to 500 ml with CCl_4 and store in the dark in a brown glass bottle. This solution contains 50 μg dithizone per ml.

f. Dithizone solution (II): Dilute 2.00 ml stock dithizone solution to 250.0 ml with CCl_4. Store in the dark in a brown glass bottle. This solution contains 0.4 μg dithizone per ml.

g. Ammonium thiocyanate reagent: Dissolve 10 g NH_4CNS in silver-free water to which 5 ml conc H_2SO_4 have been added and dilute to 500 ml with silver-free water. Store this solution in a bottle containing 25 ml dithizone solution (I).

h. Nitric acid, 1N.

i. Urea solution: Dissolve 10 g $(NH_2)_2CO$ in silver-free water and dilute to 100 ml. Store in a bottle containing 25 ml dithizone solution (I). Discard the solution upon the formation of a red film, which makes the pipeting of a clear solution impossible.

j. Hydroxylamine sulfate solution: Dissolve 20 g $(NH_2OH)_2 \cdot H_2SO_4$ in silver-free water and dilute to 100 ml. Store in a bottle containing 25 ml dithizone solution (I).

k. Sulfuric acid, 1N.

l. Stock silver solution: Dissolve 157.4 mg anhydrous silver nitrate, $AgNO_3$, in silver-free water to which 14 ml conc H_2SO_4 have been added and dilute to 1,000 ml with silver-free water; 1.00 ml = 100 μg Ag.

m. Standard silver solution: Immediately before use, dilute 10.00 ml stock solution to 1,000 ml with silver-free water; 1.00 ml = 1.00 μg Ag.

4. Procedure

a. Sample treatment: To 100 ml sample in a 500-ml separatory funnel add 11 ml conc H_2SO_4. Extract the silver by adding 5 ml dithizone solution (I) and shaking for 1 min. Collect

† Eastman No. 3092 or equivalent.

the organic phase and any scum in a 25-ml centrifuge tube. Transfer the scum formed to the centrifuge tube because it may contain an appreciable amount of silver. Repeat the extraction twice more with 5-ml portions of dithizone solution (I) and add the extracts and scum to the centrifuge tube. Reject the aqueous phase. If a larger sample is required, use two centrifuge tubes to collect the dithizone extracts. For a 500-ml sample, use at least two 5-ml portions dithizone solution (I). Centrifuge, discard the aqueous phase, and add 2 ml silver-free water. Recentrifuge and discard the aqueous phase. Transfer the silver dithizonate layer to a 60-ml separatory funnel. Add 4 ml ammonium thiocyanate reagent to the centrifuge tube to collect any remaining extract, gently agitate, and transfer quantitatively to the separatory funnel. Shake for 1 min and with a suction pipet transfer as much of the aqueous phase as possible to a Vycor dish. Repeat the addition of 4 ml ammonium thiocyanate reagent, gently agitate, and transfer the aqueous phase two more times. Run off the organic layer and add the last few drops of the aqueous phase to the dish. Add 1.5 ml conc H_2SO_4 and evaporate to dryness by first evaporating to fumes by heating from above with an infrared lamp and then by heating the sample from below with a hot plate and above with an infrared lamp. Keep the heating temperature low enough to prevent bumping. Add 0.6 ml 1*N* HNO_3 and warm to dissolve all the solid residue. Add 1 ml each of urea and hydroxylamine sulfate solutions, and digest the resultant solution for 5 min near the boiling point, adding silver-free water dropwise to prevent caking. Allow the solution to cool to room temperature. Transfer the solution to a 10-ml micro test tube, rinsing the Vycor dish twice with 2-ml portions 1*N* H_2SO_4.

b. Extraction of silver: Add 1 ml dithizone solution (II) and extract the silver by agitation of the organic and aqueous phases together for 2 min with the aid of a thin glass rod flattened at the bottom. If the organic phase has a greenish hue, the amount of silver can be estimated as less than 1.5 μg. If the organic phase is a clear yellow (showing that there is no excess of dithizone), add further 1-ml portions dithizone solution (II) and repeat the extraction until a mixed color is obtained. Record the total volume, *A*, of dithizone solution (II) used.

c. Visual colorimetric estimation: Prepare the standards by placing in each of the nine micro test tubes 1 ml dithizone solution (II) and then 0, 0.20 . . . 1.60 ml standard silver solution, and 3.0, 2.8 . . . 1.4 ml 1*N* H_2SO_4. Extract the silver as described in ¶ 4b above, starting with the solution of lowest concentration.

d. Photometric measurement: Prepare a standard curve by adding known amounts of silver in the range 0.20 to 1.50 μg to 0.3 ml 1*N* HNO_3, 1 ml each of urea and hydroxylamine sulfate solutions. After the addition of 1 ml dithizone solution (II), extract the silver, using the same method as with the samples. Measure the absorbance at or near 620 mμ, using special cells of 1-cm light path but of reduced width so as to contain, when full, no more than about 1 ml. Zero the spectrophotometer on a cell containing dithizone solution (II) at an absorbance reading of 1.0 (or 10% transmittance) and read the samples and standards against this setting. Since the samples and standards will give a lesser absorbance reading, plot the difference between the constant absorbance of 1.0 for the dithizone and the absorbance readings for each standard and sample in order to obtain a positive-sloping standard curve.

e. Subtract the blank value obtained by carrying 100 ml silver-free water through the entire process.

5. Calculation

$$\text{mg/l Ag} = \frac{\mu\text{g Ag}}{\text{ml sample}} \times A$$

where A = total volume of dithizone solution (II) used to extract the silver for the final colorimetric measurement.

6. Precision and Accuracy

A synthetic unknown sample containing 150 μg/l Ag, 500 μg/l Al, 50 μg/l Cd, 110 μg/l Cr, 470 μg/l Cu, 300 μg/l Fe, 70 μg/l Pb, 120 μg/l Mn and 650 μg/l Zn in distilled water was determined by the dithizone method, with a relative standard deviation of 61.0% and a relative error of 66.6% in 14 laboratories.

152 C. Spectrographic Method (TENTATIVE)

1. General Discussion

a. Principle: A sample of potable water is diluted with lithium sulfate solution, and a palladium solution is added as an internal standard. Standards are made by adding appropriate amounts of silver to a potable-water blank with less than 0.5 μg/l silver and diluting this with the lithium sulfate spectrobuffer solution and the palladium internal-standard solution. The diluted sample is evaporated in a glass beaker to dryness in a 150 C oven. The residue is scraped loose and crushed to homogeneity with a spatula, and an aliquot is transferred to a platform graphite electrode and arced to completion. Spectrogram densitometer readings are made on the Ag 3280.7 and the Pd 3242.7 line transmittances, and are converted to a ratio of line intensities from emulsion calibration data. The Ag/Pd intensity ratio is converted to μg/l Ag from the standard working curve. The method is suitable for the determination of silver in the concentration range 10–500 μg/l.

b. Interference: No elements in the concentrations encountered in potable water interfere.

c. Minimum detectable concentration: 0.2 μg Ag. With a 20-ml sample this represents 10 μg/l Ag. The 20-ml Li_2SO_4 solution produces 114 mg residue at 150 C. A 20-ml sample for most potable waters produces about 7 mg residue or a 6% contribution to the matrix. If a sample with half the total residue is determined, 40 ml can be taken and 5 μg/l Ag can be determined. The upper concentration limit can be extended by diluting the sample appropriately with a low-silver (less than 0.5 μg/l Ag) potable-water blank, such as is used to make up the standards.

2. Apparatus

Any commercially available spectrographic equipment meeting the following specifications is satisfactory:

a. Excitation: Excitation is provided by an ARL Multisource * Model No. 5700, or equivalent, adjusted to give a fully rectified d-c arc discharge, 13 amp at 300 V.

b. Spectrograph: The ARL 1.5-m grating spectrograph, or equivalent, with a reciprocal linear dispersion of 7 angstroms (Å) per millimeter over the 2,300–4,500 Å spectral range. For this method, only the 3,200–3,300 Å region is utilized.

c. Electrode system: The lower sample electrode (anode) is a ¼-in. diameter, high-purity graphite preform, 30-degree angle platform with center post,† and the upper is a ¼-in. diameter (a slightly smaller diameter in the upper electrode may be preferable in instances of trouble caused by arc wandering), high-purity graphite preform with center post and 3/36-in. diameter undercut. The analytical gap is maintained at 5 mm.

d. Recording equipment: The spectrum is recorded on Eastman SA No. 2 film or plates, or No. 1 film or plates, or equivalent.

e. Densitometer: Transmittance readings of spectral lines are measured with the ARL No. 5400 film densitometer or equivalent.

f. Developing equipment: Films are developed in a thermostatically controlled, rocking developing machine, washed in a film washer, and dried in a stream of warm air.

g. Calculating equipment: A sliding-scale calculating board is used to convert transmittance readings to intensity ratios based on film calibration data.

* Manufactured by Applied Research Labs., Glendale, Calif.

† United Carbon Products, Bay City, Mich., Nos. 104U and 104L, or National Carbon Co., New York, N.Y., Nos. L3948 and L3963.

h. Beakers, 250-ml, tall electrolytic type, Corning No. 1140, or equivalent.

i. Balance, capable of weighing to 0.1 mg.

3. Reagents

a. Palladium internal-standard solution: Dissolve 66.7 mg palladium chloride, $PdCl_2$, in 10 ml 0.1*N* HCl by heating up to 60 C and then dilute with distilled water to 1,000 ml. This solution contains 40 mg/l Pd.

b. Lithium sulfate solution: Dissolve 5.5 g $Li_2SO_4 \cdot H_2O$ in 1 liter distilled water. This solution contains 4.75 g/l Li_2SO_4 and yields a residue of 5.7 mg/ml at 150 C.

c. Cementing solution: Dissolve 39 g sucrose in 300 ml absolute methyl alcohol and 100 ml distilled water.

d. Stock silver solution: Dissolve 126.0 mg anhydrous silver nitrate, $AgNO_3$, in distilled water and dilute to 1,000 ml. This solution contains 80.0 mg/l Ag.

e. Standard silver solution: Dilute 5.00 ml stock silver solution to 1,000 ml with distilled water. Store overnight to allow the plating-out process to reach equilibrium. Discard this dilute solution and make again in the same flask just before using. This solution contains 400 μg/l Ag, or 0.40 μg Ag per 1.00 ml.

f. Low-silver potable-water blank: Use a potable water with about 250–450 mg/l total residue containing less than 0.5 μg/l Ag to make up the silver standards. Determine the silver concentration in the blank water by a semiquantitative spectrographic method. This range of total residue enables samples of potable water with approximately 150–800 mg/l total residue to be analyzed within 5% from the same standard working curve. When markedly different types of waters are to be analyzed, a similar type of blank water must be used to make the standard working curve.

4. Procedure

a. Preparation of sample for arcing: Take a sample containing 10–500 μg/l Ag and 150–800 mg/l total residue. See ¶s 1c and 3f for the analysis of other waters.

1) DETERMINATION OF TOTAL RESIDUE—Determine the amount of total residue in 20.0 ml of the water sample to be analyzed after evaporation, either by weighing the residue on evaporation of 20 ml at 150 C or by multiplying its specific conductance in micromhos by 0.62×0.020. (Example: If the specific conductance is 646 μmho, then $646 \times 0.62 \times 0.020 = 8.0$ mg total residue.)

2) SAMPLE TREATMENT AND EVAPORATION—Add 1.0 ml Pd internal-standard solution and 20 ml Li_2SO_4 solution to 20.0 ml sample to be analyzed in a 250-ml tall-type electrolytic beaker and evaporate to dryness in a 150 C oven. When the volume is down to about 5–10 ml, swirl the beaker a bit to redissolve the salts which have dried on the sides of the beaker, thus concentrating the residue as much as possible on the bottom.

3) PREPARATION OF RESIDUE—Scrape the residue in the beaker loose from the glass and grind to a homogeneous powder against the side of the beaker with a small stainless steel spatula or a silver-free monel spatula.

4) TRANSFER OF RESIDUE TO ELECTRODE—Weigh a 5.0-mg sample of the ground residue, transfer to the sample electrode, add 3 drops of the cementing solution, and heat over a spirit lamp or small burner until caramelized (until further heating does not produce steam and the residue smells like caramel). Sometimes it is easier to transfer the residue to the electrode if the electrode is first wetted with 1 drop of cementing solution.

b. Preparation of standards for arcing: Prepare exactly as the regular samples except that a standard sample is substituted for the 20.0 ml of sample to be analyzed [see ¶ 4a(2)]. Make the standard sample by adding 0.50, 2.00, 8.00 and 25.0 ml, respectively, of the standard silver solution to each of four 20-ml aliquots of the low-silver potable-water blanks, corresponding respectively to 10, 40, 160 and 500 μg/l Ag.

c. Spectrograph operations: Properly adjust the electrode system and operate the spectrograph and its accessories according to the manufacturer's instructions. Treat the sample and standards in the same manner.

1) EXCITATION—Set the following arc discharge-circuit constants for Multisource (see ¶ 2a): voltage, 300 V; capacitance, 62 microfarads; inductance, 460 microhenries; resistance, 20 ohms $(10 + 10)$; average current, 13 amp on short, 11–12 amp during run.

2) EXPOSURE CONDITIONS—In the spectral region of 2,300–4,500 Å, use 3,200–3,300 Å. The slit width and length depend on the spectrograph and densitometer used; however, a 55-μ width has been found satisfactory. Burn the sample and standards to completion (until the platform is gone). Use filters or sectors to expose to background (7.5% of total light has proved satisfactory).

d. Photographic processing: Develop and fix the film as follows:

emulsion, Eastman SA No. 2; developer, Eastman D-19, rocked 3 min at 68 F; stop bath, 50 ml conc (glacial) acetic acid diluted to 1 liter, 10 sec; fixing, Eastman F-5, 3 min; washing, running water, 3 min; drying, blower and heater, 5 min.

e. Estimation of silver concentration: Read the transmittance of the spectral lines Ag 3280.7Å and Pd 3242.7Å with the film densitometer. Convert the transmittance readings to intensity ratios based on film calibration data. Convert the Ag/Pd intensity ratio to mg/l Ag from the standard working curve.

f. Standard working curve: Plot mg Ag against the intensity ratio of Ag 3280.7 to Pd 3242.7 on log-log paper (2×2 cycles) with data from standard samples. Once the working curve is established, use it for all future samples unless they differ markedly (more than 100% in total residue) from the low-silver potable-water blank used to make up the standard samples.

5. Precision and Accuracy

Based on the fit of standard samples with the working curve and the precision of independent determinations, the accuracy of the method is estimated to be within about 10% of the true value.

152 D. Bibliography

General

WEST, F. K., P. W. WEST & F. A. IDDINGS. 1966. Adsorption of traces of silver on container surfaces. *Anal. Chem.* 38:1566.

DYCK, W. 1968. Adsorption of silver on borosilicate glass. Effect of pH and time. *Anal. Chem.* 40:454.

Dithizone Method

PIERCE, T. B. 1960. Determination of trace quantities of silver in trade effluents. *Analyst* 85:166.

Spectrographic Method

HARVEY, C. E. 1947. *A Method of Semi-quantitative Spectrographic Analysis.* Applied Research Laboratories, Glendale, Calif.

UMAN, G. A. 1963. Spectrochemical method for silver. *JAWWA* 55:205.

153 SODIUM

Sodium ranks sixth among the elements in order of abundance; therefore, it is present in most natural waters. The levels may vary from negligible to appreciable. Relatively high concentrations may be found in brines and hard waters softened by the sodium exchange process. The ratio of sodium to total cations is important in agriculture and human pathology. Soil permeability has been found to be detrimentally affected by a high sodium ratio, while certain diseases require water with a low sodium concentration.

A limiting concentration of 2 to 3 mg/l is recommended in feedwaters destined for high-pressure boilers. When necessary, sodium is removed by the hydrogen-exchange process or by distillation.

1. Selection of Method: The flame photometric method (*A*) is more rapid and sensitive and generally more accurate than the gravimetric method, especially for sodium concentrations below 10 mg/l; but a special instrument and much preliminary work are required before samples can be run routinely. The gravimetric method (*B*) is used if a flame photometer is not available or if a check on the flame photometric result by an independent method is desired.

2. Storage of sample: Alkaline samples or samples containing low sodium concentrations should be stored in polyethylene bottles in order to eliminate the possibility of contamination of the sample due to leaching of the glass container. Solutions attack glass and consequently become contaminated with sodium which is present in the glass.

153 A. Flame Photometric Method

1. General Discussion

a. Principle: Trace amounts of sodium can be determined in either a direct-reading or an internal-standard-type flame photometer at a wavelength of 589 mμ. The sample is sprayed into a gas flame and excitation is carried out under carefully controlled and reproducible conditions. The desired spectral line is isolated by the use of interference filters or by a suitable slit arrangement in light-dispersing devices such as prisms or gratings. The intensity of light is then measured by a phototube potentiometer or other appropriate circuit. The intensity of light at 589 mμ is approximately proportional to the concentration of the element. The calibration curve may be linear but has a tendency to level off in the upper reaches. The optimum lithium concentration may vary among individual flame photometers operating on the internal-standard principle and must therefore be ascertained for the instrument at hand. In those cases where the alignment of the wavelength dial with the prism is not precise in the available photometer, the exact wavelength setting, which may be slightly more or less than 589 mμ, can be determined from the maximum needle deflection and then used for the emission measurements.

b. Interference: Burner-clogging particulate matter should be removed from the sample by filtration through a quantitative filter paper of medium retentiveness. Incorporation of a nonionic detergent in the lithium standard may assure proper aspirator function.

The problem of interference can be minimized by the following approaches:

1) Operation in the lowest practical sodium range.

2) Resort to the internal-standard or standard-addition technic.

3) Addition of radiation buffers.

4) Introduction of identical amounts

of the same interfering substances into the calibration standards that are present in the sample.

5) Preparation of a family of calibration curves embodying added concentrations of a common interference.

6) Application of an experimentally determined correction in those instances where the sample contains a single important interference.

7) Removal of the interfering ions.

The standard-addition approach is described in the flame photometric method for strontium. Its use involves the addition of an identical portion of the sample to each standard and determination of the sample concentration by mathematical or graphical evaluation of the calibration data.

Potassium and calcium have been reported to interfere with the sodium determination by the internal-standard method if the potassium-to-sodium ratio is 5:1 or greater and the calcium-to-sodium ratio is 10:1 or higher. When these ratios are exceeded, the calcium and potassium should be determined first so that the approximate concentration of interfering ions may be added, if necessary, to the sodium calibration standards. Magnesium interference does not appear until the magnesium-to-sodium ratio exceeds 100, a rare occurrence. Among the common anions capable of causing radiation interference are chloride, sulfate and bicarbonate in relatively large amounts.

c. Minimum detectable concentration: The better flame photometers can be used for the determination of sodium levels approximating 100 μg/l. With proper modifications in technic the sodium level can be extended to 10 μg/l or lower.

2. Apparatus

a. Flame photometer, either direct-reading or internal-standard type.

b. Glassware: Rinse all glassware with 1 + 15 nitric acid followed by several portions of deionized distilled water to avoid contamination errors.

3. Reagents

In order to minimize sodium pickup, store all solutions in plastic bottles. Use small containers to reduce the amount of dry element which may be picked up from the bottle walls when the solution is poured. Shake each container thoroughly to wash the accumulated salts from the walls before the solution is poured.

a. Deionized distilled water: Use deionized distilled water for the preparation of all reagents, calibration standards, and as dilution water.

b. Stock sodium solution: Dissolve 2.542 g NaCl dried at 140 C and dilute to 1,000 ml with deionized distilled water to form a solution containing 1.00 mg Na per 1.00 ml.

c. Intermediate sodium solution: Dilute 10.00 ml stock sodium solution with deionized distilled water to 100.0 ml to form a solution containing 100 μg Na per 1.00 ml. Use this intermediate solution for preparing the calibration curve in the sodium range of 1–10 mg/l.

d. Standard sodium solution: Dilute 10.00 ml intermediate sodium solution with deionized distilled water to 100 ml to form a solution containing 10.0 μg Na per 1.00 ml. Use this solution for preparing the calibration curve in the sodium range of 0.1–1.0 mg/l.

e. Standard lithium solution: Use either lithium chloride (1) or lithium nitrate (2) for the preparation of the standard lithium solution, which contains 1.00 mg Li per 1.00 ml.

1) Dry LiCl overnight in an oven at 105 C. Weigh rapidly 6.109 g, dissolve in deionized distilled water, and dilute to 1,000 ml.

2) Dry $LiNO_3$ overnight in an oven at 105 C. Weigh rapidly 9.935 g, dissolve in deionized distilled water, and dilute to 1,000 ml.

Prepare a new calibration curve whenever the standard lithium solution must be replenished. Where circumstances warrant, alternatively prepare a standard lithium solution containing 2.00 mg or even 5.00 mg Li per 1.00 ml.

4. Procedure

a. Precautions: Locate the flame photometer in an area away from direct sunlight or the constant light emitted by an overhead fixture, and free of drafts, dust and tobacco smoke. Guard against contamination arising from corks, filter paper, perspiration, soap, cleansers, cleaning mixtures and inadequately rinsed apparatus.

b. Instrument operation: Because the differences between the makes and models of satisfactory flame photometers render impossible the formulation of detailed instructions applicable to every instrument, follow the manufacturer's recommendation for the selection of the proper photocell and wavelength, the adjustment of the slit width and sensitivity, the appropriate fuel and air or oxygen pressures, and the steps for warm-up, correcting for flame background, rinsing of the burner, ignition of sample, and measurement of emission intensity.

c. Direct-intensity measurement: Prepare a blank and sodium calibration standards in stepped amounts in any of the following applicable ranges: 0–1.0, 0–10, or 0–100 mg/l. Starting with the highest calibration standard and working toward the most dilute, measure the emission at 589 mμ. Repeat the operation with both the calibration standards and the samples a sufficient number of times to secure a reliable average reading for each solution. Construct a calibration curve from the sodium standards. Determine the sodium concentration of the sample by consulting the calibration curve. Where a large number of samples must be run routinely, reference to the calibration curve provides sufficiently accurate results. If greater precision and accuracy are desired, and ample time is available, resort to the bracketing approach described in ¶ 4e below.

d. Internal-standard measurement: To a carefully measured volume of the sample (or a diluted aliquot of the sample), each sodium calibration standard, and a blank, add, with a volumetric pipet, an appropriate volume of standard lithium solution. Then follow all the steps prescribed in ¶ 4c above for the direct-intensity measurement.

e. Bracketing approach: From the calibration curve, select and prepare the sodium standards that immediately bracket the emission intensity of the sample. Determine the emission intensities of the bracketing standards (one sodium standard slightly less and the other slightly greater than the sample) and the sample as nearly simultaneously as possible. Repeat the determination on both the bracketing standards and the sample. Calculate the sodium concentration by the equation presented in ¶ 5b, and average the several findings for a final result.

5. Calculation

a. For direct reference to the calibration curve:

$$\text{mg/l Na} = (\text{mg/l Na in aliquot}) \times D$$

b. For the bracketing approach:

$$\text{mg/l Na} = \left(\frac{(B - A)(s - a)}{(b - a)} + A\right) D$$

in which

B = mg/l Na concentration of the upper bracketing standard
A = mg/l Na concentration of the lower bracketing standard
b = emission intensity of the upper bracketing standard
a = emission intensity of the lower bracketing standard
s = emission intensity of the sample
D = dilution ratio

$$= \frac{\text{ml sample} + \text{ml distilled water}}{\text{ml sample}}$$

6. Precision and Accuracy

A synthetic unknown sample containing 19.9 mg/l Na, 108 mg/l Ca, 82 mg/l Mg, 3.1 mg/l K, 241 mg/l chloride, 250 μg/l nitrite N, 1.1 mg/l nitrate N, 259 mg/l sulfate, and 42.5 mg/l total alkalinity (contributed by $NaHCO_3$) was determined by the flame photometric method, with a relative standard deviation of 17.3% and a relative error of 4.0% in 35 laboratories.

153 B. Gravimetric Method

1. General Discussion

a. Principle: Sodium is precipitated as sodium zinc uranyl acetate hexahydrate, $NaC_2H_3O_2 \cdot Zn(C_2H_3O_2)_2 \cdot 3UO_2(C_2H_3O_2)_2 \cdot 6H_2O$, by adding a large volume of zinc uranyl acetate reagent, previously saturated with the sodium salt, to a small volume of the concentrated sample. To precipitate sodium quantitatively, at least 10 ml of reagent must be added for every 1 ml of sample and the mixture must be allowed to stand for at least 60 min. Because the solubility of sodium zinc uranyl acetate hexahydrate in water is fairly great, the precipitate, after being collected in a filter crucible, is first washed with successive small portions of the reagent solution saturated with the triple salt, and then with 95% ethyl alcohol, also saturated with the triple salt. Next, the precipitate is washed with diethyl ether to remove the alcohol, and finally a stream of air is drawn through the crucible to evaporate the ether. The precipitate is weighed in the air-dry state.

b. Interference: Lithium interferes by forming a slightly soluble salt with the reagent. Potassium interferes if there are more than 25 mg in the 1-ml solution being tested. Organic acids, such as oxalic, citric and tartaric, interfere, as do anions like phosphate which give precipitates with the reagent. Sulfate must be absent when much potassium is present, because potassium sulfate is only slightly soluble in the reagent. If the potassium and sulfate concentrations are known, the maximum possible error due to the precipitation of K_2SO_4 can be calculated. Usually this error will be negligible because the potassium concentration in potable water is generally low, and also because the calculation factor, 0.01495, for converting weight of sodium is very low. Upon evaporation of the sample, silica may, if present, become partially dehydrated and precipitate out. Except in extreme cases, the error caused by silica will be negligible for various reasons: (a) The precipitation of silica is by no means complete; (b) some of the dehydrated silica adheres strongly to the glass surface of the beaker and is not transferred to the crucible to be weighed with the sodium salt; (c) because of the high ratio of the weight of the triple salt to that of sodium, the slight increase in the weight of precipitate due to precipitated silica has a relatively small effect on the calculated sodium concentration. A method for compensation of errors caused by precipitation of uranyl phosphate and silica is described in the procedure.

2. Apparatus

a. Beakers, 20-ml, pyrex.

b. Fritted-glass crucibles, 30-ml, pyrex, of medium porosity; or porous porcelain crucibles.

c. Vacuum pump or aspirator, with manifold and individual petcocks.

3. Reagents

a. Zinc uranyl acetate reagent: Mix 2.7 ml conc (glacial) acetic acid with 100 ml distilled water. Add 10 g uranyl acetate dihydrate, $UO_2(C_2H_3O_2)_2 \cdot 2H_2O$, and 30 g zinc acetate dihydrate, $Zn(C_2H_3O_2)_2 \cdot 2H_2O$, to the solution and warm to dissolve. On cooling, add 2–3 mg sodium chloride, NaCl, allow the mixture to stand for 24 hr or more and filter off the precipitate of sodium zinc uranyl acetate, thus leaving the reagent saturated with the triple salt. Store the solution in a pyrex bottle.

b. Ethyl alcohol wash solution: Saturate 95% ethyl alcohol with pure sodium zinc uranyl acetate and decant or filter the solution just prior to use. Prepare the sodium zinc uranyl acetate by adding 25 ml zinc uranyl acetate reagent to 2 ml sodium chloride solution (10 mg NaCl), stirring, collecting the precipitate in a sintered-glass crucible, and washing 3 times with conc (glacial) acetic acid and finally 3 times with diethyl ether.

c. Diethyl ether.

4. Procedure

If necessary, remove any suspended matter from the sample by filtration. Select a sample volume containing less than 8 mg Na and less than 25 mg K. Pipet the clear sample into a 20- or 50-ml pyrex beaker and evaporate to dryness on a steam or hot water bath. Cool the residue to room temperature, add 1.0 ml distilled water and rub with a stirring rod. If the residue fails to dissolve, add more 1.0-ml increments of distilled water to put the residue into solution. Ignore a feathery turbidity of $CaSO_4$ at this point because of its subsequent solubility in the zinc uranyl acetate reagent.

Treat with zinc uranyl acetate reagent in the ratio of 10 ml reagent for each 1.0-ml increment of distilled water required to dissolve the residue. Mix, cover the beaker, and allow to stand for 1 hr. Stir periodically to prevent the formation of a supersaturated solution. Collect the precipitate under suction in a weighed medium-porosity sintered-glass crucible. Substitute a porous-bottomed porcelain filtering crucible if desired. Drain the filter as dry as possible under suction. Wash the beaker, crucible and precipitate 5 to 8 times with 2-ml portions of zinc uranyl acetate reagent. Drain the crucible completely after the last wash in order to remove traces of the zinc uranyl acetate reagent. Next wash 5 times with 2-ml portions of ethyl alcohol wash solution. Conclude the washing with 3 small portions of diethyl ether.

Continue the suction for a few minutes until the diethyl ether is volatilized and the precipitate is dry. Wipe the outside and inner bottom ring of the crucible with a cloth if salts have crystallized there. Transfer the crucible to the balance case and weigh after 10 to 15 min, and again 10 min later to check on the constancy of the weight. Return the crucible to the suction apparatus and dissolve the sodium zinc uranyl acetate by passing 100 ml warm distilled water in small portions through the filter. Dry the crucible with ethyl alcohol wash solution and diethyl ether, as previously directed, and reweigh. The difference in the weight before and after the distilled water treatment represents the weight of the sodium zinc uranyl acetate.

5. Calculation

$$\text{mg/l Na} = \frac{A \times 14.95}{\text{ml sample}}$$

where A = mg triple-salt precipitate.

6. Precision and Accuracy

A synthetic unknown sample containing 19.9 mg/l Na, 108 mg/l Ca, 82 mg/l Mg, 3.1 mg/l K, 241 mg/l chloride, 250 μg/l nitrite N, 1.1 mg/l nitrate N, 259 mg/l sulfate, and 42.5 mg/l total alkalinity (contributed by $NaHCO_3$) was determined by the gravimetric method, with a relative standard deviation of 11.3% and a relative error of 0.5% in four laboratories.

153 C. Bibliography

Flame Photometric Method

BARNES, R. B. et al. 1945. Flame photometry: A rapid analytical method. *Ind. Eng. Chem.,* Anal. Ed. 17:605.

BERRY, J. W., D. G. CHAPPELL & R. B. BARNES. 1946. Improved method of flame photometry. *Ind. Eng. Chem.,* Anal. Ed. 18:19.

PARKS, T. D., H. O. JOHNSON & L. LYKKEN. 1948. Errors in the use of a model 18 Perkin-Elmer flame photometer for the determination of alkali metals. *Anal. Chem.* 20:822.

BILLS, C. E. et al. 1949. Reduction of error in flame photometry. *Anal. Chem.* 21: 1076.

GILBERT, P. T., R. C. HAWES & A. O. BECKMAN. 1950. Beckman flame spectrophotometer. *Anal. Chem.* 22:772.

WEST, P. W., P. FOLSE & D. MONTGOMERY. 1950. Application of flame spectrophotometry to water analysis. *Anal. Chem.* 22:667.

FOX, C. L. 1951. Stable internal-standard flame photometer for potassium and sodium analyses. *Anal. Chem.* 23:137.

AMERICAN SOCIETY FOR TESTING AND MATERIALS. 1952. Symposium on flame photometry. Special Technical Pub. 116, ASTM, Philadelphia.

COLLINS, C. G. & H. POLKINHORNE. 1952. An investigation of anionic interference in the determination of small quantities of potassium and sodium with a new flame photometer. *Analyst* 77:430.

WHITE, J. U. 1952. Precision of a simple flame photometer. *Anal. Chem.* 24:394.

MAVRODINEANU, R. 1956. Bibliography on

analytical flame spectroscopy. *Applied Spectroscopy* 10:51.

MELOCHE, V. W. 1956. Flame photometry. *Anal. Chem.* 28:1844.

BURRIEL-MARTI, F. & J. RAMIREZ-MUNOZ. 1957. *Flame Photometry: A Manual of Methods and Applications.* D. Van Nostrand Co., Princeton, N. J.

DEAN, J. A. 1960. *Flame Photometry.* McGraw-Hill Publishing Co., New York.

Gravimetric Method

BARBER, H. H. & I. M. KOLTHOFF. 1928 and 1929. A specific reagent for the gravimetric determination of sodium. *J. Amer. Chem. Soc.* 50:1625; 51:3233.

KOLTHOFF, I. M., E. J. MEEHAN, E. B. SANDELL & S. BRUCKENSTEIN. 1969. *Quantitative Chemical Analysis* (4th ed.). Macmillan Co., New York.

154 SPECIFIC CONDUCTANCE

Specific conductance yields a measure of a water's capacity to convey an electric current. This property is related to the total concentration of the ionized substances in a water and the temperature at which the measurement is made. The nature of the various dissolved substances, their actual and relative concentrations, and the ionic strength of the water sample vitally affect the specific conductance.

An aqueous system containing dissociated molecules will conduct an electric current. In a direct-current field the positive ions migrate toward the negative electrode, while the negatively charged ions migrate toward the positive electrode. Most inorganic acids, bases and salts (such as hydrochloric acid, sodium carbonate and sodium chloride) are good conductors. Conversely, molecules of such organic compounds as sucrose and benzene do not dissociate in aqueous solution and therefore conduct a current very poorly, if at all.

Freshly distilled water has a specific conductance of 0.5 to 2 micromhos/cm, rising after a few weeks of storage to a value of 2 to 4 micromhos/cm. This increase from zero results principally from the absorption of atmospheric carbon dioxide, and to a lesser extent ammonia.

Most raw and finished waters in the United States exhibit a specific conductance from about 50 to 500 micromhos/cm, with highly mineralized water in the range of 500 to 1,000 micromhos/cm and even higher. Domestic sewage reflects to a degree the characteristics of the water supply serving the district. Some industrial wastes may have specific conductance values well in excess of 10,000 micromhos/cm.

A number of practical applications are made of specific conductance measurements, as follows:

a) The purity of distilled and deionized water can be checked by the determination.

b) The variations in the dissolved mineral concentration of raw water or wastewater samples can be quickly noted. The minor seasonal variations found in reservoir waters sharply contrast with the daily fluctuations prevailing in some polluted river waters. Sewage containing significant trade wastes may also evidence a considerable daily variation.

c) Conductivity measurements afford an idea of the aliquots which may prove useful for the common chemical determinations. They also offer a means for checking the results of a chemical analysis, as described in the Introduction, Section 100 C.2.

d) Specific conductance measurements make possible the determination of the amount of ionic reagent needed in certain precipitation and neutralization reactions, the end point being denoted by a change in the slope of the conductivity curve.

e) The amount of dissolved ionic matter in a sample may often be estimated by multiplying the specific conductance by an empirical factor. This factor may vary from 0.55 to 0.9, depending on the soluble components of the particular water and on the temperature of the measurement. Relatively high factors may be required for saline or boiler waters, whereas lower factors may apply where considerable hydroxide or free acid is present. Even though sample evaporation results in the change of bicarbonate to carbonate, an empirical factor is often derived for a comparatively constant water supply by dividing the dissolved residue by the specific conductance. The filtrable residue may be determined by evaporation. An approximation of the me/l of either cations or anions in some waters may be possible by multiplying the micromhos by 0.01.

1. General Discussion

The standard unit of electrical resistance is the ohm. The standard unit of electrical conductance is its inverse, the mho, or the recently adopted Siemen. Inasmuch as the measurement of conductance or resistance implies the use of two electrodes 1 cm square placed 1 cm apart, specific conductance is generally reported as micromhos/cm or microSiemens/cm, although the units micromhos or microSiemens alone are also widely accepted. A conductance cell and a Wheatstone bridge are essential for measuring the electrical resistances of the sample and of a potassium chloride solution of known specific conductance at the same temperature. Inasmuch as specific conductance varies directly with the temperature of the sample, the result is conventionally reported at 25 C. For control work, factors based on 0.01*M* potassium chloride, as shown in Figure 26, are frequently applied to correct to 25 C the specific conductance of simple water samples tested at any temperature from 0 to 30 C. A better curve

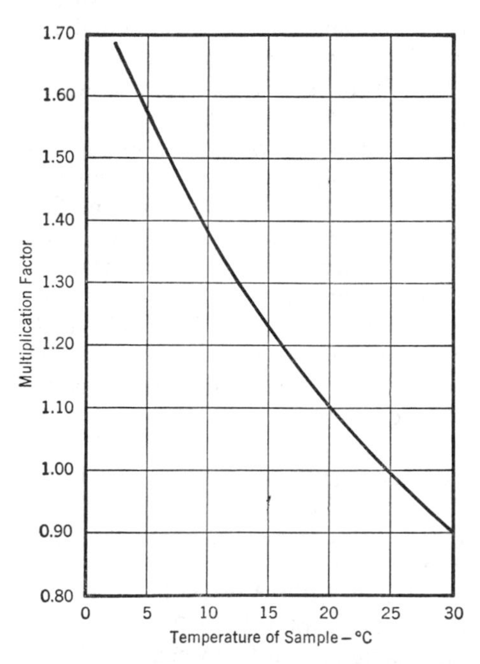

Figure 26. Factors for converting specific conductance of water to equivalent values at 25 C (based on 0.01*M* KCl solution).

will be obtained for a water or wastewater by chilling the sample to 0 C and then determining the specific conductance at intervals of a few degrees as the sample slowly warms to room temperature.

2. Apparatus

Self-contained conductance instruments meeting the specifications described in this section are available commercially and are suitable for conductance measurements.

a. Wheatstone bridge, capable of being read with an accuracy of 1% or better.

b. Source of electrical current: Either alternating or direct current may be used. A null indicator consisting of an a-c galvanometer or an electron-ray "magic eye" tube operates satisfactorily on 25 to 60 cycles, whereas an instrument incorporating a telephone receiver often requires 1,000 to 3,000 cycles. An isolating transformer will minimize electrical shock, equipment damage, and erroneous or erratic results when the current is derived from the electrical mains. Best results with direct current are obtained when the power input is limited to 1 watt.

c. Specific conductance cell:

1) PLATINUM-ELECTRODE TYPE—Specific conductance cells containing platinized electrodes are available in either the pipet or the immersion form. Cell choice will depend on the expected range of specific conductances. A cell constant of 0.1 is suitable for solutions of low conductivity, 100 micromhos/cm or less; a cell constant of 1 for solutions of moderate conductivity; and a cell constant of 10 for highly conducting solutions such as brines. In spite of the fact that the practical limits for measuring resistance are approximately 50 to 100,000 ohms, that cell should be used which will give an actual cell resistance in the range of 500 to 10,000 ohms. The range for the complete instrument assembly on hand should be checked experimentally by comparing the instrumental results with the true conductances of the potassium chloride solutions listed in Table 154 (1). New cells should be cleaned with chromic-sulfuric acid cleaning mixture and the electrodes platinized before use. Subsequently, they should be cleaned and replatinized whenever the readings become erratic or when inspection shows that any of the platinum black has flaked off. To platinize, prepare a solution of 1 g chloroplatinic acid (platinum chloride) and 12 mg lead acetate in 100 ml water. Immerse the electrodes in this solution and connect both to the negative terminal of a 1.5-V dry cell battery. Connect

TABLE 154(1): CONDUCTANCES OF POTASSIUM CHLORIDE SOLUTIONS AT 25 C *

Concentration M	Conductance (μmho/cm)	
	Equivalent	Specific
0	149.85	
0.0001	149.43	14.94†
0.0005	147.81	73.90
0.001	146.95	147.0
0.005	143.55	717.8
0.01	141.27	1,413
0.02	138.34	2,767
0.05	133.37	6,668
0.1	128.96	12,900
0.2	124.08	24,820
0.5	117.27	58,640
1	111.87	111,900

* Data drawn from Robinson & Stokes.[1]
† Computed from equation given in Lind et al.[2]

the positive side of the battery to a piece of platinum wire and dip the wire into the solution. The amount of current should be such that only a small quantity of gas is evolved. The electrolysis should be continued until both cell electrodes are coated with platinum black. The platinizing solution may be saved for subsequent use. The electrodes should be rinsed thoroughly and when not in use must be kept immersed in distilled water.

2) NONPLATINUM - ELECTRODE TYPE—Specific conductance cells containing electrodes constructed from durable common metals (stainless steel among others) are widely used for continuous monitoring and field studies.

d. Water bath, provided with racks of corrosion-resistant material, such as copper, brass, or stainless steel, in which tubes of samples may be held. Large test tubes are convenient for holding the samples.

3. Reagents

a. Standard potassium chloride, 0.0100*M*: Dissolve 745.6 mg anhydrous KCl in freshly boiled double-distilled water and make up to 1,000 ml at 25 C. This is the standard reference solution, which at 25 C has a specific conductance of 1,413 micromhos/cm. It is satisfactory for most waters when using a cell with a constant between 1 and 2. For other cell constants, stronger or weaker potassium chloride solutions listed in Table 154(1) will be needed. Store in glass-stoppered pyrex bottles.

4. Procedure

a. Temperature adjustment: Select a water bath of sufficient size to hold the required samples and standards, and locate it in an area where temperature fluctuations are minimal. Since the specific conductance varies about 2% per degree Centigrade, maintain the temperature of the water bath at 25 C for best results. If an exact 25 C is impossible to maintain, operate in the temperature range between 20 and 30 C.

Place four tubes of standard potassium chloride solution in the water bath. Place two tubes of each sample to be measured in the water bath and allow the tubes 30 min to reach thermal equilibrium.

b. Conductance measurement: Rinse the conductivity cell in three of the tubes of potassium chloride solution and measure the resistance of the fourth solution. Record this value as R_{KCl}. Next rinse the cell with one tube of the first water sample, being sure that the rinsing is very thorough, and measure the resistance of the second tube; proceed in the same way until all the water samples have been measured. Do not measure the resistance of the KCl solution again unless there is a temperature drift of more than a few tenths of a degree during the set of measurements. Repeat the KCl measurement, however, with every subsequent set of water samples. If samples are encountered which differ in conductivity by a factor of 5 or more from the conductivity of the KCl, minimize carry-over from one sample to the next by using three tubes of each sample. Where this is done, rinse the cell with two tubes and make the measurement in the third tube.

5. Calculation

a. The cell constant, *C,* is equal to the product of the measured resistance, in ohms, of the standard potassium chloride solution, and the specific conductance, in mhos per centimeter, of standard solution; $C = R_{KCl} \times 0.001413$ if the measurement is made at 25 C.

b. The specific conductance (mho/cm) of the water sample at 25 C is equal to the cell constant, *C*, divided by the resistance, in ohms, of the sample, R_s, measured at 25 C:

$$\text{Specific conductance} = \frac{C}{R_s}$$

The specific conductance of most waters is so low that it is standard practice to express it in micromhos/cm. The recently introduced unit of microSiemens/cm is equivalent to micromhos/cm.

c. If the temperature of measurement is not exactly 25 C, it may be more convenient to calculate the specific conductance at 25 C according to the equation:

$$\text{Specific conductance} = \frac{1{,}413 \times R_{KCl}}{R_s} \text{ micromhos/cm}$$

where R_{KCl} and R_s are measured at the same temperature, preferably near room temperature, and in the range from 20 to 30 C.

6. Precision and Accuracy

The precision and accuracy with which the conductance of water can be determined depends on the equipment being used. A precision and accuracy of about ±5% are possible with the better commercial instruments.

7. References

1. R. A. ROBINSON & R. H. STOKES. 1959. *Electrolyte Solutions* (2nd ed.). Academic Press, New York, p. 466.
2. J. E. LIND, J. J. ZWOLENIK & R. M. FUOSS. 1959. Calibration of conductance cells at 25 C with aqueous solutions of potassium chloride. *J. Amer. Chem. Soc.* 81:1557.

8. Bibliography

JONES, G. & B. C. BRADSHAW. 1933. The measurement of the conductance of electrolytes. V: A redetermination of the conductance of standard potassium chloride solutions in absolute units. *J. Amer. Chem. Soc.* 55:1780.

ROSSUM, J. R. 1949. Conductance method for checking accuracy of water analyses. *Anal. Chem.* 21:631.

WILCOX, L. V. 1950. Electrical conductivity. *JAWWA* 42:775.

155 STRONTIUM

A typical alkaline-earth element, strontium chemically resembles calcium and thereby causes a positive error in gravimetric and titrimetric methods for the determination of calcium. As strontium has a tendency to accumulate in the bone structure, radioactive strontium 90, with a half-life of 28 years, presents a well-recognized peril to health. Naturally occurring strontium is not radioactive. For this reason, the determination of strontium in a water supply should be supplemented by a radiologic measurement to exclude the possibility that the strontium content may originate from radioactive contamination (see Section 303).

Although most potable supplies contain little strontium, some well waters in the midwestern part of the United States have exhibited levels as high as 39 mg/l.

155 A. Flame Photometric Method (TENTATIVE)

1. General Discussion

a. Principle: The flame photometric method enables the determination of strontium in the small concentrations prevalent in natural water supplies. The strontium emission is measured at a wavelength of 460.7 mμ. Because the background intensity at a wavelength of 454 mμ equals that at 460.7 mμ, and is unaffected by the variable strontium concentration, the difference in readings obtained at these two wavelengths allows an estimate of the light intensity emitted by strontium.

b. Interference: The emission intensity is a linear function of the strontium concentration and also the concentration of the other constituents in the sample. The standard addition technic distributes the same ions throughout the standards and the unknown, thereby equalizing the radiation effect of possible interfering substances in the standards and the unknown.

c. Minimum detectable concentration: Strontium levels of about 0.2 mg/l can be detected by the flame photometric method without prior concentration of the sample by evaporation.

d. Sampling and storage: Polyethylene bottles are preferable for sample storage, although pyrex containers may also be used. Analyses should be performed as soon as possible after sample collection.

2. Apparatus

*a. Spectrophotometer,** equipped with photomultiplier tube and flame accessories.

3. Reagents

a. Stock strontium solution: Weigh into a 500-ml erlenmeyer flask 1.685 g anhydrous strontium carbonate, $SrCO_3$, powder. Place a funnel in the neck of the flask and add, a little at a time, 1 + 1 HCl until all the $SrCO_3$ has dissolved. Add 200 ml distilled water and boil for a few minutes to expel the CO_2. Cool, add a few drops of methyl red indicator, and adjust to the intermediate orange color by adding 3*N* NH_4OH or 1 + 1 HCl as required. Transfer quantitatively to a 1-liter volumetric flask and dilute to the mark with distilled water; 1.00 ml = 1.00 mg Sr.

b. Standard strontium solution: Dilute 25.00 ml stock strontium solution to 1,000 ml with distilled water; 1.00 ml = 25.0 μg Sr. Use this solution for preparing Sr standards in the 1–25 mg/l range.

c. Nitric acid, conc.

4. Procedure

a. Preparation of strontium standards: Add 25.0 ml of sample, containing less than 10 mg calcium or barium and less than 1 mg strontium, to 25.0 ml of each of a series of strontium standards. Use a minimum of four strontium standards from 0 mg/l to a concentration exceeding that of the sample. For most natural waters 0, 2.0, 5.0 and 10.0 mg/l Sr standards are sufficient. Brines may require a strontium series containing 0, 25, 50 and 75 mg/l. Dilute the brine suffi-

* Beckman Model DU or equivalent.

ciently to eliminate burner splatter and clogging. Best results are obtained when the strontium concentration of the sample does not exceed 100 mg/l.

b. Concentration of low-level strontium samples: With waters containing less than 2 mg/l Sr, concentrate the samples for best results. Add 3–5 drops conc HNO_3 to 250 ml sample and evaporate to about 25 ml. Cool and make up to 50.0 ml with distilled water. Proceed as in ¶ a above. The HNO_3 concentration in the sample prepared for atomization can approach 0.2 ml per 25 ml without producing interference.

c. Flame photometric measurement: Measure the emission intensity of the prepared samples (standards plus sample) at wavelengths of 460.7 and 454 mμ. Follow the manufacturer's instructions for correct operation of the instrument available for the determination.

5. Calculation

a. Plot the net intensity (reading at 460.7 mμ minus reading at 454 mμ) against the strontium concentration which was added to the unknown sample. Because the plot forms a straight calibration line that intersects the ordinate, the unknown strontium concentration can be computed from the equation:

$$\text{mg/l Sr} = \frac{A - B}{C} \times \frac{D}{E}$$

where A = sample emission-intensity reading at 460.7 mμ, B = background radiation reading at 454 mμ, C = slope of calibration line. The ratio D/E applies only when E ml of sample is evaporated to form a concentrate of 25.0 ml, the value for D.

b. Graphical method: The strontium concentration of the sample can also be evaluated by the graphical method illustrated in Figure 27. Plot

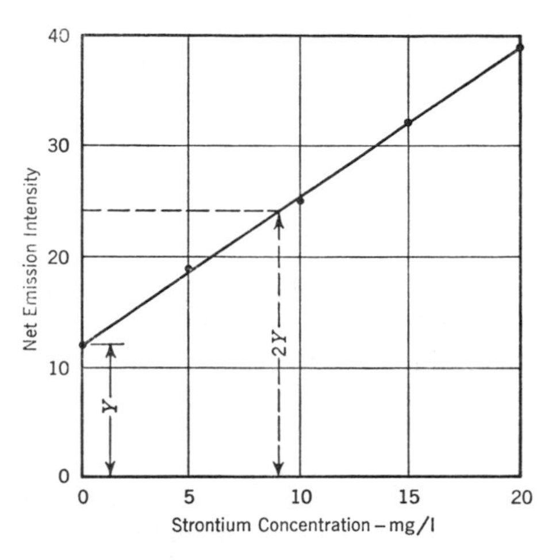

Figure 27. Graphical method of computing strontium concentration.

the net intensity against the strontium concentration which was added to the unknown sample. The calibration line in the example intersects the ordinate at 12. Thus, $Y = 12$ and $2Y = 24$. The strontium concentration of the unknown sample is found by locating the abscissa value of the point on the calibration line which has an ordinate value of 24. In the example, the strontium concentration is 9.0 mg/l.

c. Report a strontium concentration below 10 mg/l to the nearest 0.1 mg/l, and one above 10 mg/l to the nearest whole number.

6. Accuracy

Strontium concentrations in the range 12.0–16.0 mg/l can be determined with an accuracy within ± 1–2 mg/l.

155 B. Bibliography

CHOW, T. J. & T. G. THOMPSON. 1955. Flame photometric determination of strontium in sea water. *Anal. Chem.* 27:18.

NICHOLS, M. S. & D. R. MCNALL. 1957. Strontium content of Wisconsin municipal waters. *JAWWA* 49:1493.

HORR, C. A. 1959. A survey of analytical methods for the determination of strontium in natural water. *U. S. Geol. Survey Water Supply Paper* No. 1496A.

156 SULFATE

Sulfate is widely distributed in nature and may be present in natural waters in concentrations ranging from a few to several thousand mg/l. Mine drainage wastes may contribute high sulfate by virtue of pyrite oxidation. Because sodium and magnesium sulfate exert a cathartic action, the recommended sulfate concentration in potable supplies is limited to 250 mg/l.

The methods for sulfate described below are gravimetric (*A* and *B*) and turbidimetric (*C*). Several titrimetric methods are currently used for the direct or indirect determination of sulfate. Although quite satisfactory in some circumstances, they are not yet considered to be sufficiently developed to warrant recommendation for general use in water analysis. The analyst is urged, however, to become familiar with the literature on the subject of titrimetric determination of sulfate.

1. Selection of Method

Among the methods for sulfate, the choice will depend on the concentration range of sulfate and the degree of accuracy required. Dilution or concentration of the sample will bring most waters into the desired range for any of the methods. Although Method A is recognized as the preferred standard method and is the most accurate for sulfate concentrations above 10 mg/l, it is also the most time-consuming. It should be used for obtaining the theoretical ion balances and whenever results of the greatest accuracy are required. Method B is similar but substitutes drying of the filter and residue for the more rigorous heat treatment by ignition at 800 C that is required to expel occluded water. This method is acceptable in routine work where the greatest attainable accuracy is not required. Method C is more rapid and may be either more or less accurate than Methods A or B for sulfate concentrations less than 10 mg/l, depending on a number of factors, including the skill of the analyst. Although usually less accurate than Methods A or B above 10 mg/l, Method C may be applied to concentrations up to 60 mg/l.

2. Sampling and Storage

It must be noted that in the presence of organic matter certain bacteria may reduce sulfate to sulfide. To avoid this, heavily polluted or contaminated samples should be stored at low temperatures or treated with formaldehyde. Sulfite may be oxidized to sulfate by dissolved oxygen above pH 8.0. Samples containing sulfite should have the pH adjusted below this level.

156 A. Gravimetric Method With Ignition of Residue

1. General Discussion

a. Principle: Sulfate is precipitated in a hydrochloric acid medium as barium sulfate by the addition of barium chloride. The precipitation is carried out near the boiling temperature, and after a period of digestion the precipitate is filtered, washed with water until free of chlorides, ignited or dried, and weighed as $BaSO_4$.

b. Interference: The gravimetric determination of sulfate is subject to many errors, both positive and negative. In potable waters where the mineral concentration is low, these may be of minor importance. The analyst should be familiar with the more common interferences, however, so that he may apply corrective measures when necessary.

1) INTERFERENCES LEADING TO HIGH RESULTS—Suspended matter, silica, barium chloride precipitant, nitrate, sulfite and water are the principal factors in positive errors. Suspended matter may be present in both the sample and the precipitating solution; soluble silicate may be rendered insoluble and sulfite may be oxidized to sulfate during processing of the sample. Barium nitrate, barium chloride and water are occluded to some extent with the barium sulfate, although water is driven off if the temperature of ignition is sufficiently high.

2) INTERFERENCES LEADING TO LOW RESULTS—Alkali metal sulfates frequently yield low results. This is especially true of alkali hydrogen sulfates. Occlusion of alkali sulfate with barium sulfate causes the substitution of an element of lower atomic weight than barium in the precipitatc. Hydrogen sulfates of alkali metals act similarly and, in addition, decompose on being heated. Heavy metals, such as chromium and iron, cause low results by interfering with the complete precipitation of sulfate and by formation of heavy metal sulfates. Barium sulfate has small but significant solubility, which is increased in the presence of acid. Although an acid medium is necessary to prevent precipitation of barium carbonate and phosphate, it is important to limit its concentration to minimize the solution effect.

2. Apparatus

a. Steam bath.

b. Drying oven, equipped with thermostatic control.

c. Muffle furnace, with heat indicator.

d. Desiccator, preferably containing a desiccant with color indicator of the water content.

e. Analytical balance, capable of weighing to 0.1 mg.

f. Filters: One of the following is required:

1) PAPER—Acid-washed, ashless hard-finish filter paper sufficiently retentive for fine precipitates.

2) CRUCIBLE—Porous-bottom silica or porcelain crucible with a maximum pore size of 5 microns.

g. Filtering apparatus, appropriate to the type of filter selected.

3. Reagents

a. Methyl red indicator solution: Dissolve 100 mg methyl red sodium salt in distilled water and dilute to 100 ml.

b. Hydrochloric acid, 1 + 1.

c. Barium chloride solution: Dissolve

100 g $BaCl_2 \cdot 2H_2O$ in 1 liter distilled water. Filter through a membrane filter or hard-finish filter paper before use; 1 ml of this reagent is capable of precipitating approximately 40 mg SO_4.

d. Silver nitrate-nitric acid reagent: Dissolve 8.5 g $AgNO_3$ and 0.5 ml conc HNO_3 in 500 ml distilled water.

4. Procedure

a. Removal of cation interference: If the total cation concentration in the sample is 250 mg/l or more, or if the total heavy metal ion concentration in the sample is 10 mg/l or more, pass the sample portion intended for sulfate precipitation through a cation-removing ion-exchange column (Figure 3) as described in the Introduction, Section 100B.2b.

b. Removal of silica: If the silica concentration exceeds 25 mg/l, evaporate the sample nearly to dryness in a platinum dish on a steam bath. Add 1 ml HCl, tilt the dish, and rotate it until the acid comes in contact with the residue on the sides; continue the evaporation to dryness. Complete the drying in an oven at 180 C and if organic matter is present, char over the flame of a burner. Moisten the residue with 2 ml distilled water and 1 ml HCl, and evaporate to dryness on a steam bath. Add 2 ml HCl, take up the soluble residue in hot water, and filter. Wash the insoluble silica with several small portions of hot distilled water. Combine the filtrate and washings.

c. Precipitation of barium sulfate: Adjust the clarified sample—treated if necessary to remove interfering agents—to contain approximately 50 mg of sulfate ion in a 250-ml volume. Adjust the acidity with HCl to pH 4.5–5.0, using a pH meter or the orange color of methyl red indicator. Then add an additional 1 to 2 ml HCl. Lower concentrations of sulfate ion may be tolerated if it is impracticable to concentrate the sample to the optimum level, but in such cases it is better to fix the total volume at 150 ml. Heat the solution to boiling and, while stirring gently, add warm barium chloride solution slowly until precipitation appears to be complete; then add about 2 ml in excess. If the amount of precipitate is small, add a total of 5 ml barium chloride solution. Digest the precipitate at 80–90 C, preferably overnight but for not less than 2 hr.

d. Preparation of filters:

1) PAPER—Prepare in the conventional manner.

2) SILICA OR PORCELAIN CRUCIBLE—Preignite at 800 C for 1 hr, cool in a desiccator, and weigh.

e. Filtration and weighing: Mix a small amount of ashless filter paper pulp with the barium sulfate and filter at room temperature. The pulp aids filtration and reduces the tendency of the precipitate to creep. Wash the precipitate with small portions of warm distilled water until the washings are free of chloride, as indicated by testing with silver nitrate-nitric acid reagent. Dry the filter and the precipitate, and ignite at 800 C for 1 hr. *Do not allow the filter paper to flame.* Cool in a desiccator and weigh.

5. Calculation

$$\text{mg/l } SO_4 = \frac{\text{mg } BaSO_4 \times 411.5}{\text{ml sample}}$$

6. Precision and Accuracy

A synthetic unknown sample containing 259 mg/l sulfate, 108 mg/l Ca,

82 mg/l Mg, 3.1 mg/l K, 19.9 mg/l Na, 241 mg/l chloride, 250 μg/l nitrite N, 1.1 mg/l nitrate N, and 42.5 mg/l total alkalinity (contributed by $NaHCO_3$) was determined by the gravimetric method, with a relative standard deviation of 4.7% and a relative error of 1.9% in 32 laboratories.

156 B. Gravimetric Method with Drying of Residue

1. General Discussion

Refer to Method A, preceding.

2. Apparatus

With the exception of the filter paper, all of the apparatus cited in Section 156A.2 is required, plus the following:

a. Filters: Use one of the following:

1) FRITTED-GLASS FILTER, fine ("F") porosity, with a maximum pore size of 5 microns.

2) MEMBRANE FILTER, with a pore size of about 0.45 microns.

b. Filtering apparatus, appropriate to the type of filter selected. (Coat the holder used for the membrane filter with silicone fluid to prevent the precipitate from adhering to it.)

3. Reagents

All the reagents listed in Section 156A.3 are required, and in addition:

*a. Silicone fluid.**

b. Anticreep fluid: Commercial nonionic wetting agents are satisfactory.

4. Procedure

a. Removal of interference: Refer to Section 156A.4a and b.

b. Precipitation of barium sulfate: Refer to Section 156A.4c.

c. Preparation of filters:

1) SILICA OR PORCELAIN CRUCIBLE—Dry to constant weight † in an oven maintained at 105 C or higher, cool in a desiccator, and weigh.

2) FRITTED-GLASS FILTER—Dry as in (1).

3) MEMBRANE FILTER—Place the filter on a piece of filter paper or a watch glass and dry to constant weight † in a vacuum oven at 80 C, while maintaining a vacuum of at least 25 in. of mercury, or in a conventional oven at a temperature of 103–105 C. Cool in a desiccator and weigh the membrane only.

d. Filtration and weighing: Filter the barium sulfate at room temperature. Wash the precipitate with several small portions of warm distilled water until the washings are free of chloride, as indicated by testing with silver nitrate-nitric acid reagent. If the membrane filter is used, add a few drops of anticreep solution to the suspension before filtering and also to the wash water, to prevent adherence of the precipitate to the holder. Dry the filter with precipitate by the same procedure used in the preparation of the filter. Cool in a desiccator and weigh.

5. Calculation

$$\text{mg/l } SO_4 = \frac{\text{mg } BaSO_4 \times 411.5}{\text{ml sample}}$$

* "Desicote" (Beckman) or equivalent.

† Constant weight is defined as a change of not more than 0.5 mg in two successive operations consisting of heating, cooling in a desiccator, and weighing.

156 C. Turbidimetric Method

1. General Discussion

a. Principle: Sulfate ion is precipitated in a hydrochloric acid medium with barium chloride in such manner as to form barium sulfate crystals of uniform size. The absorbance of the barium sulfate suspension is measured by a nephelometer or transmission photometer and the sulfate ion concentration is determined by comparison of the reading with a standard curve.

b. Interference: Color or suspended matter in large amounts will interfere with this method. Some suspended matter may be removed by filtration. If both are small in comparison with the sulfate ion concentration, interference is corrected for as indicated in ¶ 4d below. Silica in excess of 500 mg/l will interfere, and in waters containing large quantities of organic material it may not be possible to precipitate barium sulfate satisfactorily.

There are no ions other than sulfate in normal waters that will form insoluble compounds with barium under strongly acid conditions. Determinations should be made at room temperature, which may vary over a range of 10 C without causing appreciable error.

c. Minimum detectable concentration: Approximately 1 mg/l sulfate.

2. Apparatus

a. Magnetic stirrer: It is convenient to incorporate a timing device to permit the magnetic stirrer to operate for exactly 1 min. The stirring speed should not vary appreciably. It is also convenient to incorporate a fixed resistance in series with the motor operating the magnetic stirrer to regulate the speed of stirring. If more than one magnet is used, they should be of identical shape and size. The exact speed of stirring is not critical, but it should be constant for each run of samples and standards and should be adjusted to about the maximum at which no splashing occurs.

b. Photometer: One of the following is required with preference in the order given:

1) NEPHELOMETER.

2) SPECTROPHOTOMETER, for use at 420 mμ, providing a light path of 4–5 cm.

3) FILTER PHOTOMETER, equipped with a violet filter having maximum transmittance near 420 mμ and providing a light path of 4–5 cm.

c. Stopwatch, if the magnetic stirrer is not equipped with an accurate timer.

d. Measuring spoon, capacity 0.2–0.3 ml.

3. Reagents

a. Conditioning reagent: Mix 50 ml glycerol with a solution containing 30 ml conc HCl, 300 ml distilled water, 100 ml 95% ethyl or isopropyl alcohol, and 75 g sodium chloride.

b. Barium chloride, crystals, 20–30 mesh.

c. Standard sulfate solution: Prepare a standard sulfate solution as described in (1) or (2); 1.00 ml = 100 μg SO_4.

1) Prepare by diluting 10.41 ml of the standard 0.0200*N* H_2SO_4 titrant specified in Alkalinity, Section 102.3c, to 100 ml with distilled water.

2) Dissolve 147.9 mg anhydrous sodium sulfate, Na_2SO_4, in distilled water and dilute to 1,000 ml.

4. Procedure

a. Formation of barium sulfate turbidity: Measure 100 ml sample, or a suitable aliquot made up to 100 ml, into a 250-ml erlenmeyer flask. Add exactly 5.00 ml conditioning reagent and mix in the stirring apparatus. While the solution is being stirred, add a spoonful of barium chloride crystals and begin the timing immediately. Stir for exactly 1 min at a constant speed.

b. Measurement of barium sulfate turbidity: Immediately after the stirring period has ended, pour some of the solution into the absorption cell of the photometer and measure the turbidity at 30-sec intervals for 4 min. Since maximum turbidity usually occurs within 2 min and the readings remain constant thereafter for 3–10 min, consider the turbidity to be the maximum reading obtained in the 4-min interval.

c. Preparation of calibration curve: Estimate the sulfate concentration in the sample by comparing the turbidity reading with a calibration curve secured by carrying sulfate standards through the entire procedure. Space the standards at 5 mg/l increments in the 0 to 40 mg/l sulfate range. Above 40 mg/l the accuracy of the method decreases and the suspensions of barium sulfate lose stability. Check reliability of the calibration curve by running a standard with every three or four unknown samples.

d. Correction for sample color and turbidity: Correct for the color and turbidity present in the original sample by running blanks from which the barium chloride is withheld.

5. Calculation

$$\text{mg/l } SO_4 = \frac{\text{mg } SO_4 \times 1{,}000}{\text{ml sample}}$$

6. Precision and Accuracy

A synthetic unknown sample containing 259 mg/l sulfate, 108 mg/l Ca, 82 mg/l Mg, 3.1 mg/l K, 19.9 mg/l Na, 241 mg/l chloride, 250 μg/l nitrite N, 1.1 mg/l nitrate N, and 42.5 mg/l total alkalinity (contributed by $NaHCO_3$) was determined by the turbidimetric method, with a relative standard deviation of 9.1% and a relative error of 1.2% in 19 laboratories.

156 D. Bibliography

Gravimetric Methods

HILLEBRAND, W. F. et al. 1953. *Applied Inorganic Analysis* (2nd ed.). John Wiley & Sons, New York.

KOLTHOFF, I. M., E. J. MEEHAN, E. B. SANDELL & S. BRUCKENSTEIN. 1969. *Quantitative Chemical Analysis* (4th ed.). Macmillan Co., New York.

Turbidimetric Method

SHEEN, R. T., H. L. KAHLER & E. M. ROSS. 1935. Turbidimetric determination of sulfate in water. *Ind. Eng. Chem.*, Anal. Ed. 7:262.

THOMAS, J. F. & J. E. COTTON. 1954. A turbidimetric sulfate determination. *Water & Sewage Works* 101:462.

ROSSUM, J. R. & P. A. VILLARRUZ. 1961. Suggested methods for turbidimetric determination of sulfate in water. *JAWWA* 53:873.

Other Methods

FRITZ, J. S. & S. S. YAMAMURA. 1955. Rapid microdetermination of sulfate. *Anal. Chem.* 27:1461.

FRITZ, J. S., S. S. YAMAMURA & M. J. RICHARD. 1957. Titration of sulfate following separation with alumina. *Anal. Chem.* 29:158.

BERTOLACINI, R. J. & J. E. BARNEY. 1957. Colorimetric determination of sulfate with barium chloranilate. *Anal. Chem.* 29:281.

———. 1958. Ultraviolet spectrophotometric determination of sulfate, chloride, and fluoride with chloranilic acid. *Anal. Chem.* 30:202.

157 SULFIDE

Sulfide occurs in many well waters and sometimes is formed in lakes or surface waters or even in distribution systems as a result of bacterial action on organic matter under anaerobic conditions. Varying amounts may also be found in waters receiving sewage or wastes from tanneries, paper mills, oil refineries, chemical plants and gas manufacturing works. Concentrations of a few hundredths of a milligram per liter cause a noticeable odor. Removal of sulfide odor is accomplished at the water treatment plant by aeration or chlorination.

In waters free from suspended solids, sulfide exists as a mixture of HS^- and H_2S, in proportions determined by the pH as given in Table 228(1) below. If the sample is not clear, insoluble metallic sulfides may also be present.

The colorimetric method of determination, which is described in Sulfide, Section 228B following, is applicable. Samples must be tested immediately after collection unless preserved by the addition of zinc acetate, as specified in the procedure given below.

157 A. Pretreatment of Low-Level Sulfide Samples

1. General Discussion

Many water supplies have only a few tenths or hundredths of a milligram of sulfide per liter. In these cases, it is advantageous to use zinc acetate in a procedure which, in addition to preserving the sample for up to 24 hr, causes zinc sulfide to be precipitated along with zinc hydroxide as a carrier precipitate. Upon settling, the sulfide content is concentrated into a smaller volume.

2. Reagents

a. Zinc acetate, 1M: Dissolve 22 g $Zn(C_2H_3O_2)_2 \cdot 2H_2O$ in enough distilled water to make a 100-ml solution.

b. Sodium hydroxide, 1N.

3. Procedure

Place 1 ml zinc acetate solution in a bottle of 250-ml or 500-ml capacity. Collect the sample in this bottle, measuring the amount by a mark on the bottle. Add 1 ml NaOH. Stir the solution for a minute or two to coagulate the precipitate. Allow to stand until the supernatant water is clear. Siphon off most of this water, preferably 80–95% of the sample taken, but with care to lose none of the precipitate. Pour the remaining water, with precipitate, into a graduated cylinder to measure the volume. Then, with the precipitate uniformly suspended in the water, withdraw a sample for sulfide determination as in Section 228B.4.

The amount of zinc acetate added in the foregoing procedure may be varied according to the judgment of the analyst, the aim being to get a well-settling precipitate. The volume of sodium hydroxide solution should equal the volume of zinc acetate solution in order to insure a large excess of unprecipitated zinc, without which complete precipitation of the sulfide cannot be assured.

4. Calculation

$$\text{mg/l Total sulfide} = \frac{T \times B}{A}$$

where A represents the volume of sample, B the volume of remaining sample with precipitate after decanting, and T the apparent total sulfide found in the colorimetric test.

5. Bibliography

POMEROY, R. 1954. Auxiliary pretreatment by zinc acetate in sulfide analyses. *Anal. Chem.* 26:571.

158 SULFITE

Although sulfite may occur in certain industrial wastes and polluted waters, it is most commonly found in boiler and boiler feedwaters to which sodium sulfite has been applied to reduce dissolved oxygen to a minimum and to prevent corrosion. The development of catalyzed sodium sulfite has extended its field of usefulness to the treatment of cooling, process, and distribution water systems at cold water temperatures.

1. General Discussion

a. Principle: An acidified water sample containing sulfite is titrated with a standardized potassium iodide-iodate titrant. Free iodine is released when the sulfite has been completely oxidized, resulting in the formation of a blue color in the presence of starch indicator.

b. Interference: The presence of other oxidizable substances in the water, such as organic matter and sulfide, will result in higher titration values for sulfite than are actually present. Nitrite, on the other hand, will combine with sulfite in the acid medium to destroy both, leading to low results. No interference occurs with the Dual-Purpose Dry Starch Indicator Powder because the sulfamic acid in this proprietary compound destroys the nitrite. Copper ion rapidly accelerates the oxidation of sulfite solution. Certain heavy metals may also react in a manner similar to copper. Proper sampling and immediate fixing by acid addition should minimize those difficulties.

c. Minimum detectable concentration: 2 mg/l SO_3.

2. Reagents

a. Sulfuric acid, 1 + 1.

b. Starch indicator: Either the aqueous solution (1) or the dry powders (2) and (3) may be used.

1) To 5 g starch (potato, arrowroot or soluble) in a mortar, add a little cold distilled water and grind to a paste. Pour into 1 liter of boiling distilled water, stir, and allow to settle overnight. Use the clear supernate. Preserve by adding either 1.3 g salicylic acid, 4 g zinc chloride, or a combination of 4 g sodium propionate and 2 g sodium azide to 1 liter of starch solution.

2) Soluble starch powder * provides a sharp end-point change to blue when 0.1 g of the powder is used in the presence of free iodine.

3) A dual-purpose starch indicator powder † composed of cold water-soluble starch in a sulfamic acid medium finds extensive use in control work. When this proprietary formulation is used, the sulfuric acid is omitted and 3–4 drops phenolphthalein indicator solution are added to the water sample followed by sufficient dipperfuls (1 g) of indicator powder to discharge the alkaline red color of the sample. After a final dipperful in excess is added, the sample is titrated with standard potassium iodide-iodate titrant to the appearance of a permanent blue color in the sample.

c. Standard potassium iodide-iodate titrant, 0.0125*N:* Dissolve 445.8 mg anhydrous potassium iodate, KIO_3 (primary standard grade dried for several hours at 120 C), 4.35 g potassium iodide, KI, and 310 mg sodium bicarbonate, $NaHCO_3$, in distilled water and dilute to 1,000 ml. This titrant is equivalent to 500 μg SO_3 per 1.00 ml.

3. Procedure

a. Sample collection: Collect a fresh water sample, allowing as little contact with air as possible. Cool hot samples to 50 C or below in the cooling apparatus depicted in Figure 6 (Section 100E.3). Do not filter the samples.

b. Titration: Add 1 ml H_2SO_4 (or 1 g dual-purpose starch indicator) [¶ 2b(3) above] to a 250-ml erlenmeyer flask or other titrating vessel, then measure 50 ml water sample in a graduated cylinder and transfer to the flask. Add 1 ml starch indicator solution or 0.1 g starch powder [see ¶ 2b(2) above], omitting this step if dual-purpose starch indicator powder [¶ 2b(3)] is used. Titrate with potassium iodide-iodate titrant until a faint permanent blue color develops in the sample, signaling the end of the titration. View the color change against a white background.

4. Calculation

$$\text{mg/l } SO_3 = \frac{A \times N \times 40{,}000}{\text{ml sample}}$$

$$\text{mg/l } Na_2SO_3 = \text{mg/l } SO_3 \times 1.57$$

where A = ml titration for sample and N = normality of KI-KIO_3.

* The product known as Thyodene is imported by the Magnus Chemical Co. of Garwood, N.J., and is available from the Fisher Scientific Co. of Pittsburgh, Pa., and others.

† The use of this product, known as Dual-Purpose Dry Starch Indicator Powder, is covered by U.S. Patent No. 2,963,443 issued to E. T. Erickson.

159 SURFACTANTS (ANIONIC)

The popularity of synthetic detergents (containing surface-active agents, or "surfactants") for general cleaning purposes has on occasion resulted in the frothing of some natural waters. This was especially true when alkyl benzene sulfonate (ABS) was in common use. In mid-1965, the detergent industry completed its full-scale conversion from ABS to the more biodegradable linear alkylate sulfonate (LAS). LAS is an alkyl aryl sulfonate whose structure is made up of a straight-chain alkyl group (ABS has a branched-chain alkyl group), a benzene ring, and a sulfonate. The straight-chain alkyl group is condensed with benzene to yield linear alkylate and the alkylate is then sulfonated to yield LAS.

Since the change-over, the number of detergent-caused foaming incidents has sharply dropped. As the single most widely used surfactant now is LAS, it is the most likely to be present in raw water. For this reason, LAS has been selected as the standard compound in the following two analytical methods.

1. Selection of Method

In selecting a method, it is recommended that the analyst who is interested in the LAS content of a raw water supply follow a two-step approach. He should first analyze the sample by the methylene blue method (*A*). If the concentration of methylene blue-active substances is low, 500 μg/l or so, no further analysis will generally be required because the sum of the interferences (usually positive) plus true LAS is such that LAS is not a significant factor in the water. Experience has shown that the methylene blue procedure suffices when no problems are observed in a water supply. Should the concentration of methylene blue-active substances be high, however, it becomes important to know how much represents true LAS and how much interferences. An infrared determination (*B*) is recommended in such a case, but if infrared equipment is not available, the analysis by Method B can be carried through to the recovery of the purified LAS and then completed colorimetrically by the methylene blue procedure. This alternative eliminates the need for expensive infrared equipment, which few laboratories have. The big drawback to the infrared method is that, compared to the methylene blue colorimetric process, it is fairly complicated and time-consuming. On the other hand, if the problem is of sufficient importance, the local analyst is advised to seek the help of his state board of health in obtaining an infrared determination of LAS.

159 A. Methylene Blue Method for Methylene Blue-Active Substances

1. General Discussion

a. Principle: This method depends on the formation of a blue-colored salt when methylene blue reacts with anionic surfactants, which include not only LAS but also alkyl sulfates. Thus, the materials determined are often designated methylene blue-active substances. The salt is soluble in chloroform and the intensity of color is proportional to the concentration. The intensity is measured by making spectrophotometric readings in this solvent at a wavelength of 652 mμ. The method is applicable in the 0.025–100 mg/l LAS range.

b. Interference: Both organic and inorganic compounds interfere with the determination of LAS. Some of the proved interferences can be predicted on the basis of chemical properties. Organic sulfates, sulfonates, carboxylates, phosphates and phenols—which complex methylene blue—and inorganic cyanates, chlorides, nitrates and thiocyanates—which form ion pairs with methylene blue—are among the positive interferences. Organic materials, especially amines, which compete with the methylene blue in the reaction, can cause low results. Positive errors are much more common than negative when determining anionic surfactants in water.

c. Minimum detectable concentration: 10 μg LAS.

d. Application: The methylene blue method has been successfully applied to the examination of the anionic surfactant content in water supplies destined for human consumption. Unfortunately, the numerous materials normally present in sewage, industrial wastes, and sludge can seriously interfere with the determination and lead to incorrect results and conclusions.

2. Apparatus

a. Colorimetric equipment—One of the following is required:

1) SPECTROPHOTOMETER, for use at 652 mμ, providing a light path of 1 cm or longer.

2) FILTER PHOTOMETER, providing a light path of 1 cm or longer and equipped with a red color filter exhibiting maximum transmittance near 625 mμ.

b. Separatory funnels, 500-ml, preferably with inert teflon stopcocks.

3. Reagents

a. Stock linear alkylate sulfonate (LAS) solution: Weigh an amount of the reference material (obtain from The Soap and Detergent Assn, 475 Park Avenue South, New York, N. Y. 10016) equal to 1.000 g LAS on a 100% active basis. Dissolve in distilled water and dilute to 1,000 ml; 1.00 ml = 1.00 mg LAS. Store in a refrigerator to minimize biodegradation. If necessary, prepare weekly.

b. Standard linear alkylate sulfonate (LAS) solution: Dilute 10.00 ml stock LAS solution to 1,000 ml with distilled water; 1.00 ml = 10.0 μg LAS. Prepare daily.

c. Phenolphthalein indicator solution.

d. Sodium hydroxide, 1*N.*

e. Sulfuric acid, 1*N.*

f. Chloroform.

g. Methylene blue reagent: Dissolve 100 mg methylene blue * in 100 ml distilled water. Transfer 30 ml of this solution to a 1,000-ml flask. Add 500 ml distilled water, 6.8 ml conc H_2SO_4, and 50 g monosodium dihydrogen phosphate monohydrate, $NaH_2PO_4 \cdot H_2O$. Shake until dissolution is complete. Dilute to the 1,000-ml mark.

h. Wash solution: Add 6.8 ml conc H_2SO_4 to 500 ml distilled water in a 1,000-ml flask. Then add 50 g $NaH_2PO_4 \cdot H_2O$ and shake until disso-

* Eastman No. P573 or equivalent.

lution is complete. Dilute to the 1,000-ml mark.

4. Procedure

a. Preparation of calibration curve: Prepare a series of ten separatory funnels with 0, 1.00, 3.00, 5.00, 7.00, 9.00, 11.00, 13.00, 15.00 and 20.00 ml of the standard LAS solution. Add sufficient water to make the total volume 100 ml in each separatory funnel. Treat each standard as described in ¶s 4c and 4d following, and plot a calibration curve of μg LAS versus absorbance.

b. Volume of sample: Select the volume of the water sample to be tested on the expected LAS concentration:

Expected LAS Concentration—*mg/l*	Sample Taken *ml*
0.025– 0.080	400
0.08 – 0.40	250
0.4 – 2.0	100
2 – 10	20.0
10 –100	2.00

If a sample of less than 100 ml is indicated, dilute to 100 ml with distilled water; if 100 ml or more are used, extract the entire sample.

c. Extraction and color development:

1) Add the sample solution to a separatory funnel. Make the solution alkaline by dropwise addition of 1*N* NaOH, using phenolphthalein indicator. Then discharge the pink color by dropwise addition of 1*N* sulfuric acid.

2) Add 10 ml chloroform and 25 ml methylene blue reagent. Rock vigorously for 30 sec and allow the phases to separate. Excessive agitation may cause emulsion trouble. Some samples require a longer period of phase separation than others. Before draining the chloroform layer, swirl the sample gently, then allow to settle.

3) Draw off the chloroform layer into a second separatory funnel. Rinse the delivery tube of the first separatory funnel with a small amount of chloroform. Repeat the extraction three times, using 10 ml chloroform each time. If the blue color in the water phase becomes faint and disappears, discard the sample and repeat the determination, using a smaller sample size.

4) Combine all extracts in the second separatory funnel. Add 50 ml wash solution and shake vigorously for 30 sec. Emulsions do not form at this stage. Allow to settle, swirl the contents, and then draw off the chloroform layer through glass wool into a 100-ml volumetric flask. Repeat the washing twice more with 10 ml chloroform each time. Rinse the glass wool and the funnel with chloroform. Collect the washing in the volumetric flask, dilute to the mark with chloroform, and mix well.

d. Measurement: Determine the absorbance of the solution at 652 mμ against a blank of chloroform.

5. Calculation

$$\text{mg/l Total apparent LAS} = \frac{\mu\text{g LAS}}{\text{ml sample}}$$

Report as methylene blue-active substances (MBAS).

6. Precision and Accuracy

A synthetic unknown sample containing 270 μg/l LAS in distilled water was determined, with a relative standard deviation of 14.8% and a relative error of 10.6% in 110 laboratories.

A tap water unknown sample to which were added 480 μg/l LAS was determined, with a relative standard deviation of 9.9% and a relative error of 1.3% in 110 laboratories.

A river water unknown sample to which were added 2.94 mg/l LAS was determined, with a relative standard deviation of 9.1% and a relative error of 1.4% in 110 laboratories.

159 B. Carbon Adsorption Method * (TENTATIVE)

1. General Discussion

a. Principle: This method involves the collection and isolation of a few milligrams of LAS and its quantitative determination based on infrared absorption of an amine complex of LAS. Though lengthy, this method is specific and accurate for low LAS concentrations in water and it eliminates alkyl sulfates. When an infrared spectrophotometer is not available, a colorimetric determination can be substituted by recovering the purified LAS and applying the methylene blue method (*A*).

b. Application: This method is applicable to raw-water samples only, not to sewage or industrial wastes.

c. Precaution: Most samples contain both solid and liquid phases, and LAS is highly concentrated in the solid phase. For accurate analyses, it is essential that the solids be representatively sampled or excluded.

2. Apparatus

a. Carbon adsorption tube: The glass column, about 5 × 60 cm, is charged with 100 g carbon. Screens of stainless steel or brass, about 30-mesh, divide the carbon into sections of 20, 30, 40 and 10 g (see Figure 28).

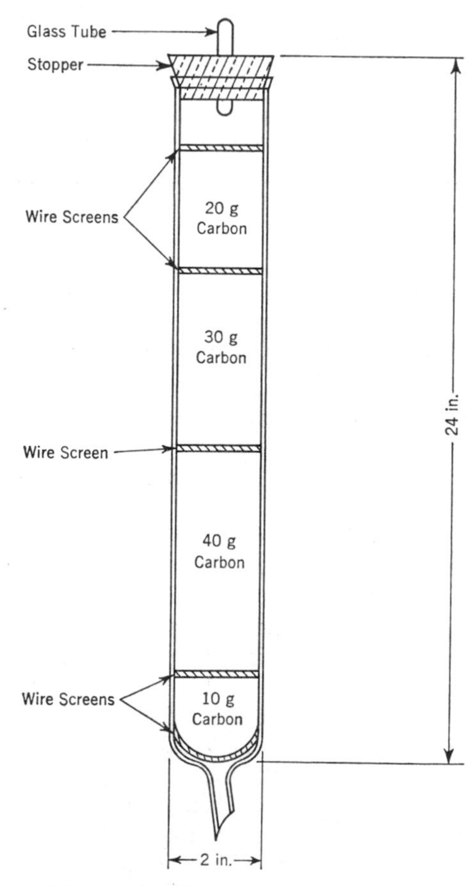

Figure 28. Carbon adsorption tube.

* This method is identical in source and substance to that developed by the Subcommittee on Analytical Methods, Technical Advisory Committee, The Soap and Detergent Association.

b. Buchner funnel, 500-ml, medium-porosity, sintered-glass.

c. pH meter.

d. Volumetric flasks, either 2 or 5 ml.

e. Separatory funnels, 500 ml.

f. Infrared spectrophotometer, for use at 2–15 microns.

g. Acid-washed glassware: All glassware used in the infrared method must be free of contamination. A thorough rinse with 1 + 1 HCl must be used to remove adsorbed LAS.

3. Reagents

a. Standard linear alkylate sulfonate (LAS), for calibration (obtain from Environmental Protection Agency, Water Quality Office, Method & Performance Evaluation Activity, 1014 Broadway, Cincinnati, Ohio 45202).

b. Activated carbon, unground, 30-mesh, for the carbon adsorption tube.†

TEST FOR IMPURITIES IN CARBON—Extract 100 g carbon by boiling 1 hr with 1 liter of benzene-alcohol solution (see ¶ 3c following). Filter the carbon, wash with 100 ml methyl alcohol, add the washings to the remainder of the solvent mixture, evaporate to dryness on a steam bath, and weigh. The residue consists of extractable organic impurities and should be less than 10 mg, not including any residue from the solvent.

c. Benzene-alcohol solution: Mix 500 ml thiophene-free benzene, 420 ml methyl alcohol, and 80 ml 0.5*N* KOH.

d. Methyl alcohol, absolute.

e. Hydrochloric acid, conc.

f. Sodium hydroxide, 1*N*.

g. Petroleum ether, boiling range 35–60 C.

h. Ethyl alcohol, 95%

i. Sulfuric acid, 1*N*.

† Nuchar C190 (Westvaco), or equivalent.

j. Buffer solution: Dissolve 6.8 g monopotassium dihydrogen phosphate, KH_2PO_4, in 1 liter of distilled water. Adjust to pH 6.8–6.9 with 6*N* NaOH.

*k. 1-methylheptylamine.**

l. Solution for extracting LAS: Dissolve 400 mg (20 drops) 1-methylheptylamine * in 400 ml chloroform. Prepare this solution daily.

m. Chloroform.

n. Carbon disulfide or carbon tetrachloride.

4. Procedure

a. Preparation of calibration curve: Place 25 mg standard LAS in a 5-gal glass vessel and dilute with about 4 gal distilled water. Mix thoroughly and, using synthetic rubberlike tubing, siphon the entire solution through the carbon column. Treat as described in ¶ 4c(1) through (7) below. Repeat with 20, 15, 10, 5 and 0 mg LAS. Make two calibration curves by plotting the LAS added as the abscissa and the absorbances of the maxima at 9.6 and 9.9 microns as the ordinate. The baseline technic is best used in determining the absorbance of the maxima.

b. Volume of sample: Estimate the concentration of LAS present in the sample. Calculate the volume of sample required to supply 10–25 mg LAS. If 2 liters or less, measure about 10 g granular activated carbon into a 2-liter glass-stoppered graduated cylinder, add the sample, and shake well for 2 min. Filter on a medium-porosity, sintered-glass Buchner funnel. If more than 2 liters of sample are required, pass through the carbon column at the rate of 10 gph or less.

c. Extraction and measurement of LAS:

1) Transfer the carbon from the Buchner funnel or column, treating the

* Eastman No. 2439 or equivalent.

sections separately, to porcelain evaporating dishes and dry at 105–110 C. Brush the dried carbon from each dish into separate 2-liter bottles or flasks with standard-taper necks and add 1 liter of benzene-alcohol solution. Add boiling chips and reflux under an air condenser for 1 hr. Filter with a vacuum through a Buchner funnel, draw off all liquid, release the vacuum, and add 100 ml methyl alcohol. Stir with a glass rod and draw off the wash with a vacuum. Wash a second time with another 100-ml portion of methyl alcohol. Return the carbon to the flask, add solvent as before, and reflux for 1 hr. While making this second extraction, evaporate the solvent from the first extract and washes. Carry out this evaporation in a 2-liter beaker on a steam bath. (A gentle stream of nitrogen or air on the surface will hasten the evaporation.)

2) Filter off the second extract and wash the carbon as before. Add the extract and washes to the beaker containing the first extract. Discard the carbon. Evaporate sufficiently to combine in one beaker the extracts from the 20-, 30- and 40-g sections of the column. Treat the extracts of the 10-g section separately throughout the entire procedure. After the solvent has been removed, take up the residue in 50 ml warm distilled water. Transfer to a 250-ml standard-taper erlenmeyer flask. Rinse the beaker with 30 ml conc HCl and add slowly to the flask. Carbon dioxide is evolved. Rinse the beaker with 50 ml distilled water and combine with the other washings in the flask. Reflux under an air condenser for 1 hr.

3) Remove the condenser and continue boiling until the volume is reduced to 20–30 ml, transfer to a steam bath, and evaporate to near dryness. (A jet of air directed on the surface of the liquid will greatly aid evaporation.) Take the solids up in 100 ml distilled water and neutralize with NaOH solution to a pH of 8–9. Extract once with 50 ml petroleum ether. Up to 70% ethyl alcohol may be added, if necessary, to break emulsions. Wash the petroleum ether twice with 25-ml portions of distilled water, discard the petroleum ether layer, and add the washes to the aqueous solution. Boil off any alcohol that was added.

4) Cool and transfer quantitatively to a 500-ml separatory funnel. Neutralize by adding H_2SO_4 until just acidic to litmus. Add 50 ml buffer solution (¶ 3j) and 2 drops methylheptylamine (¶ 3k), and shake vigorously. Add 50 ml LAS extracting solution and 25 ml chloroform. Shake for 3 min and allow the phases to separate. If an emulsion forms, draw off the lower (chloroform) phase, including any emulsion, and filter through a plug of glass wool wet with chloroform, using suction if necessary, into a 500-ml separatory funnel. Draw off the chloroform phase into a 400-ml beaker and return any aqueous solution to the first separatory funnel. Wash the glass wool plug with 10 ml chloroform and add to the chloroform extract.

5) Make an additional extraction with 50 ml LAS extracting solution and 25 ml chloroform. Shake 2 min and separate the phases [see ¶ 4c(4) preceding], if necessary. Extract a third time with 5 ml amine solution and 45 ml chloroform. Evaporate the combined chloroform extracts on a steam bath. With 10 ml chloroform, quantitatively transfer the residue to a 50-ml beaker, using three 5-ml portions of chloroform as rinses. Evaporate to dryness and continue heating on the steam bath for

30 min to remove excess amine. Take up the residue in about 1 ml carbon disulfide or carbon tetrachloride and filter through a plug of glass wool in a funnel stem (2-mm bore) into a 2- or 5-ml volumetric flask. Dilute to volume through the filter with several rinsings from the beaker.

6) Transfer a portion of the sample to an infrared cell without further dilution. Run the infrared absorption curve from 9.0 to 10.5 microns against a solvent blank. Measure the absorbance of the 9.6- and 9.9-micron peaks, using baselines from 9.5 to 9.8 and from 9.8 to 10.1 microns. From appropriate calibration curves calculate the LAS in the original sample. Report the values based on each wavelength separately (if infrared equipment is unavailable, use a colorimetric finish). Break the sulfonate-amine complex by boiling with aqueous alkali. After the amine has been boiled off (as indicated by a lack of amine odor) and suitable dilutions are made, colorimetric results should check well with infrared values.

7) Evaporate a 0.5–1.0 ml portion of the LAS solution on a sodium chloride flat. Record the absorption spectrum from 2 to 15 microns for positive qualitative identification of LAS.

PRECAUTION—The carbon adsorption should be used on all samples. It separates the LAS from many of the other substances present and reduces emulsion difficulties.

NOTE: From 10 to 50 ml of water may be lost through a 60 × 1-cm air condenser during acid hydrolysis. This loss, while not affecting the hydrolysis, reduces the amount of water that needs to be boiled off after removal of the condenser.

159 C. Bibliography

General and Colorimetric Methods

BARR, T., J. OLIVER & W. V. STUBBINGS. 1948. The determination of surface-active agents in solution. *J. Soc. Chem. Ind.* (London) 67:45.

EPTON, S. R. 1948. New method for the rapid titrimetric analysis of sodium alkyl sulfates and related compounds. *Trans. Faraday Soc.* 44:226.

EVANS, H. C. 1950. Determination of anionic synthetic detergents in sewage. *J. Soc. Chem. Ind.* (London) 69: Suppl. 2:576.

DEGENS, P. N., JR. et al. 1953. Determination of sulfate and sulfonate anion-active detergents in sewage. *J. Applied Chem.* (London) 3:54.

AMERICAN WATER WORKS ASSOCIATION. 1954. Task Group Report. Characteristics and effects of synthetic detergents. *JAWWA* 46:751.

EDWARDS, G. P. & M. E. GINN. 1954. Determination of synthetic detergents in sewage. *Sewage & Ind. Wastes* 26:945.

LONGWELL, J. & W. D. MANIECE. 1955. Determination of anionic detergents in sewage, sewage effluents, and river water. *Analyst* 80:167.

MOORE, W. A. & R. A. KOLBESON. 1956. Determination of anionic detergents in surface waters and sewage with methyl green. *Anal. Chem.* 28:161.

AMERICAN WATER WORKS ASSOCIATION. 1958. Task Group Report. Determination of synthetic detergent content of raw water supplies. *JAWWA* 50:1343.

OGDEN, C. P. et al. 1961. Determination of biologically soft and hard alkylbenzenesulfonate in detergents and sewage. *Analyst* 86:22.

MAGUIRE, O. E. et al. 1962. Field test for analysis of anionic detergents in well waters. *JAWWA* 54:665.

ABBOTT, D. C. 1962. The determination of traces of anionic surface-active materials in water. *Analyst* 87:286.
———. 1963. A rapid test for anionic detergents in drinking water. *Analyst* 88:240.
REID, V. W. et al. 1967. Determination of anionic-active detergents by two-phase titration. *Tenside* 4:292.

Carbon Adsorption Method

SALLE, E. M. et al. 1956. Determination of trace amounts of alkyl benzenesulfonates in water. *Anal. Chem.* 28:1822.

SYNTHETIC DETERGENTS: See Surfactants, Section 159.

160 TANNIN AND LIGNIN

Lignin is a plant constituent which is often discharged as a waste during the manufacture of paper pulp. Another plant constituent, tannin, may enter the water supply through the process of vegetative degradation or the wastes of the tanning industry. Tannin is also applied in the so-called internal treatment of boiler waters, where it is said to reduce scale formation by causing the production of a more easily handled sludge.

Both lignin and tannin contain aromatic hydroxyl groups which react with tungstophosphoric and molybdophosphoric acids to form a blue color. However, the reaction is not specific for lignin or tannin, inasmuch as other reducing materials respond similarly.

The nature of the substance suspected in the water sample will dictate the choice of tannic acid or lignin for use in the preparation of the standard solution. This course is necessary because it is impossible to distinguish among hydroxylated aromatic compounds. Unless tannin or lignin is definitely known to be present in the water under examination, the results of this determination may logically be reported in the more general terms of "tannin-like," "lignin-like," or simply as "hydroxylated aromatic" compounds.

1. General Discussion

a. Principle: Tannins and lignins reduce tungstophosphoric and molybdophosphoric acids to produce a blue color suitable for the estimation of concentrations up to at least 9 mg/l for tannic acid as well as lignin.

b. Minimum detectable concentration: Approximately 0.1 mg/l for tannic acid and 0.3 mg/l for lignin.

2. Apparatus

COLORIMETRIC EQUIPMENT—One of the following is required:

a. Spectrophotometer, for use at 700 mμ. A light path of 1 cm or longer yields satisfactory results.

b. Filter photometer, provided with a red filter exhibiting maximum transmittance in the wavelength range of 600–700 mμ. Sensitivity improves with increasing wavelength. A light path of 1 cm or longer yields satisfactory results.

c. Nessler tubes, matched, 100-ml, tall form, marked at 50-ml volume.

3. Reagents

a. Tannin-lignin reagent: Dissolve 100 g sodium tungstate dihydrate, $Na_2WO_4 \cdot 2H_2O$, 20 g molybdophosphoric acid (also called phosphomolybdic acid), $20MoO_3 \cdot 2H_3PO_4 \cdot 48H_2O$, and 50 ml 85% phosphoric acid, H_3PO_4, in 750 ml distilled water. Boil the liquid under reflux for 2 hr; cool and make up to 1 liter with distilled water.

b. Sodium carbonate solution: Dissolve 200 g Na_2CO_3 in 500 ml warm distilled water and dilute to 1 liter to form a saturated solution. Keep in a rubber-stoppered bottle.

c. Stock solution: Weigh 1.000 g of the tannic acid, tannin or lignin compound which is being used for boiler water treatment or is known to be a contaminant of the water sample. Dissolve in distilled water and dilute to 1,000 ml.

d. Standard solution: Dilute 10.00 ml or 50.00 ml stock solution to 1,000 ml with distilled water to form a solution containing 10.0 μg or 50.0 μg active ingredient per 1.00 ml.

4. Procedure

Add 2 ml tannin-lignin reagent to 50.0 ml of clear sample and mix well. After 5 min add 10 ml sodium carbonate solution and mix thoroughly. Wait 10 min for color development. Compare visually against simultaneously prepared standards, or make photometric readings against a reagent blank prepared at the same time. Use the following guide for the instrumental measurements in the wavelength region of 600–700 mμ:

Tannic Acid in 62-ml Final Volume *µg*	Lignin in 62-ml Final Volume *µg*	Light Path *cm*
50–600	100–1,500	1
10–150	30– 400	5

5. Bibliography

BERK, A. A. & W. C. SCHROEDER. 1942. Determination of tannin substances in boiler water. *Ind. Eng. Chem.*, Anal. Ed. 14:456.

161 TASTE

Since many statements in the Odor Section (136) refer and relate directly to the taste determination, the entire Section 136 should be studied carefully in advance of the taste determination.

1. General Discussion

The sensation of taste is much less complex than odor. Consequently, judgments on description of taste are more readily arrived at. However, taste intensity measurements are more difficult than odor threshold tests, because the physical contact of the sample with the observer produces aftereffects which are much more difficult to eliminate. Consequently, where the observed taste is actually an odor, as in the case of chlorophenols, the threshold odor test is preferred.

Taste tests are performed only on samples which are known to be sanitarily acceptable for ingestion. Samples that may be contaminated with bacteria, viruses, parasites or poisonous chemicals like arsenic dechlorinating agents, or which are derived from an unesthetic source, are not used for taste tests. A laboratory performing taste tests must observe all sanitary and esthetic precautions with regard to apparatus and containers contacting the sample. Hospital-level sanitation of these items and of the small containers for the taste sample must be scrupulously observed. Panel taste tests are not performed on wastewaters or similar untreated effluents.

The same procedures with respect to purity of taste and odor-free dilution water, sequence of dilutions, and use of panels of observers as those described under odor testing apply also to taste testing. Taste tests should be made at 40 C, as this is near body temperature and no sensation of hot or cold will be encountered.

2. Apparatus

a. Preparation of dilutions: The same dilution system is used in preparing taste samples as that described for odor tests.

b. For tasting: Each dilution, and blank, is presented to the observer in a clean 50-ml beaker. An automatic dishwasher is convenient for sanitizing these beakers between tests.

3. Procedure

Prepare a dilution series in the same way as the series described for odor testing. Present the series of unknown samples to each subject. Pair each sample with a known blank sample, both containing 15 ml of water in the 50-ml beaker. Have the subject taste the sample by taking into the mouth whatever volume of sample at 40 C is comfortable to him, holding it for several seconds and discharging it without swallowing the water. Have the subject record whether a taste or aftertaste is detectable in the unknown sample. Submit the samples in an increasing order of concentration until the subject's taste threshold has been passed.

Calculate the individual threshold and the threshold of a panel in the same manner as described for threshold odor tests.

162 TEMPERATURE

1. General Discussion

Temperature readings are used in the calculation of the various forms of alkalinity and in the saturation and stability studies with respect to calcium carbonate. In limnologic studies, water temperatures at different depths in reservoirs are required. Identification of the source of supply, such as deep wells, is often possible by temperature measurement alone. Industrial plants often require data on the temperature of water for process use or heat-transmission calculations.

Normally, temperature measurements may be made with any good grade of mercury-filled centigrade thermometer, provided it is checked occasionally against a precision thermometer certified by the National Bureau of Standards.* Field instruments should

* Some commercial thermometers may be as much as 3 C in error.

be provided with a metal case to prevent breakage.

Depth temperature required for limnologic studies may be taken with a reversing thermometer, a thermophone, or a thermistor. The thermistor is considered to be the most convenient and also to be capable of the greatest accuracy. The reading should be made with the thermometer immersed in water, preferably flowing, after a period of time sufficient to permit a constant reading.

The temperature of the water at the sampling point should be expressed to the nearest degree centigrade, or closer if more precise data are required.

2. Bibliography

WARREN, H. E. & G. C. WHIPPLE. 1895. The thermophone—A new instrument for determining temperatures. *Massachusetts Inst. Technol. Quart.* 8:125.

AMERICAN SOCIETY FOR TESTING AND MATERIALS. 1949. *Standard Specifications for ASTM Thermometers.* No. E1-58, ASTM, Philadelphia.

REE, W. R. 1953. Thermistors for depth thermometry. *JAWWA* 45:259.

163 TURBIDITY

A clear water is important in those industries where the product is destined for human consumption or for a large number of manufacturing uses. Beverage producers, food processors, and treatment plants drawing upon a surface water supply commonly rely on coagulation, settling and filtration measures to insure an acceptable effluent.

Turbidity in water is caused by the presence of suspended matter, such as clay, silt, finely divided organic and inorganic matter, plankton and other microscopic organisms. Turbidity should be clearly understood to be an expression of the optical property of a sample which causes light to be scattered and absorbed rather than transmitted in straight lines through the sample. Attempts to correlate turbidity with the weight concentration of suspended matter are impractical, as the size, shape and refractive index of the particulate materials are of great importance optically but bear little direct relationship to the concentration and specific gravity of the suspended matter.

The standard method for the determination of turbidity has been based on the Jackson candle turbidimeter. However, the lowest turbidity value which can be measured directly on this instrument is 25 units. With turbidities of treated water generally falling within the range of 0–5 units, indirect secondary methods have been required to estimate turbidities on such samples. Unfortunately, no instrument has been devised which will duplicate the results obtained on the Jackson candle turbidimeter for all samples. Owing to fundamental differences in optical systems, the results obtained with different types of secondary instruments will frequently not check closely with one another, even though the instruments are all precalibrated against the candle turbidimeter.

A further cause of discrepancies in turbidity analysis is the use of suspensions of different types of particulate matter for the preparation of instrumental calibration curves. As with the water samples, prepared suspensions have different optical properties, depending upon the particle size distributions, shapes and refractive indices. Most commercial turbidimeters available for measuring low turbidities give comparatively good indications of the intensity of light scattered in one particular direction, predominantly at right angles to the incident light. Since there is no direct relationship between the Jackson candle turbidity and the intensity of light scattered at 90 °, there is no valid basis for the practice of calibrating the 90° turbidimeters in terms of candle units.

1. Selection of method: Its greater precision, sensitivity and applicability over a wide turbidity range make the nephelometric method preferable to the visual methods. The candle turbidimeter with a lower limit of 25 turbidity units has its principal usefulness in the estimation of highly turbid waters. The bottle standards offer a practical means for checking raw and conditioned water at various stages of the treatment process.

2. Storage of sample: Turbidity should preferably be determined on the same day the sample is taken. If longer storage is unavoidable, however, samples may be stored in the dark up to 24 hr. For even longer storage, treat each 1 liter of sample with 1 g mercuric chloride. Prolonged storage before measurement is not recommended, as irreversible changes in turbidity may occur. All samples should be vigorously shaken before examination.

163 A. Nephelometric Method

1. General Discussion

a. Principle: The method presented below is based upon a comparison of the intensity of light scattered by the sample under defined conditions with the intensity of light scattered by a standard reference suspension under the same conditions. The higher the intensity of scattered light, the higher the turbidity. Formazin polymer, which has gained acceptance as the turbidity standard reference suspension in the brewing industry, is also used as the turbidity standard reference suspension for water. It is easy to prepare and is more reproducible in its light-scattering properties than the clay or turbid natural water standards previously used. The turbidity of a particular concentration of formazin suspension is defined as 40 units. This same suspension of formazin has an approximate turbidity of 40 units when measured on the candle turbidimeter; therefore, turbidity units based on the formazin preparation will approximate those derived from the candle turbidimeter but will not be identical to them.

b. Interference: The determination of turbidity is applicable to any water sample that is free of débris and coarse sediments which settle out rapidly, although dirty glassware, the presence of air bubbles, and the effects of vibrations which disturb the surface visibility of the sample will lead to false results. The presence of "true color," that is, the color of the water which is due to dissolved substances that absorb light, will cause measured turbidities to be low. This effect is generally not significant in the case of treated water.

2. Apparatus

The *turbidimeter* shall consist of a nephelometer with a light source for illuminating the sample and one or more photoelectric detectors with a readout device to indicate the intensity of light scattered at right angles to the path of the incident light. The turbidimeter should be so designed that little stray light reaches the detector in the absence of turbidity and it should be free from significant drift after a short warm-up period. The sensitivity of the instrument should permit detection of turbidity differences of 0.02 unit or less in waters having turbidity of less than 1 unit. The instrument should measure from 0 to 40 units of turbidity. Several ranges will be necessary to obtain both adequate coverage and sufficient sensitivity for low turbidities.

The sample tubes to be used with the available instrument must be of clear colorless glass. They should be kept scrupulously clean, both inside and out, and discarded when they become scratched or etched. They must not be handled at all where the light strikes them, but should be provided with sufficient extra length, or with a protective case, so that they may be handled properly. The tubes should be filled with samples and standards which have been thoroughly agitated, and sufficient time should be allowed for bubbles to escape.

Differences in physical design of turbidimeters will cause differences in measured values for turbidity even though the same suspension is used for calibration. To minimize such differences, the following design criteria should be observed:

a. Light source—Tungsten lamp operated at not less than 85% of rated voltage or more than rated voltage.

b. Distance traversed by incident light and scattered light, within the sample tube—Total not to exceed 10 cm.

c. Angle of light acceptance of the detector—Centered at 90° to the incident light path and not to exceed ±30° from 90°.

d. Maximum turbidity to be measured, 40 units.

3. Reagents

a. Turbidity-free water: Pass distilled water through a membrane filter having a pore size no greater than 100 mμ, if such filtered water shows a lower turbidity than the distilled water. Discard the first 200 ml collected. Otherwise, use the distilled water.

b. Stock turbidity suspension:

1) SOLUTION I—Dissolve 1.000 g hydrazine sulfate, $(NH_2)_2 \cdot H_2SO_4$, in distilled water and dilute to 100 ml in a volumetric flask.

2) SOLUTION II—Dissolve 10.00 g hexamethylenetetramine, $(CH_2)_6N_4$, in distilled water and dilute to 100 ml in a volumetric flask.

3) In a 100-ml volumetric flask, mix 5.0 ml solution I with 5.0 ml solution II. Allow to stand 24 hr at 25 ± 3 C, then dilute to the mark and mix. The turbidity of this suspension is 400 units.

4) Prepare solutions and suspensions monthly.

c. Standard turbidity suspension: Dilute 10.00 ml stock turbidity suspension to 100 ml with turbidity-free water. Prepare weekly. The turbidity of this suspension is defined as 40 units.

d. Dilute turbidity standards: Dilute portions of the standard turbidity suspension with turbidity-free water as required. Prepare weekly.

4. Procedure

a. Turbidimeter calibration: Follow the manufacturer's operating instructions. In the absence of a precalibrated scale, prepare calibration curves for each range of the instrument. Check the accuracy of any supplied calibration scales on an already calibrated instrument by the use of appropriate standards in the range of interest. Run at least one standard in each instrument range to be used. On those instruments which allow adjustment of sensitivity so that scale values will correspond to turbidities, *do not rely on a manufacturer's solid scattering standard for setting overall instrument sensitivity for all ranges unless the turbidimeter has been shown to be free of drift on all ranges.*

b. Measurement of turbidities less than 40 units: Shake the sample to disperse the solids thoroughly. Wait until air bubbles disappear, then pour the sample into the turbidimeter tube. Read the turbidity directly from the instrument scale or from the appropriate calibration curve.

c. Measurement of turbidities exceeding 40 units: Dilute the sample with one or more volumes of turbidity-free water until the turbidity falls between 30 and 40 units. Compute the turbidity of the original sample from the turbidity of the diluted sample and the dilution factor as shown in the calculation below. For example, if 5 volumes of turbidity-free water were added to 1 volume of sample and the diluted sample showed a turbidity of 30 units, then the turbidity of the original sample was 180 units.

Use the stock turbidity suspension of 400 units for those cases where it is necessary to calibrate turbidity for the continuous monitoring of waters which exceed 40 turbidity units. Hold the total distance traversed by incident light and scattered light to the absolute minimum consistent with low background readings if high turbidities are to be determined by the measurement of scattered-light intensities. High turbidities determined by direct measurement are likely to differ appreciably from those determined by the dilution technic.

5. Calculation

$$\text{Turbidity units} = \frac{A \times (B + C)}{C}$$

where A = turbidity units found in diluted sample, B = volume of dilution water used in ml, and C = sample volume in ml taken for dilution.

6. Interpretation of Results

a. Report turbidity readings in accordance with the following schedule:

Turbidity Range in Units	Record to the Nearest
0–1.0	0.05
1–10	0.1
10–40	1
40–100	5
100–400	10
400–1000	50
>1000	100

b. For comparison of water treatment efficiencies, it may be desirable to estimate turbidity more closely than is specified in the above tabulation. However, the uncertainties and discrepancies in turbidity measurements make it unlikely that two or more laboratories will duplicate results on the same sample more closely than specified.

163 B. Visual Methods

1. General Discussion

a. Principle: Turbidity measurements by the candle turbidimeter are based on the light path through a suspension which just causes the image of the flame of a standard candle to disappear—that is, to become indistinguishable against the general background illumination—when the flame is viewed through the suspension. The longer the light path, the lower the turbidity.

b. Interference: The determination of turbidity is applicable to the water sample that is free of debris and coarse sediments which settle out rapidly. Dirty glassware, the presence of air bubbles, and the effects of vibrations which disturb the surface visibility of the sample will lead to false results.

2. Apparatus

a. Candle turbidimeter: The instrument consists of a glass tube calibrated according to Table 163(1), a standard candle, and a support which aligns the candle and the tube. The glass tube and the candle are supported in a vertical position so that the center line of the tube passes through the center line of the candle. The candle support consists of a spring-loaded cylinder designed to keep the top of the candle pressed against the top of the support as the candle gradually burns away.

TABLE 163(1): GRADUATION OF CANDLE TURBIDIMETER

Light Path * *cm*	Turbidity Units	Light Path * *cm*	Turbidity Units
2.3	1,000	11.4	190
2.6	900	12.0	180
2.9	800	12.7	170
3.2	700	13.5	160
3.5	650	14.4	150
3.8	600	15.4	140
4.1	550	16.6	130
4.5	500	18.0	120
4.9	450	19.6	110
5.5	400	21.5	100
5.6	390	22.6	95
5.8	380	23.8	90
5.9	370	25.1	85
6.1	360	26.5	80
6.3	350	28.1	75
6.4	340	29.8	70
6.6	330	31.8	65
6.8	320	34.1	60
7.0	310	36.7	55
7.3	300	39.8	50
7.5	290	43.5	45
7.8	280	48.1	40
8.1	270	54.0	35
8.4	260	61.8	30
8.7	250	72.9	25
9.1	240		
9.5	230		
9.9	220		
10.3	210		
10.8	200		

* Measured from inside bottom of glass tube.

The top of the support for the candle must be 7.6 cm (3 in.) below the bottom of the glass tube. The glass tube must have a flat, polished optical-glass bottom and must conform to the specifications for nessler tubes as described in the General Introduction, Section 000A.6. It must be kept clean and free from scratches. The glass tube is graduated to read directly in turbidity units. Most of the glass tube should be enclosed in a metal tube when observations are being made, both for the sake of protection against breakage and in order to exclude extraneous light.

The Candle is made of beeswax and spermaceti, designed to burn within the limits of 114 to 126 grains per hour. To insure uniform results, the flame must be kept as near constant size and constant distance from the bottom of the glass tube as possible; this will require frequent trimming of the charred portion of the wick and frequent observations to be sure the candle is pushed to the top of its support. All drafts must be eliminated during measurements to prevent the flame from flickering. The candle must burn for no more than a few minutes at a time, as the flame has a tendency to increase in size. Before the candle is lighted each time, such portions of the charred wick must be removed as can easily be broken off when manipulated with the fingers.

b. Bottles for visual comparison: A matched set of 1-liter capacity, glass-stoppered bottles made of pyrex or other resistant glass.

3. Preparation of Standard Suspensions

a. Turbidity-free water: See Section 163A.3a.

b. Visual comparison standards: Prepare from natural turbid water (1) or kaolin (2).

1) NATURAL WATER—For best results, prepare from the natural turbid water of the same source as that to be tested. Determine turbidity with the nephelometer or candle turbidimeter, then dilute portions of the suspension to the turbidity values desired.

Prepare weekly suspensions of turbidities below 25 units by dilution of a more concentrated suspension which has been freshly checked.

2) KAOLIN—Add approximately 5 g kaolin to 1 liter distilled water, thoroughly agitate, and allow to stand for 24 hr. Withdraw the supernate without disturbing the sediment at the bottom. Determine turbidity with the nephelometer or candle turbidimeter. Dilute portions of the suspension to the turbidity values desired. Preserve standard suspensions by the addition of 1 g mercuric chloride to 1 liter of suspension. Shake the suspensions vigorously before each reading and check at least once a month with the nephelometer or candle turbidimeter.

4. Procedure

a. Estimation with candle turbidimeter:

1) TURBIDITIES BETWEEN 25 AND 1,000 UNITS—Pour the shaken sample into the glass tube until the image of the candle flame just disappears from view. At this stage, make certain that a uniformly illuminated field with no bright spots materializes. Add the sample slowly toward the end. After the image has been made to disappear, remove 1% of the sample to make the flame image visible again. Employ a pipet to add or remove small amounts of the sample at the end. Keep the

glass tube clean both inside and outside, and avoid scratching the glass. The accumulation of soot or moisture on the bottom of the tube will interfere with the accuracy of the results.

2) TURBIDITIES EXCEEDING 1,000 UNITS—Dilute the sample with 1 or more volumes of turbidity-free water until the turbidity falls below 1,000 units. Compute the turbidity of the original sample from the turbidity of the diluted sample and the dilution factor. For example, if 5 volumes of turbidity-free water were added to 1 volume of sample and the diluted sample showed a turbidity of 500 units, then the turbidity of the original sample was 3,000 units.

b. Estimation with bottle standards: In the range 5–100 units, compare shaken samples with standard suspensions made by diluting concentrated standard suspensions with turbidity-free water in known ratios. Place the sample and the standards in bottles of the same size, shape and type, leaving enough empty space at the top of each bottle to allow adequate shaking before each reading. Compare the sample and the standards through the sides of the bottles by looking through them at the same object and noting the distinctness with which such objects as ruled lines or newsprint can be seen. Arrange the artificial lighting above or below the bottles so that no direct light reaches the eye. Record the turbidity of the sample as that of the standard which produces the visual effect most closely approximating that of the sample.

5. Calculation

See Section 163A.5.

6. Interpretation of Results

Record the turbidity readings in the following manner:

Turbidity Range *units*	Record to Nearest:
0 – 1.0	0.1
1 – 10	1
10 –100	5
100 –400	10
400 –700	50
700 or more	100

Identify the visual approach (whether candle turbidimeter or bottle standards) used for the turbidity estimation.

163 C. Bibliography

WHIPPLE, G. C. & D. D. JACKSON. 1900. A comparative study of the methods used for the measurement of turbidity of water. *Massachusetts Inst. Technol. Quart.* 13:274.

AMERICAN PUBLIC HEALTH ASSOCIATION. 1901. Report of Committee on Standard Methods of Water Analysis. *APHA Pub. Health Papers & Reports* 27:377.

WELLS, P. V. 1922. Turbidimetry of water. *JAWWA* 9:488.

BAYLIS, J. R. 1926. Turbidimeter for accurate measurement of low turbidities. *Ind. Eng. Chem.* 18:311.

WELLS, P. V. 1927. The present status of turbidity measurements. *Chem. Rev.* 3:331.

BAYLIS, J. R. 1933. Turbidity determinations. *Water Works & Sew.* 80:125.

ROSE, H. E. & H. B. LLOYD. 1946. On the measurement of the size characteristics of powders by photo-extinction methods. *J. Soc. Chem. Ind.* (London) 65:52 (Feb.); 65:55 (Mar.).

ROSE, H. E. & C. C. J. FRENCH. 1948. On the extinction coefficient: Particle size relationship for fine mineral powders. *J. Soc. Chem. Ind.* (London) 67:283.

GILLETT, T. R., P. F. MEADS & A. L. HOLVEN. 1949. Measuring color and turbidity of white sugar solutions. *Anal. Chem.* 21:1228.

JULLANDER, I. 1949. A simple method for the measurement of turbidity. *Acta Chem. Scandinav.* 3:1309.

ROSE, H. E. 1950. Powder-size measurement by a combination of the methods of nephelometry and photo-extinction. *J. Soc. Chem. Ind.* (London) 69:266.

———. 1950. The design and use of photo-extinction sedimentometers. *Engineering* 169:350, 405.

BRICE, B. A., M. HALWER & R. SPEISER. 1950. Photoelectric light-scattering photometer for determining high molecular weights. *J. Optical Soc. America* 40: 768.

KNIGHT, A. G. 1950. The measurement of turbidity in water. *J. Inst. Water Eng.* 4:449.

HANYA, T. 1950. Study of suspended matter in water. *Bull. Chem. Soc. Japan* 23: 216.

JULLANDER, I. 1950. Turbidimetric investigations on viscose. *Svensk Papperstidn.* 22:1.

ROSE, H. E. 1951. A reproducible standard for the calibration of turbidimeters. *J. Inst. Water Eng.* 5:310.

AITKEN, R. W. & D. MERCER. 1951. Comment on "The measurement of turbidity in water." *J. Inst. Water Eng.* 5:328.

ROSE, H. E. 1951. The analysis of water by the assessment of turbidity. *J. Inst. Water Eng.* 5:521.

KNIGHT, A. G. 1951. The measurement of turbidity in water: A reply. *J. Inst. Water Eng.* 5:633.

STAATS, F. C. 1952. Measurement of color, turbidity, hardness, and silica in industrial waters. Preprint 156, American Society for Testing and Materials, Philadelphia.

PALIN, A. T. 1955. Photometric determination of the colour and turbidity of water. *Water & Water Eng.* 59:341.

CONLEY, W. R. & R. W. PITMAN. 1957. Microphotometer turbidity analysis. *JAWWA* 49:63.

PACKHAM, R. F. 1962. The preparation of turbidity standards. *Proc. Soc. Water Treatment & Exam.* 11:64.

BAALSRUD, K. & A. HENRIKSEN. 1964. Measurement of suspended matter in stream water. *JAWWA* 56:1194.

HOATHER, R. C. 1964. Comparison of different methods for measurement of turbidity. *Proc. Soc. Water Treatment & Exam.* 13:89.

EDEN, G. E. 1965. The measurement of turbidity in water. A progress report on the work of the analytical panel. *Proc. Soc. Water Treatment & Exam.* 14:27.

BLACK, A. P. & S. A. HANNAH. 1965. Measurement of low turbidities. *JAWWA* 57:901.

164 VANADIUM

Laboratory and epidemiologic evidence suggests that vanadium may play a beneficial role in the prevention of heart disease. In New Mexico, which has a low incidence of heart disease, vanadium has been found in concentrations of 20–150 μg/l. In a state where incidence of heart disease is high, vanadium was not found in the water supplies. Counterbalancing the favorable effects of trace vanadium concentrations, the pentoxide dust is reported to cause gastrointestinal and respiratory disturbances. The mean concentration found in U.S. drinking waters is 6 μg/l. Industrial applications of vanadium include dyeing, ceramics, ink and catalyst manufacture, and discharges from such sources can contribute to its presence in a water supply.

164 A. Gallic Acid Method (TENTATIVE)

1. General Discussion

a. Principle: The determination of trace amounts of vanadium in water is calculated by considering the catalytic effect it exerts on the rate of oxidation of gallic acid by persulfate in acid solution. Under the given conditions of concentrations of reactants, temperature and reaction time, the extent of oxidation of gallic acid is proportional to the existing concentration of vanadium. Vanadium is determined by measuring the absorbance of the sample at 415 mμ and comparing it with standard solutions treated in an identical manner.

b. Interference: The substances listed in Table 164(1) will interfere in

TABLE 164(1): CONCENTRATION AT WHICH VARIOUS IONS INTERFERE IN THE DETERMINATION OF VANADIUM

Ion	Concentration *mg/l*
Chromium (VI)	1.0
Cobalt (II)	1.0
Copper (II)	0.05
Iron (II)	0.3
Iron (III)	0.5
Molybdenum (VI)	0.1
Nickel (II)	3.0
Silver	2.0
Uranium (VI)	3.0
Bromide	0.1
Chloride	100.0
Iodide	0.001

the determination of vanadium if the specified concentrations are exceeded. This is not a serious problem for chromium, cobalt, molybdenum, nickel, silver and uranium, as the tolerable concentration is greater than that commonly encountered in fresh water. However, in some samples the tolerable concentration of copper and iron may be exceeded. Because of the high sensitivity of the method, interfering substances in concentrations only slightly above tolerance limits can be rendered harmless by dilution.

Traces of bromide and iodide interfere seriously, and dilution alone will not always reduce the concentration below tolerance limits. Mercuric ion may be added to complex these halides and minimize their interference; however, the mercuric ion itself interferes if an excess is present. The addition of 350 μg of mercuric nitrate per sample permits the determination of vanadium in the presence of up to 100 mg/l chloride ion and 250 μg/l each of bromide and iodide. Samples containing high concentrations of these ions must be diluted below the above values and mercuric nitrate must be added.

c. Minimum detectable concentration: 0.025 μg.

2. Apparatus

a. Water bath, capable of temperature control to 25 ± 0.5 C.

b. Colorimetric equipment—One of the following is required:

1) SPECTROPHOTOMETER, for measurements at 415 mμ, with a light path of 1–5 cm.

2) FILTER PHOTOMETER, providing a light path of 1–5 cm and equipped with a violet filter exhibiting maximum transmittance near 415 mμ.

3. Reagents

a. Stock vanadium solution: Dissolve 229.6 mg ammonium metavanadate, NH_4VO_3, in a volumetric flask containing approximately 800 ml distilled water and 15 ml of 1 + 1 nitric acid. Dilute to the 1,000-ml mark; 1.00 ml = 100 μg V.

b. Intermediate vanadium solution: Dilute 10.00 ml stock vanadium solution with distilled water to 1,000 ml in a volumetric flask; 1.00 ml = 1.00 μg V.

c. Standard vanadium solution: Dilute 10.00 ml intermediate vanadium solution with distilled water to 1,000 ml in a volumetric flask; 1.00 ml = 0.010 μg V.

d. Mercuric nitrate solution: Dissolve 350 mg $Hg(NO_3)_2 \cdot H_2O$ in 1,000 ml distilled water.

e. Ammonium persulfate-phosphoric acid reagent: Dissolve 2.5 g $(NH_4)_2S_2O_8$ in 25 ml distilled or demineralized water. Bring just to a boil, and then remove the heat and add 25 ml concentrated H_3PO_4. Let it stand approximately 24 hr before use and discard after 48 hr.

f. Gallic acid solution: Dissolve 2 g $H_6C_7O_5$ in 100 ml warm distilled water, heat to a temperature just below boiling, and filter through Whatman No. 42 paper or equivalent. Prepare a fresh solution for each set of samples.

4. Procedure

a. Preparation of standards and sample: Prepare both blank and sufficient standards by diluting 0–8.0 ml aliquots (0–0.08 μg V) of the standard vanadium solution to 10 ml with distilled or demineralized water. Pipet a volume of water sample (10.00 ml maximum) containing less than 0.08 μg V into a suitable container and adjust the volume to 10.0 ml with distilled or demineralized water. Decolorize or filter colored or turbid samples before starting the analysis. Add 1.0 ml mercuric nitrate solution to each of the blanks, standards, and samples. Place the containers in a water bath regulated to 25 ± 0.5 C and allow 30 to 45 min for the samples to come to the temperature of the bath.

b. Color development and measurement: Add 1.0 ml ammonium persulfate-phosphoric acid reagent (temperature equilibrated), swirl to mix thoroughly, and return to the water bath. Add 1.0 ml gallic acid solution (temperature equilibrated), swirl to mix thoroughly, and return to the water bath. Add the gallic acid to successive samples at intervals of 30 sec or longer to permit accurate control of the reaction time. Exactly 60 min after addition of the gallic acid, remove the sample from the water bath and measure its absorbance at 415 mμ, using distilled water as a reference. Subtract the absorbance of the blank from the absorbance of each standard and unknown. Construct a calibration curve by plotting the absorbance values of standards versus micrograms of vanadium. Determine the amount of vanadium in an unknown sample by referring to the corresponding absorbance on the calibration curve. Prepare a calibration curve with each set of samples.

5. Calculation

$$\text{mg/l V} = \frac{\mu\text{g V}}{\text{ml sample}}$$

6. Precision and Accuracy

In a synthetic unknown sample containing 6 μg/l V, 40 μg/l As, 250 μg/l Be, 240 μg/l B, and 20 μg/l Se in distilled water, vanadium was determined with a relative standard deviation of 20% and no relative error in 22 laboratories.

7. Bibliography

FISHMAN, M. J. & M. V. SKOUGSTAD. 1964. Catalytic determination of vanadium in water. *Anal. Chem.* 36:1643.

165 ZINC

Zinc is an essential and beneficial element in body growth. However, concentrations above 5 mg/l can cause a bitter astringent taste and an opalescence in alkaline waters. The zinc concentration of U.S. drinking waters has been reported to vary between 0.06 and 7.0 mg/l, with a mean of 1.33 mg/l. Zinc most commonly enters the domestic water supply from the deterioration of galvanized iron and the dezincification of brass. In such cases the presence of lead and cadmium may additionally be suspected, because they are impurities of the zinc used in galvanizing. Zinc may also appear as a result of industrial waste pollution.

1. Selection of method: Where the equipment is available, the atomic absorption spectrophotometric method is generally preferred for the determination of zinc. The dithizone and zincon colorimetric methods are useful in the absence of the sophisticated instrumentation.

2. Sampling and storage: Samples should preferably be analyzed within 6 hr after collection. The addition of hydrochloric acid will preserve the metallic ion content but requires that: (a) the acid be zinc-free; (b) the sample bottles be rinsed with acid before use; and (c) the samples be evaporated to dryness in silica dishes before they are analyzed to remove the excess HCl.

165 A. Atomic Absorption Spectrophotometric Method

See Metals, Section 129A.

165 B. Dithizone Method

1. General Discussion

a. Principle: Nearly 20 metals are capable of reacting with diphenylthiocarbazone (dithizone) to produce colored coordination compounds. These dithizonates are extractable into organic solvents such as carbon tetrachloride. Most interferences can be overcome in the zinc-dithizone reaction by adjusting the solution to pH 4.0 to 5.5 and by the addition of sufficient sodium thiosulfate. Zinc also forms a weak thiosulfate complex that tends to retard the reaction between zinc and dithizone, a reaction which is demonstrably slow and incomplete. For this reason, the determination is empirical and demands the use of an identical technic in both standardization and actual sample analysis. The duration and vigor of shaking, the volumes of sample, sodium thiosulfate and dithizone, and the pH should all be kept constant.

b. Interference: Interference from bismuth, cadmium, cobalt, copper, gold, lead, mercury, nickel, palladium, silver and stannous tin in the small quantities found in potable waters is eliminated by complexing with sodium thiosulfate and by pH adjustment. Ferric iron, residual chlorine, and other oxidizing agents convert dithizone to a yellow-brown color. The zinc-dithizone reaction is extremely sensitive, and unusual precautions must be taken to avoid contamination. Experience has shown that high and erratic blanks are often traceable to glass containing zinc oxide, surface-contaminated glassware, rubber products, stopcock greases, reagent-grade chemicals, and distilled water. The extreme sensitivity of the reaction makes it desirable to prepare and segregate glassware especially for this determination, and to extract reagents with dithizone solution to remove all traces of zinc and contaminating metals. Dithizone and dithizonates decompose rapidly in strong light. Analyses should be performed in subdued light and the solutions should not be exposed to the light of the photometer for a longer period than is necessary. Direct sunlight should also be avoided at all times.

c. Minimum detectable concentration: 1 μg Zn.

2. Apparatus

a. Colorimetric equipment: One of the following should be used, although it is also possible to make visual comparisons directly in separatory funnels:

1) SPECTROPHOTOMETER, for use at either 535 or 620 mμ, providing a light path of 2 cm.

2) FILTER PHOTOMETER, providing a light path of 2 cm and equipped with either a green filter having maximum transmittance near 535 mμ or a red filter having maximum transmittance near 620 mμ.

3) NESSLER TUBES, matched.

b. Separatory funnels, capacity 125–150 ml, Squibb form, preferably with inert teflon stopcocks. If the funnels are of identical size and shape, visual color comparisons may be made directly in them.

c. Glassware: All glassware should be rinsed with 1 + 1 HNO_3, followed by zinc-free water to avoid contamination errors.

d. pH meter.

3. Reagents

a. Zinc-free water: Use redistilled or deionized distilled water for rinsing apparatus and the preparation of solutions and dilutions.

b. Stock zinc solution: Dissolve 100.0 mg 30-mesh zinc metal in a slight excess of 1 + 1 HCl; about 1 ml is required. Then dilute to 1,000 ml with zinc-free water; 1.00 ml = 100 μg Zn.

c. Standard zinc solution: Dilute 10.00 ml zinc stock solution to 1,000 ml with zinc-free water; 1.00 ml = 1.00 μg Zn.

d. Hydrochloric acid, 0.02*N*: Dilute 1.0 ml conc HCl to 600 ml with zinc-free water. If high blanks are traced to this reagent, dilute conc HCl with an equal volume of distilled water and redistill in an all-pyrex still.

e. Sodium acetate, 2*N*: Dissolve 68 g $NaC_2H_3O_2 \cdot 3H_2O$ and dilute to 250 ml with zinc-free water.

f. Acetic acid, 1 + 7. Use zinc-free water.

g. Acetate buffer solution: Mix equal volumes of 2*N* sodium acetate solution and 1 + 7 acetic acid solution. Extract with 10-ml portions of dithizone solution (I) until the last extract remains green; then extract with carbon tetrachloride to remove excess dithizone.

h. Sodium thiosulfate solution: Dissolve 25 g $Na_2S_2O_3 \cdot 5H_2O$ in 100 ml zinc-free water. Purify by dithizone extraction as in ¶ 3g above.

i. Dithizone solution (I): Dissolve 100 mg diphenylthiocarbazone * in 1 liter carbon tetrachloride. Store in a brown glass-stoppered bottle in a refrigerator. If the solution is of doubtful quality or has been stored for a long time, the following test for deterioration can be applied: Shake 10 ml with 10 ml 1 + 99 NH_4OH. If the lower, CCl_4, layer is only slightly yellow, the reagent is in good condition.

j. Dithizone solution (II): Dilute 1 volume of dithizone solution (I) with 9 volumes of CCl_4. If stored in a brown glass-stoppered bottle in a refrigerator, this solution is good for several weeks.

k. Carbon tetrachloride.

l. Sodium citrate solution: Dissolve 10 g $Na_3C_6H_5O_7 \cdot 2H_2O$ in 90 ml zinc-free water. Purify by dithizone extraction as in ¶ 3g preceding. Use this reagent in the final cleansing of glassware.

4. Procedure

a. Preparation of colorimetric standards: To a series of 125-ml Squibb separatory funnels, thoroughly cleansed as described in ¶ 2c above, add 0, 1.00, 2.00, 3.00, 4.00 and 5.00 ml standard zinc solution equivalent, respectively, to provide 0, 1.00, 2.00, 3.00, 4.00 and 5.00 μg Zn. Bring each volume up to 10.0 ml by adding zinc-free water. To each funnel add 5.0 ml acetate buffer and 1.0 ml sodium thiosulfate solution and mix. The pH should be between 4 and 5.5 at this point. To each funnel add 10.0 ml dithizone solution (II), stopper, and shake vigorously for 4.0 min. Allow the layers to separate. Dry the stem of the funnel with strips of filter paper and run the lower CCl_4 layer into a clean *dry* absorption cell.

b. Photometric measurement: Either the red color of the zinc dithizonate can be measured at 535 mμ, or the green color of the unreacted dithizone at 620 mμ.

Set the photometer at 100% transmittance with the blank if the 535-mμ wavelength is selected; but if 620 mμ is used, set the blank at 10.0% transmittance. Plot a calibration curve. Run a new calibration curve with each set of samples.

c. Treatment of samples: If the zinc content is not within the working range, dilute the sample with zinc-free water or concentrate it in a silica dish. If the sample has been preserved with acid, evaporate an aliquot to dryness in a silica dish to remove the excess acid. Do not neutralize with sodium or ammonium hydroxide, as these alkalis usually contain excessive amounts of zinc. Using a pH meter and accounting for any dilution, adjust the sample to pH 2–3 with HCl. Transfer 10.0 ml to a separatory funnel. Complete the analysis as described in ¶ 4a, beginning with the words "To each funnel add 5.0 ml acetate buffer" and continuing to the end of the paragraph.

d. Visual comparison: If a photo-

* Eastman No. 3092 or equivalent.

metric instrument is not available, run the samples and standards at the same time. Compare the CCl_4 layers directly in the separatory funnels if these match in size and shape; otherwise transfer to matched test tubes or nessler tubes. The range of colors obtained with various amounts of zinc are roughly these:

Zinc μg	Color
0 (blank)	green
1	blue
2	blue-violet
3	violet
4	red-violet
5	red-violet

5. Calculation

$$\text{mg/l Zn} = \frac{\mu\text{g Zn}}{\text{ml sample}}$$

6. Precision and Accuracy

A synthetic unknown sample containing 650 μg/l Zn, 500 μg/l Al, 50 μg/l Cd, 110 μg/l Cr, 470 μg/l Cu, 300 μg/l Fe, 70 μg/l Pb, 120 μg/l Mn and 150 μg/l Ag in distilled water was determined by the dithizone method with a relative standard deviation of 18.2% and a relative error of 25.9% in 46 laboratories.

165 C. Zincon Method *

1. General Discussion

a. Principle: Zinc forms a blue-colored complex with 2-carboxy-2′-hydroxy-5′-sulfoformazyl benzene (zincon) in a solution buffered to pH 9.0. Other heavy metals likewise form colored complexes. Heavy metals, including zinc, are complexed by cyanide. Chloral hydrate is added specifically to free the zinc from its cyanide complex. The zinc-zincon complex is measured before other heavy metal-cyanide complexes are destroyed by chloral hydrate. Sodium ascorbate reduces the interference of manganese. The final solutions are unstable and the procedure is designed to minimize the effects of color fading.

b. Interference: The following ions interfere in concentrations exceeding those listed:

Ion	*mg/l*	Ion	*mg/l*
Cd (II)	1	Cr (III)	10
Al (III)	5	Ni (II)	20
Mn (II)	5	Cu (II)	30
Fe (III)	7	Co (II)	30
Fe (II)	9	CrO_4 (II)	50

c. Minimum detectable concentration: 1 μg Zn.

2. Apparatus

COLORIMETRIC EQUIPMENT—One of the following is required:

a. Spectrophotometer, for measurements at 620 mμ, providing a light path of 1 cm or longer.

b. Filter photometer, providing a light path of 1 cm or longer and equipped with a red filter having maximum transmittance near 620 mμ. De-

* This method, with modifications, is identical in source and substance to ASTM D1691–67.

viation from Beer's law occurs when the filter band pass exceeds 20 mμ.

3. Reagents

a. Zinc-free water, for rinsing of apparatus and preparation of solutions and dilutions. Prepare as directed in Section 165B.3a.

b. Stock zinc solution: Prepare as directed in Section 165B.3b.

c. Standard zinc solution: Dilute 10.00 ml stock zinc solution to 100 ml with zinc-free water; 1.00 ml = 10.0 μg Zn.

d. Sodium ascorbate, fine granular powder.†

e. Potassium cyanide solution: Dissolve 1.00 g KCN in 50 ml zinc-free water and dilute to 100 ml. This solution is stable for approximately 60 days. CAUTION: *Poison—potassium cyanide is extremely poisonous and more than customary precautions should be observed in its handling. Never use mouth pipets to deliver volumes of cyanide solution.*

f. Buffer solution, pH 9.0: Prepare 1*N* NaOH by dissolving 40 g sodium hydroxide in 500 ml zinc-free water and diluting to 1,000 ml. Dilute 213 ml 1*N* NaOH to approximately 600 ml with zinc-free water. Dissolve 37.8 g potassium chloride, KCl, and 31.0 g boric acid, H_3BO_3, in the solution and dilute to 1 liter.

g. Zincon reagent: Prior to use, grind the entire supply of zincon powder and mix well if it is not uniform, as evidenced by the presence of different-colored particles. Dissolve 130 mg powdered 2-carboxy-2′-hydroxy-5′-sulfoformazyl benzene (zincon) in 100 ml methyl alcohol (methanol). Let stand overnight to complete dissolution of the zincon, or use a magnetic stirrer in a closed flask.

h. Chloral hydrate solution: Dissolve 10.0 g chloral hydrate in 50 ml zinc-free water and dilute to 100 ml. Filter if necessary.

i. Hydrochloric acid, conc.

j. Sodium hydroxide, 6N.

4. Procedure

a. Preparation of colorimetric standards: To a series of 50-ml erlenmeyer flasks, thoroughly cleansed, add 0, 0.25, 0.50, 1.00, 3.00, 5.00 and 7.00 ml standard zinc solution equivalent, respectively, to provide 0, 2.50, 5.00, 10.0, 30.0, 50.0 and 70.0 μg Zn. Bring each volume to 10.0 ml by adding zinc-free water. To each flask add, in sequence, mixing thoroughly after each addition, 0.5 g sodium ascorbate, 1.0 ml KCN solution, 5.0 ml buffer solution, and 3.00 ± 0.05 ml zincon solution. Add 3.0 ml chloral hydrate solution, note the time and mix. Transfer to the absorption cell and measure the absorbance at 620 mμ *exactly* 5 min after adding the chloral hydrate solution. Use the treated blank as the reference solution for initial balancing of the photometer. For greater accuracy in the range below 10 μg Zn, prepare a separate calibration curve for this range.

b. Treatment of water samples: If dissolved zinc is desired, filter the sample. If total zinc is desired, add 1 ml conc HCl to 50 ml thoroughly mixed sample and mix well to assure the dissolution of any precipitated zinc compound. Filter and adjust to pH 7 with 6*N* NaOH. Transfer a 10.0-ml aliquot of sample containing not more

† Hoffman-LaRoche or equivalent.

than 70 μg Zn to a 50-ml erlenmeyer flask. Complete the analysis as described in ¶ 4a above, beginning with the words "To each flask add, in sequence . . .," and continue to the end of the paragraph.

Prepare as a reference solution a sample aliquot treated as above, except that 3.0 ml zinc-free water is substituted for the 3.0 ml chloral hydrate. Use this reference solution to compensate for color, turbidity or interference not obviated by the procedure. Prepare as nearly simultaneously as possible with the sample aliquot.

5. Calculation

$$\text{mg/l Zn} = \frac{\mu\text{g Zn}}{\text{ml sample}}$$

6. Precision and Accuracy

A synthetic unknown sample containing 650 μg/l Zn, 500 μg/l Al, 50 μg/l Cd, 110 μg/l Cr, 470 μg/l Cu, 300 μg/l Fe, 70 μg/l Pb, 120 μg/l Mn and 150 μg/l Ag in distilled water was determined by the zincon method, with a relative standard deviation of 13.9% and a relative error of 17.4% in four laboratories.

165 D. Bibliography

Dithizone Method

HIBBARD, P. L. 1937. A dithizone method for measurement of small amounts of zinc. *Ind. Eng. Chem.*, Anal. Ed. 9:127.

SANDELL, E. B. 1937. Determination of copper, zinc, and lead in silicate rocks. *Ind. Eng. Chem.*, Anal. Ed. 9:464.

HIBBARD, P. L. 1938. Estimation of copper, zinc, and cobalt (with nickel) in soil extracts. *Ind. Eng. Chem.*, Anal. Ed. 10:615.

WICHMAN, H. J. 1939. Isolation and determination of traces of metals: The dithizone system. *Ind. Eng. Chem.*, Anal. Ed. 11:66.

COWLING, H. & E. J. MILLER. 1941. Determination of small amounts of zinc in plant materials: A photometric dithizone method. *Ind. Eng. Chem.*, Anal. Ed. 13:145.

ALEXANDER, O. R. & L. V. TAYLOR. 1944. Improved dithizone procedure for determination of zinc in foods. *J. Assoc. Official Agric. Chem.* 27:325.

SNELL, F. D. & C. T. SNELL. 1949. *Colorimetric Methods of Analysis* (3rd ed.). D. Van Nostrand Co., Princeton, N. J., Vol. 2, pp. 1–7, 412–419.

BARNES, H. 1951. The determination of zinc by dithizone. *Analyst* 76:220.

COOPER, S. S. & M. L. SULLIVAN. 1951. Spectrophotometric studies of dithizone and some dithizonates. *Anal. Chem.* 23:613.

SANDELL, E. B. 1959. *Colorimetric Determination of Traces of Metals* (3rd ed.). Interscience Publishers, New York, Chapter 49 and pp. 144–176.

Zincon Method

PLATTE, J. A. & V. M. MARCY. 1959. Photometric determination of zinc with zincon. *Anal. Chem.* 31:1274.

AMERICAN SOCIETY FOR TESTING AND MATERIALS. 1969. *Book of ASTM Standards*, Part 23. Water; Atmospheric analysis. ASTM, Philadelphia.

PART 200

PHYSICAL, CHEMICAL AND BIOASSAY EXAMINATION OF POLLUTED WATERS, WASTEWATERS, EFFLUENTS, BOTTOM SEDIMENTS AND SLUDGES

200 INTRODUCTION

The procedures described in Part 200 of this manual are intended for the physical and chemical examination of wastewaters of both domestic and industrial origin, treatment plant effluents, polluted waters, sludges and bottom sediments. An effort has been made to present methods which apply as generally as possible and to indicate modifications which are required for samples of unusual composition, such as certain industrial wastes. However, because of the wide variety of industrial wastes, the procedures given here cannot cover all possibilities and may not be suitable for all wastes and combinations of wastes. Hence, some modification of a procedure may be necessary in specific instances. Whenever a procedure is modified, the nature of the modification must be plainly stated in the report of results. The procedures which are indicated as being intended for the examination of sludges and bottom sediments may not apply without modification to chemical sludges or slurries.

200 A. Collection of Samples

Only representative samples should be used for examination. The great variety of conditions under which collections must be made renders it impossible to prescribe a fixed procedure. In general, the sampling procedure should take account both of the tests or analyses to be performed and of the purpose for which the results are needed.

When the purpose of testing is to determine average concentrations—for example, for the calculation of plant loading or plant efficiency—a 24-hr composite sample is considered standard for most determinations. When the purpose is to show peak concentrations, the duration of peak loads, or the occurrence of variations, grab or catch samples collected at suitable intervals, and separately analyzed, are more appropriate. The sampling interval should be chosen on the basis of the frequency with which changes may be expected, and may vary from as little as 5 min to as long as an hour or more. Under other circumstances, a composite sample representing one shift, or a shorter time period, or a complete cycle of a periodic operation may be required. Evaluation of the effects of special, variable or irregular discharges and operations may require composite samples representing the periods during which such wastes are present.

For determination of components or characteristics which are subject to significant and unavoidable changes on storage, composite samples cannot be used. Such determinations should be performed on individual samples as soon as possible after collection, and preferably at the sampling point.

Analyses for all dissolved gases, residual chlorine, soluble sulfides, temperature, and pH are examples of determinations of this type.

Individual portions should be taken in a wide-mouth bottle having a diameter of at least 35 mm at the mouth and a capacity of at least 120 ml. These portions should be collected each hour —in some cases each half hour or even every 5 min—and mixed at the end of the sampling period, or combined in a single bottle as collected. If preservatives are to be used, they should be added to the sample bottle initially, so that all portions of the composite are preserved as soon as collected. Analysis of individual samples may sometimes be necessary.

It is desirable, and often absolutely essential, to combine the individual samples in volumes proportionate to the volume of flow. A final volume of 2–3 liters is sufficient for sewage, effluents and wastes.

Automatic sampling devices are available but should not be used unless the sample is preserved as described below. Sampling devices, including bottles, should be cleaned daily of all growths of sewage organisms.

Great care must be used in sampling sewage sludges, sludge banks, and muds. No definite procedure can be given, but every possible precaution should be taken to obtain a representative sample.

200 B. Preservation of Samples

Preservation of samples is difficult because almost all preservatives interfere with some of the tests. Immediate analysis is ideal. Storage at a low temperature (4 C) is perhaps the best way to preserve most samples until the next day. Chemical preservatives are to be used only when they are shown not to interfere with the examinations being made. When used, they should be added to the sample bottle initially, so that all portions of the composite are preserved as soon as collected. No single method of preservation is entirely satisfactory, and the preservative should be chosen with due regard to the determinations that are to be made. All methods of preservation may be inadequate when applied to suspended matter. Formaldehyde affects so many of the determinations that its use is not recommended.

DISSOLVED OXYGEN—Samples for this determination are preserved as directed under Oxygen (Dissolved).

BIOCHEMICAL OXYGEN DEMAND—Samples must be free from all preservatives. When samples are composited, the individual or composite sample must be chilled immediately to 3–4 C and kept at this temperature during the compositing period. In samples stored at room temperature, the BOD may drop 10–40% within 6 hr, but in some instances it may rise.

CHEMICAL OXYGEN DEMAND—Samples for determining COD by the dichromate method should be preserved by adding sufficient H_2SO_4 to obtain a final pH value of 2–3.

a. Nitrogen balance: The nitrogen balance may be preserved for 24 hr by adding sufficient H_2SO_4 to produce 1,500 mg/l acidity in the sample, equivalent to pH 2–3. This treatment will lower the suspended matter and settleable matter and will not preserve the nitrogen balance longer than 24 hr.

b. Sludge and sediment samples: When analyses cannot be made immediately, samples may be preserved with 5 g sodium benzoate, or 1 ml conc H_2SO_4, for each 80 g of sample, provided that these preservatives do not interfere with the tests to be made. Sludge or mud samples cannot be preserved with chloroform or sodium benzoate when grease is to be determined.

200 C. Expression of Results

Results should be expressed as milligrams per liter (mg/l). If the concentration is less than 1 mg/l, the results may be expressed as micrograms per liter (μg/l). The use of micrograms per liter is encouraged when concentrations are less than 0.1 mg/l.

If the concentration is greater than 10,000 mg/l, the results should be expressed as a percent, 1% being equivalent to 10,000 mg/l. In solid samples and liquid wastes of high specific gravity, a correction must be made if the results are expressed as ppm or percent by weight:

$$\text{ppm by weight} = \frac{\text{mg/l}}{\text{sp gr}}$$

$$\text{\% by weight} = \frac{\text{mg/l}}{10{,}000 \times \text{sp gr}}$$

In such cases, if the result is given in mg/l, the specific gravity must be stated.

200 D. Methods Evaluation by the Committee

The Committee on Standard Methods of the Water Pollution Control Federation has attempted to establish the precision and accuracy of the methods in Part 200. For many methods, results were obtained from ten replicate determinations on 10 different days or, when necessary, from five replicate samples on 20 days.

Most methods studied were found to be statistically reliable, and the standard deviations given may be used with some confidence in statistical prediction. If a method has been found statistically unreliable, this is indicated in the statements on precision under the method. The standard deviations of unreliable methods cannot safely be used for statistical prediction, but may be of some value for indicating roughly the variation that may be expected.

In expressing the evaluation data on

each test, the number of analysts and determinations is given in shorthand form; for example, "$n = 5$; 56×10," which means that 5 different analysts ran 56 separate sets of 10 determinations each, making a total of 560 determinations. Usually the precision is expressed as the standard deviation in original units of measurement—i.e., milligrams or milliliters. In a few instances, the precision is expressed as the coefficient of variation C_v (the ratio of the standard deviation to the average), expressed as a percentage:

$$C_v = \frac{100\,\sigma}{\bar{x}}$$

The standard deviation given with each method is based on careful laboratory examination. No attempt has been made to obtain the standard deviation under research conditions, or with the use of specially calibrated apparatus or glassware. The values given are to be regarded as provisional in nature and subject to change on further study. In general, the standard deviations given may be regarded as being too high rather than too low.

200 E. Bibliography

JEWELL, M. E. 1920. Experiments on the preservation of mud samples. *Illinois State Water Survey Bull.* 16:206.

HATFIELD, W. D. & G. E. PHILLIPS. 1941. Preservation of sewage samples. *Water Works & Sew.* 88:285.

201 ACIDITY AND ALKALINITY

Acidity and alkalinity measurements provide a quantitative measure of the ability of a given sample to neutralize strong bases or strong acids, respectively, to an arbitrarily designated pH or indicator end point. Both results are expressed as mg/l $CaCO_3$, implying an acidity which is theoretically neutralized by this amount of $CaCO_3$, or an alkalinity which is equivalent to this amount of $CaCO_3$. The magnitude of the measured value may vary significantly with the end-point pH used in the determination. Acidity and alkalinity are measures of a gross property of the sample and cannot be interpreted in terms of specific substances unless the general chemical composition of the sample is known. The hydroxide-carbonate - bicarbonate relationships based upon alkalinity measurements which are discussed in Part 100 are not generally applicable to polluted waters or waste systems.

In addition to providing information relative to the amounts of acid or base required to neutralize a given sample to a specific pH, these measurements provide an indication of changes if the source of the sample is known to have generally stable operating levels of alkalinity or acidity. The general significance of these measurements is indicated under the sample types listed under Procedure, ¶ 4d below.

1. General Discussion

a. Principles: Acidity and alkalinity, as defined by these methods, are relative quantities dependent upon the end-point indicator or pH employed. For purposes of standardization of the analysis procedures, the end points of pH 3.7 (methyl orange) and 8.3 (phenolphthalein) have been selected arbitrarily. Since industrial wastewaters may contain considerable acidity or alkalinity of a noncarbonate nature, the pH of 3.7, at the extreme end of the methyl orange indicator range, has been selected arbitrarily as the point to which titrations should be carried. The sliding equivalence pH range from 5 to 4 recommended in Part 100 for the titration of unpolluted waters, where the carbon dioxide, carbonate and bicarbonate equilibrium normally prevails, may be inapplicable to wastewater samples.

A sample of intermediate pH will therefore exhibit both alkalinity to methyl orange and acidity to phenolphthalein. This will be true even if the sample happens to be originally at pH 7.0, the neutral point of the pH scale.

The titrations to the designated standard pH values may not represent complete neutralization of all acidity or alkalinity components, but are to be employed unless a potentiometric titration curve indicates a distinct inflection point which can be employed to definite advantage when dealing with known components of a sample. The potentiometric end-point pH or indicator used should be specified with the results of the analysis.

Extreme care must be exercised when attempts are made to interpret the results of acidity and alkalinity determinations in terms of specific chemical components in the sample rather than as a gross characteristic of the sample, which represents the summation of all components either wholly or partially titrated. Certain empirical classifications of acidity and alkalinity have found practical application as indicators of pollution or wastewater effluent changes. These are the designations of "methyl orange and phenolphthalein acidity or alkalinity."

Methyl orange acidity is represented by the acidity determined by titration with NaOH to pH 3.7 (methyl orange end point). It represents the sum of all strong mineral acids, partial neutralization of weak organic and inorganic acids, and possibly some hydrolysis.

Phenolphthalein acidity is determined by titration with NaOH to pH 8.3 (phenolphthalein end point). It represents the sum of methyl orange acidity, plus a major portion of acidity due to weak organic acids, weak inorganic acids, and metal ions hydrolyzing or forming hydrous oxide precipitates.

In a similar manner, titrations with standard acid solutions to pH 8.3 (phenolphthalein end point) or pH 3.7 (methyl orange end point) represent phenolphthalein alkalinity and methyl orange alkalinity respectively. Phenolphthalein alkalinity is a measure of the sum of free hydroxide, carbonate and other organic or inorganic substances partially or wholly neutralized at pH 8.3. Methyl orange alkalinity represents the sum of phenolphthalein alkalinity, plus a major portion of the alkalinity due to weak organic and inorganic bases.

The terms "free acidity or alkalinity"

and "total acidity or alkalinity" are not generally applicable to polluted water and wastewater samples, and their use should be avoided to prevent misinterpretation of the data.

b. Selection of method: The standard methods for the determination of acidity and alkalinity in wastewaters and polluted water are essentially those presented in Part 100. The principal difference rests in the pH value specified for the end point. The pH 3.7 (methyl orange) and pH 8.3 (phenolphthalein) end points have been designated arbitrarily for the standard methods, for reasons explained in Section 201.1a. However, for control purposes where sufficient information is available with respect to known components in a waste sample, the use of any other pH or color indicator corresponding to an inflection point in a potentiometric titration may provide useful information. Other color indicators changing color close to the methyl orange end point may be substituted by the analyst for convenience in routine control testing, but will not constitute a standard method analysis. In all cases, the specific indicator or pH used should be specified with the results. (See ¶ 5, following.)

The potentiometric titration using a properly calibrated pH meter or electrically operated titrimeter is to be employed for colored or turbid waters and for all cases where difficulties arise in determining a color indicator end point.

For industrial wastes such as iron pickle liquors, acid mine drainage, or other samples containing appreciable amounts of iron, aluminum or other hydrolyzable metal salts, the alkalinity and acidity should be determined by the hot titration procedure.

c. Selection of sample size and reagent normalities: The range of acidities and alkalinities found in wastewaters and polluted waters is so large that a single sample size and normality of acid or base used as a titrant cannot be specified. It is desirable to use a sufficiently large volume of titrant (20 ml or more from a 50-ml buret) to obtain good relative precision in the volume measurement, while at the same time keeping the sample volume sufficiently small to permit sharp end points. The following table serves as a guide to the selection of sample size and titrant normality for various ranges of acidities and alkalinities:

Sample Range mg/l $CaCO_3$	Normality of Titrant	Sample Size *ml*
0–500	0.0200	100
400–1000	0.0200	50
500–1250	0.0500	100
1000–2500	0.0500	50
1000–2500	0.1000	100
2000–5000	0.1000	50
4000–10,000	0.1000	25

d. Sampling and storage: Samples should be collected in polyethylene or borosilicate glass (pyrex or equivalent) bottles, and stored at a low temperature if storage is required. Since waste samples may be subject to microbiological action and to loss or gain of carbon dioxide when exposed to the air, it is highly desirable that all samples be analyzed as soon as possible after collection. Agitation and prolonged exposure to air should be avoided.

2. Apparatus

Any of the commercial instruments for measuring pH with a glass electrode can be used. Standardize the instrument according to the manufacturer's instructions. Exercise care with reference to the directions regarding temperature compensation, electrode limitations, and cleanliness of electrodes.

3. Reagents

All reagents are prepared and standardized according to the directions in Part 100 under Acidity and Alkalinity (Sections 101.3 and 102.3 respectively). For NaOH or H_2SO_4 normalities of 0.05 use a 1 + 1 dilution of the stock 0.1*N* solutions. Increase the prescribed weights of standards employed in the standardization of the 0.1 and 0.05*N* solutions by the appropriate factors of 5 and 2.5 respectively.

4. Procedure

The general procedures to be employed are those given in Part 100, Acidity and Alkalinity (Sections 101.4 and 102.4, respectively), using an appropriate size of sample and a titrant of appropriate normality as indicated in ¶ 1c above. In the sections which follow, the procedure and significance of these tests are described for the major sample types generally subjected to these tests.

a. Surface streams: Surface waters are normally neutral in pH or slightly alkaline. Methyl orange alkalinity is the only test commonly run. River waters vary widely in alkalinity, from stable levels of 10–20 mg/l $CaCO_3$ to levels near 300 mg/l $CaCO_3$, which may vary by 50% during a year.[1] Alkalinity data are indicative of changes in stream quality or pollution load only when results vary significantly from known normal levels, or when point samples differ from the bulk of the stream.

A 100-ml portion of clear supernatant from settled samples, measured by volumetric pipet, should be titrated with 0.02*N* H_2SO_4 according to the procedure given in Alkalinity, Section 102.4. Color indicators are generally applicable.

b. Domestic sewage: Domestic sewage normally has a neutral or slightly alkaline pH and exhibits an alkalinity only slightly greater than the water supply from which it is derived. Methyl orange alkalinity is the test commonly employed unless industrial waste discharge to the system is indicated. Sharp changes from normal alkalinity levels, the presence of phenolphthalein alkalinity or methyl orange acidity, are indicators of industrial waste discharge.

A 100-ml portion of a settled sample, measured by volumetric pipet, should be titrated with 0.02*N* H_2SO_4 according to the procedure given in Alkalinity, Section 102.4. Color indicators are generally applicable. Where results deviate from normal conditions, acidity determinations should be made according to the procedure given in Acidity, Section 101.4.

c. Anaerobic digester supernatants: Methyl orange alkalinity is commonly determined on anaerobic digester supernatants for purposes of control of the digestion process. This measurement and the determination of volatile acids have been suggested as defined indices of digester condition and failure prediction.[2] The methyl orange alkalinity measures essentially all bicarbonate alkalinity, approximately 70% of the volatile acid salt alkalinity, and a generally small alkalinity due to other components in the digester. Normal alkalinities are below 4,000 mg/l $CaCO_3$; high alkalinity units may operate well in the region of 4,000–6,000 mg/l $CaCO_3$.[3] Malfunctioning or "sick" digesters may reach alkalinities as high as 10,000 mg/l $CaCO_3$.

A suitable-size sample (see ¶ 1c) of settled or centrifuged supernatant is titrated potentiometrically with 0.1*N* H_2SO_4. Color indicators are not applicable.

d. Industrial wastes: Acidity and alkalinity measurements on complex industrial waste effluents can be interpreted only in terms of methyl orange and phenolphthalein acidities and alkalinities. Where waste streams are relatively simple and contain known major components, a potentiometric curve plotting pH vs. ml of titrant may reveal sufficiently well-defined inflection points to permit the determination of individual components. Titrations to the indicated pH values, potentiometrically or with the use of color indicators, may prove useful for plant control or treatment purposes, but shall not constitute a standard method of analysis unless the pH values of 3.7 and 8.3 are used.

e. Wastes and waters containing iron, aluminum and other hydrolyzable metal salts: Some wastes, such as iron pickle liquors and acidic mine effluents, contain large amounts of the salts of ferrous and ferric iron and aluminum, with possibly some excess acid and other metallic salts. Alkaline receiving waters contain bicarbonate and sometimes carbonate, and the alkalinity, as measured by this procedure, are dependent upon the metallic elements after evolution of carbon dioxide. The procedures which follow are suitable for mine waters, acid wastes and their receiving streams and give stoichiometrically equivalent values.

The acidity, as measured by this procedure, is caused by the presence of mineral acids or the hydrolyzable salts of mineral acids. The amount of acidity, for control purposes, is determined by titration of a hot sample with a standard solution of a strong base to a predetermined end point. The alkalinity is determined by acidifying a hot sample with standard acid and back-titrating with standard alkali. Phenolphthalein is used as the end-point indicator for both determinations. The solution is titrated hot in order to insure complete hydrolysis of the acid-producing salts.

The presence of ferrous or ferric iron produces precipitates of iron hydroxide varying in color from green through black to yellow. These precipitates may mask the end point, and extreme care is necessary to determine the color change. Aluminum is amphoteric and thus is soluble in alkali; large concentrations may give high results unless extreme care is exercised in determining the color change. A fleeting end point indicates the presence of aluminum.

PHENOLPHTHALEIN ACIDITY (at boiling temperature): Add several drops of phenolphthalein indicator solution to a sample of suitable size. The size of sample depends on the normality of the sodium hydroxide titrant and the concentration of the acid in the waste. The amount of reagent required should be between 10 and 25 ml. The tabulation at the end of ¶ 1c may be used as a guide, but the sample volume should be half that specified in the tabulation if the acidity is more than 250 mg/l. Boil the sample for 2 min and titrate the hot sample with sodium hydroxide to a pink end point.

ALKALINITY (at boiling temperature; sample pH 3.7 or above): The alkalinity determination requires the complete removal of carbonate and bicarbonate. Follow the same procedure as for acidity but add a measured volume of standard sulfuric acid until the solution remains colorless after boiling. Back-titrate with standard sodium hydroxide to a pink end point.

CALCULATION: Phenolphthalein alkalinity (B.P.) as mg/l $CaCO_3$

$$= \frac{(AB - CD) \times 50{,}000}{E}$$

where

A = ml sulfuric acid added
B = normality of sulfuric acid
C = ml sodium hydroxide titrant used
D = normality of sodium hydroxide and
E = ml sample

A negative value is acidity.

f. Other samples: All analyses on samples not specifically included in the preceding sections shall be run on the supernatant from settled samples according to the procedures of Part 100, using appropriate-size samples and reagent concentrations.

5. Calculations and Expression of Results

With the exception of the alkalinity procedure of Section 201.4e, which requires a back-titration, all alkalinity and acidity determinations are calculated according to the following formula:

$$\text{mg/l } CaCO_3 = \frac{\text{ml of titrant} \times N \text{ of titrant} \times 50{,}000}{\text{ml of sample}}$$

The N of titrant is the experimental normality of the acid or base used as determined in the standardization process.

Reported results should clearly indicate the indicator used, its pH equivalent, or the specific pH employed. Examples are given below:

1—Methyl orange alkalinity = 400 mg/l $CaCO_3$
2—Phenolphthalein alkalinity = 55 mg/l $CaCO_3$
3—Methyl orange acidity = 120 mg/l $CaCO_3$
4—pH 4.00 Acidity = 180 mg/l $CaCO_3$
5—Phenolphthalein acidity (B.P.) = 460 mg/l $CaCO_3$

Results 1, 2 and 3 represent conventional standard methods. Result 4 is an acidity determined by titration with base to pH 4.00. Result 5 represents an acidity determination using phenolphthalein at the sample boiling point. If reported values are desired in milliequivalents of acid or base per liter, the reported values are divided by 50.

$$\text{me/l} = \frac{\text{mg/l } CaCO_3}{50}$$

6. Precision

A standard deviation of 0.08 ml can be expected, using water or sewage samples and the indicators phenolphthalein and methyl orange. Precision data using potentiometric titrations are not available but comparable precision would be expected. In strongly polluted water or in waste streams containing constituents which act as buffers at the designated end points, precision varies with the samples and is not as precise.[4]

7. References

1. NATIONAL WATER QUALITY NETWORK. 1962. *Annual Compilation of Data.* U. S. Department of Health, Education & Welfare, PHS, Washington, D. C.
2. POHLAND, F. G. & D. E. BLOODGOOD.

1963. Laboratory studies on mesophilic and thermophilic anaerobic sludge digestion. *JWPCF* 35:11.
3. WPCF. *Anaerobic Sludge Digestion.* Manual of Practice No. 16. WPCF (1967); *JWPCF* 38:1925 (1966).
4. WEBER, W. J., JR. & W. STUMM. Mechanism of hydrogen ion buffering in natural waters. *JAWWA* 55:1553 (1963); Corrections. *JAWWA* 56:386 (1964).

See also Sections 101.6 and 102.7, bibliographies for Acidity and Alkalinity in the preceding Part 100.

202 APPEARANCE

When it is desirable to record the general physical appearance of the sample, any terms which best describe the characteristics of the individual sample should be used. No standard methods or standard terminology are recommended.

For liquid samples, it is often desirable to supplement or replace the description of appearance by the determination of color. Also, for liquid samples which are relatively clear, the determination of turbidity may be appropriate.

CADMIUM: See Heavy Metals, Section 211(II)B.

CALCIUM: See Metals (Groups I and II), Section 210.

203 CHLORIDE

Chloride, in the form of Cl ion, is one of the major inorganic anions which is increased in sewage over the raw water because sodium chloride is a common article of diet and passes unchanged through the digestive system. Along the sea coast, chloride may be present in high concentrations because of leakage of salt water into the sewer system. It may also be increased by industrial processes.

Selection of method: Three methods are presented for the determination of chlorides. The argentometric method (*A*) is suitable for use when 0.15–10 mg Cl are present in the portion of sample titrated. The mercuric nitrate method (*B*) is given for its easier end point. The potentiometric method (*C*), given below, is suitable for colored or turbid samples in which colored end points might be difficult to observe. The potentiometric method can also be used without a pretreatment step for solutions containing ferric ions (if not present in an amount greater than the chloride concentration), chromic phosphate, ferrous and other heavy metal ions.

203 A. Argentometric Method

If the sample contains sulfide, acidify an appropriate volume of sample, diluted if necessary to 50.0 ml, with H_2SO_4 and oxidize the sulfide by heating with H_2O_2 for a few minutes. Cool and neutralize with $NaHCO_3$, dilute to the original volume, and determine chloride by the argentometric method as in Section 112A.

203 B. Mercuric Nitrate Method

See Chloride, Section 112B.

203 C. Potentiometric Method

1. General Discussion

a. Principle: Chloride is determined by potentiometric titration with silver nitrate solution using a glass and silver–silver chloride electrode system. During titration an electronic voltmeter is used to detect the change in potential between the two electrodes. The end point of the titration is that instrument reading at which the greatest change in voltage has occurred for a small and constant increment of silver nitrate added.

b. Interference: Iodide and bromide also are titrated as chloride. Ferricyanide causes high results and must be removed. Chromate and dichromate interfere and should be reduced to the chromic state or removed. Ferric iron interferes if present in an amount that is substantially higher than the amount of chloride. Chromic ion, ferrous iron, and phosphate do not interfere.

Grossly contaminated samples usually require pretreatment. Where contamination is minor, some contaminants can be destroyed simply by the addition of nitric acid.

2. Apparatus

a. Glass and silver–silver chloride electrodes: The latter is a silver electrode coated with silver chloride and may be prepared in the laboratory if desired, but can be purchased for use with specified instruments. Instructions on the use and care of the electrodes are supplied by the manufacturer.

b. Electronic voltmeter, to measure the potential difference between the electrodes: Many laboratories may find it possible to convert a pH meter to this use by substitution of the appropriate electrode.

c. Mechanical stirrer, with plastic-coated or glass impeller.

3. Reagents

a. STANDARD SODIUM CHLORIDE SOLUTION, $0.0141N$—Dissolve 8.243 g NaCl, dried at 105 C, in distilled water and dilute to exactly 500 ml. Dilute 50.0 ml of this solution to exactly 1,000 ml. The final solution contains 0.500 mg Cl per 1.00 ml.

b. NITRIC ACID, conc.

c. STANDARD SILVER NITRATE TITRANT, $0.014N$—Dissolve 2.40 g $AgNO_3$ in distilled water and dilute to 1,000 ml. Standardize this solution by titrating exactly 10.0 ml standard NaCl solution using the procedure described in Section 4a below. Adjust the $AgNO_3$ titrant to the same normality as the NaCl solution; 1.00 ml = 0.500 mg Cl.

$$\text{Normality of } AgNO_3 = \frac{10.0 \times 0.0141}{\text{ml } AgNO_3}$$

d. SPECIAL REAGENTS FOR PRETREATMENT—

1) Sulfuric acid, 1 + 1.

2) Hydrogen peroxide, 30%.

3) Sodium hydroxide, $1N$.

4a. Standardization

1) Inasmuch as the various instruments that can be used in this determination differ in operating details, the manufacturer's instructions should be followed. Necessary mechanical adjustments should be made. Then, after allowing sufficient time for warm-up (10 min), the internal electrical components are balanced to give an instrument setting of 0 mV or, if a pH meter is used, a pH reading of 7.0.

2) Place 10.0 ml standard NaCl solution in a 250-ml beaker, dilute to about 100 ml, and add 2.0 ml conc HNO_3. Immerse the stirrer and the electrodes in the solution.

3) Set the instrument to the desired range of millivolts or pH units. Start the stirrer.

4) Add standard $AgNO_3$ titrant, recording the scale reading after each addition. At the start, large increments of $AgNO_3$ may be added; then, as the end point of the reaction is approached, smaller and equal increments (0.1 or 0.2 ml) should be added at longer intervals, so that the exact end point can be determined. Determine the volume of $AgNO_3$ used at the point at which there is the greatest change in instrument reading per unit addition of $AgNO_3$.

5) A differential titration curve should be plotted if the exact end point cannot be determined by inspection of the data. Plot the change in instrument reading for equal increments of $AgNO_3$ against the volume of $AgNO_3$ added, using the average of the buret readings before and after each addition. The procedure is illustrated in Figure 29.

4b. Procedure

1) Pipet exactly 100.0 ml of sample, or an aliquot containing not more than 10 mg chloride, into a 250-ml

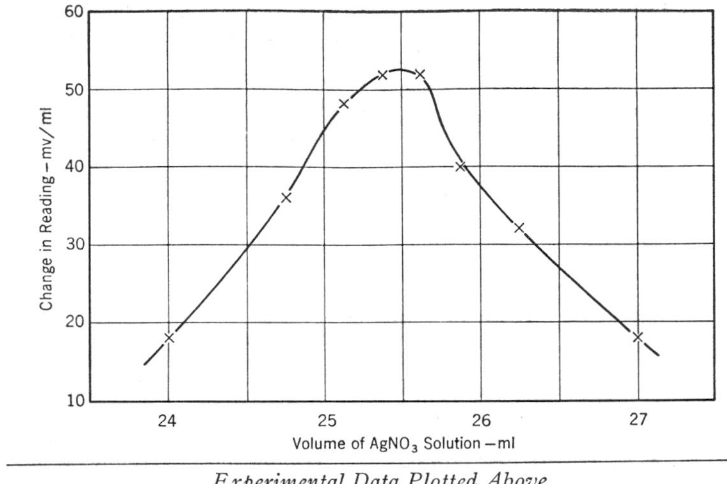

Experimental Data Plotted Above

Volume, *ml*	23.50	24.50	25.00	25.25	25.50	25.75	26.00	26.50	27.50
Change, *mV/ml*	18	36	48	52	52	40	32	18	

Figure 29. Example of differential titration curve (end point is 25.5 ml).

beaker. In the absence of interfering substances, proceed with ¶ 3 below.

2) In the presence of organic compounds, sulfite or other interferences (such as large amounts of ferric iron or substantial amounts of cyanide or sulfide), acidify the sample with H_2SO_4, using litmus paper. Boil for 5 min to remove volatile compounds. Add more H_2SO_4, if necessary, to keep the solution acidic. Add 3 ml H_2O_2 and boil for 15 min, adding chloride-free distilled water to keep the volume above 50 ml. Dilute to 100 ml, add NaOH solution dropwise until alkaline to litmus, then 10 drops in excess. Boil for 5 min, filter into a 250-ml beaker, and wash the precipitate and paper several times with hot distilled water.

3) Add conc HNO_3 dropwise until acidic to litmus paper, then 2.0 ml in excess. Cool and dilute to 100 ml if necessary. Immerse the stirrer and the electrodes in the sample and start the stirrer. After making the necessary adjustments of the instrument according to the manufacturer's instructions, set the selector switch to the appropriate setting for measuring the difference of potential between the electrodes.

4) Complete the determination by titrating according to ¶ 4a(4). If an end-point reading has been established from previous determinations for similar samples and conditions, this predetermined end point can be used. For the most accurate work, a blank titration should be made by carrying chloride-free distilled water through the procedure.

5. Calculation

$$\text{mg/l Cl} = \frac{(A - B) \times N \times 35.45 \times 1{,}000}{D}$$

where A = ml $AgNO_3$, B = ml blank, N = normality of titrant, and D = ml sample.

6. Precision and Accuracy

In the absence of interfering substances, the precision and accuracy are estimated to be about 0.12 mg for 5 mg Cl, or 2.5% of the amount present. When pretreatment is required for removal of interfering substances, the precision and accuracy are reduced to about 0.25 mg for 5 mg Cl, or 5% of the amount present.

203 D. Bibliography

HAZEN, A. 1889. On the determination of chlorine in water. *Amer. Chem. J.* 11:409.

KOLTHOFF, I. M. & N. H. FURMAN. 1931. *Potentiometric Titrations* (2nd ed.). John Wiley & Sons, New York.

REFFENBURG, H. B. 1935. Colorimetric determination of small quantities of chlorides in water. *Ind. Eng. Chem.*, Anal. Ed. 7:14.

CALDWELL, J. R. & H. V. MEYER. 1935. Chloride determination. *Ind. Eng. Chem.*, Anal. Ed. 7:38.

WALTON, H. F. 1952. *Principles and Methods of Chemical Analysis.* Prentice-Hall, Inc., Englewood Cliffs, N. J.

SERFASS, E. J. & R. F. MURACA. 1954. *Procedures for Analyzing Metal-Finishing Wastes.* Ohio River Valley Water Sanitation Commission, Cincinnati, p. 80.

WILLARD, H. H., L. L. MERRITT & J. A. DEAN. 1958. *Instrumental Methods of Analysis* (3rd ed.). D. Van Nostrand Co., Princeton, N. J.

FURMAN, N. H., Ed. 1962. *Standard Methods of Chemical Analysis* (6th ed.). D. Van Nostrand Co., Princeton, N. J., Vol. I.

204 CHLORINE (RESIDUAL)

The determination of residual chlorine in samples containing organic matter presents problems which are not encountered when the determination is performed in clean water samples. Because of the presence of organic compounds, particularly organic nitrogen, the residual chlorine exists in a combined state. A considerable amount of residual may exist in this form, and at the same time there may be appreciable unsatisfied chlorine demand. The addition of the reagents in the determination may change the relationships so that the residual chlorine is lost during the course of the procedure. In sewage, the differentiation of free available chlorine from combined available chlorine is not ordinarily made. Sewage chlorination is seldom carried to the point necessary to produce free available chlorine.

The determination of residual chlorine in industrial wastes is similar to the determination in sewage when the waste contains organic matter, but may be similar to the determination in water when the waste is low in organic matter.

The methods given below are useful

for the determination of residual chlorine in wastewaters and treated effluents, but the method must be selected in accordance with the composition of the sample being tested. Some industrial wastes, or mixtures of wastes with domestic sewage, may require certain precautions and modifications in order to obtain satisfactory results.

Selection of method: Free available chlorine can be determined, in the substantial absence of organic nitrogen, by the procedure in Chlorine (Residual), Section 114B. This method is not subject to interference from color, turbidity, iron, manganese, or nitrite nitrogen.

For samples containing significant amounts of organic matter such as many wastewaters and some effluents, the iodometric method (A) should be used to prevent contact between the full concentration of liberated iodine and the sample. Either the amperometric or the starch-iodide end point may be used. In the absence of interference, the two modifications give concordant results. The amperometric end point is inherently more accurate and is free of interference from color and turbidity, which can cause difficulty with the starch-iodide end point. On the other hand, certain metals and complex anions which may occur in some industrial wastes interfere in the amperometric titration and therefore indicate the use of another method for such wastewaters. Silver in the soluble silver cyanide complex ion, in concentrations as low as 1.0 mg/l silver, poisons the cell at pH 4.0 but not at 7.0, and the silver ion, in the absence of the cyanide complex, gives extensive response in the current at pH 4.0 and gradually poisons the cell at all pH levels. Cuprous copper in the soluble copper cyanide ion, in concentrations at least as low as 5 mg/l copper, poisons the cell at pH 4.0 and 7.0. Although manganese, iron and nitrite may interfere with this method, the interference is minimized by buffering to pH 4.0 before addition of KI. An unusually high content of organic matter may cause some uncertainty in the end point. Whenever manganese, iron and nitrites are definitely absent, this uncertainty can be reduced and precision improved by buffering below pH 4.0—even as low as pH 3.0.

Regardless of the method of end-point detection, either phenylarsine oxide or thiosulfate may be used as the standard reducing reagent, depending on convenience. The former is more stable and is to be preferred, other things being equal.

The orthotolidine method (B) consistently gives lower values than the iodometric method. The magnitude of the difference seems to depend on the concentration of organic matter. In pure water, both methods give essentially the same result. In ordinary settled sewage, the difference in residual chlorine can be of the order of 2–5 mg/l. In many sewage and waste mixtures even greater differences may be found. The cause may be either more tightly combined chlorine, which is unreactive to orthotolidine, or an actual loss of available chlorine by the activation effect when the pH is lowered in the orthotolidine determination. When nitrite nitrogen is present in amounts greater than 2 mg/l, the orthotolidine method should not be used. It may also be undesirable for use in the presence of manganic manganese.

The arsenite-orthotolidine test (C) is preferable to the orthotolidine method if iron and manganese are present in the waste and the organic nitrogen content is low.

Method D, a rapid spot plate test for field use, describes a technic which may also be applicable to plant control work.

204 A. Iodometric Method

1. General Discussion

a. Principle: Refer to Residual Chlorine, Section 114A.1a and Section 114 F.1a preceding. As used in sewage, the end-point signal is reversed because the unreacted standard reducing agent remaining in the sample is titrated with standard iodine or standard iodate, rather than directly titrating the iodine released. This indirect procedure is necessary regardless of the method of end-point detection, in order to avoid any contact between the full concentration of liberated iodine and the sewage.

b. Interference: Manganese, iron and nitrite interference may be minimized by buffering to pH 4.0 before the addition of KI. An unusually high content of organic matter may cause some uncertainty in the end point. Whenever manganese, iron and nitrite are definitely absent, this uncertainty can be reduced and precision improved by acidification to pH 1.0.

2. Apparatus

For a description of the amperometric end-point detection apparatus and a discussion of its use, refer to Residual Chlorine, Section 114F.2.

3. Reagents

a. Standard phenylarsine oxide solution, 0.00564*N:* Dissolve approximately 0.8 g phenylarsine oxide powder in 150 ml 0.3*N* NaOH solution. After settling, decant 110 ml of this solution into 800 ml distilled water and mix thoroughly. Bring to pH 6–7 with 6*N* HCl and dilute to 950 ml with distilled water.

STANDARDIZATION—Accurately measure 5–10 ml freshly standardized 0.0282*N* iodine solution into a flask and add 1 ml KI solution. Titrate with phenylarsine oxide solution, using starch solution as an indicator. Adjust to exactly 0.00564*N* and recheck against the standard iodine solution; 1.00 ml = 200 μg available chlorine. (CAUTION: *Toxic—take care to avoid ingestion.*)

b. Standard sodium thiosulfate solution, 0.1*N:* Dissolve at least 25 g $Na_2S_2O_3 \cdot 5H_2O$ in 1 liter freshly boiled distilled water. Bacterial decomposition may be avoided by the addition of 5 ml chloroform or 1 g NaOH per liter. Store for at least 2 weeks before standardizing.

STANDARDIZATION—To 80 ml distilled water add, with constant stirring, 1 ml conc H_2SO_4, 10.0 ml of either 0.1*N* potassium biniodate solution containing 3.250 g/l $KH(IO_3)_2$ or 0.1*N* potassium dichromate solution containing 4.904 g/l $K_2Cr_2O_7$, and 15 ml KI solution. Allow to stand 6 min in subdued light at laboratory temperature and then dilute to 400 ml if $K_2Cr_2O_7$ was used or to 200 ml if biniodate was used. Titrate the liberated iodine with the thiosulfate solution being standardized, adding starch solution toward the end of the titration. Exactly 10.00 ml of thiosulfate should be required if the solutions under comparison are of equal strength.

c. Standard sodium thiosulfate solution, 0.00564*N:* Prepare by dilution of 0.1*N* sodium thiosulfate (see ¶ b preceding). For maximum stability of the dilute solution, prepare it by diluting an aged 0.1*N* solution with freshly boiled distilled water (to minimize bacterial action) and add 10 mg HgI_2 and 4 g $Na_4B_4O_7$ per liter. Standardize this thiosulfate solution daily, in accordance with the directions given above, using 0.00564*N* $K_2Cr_2O_7$ solution if desired. The use of an automatic buret of a type in which rubber does not come in contact with the solution is advisable; 1.00 ml = 200 μg available chlorine.

d. Potassium iodide, crystals.

e. Acetate buffer solution, pH 4.0: Dissolve 146 g anhydrous $NaC_2H_3O_2$, or 243 g $NaC_2H_3O_2 \cdot 3H_2O$, in 400 ml distilled water, add 480 g conc acetic acid, and dilute to 1 liter with distilled water.

f. Standard arsenite solution, 0.1*N:* Accurately weigh a stoppered weighing bottle containing approximately 4.95 g arsenic trioxide, As_2O_3. Transfer without loss to a 1-liter volumetric flask and again weigh the bottle. Do not attempt to brush out the adhering oxide. Moisten the As_2O_3 with water and add 15 g NaOH and 100 ml distilled water. Swirl the contents of the flask gently until the As_2O_3 is in solution. Dilute to 250 ml with distilled water and saturate the solution with CO_2, thus converting all the NaOH to sodium bicarbonate. Dilute to the mark, stopper the flask, and mix thoroughly. A solution thus prepared will preserve its titer almost indefinitely. (CAUTION: *Toxic —take care to avoid ingestion.*)

$$\text{Normality} = \frac{\text{g } As_2O_3}{49.455}$$

g. Standard iodine solution, 0.1*N:* Dissolve 40 g KI in 25 ml distilled water, add 13 g resublimed iodine, and stir until dissolved. Transfer to a 1-liter volumetric flask and dilute to the mark.

STANDARDIZATION—Accurately measure 40–50 ml 0.1*N* arsenite solution into a flask and titrate with the 0.1*N* iodine solution, using starch solution as indicator. To obtain accurate results, it is absolutely necessary that the solution be saturated with CO_2 at the end of the titration. A current of CO_2 may be passed through the solution for a few minutes just before the end point is reached, or a few drops of HCl may be added to liberate sufficient CO_2 to saturate the solution.

h. Standard iodine titrant, 0.0282*N:* Dissolve 25 g KI in a little distilled water in a 1-liter volumetric flask, add the proper amount of 0.1*N* iodine solution exactly standardized to yield a 0.0282*N* solution, and dilute to 1 liter. For accurate work, standardize this solution daily in accordance with directions given in ¶ 3g above, using 5–10 ml of arsenite solution. Store in amber bottles or in the dark, protecting the solution from direct sunlight at all times and keeping it from all contact with rubber.

i. Starch indicator: Either the aqueous solution or soluble starch powder mixtures may be used for detection of the iodine end point.

To prepare the aqueous solution, place 5 g starch (potato, arrowroot or soluble) in a mortar, add a little cold water, and grind to a thin paste. Pour into 1 liter of boiling distilled water, stir, and allow to settle overnight. Use the clear supernate. Preserve with 1.25 g salicylic acid or with 4 g zinc chloride per liter.

j. Standard iodate titrant, 0.00564*N:* Dissolve 201.2 mg primary standard grade KIO_3,* which has previously been dried 1 hr at 103 C, in distilled water and dilute to 1 liter.

k. Phosphoric acid solution, 1 + 9.

4. Procedure

a. Amperometric end point:

1) VOLUME OF SAMPLE—For residual chlorine concentrations of 10 mg/l or less, titrate 200 ml. For residual chlorine concentrations above this range, use proportionately less of the sample. Use a sample of such size that not more than 10 ml phenylarsine oxide solution is required.

2) PREPARATION FOR TITRATION—To a beaker suitable for use with the apparatus add 5.0 ml 0.00564*N* phenylarsine oxide solution or 0.00564 *N* thiosulfate solution, KI in excess (approximately 1 g), and 4 ml acetate buffer solution or sufficient to reduce the pH to between 3.5 and 4.2. Then add 200 ml of sample and mix thoroughly. Because 1 ml phenylarsine oxide reagent consumed by a 200-ml sample represents 1 mg/l available chlorine, use 5 ml reagent solution for residual chlorine concentrations up to 5 mg/l and 10 ml reagent solution for residual chlorine concentrations of 5 to 10 mg/l. The following is suggested as a possible dilution method: Add 10.0 ml reagent solution, excess KI (approximately 1 g), and 4 ml acetate buffer solution or sufficient to reduce the pH to between 3.5 and 4.2 to the beaker or graduate. Dilute to 100 ml with distilled water and then add 100 ml of the sample for which the residual chlorine concentration is to be determined.

3) TITRATION—Add 0.0282*N* iodine titrant in small increments from a 1-ml pipet or a 1-ml buret. Observe the response of the meter needle as iodine is added to the sample: The pointer remains practically stationary until the end point is approached, whereupon each iodine increment causes a temporary deflection of the microammeter, with the pointer dropping back to its original position. Stop the titration at the end point when a small increment of iodine titrant gives a definite pointer deflection upscale and the pointer does not return promptly to its original position. Record the volume of iodine titrant used to reach the end point.

b. Starch-iodide end point:

1) VOLUME OF SAMPLE—For residual chlorine concentrations of 10 mg/l or less, take a 200-ml sample for titration. For greater residual chlorine concentrations, use proportionately less of the sample.

2) TITRATION WITH STANDARD IODINE—Place 5.00 ml 0.00564*N* phenylarsine oxide solution or 0.00564*N* thiosulfate solution in a flask or white porcelain casserole. Add excess KI (approximately 1 g), and 4 ml acetate buffer solution, or sufficient to reduce the pH to between 3.5 and 4.2. Pour in the sample and mix with a stirring rod. Just prior to titration with 0.0282*N* iodine, add 1 ml starch solution for each 200 ml of sample. Titrate to the first appearance of blue color, which persists after complete mixing.

* Mallinckrodt No. 1093 or equivalent.

Because 1 ml 0.00564*N* reagent solution consumed by a 200-ml sample represents 1 mg/l available chlorine, use 5 ml reagent for residual chlorine concentrations up to 5 mg/l, 10 ml reagent for residual chlorine concentrations of 5–10 mg/l, and proportionately larger volumes of reagent for higher concentrations.

3) TITRATION WITH STANDARD IODATE—To 200 ml distilled water add, with agitation, exactly 5.00 ml 0.00564*N* thiosulfate solution, an excess of KI (approximately 0.5 g), 2 ml 10% phosphoric acid solution and 1 ml starch solution, in the order given, and immediately titrate * with 0.00564*N* iodate solution to the first appearance of a blue color, which persists after complete mixing. Designate the volume of iodate solution used as *A*. Repeat the procedure as given, substituting 200 ml sample for the 200 ml distilled water. If the sample is colored or turbid, titrate to the first change in color, using for comparison another portion of sample with phosphoric acid added. Designate the volume of iodate solution used in titrating the sample as *B*. Because 1 ml 0.00564*N* reagent solution consumed by a 200-ml sample represents 1 mg/l available chlorine, use 5 ml thiosulfate solution for residual chlorine concentrations up to 5 mg/l, 10 ml thiosulfate solution for residual chlorine concentrations of 5–10 mg/l, and proportionately larger volumes of thiosulfate solution for higher concentrations.

* Titration may be delayed up to 10 min without appreciable error if the phosphoric acid is not added until immediately before the titration.

5. Calculation

a. Titration with standard iodine:

$$\text{mg/l Cl} = \frac{(A - 5B) \times 200}{C}$$

where A = ml 0.00564*N* reagent, B = ml 0.0282*N* I, and C = ml sample.

b. Titration with standard iodate:

$$\text{mg/l Cl} = \frac{(A - B) \times 200}{C}$$

where A and B are as given in ¶ 4b(3) above and C = ml sample.

204 B. Orthotolidine Method

1. General Discussion

The determination of residual chlorine in water by the orthotolidine method is discussed in Residual Chlorine, Section 114C, which describes the many pitfalls of the test and the precautions to be observed. Particular attention is called to the importance of warming the sample to 20 C, after the addition of orthotolidine, in order to complete the reaction. If the sample is warmed before the addition of orthotolidine, there will be further reaction between chlorine and organic matter, resulting in a low value for residual chlorine.

The concentration of acid in the orthotolidine reagent will produce a suitable pH value in the sample if its alkalinity is 1,000 mg/l or less. Samples of higher alkalinity require the addition of more orthotolidine reagent than is specified.

2. Apparatus

Comparator, turbidity-compensating.

3a. Standards

See Residual Chlorine, Section 114 C.3a and 3b preceding.

3b. Reagent

See Residual Chlorine, Section 114C.3c preceding.

4. Procedure

a. Add a 10-ml sample of chlorinated sewage to a cell or test tube containing 1 ml orthotolidine solution. If the temperature of the sample is less than 20 C, bring it to that temperature quickly after mixing it with orthotolidine by placing the tube in hot water until the specified temperature is reached.

b. Place the treated sample in the dark during color development. Take the reading when the color reaches its maximum intensity and before fading begins, usually in less than 5 min and in some cases immediately.

c. Compare the colors in a turbidity-compensating comparator with color standards prepared as directed in Residual Chlorine, Section 114C.3a and 3b preceding. If permanent standards are used, note that the amount of sample is but 10 ml and the depth of liquid viewed is not the same as in Tables 114 (2) and 114(3); adjustments may have to be made accordingly. The standards most commonly used represent 0.0, 0.10, 0.20, 0.40, 0.60, 0.80 and 1.00 mg/l Cl.

204 C. Arsenite-Orthotolidine Method

1. Apparatus

The same apparatus is required as for the OTA test in water; see Residual Chlorine, Section 114D.2 preceding.

2. Reagents

The same reagents are required as for the OTA test in water; see Residual Chlorine, Section 114D.3.

3. Procedure

a. Label two comparator cells or French square bottles "A" and "B." Use 1 ml orthotolidine reagent in 10-ml cells, 1.5 ml in 15-ml cells, and the same ratio for other volumes of sample. Use the same volume of sodium arsenite solution as orthotolidine reagent.

b. To Cell A, containing sodium arsenite solution, add a measured volume of sample. Mix quickly and immediately add orthotolidine reagent. Mix quickly and compare with color standards when maximum color develops—usually in less than 5 min. Record the result as the *A* value, which represents interfering color.

c. To Cell B, containing orthotolidine reagent, add a measured volume of sample. Mix quickly and compare with color standards when maximum color develops—usually in less than 5 min. Record the result as the *B* value, which represents the total amount of residual chlorine present and of interfering color.

d. For more accurate readings, place both cells in the comparator in such relative positions that the color compensation is made directly.

4. Calculation

If color compensation is not made directly:

$$\text{mg/l total residual Cl} = B - A$$

where *A* is the result from ¶ 3b and *B* is the result from ¶ 3c above.

204 D. Spot Plate Test for Field Use

The following rapid spot plate technic offers simplicity and speed for plant control work and field use.

1. Apparatus

a. Spot plates, containing several depressions.

b. Pipets, large bore, 1-ml, fitted with pipet bulbs.

2. Reagents

a. Orthotolidine reagent: Prepare as directed in Section 114C.3e for the Orthotolidine Method (Residual Chlorine).

b. Permanent standard solutions: Prepare as directed in Residual Chlorine, Section 114C.3b, and adjust color intensities and hues to match temporary standards in spot plates.

3. Procedure

Add 3 drops of orthotolidine reagent to a depression in the spot plate. By means of the pipet bulb, pipet 1 ml of the sample under examination directly and rapidly into the orthotolidine reagent and stir with the tip of the pipet. The color will usually develop within 45 sec to 1 min and fade thereafter.

Compare the color developed with permanent or temporary standards pipeted into another spot plate, testing several samples at the same time if desired. The minimum readable color is produced by a chlorine concentration between 0.05 and 0.1 mg/l.

204 E. Bibliography

LEA, C. 1933. Chemical control of sewage chlorination: The use and value of orthotolidine test. *J. Soc. Chem. Ind.* (London) 52:245T.

SYMONS, G. E. 1937. A modification of the chlorine demand test and the orthotolidine test for residual chlorine. *Sewage Works J.* 9:569.

AMERICAN WATER WORKS ASSOCIATION. 1943. Committee Report. Control of Chlorination. *JAWWA* 35:1315.

GILCREAS, F. W. & F. J. HALLINAN. 1944.

The practical use of the orthotolidine-arsenite test for residual chlorine. *JAWWA* 36:1343.

MARKS, H. C., R. JOINER & F. B. STRANDSKOV. 1948. Amperometric titration of residual chlorine in sewage. *Water & Sewage Works* 95:175.

STRANDSKOV, F. B., H. C. MARKS & D. H. HORCHIER. 1949. Application of a new residual chlorine method to effluent chlorination. *Sewage Works J.* 21:23.

NUSBAUM, I & L. A. MEYERSON. 1951. Determination of chlorine demands and chlorine residuals in sewage. *Sewage & Ind. Wastes* 23:968.

MARKS, H. C., D. B. WILLIAMS & G. U. GLASGOW. 1951. Determination of residual chlorine compounds. *JAWWA* 43:201.

MARKS, H. C. & N. S. CHAMBERLIN. 1953. Determination of residual chlorine in metal finishing wastes. *Anal. Chem.* 24:1885.

205 CHLORINE REQUIREMENT

"Chlorine demand," as defined in Part 100, is of little significance in relation to the objectives of wastewater chlorination. "Chlorination requirement" is a more applicable term.

The chlorine requirement is defined as the amount of chlorine which must be added per unit volume to produce the desired result under stated conditions. The result (i.e., the purpose of chlorination) may be based on any of a number of criteria, such as a stipulated coliform density, a specified residual chlorine concentration, the destruction of a chemical constituent, or others. In each instance a definite chlorine dosage will be necessary. This dosage constitutes the chlorine requirement.

In those cases where the desired result is a specified residual chlorine concentration, residuals may be determined by either the iodometric or the orthotolidine method. It is important that the same method be used for both laboratory testing and operational control.

In reporting results, the following information must be included: (1) the conditions of chlorination, such as pH, contact time, and temperature; (2) the result achieved; (3) the method used for determining the result; and (4) the chlorine dosage required to produce the desired result (i.e., the chlorine requirement).

205 A. Method for Control of Disinfection

1. General Discussion

For control of the disinfection process the chlorine requirement can be determined on either a plant or a laboratory scale. In plant tests the flow of sewage, quantity of chlorine used, contact time, residual chlorine concentration, and bacteriological results are determined. Sufficient replication may establish a correlation between bacteriological results and residual chlorine concentration. If so, operational control may then be based on residual chlorine determinations. Bacteriological tests should be performed periodically to verify the correlation.

In plant studies the test should be run with the minimum and average contact times corresponding to different flow conditions, to determine the average and the variations from the average of the number of organisms in the effluent. Similarly, in laboratory studies more than one contact time should be used to establish minimum and average chlorine requirements compatible with the stipulated microbial densities and permissible variations.

It is to be understood that chlorine requirement is not an absolute value which can be used to compare the results from place to place and from time to time. It is rather a practical and realistic approach to the control of sewage disinfection and to an estimate of the chlorine required.

The orthotolidine test may not be suitable for the determination of chlorine requirement in some cases, because often, with no residuals, as determined by this method, substantial reductions in organisms are obtained.

For a given sewage, the same amount of added chlorine will result in a higher residual value by the iodometric method than by the orthotolidine method.

The chlorine requirement for disinfection of a given waste may be defined as the amount of chlorine which must be added per unit volume of waste to produce the desired residual chlorine concentration after a definite contact time. Residual chlorine and contact time will have been chosen to give a stipulated result in terms of coliform density or other characteristic.

The results of such determinations may also be used for measuring the increase in chlorine requirement at the treatment plant due to the discharge of the waste into the sewer and for assessing the cost of chlorination attributable to the particular contributor to the plant.

When there are a number of contributors to a common treatment plant, the necessary value of residual chlorine will be based on the treatment plant effluent. The chlorine requirement for each contributor will then be the additional amount of chlorine necessary to produce the stipulated residual chlorine concentration after dilution of the waste with treatment plant effluent in the same volumetric ratio as actually occurs.

2. Reagents

All the reagents necessary for the determination of residual chlorine by the selected method are required, and in addition:

a. Standard chlorine solution: Pass chlorine gas through distilled water or tap water until the solution contains approximately 1.0 mg chlorine per ml. Since this solution is not stable, prepare it fresh daily, or standardize it each time it is used, according to directions in Residual Chlorine, Section 114C.3a, using 5 ml chlorine water and 0.025*N* thiosulfate solution. Calculate the strength as follows:

$$\text{mg/ml Cl} = \frac{(A \pm B) \times N \times 35.45}{\text{ml sample}}$$

where A = ml titration for sample, B = ml titration for blank which may be positive or negative, and N = normality of $Na_2S_2O_3$.

b. Sodium sulfite solution: Dissolve

10 g anhydrous Na_2SO_3 in 100 ml distilled water and heat to boiling to sterilize. Prepare daily.

3. Procedure

a. Measurement of samples: In each of a series of 1-liter beakers, jars or flasks, place a 500-ml portion of the sewage.

b. Addition of chlorine: Select dosages and increments of chlorine which are suited to the type and concentration of the waste being tested and to the purpose of chlorination. Use a range of dosages which includes at least one that is believed certain to produce the desired result. While stirring gently and constantly, add the selected quantities of chlorine to the various waste samples.

c. Determination of residual chlorine: At the end of the stipulated contact times, determine residual chlorine on each portion of the sewage by one or more of the procedures given in Section 204A or 204B.

NOTE: In following the procedure for Method B, it is permissible, after completing preparations for titration, to set the samples aside until portions have been removed from the original sample for other tests.

d. Determination of degree of disinfection: Immediately after the aliquots have been removed for determination of residual chlorine, add 0.5 ml sodium sulfite solution to each of the sample portions and estimate the number of organisms surviving by one of the procedures given in Sections 406–412, inclusive (tests for the presence of members of the coliform group).

4. Calculation

The chlorine requirement is the amount of chlorine that must be added per unit volume to produce the stipulated bacteriological quality.

5. Precision

The precision of the chlorine requirement as determined by this procedure is poor on the basis of a single sample, because of the inaccuracies of the enumeration of surviving organisms. In order to establish the chlorine requirement for a given coliform density in the effluent with suitable precision, the test should be repeated at least ten times on different samples using otherwise identical conditions.

205 B. Methods for Purposes Other Than Disinfection Control

When chlorine is used for such purposes as odor control, BOD reduction, slime and insect control on trickling filters, and control of activated-sludge bulking, chlorine requirement is defined as the quantity of chlorine that must be added to produce the desired result. In most of the cases mentioned, chlorine requirement is best determined on a plant basis. Occasionally, laboratory tests may be more suitable, as in BOD reduction. If residual chlorine tests are to be used for control, either the iodometric or the orthotolidine method may be used at the option of the analyst.

When industrial wastes are to be chlorinated for such purposes as the destruction of chemicals or the reduction of undesirable qualities in effluents, the same general concept of chlorine requirement as developed for disinfection purposes can be applied. pH values may be varied according to the conditions and purposes of the chlorine treatment. Instead of using bacteriological examination as the criterion of chlorine requirement, the requirement is based on the objective for which chlorine is applied. For example, if chlorine is applied for phenol destruction, the chlorine requirement is based on the actual phenol concentration desired. Contact times may be varied in conjunction with the quantity of chlorine applied, compatible with the accomplishment of the objective. All conditions of the test should be specified.

The procedure is analogous to the one given for disinfection control (Section 205A.3) preceding.

CHROMIUM: See Heavy Metals, Section 211(II)C.

206 COLOR

Color is not normally determined on sewages, but it is often an important constituent in industrial wastes. The methods described are intended primarily for industrial wastes but may be applied to other liquid samples if the determination of color is necessary.

For solid samples, such as sludges and sediments, no standard terms are recommended. The color of such samples may be described in any suitable terms.

The color of a sample is considered to be the color of the light transmitted by the solution after removing the suspended material, including the pseudocolloidal particles. It is recognized that the color characteristics of some samples are affected by the light reflection from the suspended material present. However, until a suitable method is available for making solution reflectance determinations, the color measurements will be limited to the characteristics of light transmitted by clarified wastes. Suspended materials are removed by filtration through a standard filter aid medium. Color adsorption by calcined filter aids is practically negligible for the quantity of filter aid required. Centrifuging is not used because the results will vary with the size and speed of the centrifuge. Furthermore, particles with a specific gravity lower than that of water will tend to float or remain in suspension.

The color of the filtered sample is expressed in terms which describe the sensation realized when viewing the waste. The hue (red, yellow, green, etc.) of the color is designated by the term *dominant wavelength,* the degree of brightness by *luminance,* and the saturation (pastel, pale, etc.) by *purity.* These values are best determined from the light transmission characteristics of the filtered waste by means of a spectrophotometer (Section 206A.1). A rapid method which uses three color filters and a filter photometer is given as Method B following. It is not as accurate as Method A but will give very satisfactory results. The light transmission data are converted to the color classification terms by using standards adopted by the International Commission on Illumination (CIE), and the selected-ordinate method.

206 A. Spectrophotometric Method

1. Apparatus

a. Spectrophotometer, having 10-mm absorption cells, a narrow (10 mμ or less) spectral band, and an effective operating range from 400 to 700 mμ.

b. Filtration system, consisting of the following (see Figure 30):

1) FILTRATION FLASKS, 250-ml, with side tubes.

2) WALTER CRUCIBLE HOLDER.

3) MICROMETALLIC FILTER CRUCIBLE, average pore size 40 microns.

4) CALCINED FILTER AID.*

5) VACUUM SYSTEM.

2. Procedure

a. Preparation of sample: Bring two 50-ml samples to room temperature. Use one sample at the original pH value; adjust the pH value of the other to 7.6 by using conc H_2SO_4 or NaOH as required. A standard pH is necessary because of the variation of color with pH. Remove excessive quantities of suspended materials by centrifuging. Treat each sample separately, as follows:

Thoroughly mix 0.1 g filter aid in a 10-ml portion of centrifuged sample

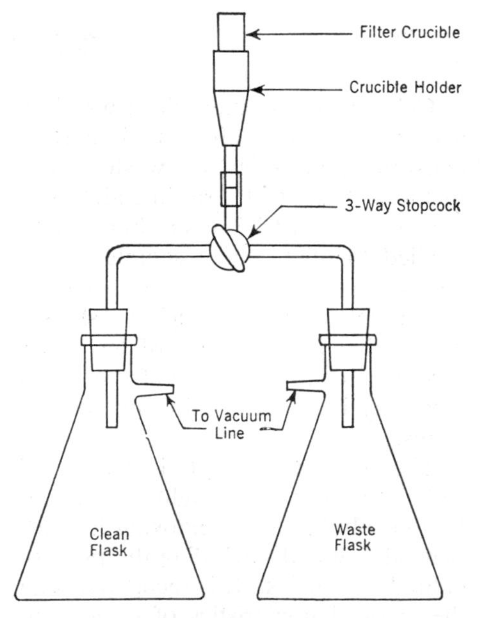

Figure 30. Filtration system for color determinations.

* Celite No. 505 (Johns-Manville Corporation) or equivalent.

TABLE 206(1): SELECTED ORDINATES FOR SPECTROPHOTOMETRIC COLOR DETERMINATIONS *

Ordinate No.	X	Y	Z
	Wavelength—mμ		
1	424.4	465.9	414.1
2*	435.5*	489.5*	422.2*
3	443.9	500.4	426.3
4	452.1	508.7	429.4
5*	461.2*	515.2*	432.0*
6	474.0	520.6	434.3
7	531.2	525.4	436.5
8*	544.3*	529.8*	438.6*
9	552.4	533.9	440.6
10	558.7	537.7	442.5
11*	564.1*	541.4*	444.4*
12	568.9	544.9	446.3
13	573.2	548.4	448.2
14*	577.4*	551.8*	450.1*
15	581.3	555.1	452.1
16	585.0	558.5	454.0
17*	588.7*	561.9*	455.9*
18	592.4	565.3	457.9
19	596.0	568.9	459.9
20*	599.6*	572.5*	462.0*
21	603.3	576.4	464.1
22	607.0	580.4	466.3
23*	610.9*	584.8*	468.7*
24	615.0	589.6	471.4
25	619.4	594.8	474.3
26*	624.2*	600.8*	477.7*
27	629.8	607.7	481.8
28	636.6	616.1	487.2
29*	645.9*	627.3*	495.2*
30	663.0	647.4	511.2
Factors When 30 Ordinates Used			
	0.03269	0.03333	0.03938
Factors When 10 Ordinates Used			
	0.09806	0.10000	0.11814

* Insert in each column the transmittance value (%) corresponding to the wavelength shown. Where limited accuracy is sufficient, only the ordinates marked with an asterisk need be used.

and filter the slurry to form a precoat in the filter crucible. Direct the filtrate to the waste flask as indicated in Figure 30. Mix 40 mg filter aid in a 35-ml portion of the centrifuged sample. While the vacuum is still in effect, filter through the precoat and pass the filtrate to the waste flask until clear; then direct the clear-filtrate flow to the clean flask by means of the three-way stopcock and collect 25 ml for the transmittance determination.

b. Determination of light transmission characteristics: Thoroughly clean the 10-mm absorption cells with detergent and rinse with distilled water. Rinse twice with filtered sample, clean the external surfaces with lens paper, and fill the cell with filtered sample.

Determine the transmittance values (in percent) for the sample at each of the visible wavelength values presented in Table 206(1), using the 10 ordinates marked with an asterisk for fairly accurate work and all 30 ordinates for increased accuracy. Set the instrument to read 100% transmittance on the distilled water blank and make all determinations with a narrow spectral band.

3. Calculation

a. Tabulate the transmittance values corresponding to the wavelengths shown in Columns X, Y, and Z in Table 206(1). Total each of the transmittance columns and multiply the totals by the appropriate factors (for 10 or 30 ordinates) shown at the bottom of the table, to obtain tristimulus values X, Y and Z. The tristimulus value Y is the *percent luminance* of the waste.

b. Calculate the trichromatic coefficients x and y from the tristimulus values X, Y and Z by the following equations:

$$x = \frac{X}{X+Y+Z}$$

$$y = \frac{Y}{X+Y+Z}$$

Locate point (x, y) on one of the chromaticity diagrams in Figure 31 and determine the dominant wavelength (in mμ) and the purity (in percent) directly from the diagram.*

Determine the hue from the dominant-wavelength value, according to the ranges in Table 206(2).

4. Expression of Results

Express the color characteristics (at pH 7.6 and at the original pH) in terms of *dominant wavelength* (mμ, to the nearest unit), *hue* (e.g., blue, blue-green, etc.), *luminance* (percent, to the nearest tenth), and *purity* (percent, to the nearest unit). Report the type of instrument (i.e., spectrophotometer), the number of selected ordinates (10 or 30), and the spectral band width (mμ) which were used.

* If more accurate values are desired, larger charts are presented in Hardy's *Handbook of Colorimetry* (See Bibliography following, Section 206 C).

TABLE 206(2): COLOR HUES FOR DOMINANT-WAVELENGTH RANGES

Wavelength Range *mμ*	Hue
400–465	violet
465–482	blue
482–497	blue-green
497–530	green
530–575	greenish yellow
575–580	yellow
580–587	yellowish orange
587–598	orange
598–620	orange-red
620–700	red
400–530c	blue-purple
530c–700	red-purple

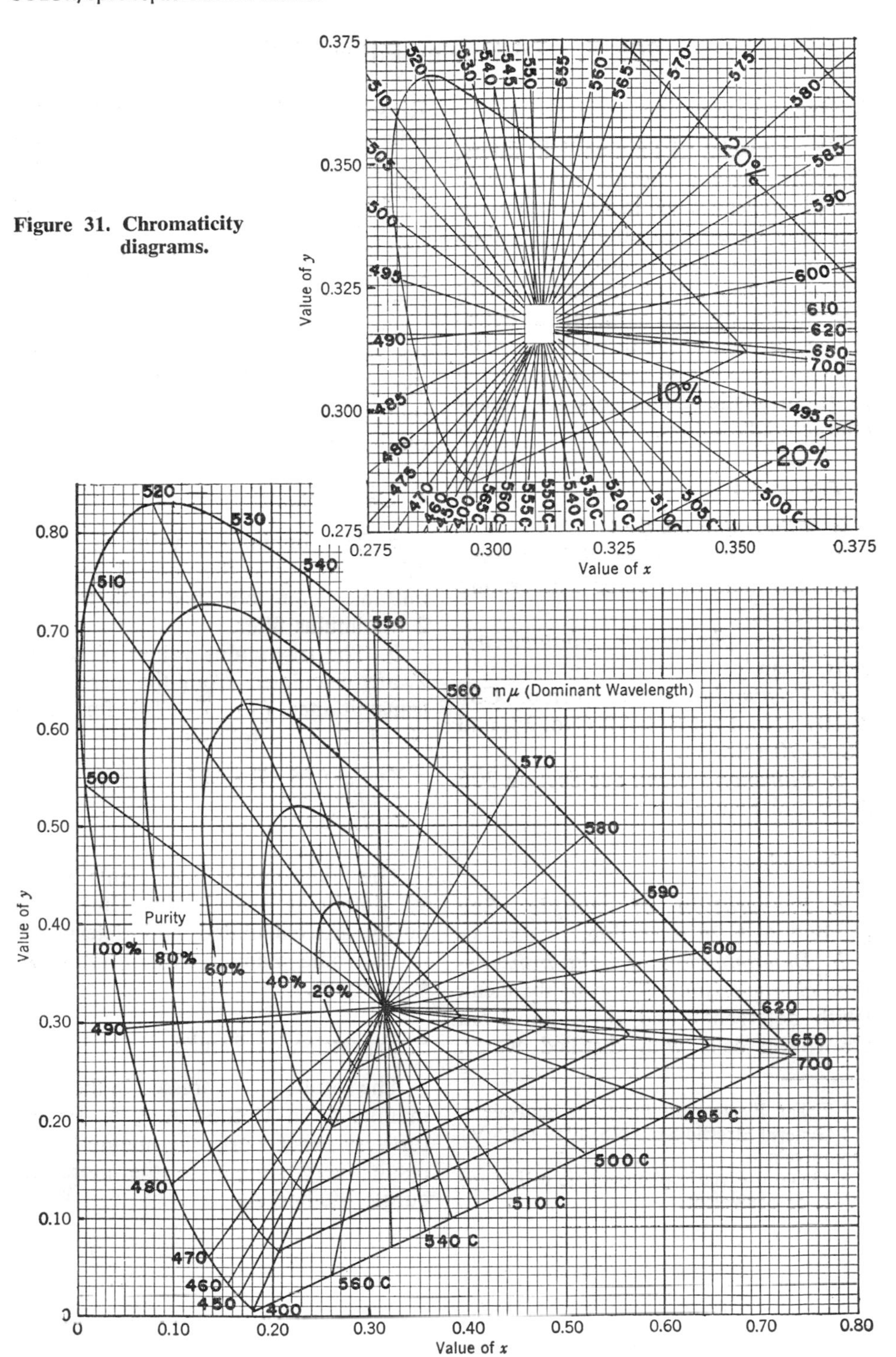

Figure 31. Chromaticity diagrams.

206 B. Tristimulus Filter Method

1. General Discussion

Three special tristimulus light filters, combined with a specific light source and photoelectric cell in a filter photometer may be used to obtain color data suitable for routine control purposes.

The percentage of tristimulus light transmitted by the solution is determined for each of the three filters. The transmittance values are then converted to trichromatic coefficients and color characteristic values.

2. Apparatus

a. Filter photometer.†

b. Filter photometer light source: Tungsten lamp at a color temperature of 3,000 K.‡

c. Filter photometer photoelectric cells, 1 cm.§

d. Tristimulus filters: Corning CS–3–107 (No. 1), CS–4–98 (No. 2), and CS–5–70 (No. 3).

e. Filtration system: See Section 206 A.1b and Figure 30.

3. Procedure

a. Preparation of sample: See Method A, ¶ 2a preceding.

b. Determination of light transmission characteristics: Thoroughly clean (with detergent) and rinse the 1-cm absorption cells with distilled water. Rinse each absorption cell twice with filtered sample, clean the external surfaces with lens paper, and fill the cell with filtered sample.

Place a distilled water blank in another cell and use it to set the instrument at 100% transmittance. Determine the percentage of light transmission through the sample for each of the three tristimulus light filters, with the filter photometer lamp intensity switch in a position equivalent to 4 V on the lamp.

4. Calculation

a. The luminance value is determined directly as the percentage transmittance value obtained with the No. 2 tristimulus filter.

b. The tristimulus values X, Y and Z are calculated from the percentage transmittance (T_1, T_2, T_3) for filters No. 1, 2, 3, as follows:

$$X = T_3 \times 0.06 + T_1 \times 0.25$$
$$Y = T_2 \times 0.316$$
$$Z = T_3 \times 0.374$$

The trichromatic coefficients x and y, dominant wavelength, hue, and purity are calculated and determined in the same manner as in Method A, ¶ 3b above.

5. Expression of Results

The results are expressed in the same manner as in Method A, ¶ 4. Except for very exact work, this method gives results very similar to the more accurate Method A.

† Fisher Electrophotometer or equivalent.

‡ General Electric lamp No. 1719 (at 6 V) or equivalent.

§ General Electric photovoltaic cell, Type PV–1, or equivalent.

206 C. Bibliography

HARDY, A. C. 1936. *Handbook of Colorimetry*. Technology Press, Boston, Mass.

OPTICAL SOCIETY OF AMERICA. 1943. Committee Report. The concept of color. *J. Optical Soc. Amer.* 33:544.

RUDOLFS, W. & W. D. HANLON. 1951. Color in industrial wastes. I. Determination by spectrophotometric method. *Sewage & Ind. Wastes* 23:1125.

JONES, H. et al. 1952. *The Science of Color*. Thomas Y. Crowell Co., New York.

JUDD, D. D. 1952. *Color in Business, Science, and Industry*. John Wiley & Sons, New York.

COPPER: See Heavy Metals, Section 211(II)E.

207 CYANIDE

In the examination of industrial wastes and other waters, "cyanide" refers to all of the CN groups in the cyanide compounds present that can be determined as the cyanide ion, CN^-, by the methods used. The cyanide compounds in which cyanide can be obtained as CN^- are classed as simple and complex cyanides.

The simple cyanides are represented by the formula $A(CN)_x$, where A is an alkali (sodium, potassium, ammonium) or a metal, and x, the valence of A, is the number of CN groups. In the soluble compounds, particularly the simple alkali cyanides, the CN group is present as CN^-.

The complex cyanides have a variety of formulas, but the alkali-metallic cyanides normally can be represented by $A_yM(CN)_x$. In this formula, A represents the alkali present y times, M the heavy metal (ferrous and ferric iron, cadmium, copper, nickel, silver, zinc or others), and x the number of CN groups; x is equal to the valence of A taken y times plus that of the heavy metal. In these soluble alkali-metallic cyanides, the anion is not the CN groups but the radical, $M(CN)_x$.

The cyanides show varying degrees of chemical activity. The simple cyanides are readily changed to HCN during distillation with acid. Many of the metal cyanides, such as those of cadmium, copper, nickel and zinc, react almost as readily. The iron cyanide complexes under similar conditions show greater resistance to decomposition to HCN, whereas those of cobalticyanides decompose very slowly.

The cyanide ion, CN^-, is very toxic. Because the simple alkali cyanides form CN^- when dissolved in aqueous solution, they, too, normally display intense toxicity. Many of the alkali-metallic cyanides are rather stable in aqueous solution and therefore normally have little or no toxicity. Under certain conditions, some not well defined, these complexes decompose to display varying degrees of toxicity, depending on the metal present and the proportion of the CN groups converted to the simpler alkali cyanides with their toxic CN^-.

The presence of cyanide in water has a significant effect on the biologic activity of the system. For example, Dodge and Reams [1] report that the threshold limit of toxicity at infinite time for fish appears to be 0.1 mg/l as CN^-. Ludzack and colleagues [2] found that the microorganisms responsible for self-purification were inhibited by a CN^- content of 0.3 mg/l or above. The toxicity limits are affected by water quality, temperature, and type and size of organisms; hence, definite effects are difficult to establish but the values quoted indicate the nature of the effects due to cyanides in water.

Selection of Method

Procedures are given below for the removal of interfering substances and the conversion of all cyanides, except cobalticyanides, to the simple ion, CN^-, by preliminary treatment of the sample; and for the determination of the CN^- after such treatment.

The screening procedure selected for the preliminary treatment of the sample is applicable to many types of waters. The procedure was found effective on relatively pure water, river water, sewage, and several industrial wastes, including those from gas and coke operations, petroleum refining, and plating.

The preliminary screening procedure eliminates or reduces interference to a minimum. Such screening is subject to modification to conform to the nature of the interference. Distillation is an important part of the screening procedure because it not only isolates cyanide from most interferences, but converts most cyanide complexes into the simple CN^- that is readily measured by titration or color test. It is permissible to omit the distillation procedure when it is known that the sample contains only simple cyanides of the alkalis and is completely free of all interferences.

If all of the conditions for direct determination of CN^-, except turbidity, are met, it may be possible to extract the pyridine-pyrazolone color, thereby avoiding distillation. This procedure is similar to that of Nusbaum and Skupeko [3] and is very effective where turbidity is the principal interference. In such cases, the reliability of the test would be verified if the same results were obtained with and without distillation.

The concentration of the cyanide in the sample following the preliminary screening procedure can be determined by the modified Liebig titration method, Method B, using the rhodanine internal indicator of Ryan and Culshaw,[4] or by a colorimetric method, Method C, using pyridine-pyrazolone as outlined by Epstein.[5]

The proposal by Serfass and colleagues [6] that the titration method be used for samples with a cyanide concentration greater than 1 mg/l as CN and that the colorimetric method be used below this level has been justified by the sensitivity and precision of the two methods at the respective cyanide levels. If the cyanide concentration is unknown, the colorimetric method is used only when titration of part of the distillate indicates a concentration of less than 1 mg/l as CN.

The titration method can be adapted for high concentrations of cyanide by increasing the strength of silver nitrate solution, by taking smaller samples and diluting before distillation, or by taking smaller aliquots of distillate and diluting before titration.

207 A. Preliminary Treatment of Samples

CAUTION—Due care should be exercised in the manipulation of cyanide samples because of the toxicity involved. They should be processed in a hood or other well-ventilated area. Avoid inhalation or ingestion of the sample or products of the sample. Do not attempt to acidify a sample unless liberated HCN can be trapped or controlled.

1. General Discussion

a. Principle: The nature of the preliminary treatment will vary according to the interfering substance present. Sulfide, fatty acids and oxidizing agents are removed by special procedures that are more or less self-explanatory. Most other interfering substances are removed by distillation. The importance of the distillation procedure cannot be overemphasized. This step not only eliminates interference, but also results in the conversion of the cyanide into simple sodium cyanide, which may readily be measured by titration or color test.

The color test, in particular, is sensitive to variations in salt concentration. Although the pyridine-pyrazolone color reaction is reproducible through a pH range of 3 to 8, significant variations in salt concentration result in changes in the absorbance of the color. Therefore, it is essential to isolate these salts so that a controlled salt concentration may be used for all aliquots of the distillate and the standards, as provided in the colorimetric test.

Distillation of the sample in the presence of sulfuric acid readily converts the simple cyanides into HCN. Complex iron cyanides and a few others are not easily decomposed, but many, such as those of cadmium, copper, nickel, silver and zinc, are also converted to HCN by boiling in the presence of acid. The conversion is hastened in the presence of magnesium and mercuric salts. These salts are extremely effective in reducing the ferrocyanides and ferricyanides to magnesium and mercuric simple cyanides, which in turn are readily decomposed by the acid to HCN. In spite of this favorable transition, an additional distillation period is required for conversion of all cyanide to HCN. Complete decomposition of the cobalticyanide complex does not occur even after distilling the sample under similar conditions for more than 24 hr.

The HCN gas and water vapor are evolved from the boiling sample. Through refluxing and use of an air stream, the water vapor is returned to the distilling flask and the HCN is swept over into a caustic solution, where it is converted to simple sodium cyanide for test.

b. Interference: Common interferences in the analysis for cyanide include: sulfide, heavy-metal ions, fatty acids, and other steam-distillable organic compounds which adversely affect the silver nitrate titration; thiocyanate, cyanate, glycine, urea or other substances which may hydrolyze to form cyanide under analytical conditions; substances contributing color or turbidity, affecting both titration and color development; and oxidizing agents which are likely to result in the destruction of cyanide during manipulation, particularly during the distillation stage.

1) SULFIDE is removed by treating the alkaline sample at pH 11.0 with small increments of powdered lead carbonate. Black lead sulfide precipitates in samples containing sulfide. Repeat this operation until no more lead sulfide forms. Filter and rinse the precipitate, add the rinse water to the filtrate, and use an aliquot for analysis. Avoid a large excess of lead carbonate and a long period of contact, in order to minimize complexing or occlusion of the cyanide with the precipitated material.

2) FATTY ACIDS form soaps under alkaline titration conditions and render it difficult or impossible to detect the end point. This type of interference may be removed by an extraction, as suggested by Kruse and Mellon.[7] The sample should be acidified with acetic acid to pH 6–7 and extracted with isooctane, hexane or chloroform (preference in the order named). One extraction with a solvent volume equal to 20% of the sample volume is usually adequate to reduce the fatty acids to a point below the interference level. Avoid multiple extractions or a long contact time at a low pH, in order to keep the loss of HCN at a minimum.

3) OXIDIZING AGENTS are removed by the procedure outlined by Serfass and colleagues.[6] If the sample tests positively with starch-iodide paper, titrate with sodium sulfite (12.6 g anhydrous Na_2SO_3 per liter of solution) until a negative test is obtained.

4) OTHER INTERFERING SUBSTANCES —After the removal of sulfides, fatty acids and oxidizing agents, if necessary most other interferences can be removed by distillation.

c. Preservation of samples: Because most cyanides are very reactive and unstable, analysis should be made as soon as possible after sampling. If the sample cannot be analyzed immediately, add NaOH to raise the pH to 11.0 or above, and store in a cool place.

2. Apparatus

The following apparatus (see Figure 32) is required:

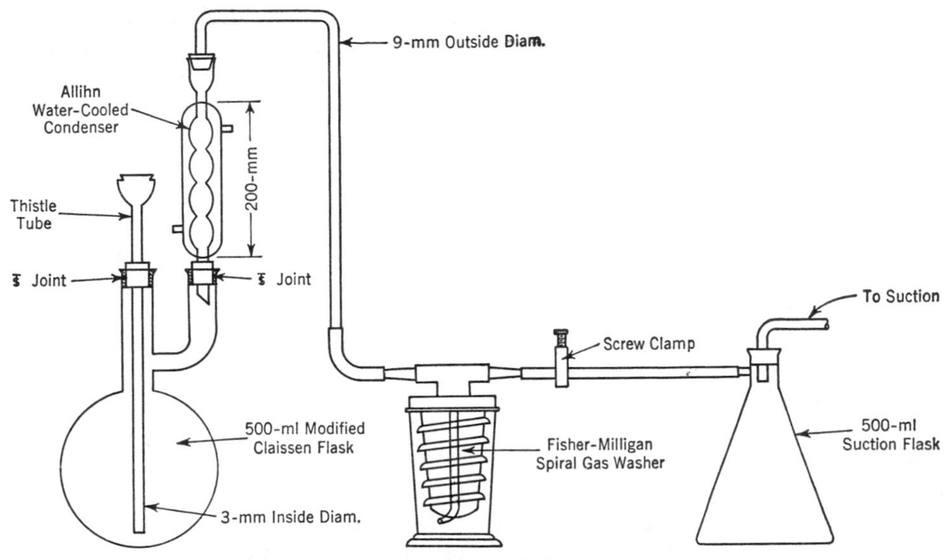

Figure 32. Cyanide distillation apparatus.

a. Modified Claissen flask, 500-ml, having ₴ joints, with side-arm delivery tube removed and opening sealed.

b. Air inlet, consisting of a thistle tube with ₴ joint, having a glass tube (3-mm I.D.) fused to the joint and extended to ¼ in. from the bottom of the modified Claissen flask.

c. Allihn-type condenser, with ₴ joint to fit the modified Claissen flask.

d. Gas washer, spiral-flow type, liquid capacity 100–250 ml (such as the modified Milligan washer), fitted with a rubber tube with a pinch clamp in the bottom.

e. Suction flask, 500-ml capacity.

f. Water aspirator.

g. Heating element, for the modified Claissen flask.

h. Connecting tubing, rubber or glass as indicated.

3. Reagents

a. Sodium hydroxide solution, 1*N*.

b. Mercuric chloride solution: Dissolve 34 g $HgCl_2$ in 500 ml distilled water. (CAUTION: *Toxic—take care to avoid ingestion.*)

c. Magnesium chloride solution: Dissolve 51 g $MgCl_2 \cdot 6H_2O$ in 100 ml distilled water.

d. Sulfuric acid, conc.

4. Procedure

a. Add the sample, containing not more than 500 mg CN (diluted if necessary to 250–500 ml with distilled water), to the Claissen flask. Add exactly 50 ml 1*N* NaOH solution to the gas washer and dilute, if necessary, with distilled water to obtain an adequate depth of liquid in the absorber. Connect the train, consisting of boiling flask air inlet, flask, condenser, gas washer, suction flask trap and aspirator. Adjust the suction so that approximately one bubble of air per second enters the boiling flask through the air inlet. This air rate will effectively act as a carrier for the HCN gas from flask to absorber and will usually prevent a reverse flow of HCN through the air inlet. If the air rate does not prevent the sample from backing up in the delivery tube, the airflow rate may be increased up to two bubbles per second without loss in efficiency. If the air rate becomes too high, the gas washer will not trap all the HCN.

b. Add 20 ml mercuric chloride solution and 10 ml magnesium chloride solution through the air inlet tube. Rinse the tube with distilled water and allow the airflow to mix the flask contents for 3 min. Slowly add conc H_2SO_4 in an amount equal to 5 ml for each 100 ml of solution in the distilling flask and rinse the air inlet once more.

c. Heat at a rate which will provide rapid boiling but will not flood the condenser inlet or permit vapors to rise more than halfway into the condenser. Reflux for 1 hr. Turn off the heat but continue the airflow. After 15 min of cooling, drain the gas washer contents into a separate container. Rinse the connecting tube from the condenser to the gas washer with distilled water, add the rinse water to the drained liquid, and dilute to 250 ml in a volumetric flask.

d. Determine the cyanide content by the titration method (*B*) if the cyanide concentration is greater than 1 mg/l as CN and by the colorimetric method (*C*) if the cyanide is below this level. If the cyanide concentration is unknown, it is recommended that 200 ml of the distillate be titrated by Method B. If the cyanide value is then found to be below the desired limit of 1 mg/l as CN, the remaining 50 ml of the distillate is diluted, if necessary, and examined as indicated in Method C.

e. Refill the gas washer with a fresh charge of 1*N* NaOH solution and repeat the reflux procedure.

f. If the sample includes only readily hydrolyzed cyanides, the absorber liquid from the first reflux will contain all the available cyanide; if stable complex cyanides are present, a significant yield will appear in the absorber liquid from the second or from several successive periods, depending on the degree of stability.

207 B. Titration Method

1. General Discussion

a. Principle: The CN^- in the alkaline distillate from the preliminary screening procedure is titrated with a standard solution of $AgNO_3$ to form the soluble cyanide complex, $Ag(CN)_2^-$. As soon as all the CN^- has been complexed and a small excess of Ag^+ has been added, the excess Ag^+ is detected by the silver-sensitive indicator, para-dimethylaminobenzalrhodanine, which immediately turns from a yellow to a salmon color. The indicator is sensitive to about 0.1 mg/l Ag. If the titration shows that CN^- is below 1 mg/l, another aliquot is examined colorimetrically. The titration method can be adapted for high concentration, as noted under selection of method.

b. Interference: All interferences are eliminated or reduced to a minimum by using only a distillate from the preliminary screening procedure.

c. Minimum detectable concentration: About 0.1 mg Ag, or about 0.05 mg CN. If all of the distillate from a 500-ml sample is used in the determination, the minimum detectable concentration approaches 0.1 mg/l CN.

2. Apparatus

a. Koch microburet, 5-ml capacity.

3. Reagents

a. Sodium hydroxide solution, 1N: Dissolve 4 g NaOH in 100 ml distilled water.

b. Indicator solution: Dissolve 0.02 g paradimethylaminobenzalrhodanine in 100 ml acetone.

c. Standard silver nitrate titrant, 0.0192N: Dissolve 3.27 g $AgNO_3$ in 1 liter distilled water. Standardize against standard NaCl solution, using the argentometric method with K_2CrO_4 indicator, as directed in Chloride, Section 112A.2; 1.00 ml of this solution is equivalent to 1.00 mg CN.

4. Procedure

a. If preliminary treatment has included distillation, take an aliquot of the distillate without pH adjustment. If the sample has not been distilled, adjust the pH to 11.0 or above with 1*N* sodium hydroxide solution. Dilute the aliquot to 250 ml or some other convenient volume to be used for all titrations. Add 0.5 ml indicator solution.

b. Titrate with standard silver nitrate titrant to the first change in color from a canary yellow to a salmon hue. Titrate a blank containing the same amount of alkali and water.

It is advisable to adjust the sample size or the strength of $AgNO_3$ titrant so that the titration requires 2–10 ml. The analyst should use the amount of indicator that gives him the best result; the same amount should be used for all titrations. Most analysts find this titration difficult for the first few trials, and this is reflected in high blank values. As the analyst becomes accustomed to the end point, blank titrations decrease to 1 drop or less and precision improves accordingly.

5. Calculation

$$\text{mg/l CN} = \frac{(A - B) \times 1{,}000}{\text{ml original sample}} \times \frac{250}{\text{ml aliquot}}$$

where A = ml standard $AgNO_3$ for aliquot, and B = standard $AgNO_3$ for blank.

6. Precision and Accuracy

The modified Liebig titration, when used at a cyanide level above 1 mg/l CN, has a coefficient of variation * of 2.0% for distilled samples or for relatively clear samples without significant interference. Extraction and removal of sulfide or oxidizing agents tend to increase the variation to a degree determined by the amount of manipulation required and the type of sample. The limit of sensitivity is approximately 0.1 mg/l CN, but at this point the color change is indistinct. At 0.4 mg/l the coefficient of variation is four times that at a concentration level greater than 1.0 mg/l CN.

* See Introduction, Section 200 D.

207 C. Colorimetric Method

1. General Discussion

a. Principle: The CN^- in the alkaline distillate from the preliminary screening procedure is converted to cyanogen chloride, CNCl, by reaction with chloramine-T at a pH less than 8 without hydrolyzing to the cyanate. After the reaction is complete, the CNCl forms a blue dye on the addition of a pyridine-pyrazolone reagent. If the dye is kept in an aqueous solution, the absorbance is read at 620 mμ. To obtain colors of comparable intensity, it is essential to have the same salt content in both the sample and the standards.

The above test, proposed by Epstein,[5] can be modified to improve sensitivity and precision by extracting the color with butyl alcohol and then reading the absorbance at 630 mμ. If the color is too intense, provision is made to use smaller aliquots for color development.

b. Interference: All interferences are eliminated or reduced to a minimum by using only a distillate from the preliminary screening procedure.

2. Apparatus

a. Colorimetric equipment—One of the following is required:

1) SPECTROPHOTOMETER, for use at 620–630 mμ, providing a light path of 1 cm.

2) FILTER PHOTOMETER, providing a light path of 1 cm and equipped with a red filter having maximum transmittance at 620–630 mμ.

b. Reaction tubes, consisting of test tubes, approximately 1 × 8 in., fitted with rubber stoppers.

3. Reagents

a. Sodium hydroxide solution, 0.2*N:* Dissolve 8 g NaOH in 1 liter distilled water.

b. Acetic acid, conc and 1 + 4.

c. Stock cyanide solution: Dissolve 2.51 g potassium cyanide, KCN, in 1 liter water. Standardize as directed in Method B, ¶ 4b, against silver nitrate. The solution loses strength gradually and must be rechecked every week. Approximate strength, 1 ml = 1 mg CN. (CAUTION: *Toxic—take care to avoid ingestion.*)

d. Standard cyanide solution: Dilute 10 ml stock cyanide solution to 1,000 ml with distilled water, mix, and make a second dilution of 10 ml to 100 ml; 1.00 ml = 1.0 μg CN. This solution must be prepared daily. (CAUTION: *Toxic—take care to avoid ingestion.*)

e. Chloramine-T solution: Dissolve 1 g in 100 ml water. Prepare daily.

f. 1-Phenyl-3-methyl-5-pyrazolone solution: Prepare a saturated aqueous solution (approximately 0.5 g/100 ml) by adding the pyrazolone to water at approximately 75 C. Agitate occasionally as the solution cools to room temperature. If necessary, the pyrazolone (melting point 127–128 C) can be purified by recrystallization from ethyl alcohol. Usually this is not required.

g. Pyridine.

h. Bis-pyrazolone: Dissolve 17.4 g of 1-phenyl-3-methyl-5-pyrazolone in 100 ml ethyl alcohol. Add 25 g phenyl hydrazine, freshly distilled, under reduced pressure. Reflux in an all-glass apparatus. Several hours of refluxing are necessary to produce the bis-pyrazolone, which is indicated by formation of crystals in the reflux mixture. A reflux of 6–8 hr, followed by standing at room temperature overnight, and a 1–2 hr reflux the following day are generally adequate for a good yield. Filter while hot, wash with hot 95% ethyl alcohol, and air-dry. The product (melting point greater than 320 C) is stable indefinitely in dry form.*

i. Mixed pyridine-pyrazolone reagent: Mix 125 ml of the filtered saturated aqueous solution of pyrazolone with a filtered solution containing 0.025 g bis-pyrazolone dissolved in 25 ml pyridine. Several minutes of mixing are usually necessary to dissolve the bis-pyrazolone in pyridine. The mixed reagent develops a pink color on standing, but if used within 24 hr this does not affect the color production with cyanide. Prepare daily.

j. n-Butyl alcohol.

k. Disodium hydrogen phosphate solution: Dissolve 5 g anhydrous Na_2HPO_4 in 100 ml water.

4. Procedure

a. Prepare one or more aliquots of the absorption liquid obtained from the distillation procedure in reaction tubes which, together with their stoppers, have been carefully rinsed with distilled water. Dilute each to 15 ml with 0.2*N* NaOH, and neutralize with 1 + 4 acetic acid to pH 6–7.

b. Prepare a blank by adding 15 ml 0.2*N* NaOH to a carefully rinsed reaction tube. Also prepare a series of standards containing 0.2, 0.4, 0.6, 0.8 and 1.0 μg CN. Neutralize blank and standards to pH 6–7 with 1 + 4 acetic acid. The amount of the acid for all diluted aliquots, the blank, and the standards should be approximately the same.

c. Add 0.2 ml chloramine-T solution, stopper, and mix by inversion two or three times. Allow 1–2 min for the reaction.

d. Add 5.0 ml of mixed pyridine-pyrazolone reagent, stopper, and mix by inversion. Allow 20 min for color development.

e. If the aqueous color is to be measured, dilute all reaction tubes accurately to a definite volume—usually 25 ml—mix, and read absorbance at 620 mμ on all samples and standards. If the color of the distillate aliquot is too intense, repeat the test using a smaller sample or aliquot.

f. Greater sensitivity is possible if extracted color is used for the spectrophotometric reading, as follows: At the end of the color development period add 1 ml disodium hydrogen phosphate solution and 10 ml carefully measured butyl alcohol. Stopper and mix by inversion. If the emulsion formed by the two-phase system does not break within 1 to 3 min, add more of the phosphate solution and mix again. Withdraw an aliquot of the alcohol layer and measure the absorbance at 630 mμ. A large sample volume or trace quantities of cyanide may require a modified solvent volume.

The pyridine-pyrazolone color will not develop quantitatively in the alcohol layer if the phosphate is added before the color development is essentially complete in the aqueous phase.

5. Calculation

$$\mu g/l\ CN = \frac{\mu g\ CN\ in\ sample\ from\ calibration\ curve \times 1{,}000}{ml\ original\ sample\ representing\ colored\ sample}$$

* Bis-pyrazolone may also be obtained commercially: Eastman No. 6969 or equivalent.

6. Precision and Accuracy

The pyridine-pyrazolone sensitivity data given below are for a final volume of 25 ml after color development on the aqueous readings and in 10 ml of added solvent for extracted samples. The absorbances of the extracted samples were read in 1-cm cells. The color was extracted from a 25-ml volume in order to compare data with the aqueous readings, but no detectable difference in precision was obtained on extractions where 100 ml of sample was used.

For aqueous color readings, the coefficient of variation was 1.7%, the sensitivity 0.5 μg, and the effective range 1–5 μg. For extracted color readings, the respective figures were 3.9%, 0.1 μg, and 0.2–2.0 μg.

Sensitivity is defined as the amount of CN required to produce an absorbance of 0.05 or above with a precision not more than twice the coefficient of variation given. Effective range is the amount of CN present in the reaction tubes—containing 25 ml aqueous or 10 ml solvent—that results in an absorbance reading from 0.1 to 1.0.

The sensitivity of the extracted sample is determined by the ratio of water to solvent volume. The values given are for distilled samples. A turbid sample showed approximately the same precision on the extracted readings with a large increase in variation for the aqueous readings.

207 D. References

1. B. F. DODGE & D. C. REAMS. 1949. Critical review of the literature pertaining to disposal of waste cyanide solutions. *Amer. Electroplaters Soc. Res. Rep.* 14:1.
2. F. J. LUDZACK, et al. 1951. Effect of cyanide on biochemical oxidation in sewage and polluted water. *Sewage & Ind. Wastes* 23:1298.
3. I. NUSBAUM & P. SKUPEKO. 1951. Determination of cyanides in sewage and polluted waters. *Sewage & Ind. Wastes,* 23:875.
4. J. A. RYAN & G. W. CULSHAW. 1944. The use of *p*-dimethylaminobenzylidene rhodanine as an indicator for the volumetric determination of cyanides. *Analyst* 69:370.
5. J. EPSTEIN. 1947. Estimation of microquantities of cyanide. *Anal. Chem.* 19:272.
6. E. J. SERFASS et al. 1952. Analytical method for the determination of cyanides in plating wastes and in effluents from treatment processes. *Plating* 39:267.
7. J. M. KRUSE & M. G. MELLON. 1951. Colorimetric determination of cyanides. *Sewage & Ind. Wastes* 23:1402.

207 E. Bibliography

RUCHHOFT, C. C. et al. 1949. *Tentative Methods for Analysis of Cadmium, Chromium, and Cyanide in Water.* U. S. Public Health Service, Environmental Health Center, Cincinnati, Ohio.

HUGHES, E. K. 1952. Suggested nonmenclature in applied spectroscopy. *Anal. Chem.* 24:1349.

LUDZACK, F. J. et al. 1954. Determination of cyanides in water and waste samples. *Anal. Chem.* 26:1784.

DENSITY INDEX: See Tests on Activated Sludge, Section 230D.

DETERGENTS: See Surfactants, Section 229.

208 FLUORIDE

1. General Discussion

Color, turbidity and other interfering substances cannot be removed from wastewater and highly polluted water by a single distillation. Separation of fluoride ions from the primary distillate by magnesium oxide and redistillation from a water suspension of the oxide produce a clear distillate, free of interfering substances, which can be analyzed readily.

2. Apparatus

The same apparatus is required as for the fluoride determination in water; see Part 100, Fluoride, Preliminary Distillation Step, Section 121A.

3. Reagents

In addition to reagents listed in Part 100, Fluoride, Section 121A, the following is required:

a. Magnesium oxide, light powder.

4. Procedure

Collect the primary distillate in the same manner as described in Fluoride, Preliminary Distillation Step (Section 121A). Use 300 ml sample or a suitable aliquot made up to 300 ml. Make the distillate just alkaline to phenolphthalein and bring to a boil. Add 0.5 g magnesium oxide. Continue boiling for 5 min. Separate the magnesium oxide (containing fluoride) by centrifuging. Wash the magnesium oxide into a distilling flask, dilute to 300 ml, and repeat the distillation procedure as in the preliminary distillation step for fluoride (Section 121A.4). Measure the fluoride by the colorimetric or electrode methods described in Section 121B and C.

5. Bibliography

VENKATESWARLU, P. & D. NARAYANA RAO. 1954. Estimation of fluorine in biological material. *Anal. Chem.* 20:766.

209 GREASE

1. Limitations: In the determination of grease, an absolute quantity of a specific substance is not measured. Rather, groups of substances with similar physical characteristics are determined quantitatively, based on their mutual solubility in the solvent used. Grease may therefore be said to include fatty acids, soaps, fats, waxes, oils and any other material which is extracted by the solvent from an acidified sample and which is not volatilized during evaporation of the solvent. It is important that this limitation be clearly understood. Unlike some constituents—which represent distinct chemical elements, ions, compounds or groups of compounds—greases are in effect defined by the method used for their determination.

The methods presented here have been found suitable for biological lipids and long-chain mineral hydrocarbons, when these occur at the concentrations which are usual in domestic wastewaters. However, samples which contain certain industrial wastes may require modification of the methods,[1, 2] due to the presence of either excessive concentrations of natural greases or synthetic or modified compounds which are not well recovered by the standard procedures.

Modern industry employs a number of long-chain carbon compounds as lubricants and emulsifiers, as well as for other more specialized purposes. Often the composition of these materials differs from that of natural greases and oils, and may render them more soluble in water or more easily emulsified than the natural products. As a result, they behave as greases and oils in treatment processes and the receiving water, but the problems they cause may be accentuated by their special properties. There is evidence that the procedures described here may fail to give complete recovery of products of this kind.[1, 2]

Consequently, various laboratories have found it necessary to modify the methods given here, in order to obtain meaningful results when dealing with specific industrial wastes or other specialized problems. Some report that recovery of solubilized or emulsified oil derivatives is greatly improved if the sample is saturated with sodium chloride (300 g per liter of sample) immediately after sample acidification to pH 1.0 (Section 209A.4a).[3] At times it has been found necessary to subject the filtrate in Methods A and B to wet extraction with the solvent used in order to realize consistently good quantitative results. These modifications and others are perfectly valid for use in special circumstances, as long as it is recognized that they do have the effect of changing the spectrum of compounds determined by the method. As always, any modification of procedure which is introduced to cope with an unusual problem should be described exactly when the results are reported.

2. Significance: Greases and oils are particularly resistant to anaerobic digestion, and when present in sludge they cause excessive scum accumulation in digesters, clog the pores of filters, and deter the use of the sludge as fertilizer.

When these substances are discharged in wastewater or treated effluents, they often cause surface films and shoreline deposits.

A knowledge of the quantity of grease present in a waste is helpful in overcoming difficulties in plant operation, in determining plant efficiencies, and in controlling the subsequent discharge of grease to receiving streams. A knowledge of the amount of grease present in sludge can aid in the diagnosis of digestion and dewatering problems and indicate the suitability of a particular sludge for use as a fertilizer.

3. Selection of method: For liquid samples, two extraction methods are presented: the Soxhlet method (*A*) and the tentative semiwet method (*B*). An elapsed time of 6 hr is required to complete a determination by Method A, whereas Method B requires 2 hr. However, the personnel time (1½ hr) is the same for each. Of the two, Method A has the greater precision and accuracy. Both methods have been found to give reproducible results for grease concentrations up to 650 mg/l. Methods A and B are not intended for use with sludges or other solid and semisolid samples. Method C is a modification of the Soxhlet method which is suitable for sludges and similar materials. Method D separates the total grease into two fractions on the basis of the polar or nonpolar nature of the compounds present and determines these fractions separately.

4. *Sampling and storage:* In sampling water, wastewater and effluents, whenever possible collect representative samples in a wide-mouth bottle calibrated to hold a measured volume and perform the initial steps of the procedure in the sample bottle. When information is required concerning the average grease concentration of a waste over an extended period, the examination of individual portions collected at prescribed time intervals can be used to eliminate losses of grease on sampling equipment during collection of a composite sample.

In sampling sludges, every possible precaution must be taken to obtain a representative sample. When analysis cannot be made immediately, samples may be preserved with 1 ml conc H_2SO_4 for each 80 g of sample. Samples should never be preserved with chloroform or sodium benzoate when grease is to be determined.

209 A. Soxhlet Extraction Method

1. General Discussion

a. Principle: Soluble metallic soaps are hydrolyzed by acidification. The solid or viscous grease is separated from the liquid sample by filtration. Grease is then extracted in a Soxhlet apparatus using hexane or trichlorotrifluoroethane, and the residue remaining after evaporation of the solvent is weighed to determine the grease content of the sample. Compounds volatilized at or below 103 C will be lost when the filter is dried.

b. Interference: The method is entirely empirical, and duplicate results can be obtained only by strict adherence to all details. By definition, any material recovered is called grease and any filtrable organic-soluble substances, such as elemental sulfur and certain organic dyes, will be extracted as grease. The rate and time of extraction in the Soxhlet apparatus must be exactly as directed because of varying solubilities of different greases in the solvents. In addition, the length of time required for drying and cooling the extracted grease cannot be varied. There may be a gradual increase in weight, presumably due to the absorption of oxygen, or a gradual loss of weight due to volatilization.

2. Apparatus

a. Extraction apparatus, Soxhlet.

b. Vacuum pump, or other source of vacuum.

c. Buchner funnel, 12-cm.

d. Electric heating mantle.

3. Reagents

a. Hydrochloric acid, conc.

b. Organic solvent: Either *n*-hexane or trichlorotrifluoroethane may be used for extraction purposes. The latter, being nonflammable, is preferable from the standpoint of laboratory safety. The solvent used should leave no measurable residue on evaporation.

1) *n*-HEXANE, boiling point 69 C.

2) TRICHLOROTRIFLUOROETHANE,* bp 47.5 C.

c. Filter paper, Whatman No. 40, 11 cm.

d. Muslin cloth disks, 11 cm.

e. Diatomaceous-silica filter aid suspension,† 10 g per liter distilled water.

4. Procedure

a. Collect 1 liter of sewage in a wide-mouth bottle marked at 1 liter. Acidify to pH 1.0; generally, 10 ml conc HCl is sufficient.

b. Prepare a filter consisting of a muslin cloth disk overlaid with filter paper. Wet the paper and muslin and press down the edges of the paper. Using a vacuum, pass 100 ml filter aid suspension through the prepared filter and wash with 1 liter distilled water. Apply a vacuum until no more water passes the filter.

c. Filter the acidified sample through the prepared filter. Apply a vacuum until no more water passes the filter.

d. Remove the filter paper to a watch glass with a forceps. Add the material adhering to the edges of the muslin cloth disk. Wipe the sides and bottom of the collecting vessel, the stirring rod, and the Buchner funnel with bits of filter paper soaked in the solvent to be used, taking care to remove all films caused by grease and to collect all solid material. Add the bits of filter paper to the filter paper on the watch glass. Roll the filter paper and the bits of filter paper and fit them into a paper extraction thimble. Add any bits of material remaining on the watch glass. Wipe the watch glass with a bit of filter paper soaked in solvent and place in the paper extraction thimble.

e. Dry the thimble with the filter paper in a hot-air oven at 103 C for 30 min. Fill the thimble with small glass beads. Weigh the extraction flask and extract the grease in a Soxhlet apparatus, using hexane or trichlorotrifluoroethane at a rate of 20 cycles per hour for 4 hr. Time from the first cycle.

f. Distill the solvent from the extraction flask in a water bath at 85 C, or in an electric heating mantle adjusted for slow distillation (the solvent may be reused if it is redistilled). Dry by placing the flask on a steam bath and draw air through the flask by means of a vacuum applied for 15 min.

g. Cool in a desiccator for 30 min and weigh.

---

* Freon TF, Freon PCA, Freon 113, or equivalent. Suitable grades are available commercially.

† Hyflo Super-Cel (Johns-Manville Corp.) or equivalent.

5. Calculation

$$\text{mg/l total grease} = \frac{\text{mg increase in weight of flask} \times 1{,}000}{\text{ml sample}}$$

6. Precision and Accuracy

The accuracy of this determination cannot be measured directly in wastewaters. The following data, obtained on synthetic samples, may be considered indicative for natural animal, vegetable and mineral products, but cannot be applied to the specialized industrial products discussed in the introduction to these methods.

Using synthetic samples containing various amounts of Crisco and Shell S.A.E. No. 20 oil, an average recovery of 98.7% was obtained, with a standard deviation of 1.86%. Ten replicates each of two sewages yielded standard deviations of 0.76 mg and 0.48 mg.

209 B. Semiwet Extraction Method (TENTATIVE)

1. General Discussion

a. Principle: The principle is the same as in Method A, except that contact between the solvent and grease is forced mechanically with a glass stirring rod.

b. Interference: Because of the variable composition of grease, it is impossible to say that a fixed, practicable number of direct extractions removes a determinable percentage of the total grease in all types of sewage. If a limit is set on the number of extractions—even as high as ten—the more difficultly soluble fractions of grease may not be determined by this method. As in Method A, certain nongrease substances will be extracted by hexane. Moreover, strict adherence to all details must be observed if reproducible results are to be obtained.

2. Apparatus

a. Buchner funnel, 12-cm.

b. Distilling flask, 300-ml.

3. Reagents

Same as Method A, ¶s 3a–e.

4. Procedure

a. Follow the same procedure as in Method A to the point in ¶ 4d where the filter paper has been removed from the Buchner funnel. Instead of placing it in an extraction thimble, place it in a 300-ml erlenmeyer flask. Also add the bits of filter paper used for wiping the flask.

b. Add 25 ml hexane or trichlorotrifluoroethane to the flask. With the aid of a stirring rod of suitable length flattened at one end, stir the paper around in the solvent for 1 min. Occasionally squeeze the paper between the stirring rod and the wall of the flask. Allow the material to settle momentarily, then pour the solvent into a 12-cm funnel fitted with 18.5-cm Whatman No. 40 filter paper. Collect the solvent in a 300-ml distilling flask.

c. Repeat the above extraction

nine more times, collecting all of the solvent in the one distilling flask.

d. Wash the filter paper in the funnel with solvent, using a glass rod to aid in dissolving the grease on the paper by rubbing the visible residues while applying a stream of solvent to the same spot. Add the washings to the contents of the flask.

e. Distill the solvent from the distilling flask in a water bath at 85 C, or in an electric heating mantle adjusted for slow distillation, to a volume of approximately 25 ml. Transfer to a smaller tared flask, using a 6-cm glass funnel, and rinse the larger flask and funnel with two small portions of solvent, adding the rinsings to the tared flask.

f. Distill the solvent from the tared flask in a water bath at 85 C. Dry by placing on a steam bath and draw air through the flask by means of a vacuum applied for 15 min.

g. Cool in a desiccator for 30 min and weigh.

5. Calculation

See Method A, ¶ 5.

6. Precision and Accuracy

The accuracy of this determination cannot be measured directly in wastewaters. The following data, obtained on synthetic samples, may be considered indicative for natural animal, vegetable, and mineral products, but cannot be applied to the specialized industrial products discussed in the introduction to these methods.

Using 100.0 mg Crisco as a standard grease, an average recovery of 98.2% was obtained, with a standard deviation of ±4.0 mg. Analysis of 10 replicate samples of a domestic sewage yielded a standard deviation of ±2.58 mg.

209 C. Extraction Method for Sludge Samples

1. General Discussion

a. Principle: Drying of acidified sludges by heating leads to low results. Magnesium sulfate monohydrate is capable of combining with 75% of its own weight in water in forming the heptahydrate. Magnesium sulfate monohydrate can be used to dry sludge. After drying, the grease can be extracted with hexane or trichlorotrifluoroethane.

b. Interference: Refer to Method A, ¶ 1b preceding.

2. Apparatus

a. Extraction apparatus, Soxhlet.

b. Vacuum pump, or other source of vacuum.

3. Reagents

a. Hydrochloric acid, conc.

b. Magnesium sulfate monohydrate: Prepare $MgSO_4 \cdot H_2O$ by drying overnight a thin layer of $MgSO_4 \cdot 7H_2O$ in an oven at 103 C.

c. Organic solvent: Either *n*-hexane or trichlorotrifluoroethane may be used for extraction purposes.

1) *n*-HEXANE, boiling point 69 C.

2) TRICHLOROTRIFLUOROETHANE,* bp 47.5 C.

---

* Freon TF, Freon PCA, Freon 113, or equivalent.

d. Grease-free cotton: Nonabsorbent cotton after extraction with *n*-hexane or trichlorotrifluoroethane.

4. Procedure

a. In a 150-ml beaker weigh a sample of wet sludge, 20 ± 0.5 g, of which the dry-solids content is known. Acidify to pH 2.0 (generally, 0.3 ml conc HCl is sufficient). Add 25 g magnesium sulfate monohydrate. Stir to a smooth paste and spread on the sides of the beaker to facilitate subsequent removal. Allow to stand until solidified, 15 to 30 min. Remove the solids and grind in a porcelain mortar. Add the powder to a paper extraction thimble. Wipe the beaker and mortar with small pieces of filter paper moistened with solvent and add to the thimble. Fill the thimble with small glass beads. Extract in a Soxhlet apparatus, using hexane or trichlorotrifluoroethane at a rate of 20 cycles per hour for 4 hr.

b. If any turbidity or suspended matter is present in the extraction flask, remove by filtering through grease-free cotton into another weighed flask. Rinse flask and cotton with solvent. Distill the solvent from the extraction flask in water at 85 C. Dry by placing on a steam bath and drawing air through the flask with a vacuum for 15 min.

c. Cool in a desiccator for 30 min and weigh.

5. Calculation

Grease as % dry solids

$$= \frac{\text{gain in weight of flask (g)} \times 100}{\text{weight of wet solids (g)} \times \text{\% dry solids}}$$

6. Precision

The examination of six replicate samples of sludge yielded a standard deviation of 4.6%

209 D. Hydrocarbon and Fatty Matter Content of Grease

In the absence of specially modified industrial products, greases are composed primarily of fatty matter from animal and vegetable sources and hydrocarbons of petroleum origin. A knowledge of the percentage of each of these constituents in the total grease minimizes the difficulty in determining the major source of the grease and simplifies the correction of grease problems in sewage treatment plant operation and stream pollution abatement.

Using the method described, reproducible results have been obtained for concentrations up to 650 mg/l.

1. General Discussion

a. Principle: Activated alumina has the ability to adsorb polar materials. If a solution of grease dissolved in hexane or trichlorotrifluoroethane is passed through a column of activated alumina, the grease will be adsorbed on the surface of the alumina. Further passage of pure solvent through the column will elute the nonpolar material that has been retained on the column. Because petroleum is composed chiefly of nonpolar hydrocarbons, and fatty acids and esters are polar, this procedure effects a separation.

b. Interference: The more polar hydrocarbons, such as the complex aromatic compounds and the hydrocarbon derivatives of chlorine, sulfur and nitrogen, will be retained on the column and determined as fatty matter. Any compounds other than hydrocarbons and fatty matter recovered by the procedures for the determination of grease also interfere.

2. Apparatus and Reagents

All the apparatus and reagents listed in Method A, Sections 2 and 3, are required, plus the following:

a. Adsorption alumina, 80–200 mesh. Since the quality of alumina from various sources may be variable, reactivate before use as directed in ¶ 3a unless test runs prove this treatment of new material to be unnecessary.

3. Procedure

a. Preparation of adsorption column: Take a 30-cm piece of glass tubing (1-cm I.D.) and draw out one end over a flame to an opening of 1-mm inside diameter. Pack the drawn end of the tube with glass wool to a depth of 4 cm. Fill the tube with adsorption alumina to an overall height of 16 cm (12 cm of alumina). Place a small plug of glass wool in the column on the surface of the alumina. Since the alumina in the column is capable of adsorbing about 700 mg of polar material, repack with fresh alumina before this limit has been reached. Reactivate used alumina for reuse by ignition for 5 hr at 600 C in a muffle furnace.

b. Sample treatment: Dissolve, in 10 ml hexane or trichlorotrifluoroethane, the grease in the flask after completion of the grease procedure and pass through the adsorption column. Collect the solvent in a tared flask.

Elute the nonpolar material in the column with seven 10-ml portions of solvent and collect the eluate in the tared flask. Add each successive portion of solvent when the level of the preceding portion reaches the top of the alumina in the column.

Distill the solvent from the flask in a water bath at 85 C or in an electric heating mantle adjusted for slow distillation. Dry by placing the flask on a steam bath and draw air through the flask by means of a vacuum applied for 15 min. Cool the flask in a desiccator for 30 min and weigh.

4. Calculation

$$\% \text{ hydrocarbon} = \frac{A \times 100}{B}$$

where A = mg increase in weight of flask, B = total grease, and percent fatty matter = 100 − percent hydrocarbon.

5. Precision and Accuracy

The accuracy of this determination cannot be determined directly in wastewaters. The following data, obtained on synthetic samples, may be considered indicative for natural animal, vegetable and mineral products, but cannot be applied to the specialized industrial products discussed in the introduction to these methods.

Using the hydrocarbon determination on 18 synthetic samples containing known amounts of Crisco and Shell S.A.E. No. 20 motor oil, an average of only 91.5% of the oil was recovered, with a standard deviation of 2.68 mg. The low percentage recovery was due to the presence of polar material in the oil. Ten replicates each of two sewages yielded standard deviations of 0.26 mg and 1.06 mg, respectively.

For the determination of the fatty matter content of the grease, the analysis of 18 samples showed an average recovery of 103.9%, with a standard deviation of 3.11 mg. The high results are related to the presence of polar material in the oil added. Ten replicates each of two sewages yielded standard deviations of 0.81 mg and 1.23 mg, respectively.

209 E. References

1. G. CHANIN, E. H. CHOW, R. B. ALEXANDER & J. F. POWERS. 1968. Scum analysis: A new solution to a difficult problem. *Waterworks & Wastes Eng.* 5, 6:49.
2. M. J. TARAS & K. A. BLUM. 1968. Determination of emulsifying oil in industrial wastewater. *JWPCF* Research Suppl. 40:R404.

209 F. Bibliography

HATFIELD, W. D. & G. E. SYMONS. 1945. The determination of grease in sewage. *Sewage Works J.* 17:16.

STEPHENSON, R. J. 1949. Estimation of grease in sewage sludges. *Analyst* 74:257.

GILCREAS, F. W., W. W. SANDERSON & R. P. ELMER. 1953. Two new methods for the determination of grease in sewage. *Sewage & Ind. Wastes* 25:1379.

FIESER, L. F. & M. FIESER. 1956. *Organic Chemistry* (3rd ed.). Reinhold Publishing Corp., New York, page 109.

LEDERER, E. & M. LEDERER. 1957. *Chromatography: A Review of Principles and Applications* (2nd ed.). D. Van Nostrand Co., Princeton, N. J., page 103.

ULLMANN, W. W. & W. W. SANDERSON. 1959. A further study of methods for the determination of grease in sewage. *Sewage & Ind. Wastes* 31:8.

CHANIN, G., E. H. CHOW, R. B. ALEXANDER & J. F. POWERS. 1967. A safe solvent for oil and grease analyses. *JWPCF* 39:1892.

IRON: See Heavy Metals, Section 211(II)F.

LEAD: See Heavy Metals, Section 211(II)G.

LITHIUM: See Metals (Groups I and II), Sections 210 and 126.

MAGNESIUM: See Metals (Groups I and II), Section 210.

MANGANESE: See Heavy Metals, Section 211(II)H.

210 METALS (Groups I and II) (TENTATIVE)

The methods described below for pretreatment of samples for the determination of metals in Groups I and II can be satisfactorily applied for the determination of calcium, lithium, magnesium, potassium, sodium and strontium. This pretreatment eliminates interfering materials, which may prohibit the direct determination of these metals in wastewaters, effluents and polluted water.

1. General Discussion

If the sample contains considerable organic matter, ashing by either wet or dry methods will be necessary. If the elements of interest are volatile at ashing temperature, wet ashing is preferable. If a sample of sufficient size is ashed and the ash dissolved, suitable aliquots can then be used for the individual determinations.

2. Reagents

a. *Nitric acid,* conc.
b. *Hydrogen peroxide,* 30%.
c. *Hydrochloric acid,* conc.
d. *Ammonium hydroxide,* conc.

3. Procedure

Either digestion with nitric acid (¶ a below) or dry ashing (¶ b below) may be used.

a. Digestion with nitric acid: Measure a sample of suitable size into a 250-ml erlenmeyer flask, acidify with nitric acid, and evaporate to dryness on a steam bath. Add approximately 25 ml conc nitric acid to the solids in the flask and heat to near boiling. Evaporate the acid to a small volume, taking precautions to prevent spattering. The presence of unoxidized organic matter is indicated by brown fumes. Complete the ashing by repeated additions of nitric acid or nitric acid plus small quantities of hydrogen peroxide. The residue on final drying should be white unless such elements as iron or copper are present. Proceed to ¶ 3c.

b. Dry ashing: Evaporate a sample of suitable size to dryness on a steam bath in a platinum or Vycor evaporating dish. Transfer the dish to a muffle furnace and heat the sample to a white ash. The ashing temperature to be used depends on the elements to be determined in the sample. If volatile elements are present, keep the temperature at 400–450 C for as many hours as required. If sodium only is to be determined, ash the sample at a temperature up to 600 C.

c. Final sample preparation: Dissolve the sample ash prepared according to ¶ a or ¶ b above in a minimum amount of conc HCl and warm distilled water. Filter the diluted sample, neutralize with conc NH_4OH, and adjust to a known volume.

d. Determinations: Following pretreatment, determine calcium, lithium, magnesium, potassium, sodium and strontium in wastewater and polluted water by the methods described in Part 100. For best results, apply flame photometric methods for the determination of lithium, potassium, sodium and strontium, and gravimetric methods for calcium and magnesium. For less accurate work, use the alternative methods given in Part 100. When applying flame photometric methods, adjust the acid concentrations of the standards to that of the sample being analyzed.

4. Bibliography

WEST, P. W., P. FOLSE & D. MONTGOMERY. 1950. Application of flame spectrophotometry to water analysis, determination of sodium, potassium and calcium. *Anal. Chem.* 22:667.

POLUEKTOVE, N. S. 1961. *Techniques in Flame Photometric Analysis.* Consultants Bureau, New York, page 219.

HARLEY, J. 1967. *Manual of Standard Procedures.* U. S. Atomic Energy Commission. Document No. NYO-4700.

211 METALS (HEAVY)

The presence of metals in domestic sewage, industrial effluents, and receiving streams is a matter of serious concern because the possible toxic properties of these materials may adversely affect sewage treatment systems or the biological systems of the receiving streams. Metals may be determined satisfactorily by atomic absorption spectroscopy, polarography or colorimetric methods. The instrumental methods are preferable because they are rapid and do not require extensive separation technics. Many of the colorimetric methods recommended for determination of these metals individually must include procedures for the elimination of interference from other metals occurring simultaneously in the waste sample. Procedures are given herein for the determination of cadmium, chromium, copper, iron, lead, manganese, nickel and zinc.

Preliminary treatment of the samples is necessary, and appropriate methods are described for each type of analysis. The sample preparation must be carefully carried out to avoid difficulties in the subsequent metals determination.

1. Sampling and Sample Preservation

Serious errors may be introduced during sampling and storage. Errors may occur because of (a) contamination from the sampling device, (b) failure to remove residues of previous samples from the sample container, and (c) loss of metal by adsorption on the sample container. These errors may be avoided by insuring that all materials coming in contact with the sample are glass or polyethylene, that the sample container is thoroughly washed and rinsed with 1 + 1 nitric acid, then with redistilled water before reuse, and by the addition of 5 ml concentrated nitric acid per liter of sample at the time of collection to minimize adsorption of metals on the container.

2. General Precautions

Great care must be taken in the laboratory to avoid the introduction of contaminating metals from glassware and distilled water. All water used in the preparation of reagents and in the determination of metals should be distilled water which has been redistilled in an all-glass apparatus or passed through a mixed-bed ion-exchange column. All glassware used should be cleaned thoroughly, then rinsed with 1 + 1 nitric acid, and finally with redistilled water.

I—ATOMIC ABSORPTION SPECTROPHOTOMETRY

Metals in solution may be readily determined by atomic absorption spectroscopy. The method is simple, rapid and applicable to a large number of metals. Relative freedom from interference eliminates the need for extensive preparation and separation technics. When a suitable instrument is available, the atomic absorption methods are preferable to colorimetric procedures in the analysis of most wastewater samples, although concentration of the sample or solvent extraction may be required to obtain maximum sensitivity. Because the flame oxidizes the metals to the highest valence state, only the total concentration of each metal can be measured.

Specific methods for the determination of metals by atomic absorption are presented in Section 129A. The pretreatment of samples by autoclaving may be used, or the digestion procedure below may be followed.

211 (I)A. Preliminary Treatment of Samples

1. General Discussion

Since organic constituents in the sample do not usually interfere, a rigorous destruction of these materials is not necessary. To prevent clogging of the burner and to insure that all the metal is atomized, it is necessary to dissolve particulate matter. The acid digestion is designed to bring all metals into solution.

Because no preliminary separations are required, a single aliquot of the sample may be digested for all subsequent analyses. The usual volume required for a single determination is 3–5 ml—thus, 100 ml of digested sample is ample for most purposes.

2. Apparatus

a. Sintered-glass filter crucibles, fine-porosity, with holder; Gooch crucibles with glass fiber filter disks may be used.

b. Vacuum pump or aspirator.

All glassware should be cleaned thoroughly, then rinsed with 1 + 1 HNO_3, and finally rinsed with glass-redistilled water.

3. Reagents

a. Nitric acid, conc.

b. Hydrochloric acid, conc.

c. Redistilled water: Distilled water redistilled in all-glass apparatus.

4. Procedure

If the sample was not acidified at the time of collection, as instructed under Sampling and Sample Preparation (Section 211.1 above), adjust to pH 4 with concentrated nitric acid, then add an additional 5 ml concentrated nitric acid per liter of sample.

Agitate the sample thoroughly. Measure 100 ml with a pipet or volumetric flask and transfer it to a 250-ml conical flask. Add 5 ml conc HCl, then heat on a steam bath or hot plate for 15 min.

Cool slightly, then filter with suction through a sintered-glass or porcelain filter crucible into a clean filter flask. Rinse the filter with a few ml of redistilled water. Transfer the filtrate to a 100-ml volumetric flask and rinse the filter flask with 5 ml redistilled water. Dilute to the 100-ml mark and mix thoroughly. Use this solution directly for determination of all metals except lead and manganese, for which special procedures are required.

II—COLORIMETRY

211 (II)A. Preliminary Treatment of Samples

1. General Discussion

Because metals readily form complex ions with possible organic constituents of waste or sewage, it is generally necessary that organic matter be destroyed in a preliminary treatment. The recommended treatment is digestion, either with a mixture of nitric and sulfuric acids, or—when the organic matter is difficult to oxidize—with nitric and perchloric acids. In addition to destroying organic matter, acid digestion of the sample eliminates possible interference from cyanide, nitrite, sulfide, sulfite, thiosulfate and thiocyanate.

A single sample of suitable size may be digested and aliquots of the sample are used for determination of the individual metals. The volume of sample to be taken for digestion may be estimated by summing the volumes needed for determination of each of the constituents, as given in the directions for the individual determinations.

2. Apparatus

a. Sintered-glass filter crucibles, fine porosity, with holder. Gooch crucibles with glass fiber filters may be used.

All glassware should be cleaned thoroughly, then rinsed with 1 + 1 HNO_3, and finally rinsed with glass-redistilled water.

b. Infrared lamp (optional).

3. Reagents

1) Methyl orange indicator solution.

2) Sulfuric acid, conc.

3) Nitric acid, conc.

4) Hydrogen peroxide, 30%.

5) Redistilled water: Distilled water redistilled in all-glass apparatus or passed through a deionizing column. (See Ammonia Nitrogen, Section 132A.3a.)

6) Perchloric acid, 60%.

7) Special reagent—ammonium acetate solution: Dissolve 400 g $NH_4C_2H_3O_2$ in 600 ml redistilled water. This solution is required only if lead is to be determined in the presence of sulfate.

Total iron and heavy-metal impurities in the reagent acids should not exceed 0.0001%. Blanks must be prepared in any event, but if the metallic impurities are greater than this, the blanks will be too large and variable for precise determinations of small concentrations of the metals. When the amounts of acid specified are used, 0.0001% of heavy-metal impurity will add about 0.03 mg of heavy metals to the sample.

4a. Digestion with Sulfuric Acid

1) Agitate the sample to obtain a homogeneous suspension. Measure a suitable volume (as determined from the tabulation) with a pipet or volumetric flask and transfer it to an evaporating dish or casserole. (If the volume required is greater than 250 ml, transfer in portions as the sample evaporates.)

Concentration *mg/l*	Volume *ml*
<1	1,000
1–10	100
10–100	10
100–1,000	1

Acidify the transferred sample or portion of sample to methyl orange with conc H_2SO_4, then add 5 ml conc HNO_3 and 2 ml 30% H_2O_2 to reduce chromate. Evaporate on a steam bath or hot plate to 15–20 ml, covering the vessel with a watch glass, when necessary, to avoid loss of material by spattering. An infrared lamp may be placed over the sample to hasten the evaporation.

2) Transfer the evaporated solution, together with any solids remaining in the dish, to a 125-ml conical flask. Add another 5 ml conc HNO_3, which has been used to rinse the evaporating dish or casserole; 10 ml conc H_2SO_4; and a few glass beads, carborundum chips or Hengar granules to minimize bumping. Evaporate on a hot plate (in a hood) until dense white fumes of SO_3 just appear in the flask, but do not continue heating beyond this point. If the solution is not clear, add another 10 ml HNO_3 and repeat the evaporation to fumes of SO_3. Be sure that all HNO_3 is removed, as indicated by the clarity of the solution and the absence of brownish fumes in the flask.

3) Cool the solution to room temperature and dilute carefully to about 50 ml with redistilled water. Heat nearly to boiling to dissolve slowly soluble salts, then filter through a sintered-glass or porcelain filter crucible into a thoroughly clean filter flask. Rinse the sample flask with two 5-ml portions of redistilled water, passing them through the crucible to wash any residue on the filter. (A filtering device which allows collection of the filtrate directly in a 100-ml volumetric flask may be used and, if available, is to be preferred.) Transfer the filtrate to a 100-ml volumetric flask and rinse the filter flask with two 5-ml portions of redistilled water, adding these rinsings to the volumetric flask. Finally dilute the solution in the volumetric flask to the 100-ml mark and mix thoroughly. The resulting solution is about $3N$ in H_2SO_4. Take aliquots of this solution for the determination of the metals; for the determination of lead, also use the solution obtained in the following section:

4) If the sample contains much lead, some of it will be present as $PbSO_4$ in the residue on the filter; this must be dissolved and measured as a part of the lead determination. Add 50 ml ammonium acetate solution to the conical flask in which the digestion was carried out and heat to incipient boiling, rotating the flask occasionally to wet thoroughly all interior areas on which residue might have deposited. Reconnect the filter and draw the hot ammonium acetate solution through it slowly to dissolve the

$PbSO_4$. Transfer the filtrate to a 100-ml volumetric flask, allow it to cool to room temperature, dilute to the mark, mix thoroughly, and set aside for the determination of lead.

4b. Digestion with Nitric and Perchloric Acids

CAUTION: Heated mixtures of concentrated perchloric acid and organic matter may explode violently. To avoid this hazard, observe the following precautions: (a) Do not add perchloric acid to a hot solution that may contain organic matter. (b) Always pretreat samples containing organic matter with HNO_3 prior to addition of $HClO_4$. (c) Use a mixture of nitric and perchloric acids in starting the digestion step. (d) Avoid repeated fumings of perchloric acid in ordinary hoods. For routine operations use hoods of stone or asbestos-cement. Alternatively, for occasional work with $HClO_4$, use glass fume eradicators * attached to a water pump.

1) Measure a sample, acidify to methyl orange with HNO_3, add another 5 ml conc HNO_3, and evaporate the sample as in ¶ 4a(1). Transfer the evaporated sample to a 125-ml conical flask as in ¶ 4a(2), cool, and add 5 ml HNO_3 and 10 ml 70% $HClO_4$. After adding a few boiling chips, heat on a hot plate and evaporate gently until dense white fumes of $HClO_4$ just appear. If the solution is not clear at this point, add 10 ml HNO_3, cover the neck of the flask with a watch glass, and keep the solution just barely boiling until it clears.

2) Cool the digested solution, dilute to about 50 ml with redistilled water, and boil to expel any chlorine or oxides of nitrogen. Then filter the sample as in ¶ 4a(3), transfer the filtrate and washings to a 100-ml volumetric flask, cool, dilute to the mark, and mix thoroughly. The resulting solution is about 0.8*N* in $HClO_4$. Take aliquots of this solution for the determination of individual metals just as from the solution obtained in ¶ 4a(3).

3) If lead is to be determined and if sulfate is present in the sample, treat the residue from the filtration as directed in ¶ 4a(4).

4c. Digestion of Sludges Having High or Refractory Organic Content

Transfer a sample, measured as in ¶ 4a(1), to a suitable evaporating dish or casserole and evaporate to 15–20 ml on a steam bath. Then add 12 ml conc HNO_3 and evaporate on a hot plate to near dryness. Repeat the addition of HNO_3 and evaporation. Use 25 ml 1 + 1 HNO_3 to transfer the residue to a 250-ml conical flask (add 10 ml to the residue to assist in the transfer and use the other 15 ml for rinsing the evaporating dish). Add 25 ml 60% $HClO_4$ and boil until nearly dry, or until the solution is clear and white fumes of $HClO_4$ have appeared. Cool, add 50 ml redistilled water, and proceed with ¶ 4b(2).

4d. Dithizone Solutions

Diphenylthiocarbazone (dithizone) is the colorimetric reagent for the determination of cadmium, lead and zinc. To insure satisfactory results, dithizone solutions must be purified to remove the oxidation product, diphenylthiocarbondiazone, which is generally present as a contaminant. Directions below pro-

* Such as are obtainable from G. F. Smith Chemical Company, Columbus, Ohio.

vide for the preparation of purified stock solutions of dithizone in chloroform and carbon tetrachloride. The solutions must be refrigerated at all times and the working solutions for the specific metal determinations must be prepared daily.

1) Stock dithizone solution I (chloroform): Dissolve 250 mg dithizone crystals in 50 ml $CHCl_3$, filter through a small paper, and wash the filter with several small portions of $CHCl_3$. Transfer the filtrate to a separatory funnel and extract with portions of 1 + 99 NH_4OH until the $CHCl_3$ layer is nearly devoid of green color. Discard the $CHCl_3$ layer and wash the combined extracts with four 15-ml portions of $CHCl_3$. Discard the $CHCl_3$ extracts. Precipitate the dithizone by addition of 2 ml conc HCl; shake to completely neutralize the ammonia. Extract the precipitated dithizone with 25-ml portions of $CHCl_3$ and finally dilute the combined extracts with pure $CHCl_3$ to a volume of 250 ml. Keep the solution in the refrigerator.

2) Stock dithizone solution II (carbon tetrachloride): Dissolve 125 mg dithizone in 50 ml $CHCl_3$ and filter through a small filter paper. Wash filter paper with small portions of pure $CHCl_3$ and combine all filtrates. Extract the filtrates with 1 + 99 NH_4OH until the $CHCl_3$ layer is nearly devoid of green color. Wash the aqueous layer with pure CCl_4 to remove traces of $CHCl_3$ and any diphenylthiocarbondiazone. Reject the CCl_4 extracts. Neutralize the NH_4OH by shaking well with 2 ml conc HCl. Extract the precipitated dithizone with pure CCl_4. Dilute the extracts to 500 ml with pure CCl_4. Keep this solution in a refrigerator.

211 (II)B. Method for Cadmium (TENTATIVE)

1. General Discussion

a. Principle: Cadmium ions, like those of many other metals, form an intense red compound with diphenylthiocarbazone (dithizone) which can be extracted into carbon tetrachloride and used for the colorimetric determination of cadmium. When the extraction is carried out from a strongly basic solution, only a few substances—silver, mercury, copper, nickel and cobalt—interfere, and these can be removed by preliminary extractions.

After digestion of the sample with HNO_3-H_2SO_4 or with HNO_3-$HClO_4$ to decompose organic matter, any large amount of silver present is precipitated as AgCl. Copper and mercury, together with remaining silver, are then removed by an extraction with dithizone in chloroform at pH 2. The solution is adjusted to pH 9, and nickel is removed by addition of dimethylglyoxime and extraction with chloroform; any cobalt present is complexed with dimethylglyoxime, so that it will not react with dithizone.

The solution is then made strongly basic and cadmium is extracted with dithizone in chloroform. Zinc extracted with the cadmium from this basic solution is removed by washing the chloroform solution with 0.5*N* NaOH. Finally, the cadmium is determined by measuring the absorbance of the cadmium-dithizone complex in chloroform at a wavelength of 515 mμ, or with a suitable filter.

b. Interference: When the recommended procedure is used, the major interference is from massive amounts of zinc; if the zinc-cadmium ratio is large (greater than 500:1) it is difficult to extract the last traces of cadmium and low results are obtained. Otherwise, quantities of cadmium from 2.5 to 25 μg can be determined readily in the presence of 0.25 mg each of copper, cobalt and zinc, and 2.5 mg each of acetate, aluminum, antimony, arsenic, bismuth, chromium, cyanide, iron, lead, manganese, mercury, nickel, phosphate, silver, sulfite, tartrate, thiocyanate, thiosulfate, tin, and other common ions.

c. Minimum detectable concentration: The quantity of cadmium required to give a net absorbance of 0.01 (98% transmittance) at 515 mμ in the final chloroform solution is about 0.5 μg when a 1-cm absorption cell is used. When 50 ml of initial sample are taken, this corresponds to 10 μg/l.

d. Sampling and storage: Because of the great sensitivity of the method and the ready adsorbability of cadmium ions on surfaces, great care should be used to clean sampling vessels thoroughly. Polyethylene vessels are recommended. Glass vessels after normal cleaning should be washed with 1 + 1 HNO_3 and then rinsed with redistilled water.

Samples should be acidified with HNO_3 and an excess of 5 ml HNO_3 per liter of sample added at the time of collection.

2. Apparatus

a. Volumetric pipets, 5 ml.

b. Colorimetric equipment: One of the following, equipped with absorption cells providing a 1-cm light path and having lids for stoppers, is required:

1) SPECTROPHOTOMETER, for use at 515 mμ.

2) FILTER PHOTOMETER, equipped with a green filter, exhibiting maximum light transmission near 515 mμ.

c. Separatory funnels, 125-ml Squibb form, with ground-glass or teflon stopcocks and stoppers. Amber or low-actinic ware is convenient but not essential. Wash with 1 + 1 HNO_3 following normal cleaning and then rinse thoroughly with redistilled water.

d. Volumetric flasks, 25-ml, with ground-glass stoppers. Amber or low-actinic ware is desirable but not essential. Clean as described in ¶ c preceding.

3. Reagents

a. Stock cadmium solution: Dissolve 100.0 mg pure cadmium metal in 20 ml distilled water and 5 ml conc HCl, and dilute to 1,000 ml with redistilled water. Store this solution in a polyethylene container.

b. Standard cadmium solution: To 5.00 ml stock cadmium solution add 2 ml conc HCl and dilute to 200 ml with redistilled water. Prepare as needed and use the same day; 1.00 ml = 2.50 μg Cd.

c. Redistilled water: Distilled water redistilled in all-glass apparatus.

d. Potassium sodium tartrate solution: Dissolve 50 g $KNaC_4H_4O_6 \cdot 4H_2O$ in 250 ml distilled water. Place in a separatory funnel and shake with 50-ml portions of dithizone solution (II) in carbon tetrachloride to purify from heavy-metal impurities. Remove the dithizone and its yellow oxidation product by extraction with portions of chloroform until the extracts remain colorless. Finally, extract with carbon tetrachloride to remove any chloroform. Store in a polyethylene bottle.

e. Sodium hydroxide solution, 6N.

f. Carbon tetrachloride, ACS grade or purified as follows: Reflux 500 ml CCl_4 with 100 ml 1.25*N* NaOH for 2 hr; separate the CCl_4 layer, wash it with 100 ml distilled water, dry it over anhydrous $CaCl_2$, and then distill over CaO. Avoid or redistill CCl_4 that comes in containers with metal or metal-lined caps.

g. Hydrochloric acid, conc.

h. Dithizone solution (I): Use stock dithizone solution (chloroform).

i. Dithizone solution (II): Dilute 40 ml stock dithizone solution (carbon tetrachloride) to 100 ml with pure carbon tetrachloride. Prepare daily.

j. Chloroform: Avoid or redistill material that comes in containers with metal-lined caps.

k. Ammonium hydroxide, conc: Place 660 ml redistilled water in a 1-liter polyethylene bottle and chill by immersion in an ice bath. Pass ammonia gas from a cylinder through a glass-wool trap into the chilled bottle until the volume of liquid has increased to 900 ml. As an alternate technic in preparing the ammonium hydroxide, place 900 ml conc reagent ammonium hydroxide in a 1,500-ml distillation flask and distill into a chilled 1-liter polyethylene bottle, containing initially 250 ml redistilled water, until the volume of liquid in the bottle has increased to 900 ml, keeping the condenser tip below the surface of the liquid.

l. Dimethylglyoxime solution: Dissolve 1 g dimethylglyoxime in 100 ml 95% ethyl alcohol.

m. Sodium hydroxide solution, 1N: Dissolve 10 g NaOH in 490 ml redistilled water. Store in a polyethylene container.

4. Procedure

a. Preparation of calibration curve: Pipet 1.00–10.00 ml portions of the standard cadmium solution into 125-ml separatory funnels (amber). Dilute each to about 15–20 ml with redistilled water and add 10 ml potassium sodium tartrate solution and 4.2 ml 6*N* NaOH. Then continue with ¶s 4b(5) and 4b(8) of the procedure.

Transfer a suitable portion of each final solution to a 1-cm absorption cell and measure its absorbance at 515 mμ or with a green filter having maximum transmission near this wavelength. As reference, use either pure CCl_4 or a blank prepared by carrying 20 ml redistilled water through the procedure employed for the standards. If pure CCl_4 is used as the reference, correct the absorbance readings of the standards by subtracting the absorbance of a blank prepared as described.

Construct a calibration chart by plotting corrected absorbance values against micrograms of cadmium.

b. Treatment of sample:

1) Pipet a measured aliquot containing 2.5–20 μg Cd from the digested sample, prepared according to directions given under Preliminary Treatment of Samples, into a 150-ml beaker.

If a separate sample for cadmium is desired, measure a volume of sewage or waste containing 25–200 μg Cd, treat it according to Preliminary Treatment of Samples and use a 10.00-ml aliquot of the final solution.

Add 0.2 ml conc HCl to precipitate silver, stir, and let stand 2 min. Filter, if necessary, and wash. To the combined filtrate and washings add 5 ml potassium sodium tartrate solution and adjust to pH 2.0 with conc HCl or NH_4OH.

2) Transfer the adjusted solution to a 125-ml separatory funnel and extract with 5-ml portions of dithizone solution (I) in chloroform until the dithizone layer remains green. Discard the extracts. Then wash with 10-ml portions of chloroform until the organic layer remains colorless, discarding the washings. Finally, wash with a 5-ml portion of CCl_4 and discard the washing.

3) Transfer the aqueous solution to a 150-ml beaker, add 5 ml potassium sodium tartrate solution, and adjust to pH 8.5–9.0 with conc NH_4OH. Return the solution quantitatively to the separatory funnel.

4) Add 5 ml dimethylglyoxime solution and shake vigorously for 30 sec. Extract with three or more 10-ml portions of $CHCl_3$ until any white precipitate of excess dimethylglyoxime has been removed. Discard the extract. Wash the aqueous layer with 5 ml CCl_4 and discard the washing.

NOTE: In the absence of copper, mercury or silver, ¶ 4b(2) may be omitted; in the absence of nickel or cobalt, ¶ 4b(4) may be omitted.

5) Add 4.2 ml 6*N* NaOH to the aqueous layer in the separatory funnel and mix. Add 5 ml dithizone solution (II) in CCl_4 and shake thoroughly. Transfer the CCl_4 layer to a clean separatory funnel (amber) and reextract the aqueous layer with a second 5-ml portion of dithizone solution (II) in CCl_4. Combine the organic layer with the first one. Continue extracting with 3-ml portions of the dithizone in CCl_4 until the organic extracts remain colorless or only slightly yellow, adding these additional extracts to the previous ones.

6) Wash the combined organic extracts twice with 10 ml 1*N* NaOH plus 10 ml distilled water, then once with 20 ml distilled water; discard the aqueous layer in each instance.

7) Filter the red solution of cadmium-dithizone complex through a small filter paper into a 25-ml volumetric flask. Wash the filter paper with a little CCl_4 and add the washing to the contents of the volumetric flask. Dilute to the mark with CCl_4 and mix well.

NOTE: During extraction of the cadmium [¶s 4b(5)–(7)] it is advisable to darken the room unless amber or low-actinic glassware is used. Towels may be wrapped around the separatory funnels and volumetric flask to prevent sunlight from accelerating the light-sensitive decomposition of the solution.

8) Transfer a suitable portion of the CCl_4 solution to a 1-cm absorption cell and measure its absorbance within 15 min at a wavelength of 515 mμ or with a suitable green filter against a blank of pure CCl_4. From the observed absorbance subtract that of a reagent blank prepared by carrying 10 ml redistilled water through the entire procedure, including initial digestion. From the corrected absorbance determine the cadmium in the sample ana-

lyzed by reference to the calibration chart prepared according to Section 211(II)B.4a preceding.

5. Calculation

$$\text{mg/l Cd} = \frac{\mu\text{g Cd}}{\text{ml sample}} \times \frac{100}{\text{ml aliquot}}$$

211 (II)C. Method for Total Chromium

1. General Discussion

a. Principle: Hexavalent chromium reacts with diphenylcarbazide in acidic medium to produce a red-violet coloration of unknown composition suitable for determination of low concentrations of chromium. The reaction is very sensitive, the absorbancy index per gram atom of chromium for the colored product being about 40,000 near 540 mμ. The colored product is not very stable; appreciable fading is noted after about 1 hr.

After the sample has been digested with HNO_3-H_2SO_4 or HNO_3-$HClO_4$ to decompose organic matter, the acidity is adjusted to 0.5*N*, and the chromium is oxidized to the hexavalent state with potassium permanganate. Excess permanganate is reduced with sodium azide. Addition of an excess of diphenylcarbazide yields the red-violet product; its absorbance at 540 mμ is measured photometrically.

b. Interference: The reaction with diphenylcarbazide is nearly specific for chromium. Hexavalent molybdenum and mercury salts will react to form color with the reagent, but the intensities are much lower than that for chromium at the specified pH. Concentrations of molybdenum and mercury up to 200 mg/l can be tolerated. Vanadium interferes to the greatest extent but can be present in a concentration up to ten times that of chromium without causing trouble. Potential interference from permanganate is eliminated by the prior reduction with azide. Of the remaining common elements only ferric iron, in the form of yellow or yellow-brown compounds, may interfere; in the absence of chlorides and with sulfuric and phosphoric acids present, the ferric ion color is not strong and no difficulty is encountered if the absorbance is measured photometrically at the appropriate wavelength. Large amounts of some metals cause low results by consuming the diphenylcarbazide reagent.

Interfering amounts of molybdenum, vanadium, iron and copper can be removed by extraction of the cupferrates of these metals into chloroform. Procedure for this extraction is provided, but it should be included only when needed, for the presence of residual cupferron and chloroform in the aqueous solution complicates the later oxidation of chromium with permanganate. Therefore, the extraction is followed by additional treatment with acid fuming in order to decompose these compounds.

c. Minimum detectable concentration: The quantity of chromium required to give a net absorbance of 0.01 (98% transmittance) at 540 mμ is 1 μg with a 1-cm light path. When 100 ml of initial sample are taken, this corresponds to 10 μg/l.

d. Sampling and storage: In addition to the usual procedures and precautions for collection of samples of sewage or wastes, special care is needed to minimize adsorption of chromium on the walls of the sampling container. The sample should be acidified at the time of collection with HNO_3, and an excess 5 ml HNO_3 per liter of sample should be added.

2. Apparatus

a. Colorimetric equipment—One of the following is required:

1) SPECTROPHOTOMETER, for use at 540 mμ, providing a light path of 1 cm or longer.

2) FILTER PHOTOMETER, providing a light path of 1 cm or longer and equipped with a greenish yellow filter having maximum transmittance near 540 mμ.

b. Separatory funnels, 125-ml, Squibb form, with glass or teflon stopcock and stopper.

3. Reagents

a. Stock chromium solution: Dissolve 141.4 mg $K_2Cr_2O_7$ in distilled water and dilute to 1 liter; 1.00 ml = 50.0 μg Cr.

b. Standard chromium solution: Dilute 10.00 ml stock chromium solution to 100 ml; 1.00 ml = 5.00 μg Cr.

c. Nitric acid, conc.

d. Sulfuric acid, 1 + 1.

e. Perchloric acid, 60%.

f. Methyl orange indicator solution.

g. Hydrogen peroxide, 30%.

h. Redistilled water: Distilled water redistilled in all-glass apparatus.

i. Ammonium hydroxide, conc.

j. Phosphoric acid, 85%.

k. Potassium permanganate solution: Dissolve 4 g $KMnO_4$ in 100 ml water.

l. Sodium azide solution: Dissolve 0.5 g NaN_3 in 100 ml water.

m. Diphenylcarbazide solution: Dissolve 0.25 g 1,5-diphenylcarbazide in 50 ml acetone. Store in a brown bottle. Discard when the solution becomes discolored.

n. Chloroform: Avoid or redistill material that comes in containers with metal or metal-lined caps.

o. Cupferron solution: Dissolve 5 g $C_6H_5N(NO)ONH_4$ in 95 ml distilled water.

4. Procedure

a. Preparation of calibration curve: To compensate for possible slight losses of chromium during digestion or other operations of the analysis, treat the chromium standards by the same procedure as the sample. Accordingly, pipet measured volumes of standard chromium solution (5 μg/ml) ranging from 2.00 to 20.0 ml, to give standards for 10–100 μg Cr, into 250-ml beakers or conical flasks. Add H_2O_2 and either HNO_3 and H_2SO_4 or HNO_3 and $HClO_4$ depending on the method used under Preliminary Treatment of Samples, and proceed with digestion and subsequent treatment of the standards just as if they were samples, also carrying out cupferron treatment of the standards if this is required for the samples.

Develop the color as for the samples, transfer a suitable portion of each colored solution to a 1-cm absorption cell, and measure the absorbance at 540 mμ. As reference, use distilled water. Correct the absorbance readings on the standards by subtracting the absorbance of a reagent blank carried through the method.

Construct a calibration curve by plotting corrected absorbance values against micrograms of chromium.

b. Treatment of sample:

1) Prepare the sample according to directions [Section 211(II)A], Preliminary Treatment of Samples, by reducing chromium with hydrogen peroxide and preferably using the nitric-sulfuric acid treatment. Pipet an aliquot of digested sample containing 10–100 μg chromium into a 125-ml separatory funnel if the cupferron treatment is necessary (¶ 1b above) or into a 125-ml conical flask if treatment with cupferron can be omitted. Proceed either with the extraction of cupferrates as in ¶ 4b(2) below or with neutralization and subsequent treatment according to ¶ 4b(3) below.

2) SEPARATION OF MOLYBDENUM, VANADIUM, IRON, AND COPPER WITH CUPFERRON—Dilute the filtered digestate in the 125-ml separatory funnel to about 40 ml with distilled water and chill in an ice bath. Add 5 ml ice cold cupferron solution, shake well, and allow to stand in the ice bath for 1 min. Extract the solution in the separatory funnel with three successive 5-ml portions of chloroform; shake each portion thoroughly with the aqueous solution, allow the layers to separate, and then withdraw and discard the chloroform extract. Transfer the extracted aqueous solution to a 125-ml conical flask, washing the separatory funnel with a small amount of distilled water and adding the wash water to the flask. Boil the solution in the flask for about 5 min to volatilize the chloroform, and cool. Add 5 ml HNO_3 and sufficient H_2SO_4 to have about 3 ml present. Boil the samples to the appearance of SO_3 fumes. Cool slightly, carefully add 5 ml HNO_3, and again boil to fumes to complete the decomposition of organic matter. Cool, then wash sides of flask and boil once more to SO_3 fumes to eliminate all HNO_3. Cool samples and add 25 ml water.

3) Using methyl orange as indicator, add conc NH_4OH until the solution in the flask is just basic. Then add 1 + 1 H_2SO_4 dropwise until it is acidic, plus 1 ml (20 drops) in excess. Adjust volume of the solution to about 40 ml, add a boiling chip, and heat to boiling. Add 2 drops potassium permanganate solution to give a dark red color. If fading occurs, add additional drops of $KMnO_4$ to maintain an excess of about 2 drops. Boil the solution for 2 min longer. Add 1 ml sodium azide solution and continue gently boiling. If the red color does not fade completely after boiling for approximately 30 sec, add another 1 ml sodium azide solution. Continue boiling for 1 min after the color has faded completely, then cool. Add 0.25 ml (5 drops) H_3PO_4.

4) Transfer the cooled solution to a 100-ml volumetric flask, dilute to 100 ml, and mix. Add 2.0 ml diphenylcarbazide solution, mix, and allow to stand 5–10 min for full color development. Then transfer an appropriate portion of the solution to a 1-cm absorption cell and measure its absorbance at 540 mμ. As reference use distilled water. Correct the absorbance reading of the sample by subtracting the absorbance of a blank carried through the method (see also note below). From the corrected absorbance, determine the micrograms of chromium present by reference to the calibration curve.

NOTE: If the solution is turbid after dilution to 100 ml in ¶ 4b(4) above, take an absorbance reading before addition of the carbazide reagent, and correct the absorbance reading of the final colored solution by subtracting the absorbance measured previously.

5. Calculation

$$mg/l\ Cr = \frac{A \times 100}{B \times C}$$

where A = μg Cr, B = ml original sample, and C = ml aliquot from 100 ml digested sample.

211 (II)D. Method for Hexavalent Chromium

1. General Discussion

Soluble hexavalent chromium, in the absence of interfering amounts of substances such as molybdenum, vanadium and mercury, may be determined colorimetrically by reaction with diphenylcarbazide in acid solution.

2. Apparatus

a. Filter, sintered-glass or membrane.

b. Colorimetric equipment, as specified for Method for Total Chromium, Section 211 (II) C.2a above.

3. Reagents

a. Standard chromium solution: Prepare as directed in Method for Total Chromium, ¶s 3a and 3b.

b. Redistilled water: Distilled water redistilled in all-glass apparatus.

c. Ammonium hydroxide, conc.

d. Sulfuric acid, 1 + 1.

e. Phosphoric acid, 85%.

f. Diphenlycarbazide solution: Prepare as directed in Method for Total Chromium, ¶ 3m.

4. Procedure

a. Preparation of calibration curve: Pipet measured volumes of the standard chromium solution (5 μg/ml) ranging from 2.00 to 20.0 ml into 100-ml volumetric flasks. Add 2.0 ml 1 + 1 H_2SO_4 and 5 drops (0.25 ml) H_3PO_4 and dilute to 100 ml. Add 2.0 ml diphenylcarbazide solution, mix, and allow to stand for 5 min for full color development. Measure the absorbance at 540 mμ. As reference, use distilled water. Correct the absorbance readings on the standards by subtracting the absorbance of a reagent blank carried through the method. Construct a calibration curve by plotting corrected absorbance against micrograms of chromium.

b. Treatment of sample: If necessary, filter a sample containing 10–100 μg Cr through a sintered-glass or membrane filter into a 125-ml conical flask. Adjust the solution until it is acidic to litmus paper by adding conc NH_4OH or 1 + 1 H_2SO_4, then add 1.0 ml 1 + 1 H_2SO_4 and 0.3 ml H_3PO_4. Determine hexavalent chromium by completing the procedure according to Method C, ¶ 4b(4).

If turbidity or color is present in the sample before color formation, deduct from the final absorbance reading the absorbance obtained on the sample carried through the procedure without addition of diphenylcarbazide.

5. Calculation

$$mg/l\ Cr = \frac{\mu g\ Cr}{ml\ sample}$$

211 (II)E. Method for Copper

1. General Discussion

a. Principle: Cuprous ion in neutral or slightly acidic solution reacts with 2,9-dimethyl-1,10-phenanthroline ("neocuproine") to form a complex in which 2 moles of the neocuproine are bound by 1 mole of Cu^+ ion. The complex can be extracted by a number of organic liquids, including a chloroform-methanol mixture, to give an orange-colored solution with a molar absorbancy index of about 8,000 at 457 mμ. The reaction is virtually specific for copper; the color system follows Beer's law up to a concentration of 0.2 mg Cu per 25 ml of organic solvent; full color development is obtained with the pH of the aqueous system between 3 and 9; the color system is stable in chloroform-methanol for several days.

After digestion of the sewage or waste with acid to destroy organic matter and to remove interfering anions (see Preliminary Treatment of Samples), the sample is treated with hydroxylamine-hydrochloride to reduce copper to the cuprous condition, and with sodium citrate to complex metallic ions which might give precipitates when the pH is raised. The pH is adjusted to 4–6 by the addition of ammonia, a solution of neocuproine in methanol is added, and the resultant complex is extracted into chloroform. After dilution of the chloroform to an exact volume with methanol, the absorbance of the solution is measured at 457 mμ.

b. Interference: Determination of copper by the recommended procedure is substantially free from interference by other metal ions. There have been reports that large amounts of chromium and tin may interfere. Potential interference from chromium can be avoided by addition of sulfurous acid to reduce chromate and complex chromic ion; in the presence of much tin or excessive amounts of other oxidizing ions, additional hydroxylamine—up to 20 ml—should be employed.

Cyanide and sulfide produce strong interference but are removed during the digestion procedure, as are organic materials which might lead to difficulties.

c. Minimum detectable concentration: For the recommended procedure the minimum detectable concentration, corresponding to 0.01 absorbance or 98% transmittance, is 3 μg Cu when a 1-cm cell is used and 0.6 μg Cu when a 5-cm cell is used. When the initial volume of sample corresponding to the aliquot taken is 100 ml, these concentrations become 30 and 6 μg/l Cu, respectively.

d. Sampling and storage: Precautions for sampling and storage described in the introduction should be followed. Acidification, as described there, is especially important when the concentration of copper is less than 1 mg/l.

2. Apparatus

a. Colorimetric equipment—One of the following is required:

1) SPECTROPHOTOMETER, for use at 457 mμ, providing a light path of 1 cm or longer.

2) FILTER PHOTOMETER, providing

a light path of 1 cm or longer and equipped with a narrow-band violet filter having maximum transmittance in the range 450–460 mμ.

b. Separatory funnels, 125-ml, Squibb form, with glass or teflon stopcock and stopper.

3. Reagents

a. Redistilled water, copper-free: Most ordinary distilled water contains detectable amounts of copper. Redistilled water, prepared by distillation of singly distilled water in a resistant-glass still, or distilled water passed through an ion-exchange unit, should be used for the preparation of all reagents and for all dilutions or other operations performed in connection with copper determinations.

b. Stock copper solution: To 200.0 mg polished electrolytic copper wire or foil in a 250-ml conical flask, add 10 ml redistilled water and 5 ml conc HNO_3. After the reaction has slowed, warm gently to complete dissolution of the copper and then boil to expel oxides of nitrogen, using precautions to avoid loss of copper. Cool, add about 50 ml redistilled water, transfer quantitatively to a 1-liter volumetric flask, and dilute to the mark with redistilled water; 1 ml = 200 μg Cu.

c. Standard copper solution: Dilute 50.00 ml stock copper solution to 500 ml with redistilled water; 1.00 ml = 20.0 μg Cu.

d. Sulfuric acid, conc.

e. Perchloric acid, 60%.

f. Hydroxylamine-hydrochloride solution: Dissolve 50 g $NH_2OH \cdot HCl$ in 450 ml redistilled water.

g. Sodium citrate solution: Dissolve 150 g $Na_3C_6H_5O_7 \cdot 2H_2O$ in 400 ml redistilled water. Add 5 ml hydroxylamine hydrochloride solution and 10 ml neocuproine reagent. Extract with 50 ml chloroform to remove copper impurities, and discard the chloroform layer.

h. Ammonium hydroxide, 5N: Dilute 330 ml conc NH_4OH (28–29%) to 1,000 ml with redistilled water. Store in a polyethylene bottle.

i. Congo red paper, or other pH test paper showing a color change in the pH range 4–6.

j. Neocuproine reagent: Dissolve 100 mg 2,9-dimethyl-1,10-phenanthroline hemihydrate * in 100 ml methyl alcohol. This solution is stable under ordinary storage conditions for a month or more.

k. Chloroform: Avoid or redistill material that comes in containers with metal-lined caps.

l. Methyl alcohol.

4. Procedure

a. Preparation of calibration curve: Pipet accurately measured volumes of standard copper solution ranging from 1.00 to 10.00 ml (20.0–200 μg Cu) into 150-ml beakers, dilute to 10 ml with redistilled water, and add 1 ml of either H_2SO_4 or $HClO_4$, depending upon which acid is to be used for digestion of the samples. Add hydroxylamine-hydrochloride solution and sodium citrate solution, and then neutralize as described in ¶ 4b(2) below; transfer to a 125-ml separatory funnel and carry through the extraction

---

* Such as is obtainable from G. F. Smith Chemical Company, Columbus, Ohio.

procedure as described in ¶ 4b(3) following.

Transfer an appropriate portion of each final solution to a 1-cm absorption cell and measure the absorbance at 457 mμ or with a filter for 450–460 mμ. As reference use either pure chloroform or a reagent blank prepared by carrying 10 ml redistilled water plus 1 ml H_2SO_4 or $HClO_4$ through the procedure. If pure chloroform is used, the measured absorbance values must be corrected by subtracting the absorbance of a reagent blank carried through the procedure as described.

Construct a calibration curve by plotting absorbance value against micrograms of copper.

To prepare a calibration curve for smaller amounts of copper, dilute 10.0 ml of the standard copper solution to 100 ml. Then carry 1.00- to 10.00-ml volumes of this diluted standard through the previously described procedure, but use 5-cm cells for measurements of absorbance.

b. Treatment of sample:

1) If copper is the only heavy metal to be determined, take a sample of sewage or waste containing 0.1–1 mg Cu and treat it with the digestion procedure described under Preliminary Treatment of Samples. If several heavy metals are to be determined, the directions for size of sample given therein should be followed.

2) Pipet exactly 10.00 ml, or other suitable aliquot containing 4–200 μg Cu, from the solution for analysis obtained from preliminary treatment, into a 125-ml separatory funnel. Dilute to 10 ml with redistilled water if a smaller aliquot has been used. Add 5 ml hydroxylamine-hydrochloride solution and 10 ml sodium citrate solution and mix thoroughly. Adjust the pH to approximately 4 by addition of 1-ml increments of ammonium hydroxide until congo red paper is just definitely red or other suitable pH test paper indicates a value between 4 and 6. (About 6 ml ammonium hydroxide is needed for each 10 ml of sample if digestion with H_2SO_4 was used, about 1.8 ml for each 10 ml if digestion with $HClO_4$ was used.)

3) Add 10 ml neocuproine reagent and 10 ml chloroform. Stopper and shake vigorously for 30 sec or more to extract the copper-neocuproine complex into the chloroform. Allow the mixture to separate into two layers and then withdraw the lower chloroform layer into a 25-ml volumetric flask, taking care not to transfer any of the aqueous layer. Repeat the extraction of the water layer with an additional 10 ml chloroform and add this extract to the previous one. Dilute the combined extracts exactly to the 25-ml mark with methyl alcohol, stopper, and mix thoroughly.

4) Transfer an appropriate portion of the final organic solution to a suitable absorption cell (1-cm for 40–200 μg Cu; 5-cm for lesser amounts) and measure the absorbance at 457 mμ or with a filter for 450–460 mμ. As reference, use either pure chloroform or a sample blank prepared by carrying 10 ml redistilled water through the complete digestion and subsequent procedure. If pure chloroform is used, correct the measured absorbance values by subtracting the absorbance of a sample blank prepared as described.

From the measured or corrected absorbance, determine the micrograms of copper in the final solution by reference to the appropriate calibration curve.

5. Calculation

$$\text{mg/l Cu} = \frac{\mu\text{g Cu}}{\text{ml sample}} \times \frac{100}{\text{ml aliquot}}$$

211 (II)F. Method for Iron

1. General Discussion

a. Principle: Ferrous iron reacts with 1,10-phenanthroline in aqueous solution to form an orange-red complex exhibiting maximum light absorption at a wavelength of 508 mμ. The absorbance of the colored solution is proportional to the concentration of iron; the intensity of color is independent of pH between 3 and 9; the color is stable indefinitely.

The sample is first digested with H_2SO_4 or $HClO_4$ to destroy organic matter, to remove interfering anions such as cyanide and nitrite, and to insure complete dissolution of the iron. The resulting solution is made $7N$–$8N$ in HCl, and the iron is separated from interfering substances by extraction of $FeCl_3$ into isopropyl ether. After re-extraction of the iron into water, it is reduced with hydroxylamine; the color complex is formed in acetate-buffered solution by the addition of a solution of phenanthroline. The absorbance of the resulting solution near 510 mμ is measured with a spectrophotometer or filter photometer.

b. Interference: Numerous metal ions, including those of chromium, copper, nickel, cobalt, zinc, cadmium and mercury, may interfere with determination of iron by phenanthroline. Also, anions that complex iron, such as phosphate or polyphosphate, fluoride, citrate, tartrate and oxalate, may retard or impair color development. All of these potential interferences are eliminated by the extraction procedure.

c. Minimum detectable concentration: The ferrous-phenanthroline complex has a molar absorbancy index equal to about 11,000 at 508 mμ. In a 100-ml final volume the method will detect 5 μg Fe if a 1-cm cell is used for photometric measurement and 1 μg Fe if a 5-cm cell is used (98% light transmittance or 0.01 absorbance). If the volume of initial sample is 100 ml, the concentrations are 50 μg/l and 10 μg/l with the 1-cm and 5-cm cells, respectively.

d. Sampling and storage: Normal precautions for sampling and storage, as described in Sampling and Sample Preservation, should be observed. Because procedures are given only for determination of total iron, no special precautions to prevent oxidation, reduction, solution or precipitation of iron need be taken.

2. Apparatus

a. Colorimetric equipment: One of the following types of photometers, equipped with absorption cells providing light paths of 1 cm or longer, is required:

1) SPECTROPHOTOMETER, for use at 510 mμ.

2) FILTER PHOTOMETER, equipped with a green filter having maximum transmittance near 510 mμ.

b. Separatory funnels, 125-ml, Squibb form, with ground-glass or teflon stopcocks and stoppers.

3. Reagents

a. Stock iron solution: Dissolve 200.0 mg electrolytic iron wire or "iron wire for standardizing," which has been rubbed with fine sandpaper to produce a bright surface, in 20 ml 1 + 5 H_2SO_4 and allow the reaction to proceed until the iron is completely dissolved. Then dilute to 1,000 ml with distilled water; 1.00 ml = 200 μg Fe. Prepare fresh at least every 6 months.

b. Standard iron solution: Prepare this solution the day it is to be used. Dilute 25.0 ml stock iron solution to 500 ml with iron-free distilled water; 1.00 ml = 10.0 μg Fe.

c. Hydroxylamine-hydrochloride solution: Dissolve 50 g $NH_2OH \cdot HCl$ in 450 ml distilled water. Prepare fresh every few days.

d. Sodium acetate solution: Dissolve 200 g $NaC_2H_3O_2 \cdot 3H_2O$ in 800 ml distilled water.

e. Phenanthroline solution: Dissolve 0.5 g 1,10-phenanthroline, $C_{12}H_8N_2 \cdot H_2O$, in 500 ml distilled water, warming to 80–90 C to dissolve, as required. Alternatively, add a few drops of conc HCl to assist in dissolving the reagent.

f. Hydrochloric acid, conc, containing less than 0.00005% of iron.

g. Diisopropyl or isopropyl ether.

h. Sulfuric acid, 1 + 5.

4. Procedure

a. Preparation of calibration curves:

1) RANGE 0–100 μg FE PER 100 ML OF FINAL SOLUTION—Pipet 2.0, 4.0, 6.0, 8.0 and 10.0 ml standard iron solution into 100-ml volumetric flasks. Add 1.0 ml $NH_2OH \cdot HCl$ solution and 1 ml sodium acetate solution to each flask. Dilute each to about 75 ml with distilled water, add 10 ml phenanthroline solution, dilute to volume, mix thoroughly, and let stand for 10 min. Then measure the absorbance of each solution in a 5-cm cell at 508 mμ or with a green filter near 510 mμ against a reference blank prepared by treating distilled water with specified amounts of all reagents except the standard iron solution. Alternatively, if distilled water is used as a reference, correct the absorbance values for standard concentrations of iron by subtracting the absorbance value for a reagent blank against distilled water. From the data obtained, construct a calibration curve for absorbance against milligrams of iron.

2) RANGE 50–500 μg FE PER 100 ML OF FINAL SOLUTION—Follow the procedure specified in the preceding paragraph, but use 10.0, 20.0, 30.0, 40.0 and 50.0 ml standard iron solution and measure the absorbance values in 1-cm cells.

b. Treatment of sample:

1) If a digested sample has been prepared according to the directions given in the section on Preliminary Treatment of Samples, pipet a 10.0-ml portion or other suitable aliquot containing 20–500 μg Fe into a 125-ml separatory funnel. If the volume taken is less than 10 ml, add distilled water to make up the volume to 10 ml. To the separatory funnel add 15 ml conc HCl for a 10-ml aqueous volume; or, if the aliquot taken was greater than 10.0 ml, add 1.5 ml conc HCl for every milliliter of sample used. Mix, cool, and proceed with ¶ 4b(3) below.

2) To prepare a sample for specific determination of iron, measure a suitable volume of sewage or waste containing 20–500 μg Fe and carry it through either of the digestion procedures described under Preliminary Treatment of Samples. However, use only 5 ml H_2SO_4 or $HClO_4$ rather than the 10 ml specified there; also, omit the H_2O_2. When digestion is complete, cool the digested sample, dilute with just 10 ml distilled water, heat almost to boiling to dissolve slowly soluble salts, and if the sample is still cloudy, filter through a glass-fiber, sintered-glass, or porcelain filter, washing with 2–3 ml distilled water. Transfer the filtrate or the clear solution quantitatively to a 25-ml volumetric flask or graduate and make up to 25 ml with distilled water. Empty the flask or graduate into a 125-ml separatory funnel, rinsing with 5 ml conc HCl which is added to the funnel, and then add an additional 25 ml conc HCl measured with the same graduate or flask. Mix and cool to room temperature.

3) Extract the iron from the HCl solution in the separatory funnel by shaking for 30 sec with 25 ml isopropyl ether. Draw off the lower acid layer into a second separatory funnel. Extract the acid solution again with 25 ml isopropyl ether, drain the acid layer into a suitable clean vessel, and combine the second portion of isopropyl ether with the first. Pour the acid layer back into the second separatory funnel and extract once more with 25 ml isopropyl ether. Withdraw and discard the acid layer, then add the ether layer to the lower layers in the original funnel. Do not accept the persistence of a yellow color in the HCl solution after three extractions as evidence of incomplete separation of iron, because copper, which is not extracted, gives a similar yellow color.

Shake the combined ether extracts with 25 ml distilled water to return the iron to the aqueous phase and transfer the lower aqueous layer to a 100-ml volumetric flask. Repeat the extraction with a second 25-ml portion of distilled water, adding this to the first aqueous extract. Discard the ether layer.

4) Add to the volumetric flask containing the combined aqueous extract 1 ml $NH_2OH \cdot HCl$ solution, 10 ml phenanthroline solution, and 10 ml sodium acetate solution. Dilute to 100 ml with distilled water, mix thoroughly, and let stand for 10 min. Measure the absorbance at 510 mμ, using a 5-cm absorption cell for amounts of iron less than 100 μg or a 1-cm cell for quantities from 100 to 500 μg. As reference, either distilled water or a sample blank prepared by carrying the utilized quantities of acids through the entire analytical procedure may be used. If distilled water is used as reference, the absorbance of the sample must be corrected by subtracting the absorbance of a sample blank prepared as described.

Determine the micrograms of iron in the sample used from the absorbance (corrected, if necessary) by reference to the calibration curve prepared according to ¶ 4a(1) and (2) preceding.

5. Calculation

a. When the sample has been treated according to ¶ 4b(1):

$$\text{mg/l Fe} = \frac{\mu\text{g Fe}}{\text{ml sample}} \times \frac{100}{\text{ml aliquot}}$$

b. When the sample has been treated according to ¶ 4b(2):

$$\text{mg/l Fe} = \frac{\mu\text{g Fe}}{\text{ml sample}}$$

211 (II)G. Method for Lead (TENTATIVE)

1. General Discussion

a. Principle: Lead forms a pink complex, lead dithizonate, with dithizone in carbon tetrachloride solution. Interfering metals are removed by preliminary extraction at pH 2 to 3.

After removal of the interfering elements, tartrate is added to prevent the formation of hydroxide, and the solution is brought to pH 8–9 with ammonium hydroxide and sodium cyanide. Lead is then extracted with a dilute solution of dithizone. Because an excess of dithizone is used, the pink color of the lead dithizonate is masked by the intense green color of the excess dithizone. This excess is removed from the carbon tetrachloride layer with alkaline cyanide solution, leaving the lead dithizonate in the organic solvent. The solution of lead dithizonate is diluted to a given volume and the color intensity determined by a colorimeter or spectrophotometer, or by comparison with standards.

The use of hydrazine acetate as the reducing agent may cause some difficulties, inasmuch as the reduction of ferric and stannic ions proceeds quite slowly. The preliminary reduction must be carried out carefully in accordance with the procedure.

b. Interference: The elements that interfere with the extraction of lead in cyanide medium at pH 8 to 9 are bismuth, stannous tin, and thallium. Thallium is so rarely encountered that its interference is hardly worth consideration. On the other hand, bismuth—and in particular, tin—occur quite frequently; hence, special attention must be given to them.

The sample is first fumed with perchloric and nitric acids to remove organic compounds and then is reduced with hydrazine acetate to lower the oxidation state of those elements and compounds which are capable of oxidizing dithizone. The reduction assures that tin and iron exist in the lower valence state. At pH 2 to 3, dithizone forms complexes with bismuth, copper, mercury, silver and tin. Thus, both bismuth and tin are removed so that they cannot interfere with the lead extraction at pH 8 to 9. Because there may be relatively large quantities of bismuth, tin or copper, a strong solution of dithizone in chloroform must be used to extract these elements.

c. Application: The method was developed to determine 0–75 μg Pb in the presence of 100 μg of each of the following ions: Ag, Hg, Bi, Cu, Cd, As, Sb, Sn, Fe, Al, Cr, Ni, Co, Mn, Zn, Ca, Sr, Ba, Mg, Na, K and NH_4.

2. Apparatus

a. Colorimetric equipment—One of the following is required:

1) SPECTROPHOTOMETER, for use at 520 mμ, providing a light path of 1 cm or longer.

2) FILTER PHOTOMETER, providing a light path of 1 cm or longer and equipped with a green filter having maximum transmittance near 520 mμ.

b. pH meter.

c. Separatory funnels, 125-ml, Squibb form, with ground-glass stoppers.

3. Reagents

a. Redistilled water: Distilled water redistilled in all-glass apparatus.

b. Stock lead solution: Dissolve 100.0 mg of the purest lead metal in a mixture of 2 ml conc HNO_3 and 2 ml distilled water. Heat gently if necessary. Dilute to 1,000 ml with distilled water. Store in polyethylene bottles; 1.00 ml = 100 μg Pb.

c. Standard lead solution: Dilute 10.00 ml stock lead solution to 100 ml with redistilled water. Prepare as needed and use the same day; 1.00 ml = 10.0 μg Pb.

d. Phenolphthalein indicator solution.

e. Ammonium hydroxide, conc. Prepare as in Section 211(II)B.3k.

f. Ammonium hydroxide, 1 + 1.

g. Hydrazine acetate solution: Mix 15 ml lead-free hydrazine hydrate (64 per cent hydrazine) * with 50 ml conc acetic acid and dilute to 100 ml with distilled water.

h. Sodium tartrate solution: Dissolve 10 g $Na_2C_4H_4O_6 \cdot 2H_2O$ in 100 ml distilled water. To purify, shake with dithizone solution (II) in carbon tetrachloride until the organic solvent layer appears pure green in color. Wash away the traces of dithizone by extraction with pure $CHCl_3$ until the solution is water white. Then extract twice with CCl_4.

i. Tartaric acid solution: Dissolve 50 g $H_2C_4H_4O_6$ in 100 ml distilled water.

j. Dithizone Solution (I): Use stock dithizone solution (chloroform).

k. Dithizone Solution (II): Use stock dithizone solution (carbon tetrachloride).

l. Chloroform: All chloroform, especially the reclaimed solvent, must be treated as follows: Drain off all water. Wash with conc H_2SO_4 until the solvent and the acid layers are clear and colorless. Use 50 to 100 ml acid per liter of solvent. Shake the solvent with a dilute solution of sodium bicarbonate and then wash thoroughly. Add calcium oxide to dry the solvent. Separate from the CaO and add 2% of its volume of pure absolute methyl alcohol. Distill the solvent slowly while keeping a pellet of CaO in the still. Reject the first 50 to 100 ml and do not allow the still to go to dryness.

m. Carbon tetrachloride: If ACS grade is not available, commercial grade and solvent to be reclaimed must be treated as follows: Shake 1,000 ml solvent with 50 ml 50% aqueous solution of KOH. Repeat this extraction several times. Wash the CCl_4 with 25–50 ml portions of conc H_2SO_4 several times. The final washing with the acid should show no discoloration. Wash the CCl_4 with a dilute solution of sodium bicarbonate; wash repeatedly with water until the washings are

---

* Such as may be obtained from Matheson Scientific, Inc.

perfectly neutral to litmus paper. Dry overnight with $CaCl_2$ and distill, or instead of drying overnight, distill about 10% of the solvent and then collect the clear distillate. Do not distill the last 50 to 100 ml after collecting the main fraction.

n. Thymol blue indicator solution: Dissolve 0.4 g indicator in 100 ml distilled water.

o. Potassium cyanide solution: Dissolve 10 g KCN in 100 ml distilled water. (CAUTION: *Toxic—take care to avoid ingestion.*)

p. Alkaline potassium cyanide solution: To 175 ml pure conc NH_4OH add 15 ml potassium cyanide solution and 7.5 ml lead-free sodium sulfite solution (10 g in 100 ml water). Dilute to 500 ml with distilled water. To remove the lead from sodium sulfite, dissolve 10 g Na_2SO_3 in 100 ml distilled water and extract with dithizone solution (I) until the color of the organic layer is pure green. Remove traces of $CHCl_3$ by 4–5 extractions with pure CCl_4.

q. Hydrochloric acid, conc. If necessary, distill in a pyrex apparatus. The distillate will be approximately 22% HCl.

4. Procedure

a. Sample pretreatment: For the lead determination, the nitric acid-perchloric acid digestion is preferred. If the nitric acid-sulfuric acid digestion is used in the preliminary treatment, two determinations of lead are necessary, one on the solution resulting from the HNO_3-H_2SO_4 digestion and one on the ammonium acetate extract of the residue as described in Preliminary Treatment of Samples.

Pipet an aliquot of the digested sample containing 10–100 μg Pb into a 125-ml beaker.

b. Preparation of calibration standards: Prepare a series of standards ranging from 1 to 10 ml solution (1.00 ml = 10.0 μg Pb) and carry these standards, together with a redistilled water blank, through the same procedure as the sample.

c. Preliminary reduction: Dilute the sample with 10 ml redistilled water. Add 10–15 drops (0.5–0.75 ml) phenolphthalein indicator solution and neutralize with 1 + 1 NH_4OH. Add 20 ml hydrazine acetate solution and heat to 90–95 C in a water bath for at least 10 min. Cool.

In the absence of tin and bismuth, proceed to ¶ e below.

d. Removal of bismuth and tin interference: Add 20 ml sodium tartrate solution. Adjust the pH to about 2.5, using a pH meter, by adding either 1 + 1 ammonium hydroxide or tartaric acid solution. Transfer to a separatory funnel.

Extract the solution in the funnel with 3-ml portions of dithizone solution (I) until the organic layer has a pure green color. Shake well each time and carefully drain off and discard the chloroform layer.

Extract the solution with two 5-ml portions of pure chloroform to remove the entrained dithizone. Discard the chloroform layers. Remove the remaining chloroform by extracting with 5 ml CCl_4. Discard the CCl_4 layer.

e. Extraction of lead: Add 10 ml sodium tartrate solution and 5 drops thymol blue indicator solution. If necessary, add conc NH_4OH to make the indicator turn blue.

Add 10 ml potassium cyanide solution (¶ 3*o* preceding). Adjust the pH to 8.5 by adding tartaric acid solution or 1 + 1 NH_4OH until the indicator turns green.

Extract with 5 ml dithizone solution (II). Shake well and carefully transfer the solvent layer to another separatory funnel.

Successively extract the aqueous phase with 2-ml portions of dithizone solution (II) until the green color of dithizone persists for at least two extractions. Combine all these extractions with the one from the previous step. When multiple samples are run, as with a calibration curve, be sure to use the same amount of dithizone solution for all extractions. The color of the blank increases somewhat as the number of extractions increases. Extract the aqueous phase with 5 ml pure CCl_4 and add it to the other extracts.

To the combined CCl_4 extracts, add 20 ml alkaline potassium cyanide solution and shake well. Drain off the CCl_4 layer into a 25- or 50-ml volumetric flask. Extract the aqueous phase with two 2-ml portions of pure CCl_4. Combine all the extracts and discard the aqueous layer.

Dilute the extracts in the volumetric flask to the mark by adding pure CCl_4 and shake well.

f. Color measurement: Filter the CCl_4 solution through small dry papers to remove suspended droplets of water. Read the absorbance of this solution at 520 mμ using pure CCl_4 as a reference. Subtract the absorbance of the blank from that of the sample readings.

5. Calculation

$$\text{mg/l Pb} = \frac{\mu\text{g Pb}}{\text{ml sample}} \times \frac{100}{\text{ml aliquot}}$$

211 (II)H. Method for Manganese

1. General Discussion

a. Principle: Manganese is readily determined in small concentrations by oxidizing it in acidic solution to the intensely colored permanganate ion and measuring the absorbance of the resulting solution at a wavelength of 525 mμ. Either periodate or persulfate can be employed as the oxidizing agent; oxidation with persulfate is used in the method described here because of its greater speed, especially for traces of manganese. Oxidation with periodate can be carried out as described for the determination of manganese in water, using an appropriate aliquot of the digestate obtained according to Section 211 (I) A, Preliminary Treatment of Samples.

After the sample has been digested with acid to oxidize organic matter and to volatilize chloride as HCl, phosphoric acid is added to form a colorless complex with ferric ion. Oxidation with the persulfate ion is carried out in hot acidic solution in the presence of silver as a catalyst. The resulting permanganate color is stable for at least 24 hr if excess persulfate is present and the solution is kept from contact with organic matter, including dust.

b. Interference: The most important interferences are organic matter, chloride ion, and other reducing substances, which may cause unstable colors by reducing permanganate. Chloride ion, by forming AgCl, also interferes with the catalytic action of silver and produces turbidity. Potential interference from all these substances is eliminated by proper performance of the acidic digestion and oxidation. Other colored ions, notably ferric iron, copper, nickel and dichromate, interfere by contributing to the absorption of light at 525 mμ. The interference of iron is avoided by addition of phosphoric acid. That of the other ions is compensated for by using as a photometric blank a portion of the sample from which the permanganate color has been bleached by reduction.

c. Minimum detectable concentration: The absorbency index of permanganate per gram atom of manganese at 525 mμ is about 2,300. The minimum detectable quantity is 30 μg Mn when a 1-cm cell is used for photometric comparison, or 5 μg Mn when a 5-cm cell is used (98% transmittance). If the volume of sample used is 100 ml, these quantities correspond to 300 and 50 μg/l, respectively.

2. Apparatus

COLORIMETRIC EQUIPMENT—One of the following, equipped with suitable absorption cells providing light paths of 1 cm or longer, is required:

a. Spectrophotometer, for use at 525 mμ.

b. Filter photometer, equipped with a green filter exhibiting maximum transmittance near 525 mμ.

3. Reagents

a. Stock manganese solution: Dissolve 1.8 g potassium permanganate, $KMnO_4$, in about 450 ml distilled water in a 1-liter conical flask and heat for 4–5 hr at 70–80 C, protecting the mouth of the flask against intrusion of dust. Filter while hot through a fritted-glass, glass-fiber or asbestos filter, collecting the filtrate in a thoroughly clean flask. Transfer the filtrate to a 500-ml volumetric flask, add 2 ml H_2SO_4, cool to room temperature, and dilute to the mark with distilled water.

Within 24 hr standardize oxidimetrically against sodium oxalate, following the procedure described in Calcium, Section 110B.3c, except that samples 0.2–0.4 g (weighed to 0.1 mg) should be used. (The standardization must be carried out promptly before any permanganate has decomposed or has been reduced, so that the total manganese content and the oxidimetric titer will correspond. As decomposition subsequent to the standardization will not change the manganese content of the acidified solution, standard manganese solutions may be prepared at any time, based on the initial oxidimetric titer but not on any subsequent oxidimetric titer.)

b. Standard manganese solution: The volume of stock solution required to prepare 1 liter of a solution containing 50 mg/l Mn is 4.55 divided by the normality of $KMnO_4$. Transfer exactly this volume, measured to 0.1 ml by means of a buret, to a 250-ml beaker or conical flask. Add 5 ml conc H_2SO_4 and then $NaHSO_3$ solution dropwise, with stirring, until the pink color of permanganate disappears. Heat the solution and boil gently for a few minutes to remove excess SO_2. Cool and transfer quantitatively to a 1-liter volumetric flask, rinsing the beaker or flask several times with distilled water. Dilute to 1,000 ml with distilled water; 1.00 ml = 50.0 μg Mn.

c. Sulfuric acid, conc.

d. Nitric acid, conc.

e. Phosphoric acid, 6M: Dilute 400 ml 85% H_3PO_4 with 600 ml distilled water.

f. Silver nitrate solution, 0.1N: Dissolve 1.7 g $AgNO_3$ in 100 ml distilled water.

g. Ammonium persulfate, solid.

h. Perchloric acid, 60%.

i. Sodium nitrite solution: Dissolve 5 g $NaNO_2$ in 95 ml distilled water.

j. Special reagents for preparation of standard manganese solution:

1) SODIUM BISULFITE SOLUTION—Dissolve 10 g $NaHSO_3$ in 90 ml distilled water.

2) SODIUM OXALATE, primary standard, $Na_2C_2O_4$.

4. Procedure

a. Preparation of calibration curve:

1) RANGE 0–0.5 MG MN PER 100 ML OF FINAL SOLUTION—Pipet 1.00, 2.00, 4.00, 6.00 and 10.00 ml standard manganese solution into 250-ml conical flasks. To each flask add 25 ml distilled water, 1 ml conc H_2SO_4, 0.5 ml conc HNO_3, 20 ml 6*M* H_3PO_4, 1 ml silver nitrate solution, and 1 g $(NH_4)_2S_2O_8$. Heat to boiling on a hot plate and boil gently for 1 min. Remove from the hot plate, add 0.2 g $(NH_4)_2S_2O_8$, and allow to stand for 1 min longer; then cool with running water. Transfer each solution quantitatively to a 100-ml volumetric flask, dilute to 100 ml with distilled water free of reducing substances, and mix thoroughly. Measure the absorbance of each solution in a 5-cm cell at a wavelength of 525 mμ or with a green filter for wavelengths near this value, using as reference a reagent blank prepared by carrying 25 ml distilled water through the procedure. Construct a calibration curve, plotting absorbance against milligrams of manganese.

2) RANGE 0.2–2.0 MG MN PER 100 ML OF FINAL SOLUTION—Follow the procedure specified in ¶ 4a(1) above, but use 5.00, 10.00, 20.0, 30.0 and 40.0 ml standard manganese solution and measure the absorbance values in 1-cm cells.

b. Treatment of sample:

1) If a digested sample has been prepared according to the directions given in Preliminary Treatment of Samples, pipet a 10.0-ml portion or other suitable aliquot containing 0.05–2.0 mg Mn into a 250-ml conical flask. Add 25 ml distilled water if the aliquot taken is less than 50 ml and proceed with ¶ 4b(3) below.

2) To prepare a solution for specific determination of manganese, measure a suitable volume of sewage or waste containing 0.02–2.0 mg Mn and carry it through either of the digestion procedures described under Preliminary Treatment of Samples. However, use only 5 ml H_2SO_4 or $HClO_4$ rather than the 10 ml specified there and omit the addition of H_2O_2. When digestion is complete, cool the digested sample, add 25 ml distilled water, and heat almost to boiling to dissolve slowly soluble salts. Filter through a glass-fiber, sintered-glass or porcelain filter to remove any cloudiness, washing the vessel and the filter with small portions of distilled water. Transfer the filtrate or clear solution quantitatively to a 250-ml conical flask and dilute to about 70 ml.

3) Add 20 ml 6*M* H_3PO_4, 1 ml silver nitrate solution, and 1 g $(NH_4)_2S_2O_8$ to the solution from ¶s 4b(1) or 4b(2) above. Heat to boiling on a hot plate and boil gently for 2 min. If the solution is brownish or turbid at this point because of incomplete oxidation of organic matter, add 1 g $(NH_4)_2S_2O_8$ more and continue boiling for 10 min. If, at the end of this time, the solution has still not cleared, add sodium bisulfite solution dropwise and reduce MnO_2 and MnO_4^-; then repeat the persulfate oxidation.

Remove the oxidized solution from the hot plate, add an additional 0.2 g $(NH_4)_2S_2O_8$, allow to stand for 1 min, then cool in running water to room temperature. Transfer the solution quantitatively to a 100-ml volumetric flask, dilute to the mark with distilled water, and mix thoroughly.

4) Pipet 50 ml of the solution from the preceding paragraph into a second 100-ml volumetric flask to make the reference solution. To the transferred portion add sodium nitrite solution dropwise, mixing thoroughly after each drop, until the permanganate color is destroyed. No more than 2 drops should be required.

5) Transfer suitable portions of the sample solution and the bleached solution to absorption cells of appropriate optical path and determine the absorbance due to permanganate in one of two ways:

i—By measuring the absorbance of the sample solution against that of the bleached solution as reference at a wavelength of 525 mμ or with a green filter having maximum transmission near 525 mμ.

ii—By measuring the absorbances of both sample solution and bleached solution against distilled water at the designated wavelength and subtracting the absorbance of the bleached solution from that of the sample.

The former technic gives greater sensitivity and precision in the presence of large concentrations of other colored ions. However, it may be impossible to set the photometer at 0 absorbance or 100% transmittance when the bleached solution contains large concentrations of colored ions. (The slit width of the spectrophotometer should not be changed from that used in preparing the calibration curve.) The latter technic must then be employed.

NOTE: The procedure described compensates for the interference of colored ions in the sample but does *not* correct for manganous impurities in the reagents. Difficulties from this source are not likely. However, manganous impurities can be determined by carrying two portions of distilled water through the complete digestion and analytical procedure, except that one of them is not heated after the addition of ammonium persulfate. Measurement of the absorbance of the heated against the unheated solution at 525 mμ gives a reagent correction to be applied to the absorbance of the sample.

Determine the milligrams of manganese in the final solution from the net absorbance by reference to the appropriate calibration curve prepared according to ¶ 4a(1) or (2) preceding.

5. Calculation

a. when the sample has been treated according to ¶ 4b(1):

$$\text{mg/l Mn} = \text{mg Mn} \times \frac{1{,}000}{\text{ml sample}} \times \frac{100}{\text{ml aliquot}}$$

b. When the sample has been treated according to ¶ 4b(2):

$$\text{mg/l Mn} = \text{mg Mn} \times \frac{1{,}000}{\text{ml sample}}$$

211 (II)I. Heptoxime Method for Nickel (TENTATIVE)

1. Principle

Following preliminary digestion with the HNO_3-H_2SO_4 mixture, iron and copper are removed by extraction of the cupferrates with chloroform. The nickel is separated from other ions by extraction of the nickel heptoxime complex with chloroform, reextracted into the aqueous phase with hydrochloric acid, and determined colorimetrically in the acidic solution with heptoxime in the presence of an oxidant.

2. Apparatus

a. Colorimetric equipment—One of the following is required:

1) SPECTROPHOTOMETER, for use at 445 mμ, providing a light path of 1 cm or longer.

2) FILTER PHOTOMETER, providing a light path of 1 cm or longer and equipped with a violet filter with maximum transmittance near 445 mμ.

b. Separatory funnels, 125-ml, Squibb form, with ground-glass stoppers.

3. Reagents

a. Standard nickel sulfate solution: Dissolve 447.9 mg $NiSO_4 \cdot 6H_2O$ in 1,000 ml distilled water; 1.00 ml = 100 μg Ni.

b. Hydrochloric acid, 1.0*N*.

c. Bromine water: Saturate distilled water with bromine.

d. Ammonium hydroxide, conc.

e. Heptoxime reagent: Dissolve 0.1 g 1,2-cycloheptanedionedioxime* (heptoxime) in 100 ml 95% ethyl alcohol.

f. Ethyl alcohol, 95%.

g. Sodium tartrate solution: Dissolve 10 g $Na_2C_4H_4O_6 \cdot 2H_2O$ in 90 ml distilled water.

h. Methyl orange indicator solution.

i. Sodium hydroxide, 6*N*.

j. Acetic acid, conc.

k. Cupferron solution: Dissolve 1 g cupferron in 100 ml distilled water. Store in a refrigerator or make up fresh for each series of determinations.

l. Chloroform.

m. Hydroxylamine - hydrochloride solution: Dissolve 10 g $NH_2OH \cdot HCl$ in 90 ml distilled water. Make up daily.

4. Procedure

a. Preparation of calibration curve: Pipet aliquots of the standard nickel sulfate solution into 100-ml volumetric flasks. The series should cover from 50 to 250 μg Ni if 1-cm cells are used. Add 25 ml 1.0*N* HCl and 5 ml bromine water. Cool with cold running tap water and add 10 ml conc NH_4OH. Then immediately add 20 ml heptoxime reagent and 20 ml ethyl alcohol. Dilute to volume with distilled water and mix.

Measure absorbance at 445 mμ 20 min after addition of the reagent, using a reagent blank as reference.

b. Treatment of sample:

1) SEPARATION OF COPPER AND IRON—Take an aliquot of the original sample [prepared by digesting with HNO_3-H_2SO_4 mixture as directed in ¶s 4a(1)–(4) of Preliminary Treatment of Samples] containing from 50 to 250 μg Ni, place in a separatory funnel, and add 10 ml sodium tartrate solution, 2 drops (0.1 ml) methyl orange indicator, and enough 6*N* NaOH to make the solution basic to the indicator.

* Such as is obtainable from Hach Chemical Company, Ames, Iowa.

Add 1 ml acetic acid and cool by placing the separatory funnel under cold running tap water. Add 4 ml fresh cupferron reagent and extract any precipitate formed with 10 ml $CHCl_3$. Allow the layers to separate and add more cupferron until a white silky precipitate forms, which indicates that an excess of cupferron is present.

Shake the mixture, allow the layers to separate, and discard the $CHCl_3$ layer. Extract again with 10 ml $CHCl_3$ and discard the $CHCl_3$ layer. Add 1 ml fresh $NH_2OH \cdot HCl$ solution, mix, and let stand a few minutes.

2) SEPARATION OF NICKEL—Add 10 ml heptoxime reagent and extract the nickel complex with one 15-ml and then two 10-ml portions of $CHCl_3$. If the $CHCl_3$ layer is not colorless with the third extraction, continue until it is. Collect the $CHCl_3$ layers in a separatory funnel. Extract the nickel from the $CHCl_3$ by shaking with 15 ml 1.0*N* HCl. After allowing the layers to separate, draw off the $CHCl_3$ layer into another separatory funnel, and rinse with 10 ml 1.0*N* HCl, which is added to the 15-ml portion of HCl.

Determine the absorbance of the solution as directed in ¶ 4a.

5. Calculation

$$\text{mg/l Ni} = \frac{\mu\text{g Ni}}{\text{ml sample}} \times \frac{100}{\text{ml aliquot}}$$

211 (II)J. Dimethylglyoxime Method for Nickel (TENTATIVE)

If desired, dimethylglyoxime may be used instead of heptoxime to develop the color with nickel. The conditions of color formation are identical, but separate curves must be prepared. The rate of color development is slightly different for the two reagents so that, with dimethylglyoxime, readings are taken exactly 10 min after addition of the reagent, whereas, with heptoxime, readings are taken exactly 20 min after addition of the reagent. Both systems are measured at 445 mμ. The heptoxime system is more stable. Dimethylglyoxime cannot be substituted for heptoxime in the extraction process, Method I, ¶ 4b(2), under the conditions prescribed.

The calculation is the same as in Method I preceding.

211 (II)K. Method for Zinc (TENTATIVE)

1. Principle

Zinc is separated from other metals by extraction with dithizone and is then determined by measuring the color of the zinc-dithizone complex in carbon tetrachloride. Specificity in the separation is achieved by extracting from a nearly neutral solution containing bis(2-hydroxyethyl)dithiocarbamyl ion and cyanide ion, which prevents moderate concentrations of cadmium, copper, lead and nickel from reacting with dithizone. If excessive amounts of these metals are present, the special procedure given in ¶ 4b(2) below must be followed.

The color reaction is extremely sensitive and precautions must be taken to avoid introducing extraneous zinc during the analysis. Contamination may arise from water, reagents and glassware, such as beakers and separatory funnels, on which zinc has been adsorbed during previous use. Appreciable blanks are generally found, and the analyst must satisfy himself that these blanks are representative and reproducible.

2. Apparatus

a. Colorimetric equipment—One of the following is required:

1) SPECTROPHOTOMETER, for use at 535 mμ, providing a light path of 1 cm or longer.

2) FILTER PHOTOMETER, providing a light path of 1 cm or longer and equipped with a greenish yellow filter with maximum transmittance near 535 mμ.

b. Separatory funnels, 125-ml, Squibb form, with ground-glass stoppers.

3. Reagents

a. Standard zinc solution: Dissolve 1.000 g zinc metal in 10 ml 1 + 1 HNO_3. Dilute and boil to expel oxides of nitrogen. Transfer to a 1,000-ml volumetric flask and dilute to volume; 1.00 ml = 1.00 mg Zn.

b. Redistilled water: Distilled water redistilled in all-glass apparatus.

c. Methyl red indicator: Dissolve 0.1 g methyl red sodium salt and dilute to 100 ml with distilled water.

d. Sodium citrate solution: Dissolve 10 g $Na_3C_6H_5O_7 \cdot 2H_2O$ in 90 ml water. Shake with 10 ml dithizone solution (I) to remove zinc, then filter.

e. Ammonium hydroxide, conc: Prepare according to the Method for Cadmium, Section 211 (II) B.3k.

f. Potassium cyanide solution: Dissolve 5 g KCN in 95 ml redistilled water. (CAUTION: *Toxic—take care to avoid ingestion.*)

g. Acetic acid, conc.

h. Carbon tetrachloride, zinc-free.

i. Bis(2-hydroxyethyl)dithiocarbamate solution: Dissolve 4.0 g diethanolamine and 1 ml CS_2 in 40 ml methyl alcohol. Prepare every 3 or 4 days.

j. Dithizone solution: Dilute 50 ml stock dithizone solution (carbon tetrachloride) to 250 ml with pure carbon tetrachloride. Prepare fresh daily.

k. Sodium sulfide solution (I): Dissolve 3.0 g $Na_2S \cdot 9H_2O$ or 1.65 g $Na_2S \cdot 3H_2O$ in 100 ml zinc-free water.

l. Sodium sulfide solution (II): Prepare just before use by diluting 4 ml sodium sulfide solution (I) to 100 ml.

m. Nitric acid, 6N.

n. Hydrogen sulfide.

4. Procedure

a. Preparation of calibration curve:

1) Prepare, just before use, a zinc solution containing 2.0 μg Zn per milliliter by diluting 5 ml standard zinc solution to 250 ml, then diluting 10 ml of the latter solution to 100 ml with redistilled water. Pipet 5.00, 10.00, 15.00 and 20.00 ml of the resulting solution, containing 10–40 μg Zn, into separate 125-ml separatory funnels and adjust the volumes to about 20 ml.

Set up another funnel containing 20 ml zinc-free water as a blank.

2) Add 2 drops methyl red indicator and 2.0 ml sodium citrate solution to each funnel; if the indicator is not yellow at this point, add conc NH_4OH a drop at a time until the indicator just turns yellow. Next, add 1.0 ml potassium cyanide solution and then acetic acid, a drop at a time, until the indicator just turns a neutral peach color.

3) Extract the methyl red by shaking with 5 ml CCl_4 and discard the yellow CCl_4 layer. Then add 1 ml dithiocarbamate solution. Extract with 10 ml dithizone solution, shaking for 1 min.

Draw off the CCl_4 layer into another separatory funnel and repeat the extraction with successive 5-ml portions of dithizone solution until the last one shows no change from the green dithizone color when viewed by transmitted light. Discard the aqueous layer.

4) Shake the combined dithizone extracts with a 10-ml portion of sodium sulfide solution (II), then separate the layers and repeat the washing with further 10-ml portions of Na_2S solution until the unreacted dithizone solution has been completely removed, as shown by color of the aqueous layer, which remains colorless or very pale yellow; usually three such washings are sufficient.

Finally, remove any water adhering to the stem of the funnel with a cotton swab and drain the pink CCl_4 solution into a dry 50-ml volumetric flask, using a few milliliters of fresh CCl_4 to rinse the last droplets from the funnel. Dilute to the mark with fresh CCl_4.

5) Determine the absorbance of the zinc dithizonate solutions at 535 mμ, using pure CCl_4 as a reference. Plot an absorbance-concentration curve after subtracting the absorbance of the blank. The calibration curve is linear if monochromatic light is used.

6) Clean separatory funnels by shaking several minutes successively with HNO_3, distilled water, and finally a mixture of 5 ml sodium citrate and 5 ml dithizone, to minimize the large or erratic blanks that result from the adsorption of zinc on the glass surface. If possible, reserve separatory funnels exclusively for the zinc determination and do not use for other purposes.

b. Treatment of sample:

1) After digestion of the sample as directed under Preliminary Treatment, take an aliquot containing 10–40 μg Zn, transfer to a clean 125-ml separatory funnel, and adjust the volume to about 20 ml. Determine the zinc in this solution exactly as described in the preceding procedure for preparing the calibration curve.

If more than 30 ml of dithizone solution is needed to extract the zinc completely, the aliquot taken contains too much zinc, or the quantity of other metals which react with dithizone exceeds the amount which can be withheld by the complexing agent. In the latter case, follow the procedure in ¶ 4b(2) below.

2) SEPARATION OF EXCESSIVE AMOUNTS OF CADMIUM, COPPER AND LEAD—When the quantity of these metals, separately or jointly, exceeds 2 mg in the aliquot taken, place the aliquot in a 100-ml beaker, and adjust the volume to about 20 ml and the acidity to 0.4–0.5*N*,* by adding dilute

* The normalities of the solutions obtained in the preliminary treatment are approximately 3*N* for the HNO_3-H_2SO_4 digestion and approximately 0.8*N* for the HNO_3-$HClO_4$ digestion.

HNO_3 or NH_4OH as necessary. Pass H_2S into the cold solution for 5 min. Filter off the precipitated sulfides using a sintered-glass filter, and wash the precipitate with two small portions of hot water. Boil the filtrate 3 to 4 min to remove H_2S; then cool, transfer to a separatory funnel, and determine the zinc as described in ¶ 4b(1) et seq.

5. Calculation

$$\text{mg/l Zn} = \frac{\mu\text{g Zn}}{\text{ml sample}} \times \frac{100}{\text{ml aliquot}}$$

III—POLAROGRAPHY

Colorimetric analysis of metal-bearing wastes and receiving streams is generally difficult and time-consuming. Polarographic technics are preferable to colorimetric methods because of the rapidity of analysis and because the method may be applied simultaneously to a variety of metals. The method has been developed to permit the simultaneous determination of cadmium, copper, lead, nickel and zinc.

A wide range of other metals can be determined polarographically with the selection of the proper supporting electrolyte. The sequence of supporting electrolytes used in these procedures was selected to give maximum information for the least effort and with the least danger of contamination by reagents.

211 (III)A. Preliminary Treatment of Samples

1. General Discussion

Iron, chromium, organic matter, turbidity, chlorides, oxidizing and reducing substances, and dissolved oxygen are the major interferences that are likely to be encountered. The following procedure was designed to eliminate interference of this type and must be used prior to the polarographic technic described below. Deviation from the procedure may lead either to completely erroneous results or to polarograms which are impossible to interpret.

2. Apparatus

a. Sintered-glass filter, fine-porosity, with holder. Gooch crucible with glass-fiber filter may be used.

NOTE: Rinse all glassware with 1 + 1 HNO_3, distilled water, and finally redistilled water.

3. Reagents

a. Sulfuric acid, conc.

b. Nitric acid, conc and 1 + 1.

c. Redistilled water: Distilled water redistilled in all-glass apparatus.

d. Ammonium hydroxide solution,

metal-free: Pass tank ammonia gas through a glass-wool trap into chilled redistilled water until the concentration reaches about 7*M*. Alternatively, distill 900 ml of conc NH_4OH in a 1,500-ml distilling flask into a 1-liter polyethylene bottle containing 250 ml of chilled redistilled water until the volume of liquid in the bottle has increased to 900 ml. Keep the tip of the condenser below the surface of the liquid during the distillation.

e. Sodium sulfite, crystals, reagent grade.

4. Procedure

Add 0.1 ml conc H_2SO_4 to 100 ml of sample in a pyrex erlenmeyer flask and evaporate to dense white fumes. Add conc HNO_3 to the fuming liquid drop by drop until the solution clears and becomes colorless. With some samples it is not possible to remove all the color by this procedure; however, add nitric acid until no further color change can be perceived. Wash down the sides of the flask with glass-distilled water to remove excess HNO_3 and again bring to fumes. Fuming also removes chlorides which interfere.

Neutralize the solution with the metal-free ammonia solution, using pink litmus paper to indicate the completion of neutralization. The resultant solution is roughly about 0.18*M* in $(NH_4)_2SO_4$. Boil to remove excess ammonia until the odor of ammonia disappears. Filter the solution through a sintered-glass filter and make up to 10 ml with redistilled water.

211 (III)B. Method for Cadmium, Copper, Lead, Nickel and Zinc

1. General Discussion

a. Principle: Conventional polarography is based on the unique properties displayed by an electrolytic cell consisting of a nonpolarizable reference electrode, a readily polarizable electrode in the form of a mercury drop falling from a capillary, and an electrolytic solution containing small amounts of electroreducible or electro-oxidizable material. When an increasing electromotive force is impressed across such a cell and the resulting current is plotted as a function of the applied voltage (Figure 34), a curve is obtained whose extension along the current axis is directly related to the concentration of the trace material and whose inflection point is located at a voltage characteristic of that material.

b. Interference: When the recommended procedure is followed, the only significant interferences are from large quantities of other reducible species with half-wave potentials close to that of the metal of interest. The sequence of supporting electrolytes was selected to permit interpretation of the polarograms for each of the five metals of interest even in the presence of large quantities of one or more of these metals. The method was also tested in the presence of 100 mg/l of chromium, iron and organic matter, with no detectable effect.

c. Minimum detectable concentrations: The lower limit of detection, using ordinary equipment and the dropping mercury electrode, is about $10^{-6}M$. Therefore, including a 10-to-1 concentration, the lower limits of detection are about 0.1 mg/l.

2. Apparatus

a. Polarograph: Any commercially available polarograph can be used that is capable of utilizing applied voltages of 0.00 to −2.0 V. Automatic voltage scanning and recording, although not required, are recommended.

b. Polarographic cell: Figure 33 shows the conventional polarographic cell used with the dropping mercury electrode, including the mercury reservoir. Cells of this type use the mercury pool as a reference electrode. The indicator electrode consists of small drops of mercury falling from a capillary attached to a reservoir of mercury. Other types of cells also available commercially permit the use of external standard reference electrodes. In general, selection of the type of cell to be used is left to the discretion of the analyst.

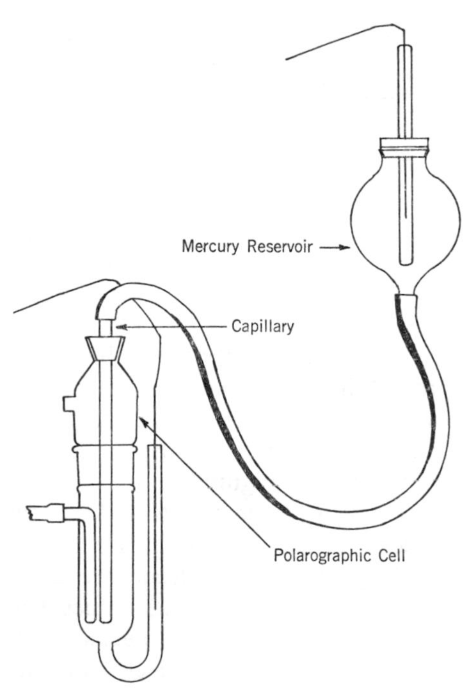

Figure 33. Polarographic cell for use with dropping mercury electrode.

c. Deaeration apparatus: Oxygen is readily reduced at the dropping mercury electrode and must be removed from the solution to be analyzed. This is generally accomplished by bubbling nitrogen through the solution. Tank nitrogen, which is usually contaminated by traces of oxygen, can be purified by passing it over copper turnings heated to 450 C. Equipment of this type is available commercially.

3. Reagents

a. Mercury, redistilled, National Formulary grade: Used mercury may be purified using commercially available oxidizers and gold adhesion filters.

b. Ammonium sulfate solution, saturated: Neutralize *7M* metal-free ammonia solution with conc H_2SO_4, adding the acid slowly with extreme caution. Extract the neutralized solution with a solution of diphenylthiocarbazone in carbon tetrachloride. Wash with carbon tetrachloride until all traces of color have been removed. Concentrate to a saturated solution by evaporation of excess water.

c. Gelatin, U.S.P. powder.

d. Ethylenediaminetetraacetic acid disodium salt, commercially available grade.

4. Procedure

a. Transfer the sample prepared according to the directions given under Preliminary Treatment of Samples to the polarographic cell. Add about 10 mg gelatin to suppress maxima which may interfere. Use a fritted-glass bubbler for better dispersion of the nitrogen and more complete deoxygenation. Place a small amount of purified mercury in the bottom of the cell to form the indicator electrode. Insert the dropping mercury electrode into the cell so that the tip is immersed in the solution. Adjust the height of the mercury reservoir to give a drop time of 4 or 5 sec.

b. Connect the cell to the polarograph and run a polarogram at suitable sensitivity, from 0.00 V to about − 1.6 V. While polarograms are being run, remove the nitrogen bubbler from the solution and hold just above the surface to maintain an atmosphere of nitrogen and prevent surface absorption of oxygen.

c. After suitable curves have been run with $(NH_4)_2SO_4$ supporting electrolyte, add sufficient NH_4OH to make the solution about 0.4*M* in NH_3. Generally 4 or 5 drops of the ammonia solution as prepared in Preliminary Treatment of Samples, ¶ 3d above, is sufficient.

d. After curves have been run in the presence of free ammonia, add about 300 mg of ethylenediaminetetraacetate disodium salt and run suitable curves.

5. Interpretation of Polarograms

a. Half-wave potentials are read off at the halfway point of the rise, as determined by inspection or by rough measurement. It is not necessary to correct for current resistance (*IR*) drop across the resistors in the measuring circuit for this type of work. Wave heights are measured vertically through

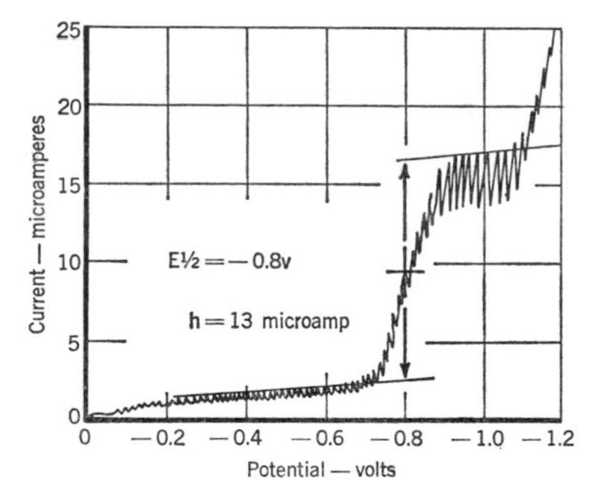

Figure 34. Interpretation of polarograms obtained using the dropping mercury electrode.

the half-wave potentials between straight-line extrapolations of the sections of the polarogram immediately preceding and following the wave. This is illustrated in Figure 34.

b. Half-wave potentials and current concentration ratios of metals at the dropping mercury electrode are given in Table 211(1). These values will serve to identify the five metals—cadmium, copper, lead, nickel and zinc —and will provide semiquantitative re-

TABLE 211(1): HALF-WAVE POTENTIALS AND CURRENT CONCENTRATION RATIOS OF METALS AT THE DROPPING MERCURY ELECTRODE

Metal	Supporting Electrolyte					
	0.18*M* $(NH_4)_2SO_4$		0.4*M* NH_4OH + 0.18*M* $(NH_4)_2SO_4$		0.4*M* NH_4OH + EDTA + 0.18*M* $(NH_4)_2SO_4$	
	Half-Wave Potential *v*	Relative Wave Height [a]	Half-Wave Potential *v*	Relative Wave Height [a]	Half-Wave Potential *v*	Relative Wave Height [a]
Copper	0.02 to 0.05	0.0076	0.17	Often not seen	0.47 to 0.51	0.0050
			0.38 to 0.45	0.0040		
Lead	0.37 to 0.40	0.0010	0.43 to 0.47	0.0010	1.13 to 1.17	0.0010
Cadmium	0.57 to 0.59	0.0036	0.67 to 0.74	0.0036	No wave	—
Nickel	1.01 to 1.03	0.0083	0.91 to 0.95	0.0083	No wave	—
Zinc	0.98	0.0083	1.19 to 1.22	0.0083	No wave	—

[a] $\mu a/\mu g$ of element.

sults which can be used to eliminate the necessity of analyzing for those metals that are absent and to determine sample size for wet analysis. For quantitative results, a similar table should be prepared by the analyst using his equipment and standard solutions of the metals of interest.

IV—BIBLIOGRAPHY

General

SERFASS, E. J. et al. 1948–51. Determination of impurities in electroplating solutions. *Plating* 35:156, 260, 458, 1019 (1948); 36:254, 818, 1034 (1949); 37:62, 166, 389, 495, 1057 (1950); 38:473 (1951).

Colorimetry

BUTTS, P. G., A. R. GAHLER & M. G. MELLON. 1950. Colorimetric determination of metals in sewage and industrial wastes. *Sewage & Ind. Wastes* 22:1543.

CHRISTIE, A. A. et al. 1957. The colorimetric determination of cadmium, chromium, copper, iron, lead, manganese, nickel, and zinc in sewage and industrial wastes. *Analyst* 82:336.

Cadmium

FISCHER, H. & G. LEOPOLDI. 1937. Determination of small quantities of cadmium with dithizone. *Mikrochim. Acta* 1:30.

SERFASS, E. J. et al. 1948. Determination of impurities in electroplating solutions. *Plating* 35:458.

SHIRLEY, R. L., W. J. BENNE & E. J. MILLER. 1949. Cadmium in biological materials and foods. *Anal. Chem.* 21:300.

SANDELL, E. B. 1959. *Colorimetric Determination of Traces of Metals* (3rd ed.). Interscience Publishers, New York.

Chromium

ROWLAND, G. P. JR. 1939. Photoelectric colorimetry—Optical study of permanganate ion and of chromium-diphenylcarbazide system. *Anal. Chem.* 11:442.

SALTZMAN, B. E. 1952. Microdetermination of chromium with diphenylcarbazide by permanganate oxidation. *Anal. Chem.* 24:1016.

URONE, P. F. 1955. Stability of colorimetric reagent for chromium, *s*-diphenylcarbazide, in various solvents. *Anal. Chem.* 27:1354.

ALLEN, T. L. 1958. Microdetermination of chromium with 1,5-diphenylcarbohydrazide. *Anal. Chem.* 30:447.

SANDELL, E. B. 1959. *Colorimetric Determination of Traces of Metals* (3rd ed.). Interscience Publishers, New York.

Copper

SMITH, G. F. & W. H. MCCURDY. 1952. 2,9-Dimethyl-1, 10-phenanthroline: New specific in spectrophotometric determination of copper. *Anal. Chem.* 24: 371.

LUKE, C. L. & M. E. CAMPBELL. 1953. Determination of impurities in germanium and silicon. *Anal. Chem.* 25:1586.

GAHLER, A. R. 1954. Colorimetric determination of copper with neocuproine. *Anal. Chem.* 26:577.

FULTON, J. W. & J. HASTINGS. 1956. Photometric determinations of copper in aluminum and lead-tin solder with neocuproine. *Anal. Chem.* 28:174.

FRANK, A. J., A. B. GOULSTON & A. A. DEACUTIS. 1957. Spectrophotometric determination of copper in titanium. *Anal. Chem.* 29:750.

Iron

FORTUNE, W. B. & M. G. MELLON. 1938. Determination of iron with *o*-phenanthroline: A spectrophotometric study. *Ind. Eng. Chem.*, Anal. Ed. 10:60.

RYAN, J. A. & G. H. BOTHAM. 1949. Iron in aluminum alloys: Colorimetric determination using 1,10-phenanthroline. *Anal. Chem.* 21:1521.

REITZ, L. K., A. S. O'BRIEN & T. L. DAVIS. 1950. Evaluation of three iron methods using a factorial experiment. *Anal. Chem.* 22:1470.

MORRIS, R. L. 1952. Determination of iron in water in the presence of heavy metals. *Anal. Chem.* 24:1376.

SANDELL, E. B. 1959. *Colorimetric Determination of Traces of Metals* (3rd ed.). Interscience Publishers, New York.

Lead

WICHMANN, H. J. 1939. Isolation and determination of traces of metals—dithizone system. *Ind. Eng. Chem.*, Anal. Ed. 11:66.

BRICKER, L. G. & K. L. PROCTOR. 1945. Application of colorimetry to the analysis of corrosion-resistant steels: Determination of lead. *Ind. Eng. Chem.*, Anal. Ed. 17:511.

SERFASS, E. J. & W. S. LEVINE. 1946. *Monthly Rev. Amer. Electroplaters Soc.* 33:1079.

ASSOCIATION OF OFFICIAL AGRICULTURAI CHEMISTS. 1960. *Official Methods of Analysis* (9th ed.). AOAC, Washington, D. C.

Manganese

WILLARD, H. H. & L. H. GREATHOUSE. 1917. Colorimetric determination of manganese by oxidation with periodate. *J. Amer. Chem. Soc.* 39:2366.

MEHLIG, J. P. 1939. Colorimetric determination of manganese with periodate. *Ind. Eng. Chem.*, Anal. Ed. 11:274.

SERFASS, E. J. & W. S. LEVINE. 1947. Determination of impurities in electroplating solutions. *Monthly Rev. Amer. Electroplaters Soc.* 34:320.

SERFASS, E. J. & R. F. MURACA. 1954. *Procedures for Analyzing Metal Finishing Wastes.* Ohio River Valley Water Sanitation Commission, Cincinnati.

SANDELL, E. B. 1959. *Colorimetric Determination of Traces of Metals* (3rd ed.). Interscience Publishers, New York.

Nickel

BUTTS, P. G., A. R. GAHLER & M. G. MELLON. 1950. Colorimetric determination of metals in sewage and industrial wastes. *Sewage & Ind. Wastes* 22: 1543.

FERGUSON, R. C. & C. V. BANKS. 1951. Spectrophotometric determination of nickel using 1,2-cycloheptanedionedioxime (heptoxime). *Anal. Chem.* 23: 448, 1486.

SERFASS, E. J. & R. F. MURACA. 1954. *Procedures for Analyzing Metal Finishing Wastes.* Ohio River Valley Water Sanitation Commission, Cincinnati.

Zinc

SERFASS, E. J. et al. 1947. *Chemist Analyst* 35:55.

SERFASS, E. J. et al. 1947. Research Report Serial No. 3, American Electroplaters Society, Newark, N. J., page 22.
SERFASS, E. J. et al. 1949. Determination of impurities in electroplating solutions. *Plating* 36:254, 818.
BUTTS, P. G., A. R. GAHLER & M. G. MELLON. 1950. Colorimetric determination of metals in sewage and industrial wastes. *Sewage & Ind. Wastes* 22: 1543.
SERFASS, E. J. & R. F. MURACA. 1954. *Procedures for Analyzing Metal Finishing Wastes.* Ohio River Valley Water Sanitation Commission, Cincinnati.
SANDELL, E. B. 1959. *Colorimetric Determination of Traces of Metals* (3rd ed.). Interscience Publishers, New York.

NICKEL: See Heavy Metals, Sections 211 (II) I and J; and Section 211 (III) B.

212 NITROGEN (AMMONIA)

Ammonia nitrogen may be determined in wastewaters, effluents, polluted waters, sludges and sediments by the methods described in Part 100 for Ammonia Nitrogen, Section 132. However, since polluted samples typically contain higher concentrations of this component than do relatively clean waters, smaller sample volumes, with appropriate dilution, are frequently required. Suitable modifications for various types of samples are indicated below in general terms, but samples of unusual composition will still require the exercise of some judgment on the part of the analyst.

a. Sampling and storage: Because organic nitrogen is progressively ammonified by biologic activity, the determination of ammonia or organic nitrogen is best made on a fresh sample. If the analysis cannot be made immediately after collection, the nitrogen balance may be maintained for not more than 24 hr with an excess of 1,500 mg/l H_2SO_4 (about 0.8 ml conc H_2SO_4 per liter).

b. Selection of method: Direct nesslerization, Ammonia Nitrogen, Section 132B, is best suited for samples which contain little or no color and turbidity and which are free from significant amounts of the interfering substances listed in Section 132.2. It has been applied successfully in samples of domestic sewage when errors of 1–2 mg/l are acceptable. Distillation, followed by nesslerization or titration (Section 132), is more accurate and precise and is less subject to interferences.

1. Procedure

Follow the preliminary distillation step and Method B described in Section 132, with the specified modifications.

a. Slightly polluted water and highly purified effluents (ammonia nitrogen below 1 mg/l): Apply the methods of Section 132 without modification.

b. Heavily polluted water, treated effluents, and fresh domestic sewage of ordinary strength (ammonia nitrogen 1–10 mg/l): Take 100–400 ml samples for distillation, or dilute 5.0 ml sample to 50 ml for direct nesslerization after clarification with zinc sulfate and sodium hydroxide. Use proportionately smaller sample volumes if higher ammonia concentrations are expected.

c. Samples containing abnormal acidity or alkalinity due to industrial wastes or other causes: Neutralize with 1*N* NaOH or 1*N* H_2SO_4 to pH 7.4 before adding the phosphate buffer for the distillation step. Determine the pH value of the solution after distillation. When the postdistillation pH falls outside the pH range 7.2–7.6, discard the sample and repeat the procedure with a greater volume of phosphate buffer. Avoid direct nesslerization of such samples.

d. Sludge or sediment samples: Rapidly weigh to within $\pm 1\%$ a wet sample, containing approximately 1 g dry solids, in a weighing bottle or crucible. Wash the sample into a 500-ml kjeldahl flask with ammonia-free distilled water, dilute to 250 ml, and determine nitrogen by distillation as directed in Section 132, Ammonia Nitrogen, Method B. Add a piece of paraffin to the distillation flask to prevent frothing. Collect 100 ml distillate in standard boric acid and titrate to the mixed-indicator end point with 0.02*N* H_2SO_4. Calculate as mg/l N.

213 NITROGEN (NITRATE)

Nitrate nitrogen may be present in small amounts in fresh domestic wastewater. However, it is seldom found in influents to treatment plants because the nitrate serves as an oxygen source in the biologically unstable wastewater. On the other hand, nitrate is often found in the effluents of biological treatment plants, because it represents the final form of nitrogen from the oxidation of organic nitrogen compounds. Trickling-filter and activated-sludge treatment plant effluents may contain from 0 to 50 mg/l nitrate nitrogen, depending on the total nitrogen content of the influent, the degree of loading, and the temperature of the sewage.

1. Selection of method: Determination of nitrate nitrogen in domestic and industrial wastewaters is much more difficult than in natural waters because of higher concentrations of numerous interfering substances such as chlorides and organic matter. Consequently, several tentative methods are presented, covering a wide range of nitrate-nitrogen concentrations. Each of these methods eliminates certain interferences but is subject to others. Thus the analyst must select the method most suitable for the kinds of samples being tested and the equipment available in his laboratory. The methods are presented approximately in the order of their relative sensitivities; no order of general preference or applicability is intended and none should be inferred. Table 213(1) summarizes the sensitivities of the various methods and the known features of their susceptibility to interferences. It is intended for use as an aid in selecting the method for a specific case.

2. Storage of sample: To prevent any change in the nitrogen balance through biological activity, the nitrate determination should be started promptly after sampling. If storage is necessary,

TABLE 213(1): INTERFERENCES IN VARIOUS METHODS FOR NITRATE

Interference	Zinc Reduction	Cadmium Reduction	Brucine	Phenol-disulfonic Acid	Chromotropic Acid
Minimum concentration †	2	10 ‡	10	10	50
Oxidants and reductants	+	↑	+		
Heavy metals	+				+
Color	+			*	
Chloride				*	
Organic matter		Unknown	+	*	
Iodate and selenium					+
Nitrite					
Sulfides		↓		*	

† NO_3^- as N in micrograms per liter.
‡ Approximate concentration.
+ Interferes.
* Method corrects for or partially eliminates interference.

samples should be kept at a temperature just above the freezing point, with or without preservatives such as H_2SO_4 (0.8 ml conc H_2SO_4/l) or $HgCl_2$ (40 mg Hg^{2+}/l). If acid preservation is employed, the sample should be neutralized to about pH 7 immediately before the analysis is begun.

213 A. Zinc Reduction Method (TENTATIVE)

1. General Discussion

a. Principle: Under controlled conditions, nitrates may be reduced to nitrites with zinc, and the nitrites determined colorimetrically in the usual manner. The amount of zinc and the contact period for reduction are critical. The reaction is temperature-dependent, and all samples must be run at a temperature near that at which the calibration curve is prepared; the lower the temperature, the greater the slope of the calibration curve and the greater the accuracy. Nitrite originally present is destroyed by sodium azide in acid solution. With a 2-cm light path, the color system obeys Beer's law to about 1.4 mg/l N, or 6.2 mg/l NO_3.

b. Interference: Strong oxidizing and reducing substances should be absent. The following ions are known to interfere: antimonous, auric, bismuth, chloroplatinate, ferric, lead, mercurous, metavanadate and silver. Cupric ions may cause low results. Colored ions which alter the color system should be absent.

c. Minimum detectable concentration: Using distilled water for sample preparation, the minimum detectable concentrations in a 50-ml sample are as follows: with a 10-cm light path, 2 μg/l N; with a 5-cm light path, 5 μg/l N; with a 2-cm light path, 10 μg/l N; and with a 1-cm light path, 40 μg/l N.

2. Apparatus

COLORIMETRIC EQUIPMENT—One of the following is required:

a. Spectrophotometer, for use at 520 mμ, providing a light path of 1 cm or longer.

b. Filter photometer, providing a light path of 1 cm or longer and equipped with a green filter having maximum transmittance near 520 mμ.

c. Nessler tubes, matched, 50-ml, tall form; or

d. Test tubes, 25 × 200 mm, Kimble No. 45048 or equivalent, fitted with cork stoppers (No. 4).

e. Filter paper, coarse, 15-cm, which will pass 50 ml of sample in 30 sec or less.

f. Measuring spoon, ¼-teaspoon capacity.

3. Reagents

a. Zinc sulfate solution: Dissolve 100 g $ZnSO_4 \cdot 7H_2O$ in distilled water and dilute to 1 liter.

b. Sodium hydroxide solution: Dissolve 240 g NaOH in 500 ml distilled water and dilute to 1 liter.

c. Stock potassium nitrate solution: Dissolve 721.8 mg anhydrous KNO_3 in distilled water and dilute to 1,000 ml. This solution contains 100 mg/l N.

d. Standard potassium nitrate solution: Dilute 50 ml stock potassium nitrate solution to 500 ml with distilled water; 1.00 ml = 10.0 μg N = 44.3 μg NO_3.

e. Sodium azide solution: Dissolve 1.0 g NaN_3 in distilled water and dilute to 1 liter. (CAUTION: *Sodium azide is toxic—take care to avoid ingestion.*)

f. Hydrochloric acid, 1 + 4.

g. Sulfanilic acid reagent: Dissolve 0.60 g sulfanilic acid in 70 ml hot distilled water, cool, dilute to 100 ml with distilled water, and mix thoroughly.

h. Zinc: Add 1.000 g finely powdered zinc to 200 g sodium chloride, NaCl, in a bottle and mix thoroughly by shaking for several minutes. Each ml (¼ level teaspoon measure) contains 5.9 mg (± 10%) Zn. Shake the mixture vigorously each time before it is used.

i. Naphthylamine hydrochloride reagent: Dissolve 0.60 g 1-naphthylamine hydrochloride in distilled water to which 1.0 ml conc HCl has been added, dilute to 100 ml with distilled water, and mix thoroughly. The reagent becomes discolored and a precipitate may form after 1 week, but it is still usable. Discard when sensitivity or reproducibility is affected. Store in refrigerator. Remove the precipitate by filtration.

j. Sodium acetate solution, 2M: Dissolve 16.4 g $NaC_2H_3O_2$ or 27.2 g $NaC_2H_3O_2 \cdot 3H_2O$ in distilled water and dilute to 100 ml. Filter if the solution is not clear.

4. Procedure

a. Preparation of calibration curve:

1) REDUCTION OF NITRATE STAN-

DARDS—Prepare a suitably spaced series of standards by accurately pipetting calculated volumes of standard potassium nitrate solution into test tubes or nessler tubes. Use tall-form 50-ml nessler tubes for convenience in mixing.

Add 1.0 ml 1 + 4 HCl and 1.0 ml sulfanilic acid reagent, dilute to about 40–45 ml, and mix thoroughly. Shake the Zn–NaCl mixture thoroughly and then add 1 ml (¼ level teaspoon measure) to sample. Invert the sample 10 times, wait 2 min, and invert 10 times more. Then filter rapidly into 50-ml volumetric flasks. Since the time of contact with zinc is critical, filter the sample 7 min after the addition of zinc.

2) COLOR DEVELOPMENT—Add 1.0 ml naphthylamine hydrochloride reagent to the filtrate and mix. Add 1.0 ml sodium acetate solution and mix. Allow 5 min for color development. Dilute to 50 ml.

3) PHOTOMETRIC MEASUREMENT—Measure the reddish purple color in a spectrophotometer at 520 mμ or in a filter photometer with a green filter having maximum transmittance near 520 mμ. Use the following light path lengths for the various nitrate nitrogen ranges:

NO_3-N Range *mg/l*	Light Path *cm*
0.4 –14.0	1
0.2 –14.0	2
0.10–10.0	5
0.02– 3.0	10

Make transmittance readings against a blank to which all reagents [as directed in ¶s 4a(1) and (2)] have been added. Prepare new calibration curves following the preparation of new reagents.

b. Preparation of visual color standards: Prepare as directed in ¶s 4a(1) and (2) above. Before use, clean the nessler tubes thoroughly with dilute HCl to remove the residual zinc remaining after reduction.

c. Treatment of Sample:

1) pH ADJUSTMENT—If the sample has been preserved with acid, neutralize to about pH 7.

2) REMOVAL OF TURBIDITY AND COLOR—If the sample contains suspended solids and color, add 1 ml zinc sulfate solution to 100 ml sample, mix thoroughly, add 0.4–0.5 ml sodium hydroxide solution to obtain a pH of 10.5 as determined with a pH meter and a high-pH glass electrode, and again mix thoroughly. Allow the treated sample to stand a few minutes, whereupon a heavy precipitate should fall, leaving the supernate clear and colorless. Clarify by centrifuging or filtering. Discard the first few ml of filtrate. Adjust the filtrate to about pH 7.

3) REMOVAL OF NITRITE INTERFERENCE—Add 1.0 ml sodium azide solution to a 50.0-ml sample in a 150-ml beaker. Add 1.0 ml 1 + 4 HCl, and concentrate by gentle boiling, without spattering, to about 40 ml. Cool to room temperature and transfer to a test tube or nessler tube. Rinse the beaker with 1–2 ml distilled water and add rinsings to the sample.

4) COLOR DEVELOPMENT AND MEASUREMENT—Complete the determination as directed in ¶s 4a(1)–(3), omitting the addition of HCl. Compare the sample with a series of visual color standards prepared according to ¶ 4b, or make transmittance readings against a sample blank to which all reagents except sulfanilic acid have been added. Check at least one point on the calibration curve with a nitrate standard of a

concentration similar to that of the sample.

5. Calculation

$$\text{mg/l nitrate N} = \frac{\text{mg nitrate N} \times 1{,}000}{\text{ml sample}}$$

$$\text{mg/l } NO_3 = \text{mg/l nitrate N} \times 4.43$$

6. Precision and Accuracy

On undiluted samples, and in the absence of interference, precision is estimated to be ± 20 μg/l N up to 1.4 mg/l, and accuracy is estimated to be 20 μg/l N in the range from 0.04 to 1.4 mg/l as nitrogen with a 2-cm light path.

213 B. Cadmium Reduction Method (TENTATIVE)

1. General Discussion

Nitrate is reduced almost quantitatively to nitrite when a sample is run through a column containing amalgamated cadmium filings. The nitrite thus produced is determined by diazotizing with sulfanilamide and coupling with N-(1-naphthyl)-ethylenediamine to form a highly colored azo dye which is measured colorimetrically. A correction may be made for any nitrite initially present in the sample.

2. Apparatus

a. Reduction columns (see Figure 35), constructed from three pieces of glass tubing joined end to end: 10 cm of 5-cm I.D. tubing is joined to 30 cm of tubing, 10-mm I.D., which in turn is joined to 35 cm of 2-mm I.D. tubing. The last tube is bent just below the joint into a U, so that it runs up parallel to the 10-mm diameter tube; its upper end is bent over to form an inverted U-siphon. This last bend should be just level with the top of the 10-mm diameter tube. Using this arrangement, liquid placed in the top reservoir should flow out of the system and stop when the level of the liquid just covers the metal filings (see below). Place a mark on the upper wide portion of the column to indicate the height of an additional 80 ml of liquid.

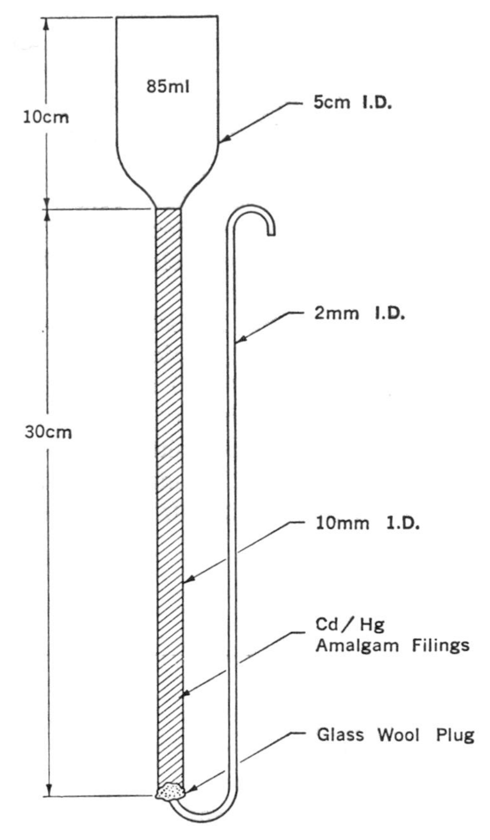

Figure 35. Reduction column.

b. Colorimetric equipment: One of the following is required—

1) SPECTROPHOTOMETER, for use at 543 mμ, providing a light path of 1 cm or longer.

2) FILTER PHOTOMETER, providing a light path of 1 cm or longer and equipped with a yellow-green filter having maximum transmittance near 543 mμ.

3. Reagents

a. Distilled water: Distilled water should be of the highest purity, preferably prepared by mixed-bed ion-exchange deionization of ordinary distilled water.

b. Ammonium chloride solution, conc: Dissolve 100 g NH_4Cl in 500 ml distilled water and store in a glass or plastic bottle.

c. Dilute ammonium chloride solution: Dilute 50 ml conc ammonium chloride solution to 2,000 ml with distilled water. Store in a glass or plastic bottle.

d. Amalgamated cadmium filings: File sticks of pure cadmium metal (reagent grade) with a coarse metal hand file (about second cut) and collect the fraction which passes a sieve with 2-mm openings and is retained on a sieve with 0.5-mm openings. Stir about 300 g of filings with 300 ml mercuric chloride solution (1 g $HgCl_2$/100 ml) for 3 min. (This amount suffices for six reduction columns.) Allow the metal particles to settle and decant off the liquid. Wash the amalgamated filings several times with distilled water, then briefly in 1 + 99 nitric acid. Wash several times with 1 + 99 HCl. Wash copiously with distilled water until no nitrite can be detected in the supernatant fluid. Store the filings in the dark under dilute ammonium chloride solution.

e. Sulfanilamide reagent: Dissolve 5 g sulfanilamide in a mixture of 50 ml conc HCl (sp gr 1.18) and about 300 ml distilled water. Dilute to 500 ml with distilled water. The solution is stable for many months.

f. N-(1-naphthyl)-ethylenediamine dihydrochloride solution: Dissolve 500 mg dihydrochloride in 500 ml distilled water. Store the solution in a dark bottle. Renew the solution once a month, or immediately when it develops a strong brown coloration.

g. Stock nitrate solution: See Zinc Reduction Method, Section 213A.3c preceding.

h. Standard nitrate solution: Dilute 4.00 ml stock standard nitrate to 2,000 ml with distilled water and use immediately; 1.0 ml = 0.20 μg NO_3-N.

4. Procedure

a. Preparation of reduction column: Pack a plug of glass wool in the bottom of a reduction column and fill the column with distilled water. Pour in sufficient amalgamated cadmium filings to produce a column 30 cm in length. Use the column size specified, because columns of lesser diameter and length give erratic results and show rapid deterioration. Wash the column thoroughly with dilute ammonium chloride solution. Use a flow rate no greater than 8 ml per min. If the rate is too fast, slow it by constricting the end of the outlet siphon or by packing more glass wool at the base of the column. Flow rates less than 5 ml per min unnecessarily increase the time for an analysis and may give low results. When not in use, cover the metal in the column with dilute ammonium chloride solution.

b. Treatment of sample:

1) Turbidity removal—If turbidity or suspended solids are present, clarify the sample by membrane filtration.

2) pH adjustment—If the pH of the sample is above 9, adjust to between 8 and 9, using a pH meter and dilute HCl.

3) Reduction of nitrate—Place 80 to 90 ml sample in a 125-ml erlenmeyer flask and add 2.0 ml conc ammonium chloride solution. Mix, and pour the sample from the flask onto the column until the marked level in the top part of the column is reached. Place a 50-ml graduated cylinder under the outlet to collect the effluent and discard any sample left in the erlenmeyer flask. Shake the flask as dry as possible and retain it for collecting the main portion of the effluent.

Allow between 25 and 30 ml effluent to collect in the cylinder and then replace it with the original erlenmeyer flask which contained the sample. Discard the contents of the cylinder. (The passage of 25–30 ml of solution removes the ammonium chloride solution or a previous sample from the voids in the reduction column. The volume flushed through is not critical provided that it exceeds 25 ml, but sufficient sample should be left in the column so that 50 ml more can be reduced. The flushing effluent should therefore not exceed about 30 ml. A maximum of about eight columns can be handled conveniently at one time. The operator should experiment to find a suitable short delay between adding the samples to successive columns so that there will be time to reject the flushing liquid from one column and replace the cylinder by the erlenmeyer flask before too much flushing liquid has escaped from the next column in line. In the case where a sample having a very low concentration of nitrate is followed by a sample with a high nitrate concentration, or vice versa, a full 30-ml volume should be used to flush the column.)

Allow the remainder of the sample to collect in the flask. When the flow of sample from the column has ceased, pour exactly 50 ml from the flask into the 50-ml measuring cylinder. Drain and discard the remaining effluent from the erlenmeyer flask. Shake the flask as dry as possible and then pour back into it the 50 ml of reduced sample from the measuring cylinder.

There is no need to wash columns between samples, but if columns are not to be reused for several hours or longer, pour 50 ml dilute ammonium chloride solution onto the top and allow it to pass through the system. Store the cadmium filings in this ammonium chloride solution and never allow them to go dry. If there are indications that the columns are becoming inactivated, as shown by a significant decrease in the color intensity produced per μg NO_3-N in the standards, empty the columns, wash the cadmium filings briefly with 1 + 99 HNO_3, and copiously, with distilled water, air-dry at about 60 C, resieve and reamalgamate. Well-prepared columns of the correct size should be stable for many weeks before such reactivation becomes necessary.

4) Color development and measurement—As soon as possible, and in any case no longer than 15 min after reduction, add to the sample 1.0 ml sulfanilamide solution from an automatic pipet. Allow the reagent to react for a period longer than 2 min but not exceeding 8 min. Add 1.0 ml 1-naphthyl-ethylenediamine solution and mix immediately. Between 10 min and 2

hr afterward, measure the absorbance of the solution against a distilled-water reagent blank, using a wavelength of 543 mμ. As a guide, use the following recommended light paths for the indicated NO_3-N concentration ranges:

Light Path Length *(cm)*	NO_3-N Concentration *μg/l*
1	2–20
5	2–6
10	less than 2

c. Standards: Use the standards both to obtain a calibration curve and to check the efficiency of the reduction columns.

Add about 110 ml dilute standard nitrate solution to clean dry 125-ml erlenmeyer flasks, and carry out the determination exactly as described for the samples, except that the volume of flushing liquid collected from each column should be 50 ml. Measure the absorbance in a cell which provides a suitable light path. Perform the determination initially in triplicate for each column and correct the mean of the three absorbances thus obtained by the absorbance of a distilled water reagent blank. Subsequently check each column once a day.

1) DETERMINATION OF F FACTOR—Determine the factor F relating absorbance in a 1-cm cell to NO_3-N concentration (mg/l) from the following equation:

$$F = \frac{0.2}{A}$$

where A is the absorbance at 543 mμ.

Reactivate the column when the value of F consistently increases beyond 0.33.

5. Calculation

$$\text{mg } NO_3\text{-N/l} = (A_s - A_b) \times \frac{F}{L} - C$$

$$\text{mg } NO_3\text{/l} = \text{mg } NO_3\text{-N/l} \times 4.43$$

where A_s = absorbance of sample
A_b = absorbance of reagent blank
F is defined in ¶ 4c(1) above.
L = light path length, cm
C = concentration of NO_2-N (separately determined).

6. Precision and Accuracy

See Section 213 C.6 following.

213 C. Brucine Method (TENTATIVE)

1. General Discussion

The reaction between nitrate and brucine produces a yellow color which can be used for the colorimetric estimation of nitrate. The intensity of the color is measured at 410 mμ. The reaction rate between brucine and nitrate ion is affected significantly by the amount of heat generated during the test. Thus the procedure seeks heat control by reagent addition sequence and incubation of the reaction mixture for a precise interval of time at a known temperature. Acid concentration and reaction time have been selected to yield optimum development and stability of color. The method works well in waters of salinities varying from that of fresh water to that of sea water. The method is recommended for the approximate range of 0.1–2 mg NO_3-N/l.

a. Interferences: All strong oxidizing or reducing agents interfere. The presence of oxidizing agents may be determined by the addition of orthotolidine reagent, as in the measurement of residual chlorine. The interference by residual chlorine may be eliminated by the addition of sodium arsenite, provided that the residual chlorine does not exceed 5 mg/l. A slight excess of sodium arsenite will not affect the determination. Ferrous and ferric iron and quadrivalent manganese give slight positive interferences, but in concentrations less than 1 mg/l these are negligible. The interference due to nitrite up to 0.5 mg NO_2-N/l is eliminated by the use of sulfanilic acid. Chloride interference is masked by the addition of excess NaCl.

High concentrations of organic matter such as in undiluted raw wastewater will usually interfere.

2. Apparatus

a. Colorimetric equipment: One of the following is required—

1) SPECTROPHOTOMETER, for use at 410 mμ providing a light path of 1 in.

2) FILTER PHOTOMETER, providing a light path of 1 in. and equipped with a violet filter having maximum transmittance between 400 and 425 mμ.

b. Safety pipet.

c. Wire racks, to hold tubes in which samples are to be incubated (Van Waters and Rogers No. 60935 or equivalent).

d. Stirred boiling water bath, with heating facility sufficient to maintain a temperature of at least 95 C when cooled samples are introduced.

e. Reaction tubes: Hard-glass test tubes, of approximate dimensions 2.5 × 15 cm, in which reaction is performed. [The 1-in. colorimeter tubes (Van Waters and Rogers No. 22366) used in conjunction with the Bausch & Lomb Spectronic 20 or equivalent are convenient, since their use avoids the necessity for a transfer, following reaction, to determine transmittance.]

3. Reagents

a. Stock nitrate solution: Dissolve 721.8 mg anhydrous potassium nitrate, KNO_3, and dilute to 1,000 ml with distilled water. This solution contains 100 mg/l N.

b. Standard nitrate solution: Dilute 10.00 ml stock nitrate solution to 1,000 ml with distilled water; 1.00 ml = 1.00 μg N. Prepare immediately prior to using.

c. Sodium arsenite solution: Dissolve 5.0 g $NaAsO_2$ and dilute to 1 liter with distilled water. (CAUTION: *Toxic—take care to avoid ingestion.*)

d. Brucine-sulfanilic acid solution: Dissolve 1 g brucine sulfate and 0.1 g sulfanilic acid in approximately 70 ml hot distilled water. Add 3 ml conc HCl, cool, and make up to 100 ml. This solution is stable for several months. The pink color that develops slowly does not affect its usefulness. (CAUTION: *Brucine is toxic—take care to avoid ingestion.*)

e. Sulfuric acid solution: Carefully add 500 ml conc H_2SO_4 to 125 ml distilled water. Cool to room temperature before using and keep tightly stoppered to prevent absorption of atmospheric moisture.

f. Sodium chloride solution: Dissolve 300 g NaCl and dilute to 1,000 ml with distilled water.

4. Procedure

a. Preparation of nitrate standards: Prepare nitrate standards in the range 0.1–1 mg/l N by diluting 1.00, 2.00, 4.00, 7.00 and 10.0 ml standard nitrate solution to 10.0 ml with distilled water.

b. Pretreatment of sample: If the sample contains residual chlorine, remove by adding 1 drop (0.05 ml) sodium arsenite solution for each 0.10 mg Cl and mix. Add 1 drop in excess to a 50-ml portion.

c. Color development: Set up the required number of reaction tubes in the wire rack, spacing them so that each tube is surrounded by empty spaces. Include a reaction tube for a reagent blank and reaction tubes for as many standards as desired. To each tube add 10.0 ml sample or an aliquot diluted to 10 ml so that the sample volume taken for analysis contains between 0.1 and 8 μg NO_3-N. Place the rack in a cool water bath and add 2 ml NaCl solution. Mix thoroughly, swirling by hand, and add 10 ml H_2SO_4 solution. In no case use a "Vortex" mixer, since this type of mixing produces inconsistent results in the analysis. Mix again thoroughly by swirling and allow to cool. At this point, if any turbidity or color is present or if optically unmatched colorimeter tubes are being used as reaction tubes, dry the tubes and read a "sample blank" value against the reagent blank tube at 410 mμ. Replace the rack of tubes in the cool water bath and add 0.5 ml brucine-sulfanilic acid reagent. Swirl the tubes to mix thoroughly and then place the rack of tubes in a well-stirred boiling water bath that maintains a temperature of not less than 95 C. After exactly 20 min, remove the samples and immerse them in a cold water bath. When thermal equilibrium is reached (at approximately room temperature), dry off the tubes with tissue and read the standards and samples against the reagent blank at 410 mμ in the spectrophotometer. Check the technic and the constancy of reaction conditions by running at least two standards with each batch of samples.

To obtain a standard curve, subtract the "sample blanks" from the final absorbance readings and plot the resultant absorbance against mg NO_3-N/l. Correct the absorbance readings of the samples by subtracting their "sample blank" values from their final absorbance values. Read the concentrations of NO_3-N directly from the standard curve.

5. Calculation

$$\text{mg/l nitrate N} = \frac{\mu\text{g } NO_3\text{-N}}{\text{ml sample}}$$

$$\text{mg/l } NO_3 = \text{mg/l nitrate N} \times 4.43$$

6. Precision and Accuracy

Five synthetic unknown samples containing nitrate and other constituents dissolved in distilled water were analyzed by the brucine and chromotropic acid methods. Three of the samples were also determined by the cadmium reduction method. The results of the participating laboratories are summarized in Table 213(2).

Sample 1 contained the following additional constituents: 400 mg/l chloride, 200 μg/l ammonia nitrogen, 230 μg/l organic phosphorus added in the form of adenylic acid, 7.00 mg/l orthophosphate phosphorus, and 3.00 mg/l polyphosphate phosphorus added as sodium hexametaphosphate.

TABLE 213(2): PRECISION AND ACCURACY DATA FOR NITRATE METHODS

Method	Nitrate-Nitrogen Concentration µg/l	No. of Laboratories	Relative Standard Deviation %	Relative Error %
B. Cadmium reduction	50	11	96.4	47.3
	500	11	25.6	6.4
	5,000	10	9.2	1.0
C. Brucine	50	50	66.7	7.6
	500	50	14.4	0.6
	1,000 *	17	5.5	6.0
	1,000 †	17	7.9	0
	5,000	50	15.4	4.5
E. Chromotropic acid	50	32	61.4	12.5
	500	34	16.4	3.5
	1,000 *	5	8.1	3.0
	1,000 †	5	1.2	0
	5,000	36	10.9	2.9

* Synthetic sample 4.
† Synthetic sample 5.

Sample 2 contained the following additional components: 400 mg/l chloride, 1.50 mg/l ammonia nitrogen, 30 µg/l organic phosphorus added in the form of adenylic acid, 100 µg/l orthophosphate phosphorus, and 80 µg/l polyphosphate phosphorus added as sodium hexametaphosphate.

Sample 3 contained the following additional constituents: 400 mg/l chloride, 800 µg/l ammonia nitrogen, 90 µg/l organic phosphorus added in the form of adenylic acid, 600 µg/l orthophosphate phosphorus, and 300 µg/l polyphosphate phosphorus added as sodium hexametaphosphate.

Sample 4 contained the following additional constituents: 10 mg/l chloride, 200 µg/l ammonia nitrogen, 1.5 mg/l organic nitrogen, 10.0 mg/l phosphate, and 5.0 mg/l silica.

Sample 5 contained the following additional constituents: 200 mg/l chloride, 800 µg/l ammonia nitrogen, 800 µg/l organic nitrogen, 5.0 mg/l phosphate, and 15.0 mg/l silica.

213 D. *Phenoldisulfonic Acid Method (TENTATIVE)*

1. General Discussion

The principles of this method are discussed in Part 100, Nitrate Nitrogen, Section 133A.

Domestic and industrial wastewaters contain more and higher concentrations of interfering substances than potable water supplies. The analyst should be aware of these interferences and know how to eliminate them. Chloride interferes at all concentrations and must be eliminated entirely. Silver sulfate is used to remove the chloride interference. Nitrite interferes in proportion to its concentration. Consequently, nitrite nitrogen must be determined and the amount subtracted from the total nitrate nitrogen concentration. Organic matter interferes if it causes turbidity or color that absorbs at 410 mμ or 480 mμ. Organic matter is eliminated by coagulation with aluminum hydroxide, and color by adsorption with activated carbon.

2. Apparatus

Same as that for Section 133A.2 (Phenoldisulfonic Acid Method).

3. Reagents

All the reagents in Section 133A.3 are required, and in addition:

a. Activated carbon for color removal: Any grade of highly adsorptive carbon will suffice. However, it must be checked for nitrate adsorption as follows: Prepare a nitrate standard containing 10 μg nitrate nitrogen per 100 ml of solution. To 50 ml of this standard, add 1 g activated carbon and stir. Filter and compare the phenoldisulfonic acid color development with that of the untreated portion of the standard. If there is no reduction in nitrate concentration, the activated carbon is ready for use.

4. Procedure

a. Removal of interferences from wastewater samples:

1) COLOR AND TURBIDITY—To 50 ml sample, add 0.5 g activated carbon and 1 ml $Al(OH)_3$ cream (floc), mix well, allow to stand for a few minutes, filter, and discard the first portion of the filtrate.

2) CHLORIDE AND NITRITE—Remove or convert as directed in Section 133A.4b and c.

b. Development of yellow color: Proceed as directed in Section 133A.4d.

5. Calculation

Same as for Section 133A.5.

6. Precision and Accuracy

See Part 100, Nitrate Nitrogen, Section 133A.6.

213 E. Chromotropic Acid Method (TENTATIVE)

1. General Discussion

a. Principle: Two moles of nitrate react with one mole of chromotropic acid to form a yellow reaction product exhibiting maximum absorbance at 410 mμ. The maximum color develops within 10 min and is stable for 24 hr. The cooling bath dissipates sufficient heat to prevent boiling of the solutions; for this reason, the temperature of the cooling bath may vary from 10 to 20 C without critically affecting the results. Residual chlorine, certain oxidants, and nitrite also yield yellow colors with chromotropic acid. However, the addition of sulfite completely eliminates the interference from residual chlorine and oxidizing agents, while urea converts nitrite to nitrogen gas. Antimony effectively masks up to 2,000 mg/l chloride, a tolerance level which can be raised to 4,000 mg/l by doubling the strength of the specified antimony reagent.

b. Interferences: The yellow color of the chloroferrate (III) complex in amounts up to 40 mg/l ferric ion is completely discharged by the addition of antimony. Barium, lead, strontium, iodide, iodate, selenite and selenate ions are incompatible with the system and form precipitates. However, their occurrence in significant amounts is unlikely in most samples. Concentrations of chromic ion exceeding 20 mg/l contribute interfering color.

c. Minimum detectable concentration: 50 $\mu g/l$ NO_3-N.

2. Apparatus

COLORIMETRIC EQUIPMENT—One of the following is required:

a. Spectrophotometer, for use at 410 mμ, providing a light path of 1 cm or longer.

b. Filter photometer, providing a light path of 1 cm or longer and equipped with a violet filter having maximum transmittance near 410 mμ.

3. Reagents

a. Redistilled water: Redistill single-distilled water from an all-pyrex still. Prepare all aqueous solutions from this double-distilled water.

b. Stock nitrate solution: See Method A, ¶ 3c above.

c. Standard nitrate solution: See Method A, ¶ 3d above.

d. Sulfite-urea reagent: Dissolve 5 g urea and 4 g anhydrous sodium sulfite, Na_2SO_3, in redistilled water and dilute to 100 ml.

e. Antimony reagent: Heat 500 mg antimony metal in 80 ml conc H_2SO_4 until all the metal has dissolved. Cool and cautiously add to 20 ml iced redistilled water. If crystals separate upon standing overnight, redissolve them by heating.

f. Chromotropic acid reagent: Purify the chromotropic acid (4,5-dihydroxy-2,7-naphthalene disulfonic acid) in the following manner. Boil 125 ml distilled water in a beaker and gradually add 15 g 4,5-dihydroxy-2,7-naphthalene disulfonic acid disodium salt, with constant stirring. To the solution add 5 g activated decolorizing charcoal. Boil the mixture for about 10 min. Add distilled water to make up the loss due to evaporation. Filter the hot solution through cotton wool. Add 5 g activated charcoal to the filtrate and boil for 10 more min. Filter, first through cotton wool and then through a filter paper to remove the charcoal completely. Cool the solution and slowly add 10 ml nitrate-free conc H_2SO_4. Boil the solution until about 100 ml are left in the beaker. Allow the solution to stand overnight. Transfer the crystals of chromotropic acid to a Buchner funnel and wash thoroughly with 95% alcohol until the crystals are white. Dry the crystals at 80 C.

Dissolve 100 mg purified chromotropic acid in 100 ml conc H_2SO_4 and store in a brown bottle. Prepare every two weeks. A colorless reagent solution signifies the absence of nitrate contamination from the sulfuric acid.

g. Sulfuric acid, conc, nitrate-free.

4. Procedure

a. Preparation of nitrate standards: Prepare nitrate standards in the range 0.10–5 mg/l N by diluting 0, 1.0, 5.0, 15, 25, 35 and 50 ml standard nitrate solution to 100 ml with redistilled water.

b. Color development: If appreciable amounts of suspended matter are present in the sample, remove by centrifugation or filtration. Pipet 2.5-ml portions of the standards, clear samples, and a blank consisting of redistilled water into dry 10-ml volumetric flasks. Use dilutions of the standards and samples containing nitrate nitrogen concentrations in the range 0.05–5 mg/l (0.125 to 12.5 μg in 2.5 ml). To each flask add 1 drop (0.05 ml) sulfite-urea reagent. Place the flasks in a tray of cold water (10–20 C) and add 2 ml antimony reagent. Swirl flasks during the addition of each reagent. After the mixtures have stood in the bath for about 4 min, add 1 ml chromotropic acid reagent, swirl flasks again, and then allow to stand in the cooling bath for 3 min more. Add conc sulfuric acid to bring the volume to the 10-ml mark. Stopper the flasks, and mix the contents by inverting each flask four times. Allow the solutions to stand for 45 min at room temperature and again adjust the volume to the 10-ml mark with conc sulfuric acid. Perform the final mixing very gently to avoid introducing gas bubbles. Read the absorbance at 410 mμ 15 min or more after the last adjustment of volume. In the reference cell of the spectrophotometer use redistilled water. Rinse the sample cell with the sample solution and then fill carefully, to avoid trapping bubbles, by holding the cell in a slanting position and pouring the solution very slowly down the side of the cell.

5. Calculation

$$\text{mg/l nitrate N} = \frac{\mu\text{g nitrate N}}{\text{ml sample}}$$

$$\text{mg/l } NO_3 = \text{mg/l nitrate N} \times 4.43$$

6. Precision and Accuracy

See Section 213C.6 preceding.

213 F. Bibliography

Zinc Reduction Method

EDWARDS, G. P. et al. 1962. Determination of nitrates in waste water effluents and water. *JWPCF* 34:1112.

Cadmium Reduction Method

STRICKLAND, J. D. H. & T. R. PARSONS. 1965. *A Manual of Sea Water Analysis* (2nd ed.). Fisheries Res. Board Canada (Ottawa) Bull. No. 125, pp. 73–77.

Brucine and Phenoldisulfonic Acid Methods

See Section 133 C, Bibliography for Nitrogen (Nitrate), preceding, and the following additional recommended source:

JENKINS, D. & L. L. MEDSKER. 1964. A brucine method for the determination of nitrate in ocean, estuarine and fresh waters. *Anal. Chem.* 36:610.

Chromotropic Acid Method

WEST, P. W. & T. P. RAMACHANDRAN. 1966. Spectrophotometric determination of nitrate using chromotropic acid. *Anal. Chim. Acta* 35:317.

214 NITROGEN (NITRITE)

Nitrite may be determined in wastewaters, effluents and polluted waters by the method described in Part 100, Nitrite Nitrogen, Section 134. Although the accuracy of the method in samples of this kind has not been determined, the precision in treated sewage effluents has been found comparable with that obtained in water samples.

215 NITROGEN (ORGANIC)

1. General Discussion

Organic nitrogen may be determined by digestion of the sample after removal of free ammonia, with subsequent distillation and titration using standard acid, or by nesslerization, as described in Part 100, Organic Nitrogen, Section 135.

a. Interference: In the presence of large quantities of nitrogen-free organic matter, it is necessary to allow an additional 50 ml of sulfuric acid–mercuric sulfate-potassium sulfate solution for each gram of solid material in the sample.

b. Storage: Because organic nitrogen in unsterilized samples is continually ammonified, the determination must be made on a freshly collected sample. When the analysis cannot be made at once, the sample must be preserved with sufficient sulfuric acid to obtain a concentration of 1,500 mg/l H_2SO_4 or more.

2. Apparatus

a. Digestion apparatus, provided with a suction takeoff to remove water vapor and sulfur trioxide fumes.

b. Distillation apparatus, kjeldahl.

c. Colorimetric equipment—One of the following is required if nesslerization is used:

1) SPECTROPHOTOMETER, for use at 400 to 425 mμ, providing a light path of 1 cm or longer.

2) FILTER PHOTOMETER, providing a light path of 1 cm or longer and equipped with a violet filter having maximum transmittance at 400 to 425 mμ.

3) NESSLER TUBES, matched, 50-ml, tall form.

3. Reagents

All the reagents listed in Part 100, Ammonia Nitrogen, Sections 132A.3 and 132B.3, are required, plus those listed in Part 100, Organic Nitrogen, Section 135.3.

4. Procedure

See Part 100, Organic Nitrogen, Section 135.4.

5. Calculation

See Part 100, Organic Nitrogen, Section 135.5.

6. Precision and Accuracy

For the range 1–5 mg/l organic

nitrogen, 97.5–98.6% was recovered by the titration method, with a precision of ± 0.03 mg/l. In the range 5–50 mg/l, 98.5–99.5% recovery was obtained, with a precision of ± 0.13 mg/l ($n = 1; 4 \times 10$).

A synthetic unknown sample containing 1,500 μg/l organic nitrogen was analyzed by nesslerization in 26 laboratories, with a standard deviation of ± 586 μg/l. At a concentration of 200 μg/l organic nitrogen, the same laboratories reported a standard deviation of ± 290 μg/l. The precision and accuracy of nesslerization for samples containing more than 1.5 mg/l organic nitrogen was not determined.

7. Bibliography

KJELDAHL, J. 1883. A new method for the determination of nitrogen in organic matter. *Z. Anal. Chem.* 22:366.

PHELPS, E. B. 1905. The determination of organic nitrogen in sewage by the Kjeldahl process. *J. Infect. Dis.* Suppl. 1:225.

MEEKER, E. W. & E. C. WAGNER. 1933. Titration of ammonia in the presence of boric acid. *Ind. Eng. Chem.*, Anal. Ed. 5:396.

BRECHER, C. 1936 and 1937. A new method for titrating ammonia in the micro-Kjeldahl determination. *Wien. Klin. Wchschr.* 49:1228; *Chem. Abstracts* 31:3818.

WAGNER, E. C. 1940. Titration of ammonia in the presence of boric acid. *Ind. Eng. Chem.*, Anal. Ed. 12:771.

MACKENZIE, H. A. & N. S. WALLACE. 1954. The Kjeldahl determination of nitrogen: A critical study of digestion conditions. *Austral. J. Chem.* 7:55.

MORGAN, G. B., J. B. LACKEY & F. W. GILCREAS. 1957. Quantitative determination of organic nitrogen in water, sewage, and industrial wastes. *Anal. Chem.* 11:833.

216 NITROGEN (TOTAL KJELDAHL)

Total kjeldahl nitrogen includes ammonia and organic nitrogen but does not include nitrite and nitrate nitrogen.

1. Procedure

a. Liquid samples: Follow the procedure described for organic nitrogen, except for the omission of the ammonia removal step (Section 135.4b). Begin with ¶ 4c, using a measured volume of 100 ml or more of sample in an 800-ml kjeldahl flask.

b. Sludge and sediment samples: Dry a sample of sludge or mud in a drying oven at 103 C, grind thoroughly to a fine powder, and dry again for 30 min at 103 C.

Weigh accurately 1.0 g dried sludge or 1.0–5.0 g dried mud into a 500-ml kjeldahl flask. Add 100 ml digestion reagent (Organic Nitrogen, Section 135.3a) and mix thoroughly. Digest slowly until frothing ceases, and for 30 min after the liquid becomes clear.

Cool, dilute to 350 ml with ammonia-free distilled water, and proceed as directed in Section 135.4d, distilling into boric acid solution. Complete the determination according to Section 135.4e(2).

Determinations by this method do

not give an accurate measure of the total nitrogen of the wet sludge. At best it is kjeldahl nitrogen minus ammonium bicarbonate or carbonate lost on drying. A more rational method for determining the total kjeldahl nitrogen in wet sludge is to determine the ammonia nitrogen and organic nitrogen as above and add the results. The results are expressed as percent N.

217 ODOR

The method for the determination of threshold odor described in this section for wastewaters differs from that presented in Section 136 for unpolluted water principally in the manner of sample presentation to the testers, and temperature. If the precautions and procedures described in either section are followed carefully, the threshold odor number obtained at the same temperature for a given sample will be equivalent. The method of reporting threshold odor results in this section is particularly applicable to more concentrated industrial wastes. The three-flask procedure described in this section has also been used extensively for determination of odor threshold of water of potable quality.

Taste tests are not generally needed and with few exceptions are not recommended for wastewaters or untreated effluents. Odor tests are important in measuring the intensity and nature of polluting sources. A combination of odor testing and instrumental analyses can be used to trace odor sources. In most cases it is necessary to make measurements of the odor in both the wastewater discharges and the receiving body if the actual relationship and effect are to be determined.

Odor effects resulting from a mixture of several chemicals are extremely complex. The blend of several odorants may produce an odor much greater in intensity than might be expected from the individual odors. There may also be the opposite effect—for example, the resulting odor may be of lesser intensity than expected. These complex effects have been demonstrated in laboratory and field studies.[1-3]

217 A. Qualitative Description

The odor of a sample may be recorded in any way that seems most appropriate. There is no suitable means of describing odor characteristics precisely. Terms formerly recommended in the 12th Edition of this manual are still used by some laboratories. For sludge and sediment samples, usually the qualitative description alone is used, with no attempt to measure intensity beyond the use of such terms as "strong," "faint," etc.

217 B. Odor Intensity Index (TENTATIVE) *

1. General Discussion

a. Principle: See Part 100, Odor, Section 136.1a.

b. Sampling and storage: See Section 136.1d. Even though all the recommended precautions are observed, storage may lead to changes in odor intensity or character through biological, chemical or physical reactions.

c. Dechlorination: Some wastewaters which have been chlorinated may require odor testing as part of a control program. In such cases it often is advisable to determine odor of the chlorinated waste and also that of dechlorinated samples to determine the effect of chloro-organic derivatives. Dechlorinate by using sodium arsenite or sodium thiosulfate, as described in Ammonia Nitrogen, Section 132A.3c(2) and (4). Add the dechlorinating agent in exact stoichiometric proportion to the residual chlorine content of the sample. Check a blank to which a similar amount of dechlorinating agent has been added to determine whether any odor has been imparted. Such odor usually disappears upon standing if excess reagent has not been added.

d. Temperature: The threshold odor results may vary as a function of temperature. The extent of this variation will depend on the chemical and physical characteristics of the odorous components. A temperature of 40 C, which approximates body temperature, is recommended for this test. Hot tests at 60 C have been used for testing drinking waters of very low threshold intensity, but this requires greater care. Many odor components readily volatilize at this temperature and the odor is frequently lost once the odor tester removes the stopper. In such cases the tester frequently cannot confirm initial response upon further inhalation. If temperatures other than 40 C are used, the results should bear this notation. It is good practice to report the sampling temperature also.

2. Apparatus

See Part 100, Odor, Section 136.2.

3. Odor-Free Water

Prepare as directed in Section 136.3.

4. Procedure

a. Precautions: Carefully observe all precautions described in Section 136.-4a.

b. Characterization: Warm a 200-ml sample in a 500-ml glass-stoppered erlenmeyer flask to 40 C in a water bath and check by normal inhalation for odor characterization. Since many wastewaters of complex composition exhibit odors other than the sample odor if diluted, and when such intermediate characterizations are desired, prepare dilutions according to ¶ 4c(1) below. Record the odor characteristic and the dilutions at which a distinct difference is noted.

c. Threshold measurement: Report the threshold odor for wastewaters and effluents as the odor intensity index †

* This method of testing odor intensity is identical to ASTM D1292.

† Threshold odor number (TON) defines the greatest dilution of the sample with odor-free water to yield the least definitely perceptible odor. These terms are related as follows:

$$TO = 2^{OII}$$

OII is used with wastewaters because of the complexity of the TON values if odorant concentration is high.

TABLE 217(1). DILUTION OF SAMPLE AND REPORTING OF RESULTS

Dilution	Volume Transferred to Odor Flask *ml* [a]	Threshold Odor Number (Dilution Factor)	Odor Intensity Index, OII
Original sample	200	1	0
	100	2	1
	50	4	2
	25	8	3
	12.5	16	4
Dilution A (25 ml of original sample diluted to 200 ml)	50	32	5
	25	64	6
	12.5	128	7
Dilution B (25 ml of dilution A diluted to 200 ml)	50	256	8
	25	512	9
	12.5	1,024	10
Dilution C (25 ml of dilution B diluted to 200 ml)	50	2,050	11
	25	4,100	12
	12.5	8,200	13
Dilution D (25 ml of dilution C diluted to 200 ml)	50	16,400	14
	25	32,800	15
	12.5	65,500	16
Dilution E (25 ml of dilution D diluted to 200 ml)	50	131,000	17
	25	262,000	18
	12.5	534,000	19
	6.25	1,050,000	20

[a] Volume in odor flask made up to 200 ml with odor-free water.

(OII), which is the number of times the original sample must be diluted in half with odor-free water for the odor to be just discernible [Table 217(1)].

1) PRELIMINARY THRESHOLD ODOR TEST—In order to minimize the number of dilutions necessary during the threshold odor test, first estimate the odor intensity by a preliminary test. Carefully transfer a sample aliquot of 25 ml by pipet to 175 ml odor-free water in a 500-ml erlenmeyer flask. Do not allow sample solution to touch the neck of the flask. Stopper flask and heat to 40 C in a water bath. Swirl or shake the flask vigorously, remove the cover, and test for the presence of odor, using normal inhalation. If no odor is found, prepare lower dilutions until odor is detected. A range of such dilutions is generally made at the start to expedite testing, but always conduct the tests from the highest dilution toward the lower dilutions. If odor is detected, make greater dilutions, always being careful not to transfer less than 10 ml of the previous dilution. Use these preliminary tests to determine the approximate threshold level.

2) THRESHOLD ODOR TEST—Prepare

a range of sample dilutions of higher and lower odorant concentration than indicated by the preliminary test, referring to Table 217(1) to facilitate this preparation. If only two persons are involved, have the one making the preliminary odor test prepare the sample dilutions for this series. Present three clean, coded, odor-free flasks for each test trial, of which two contain 200 ml odor-free water. For the first trial, use a flask containing less than half the sample concentration found to be the threshold level in the preliminary test. Heat these flasks to 40 C and offer in sets of three to the odor tester, randomizing the position of the odor-containing flasks and the two blanks. Have the odor tester shake each flask, remove the cover, and test for odor. (To prevent any odor transfer, take care not to handle the necks of the flasks.) If no odor is detected, decrease the dilution (increase concentration) and repeat the procedure until an odor is detected; then record the results. During the testing procedure, offer the dilutions in generally increasing concentration. However, especially near the threshold level, insert sets of three blanks and some repeat or lower dilutions into the sequence to discourage guessing.

Record the odor intensity index value for each tester, as well as the average and range of all tests.

5. Calculation

Calculate the odor intensity index as follows:

$$OII = 3.3 \log \frac{200}{A} + 3D$$

where A = ml of sample or ml of aliquot of the primary dilution used and D = number of 25:175 primary dilutions required to reach the determinable magnitude of odor intensity. The relationship between sample dilution and odor intensity is given in Table 217(1) preceding.

6. Interpretation

See Part 100, Odor, Section 136.6.

217 C. References

1. A. A. ROSEN, J. B. PETER & F. M. MIDDLETON. 1962. Odor thresholds of mixed organic chemicals. *JWPCF* 34:7.
2. R. A. BAKER. 1962. Critical evaluation of olfactory measurement. *JWPCF* 34: 582.
3. ———. 1963. Odor effects of aqueous mixtures of organic chemicals. *JWPCF* 35:728.

217 D. Bibliography

INGOLS, R. S. & G. M. RIDENOUR. 1948. The elimination of phenolic tastes by chloro-oxidation. *Water & Sewage Works* 95: 187.

SILVEY, J. K. G., J. C. RUSSELL, D. R. REDDEN & W. C. MCCORMICK. 1950. *Actinomycetes* and common tastes and odors. *JAWWA* 42:1018.

BRAUS, H., F. M. MIDDLETON & G. WALTON. 1951. A study of the concentration and estimation of organic chemical compounds in raw and filtered surface waters. *Anal. Chem.* 23:1160.

ETTINGER, M. B. & C. C. RUCHHOFT. 1951. Effect of stepwise chlorination on taste and odor producing intensity of some phenolic compounds. *JAWWA* 43:561.

MIDDLETON, F. M., W. GRANT & A. A. ROSEN. 1956. Drinking water taste and odor. *Ind. Eng. Chem.* 48:268.

SILVEY, J. K. G. & A. W. ROACH. 1956. *Actinomycetes* may cause tastes and odors in water supplies. *Public Works* 87:103.

BEAN, E. L. 1957. Taste and odor control at Philadelphia. *JAWWA* 49:205.

SIGWORTH, E. A. 1957. Control of odor and taste in water supplies. *JAWWA* 49:1507.

BARTHOLOMEW, K. A. 1958. Control of earthy, musty odors in water by treatment with residual copper. *JAWWA* 50:481.

BURTTSCHELL, R. H., A. A. ROSEN, F. M. MIDDLETON & M. B. ETTINGER. 1959. Chlorine derivatives of phenol causing taste and odor. *JAWWA* 51:205.

RYCKMAN, D. W. & S. G. GRIGAROPOULOS. 1959. Use of chlorine and its derivatives in taste and odor removal. *JAWWA* 51:1268.

KINNEY, J. E. 1960. Evaluating the taste and odor control problem. *JAWWA* 52:505.

ROSEN, A. A., R. T. SKEEL & M. B. ETTINGER. 1963. Relationship of river water odor to specific organic contaminants. *JWPCF* 35:777.

AMERICAN SOCIETY FOR TESTING AND MATERIALS. 1969. *Manual on Water* (3rd ed.). ASTM, Philadelphia.

OIL: See Grease, Section 209.

218 OXYGEN (DISSOLVED)

Dissolved oxygen (DO) levels in natural and wastewaters are dependent on the physical, chemical and biochemical activities prevailing in the water body. The analysis for DO is a key test in water pollution control activities and waste treatment process control.

Two methods for DO analysis are described: the Winkler or iodometric method and its modifications and the electrometric method using membrane electrodes. The iodometric method [1] is a titrimetric procedure based on the oxidizing property of DO, while the membrane electrode procedure is based on the rate of diffusion of molecular oxygen across a membrane.[2] The choice of test procedure is dependent on the interferences present, the accuracy desired and, in some cases, convenience or expedience.

218 A. Iodometric Methods

1. Principle

Improved by variations in technic and equipment and aided by instrumentation, the iodometric test remains the most precise and reliable titrimetric procedure for DO analysis. The test is based on the addition of divalent manganese solution, followed by strong alkali, to the water sample in a glass-stoppered bottle. DO present in the sample rapidly oxidizes an equivalent amount of the dispersed divalent manganous hydroxide precipitate to hydroxides of higher valency states. In the presence of iodide ions and upon acidification, the oxidized manganese reverts to the divalent state, with the liberation of iodine equivalent to the original DO content in the sample. The iodine is then titrated with a standard solution of thiosulfate.

The titration end point can be detected visually, using a starch indicator, or electrometrically, using potentiometric or dead-stop technics.[3] Experienced analysts can maintain a precision of ± 50 μg/l with visual end-point detection, and a precision of ± 5 μg/l with electrometric end-point detection.[2, 3]

The liberated iodine can also be determined directly by simple absorption spectrophotometers.[4] This method can be performed easily on a routine basis and can provide very accurate estimates for DO in the μg/l range provided that interfering particulate matter, color and chemical interferences are not present.

2. *Selection of Method*

Before using the iodometric methods, the analyst should consider the effect of interferences, oxidizing or reducing materials which may be present in the test sample. The presence of certain oxidizing agents liberates iodine from iodides (positive interference), and the presence of certain reducing agents reduces iodine to iodide (negative interference). Certain organic compounds interfere with the test by hindering the settling of the oxidized manganese precipitate and by partially obscuring the end point of the iodometric titration with starch indicator.

Several modifications of the iodometric method are prescribed to minimize the effect of interfering materials.[2] Among the more commonly used procedures are the azide modification,[5] the permanganate modification,[6] the alum flocculation modification,[7] and the copper sulfate-sulfamic acid flocculation modification.[8, 9] The azide modification (B) effectively removes the interference caused by nitrite, which is the most common interference in biologically treated effluents and incubated BOD samples. The permanganate modification (C) is used in the presence of ferrous iron. When the sample contains 5 mg/l ferric iron salts or more, potassium fluoride is added as the first reagent in the azide modification or after the permanganate treatment for ferrous iron. Alternately, Fe(III) interference may be eliminated by using 90% H_3PO_4 instead of H_2SO_4 for acidification. This procedure has not been tested for Fe(III) concentrations above 20 mg/l.

The alum flocculation modification (D) is used in the presence of suspended solids which cause interference. The copper sulfate-sulfamic acid flocculation modification (E) is used on activated-sludge mixed liquors.

3. *Collection of Samples*

Great care is required in collecting water samples for the DO analysis. Methods of sampling are highly dependent on the source to be sampled and, to a certain extent, on the method of analysis. The sample must not remain in contact with air or be agitated, since either condition would cause a change in its gaseous content. Samples from any depth in streams, lakes or reservoirs, and samples from boiler waters, need special precautions to eliminate changes in pressure and temperature. Procedures and equipment have been developed for sampling waters under pressure and unconfined waters (e.g., streams, rivers and reservoirs). Sampling procedures and the equipment needed are described in American Society for Testing and Materials Special Technical Publication No. 148–1 and in U. S. Geological Survey Water Supply Paper No. 1454.

Surface water samples are frequently collected in narrow-mouth glass-stoppered BOD bottles of 300-ml capacity with tapered ground-glass pointed stoppers and flared mouths. Special precautions are required to avoid entrainment or dissolution of atmospheric oxygen. In sampling from a line under pressure, a glass or rubber tube attached to the tap should extend to the bottom of the bottle. Allow the bottle to overflow two or three times its volume and replace the stopper so that no air bubbles are entrained.

Samplers which permit collection of DO, BOD and other samples from

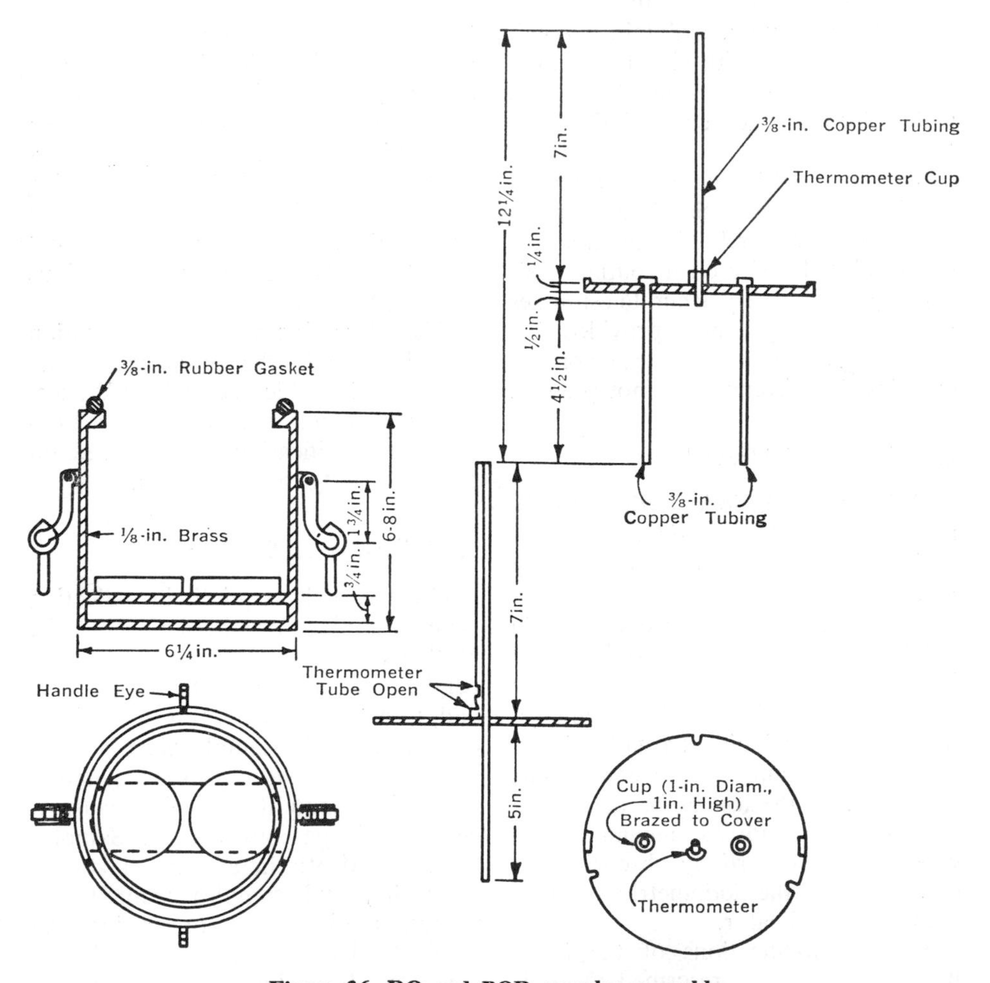

Figure 36. DO and BOD sampler assembly.

streams, ponds or tanks of moderate depth are of the APHA type shown in Figure 36. Use of a Kemmerer-type sampler is recommended for samples collected from depths greater than 5 ft. In the latter case, the sample is bled from the bottom of the sampler through a tube extending to the bottom of a 250–300 ml BOD bottle. The bottle should be filled to overflowing (overflow for approximately 10 sec), and care must be taken to prevent turbulence and the formation of bubbles while filling the bottle. The temperature of the sampled water should be recorded to the nearest degree centigrade, or more precisely, as desired.

4. *Preservation of Samples*

There should be no delay in the determination of DO on all samples that contain an appreciable oxygen or iodine demand. Samples with no iodine demand may be stored for a few hours without change after the addition of manganese sulfate solution, alkali-iodide solution and H_2SO_4, followed by shaking in the usual way. Samples stored at this point should be protected from strong sunlight and titrated as soon as possible.

For samples with an iodine demand, preservation for 4–8 hr is accomplished by adding 0.7 ml conc H_2SO_4 and 1 ml sodium azide solution (2 g NaN_3 in 100 ml distilled water) to the DO bottle. This will arrest biologic activity and maintain the DO if the bottle is stored at the temperature of collection or water-sealed and kept at a temperature of 10–20 C. As soon as possible, complete the procedure, using 2 ml manganese sulfate solution, 3 ml alkali-iodide solution, and 2 ml conc H_2SO_4.

218 B. Azide Modification

1. General Discussion

The azide modification is used for most sewage, effluent and stream samples, and is recommended especially if they contain more than 50 μg/l nitrite nitrogen and not more than 1 mg/l ferrous iron. Other reducing or oxidizing materials should be absent. If 1 ml fluoride solution is added before acidifying the sample and there is no delay in titration, the method is also applicable in the presence of 100–200 mg/l ferric iron.

2. Reagents

a. Manganese sulfate solution: Dissolve 480 g $MnSO_4 \cdot 4H_2O$, 400 g $MnSO_4 \cdot 2H_2O$, or 364 g $MnSO_4 \cdot H_2O$ in distilled water, filter, and dilute to 1 liter. The manganese sulfate solution should not give a color with starch when added to an acidified solution of potassium iodide.

b. Alkali-iodide-azide reagent: The reagent may be prepared in the traditional way (*1*), or in the form (*2*), which contains an increased amount of iodide.

1) Dissolve 500 g sodium hydroxide, NaOH (or 700 g potassium hydroxide, KOH), and 135 g sodium iodide, NaI (or 150 g potassium iodide, KI) in distilled water and dilute to 1 liter. To this solution add 10 g sodium azide, NaN_3, dissolved in 40 ml distilled water. Potassium and sodium salts may be used interchangeably. This reagent should not give a color with starch solution when diluted and acidified.

2) Dissolve 400 g sodium hydroxide in 500 ml boiled and cooled distilled water, cool slightly, and then dissolve 900 g sodium iodide in the caustic solution. Dissolve 10 g sodium azide in 40 ml distilled water. Add the latter to the former and dilute, if necessary, to 1 liter. The final volume may be slightly over 1 liter owing to the very high concentrations of dissolved salts. The amount of sodium iodide is sufficient to determine up to 40 mg/l DO. With this reagent, use the following revised volumes in ¶ 3a of the procedure: 2.5 ml alkali-iodide-azide reagent and 2 ml conc H_2SO_4.

c. Sulfuric acid, conc: The strength of this acid is about 36*N*. Hence, 1 ml is equivalent to about 3 ml of the alkali-iodide-azide reagent.

d. Starch: Either the aqueous solution or soluble starch powder mixtures may be used.

Prepare the aqueous solution by adding a cold water suspension of 5 g arrowroot or soluble starch to approximately 800 ml of boiling water, with stirring. Dilute to 1 liter, allow to boil a few minutes, and let settle overnight. Use the clear supernate. This solution may be preserved with 1.25 g salicylic acid per liter or by the addition of a few drops of toluene.

e. Sodium thiosulfate stock solution, 0.10*N:* Dissolve 24.82 g $Na_2S_2O_3 \cdot 5H_2O$ in boiled and cooled distilled water and dilute to 1 liter. Preserve by adding 5 ml chloroform or 1 g NaOH per liter.

f. Standard sodium thiosulfate titrant, 0.0250*N:* Prepare either by diluting 250.0 ml sodium thiosulfate stock solution to 1,000 ml or by dissolving 6.205 g $Na_2S_2O_3 \cdot 5H_2O$ in freshly boiled and cooled distilled water and diluting to 1,000 ml. Standard sodium thiosulfate solution may be preserved by adding 5 ml chloroform or 0.4 g NaOH per liter, or 4 g borax and 5–10 mg HgI_2 per liter. Standard sodium thiosulfate solution, exactly 0.0250*N*, is equivalent to 200 μg DO per 1.00 ml.

Standardize with (1) biniodate or (2) dichromate:

1) STANDARD POTASSIUM BINIODATE SOLUTION, 0.0250*N*—A stock solution equivalent in strength to 0.100*N* thiosulfate solution contains 3.249 g/l $KH(IO_3)_2$. The biniodate solution equivalent to the 0.0250*N* thiosulfate contains 812.4 mg/l $KH(IO_3)_2$ and may be prepared by diluting 250 ml stock solution to 1 liter.

STANDARDIZATION: Dissolve approximately 2 g KI, free from iodate, in an erlenmeyer flask with 100 to 150 ml distilled water; add 10 ml 1 + 9 H_2SO_4, followed by exactly 20.00 ml standard biniodate solution. Dilute to 200 ml and titrate the liberated iodine with the thiosulfate titrant, adding starch toward the end of the titration, when a pale straw color is reached. Exactly 20.00 ml 0.0250*N* thiosulfate should be required when the solutions under comparison are of equal strength. It is convenient to adjust the thiosulfate solution to exactly 0.0250*N*.

2) STANDARD POTASSIUM DICHROMATE SOLUTION, 0.0250*N*—Potassium dichromate may be substituted for biniodate. A solution equivalent to 0.0250*N* sodium thiosulfate contains 1.226 g/l $K_2Cr_2O_7$. The $K_2Cr_2O_7$ should be previously dried at 103 C for 2 hr. The solution should be prepared in a volumetric flask.

STANDARDIZATION: Same as with biniodate, except that 20.00 ml standard dichromate solution are used. Place in the dark for 5 min, dilute to approximately 400 ml, and titrate with 0.0250*N* thiosulfate solution.

g. Special reagent—potassium fluoride solution: Dissolve 40 g $KF \cdot 2H_2O$ in distilled water and dilute to 100 ml.

3. Procedure

a. To the sample as collected in a 250–300 ml bottle, add 2 ml * manganese sulfate solution, followed by 2 ml* alkali-iodide-azide reagent, well below the surface of the liquid; stopper with care to exclude air bubbles and mix by inverting the bottle at least 15 times. When the precipitate settles, leaving a clear supernate above the manganese hydroxide floc, shake again. With sea water, at least a 2-min period of contact with the precipitate will be required. After at least 2 min of settling has produced at least 100 ml of clear supernate, carefully remove the stopper and immediately add 2.0 ml conc H_2SO_4 by allowing the acid to run down the neck of the bottle, restopper, and mix by gentle inversion until dissolution is complete. The iodine should be uniformly distributed throughout the bottle before decanting the amount needed for titration. This should correspond to 200 ml of the original sample after correction for the loss of sample by displacement with the reagents has been made. Thus, when a total of 4 ml (2 ml each) of the manganese sulfate and alkali-iodide-azide reagents is added to a 300-ml bottle, the volume taken for titration should be $200 \times 300/(300 - 4) = 203$ ml.

b. Titrate with 0.0250*N* thiosulfate solution to a pale straw color. Add 1–2 ml starch solution and continue the titration to the first disappearance of the blue color. If the end point is overrun, the sample may be back-titrated with 0.0250*N* biniodate solution, which is added dropwise, or by an additional measured volume of sample. Correction for the amount of biniodate solution or sample should be made. Subsequent recolorations due to the catalytic effect of nitrite, or to traces of ferric salts which have not been complexed with fluoride, should be disregarded.

* Although 2-ml quantities of the reagents insure better contact with less agitation, it is permissible to use 1-ml reagent quantities with 250-ml bottles.

4. Calculation

a. Because 1 ml 0.0250*N* sodium thiosulfate titrant is equivalent to 0.200 mg DO, each milliliter of sodium thiosulfate titrant used is equivalent to 1 mg/l DO when a volume equal to 200 ml of original sample is titrated.

b. If the results are desired in milliliters of oxygen gas per liter, corrected to 0 C and 760 mm pressure, multiply mg/l DO by 0.70.

c. To express the results as percent saturation at 760 mm atmospheric pressure, the solubility data in Table 218 (1) may be used. Equations for correcting the solubilities to barometric pressures other than mean sea level are given below the table.

d. The solubility of oxygen in distilled water at any barometric pressure, P (mm Hg), temperature, $t°$ C, and saturated vapor pressure, u (mm Hg), for the given t, may be calculated between the temperature of 0 and 30 C by:

$$\text{mg/l DO} = \frac{(P - u) \times 0.678}{35 + t}$$

and between 30 and 50 C by:

$$\text{mg/l DO} = \frac{(P - u) \times 0.827}{49 + t}$$

TABLE 218(1): SOLUBILITY OF OXYGEN IN WATER EXPOSED TO WATER-SATURATED AIR *

Temperature in °C	Chloride Concentration in Water—*mg/l*					Difference per 100 mg Chloride
	0	5,000	10,000	15,000	20,000	
	Dissolved Oxygen—*mg/l*					
0	14.6	13.8	13.0	12.1	11.3	0.017
1	14.2	13.4	12.6	11.8	11.0	0.016
2	13.8	13.1	12.3	11.5	10.8	0.015
3	13.5	12.7	12.0	11.2	10.5	0.015
4	13.1	12.4	11.7	11.0	10.3	0.014
5	12.8	12.1	11.4	10.7	10.0	0.014
6	12.5	11.8	11.1	10.5	9.8	0.014
7	12.2	11.5	10.9	10.2	9.6	0.013
8	11.9	11.2	10.6	10.0	9.4	0.013
9	11.6	11.0	10.4	9.8	9.2	0.012
10	11.3	10.7	10.1	9.6	9.0	0.012
11	11.1	10.5	9.9	9.4	8.8	0.011
12	10.8	10.3	9.7	9.2	8.6	0.011
13	10.6	10.1	9.5	9.0	8.5	0.011
14	10.4	9.9	9.3	8.8	8.3	0.010
15	10.2	9.7	9.1	8.6	8.1	0.010
16	10.0	9.5	9.0	8.5	8.0	0.010
17	9.7	9.3	8.8	8.3	7.8	0.010
18	9.5	9.1	8.6	8.2	7.7	0.009
19	9.4	8.9	8.5	8.0	7.6	0.009
20	9.2	8.7	8.3	7.9	7.4	0.009
21	9.0	8.6	8.1	7.7	7.3	0.009
22	8.8	8.4	8.0	7.6	7.1	0.008
23	8.7	8.3	7.9	7.4	7.0	0.008
24	8.5	8.1	7.7	7.3	6.9	0.008
25	8.4	8.0	7.6	7.2	6.7	0.008

* At a total pressure of 760 mm Hg. Under any other barometric pressure, P (mm; or P', in.), the solubility, S' (mg/l), can be obtained from the corresponding value in the table by the equation:

$$S' = S\frac{P - p}{760 - p}$$

in which S is the solubility at 760 mm (29.92 in.) and p is the pressure (mm) of saturated water vapor at the temperature of the water. For elevations less than 3,000 ft and temperatures below 25 C, p can be ignored. The equation then becomes:

$$S' = S\frac{P}{760} = S\frac{P'}{29.92}$$

Dry air is assumed to contain 20.90% oxygen. (Calculations made by Whipple and Whipple, 1911. *J. Amer. Chem. Soc.* 33:362.)

TABLE 218(1): SOLUBILITY OF OXYGEN IN WATER EXPOSED TO WATER-SATURATED AIR * (*Continued*)

Temperature in °C	Chloride Concentration in Water—*mg/l*					Difference per 100 mg Chloride
	0	5,000	10,000	15,000	20,000	
	Dissolved Oxygen—*mg/l*					
26	8.2	7.8	7.4	7.0	6.6	0.008
27	8.1	7.7	7.3	6.9	6.5	0.008
28	7.9	7.5	7.1	6.8	6.4	0.008
29	7.8	7.4	7.0	6.6	6.3	0.008
30	7.6	7.3	6.9	6.5	6.1	0.008
31	7.5					
32	7.4					
33	7.3					
34	7.2					
35	7.1					
36	7.0					
37	6.9					
38	6.8					
39	6.7					
40	6.6					
41	6.5					
42	6.4					
43	6.3					
44	6.2					
45	6.1					
46	6.0					
47	5.9					
48	5.8					
49	5.7					
50	5.6					

5. Precision and Accuracy

The DO in distilled water can be determined with a precision, expressed as a standard deviation, of about 20 μg/l, and, in sewage and secondary effluents, of about 60 μg/l. In the presence of appreciable interference, even with the proper modifications the standard deviation may be as high as 100 μg/l. Still greater errors may occur in the testing of waters having organic suspended solids or heavy pollution. Errors due to carelessness in collecting samples, prolonging the completion of the test, or selection of an unsuitable modification should be avoided.

218 C. Permanganate Modification

1. General Discussion

The permanganate modification should be used only on samples containing ferrous iron.

High concentrations of ferric iron (up to several hundred milligrams per liter), such as may be present in acid mine water, may be overcome by the addition of 1 ml potassium fluoride and azide, providing the final titration is made immediately upon acidification.

This modification is ineffective for the oxidation of sulfite, thiosulfate, polythionate or the organic matter in sewage. The error with samples containing 0.25% by volume of digester waste from the manufacture of sulfite pulp may amount to 7–8 mg/l DO. With such samples, a crude accuracy may be secured through preliminary treatment with the alkali-hypochlorite modification.[10] At best, however, the latter procedure gives low results, the deviation amounting to 1 mg/l for samples containing 0.25% of digester wastes.

2. Reagents

All the reagents required for Method B, and in addition:

a. Potassium permanganate solution: Dissolve 6.3 g $KMnO_4$ in distilled water and dilute to 1 liter.

b. Potassium oxalate solution: Dissolve 2 g $K_2C_2O_4 \cdot H_2O$ in 100 ml distilled water; 1 ml of this solution is sufficient for the reduction of about 1.1 ml of the permanganate solution.

3. Procedure

a. To the sample collected in a 250–300 ml bottle add, below the surface, exactly 0.7 ml conc H_2SO_4 followed by 1 ml potassium permanganate solution and 1 ml potassium fluoride solution. Stopper and mix by inversion. It is essential to add not more than 0.7 ml conc H_2SO_4 as the first step of pretreatment. For this reason, it is best that the acid be added with a 1-ml pipet graduated to 0.1 ml. The amount of permanganate added should be sufficient to obtain a violet tinge which persists for 5 min. If the permanganate color is destroyed in a shorter time, add additional potassium permanganate solution, but avoid large excesses.

b. Remove the permanganate color completely by adding 0.5–1.0 ml potassium oxalate solution. Mix well and allow to stand in the dark (the reaction takes place more readily in the dark). Excess oxalate causes low results; add only an amount of oxalate which completely decolorizes the potassium permanganate without having an excess of more than 0.5 ml. Decolorization should occur in 2–10 min. If it is impossible to decolorize the sample without adding a large excess of oxalate, the DO result will be of little value.

c. From this point the procedure closely parallels that in Section 218B.3. Add 2 ml manganese sulfate solution, followed by 3 ml alkali-iodide-azide reagent. Stopper, mix, and allow the precipitate to settle. Remix for 20 sec and allow the precipitate to settle a second time; then acidify with 2 ml conc H_2SO_4. When 0.7 ml acid, 1 ml potassium permanganate solution, 1 ml potassium oxalate solution, 2 ml manganese sulfate solution, and 3 ml alkali-iodide-azide (or a total of 7.7 ml of reagents) are used in a 300-ml bottle, the volume of the sample to be taken for titration is $200 \times 300/(300-7.7) = 205$ ml.

This correction is slightly in error because the potassium permanganate solution is near saturation in DO and 1 ml would add about 0.008 mg of oxygen to the DO bottle. However, since the precision of the method (standard deviation, 0.06 ml of thiosulfate titration, or 0.012 mg oxygen) is 50% greater than the error, it does not seem necessary to complicate the volume correction further by allowing for this small error. When substantially more potassium permanganate solution is used routinely, a solution several times more concentrated should be employed, so that 1 ml will generally satisfy the permanganate demand.

218 D. Alum Flocculation Modification

1. General Discussion

Samples high in suspended solids may consume appreciable quantities of iodine in acid solution. This interference may be removed by alum flocculation.

2. Reagents

All the reagents required for the azide modification (Section 218B.2) and in addition:

a. Alum solution: Dissolve 10 g aluminum potassium sulfate, $AlK(SO_4)_2 \cdot 12H_2O$, in distilled water and dilute to 100 ml.

b. Ammonium hydroxide, conc.

3. Procedure

Collect a sample in a glass-stoppered bottle of 500–1,000 ml capacity, using the same precautions as for regular DO samples. Add 10 ml alum solution, followed by 1–2 ml conc NH_4OH. Stopper and invert gently for about 1 min. Settle quiescently for about 10 min and then siphon the clear supernate into a 250–300 ml DO bottle until it overflows. Avoid aeration and keep the siphon submerged at all times. Continue the sample treatment as in Section 218B.3 or an appropriate modification.

218 E. Copper Sulfate-Sulfamic Acid Flocculation Modification

1. General Discussion

This modification is used for biologic flocs such as activated sludge mixtures, which have high oxygen utilization rates.

2. Reagents

All the reagents required for the azide modification (Section 218B.2) and, in addition, the following:

a. Copper sulfate-sulfamic acid in-

hibitor solution: Dissolve 32 g technical grade sulfamic acid, NH_2SO_2OH, without heat in 475 ml distilled water. Dissolve 50 g copper sulfate, $CuSO_4 \cdot 5H_2O$, in 500 ml water. Mix the two solutions together and add 25 ml conc acetic acid.

3. Procedure

Add 10 ml copper sulfate–sulfamic acid inhibitor to a 1-qt wide-mouth or 1-liter glass-stoppered bottle. Insert the bottle in a special sampler designed so that the bottle fills from a tube near the bottom and overflows only 25 to 50% of bottle capacity. Collect the sample, stopper, and mix by inversion. Allow the suspended solids to settle quiescently and siphon the relatively clear supernatant liquor into a 250–300 ml DO bottle. Continue the sample treatment as rapidly as possible by the azide (Section 218B.3) or other appropriate modification.

218 F. Membrane Electrode Method (TENTATIVE)

1. General Discussion

Various modifications of the iodometric method have been developed to eliminate or minimize the effects of interferences; nevertheless, the method is still inapplicable in a variety of industrial and domestic wastewaters.[11] Moreover, the iodometric method is not ideally suited for field testing and cannot be adapted easily for continuous monitoring purposes or for dissolved oxygen determinations *in situ.*

Polarographic methods using the dropping mercury electrode or the rotating platinum electrode have not always been reliable for the DO analysis in sewage and industrial wastewaters, as impurities present in the test solution can cause electrode poisoning or other interferences.[12, 13] With the membrane-covered electrode systems these problems are minimized, since the sensing element is protected by an oxygen-permeable plastic membrane which serves as a diffusion barrier against impurities.[14–16] Under steady-state conditions the current is directly proportional to the DO concentration* in the test solution.

Membrane electrodes of the polarographic [14] as well as the galvanic [15] type have been used for DO measurements in lakes and reservoirs,[17] for stream survey and control of industrial effluents,[18, 19] for continuous monitoring of DO in activated sludge units,[20] and in estuarine and oceanographic studies.[21] Being completely submersible, membrane electrodes are well suited for analysis *in situ.* Their portability and ease of operation and maintenance render them particularly convenient for field applications. In laboratory investigations, membrane electrodes have been used for continuous DO analysis in bacterial cultures, including the BOD test.[15, 22]

Membrane electrodes provide an excellent method for DO analysis in polluted waters, highly colored waters, and strong waste effluents. They are

* Fundamentally the current is directly proportional to the activity of molecular oxygen.[2]

recommended for use especially under conditions which are not expedient for use of the iodometric method, or when that test and its modifications are subject to serious errors caused by interferences.

a. Principle: Oxygen-sensitive membrane electrodes of the polarographic as well as the galvanic type are basically composed of two solid metal electrodes in contact with a certain volume of supporting electrolyte which is separated from the test solution by a selective membrane. The basic difference between the galvanic and the polarographic system is that in the former the electrode reaction is spontaneous (similar to that in a fuel cell), while in the latter an external source of applied voltage is needed to polarize the indicator electrode. Polyethylene and teflon membranes are commonly used, since they are permeable to molecular oxygen and possess a certain degree of ruggedness.

Membrane electrodes are commercially available in some variety. In all these instruments the "diffusion current" is linearly proportional to the concentration of molecular oxygen in the test solution. The current can be converted easily to concentration units (e.g., mg/l) by a number of calibration procedures.

Membrane electrodes exhibit a relatively high temperature coefficient, which is largely due to changes in the membrane permeability.[16] The effect of temperature on the electrode sensitivity, ϕ (μamp/mg/l), can be expressed by the following simplified relationship:[16]

$$\log \phi = 0.43\, mt + b$$

where t is the temperature in degrees centigrade, m is a constant which depends on the membrane material, and b is a constant which largely depends on the membrane thickness. It is apparent that if ϕ and m are determined for one temperature, it is possible to calculate the sensitivity, at any desired temperature, as follows:

$$\log \phi = \log \phi_o + 0.43\, m(t - t_o)$$

Nomographic charts for temperature correction can easily be constructed[2] and they are available from certain manufacturers. An example is shown in Figure 37, in which for simplicity the

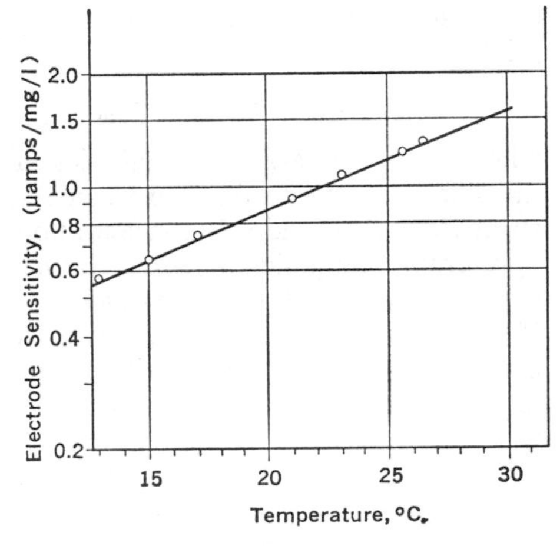

Figure 37. The effect of temperature on sensitivity.

sensitivity is plotted versus the temperature centigrade on semilogarithmic coordinates. It is recommended that one or two points be checked frequently so as to confirm the original calibration. If calibration changes, the new calibration should be parallel to the original, provided that the same membrane material is used.

Temperature compensation can be made automatically also, by using thermistors in the electrode circuit.[14] However, thermistors may not compensate fully over a wide temperature range. For certain applications where high accuracy is required, it is recommended that calibrated nomographic charts be used to correct for the temperature effect.

In order to use the DO membrane electrode in estuarine waters or in wastewaters with varying ionic strength, a correction should be made for the effect of salting-out on electrode sensitivity.[2, 16] This effect is particularly significant for large changes in the salt content of the test solution. The electrode sensitivity varies with the salt concentration according to the following relationship:

$$\log \phi_s = 0.43\, m_s\, C_s + \log \phi_o$$

where ϕ_s and ϕ_o are the sensitivities in the salt solution and distilled water respectively, C_s is the salt concentration (preferably the ionic strength), and m_s is a constant (salting-out coefficient). If ϕ_o and m_s are determined, it is then possible to calculate the sensitivity for any value of C_s. It is possible to use specific conductance to approximate the salt content in the test solution (C_s). This is particularly applicable to estuarine waters. Figure 38 shows calibration curves for sensitivity of varying salt solutions at different temperatures.

b. Interference: Plastic films used with the membrane electrode systems are permeable to a variety of gases besides oxygen, none of which is easily depolarized at the indicator electrode. However, prolonged use of membrane electrodes in waters containing such gases as H_2S tends to lower the cell sensitivity. The effect of this interference is eliminated by frequent changing and calibration of the membrane electrode.

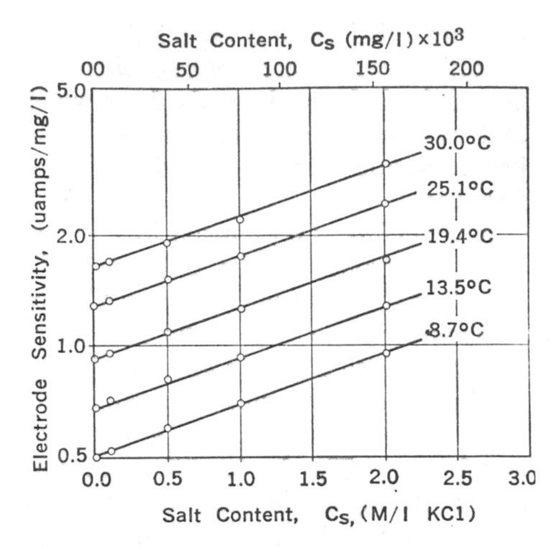

Figure 38. The salting-out effect at different temperatures.

c. Sampling: Membrane electrodes offer the advantage of analysis *in situ* and therefore eliminate errors caused by sample handling and storage. In the event sampling is required, the same precautions suggested for the iodometric method are recommended.

2. Apparatus

a. Oxygen-sensitive membrane electrode, polarographic or galvanic, with appropriate meter.

3. Procedure

a. CALIBRATION—Because the differences between makes and models of satisfactory electrodes and meters render it impossible to formulate detailed instructions applicable to every instrument, follow the manufacturer's calibration procedure exactly in order to obtain the guaranteed precision and accuracy. Generally, calibrate the membrane electrode by reading against air or a water sample of known DO concentration (determined by the iodometric method) as well as in a sample with zero DO. (Add excess sodium sulfite and a trace of $CoCl_2$ to bring the DO to zero.) Preferably calibrate with samples of the water under test. Avoid an iodometric calibration where interfering substances are suspected. The following illustrate the recommended procedures:

1) Fresh water: For river and lake samples where pollution is relatively light and interfering substances are absent, calibrate in the test solution or distilled water, whichever is more convenient.

2) Salt water: Use samples of sea water, or waters having a constant salt concentration in excess of 1,000 mg/l, directly for calibration.

3) Fresh water containing pollution or interfering substances: Calibrate with distilled water because of the erroneous results which will occur with the test solution.

4) Salt water containing pollution or interfering substances: Calibrate with a sample of clean water containing the same salt content as the test solution. Add a strong potassium chloride solution [see Specific Conductance, Section 154.3 and Table 154(1)] to distilled water to produce the same specific conductance as the test sample. In the case of polluted ocean waters, calibrate with a sample of unpolluted sea water.

5) Estuary water containing varying quantities of salt: Calibrate with a sample of uncontaminated sea water or distilled or tap water. Determine the chloride or salt concentration of the test sample and revise the calibration to take into account the change of oxygen solubility in the estuary water.[2]

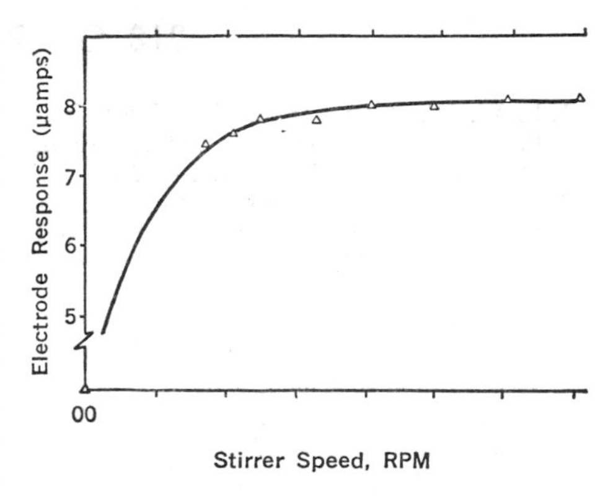

Figure 39. The effect of stirring on electrode response.

b. SAMPLE MEASUREMENT—Observe all the precautions recommended by the manufacturer to insure acceptable results. Exercise care in properly charging the electrode system to avoid contamination of the sensing element and also the trapping of minute air bubbles under the membrane, which can lead to lowered response and high residual current. Provide sufficient flow of the test solution across the membrane surface to overcome erratic response (see Figure 39 for a typical example of the effect of stirring).

c. VALIDATION OF TEMPERATURE EFFECT—Check frequently one or two points to confirm the applicability of the temperature correction data.

4. Precision and Accuracy

In most commercially available membrane electrode systems the operator can obtain an accuracy of ± 0.1 mg/l DO and a precision of ± 0.05 mg/l DO.

218 G. References

1. L. W. WINKLER. 1888. The determination of dissolved oxygen in water. *Berlin. Deutsch. Chem. Gesellsch.* 21:2843.
2. K. H. MANCY & T. JAFFE. 1966. Analysis of dissolved oxygen in natural and waste waters. USPHS Pub. No. 999-WP-37, Washington, D. C.
3. E. C. POTTER & G. E. EVERITT. 1957. Advances in dissolved oxygen microanalysis. *J. Applied Chem.* 9:642.
4. C. S. OULMAN & E. R. BAUMANN. 1956. A colorimetric method for determining dissolved oxygen. *Sewage & Ind. Wastes* 28:1461.
5. G. ALSTERBERG. 1925. Methods for the determination of elementary oxygen dissolved in water in the presence of nitrite. *Biochem. Z.* 159:36.
6. S. RIDEAL & G. G. STEWART. 1901. The determination of dissolved oxygen in waters in the presence of nitrites and of organic matter. *Analyst* 26:141.
7. C. C. RUCHHOFT & W. A. MOORE. 1940. The determination of biochemical oxygen demand and dissolved oxygen of river mud suspensions. *Ind. Eng. Chem.*, Anal. Ed. 12:711.
8. O. R. PLACAK & C. C. RUCHHOFT. 1941. Comparative study of the azide and Rideal-Stewart modifications of the Winkler method in the determination of biochemical oxygen demand. *Ind. Eng. Chem.*, Anal. Ed. 13:12.
9. C. C. RUCHHOFT & O. R. PLACAK. 1942. Determination of dissolved oxygen in activated-sludge sewage mixtures. *Sewage Works J.* 14:638.
10. E. J. THERIAULT & P. D. MCNAMEE. 1932. Dissolved oxygen in the presence of organic matter, hypochlorites, and sulfite wastes. *Ind. Eng. Chem.*, Anal. Ed. 4:59.
11. J. J. MCKEOWN, L. C. BROWN & G. W. GOVE. 1967. Comparative studies of dissolved oxygen analysis methods. *JWPCF* 39:1323.
12. W. R. LYNN & D. A. OKUN. 1955. Experience with solid platinum electrodes in the determination of dissolved oxygen. *Sewage & Ind. Wastes* 27:4.
13. K. H. MANCY & D. A. OKUN. 1960. Automatic recording of dissolved oxygen in aqueous systems containing surface active agents. *Anal. Chem.* 32:108.
14. D. E. CARRITT & J. W. KANWISHER. 1959. An electrode system for measuring dissolved oxygen. *Anal. Chem.* 31:5.
15. K. H. MANCY & W. C. WESTGARTH. 1962. A galvanic cell oxygen analyzer. *JWPCF* 34:1037.
16. K. H. MANCY, D. A. OKUN & C. N. REILLEY. 1962. A galvanic cell oxygen analyzer. *J. Electroanal. Chem.* 4:65.
17. C. M. WEISS & R. T. OGLESBY. 1963. Instrumentation for monitoring water quality in reservoirs. American Water Works Association, 83rd Annual Conference, New York.
18. E. J. CLEARY. 1962. Introducing the ORSANCO robot monitor. *Proc. Water Quality Meas. & Instrument.* Pub. No. 108, USPHS, Washington, D. C.
19. F. J. H. MACKERETH. 1964. An improved galvanic cell for determination of oxygen concentrations in fluids. *J. Sci. Instruments* 41:38.
20. F. SULZER & W. M. WESTGARTH. 1962. Continuous D.O. recording in activated sludge. *Water & Sewage Works* 109:376.
21. A. C. DUXBURY. 1963. Calibration and use of a galvanic type oxygen electrode in field work. *Limnol. & Oceanogr.* 8:483.
22. H. J. LIPNER, L. R. WITHERSPOON & V. C. CHAMPEAUS. 1964. Adaptation of a galvanic cell for microanalysis of oxygen. *Anal. Chem.* 36:204.

218 H. Bibliography

BRIGGS, R. & M. VINEY. 1964. The design and performance of temperature compensated electrodes for oxygen measurements. *J. Sci. Instruments* 41:78.

219 OXYGEN DEMAND (BIOCHEMICAL)*

1. Discussion

The biochemical oxygen demand (BOD) determination described herein constitutes an empirical test, in which standardized laboratory procedures are used to determine the relative oxygen requirements of wastewaters, effluents and polluted waters. The test has its widest application in measuring waste loadings to treatment plants and in evaluating the efficiency (BOD removal) of such treatment systems. Comparison of BOD values cannot be made unless the results have been obtained under identical test conditions.

The test is of limited value in measuring the actual oxygen demand of surface waters, and the extrapolation of test results to actual stream oxygen demands is highly questionable, since the laboratory environment does not reproduce stream conditions, particularly as related to temperature, sunlight, biological population, water movement and oxygen concentration.

Complete stabilization of a given waste may require a period of incubation too long for practical purposes. For this reason, the 5-day period has been accepted as standard. For certain industrial wastes, however, it may be advisable to determine the oxidation curve obtained. Conversion of data from one incubation period to another can only be made if such special studies are carried out. Studies in recent years have shown that the exponential rate of carbonaceous oxidation, k, at 20 C rarely has a value of 0.1, although it may vary from less than one-half to more than twice this value. This fact usually makes it impossible to calculate the ultimate carbonaceous demand, L, of a sample from 5-day BOD values unless the k value has been determined on the sewage, wastewater or stream under consideration. It appears from recent work that the exponential interpretation of BOD rate curves is a gross oversimplification; the analyst should not be surprised if a good exponential fit is not obtained.

* BOD, Biochemical Oxygen Demand.

2. Apparatus

a. Incubation bottles, 250–300 ml capacity, with ground-glass stoppers: Bottles should be cleaned with a good detergent and thoroughly rinsed and drained before use. As a precaution against drawing air into the dilution bottle during incubation, a water seal is recommended. Satisfactory water seals are obtained by inverting the bottles in a water bath or adding water to the flared mouth of special BOD bottles.

b. Air incubator or water bath, thermostatically controlled at 20 C ± 1 C: All light should be excluded to prevent formation of DO by algae in the sample.

3. Reagents

a. Distilled water: Water used for solutions and for preparation of dilution water must be of the highest quality, distilled from a block tin or all-glass still; it must contain less than 0.01 mg/l copper and be free of chlorine, chloramines, caustic alkalinity, organic material or acids.

b. Phosphate buffer solution: Dissolve 8.5 g potassium dihydrogen phosphate, KH_2PO_4, 21.75 g dipotassium hydrogen phosphate, K_2HPO_4, 33.4 g disodium hydrogen phosphate heptahydrate, $Na_2HPO_4 \cdot 7H_2O$, and 1.7 g ammonium chloride, NH_4Cl, in about 500 ml distilled water and dilute to 1 liter. The pH of this buffer should be 7.2 without further adjustment. Discard the reagent (or any of the following reagents) if there is any sign of biological growth in the stock bottle.

c. Magnesium sulfate solution: Dissolve 22.5 g $MgSO_4 \cdot 7H_2O$ in distilled water and dilute to 1 liter.

d. Calcium chloride solution: Dissolve 27.5 g anhydrous $CaCl_2$ in distilled water and dilute to 1 liter.

e. Ferric chloride solution: Dissolve 0.25 g $FeCl_3 \cdot 6H_2O$ in distilled water and dilute to 1 liter.

f. Acid and alkali solutions, 1N: For neutralization of waste samples which are either caustic or acidic.

g. Sodium sulfite solution, 0.025N: Dissolve 1.575 g anhydrous Na_2SO_3 in 1,000 ml distilled water. This solution is not stable and should be prepared daily.

h. Seeding: The purpose of seeding is to introduce into the sample a biological population capable of oxidizing the organic matter in the wastewater. Where such microorganisms are already present, as in domestic sewage or unchlorinated effluents and surface waters, seeding is unnecessary and should not be employed.

When there is reason to believe that the sample contains very few microorganisms—as a result, for example, of chlorination, high temperature or extreme pH—the dilution water should be seeded. The standard seed material is settled domestic sewage which has been stored at 20 C for 24–36 hr. The standard seed concentration is 1–2 ml per liter of dilution water.

Some samples—for example, certain industrial wastes—may require seeding because of low microbial population, but they contain organic compounds which are not readily amenable to oxidation by domestic sewage seed. For evaluating the effect of such a waste in a treatment system, more meaningful results may sometimes be realized by the use of specialized seed material containing organisms adapted to the use of the organic compounds present. Such adapted seed is best obtained from the effluent of a biological treatment process receiving the waste in question, or from the receiving water below the point of discharge (preferably 2–5 miles below) if the waste is not being treated. When these sources are not available, adapted seed may be developed in the laboratory by continuously aerating a large sample of water and feeding it with small daily increments of the particular waste, together with soil or domestic sewage, until a satisfactory microbial population has developed. The special circumstances which call for the use of adapted seed may also require use of a seed concentration higher than the standard 1–2 ml/l. The kind and amount of seed required for such special-purpose studies must be decided on the basis of prior experience with the particular waste and the purpose for which the determination is being performed.

Adapted seed has also been used when attempting to estimate the effect of a waste on the receiving water. However, refer to the introduction to this method in this connection (Section 219.1).

4a. Procedure

1) PREPARATION OF DILUTION WATER—Before use, store the distilled

water in cotton-plugged bottles long enough to permit it to become saturated with DO; or, if such storage is not practical, saturate the water by shaking the partially filled bottle or by aerating with a supply of clean compressed air. The distilled water should be at 20 ± 1 C.

Place the desired volume of distilled water in a suitable bottle and add 1 ml each of phosphate buffer, magnesium sulfate, calcium chloride and ferric chloride solutions for each liter of water. If dilution water is to be stored in the incubator, add the phosphate buffer just prior to using the dilution water.

2) SEEDING—See ¶ 3h et seq, preceding. If the dilution water is seeded, it should be used the same day it is prepared.

3) PRETREATMENT—

i) *Samples containing caustic alkalinity or acidity:* Neutralize to about pH 7.0 with 1*N* H_2SO_4 or NaOH, using a pH meter or bromthymol blue as an outside indicator. The pH of the seeded dilution water should not be changed by the preparation of the lowest dilution of sample.

ii) *Samples containing residual chlorine compounds:* If the samples are allowed to stand for 1 to 2 hr, the residual chlorine will often be dissipated. BOD dilutions can then be prepared with properly seeded standard dilution water. Higher chlorine residuals in neutralized samples should be destroyed by adding sodium sulfite. The appropriate quantity of sodium sulfite solution is determined on a 100–1,000 ml portion of the sample by adding 10 ml of 1 + 1 acetic acid or 1 + 50 H_2SO_4, followed by 10 ml potassium iodide solution (10 g in 100 ml) and titrating with 0.025*N* sodium sulfite solution to the starch-iodide end point. Add to a volume of sample the quantity of sodium sulfite solution determined by the above test, mix, and after 10–20 min test aliquot samples for residual chlorine to check the treatment. Prepare BOD dilutions with seeded standard dilution water.

iii) *Samples containing other toxic substances:* Samples such as those from industrial wastes frequently require special study and treatment—for example, toxic metals derived from plating wastes.

iv) *Samples supersaturated with DO:* Samples containing more than 9 mg/l DO at 20 C may be encountered during winter months or in localities where algae are actively growing. To prevent loss of oxygen during incubation of these samples, the DO should be reduced to saturation by bringing the sample to about 20 C in a partly filled bottle and agitating it by vigorous shaking or by aerating with compressed air.

4) DILUTION TECHNIC—Make several dilutions of the prepared sample so as to obtain the required depletions. The following dilutions are suggested: 0.1–1.0% for strong trade wastes, 1–5% for raw and settled sewage, 5–25% for oxidized effluents, and 25–100% for polluted river waters.

(i) Carefully siphon standard dilution water, seeded if necessary, into a graduated cylinder of 1,000–2,000 ml capacity, filling the cylinder half full without entrainment of air. Add the quantity of carefully mixed sample to make the desired dilution and dilute to the appropriate level with dilution water. Mix well with a plunger-type mixing rod, avoiding entrainment of air. Siphon the mixed dilution into two BOD bottles, one for incubation and the other

for determination of the initial DO in the mixture; stopper tightly and incubate for 5 days at 20 C. The BOD bottles should be water-sealed by inversion in a tray of water in the incubator or by use of a special water-seal bottle. Prepare succeeding dilutions of lower concentration in the same manner or by adding dilution water to the unused portion of the preceding dilution.

(ii) The dilution technic may be greatly simplified when suitable amounts of sample are measured directly into bottles of known capacity with a large-tip volumetric pipet and the bottle is filled with sufficient dilution water that the stopper can be inserted without leaving air bubbles. Dilutions greater than 1:100 should be made by diluting the waste in a volumetric flask before it is added to the incubation bottles for final dilution.

5) DETERMINATION OF DO—If the sample represents 1% or more of the lowest BOD dilution, determine DO on the undiluted sample. This determination is usually omitted on sewage and settled effluents known to have a DO content of practically zero. *With samples having an immediate oxygen demand, a calculated initial DO should be used, inasmuch as such a demand represents a load on the receiving water.*

6) INCUBATION—Incubate the blank dilution water and the diluted samples for 5 days in the dark at 20 C. Then determine the DO in the incubated samples and the blank, using the azide modification of the iodometric method or a membrane electrode. Unless the membrane electrode is used, the alum flocculation method is recommended for incubated samples of muds, and the copper sulfate-sulfamic acid method for activated sludges. In special cases, other modifications may be necessary. Those dilutions showing a residual DO of at least 1 mg/l and a depletion of at least 2 mg/l should be considered the most reliable.

7) SEED CORRECTION—If the dilution water is seeded, determine the oxygen depletion of the seed by setting up a separate series of seed dilutions and selecting those resulting in 40–70% oxygen depletions in 5 days. One of these depletions is then used to calculate the correction due to the small amount of seed in the dilution water. Do not use the seeded blank for seed correction because the 5-day seeded dilution water blank is subject to erratic oxidation due to the very high dilution of seed, which is not characteristic of the seeded sample.

8) DILUTION WATER CONTROL—Fill two BOD bottles with unseeded dilution water. Stopper and water-seal one of these for incubation. The other bottle is for determining the DO before incubation. The DO results on these two bottles are used as a rough check on the quality of the unseeded dilution water. The depletion obtained should not be used as a blank correction; it should not be more than 0.2 ml and preferably not more than 0.1 ml.

9) GLUCOSE-GLUTAMIC ACID CHECK—The BOD test is a bioassay procedure; consequently, the results obtained are influenced greatly by the presence of toxic substances or the use of a poor seeding material. Experience has shown that distilled waters are frequently contaminated with toxic substances—most often copper—and that some sewage seeds are relatively inactive. The results obtained with such waters are always low.

The quality of the dilution water, the effectiveness of the seed, and the tech-

TABLE 219(1): EFFECT OF SEED TYPE AND QUALITY ON BOD RESULTS

Type of Seed	5-day Seed Correction *mg/l*	Mean 5-day BOD *mg/l*	Standard Deviation *mg/l*
Settled fresh sewage	>0.6	218	±11
Settled stale sewage	>0.6	207	± 8
River water (4 sources)	0.05–0.22	224–242	±7–13
Activated-sludge effluent	0.07–0.68	221	±13
Trickling filter effluent	0.2–0.4	225	± 8

nic of the analyst should be checked periodically by using pure organic compounds on which the BOD is known or determinable. If a particular organic compound is known to be present in a given waste, it may well serve as a control on the seed used. There have been a number of organic compounds proposed, such as glucose or glutamic acid. For general BOD work, a mixture of these (150 mg/l of each) has certain advantages. It must be understood that glucose has an exceptionally high and variable oxidation rate with relatively simple seeds. When used with glutamic acid, the oxidation rate is stabilized and is similar to that obtained with many municipal wastes (0.16–0.19 exponential rate). In exceptional cases, a given component of a particular waste may be the best choice to test the efficacy of a particular seed.

To check the dilution water, the seed material, and the technic of the analyst, prepare a standard solution containing 150 mg/l each of reagent-grade glucose and glutamic acid which have been dried at 103 C for 1 hr. Pipet 5.0 ml of this solution into calibrated incubation bottles, fill with seeded dilution water, and incubate with seed control at 20 C for 5 days. On the basis of a mixed primary standard containing 150 mg/l each of glucose and glutamic acid, the 5-day BOD varies in magnitude according to the type of seed, and precision varies with the quality of seed, as shown in Table 219(1).

Excepting the oxidized river water and effluents, a low seed correction resulted in an appreciably higher value for the standard deviation. Each seed source should be checked to determine the amount required to obtain optimum precision. If results differ appreciably from those given in Table 219(1) after considering the seed source, the technic is questionable.

4b. Immediate Dissolved Oxygen Demand

Substances oxidizable by molecular oxygen, such as ferrous iron, sulfite, sulfide and aldehyde, impose a load on the receiving water and must be taken into consideration. The total oxygen demand of such a substrate may be determined by using a calculated initial DO or by using the sum of the immediate dissolved oxygen demand (IDOD) and the 5-day BOD. Where a differentiation of the two components is desired, the IDOD should be determined. It should be understood that the IDOD does not necessarily represent the immediate oxidation by molecular DO but may represent an oxidation by the iodine liberated in the acidification step of the iodometric method.

The depletion of DO in a standard water dilution of the sample in 15 min has been arbitrarily selected as the IDOD. To determine the IDOD, the DO of the sample (which in most cases is zero) and the DO of the dilution water are determined separately. An appropriate dilution of the sample and dilution water is prepared, and the DO is determined after 15 min. The calculated DO of the sample dilution minus the observed DO after 15 min is the IDOD (mg/l) of the sample dilution.

5. Calculation

a. Definitions:

D_o = DO of original dilution water
D_1 = DO of diluted sample 15 min after preparation
D_2 = DO of diluted sample after incubation
S = DO of original undiluted sample
D_c = DO available in dilution at zero time $= D_o p + SP$
p = decimal fraction of dilution water used
P = decimal fraction of sample used
B_1 = DO of dilution of seed control before incubation
B_2 = DO of dilution of seed control after incubation
f = ratio of seed in sample to seed in control $= \frac{\%\text{ seed in } D_1}{\%\text{ seed in } B_1}$
Seed correction $= (B_1 - B_2)f$.

b. Biochemical oxygen demand:

When seeding is not required,

$$\text{mg/l BOD} = \frac{D_1 - D_2}{P}$$

When using seeded dilution water,

$$\text{mg/l BOD} = \frac{(D_1 - D_2) - (B_1 - B_2)f}{P}$$

Including IDOD if small or not determined,

$$\text{mg/l BOD} = \frac{D_c - D_2}{P}$$

c. Immediate dissolved oxygen demand:

$$\text{mg/l IDOD} = \frac{D_c - D_1}{P}$$

The DO determined on the unseeded dilution water after incubation is not used in the BOD calculations because this practice would overcorrect for the dilution water. In all the above calculations, corrections are not made for small losses of DO in the dilution water during incubation. If the dilution water is unsatisfactory, proper corrections are difficult and the results are questionable.

6. Precision and Accuracy

There is no standard against which the accuracy of the BOD test can be measured. To obtain precision data, a glucose-glutamic acid mixture was analyzed by 34 laboratories, with each laboratory using its own seed material (settled stale sewage). The geometric mean of all results was 184 mg/l and the standard deviation of that mean was ± 31 mg/l (17%). The precision obtained by a single analyst in his own laboratory was ± 11 mg/l (5%) at a BOD of 218 mg/l.

7. Bibliography

THERIAULT, E. J. 1927. The oxygen demand of polluted waters. *Pub. Health Bull.* No. 173.

MOHLMAN, F. W., G. P. EDWARDS & G. SWOPE. 1928. Technique and significance of the biochemical oxygen demand determination. *Ind. Eng. Chem.* 20:242.

THERIAULT, E. J. 1931. Detailed instructions for the performance of the dissolved oxygen and biochemical oxygen demand tests. *Pub. Health Rep.* Suppl. 90.

THERIAULT, E. J., P. D. MCNAMEE & C. T. BUTTERFIELD. 1931. Selection of dilution water for use in oxygen demand tests. *Pub. Health Rep.* 46:1084.

LEA, W. L. & M. S. NICHOLS. 1936. Influence of substrate on biochemical oxygen demand. *Sewage Works J.* 8:435.

———. 1937. Influence of phosphorus and nitrogen on biochemical oxygen demand. *Sewage Works J.* 9:34.

RUCHHOFT, C. C. & W. A. MOORE. 1940. Determination of biochemical oxygen demand in river mud and suspensions. *Ind. Eng. Chem.*, Anal. Ed. 12:711.

RUCHHOFT, C. C. 1941. Report on the cooperative study of dilution waters made for the Standard Methods Committee of the Federation of Sewage Works Associations. *Sewage Works J.* 13:669.

RUCHHOFT, C. C., O. R. PLACAK & M. B. ETTINGER. 1946. Correction of BOD velocity constants for nitrification. *Sewage Works J.* 20:832.

SAWYER, C. N. & L. BRADNEY. 1946. Modernization of the BOD test for determining the efficiency of the sewage treatment process. *Sewage Works J.* 18:1113.

HURWITZ, E. et al. 1947. Nitrification and BOD. *Sewage Works J.* 19:995.

RUCHHOFT, C. C. et al. 1948. Variations in BOD velocity constants of sewage dilutions. *Ind. Eng. Chem.* 40:1290.

GOTAAS, H. B. 1949. Effect of sea water on biochemical oxidation of sewage. *Sewage Works J.* 21:818.

BUSWELL, A. M., I. VAN METER & J. R. GERKE. 1950. Study of the nitrification phase of the BOD test. *Sewage & Ind. Wastes* 22:508.

MOHLMAN, F. W. et al. 1950. Experience with modified methods for BOD. *Sewage & Ind. Wastes* 22:31.

SAWYER, C. N. et al. 1950. Primary standards for BOD work. *Sewage & Ind. Wastes* 22:26.

220 OXYGEN DEMAND (CHEMICAL)

The chemical oxygen demand (COD) determination provides a measure of the oxygen equivalent of that portion of the organic matter in a sample that is susceptible to oxidation by a strong chemical oxidant. It is an important, rapidly measured parameter for stream and industrial waste studies and control of waste treatment plants. In the absence of a catalyst, however, the method fails to include some organic compounds (such as acetic acid) which are biologically available to the stream organisms, while including some biologic compounds (such as cellulose) which are not a part of the immediate biochemical load on the oxygen assets of the receiving water. The carbonaceous portion of nitrogenous compounds can be determined, but there is no reduction of the dichromate by any ammonia in a waste or by any ammonia liberated from the proteinaceous matter. With certain wastes containing toxic substances, this test or a total organic carbon determination may be the only method for determining the organic load. Where wastes contain only readily available organic bacterial food and no toxic matter, the results can be used to approximate the ultimate carbonaceous BOD values.

The use of exactly the same technic each time is important because only a part of the organic matter is included, the proportion depending on the chemical oxidant used, the structure of the organic compounds, and the manipulative procedure.

The dichromate reflux method has been selected for the COD determination because it has advantages over other oxidants in oxidizability, applicability to a wide variety of samples, and ease of manipulation. The test will find its major usefulness in a plant for waste control purposes after many values have been obtained and correlated with some other important parameter or parameters.

1. General Discussion

a. Principle: Most types of organic matter are destroyed by a boiling mixture of chromic and sulfuric acids. A sample is refluxed with known amounts of potassium dichromate and sulfuric acid, and the excess dichromate is titrated with ferrous ammonium sulfate. The amount of oxidizable organic matter, measured as oxygen equivalent, is proportional to the potassium dichromate consumed.

b. Interference and inadequacies: Straight-chain aliphatic compounds, aromatic hydrocarbons, and pyridine are not oxidized to any appreciable extent, although this method gives more nearly complete oxidation than the permanganate method. The straight-chain compounds are more effectively oxidized when silver sulfate is added as a catalyst; however, silver sulfate reacts with chlorides, bromides or iodides to produce precipitates which are only partially oxidized by the procedure. There is no advantage in using the catalyst in the oxidation of aromatic hydrocarbons, but it is essential to the oxidation of straight-chain alcohols and acids.

The oxidation and other difficulties caused by the presence of chlorides in the sample may be overcome by employing the following method, which is a complexing technic for the elimination of chlorides from the reaction. This is accomplished by adding mercuric sulfate to the samples before refluxing. This ties up the chloride ion as a soluble mercuric chloride complex, which greatly reduces its ability to react further.

c. Application: The method can be used to determine COD values of 50 mg/l or more with the concentrated dichromate. With the dilute dichromate, values below 10 mg/l are less accurate but may be used to indicate an order of magnitude.

d. Sampling and storage: Unstable samples should be tested without delay, and samples containing settleable solids should be homogenized sufficiently by means of a blender to permit representative sampling. If there is to be a delay before analysis, the sample may be preserved by acidification with sulfuric acid. Initial dilutions in volumetric flasks should be made on wastes containing a high COD value in order to reduce the error which is inherent in measuring small sample volumes.

2. Apparatus

a. Reflux apparatus, consisting of 250-ml erlenmeyer flasks with ground-glass 24/40 neck * and 300-mm jacket Liebig, West or equivalent condensers,† with 24/40 ground-glass joint, and a hot plate having sufficient power to produce at least 9 watts/sq in. of heating surface, or equivalent, to insure adequate boiling of the contents of the refluxing flask.

3. Reagents

a. Standard potassium dichromate solution, 0.250*N:* Dissolve 12.259 g $K_2Cr_2O_7$, primary standard grade, pre-

* Corning 5000 or equivalent.
† Corning 2360, 91548, or equivalent.

viously dried at 103 C for 2 hr, in distilled water and dilute to 1,000 ml. NOTE—Nitrite nitrogen exerts a COD of 1.14 mg per mg nitrite N. To eliminate a significant interference due to nitrites, sulfamic acid in the amount of 10 mg for every 1 mg of nitrite N in the refluxing flask may be added to the dichromate solution. Thus, 120 mg sulfamic acid per liter of dichromate solution will eliminate the interference up to 6 mg/l nitrite N in the sample if a 20-ml sample is used. Correspondingly higher concentrations of nitrite N will be protected against if an aliquot diluted to 20 ml is used. For convenience, it is recommended that the sulfamic acid be added to the standard dichromate solution, since it must be included in the distilled water blank.

b. Sulfuric acid reagent, conc H_2SO_4 containing 22 g silver sulfate, Ag_2SO_4, per 9-lb bottle (1 to 2 days required for dissolution).

c. Standard ferrous ammonium sulfate titrant, analytical-grade crystals, 0.10*N:* Dissolve 39 g $Fe(NH_4)_2(SO_4)_2 \cdot 6H_2O$ in distilled water. Add 20 ml conc H_2SO_4, cool, and dilute to 1,000 ml. This solution must be standardized against the standard potassium dichromate solution daily.

STANDARDIZATION—Dilute 10.0 ml standard potassium dichromate solution to about 100 ml. Add 30 ml conc H_2SO_4 and allow to cool. Titrate with the ferrous ammonium sulfate titrant, using 2 or 3 drops (0.10–0.15 ml) ferroin indicator.

$$\text{Normality} = \frac{\text{ml } K_2Cr_2O_7 \times 0.25}{\text{ml Fe } (NH_4)_2\ (SO_4)_2}$$

d. Ferroin indicator solution: Dissolve 1.485 g 1,10-phenanthroline monohydrate, together with 695 mg $FeSO_4 \cdot 7H_2O$ in water and dilute to 100 ml. This indicator solution may be purchased already prepared.‡

e. Silver sulfate, reagent powder (see ¶ b above).

f. Mercuric sulfate, analytical-grade crystals.

g. Sulfamic acid, analytical grade: NOTE—Required only if the interference of nitrites is to be eliminated (see ¶ a above).

4a. Procedure

1) Place 0.4 g $HgSO_4$ § in a refluxing flask. Add 20.0 ml sample, or an aliquot diluted to 20.0 ml with distilled water, and mix. Then add 10.0 ml standard potassium dichromate solution and several pumice granules or glass beads which have been previously heated to 600 C for 1 hr. Connect the flask to the condenser. Slowly add 30 ml conc H_2SO_4 containing Ag_2SO_4 through the open end of the condenser, mixing thoroughly by swirling while adding the acid. *Mix the reflux mixture thoroughly before heat is applied; if this is not done, local heating occurs in the bottom of the flask, and the mixture may be blown out of the condenser.*

Use 0.4 g $HgSO_4$, to complex 40 mg chloride ion, or 2,000 mg/l when 20 ml of sample are used. If more chloride is present, add more $HgSO_4$ to maintain a $HgSO_4$:Cl ratio of 10:1. If a slight precipitate develops, it does not adversely affect the determination.

2) Reflux the mixture for 2 hr, or use a shorter period for particular

‡ G. F. Smith Chemical Company, Columbus, Ohio.

§ $HgSO_4$ may be measured conveniently by volume, using a reagent spoon (e.g., Hach Company No. 638 or equivalent).

wastes if it has been found to give the maximum COD. Cool and then wash down the condenser with distilled water.

3) Dilute the mixture to about 150 ml with distilled water, cool to room temperature, and titrate the excess dichromate with standard ferrous ammonium sulfate, using ferroin indicator. Generally, use 2–3 drops (0.10–0.15 ml) of indicator. Although the quantity of ferroin is not critical, do not vary it among samples even when analyzed at different times. Take as the end point the sharp color change from blue-green to reddish brown, even though the blue-green may reappear within minutes.

4) Reflux in the same manner a blank consisting of 20 ml distilled water, together with the reagents.

Sample Size *ml*	0.25*N* Standard Dichromate *ml*	Conc H_2SO_4 with Ag_2SO_4 *ml*	$HgSO_4$ *g*	Normality of $Fe(NH_4)_2(SO_4)_2$	Final Volume Before Titration *ml*
10.0	5.0	15	0.2	0.05	70
20.0	10.0	30	0.4	0.10	140
30.0	15.0	45	0.6	0.15	210
40.0	20.0	60	0.8	0.20	280
50.0	25.0	75	1.0	0.25	350

4b. Alternate Procedure for Other Sample Sizes

For particular situations, use a sample size ranging from 10.0 ml to 50.0 ml, with the volumes, weights and normalities of the reagents adjusted accordingly. Consult the tabulation above for applicable ratio examples. For satisfactory results, maintain these ratios and follow the complete procedure outlined in ¶ 4a et seq. If larger samples are used, use 500-ml erlenmeyer refluxing flasks to permit titration within the refluxing flask.

4c. Alternate Procedure for Dilute Samples

Follow the standard procedure, ¶s 4a(1) to 4a(4), with two exceptions: (a) Use 0.025*N* standard potassium dichromate, and (b) perform the back-titration with 0.01*N* ferrous ammonium sulfate. Exercise extreme care with this procedure because a trace of organic matter in the glassware or the atmosphere may cause a gross error. If a further increase in sensitivity is required, reduce a larger sample volume to 20 ml (final total volume 60 ml) by boiling in the refluxing flask on a hot plate in the presence of all the reagents. Carry a blank through the same procedure. (This technic has the advantage of concentrating without significant loss of easily digested volatile materials. Hard–to–digest volatile materials such as volatile acids are lost, but an improvement is gained over ordinary evaporative concentration methods. Also, as sample volume increases, correspondingly lower concentrations of chlorides will be complexed by 0.4 g $HgSO_4$.)

4d. Determination of Standard Solution

Evaluate the technic and quality of reagents with a standard solution of either glucose or potassium acid phthalate. See ¶ 6, Precision and Accuracy, below, for reference to phthalate. Since glucose has a theoretical COD of 1.067 g/g, dissolve 468.6 mg glucose in distilled water and dilute to 1,000 ml for a 500-mg/l COD solution. Potassium acid phthalate has a theoretical COD of 1.176 g/g; therefore, dissolve 425.1 mg potassium acid phthalate in distilled water and dilute to 1,000 ml for a 500-mg/l COD solution. (A 98 to 100% recovery of the theoretical oxygen demand can be expected with potassium acid phthalate. This reagent has the advantage over glucose in that it can be chemically standardized. It is also stable over a period of time, whereas glucose may be decomposed biologically quite rapidly.)

5. Calculation

$$\text{mg/l COD} = \frac{(a-b)\,N \times 8{,}000}{\text{ml sample}}$$

where COD = chemical oxygen demand from dichromate, a = ml $Fe(NH_4)_2(SO_4)_2$ used for blank, b = ml $Fe(NH_4)_2(SO_4)_2$ used for sample, and N = normality of $Fe(NH_4)_2(SO_4)_2$.

6. Precision and Accuracy

A set of synthetic unknown samples containing potassium acid phthalate and sodium chloride was tested by 74 laboratories. At 200 mg/l COD in the absence of chloride, the standard deviation was ± 13 mg/l (coefficient of variation, 6.5%). At 160 mg/l COD and 100 mg/l chloride, the standard deviation was ± 10 mg/l (6.5%), while at 150 mg/l COD and 1,000 mg/l chloride, the standard deviation was ± 14 mg/l (10.8%).

The accuracy of this method has been determined by Moore and associates. For most organic compounds the oxidation is 95 to 100% of the theoretical value. Benzene, toluene and pyridine are not oxidized.

7. Bibliography

MUERS, M. M. 1936. Biological purification of whey solutions. *J. Soc. Chem. Ind.* (London) 55:711.

MOORE, W. A., R. C. KRONER & C. C. RUCHHOFT. 1949. Dichromate reflux method for determination of oxygen consumed. *Anal. Chem.* 21:953.

MOORE, W. A., F. J. LUDZACK & C. C. RUCHHOFT. 1951. Determination of oxygen-consumed values of organic wastes. *Anal. Chem.* 23:1297.

MEDALIA, A. I. 1951. Test for traces of organic matter in water. *Anal. Chem.* 23:1318.

SUBRAHMANYAN, P., C. SASTRY & S. PALLAI. 1959. Determination of the permanganate value for waters and sewage effluent containing nitrite. *Analyst* 84:731.

SYMONS, J. M., R. E. MCKINNEY & H. H. HASSIS. 1960. A procedure for determination of the biological treatability of industrial wastes. *JWPCF* 32:841.

DOBBS, R. A. & R. T. WILLIAMS. 1963. Elimination of chloride interference in the chemical oxygen demand test. *Anal. Chem.* 35:1064.

221 pH VALUE

1. General Discussion

An electrometric method using glass and reference electrodes with a commercial pH meter is the standard procedure for measuring pH. The general standardization and measurement procedures and necessary precautions are described in Section 144. Accurate measurements require strict adherence to the specific directions for the particular pH meter and electrodes used.

Immediately before sample measurement, the pH meter must be standardized with a buffer solution of known pH. Buffer solutions and their temperature variations are described in Section 144A.3. Standardization of the instrument with two buffer solutions of different pH values serves as a check for proper instrument response.

In the measurement of pH values of industrial wastes, effluents, sludges and similar samples, the electrodes must be thoroughly rinsed with buffer solutions between samples and after calibrating. The electrodes should be kept free of oil and grease and stored in water when not in use. In testing samples containing gaseous or volatile components which affect the pH value, any handling technic such as stirring or heating may cause loss of such components and thereby introduce error. For example, the loss of carbon dioxide from an anaerobic sludge digester sample due to stirring will result in an apparent pH value which is too high. If a sample of sludge or mud is highly buffered, a small amount of water may be added but the result cannot be considered valid unless further dilutions yield the same pH value. All dilutions should be reported along with the result.

Colorimetric pH measurements are not acceptable as standard procedures, but they may find applications in plant control or water pollution field testing, and commercial kits are available. When using colorimetric methods in any specific application, the reliability of the procedure should first be checked by the standard method. Errors in colorimetric methods may be due to a chemical reaction between the indicator and the sample, dilutions beyond the buffering capacity, adsorption effects and other possible interfering factors.

2. Precision

The precision of the electrometric determination in wastewaters, effluents and polluted waters is of the same order as that obtaining for natural and treated waters (Section 144A.5). Generally, pH values should be reported to the nearest 0.1 pH unit.

3. Bibliography

FAIR, G. M. & E. W. MOORE. 1930. Determining the pH of sewage sludges. *Sewage Works J.* 1:3.

BANTA, A. P. & R. POMEROY. 1934. Hydrogen ion concentration and bicarbonate equilibrium in digesting sludge. *Sewage Works J.* 6:234.

222 PHENOLS

Phenols, defined as hydroxy derivatives of benzene and its condensed nuclei, may occur in domestic and industrial wastewaters and in drinking water supplies. Chlorination of such waters may produce odoriferous and objectionable-tasting chlorophenols which may include *o*-chlorophenol, *p*-chlorophenol, 2,6-dichlorophenol, and 2,4-dichlorophenol.[1] Of the four procedures offered, three use the 4-aminoantipyrine colorimetric method that determines phenol, the ortho- and meta-substituted phenols, and, under the proper condition of pH, those para-substituted phenols in which the substitution is a carboxyl, halogen, methoxyl, or sulfonic acid group. Presumably, the 4-aminoantipyrine method does not determine those para-substituted phenols in which the substitution is an alkyl, aryl, nitro, benzoyl, nitroso or aldehyde group. A typical example of these latter groups is paracresol, which may be present in certain industrial wastewaters and in polluted surface waters. The fourth procedure is a gas-liquid chromatographic technic.

a. Selection of procedure: The 4-aminoantipyrine method is given in three forms: Method C, for extreme sensitivity, is adaptable for use in wastewaters containing less than 1 mg/l phenol and concentrates the color in a nonaqueous solution; Method D, used for phenol concentrations greater than 1 mg/l in which a high degree of sensitivity is not required, retains the color in the unconcentrated aqueous solution; Method E, a tentative procedure, is used where an estimation of para-substituted phenols, especially the halogenated types, is required. Method F, a tentative gas-liquid chromatographic procedure, may be applied to wastewaters or to concentrates which contain more than 1 mg/l of phenolic compounds.

222 A. Interferences, Preservation and Storage of Samples

1. *Interferences*

a. Domestic and industrial wastewaters may contain such interferences as phenol-decomposing bacteria, oxidizing and reducing substances, and alkaline pH values. Biological degradation is inhibited by the addition of $CuSO_4$ to the sample. Acidification with H_3PO_4 assures the presence of the copper ion and eliminates any chemical changes resulting from the presence of strong alkaline conditions.

b. Some of the treatment procedures used for the removal of interferences prior to analysis may result in an unavoidable loss of certain types of phenols. Consequently, some highly contaminated wastewaters may require specialized screening technics for elimination of interferences and for quantitative recovery of the phenolic compounds. It is left to the analyst to meet these specialized situations.

c. Some of the major interferences can be eliminated as follows (see Distillation Step, Section 222B, for the required reagents).

1) *Oxidizing agents,* such as chlorine and as detected by the liberation of iodine upon acidification in the presence of potassium iodide, are removed immediately after sampling by the addition of an excess of ferrous sulfate or sodium arsenite. If oxidizing agents are not removed, the phenolic compounds will be partially oxidized and the results will be low.

2) *Sulfur compounds* are removed by acidifying the sample to a pH of less than 4.0 with H_3PO_4, using methyl orange or a pH meter, and aerating briefly by stirring prior to the addition of $CuSO_4$. This should eliminate the interferences of H_2S and SO_2.

3) *Oils and tars* contain phenols, so that an alkaline extraction is required prior to the addition of $CuSO_4$. The pH of the sample is adjusted to 12–12.5 by the addition of NaOH pellets. The oil and tar are extracted from the aqueous solution by CCl_4. Discard the oil- or tar-containing layer. Any excess of CCl_4 in the aqueous layer is removed by warming on a water bath before proceeding with the distillation step.

2. Sampling

Sampling of domestic and industrial wastewaters should be done in accordance with the instructions of Section 200A, Introduction (Collection of Samples).

3. Preservation and Storage of Samples

a. Phenols in concentrations usually encountered in wastewaters are subject to biochemical and chemical oxidation. Samples should be preserved and stored unless they will be analyzed within 4 hr after collection.

b. Acidify the samples to a pH of approximately 4.0 with H_3PO_4, using methyl orange or a pH meter. If H_2S or SO_2 is known to be present, briefly aerate or stir the sample with caution.

c. Biochemical oxidation of phenols is inhibited by the addition of 1.0 g $CuSO_4 \cdot 5H_2O$ per liter of sample.

d. The sample then should be kept cold (5–10 C). Analyze the preserved and stored samples within 24 hr after collection.

222 B. Distillation Step for Methods C and D

1. Principle

The phenols are distilled at a more or less constant rate from the nonvolatile impurities. The rate of volatilization of the phenols is gradual, so that the volume of the distillate must equal that of the sample being distilled. The use of $CuSO_4$ during distillation of an acidic sample permits the formation of cupric sulfide without subsequent decomposition to H_2S. The acidic solution also prevents the precipitation of cupric hydroxide, which acts as an oxidizing agent toward phenols.

2. Apparatus

a. Distillation apparatus, all-glass, consisting of a 1-liter pyrex distilling apparatus with Graham condenser * (see Figure 18).

b. pH meter: The pH meter should conform to the requirements of Section 144A.2, pH Value, Glass Electrode Method.

3. Reagents

All reagents must be prepared with distilled water free of phenols and chlorine.

a. COPPER SULFATE SOLUTION—Dissolve 100 g $CuSO_4 \cdot 5H_2O$ in distilled water and dilute to 1 liter.

b. PHOSPHORIC ACID SOLUTION, 1+9. Dilute 10 ml 85% H_3PO_4 to 100 ml with distilled water.

c. METHYL ORANGE INDICATOR—Dissolve 0.5 g methyl orange in 1 liter distilled water.

d. SPECIAL REAGENTS FOR TURBID DISTILLATES:

1) *Sulfuric acid, 1N.*

2) *Sodium chloride.*

3) *Chloroform or ethyl ether.*

4) *Sodium hydroxide, 2.5N:* Dilute 41.7 ml 6*N* NaOH to 100 ml or dissolve 10 g NaOH in 100 ml distilled water.

4. Procedure

a. Measure 500 ml sample into a beaker, lower the pH to approximately 4.0 with the 1+9 H_3PO_4 solution using the methyl orange indicator or a pH meter, add 5 ml copper sulfate solution, and transfer to the distillation apparatus. Use a 500-ml graduated cylinder as a receiver. The additions of H_3PO_4 and $CuSO_4$ may be omitted if the sample was preserved as described in Section 222A.2 and 3 preceding.

b. Distill 450 ml of sample, stop the distillation, and when boiling ceases add 50 ml phenol-free distilled water to the distilling flask. Continue distillation until a total of 500 ml has been collected.

c. One distillation should prove sufficient for purification of the sample. Occasionally, however, the distillate is turbid. In this case, acidify the turbid distillate with 1+9 H_3PO_4, add 5 ml copper sulfate solution, and distill as described in ¶ 4b above. If the second distillate is still turbid, an extraction process, described in ¶ 4d following, is required *before* distillation of the sample.

d. Treatment when second distillate is turbid: Extract a 500-ml aliquot of the original sample as follows: Add 4 drops methyl orange indicator and sufficient 1*N* H_2SO_4 to make the solution acidic. Transfer to a separatory funnel and add 150 g NaCl. Shake with five increments of chloroform, using 40 ml in the first increment and 25 ml in each of the increments following. Place the chloroform layer in a second separatory funnel and shake with three successive increments of 2.5*N* NaOH solution, using 4.0 ml in the first increment and 3.0 ml in each of the next two increments. Combine the alkaline extracts, heat on a water bath until the chloroform has been removed, then cool and dilute to 500 ml with distilled water. Proceed with distillation as described in ¶s 4a and b above.

NOTE: Diethyl ether may be used instead of chloroform, especially if an emulsion forms when extracting the chloroform solution with NaOH. When ether is used, a better distribution coefficient is obtained for phenol between the ether and water phases and it is not necessary to use NaCl. Chloroform is preferred because of the hazards in handling ether.

* Corning No. 3360 or equivalent.

222 C. Chloroform Extraction Method *

1. General Discussion

a. Principle: The steam-distillable phenols react with 4-aminoantipyrine at a pH of 10.0 ± 0.2 in the presence of potassium ferricyanide to form a colored antipyrine dye. This dye is extracted from aqueous solution with chloroform and the absorbance is measured at 460 mμ. The concentration of phenolic compounds is expressed as μg/l of phenol (C_6H_5OH). This method covers the phenol concentration range of 0.0 to 1,000 μg/l with a sensitivity of 1 μg/l.

b. Interference: All interferences are eliminated or reduced to a minimum if the sample has been preserved and stored, and distilled in accordance with the foregoing instructions.

c. Minimum detectable concentration: The minimum detectable quantity is 0.5 μg phenol when a 25-ml $CHCl_3$ extraction with a 5-cm cell, or a 50-ml $CHCl_3$ extraction with a 10-cm cell, is used in the photometric measurement. The minimum detectable quantity is 1 μg/l phenol in a 500-ml distillate.

2. Apparatus

a. Photometric equipment: One of the following, equipped with absorption cells providing light paths of 1 to 10 cm (depending on the absorbances of the colored solutions and the individual characteristics of the photometer; in general, if the absorbance readings are greater than 1.0 in a given cell size, the next smaller size cell should be used), is required:

1) SPECTROPHOTOMETER, for use at 460 mμ.

2) FILTER PHOTOMETER, equipped with a filter exhibiting maximum light transmission near 460 mμ.

b. Funnels: Buchner type with fritted disk (such as 15-ml Corning No. 36060 or equivalent).

c. Filter paper: An appropriate 11-cm filter paper may be used for filtration of the chloroform extracts in place of the Buchner-type funnels and anhydrous sodium sulfate.

d. pH meter: Should conform to the requirements of pH Value, Glass Electrode Method, Section 144A.2.

e. Separatory funnels, 1,000-ml, Squibb form, with ground-glass stoppers and teflon stopcocks. At least eight are required.

f. Nessler tubes, matched, 50-ml, tall form.

3. Reagents

All reagents must be prepared with distilled water free of phenols and chlorine.

a. Stock phenol solution: Dissolve 1.00 g reagent-grade phenol in freshly boiled and cooled distilled water and dilute to 1,000 ml. Ordinarily this direct weighing of the phenol constitutes a standard solution. However, if extreme accuracy is required, standardize as directed in ¶ 4a below.

b. Intermediate phenol solution: Dilute 10.0 ml stock phenol solution to 1.00 g reagent-grade phenol in freshly distilled water; 1 ml = 10.0 μg phenol. Prepare a fresh solution on each day of use.

---

* Similar in principle to but different in detail from ASTM D-1783-62 (Standard). Both methods were adapted from E. Eisenstaedt. 1938. *J. Organic Chem.* 3:153.

c. Standard phenol solution: Dilute 50.0 ml intermediate phenol solution to 500 ml with freshly boiled and cooled distilled water; 1 ml = 1.0 μg phenol. Prepare this solution within 2 hr of use.

d. Bromate-bromide solution, 0.10*N:* Dissolve 2.784 g anhydrous potassium bromate, $KBrO_3$, in distilled water, add 10 g potassium bromide (KBr crystals), dissolve, and dilute to 1,000 ml.

e. Hydrochloric acid, conc.

f. Standard sodium thiosulfate titrant, 0.025*N:* Prepare and standardize as directed in Dissolved Oxygen, Azide Modification, Section 218B.2f.

g. Starch solution: Prepare as directed in Dissolved Oxygen, Azide Modification, Section 218B.2d.

h. Ammonium chloride solution: Dissolve 50 g NH_4Cl in distilled water and dilute to 1,000 ml.

i. Ammonium hydroxide, conc.

j. Aminoantipyrine solution: Dissolve 2.0 g 4-aminoantipyrine in distilled water and dilute to 100 ml. This solution should be prepared each day of use.

k. Potassium ferricyanide solution: Dissolve 8.0 g $K_3Fe(CN)_6$ in distilled water and dilute to 100 ml. Filter if necessary. Prepare fresh each week of use.

l. Chloroform.

m. Sodium sulfate, anhydrous, granular.

n. Potassium iodide, crystals.

4a. Standardization of Phenol Solution

1) To 100 ml distilled water in a 500-ml glass-stoppered conical flask, add 50.0 ml stock phenol solution and 10.0 ml 0.1*N* bromate-bromide solution. Immediately add 5 ml conc HCl and swirl the stoppered flask gently. If the brown color of free bromine does not persist, add 10.0-ml portions of bromate-bromide solution until the color does persist. Keep the flask stoppered and allow to stand for 10 min; then add approximately 1 g KI. Usually four 10-ml portions of bromate-bromide solution are required if the stock phenol solution contains 1,000 mg/l phenol.

2) Prepare a blank in exactly the same manner, using distilled water and 10.0 ml 0.1*N* bromate-bromide solution. Titrate the blank and sample with the 0.025*N* sodium thiosulfate titrant, using starch solution as the indicator.

3) Calculate the concentration of the phenol solution as follows:

$$\text{mg/l phenol} = 7.842\ (AB - C)$$

where A = ml thiosulfate for blank; B = ml bromate-bromide solution used for sample divided by 10; and C = ml thiosulfate used for sample.

4b. Procedure

1) Place 500 ml of the distillate, or a suitable aliquot diluted to 500 ml, in a 1-liter beaker. If all 500 ml of distillate is used, it may not contain more than 50 μg (0.1 mg/l) phenol. If the sample is known to contain more than 50 μg phenol, a smaller aliquot must be used. Practically, the smallest aliquot would be 50 ml that contains not more than 50 μg (1 mg/l) phenol.

2) If the approximate phenol concentration of the original sample is not known, determine by a preliminary check the proper aliquot of the distillate and of the $CHCl_3$ to use for the final determination. This may be done without $CHCl_3$ extraction by carrying out the reaction in 50-ml nessler tubes and comparing against suitable phenol standards.

3) Prepare a 500-ml distilled water blank and a series of 500-ml phenol standards containing 5, 10, 20, 30, 40 and 50 μg phenol.

4) Treat sample, blank and standards as follows: Add 10 ml ammonium chloride solution and adjust with conc NH_4OH to pH 10.0 ± 0.2. Transfer to the 1-liter separatory funnels, add 3.0 ml aminoantipyrine solution, mix well, add 3.0 ml potassium ferricyanide solution, again mix well, and allow the color to develop for 3 min. The solution should be clear and light yellow.

5) Extract immediately with $CHCl_3$, using 25 ml for 1- to 5-cm cells and 50 ml for a 10-cm cell. Shake the separatory funnel at least 10 times, allow the $CHCl_3$ to settle, shake again 10 times, and allow the $CHCl_3$ to settle again.

6) Filter each of the chloroform extracts through the filter paper or through the fritted-glass funnels containing a 5-g layer of the anhydrous sodium sulfate. Collect the dried extracts in clean cells for the absorbance measurements; do not add more $CHCl_3$.

7) Read the absorbance of the sample and standards against the blank at a wavelength of 460 mμ. Plot absorbance against μg of standard phenol solutions for the calibration curve. Estimate the phenol concentration of the sample from the calibration curve. A separate calibration curve must be constructed for each photometer and each curve must be checked periodically to insure reproducibility.

8) Calculation:

$$\mu g/l \text{ phenol} = \frac{A}{B} \times 1{,}000$$

where A = μg phenol in sample, from calibration curve, and B = ml original sample.

4c. Alternative Procedure

1) If infrequent analyses for phenol are made, the analyst may prepare only one standard phenol solution instead of a series of solutions and a calibration curve.

2) In this case, prepare 500 ml of a standard phenol solution approximately equal to the phenolic content of that portion of the original sample used for final analysis. Also prepare a 500-ml distilled water blank.

3) Proceed as described in ¶s 4b(1) through (7), except that the absorbances of the sample and the standard phenol solution are measured against the blank at 460 mμ.

4) Calculation of the phenol content of the original sample is:

$$\mu g/l \text{ phenol} = \frac{CD}{E} \times \frac{1{,}000}{B}$$

where C = μg standard phenol solution, D = absorbance reading of sample, E = absorbance of standard phenol solution, and B = ml original sample.

5. Precision and Accuracy

The precision of this method is dependent on the skill of the analyst and on the interferences present after the distillation procedure. Because the "phenol" value is based on C_6H_5OH, this method can be regarded only as an approximation and as representing the minimum amount of phenols present. This is true because the phenolic value varies as the types of phenols vary within a given sample. Therefore, it is impossible to express the accuracy of the method.

222 D. Direct Photometric Method *

1. General Discussion

a. Principle: The steam-distillable phenols react with 4-aminoantipyrine at a pH of 10.0 ± 0.2 in the presence of potassium ferricyanide to form a colored antipyrine dye. This dye is kept in an aqueous solution and the absorbance is measured at 510 mμ. Because extreme sensitivity is not required in this method, smaller distillate volumes may be used for analysis. For example, this permits determination of 0.5 mg phenol, expressed as C_6H_5OH, in a 100-ml volume of distillate. Practically, the smallest distillate volume would be 10 ml. Consequently, this method covers the phenol concentration range of 0.0 to 50 mg/l, with a sensitivity of 1 mg/l.

b. Interference: All interferences are eliminated or reduced to a minimum by using only the distillate from the preliminary distillation procedure.

c. Minimum detectable concentration: This method has considerably less sensitivity than Method C. The minimum detectable quantity is 0.1 mg phenol when a 5-cm cell is used in the photometric measurement and 100 ml distillate are used in the determination.

2. Apparatus

a. Photometric equipment: One of the following, equipped with absorption cells providing light paths of 1 to 5 cm, is required:

1) SPECTROPHOTOMETER, for use at 510 mμ.

2) FILTER PHOTOMETER, equipped with a green filter exhibiting maximum light transmittance near 510 mμ.

b. pH meter: See Method C (Section 222C.2d).

3. Reagents

The reagents are the same as for Method C (Section 222C.3).

4a. Procedure

1) Place 100 ml of the distillate, or a suitable aliquot diluted to 100 ml, in a 250-ml beaker. If all 100 ml of distillate is used it may not contain more than 0.5 mg (5.0 mg/l) phenol. If the sample is known to contain more than 0.5 mg phenol, a smaller aliquot must be used. Practically, the smallest aliquot would be 10 ml that contains not more than 0.5 mg (50 mg/l) phenol.

2) Prepare a 100-ml distilled water blank and a series of 100-ml phenol standards containing 0.1, 0.2, 0.3, 0.4 and 0.5 mg phenol.

3) Treat sample, blank and standards as follows: Add 2.0 ml ammonium chloride solution and adjust with conc NH_4OH to pH 10.0 ± 0.2. Add 2.0 ml aminoantipyrine solution, mix well, add 2.0 ml potassium ferricyanide solution, and again mix well.

4) After 15 min, transfer to cells and read the absorbance of the sample and standard against the blank at 510 mμ. Estimate the phenol content of the sample from the photometric readings by using a calibration curve as directed in Method C [Section 222C.4b (7)].

5) Calculation:

$$\text{mg/l phenol} = \frac{A}{B} \times 1{,}000$$

* Adapted from ASTM D–1783-Standard, as published in ASTM *Book of Standards,* Part 23 (1968).

where A = mg phenol in sample, from calibration curve, and B = ml original sample.

4b. Alternate Procedure

Refer to Section 222C.4c. Use the appropriate 100-ml aliquots of sample and standard phenol solutions. Proceed as described in ¶s 4a(1) through (5) preceding, except that the absorbances of sample and standard phenol solution are measured against the blank at 510 mμ. Calculation of the phenol content of the original sample is:

$$\text{mg/l phenol} = \frac{CD}{E} \times \frac{1{,}000}{B}$$

where C = mg standard phenol solution, D = absorbance of sample, E = absorbance of standard phenol solution, and B = ml original sample.

5. Precision and Accuracy

Refer to Section 222C.6.

222 E. Aminoantipyrine Method for Halogenated Phenols * (TENTATIVE)

1. General Discussion

a. Principle: This procedure involves a petroleum ether extraction of the phenols (especially the para-substituted halogenated types) from an acidified aqueous sample, an alkaline aqueous extraction of the phenols from the petroleum ether, and color development with 4-aminoantipyrine and potassium ferricyanide at pH 7.9 ± 0.1. This procedure employs 2,4-dichlorophenol for the calibration curve. Thus, any other phenol that reacts with 4-aminoantipyrine at pH 7.9 will be reported in equivalents of 2,4-dichlorophenol. This method eliminates the distillation screening procedure required for Method C.

b. Interference: Most of the organic and inorganic compounds known to interfere with 4-aminoantipyrine are eliminated by the acid extraction of the aqueous sample with petroleum ether. The precautions listed under Interferences, Preservation, and Storage of Samples, Section 222A, should be followed.

c. Minimum detectable concentration: The analytical sensitivity depends upon the size of the sample extracted and the path length of the absorbance cell. With a path length of 2.54 cm and a 100-ml sample, the sensitivity is 70 μg/l; if 1,000 ml are extracted, the sensitivity is 7 μg/l. If a path length greater than 2.54 cm is used, then a greater sensitivity is obtained.

d. Absorptivity values: Table 222 (1) presents absorptivity and molar absorptivity values for a number of phenols.

2. Apparatus

a. Spectrophotometer: Any suitable spectrophotometer providing a light path of at least 2.54 cm for use at 500 mμ.

b. Separatory funnels, Squibb form,

* And other phenols, as indicated in introductory paragraph.

TABLE 222(1): ABSORPTIVITY AND MOLAR ABSORPTIVITY VALUES OF PHENOLS

Phenol	Absorptivity 1 $cm^{-1}g^{-1}$	Molar Absorptivity
4-Cl	39.0 ± 2.7	5020 ± 350
3-Cl	102.7 ± 4.5	13200 ± 580
2-Cl	135.9 ± 2.9	17470 ± 370
2,4-Cl	86.9 ± 4.5	14170 ± 730
3,4-Cl	27.4 ± 3.1	4470 ± 505
2,5-Cl	99.0 ± 3.6	16140 ± 590
2,3-Cl	103.6 ± 4.0	16885 ± 644
2,6-Cl	104.9 ± 3.2	17100 ± 513
2,4,6-Cl	36.8 ± 2.7	7270 ± 530
2,4,5-Cl	45.3 ± 2.7	8950 ± 530
2,3,4,5,6-Cl	No reaction	No reaction
4-Br	31.0 ± 2.7	5360 ± 470
3-Br	77.0 ± 2.7	13320 ± 470
2-Br	98.0 ± 3.6	16960 ± 620
2,4-Br	55.0 ± 2.9	13860 ± 730
2,6-Br	71.0 ± 2.6	17880 ± 680
2,4,6-Br	27.4 ± 2.2	9065 ± 730
2,3,4,5,6-Br	No reaction	No reaction

250-, 500-, or 1,000-ml, glass-stoppered, with teflon stopcock.

3. Reagents

a. Hydrochloric acid, conc.

b. Petroleum ether, 30–60 C: This solvent should be purified by extraction with the 0.5*N* ammonium hydroxide before use.

c. Ammonium hydroxide, 0.5*N*: Dilute 35 ml *fresh,* conc NH_4OH to 1 liter with distilled water.

d. Phosphate buffer solution: Dissolve 104.5 g dipotassium hydrogen phosphate, K_2HPO_4, and 72.3 g potassium dihydrogen phosphate, KH_2PO_4, in distilled water and dilute to 1 liter. The pH of this buffer solution should be 6.8.

e. Aminoantipyrine solution: Refer to Method C (Section 222C.3j).

f. Potassium ferricyanide solution: Refer to Method C (Section 222C.3k).

g. 2,4-dichlorophenol, analytical reference grade.*

h. Ethyl alcohol, 95%.

i. Stock 2,4-dichlorophenol (Solution A): Dissolve 0.100 g analytical-reagent grade 2,4-dichlorophenol in 100 ml of 95% ethyl alcohol; 1 ml = 1,000 μg.

j. Intermediate 2,4-dichlorophenol (Solution B): Dilute 10.0 ml stock 2,4-dichlorophenol (Solution A) to 100.0 ml with phenol-free distilled water; 1 ml = 100 μg.

k. Standard 2,4-dichlorophenol (Solution C): Dilute 25.0 ml intermediate solution (B) to 250 ml with phenol-free distilled water; 1 ml = 10 μg.

4. Procedure

a. Extraction: Place an appropriate volume of sample and an equal volume of a distilled water blank in separatory funnels. Add 5.0 ml conc HCl. Mix.

Extract the phenols from the acidified sample with three 50-ml portions petroleum ether. Shake each extraction for 3 min. Place the combined extracts in a 250-ml separatory funnel. Wash the combined petroleum ether extracts with two 50-ml portions distilled water to remove any emulsified HCl.

Extract the phenols from the washed petroleum ether with one 10.0-ml and two 5.0-ml portions of 0.5*N* NH_4OH. Shake each extraction for 3 min.

Place the ammoniacal extracts into 50-ml volumetric flasks. Add 20.0 ml phosphate buffer solution and mix well. The pH of this solution should be 7.9 ±

* Eastman White Label #1933 or equivalent.

0.1. It may be necessary to adjust the pH value to 7.9 ± 0.1 at this point.

b. Color development and measurement: Add exactly 0.50 ml 4-aminoantipyrine solution and mix well. Add exactly 0.50 ml potassium ferricyanide solution and mix well. Bring the solution to the 50.0-ml mark with distilled water and mix well. Allow 15 min for maximum color to develop. Read the absorbance at 500 mμ against a reagent blank. Estimate the phenol concentration of the sample from the calibration curve.

c. Preparation of calibration curve: Add the appropriate volumes of standard 2,4-dichlorophenol (Solution C) to a 500-ml separatory funnel so that quantities of 0, 10, 30, 50, 70 and 100 μg are obtained. Adjust these volumes to approximately 250 ml with phenol-free distilled water. Follow the steps outlined in ¶s 4a and 4b to develop and measure the color.

Construct the calibration curve by plotting absorbance against μg 2,4-dichlorophenol. Prepare a calibration curve for each photometer and check periodically.

5. Calculation

$$\mu g/l\ \text{2,4-dichlorophenol} = \frac{A}{B} \times 1{,}000.$$

where A = μg 2,4-dichlorophenol in sample from calibration curve and B = ml of original sample.

6. Precision and Accuracy

a. This method can be regarded only as an approximation and as representing the minimum amount of phenols present because 2,4-dichlorophenol is used as the standard. Therefore, no expression of accuracy can be made.

b. The precision of this method depends on interferences present and on the skill of the analyst. Precision also varies with concentration of the phenolic compounds. Round robin tests by four laboratories and five operators on standard 2,4-dichlorophenol solutions yielded the following standard deviations:

2,4-Dichlorophenol μg	Standard Deviation ± μg
9.67	0.92
50.23	2.61
103.47	3.40

222 F. Gas-Liquid Chromatographic Method * (TENTATIVE)

1. General Discussion

This method covers a direct aqueous-injection procedure for the gas-liquid chromatographic determination of phenols, cresols, and mono- and dichlorophenols in water.[2] The method may be applied to wastewater or to concentrates which contain more than 1 mg/l of phenolic compounds.

a. Principle: This method specifies a single gas-liquid chromatographic column for the separation of phenolic compounds and a flame-ionization detector for their measurement. The peak area of each component is measured and compared with that of a known standard to obtain quantitative results. In this method, elution of character-

* Adapted from ASTM D–2580–68-Standard, as published in ASTM *Book of Standards,* Part 23 (1968).

istic phenols occurs in the following order: (1) *o*-chlorophenol, (2) phenol and *o*-cresol, (3) *m*- and *p*-cresol, (4) 2,3- 2,4- 2,5- and 2,6-dichlorophenols, (5) *m*- and *p*-chlorophenols, and (6) 3,4-dichlorophenol.

b. Interference: Particulate or suspended matter may, unless very finely subdivided, plug the needle of the microsyringe used for sample injection. Such matter may be removed by centrifugation or filtration, provided it is ascertained that compounds of interest are not also removed. A colloid mill may be used, if necessary, to prepare a colloidal solution or suspension suitable for injection. Particulate matter may serve as condensation nuclei for samples; acid treatment may often dissolve such interfering solids.

Nonphenolic organic compounds which have the same retention time as the phenolic compounds will interfere with the test. Such compounds may be eliminated by the distillation step (Section 222B) for Methods C and D.

Under strong alkaline conditions, some chlorophenols may form salts which reduce their volatility in the test. Also, some nonphenolic organics—for example, tar bases—may be more volatile in basic solutions. Simple pH adjustment to near neutral or slightly acid will eliminate these interferences.

A "ghost" or "memory peak" is an interference, showing as a peak, which appears at the same elution time as an organic component of a previous analysis. Such effect is minimized or eliminated in this method by injecting 3 μl of water between samples. This water wash usually clears the injection port, column and detector of artifacts; however, repeated wash injections may be necessary to clear the system. The electrometer should be set at maximum sensitivity during the wash injections to facilitate detection of ghosts. Glass injector inserts are recommended. Inserts are easy to clean or replace and they minimize cleanup difficulties.

It is beyond the scope of this method to describe procedures for eliminating all possible interferences which might occur, particularly with highly contaminated industrial wastewater.

Observe the precautions given in the section, Interferences, Preservation, and Storage of Samples (Section 222A).

2. Apparatus

a. Gas chromatograph, equipped with a hydrogen flame-ionization detector: A commercial or custom-designed gas chromatograph with a column oven capable of isothermal temperature control to at least 210 ± 0.2 C. A unit for temperature programming will facilitate elution of a mixture of phenolics of wide boiling-point range. This method describes an isothermal analysis using a single-column type of gas chromatograph. Temperature programming is an option of the analyst.

b. Recorder, to measure chromatographic output at a full-scale range of 1mV with a response time of 1 sec.

c. Chromatographic columns: Columns may be purchased or prepared by the analyst. Variations in column loading, length, diameter, support size, treatment, etc., are possible. Three columns are cited in this procedure. These may be modified with the understanding that the elution time and sensitivity may in consequence be altered.

1) Carbowax 20*M:* A ⅛ in. by 10 ft stainless steel column packed with 60/80 mesh Chromosorb W (acid-washed and hexamethyldisilazane-treated) coated with 20% by weight

of Carbowax 20M-TPA (terephthalic acid).

2) FREE FATTY ACID PHASE, 5 ft: A ⅛ in. by 5 ft stainless steel column packed with 70/80 mesh Chromosorb W (acid-washed) coated with 5% by weight Free Fatty Acid Phase (FFAP).*

3) FREE FATTY ACID PHASE, 10 ft: A ⅛ in. by 10 ft stainless steel column packed with 60/80 mesh Chromosorb T coated with 10% Free Fatty Acid Phase. Chromosorb T is a TFE fluorocarbon-6 product which melts at 327 C and may begin to fuse above 250 C. It is available from suppliers of gas-chromatographic materials.

d. Syringe, 10 μl.

3. Reagents

a. Carrier gases: Research-grade nitrogen or helium of highest purity.

b. Hydrogen, for use with the flame-ionization detector; may be obtained by using a hydrogen generator, or from a high-purity tank supply.

c. Water, referee-grade reagent: If only ordinary distilled water is available, treat it by *both* redistillation and deionization as described in Ammonia Nitrogen, Section 132A.3a. Test the treated water in the chromatograph to assure freedom from false peaks.

d. Phenolic compounds: Research grades of high purity are required. Highest-purity compounds may be prepared by redistillation or recrystallization, or by using a preparatory gas-chromatographic instrument. The following phenolic compounds are suggested: *o*-chlorophenol, *m*-chlorophenol, *p*-chlorophenol, *o*-cresol, *m*-cresol, *p*-cresol, 2,3-dichlorophenol, 2,4-dichlorophenol, 2,5-dichlorophenol, 2,6-dichlorophenol, 3,4-dichlorophenol, and phenol. Prepare 100 mg/l solutions in referee-grade reagent water.

4. Procedure

a. Preparation of chromatograph: Install the packed column in the chromatograph, using suitable fittings. The use of antigalling thread lubricant is advisable.

b. Check for leaks: Conduct a leak test at approximately 15 psi above the operating pressure by shutting off the downstream end of the system and pressurizing from the carrier gas supply. Shut off the cylinder valve and observe the pressure gauge. If no drop is noted in 10 to 15 min, consider the system to be tight. Locate minor leaks with aqueous soap solution but do so with caution, because soap solution entering the system may cause extraneous peaks or affect the stability of the system. Do not use the soap method for leak-testing near the ionization detector.

c. Column conditioning: Condition columns for at least 24 hr at temperatures 30 to 50 C above the expected operating temperature before use. Exercise caution to avoid exceeding the maximum allowable temperature for both the packing and the substrate. Disconnect the column at the end near the detector base to avoid deposition of volatiles on the detector during conditioning. Adjust carrier gas flow to about 20–40 ml/min for a ⅛ in.-diameter column. Occasionally inject 3 to 5 μl water during conditioning to facilitate elution of impurities.

After conditioning, connect the column to the flame-ionization detector. Adjust the hydrogen flow to the detector to about 25 ml/min for a ⅛ in.-

* Available from Varian Aerograph, Walnut Creek, Calif.

TABLE 222(2): TYPICAL OPERATING CONDITIONS FOR CHROMATOGRAPHIC COLUMN

Column and Packing	Column No. (Chromatographic Columns)		
	1 ¶ 2c(1)	2 ¶ 2c(2)	3 ¶ 2c(3)
Carrier gas	Helium	Helium	Nitrogen
Carrier gas flow, ml/min	25	35	60
Temperature, degrees Centigrade:			
Injection port	250	205	250
Column	210	147	188
Hydrogen for detector, ml/min	25	25	30
Chart speed, in./hr	12	12	12
Sensitivity, mV	1	1	1
Electrometer range	1	0.1	1
Attenuation	1	1	1
Sample volume, microliters	1	1	1
Results	a	b	c

[a] See Figures 40 and 41.
[b] See Figure 44.
[c] See Figures 42 and 43.

diameter column. Adjust the airflow as specified in the instrument being used. Ignite the hydrogen flame at the detector. Adjust the column temperature to the desired level. Adjust the carrier gas flow rate to 20–40 ml/min. Observe the recorder base line. When a base-line drift is no longer apparent, the column is ready for use.

When the series of analyses is completed and the column is to be removed and stored, seal or cap the ends.

d. Operating conditions for analysis: Typical operating conditions are summarized in Table 222(2). These operating parameters may be varied, but analytical and calibration test variations must be reconciled in calculating results. For example, either nitrogen or helium may be used as the carrier gas; recorder chart speeds of approximately 30 in./hr are commonly employed; sample sizes of 3 to 5 μl are usually injected.

e. Method of compound identification: Compound identification is based upon the retention time—the time that elapses from the introduction of the sample until the peak maximum is reached. Compare the retention times of the sample peaks with those of known standards obtained under the same operating conditions. When several related materials are eluted at the same time, reanalyze the sample with a column of a different type that effects a better separation, or supplement the chromatographic procedure with spectrographic analyses.[3] (If necessary, the various sample components may be trapped as they emerge from the system, then analyzed by other appropriate methods.

To determine the retention time of

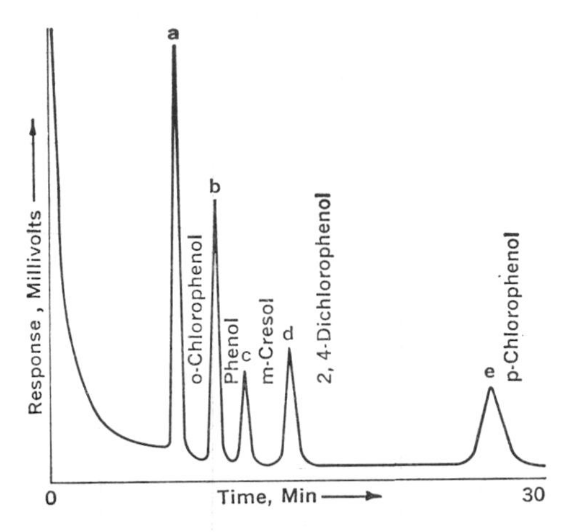

Analyses were made with 10-ft by ⅛-in. stainless steel column coated with 20 per cent Carbowax-terephthalic acid on 60/80-mesh diatomite, HMDS treated. Column temperature was 210°C, and injection temperature, 250°C. Hydrogen and helium flow rates were each 20 ml/min, at electrometer range 1 and attenuation 1, with chart speed at 12 in./hr, 1-mv full-scale response, and 1-µl sample of approximately 100-mg/l solutions of each phenolic. Peak A is for o-chlorophenol; B, phenol; C, m-cresol; D, 2, 4-dichlorophenol; E, p-chlorophenol.

Figure 40

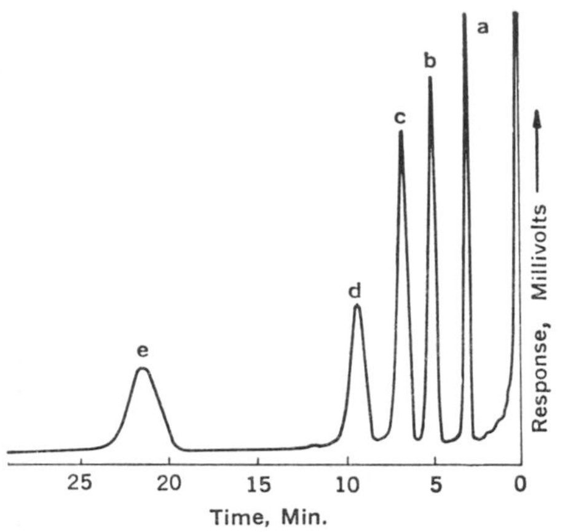

Analyses were made with 10-ft by ⅛-in. stainless steel column coated with 10 per cent polyester on 60/80-mesh fluorocarbon resin medium. Column temperature was 188°C, and injection temperature, 250°C. Flow rates for nitrogen were 60 ml/min, for hydrogen, 30 ml/min, at electrometer range 1 and attenuation 1, with chart speed at 12 in./hr., 1-mv full-scale response, and 1-µl sample of approximately 100-mg/l solutions of each phenolic. Peak A is for o-chlorophenol; B, phenol; C, m-cresol; D, 2,4-dichlorophenol; E, p-chlorophenol.

Figure 42

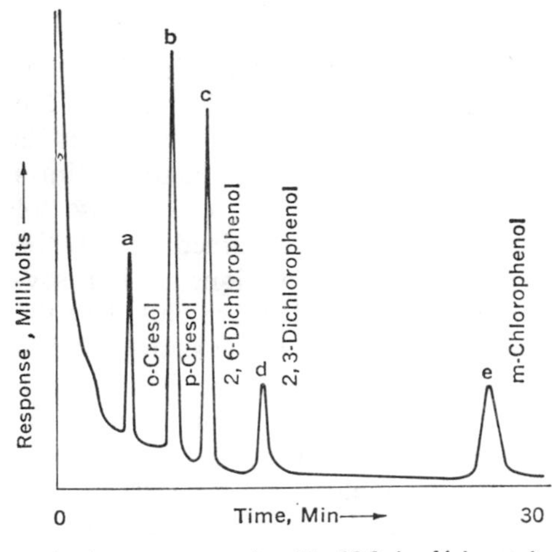

Analyses were made with 10-ft by ⅛-in. stainless steel column coated with 20 per cent Carbowax-terephthalic acid on 60/80-mesh diatomite, HMDS treated. Column temperature was 210°C, and injection temperature 250°C. Hydrogen and helium flow rates were each 20 ml/min, at electrometer range 1 and attenuation 1, with chart speed at 12 in./hr, 1-mv full scale response, and 1-µl sample of approximately 100 ml/l solutions of each phenolic. Peak A is for o-cresol; B, p-cresol; C, 2, 6-dichlorophenol; D, 2, 3-dichlorophenol; E, m-chlorophenol.

Figure 41

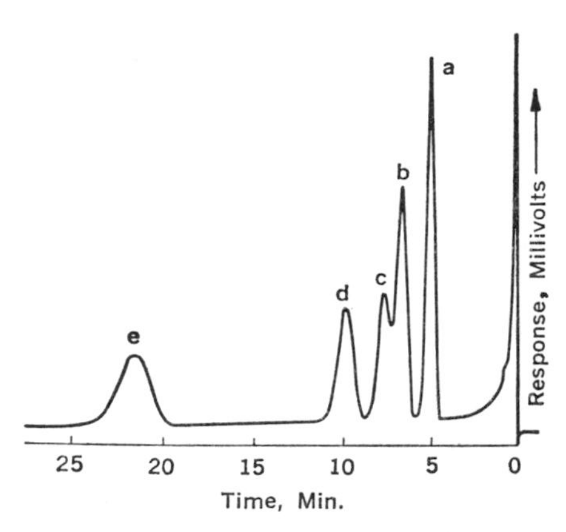

Analyses were made with 10-ft by ⅛-in. stainless steel column coated with 10 per cent polyester on 60/80-mesh fluorocarbon resin medium. Column temperature was 188°C, and injection temperature, 250°C. Flow rates for nitrogen were 60 ml/min, for hydrogen, 30 ml/min, at electrometer range 1 and attenuation 1, with chart speed at 12 in./hr., 1-mv full-scale response, and 1-µl sample of approximately 100-mg/l solutions of each phenolic. Peak A is for o-cresol; B, p-cresol, C, 2,6-dichlorophenol; D,2, 3-dichlorophenol; E, m-chlorophenol.

Figure 43

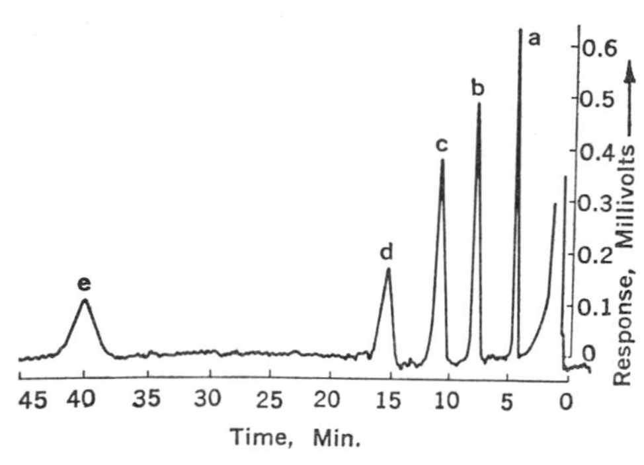

Analyses were made with 5-ft by ⅛ in. stainless steel column coated with 5 per cent polyester on acid-washed 70/80-mesh diatomite. Column temperature was 147°C. Flow rates for helium were 35 ml/min, for hydrogen, 25 ml/min, at electrometer range 0.1 and attenuation 1, with chart speed 12 in./hr, 1-mv full-scale response; for 1-λ sample. Peak A is for o-chlorophenol, 10.4 mg/l, B, phenol, 9.3 mg/l; C, m-cresol, 10.7 mg/l; D, 2,4-dichlorophenol, 10.7 mg/l; E, p-chloro-phenol, 11.2 mg/l.

Figure 44

phenol, cresols, mono- and dichlorophenols, take the following steps:

With the column at operating conditions, inject in turn a 1-μl sample of a 100 mg/l aqueous solution of each phenolic compound. Use a 10-μl syringe. Adjust the instrument attenuation so that the peak height is on scale, preferably near 50% of full scale. Mark the injection point on the recorder chart. Measure the retention time in minutes to at least two significant figures.

To eliminate errors induced by ghosting, inject water alone after each phenolic sample. Set the electrometer range and attenuation at maximum sensitivity during water washing. Inject the same volume of water as that used for the sample. Repeat water injections until a steady base line free of ghosts has been attained, after which the next sample injection may be made.

Make triplicate determinations for each phenolic compound and record the average retention value. (Mixtures of phenols having different retention intervals may be injected simultaneously to expedite the standardizations.)

CAUTION—Flush the injection syringe used for calibration with each new sample at least three times before injecting into the chromatograph.

Calculate the retentions of all the phenolic compounds relative to phenol. The relative retention times with approximate chromatograph calibration factors are shown in Table 222(3) for two columns. These calibration values are presented only for information. The analyst must determine and regularly recheck calibration values for each column and phenolic material used.

f. Calibration and standardization: The area under the peak of the chromatogram is taken as a quantitative measure of the amount of the corresponding compound. To make calibrations, select the phenolic concentration range desired (for example, 1 mg/l or 10 mg/l) and prepare fresh solutions of each compound in referee-grade reagent water.

With the column at equilibrium operating conditions, inject measured volumes (e.g., 3 μl) of the standard solutions, using the previously described procedure and observing all precautions. Continue until at least three peaks are obtained which deviate by no more than ± 1% in area at the same attenuation. Adjust the attenuation in all cases to keep the peak on scale and preferably with a height of 50% of full-scale recorder range.

Measure the peak area for each standard by triangulation, or by mechanical or electronic integration, or by weighing the peak cutouts.

If overlapping of peaks or other interaction between the components of the sample to be analyzed is anticipated, inject into the column prepared mixtures of standards representing the phenolic compounds expected in the sample. Measure the peak areas as for the pure compounds. Express the results as nanograms per unit area.

Typical calibration factors are shown in Table 222(3). These must not be used in quantitative analysis and are presented only as a guide.

g. Sample treatment: With the column at operating conditions, inject 1 to 3 μl of sample into the injection port. Determine the retention times of the phenols in the sample. If necessary, adjust the attenuation to keep the highest peak on scale for the major phenolic component in the sample. Perform triplicate determinations at identical column and instrument conditions; flush as required to eliminate artifacts. Characterize and measure the peak areas obtained. Average the results of the triplicate determinations.

5. Calculation

a. Each peak should be characterized by a retention time. Supplementary tests, such as infrared and ultraviolet, used in the characterization of trapped fractions, should be reported.

b. For those peak areas representing two or more phenolic compounds, an average value of the calibration obtained with the standards may be used in the calculation; or the area may be measured as a given material, with the notation in the results reported that other components have comparable elution intervals and may be represented.

c. Calculate the concentration of each component by the equation:

TABLE 222(3): CHROMATOGRAPHIC RETENTION TIMES

Phenolic Compound	Boiling Point	Relative Retention [b]	Calibration Factor [a, b] ng per sq in.	Relative Retention [c]	Calibration Factor [a, c] ng per sq in.
Phenol	182 C	1.0	45.2	1.0	28.8
o-Cresol	192 C	1.0	51.0	1.0	27.0
m-Cresol	203 C	1.3	51.9	1.3	30.5
p-Cresol	202 C	1.3	51.3	1.3	31.3
o-Chlorophenol	176 C	0.8	86.7	0.6	44.8
m-Chlorophenol	214 C	3.6	106	3.6	45.4[b]
p-Chlorophenol	217 C	3.6	125	3.6	46.5[b]
2,3-Dichlorophenol	—	1.8	76.5	1.9	46.8
2,4-Dichlorophenol	210 C	1.8	117	1.9	55.3
2,5-Dichlorophenol	210 C	1.8	113	1.9	50.4
2,6-Dichlorophenol	220 C	1.6	71.5	1.5	50.0
3,4-Dichlorophenol	254 C	—	—	11.5	43.0[b]

[a] Calibration in nanograms (10^{-9} g)/sq in. at chart speed of 90 in./hr, 1-mV response, range 1, attenuation 1.
[b] Column at 210 C.
[c] Column at 188 C.

$$\text{Phenolic Compound(s), mg/l} = \frac{A \times B}{C}$$

where A = area of sample peak in sq in., B = calibration factor in nanograms per sq in., and C = sample volume in microliters.

6. Precision

The precision of this method has been tested using four master solutions, each containing four phenolic compounds. The compositions of the master solutions were as follows:

Phenolic Compounds	Master Solution (mg/liter)			
	1	2	3	4
Phenol	20	80	40	10
m-Cresol	40	10	20	80
o-Chlorophenol	10	20	80	40
2,4-Dichlorophenol	80	40	10	20

The respective precisions may be expressed as follows:

Phenol: $S_T = 0.048X + 0.6$
$S_O = 0.017X + 0.3$
m-Cresol: $S_T = 0.029X + 2.2$
$S_O = 0.014X + 0.7$
o-Chlorophenol: $S_T = 0.083X + 1.2$
$S_O = 0.031X + 0.2$
2,4-Dichlorophenol: $S_T = 0.172X + 0.1$
$S_O = 0.036X + 1.2$

where: S_T = overall precision in mg/liter, S_O = single-operator precision in mg/liter, and X = concentration of phenolic determined in mg/liter.

Additional Information

The information in Tables 222(4) and 222(5) is presented to aid the analyst.

TABLE 222(4): COMPARISON OF PHENOLIC ANALYTICAL PROCEDURES[c]

Phenolic Compound	Concentration, mg/liter		
	By Weight	4-Amino-anti-pyrine[a]	GLC
Phenol	1.06	0.97	0.97
o-Cresol	1.04	0.64	1.03
m-Cresol	1.02	0.38	1.03
p-Cresol	1.00	0.00	1.00
			3.94[b]
Composite	4.12[c]	2.40	4.11[d]

[a] Reported as phenol; ASTM Method D 1783, Test for Phenolic Compounds in *Industrial Water and Industrial Wastewater;* average of two analyses.

[b] Based on *m*- and *p*-cresol of 2.01, plus *o*-cresol and phenol as phenol of 1.93; average of four analyses.

[c] Composite of the four phenolics.

[d] Based on *m*- and *p*-cresols of 2.01, plus *o*-cresol and phenol, equal concentrations, with calibration factors averaged.

TABLE 222(5): EFFECT OF PH IN GLC ANALYSES OF 2,4-DICHLOROPHENOL

pH	4.5	7.7	9.7	10.8	11.7
Peak area (sq in.)	2.88	2.90	2.90	2.93	1.08

[a] Column and operating conditions: column, 5 ft by ⅛ in., stainless steel; 5% FFAP, 60/80 Chromosorb W. Flow rates and temperature: hydrogen, 25 ml/min; nitrogen, 25 ml/min. Tc = 176 C; Ti = 205 C; R = 0.1, x, 1; 3 samples in distilled water; chart, 90 in./hr; pH adjusted by NaOH; 1 mV full scale. Initial dichlorophenolic concentration, 5 mg/liter.

222 G. References

1. R. H. BURTSCHELL et al. 1959. Chlorine derivatives of phenol causing taste and odor. *JAWWA* 51:205.
2. R. A. BAKER. 1966. Phenolic analyses by direct aqueous injection gas chromatography. *JAWWA* 58:751.
3. ———. 1966. Trace organic analyses by aqueous gas-liquid chromatography. *J. Air & Water Poll.* 10:591.

222 H. Bibliography

SCOTT, R. D. 1931. Application of a bromine method in the determination of phenols and cresols. *Ind. Eng. Chem.*, Anal. Ed. 3:67.

EMERSON, E., H. H. BEACHAM & L. C. BEEGLE. 1943. The condensation of aminoantipyrine. II. A new color test for phenolic compounds. *J. Organic Chem.* 8:417.

ETTINGER, M. B., S. SCHOTT & C. C. RUCHHOFT. 1943. Preservation of phenol content in polluted river water samples previous to analysis. *JAWWA* 35:299.

ETTINGER, M. B. & R. C. KRONER. 1949. The determination of phenolic materials in industrial wastes. *Proc. 5th Ind. Waste Conf.* (Purdue Univ.), page 345.

ETTINGER, M. B., C. C. RUCHHOFT & R. J. LISHKA. 1951. Sensitive 4-aminoantipyrine method for phenolic compounds. *Anal. Chem.* 23:1783.

DANNIS, M. 1951. Determination of phenols by the aminoantipyrine method. *Sewage & Ind. Wastes* 23:1516.

MOHLER, E. F. JR. & L. N. JACOB. 1957. Determination of phenolic-type compounds in water and industrial waste waters: Comparison of analytical methods. *Anal. Chem.* 29:1369.

GORDON, G. E. 1960. Colorimetric determination of phenolic materials in refinery waste waters. *Anal. Chem.* 32: 1325.

OCHYNSKI, F. W. 1960. The absorptiometric determination of phenol. *Analyst* 85: 278.

FAUST, S. D. & O. M. ALY. 1962. The determination of 2,4-dichlorophenol in water. *JAWWA* 54:235.

FAUST, S. D. & E. W. MIKULEWICZ. 1967. Factors influencing the condensation of 4-aminoantipyrine with derivatives of hydroxybenzene. II. Influence of hydronium ion concentration on absorptivity. *Water Research* 1:509.

BAKER, R. A. & B. A. MALO. 1967. Phenolics by aqueous injection gas chromatography. *Environ. Sci. & Technol.* 1:997.

223 PHOSPHATE

Phosphorus occurs in natural waters and in wastewaters almost solely in the form of various types of phosphate. These forms are commonly classified into orthophosphates, condensed phosphates (pyro-, meta-, and polyphosphates) and organically bound phosphates. These forms of phosphate may occur in the soluble form, in particles of detritus, or in the bodies of aquatic organisms.

The various forms of phosphate find their way into wastewaters, effluents and polluted waters from a variety of sources. Small amounts of certain condensed phosphates are added to some water supplies in the course of treatment. Larger quantities of the same compounds may be added when the water is used for laundering or other cleaning, since these materials are major constituents of many commercial cleaning preparations. Orthophosphates applied to agricultural or residential cultivated land as fertilizers are carried into surface waters with storm runoff and to a lesser extent with melting snow. Organic phosphates are formed primarily in biological processes; hence, they are contributed to sewage in body wastes and food residues, or they may be formed from orthophosphates in biological treatment processes or by life in the receiving water.

Phosphorus is an element which is essential to the growth of organisms and it can often be the nutrient that limits the growth which a body of water can support. In instances where phosphorus is a growth-limiting nutrient, the discharge of raw or treated sewage, agricultural drainage or certain industrial wastes to a receiving water may stimulate the growth, in nuisance quantities, of photosynthetic aquatic micro- and macroorganisms.

Phosphates occur in bottom sediments and in biological sludges, both as precipitated inorganic forms and incorporated into organic compounds.

1. Definition of Terms

Phosphate analyses embody two general procedural steps: (a) conversion of the phosphorus form of interest to soluble orthophosphate, and (b) colorimetric determination of soluble orthophosphate. The separation of phosphorus into its various forms is largely analytically defined, but the analytical differentiations have been selected so that they may be used for interpretive purposes.

Separation of "filtrable" (or "dissolved") from "particulate" forms of phosphate depends on filtration through a 0.45-μ membrane filter. The selection of membrane filtration over depth filtration is made because of the greater likelihood of obtaining a consistent separation of particle sizes by the membrane filtration technic. No claim is made that filtration through 0.45-μ membrane filters is a true separation of suspended and soluble forms of phosphate; it is merely a convenient and replicable analytical technic designed to make a gross separation. This is reflected in the use of the term "filtrable" (rather than "soluble") to describe the phosphorus forms determined in the filtrate which passes the 0.45-μ membrane.

The phosphates which respond to the colorimetric tests without preliminary hydrolysis or oxidative digestion of the sample are considered as "orthophosphate." Strictly speaking, a small fraction of any condensed phosphates present is usually hydrolyzed unavoidably in the procedure, and thus is reported as a part of the orthophosphate. Orthophosphates occur both in filtrable (dissolved) and in particulate form.

Acid hydrolysis at boiling-water temperature is designed to convert filtrable and particulate condensed phosphates to filtrable orthophosphate. The hydrolysis unavoidably releases some phosphate from organic compounds, but this factor has been reduced to a minimum (consistent with good condensed phosphate hydrolysis) by judicious selection of acid strength and hydrolysis time and temperature. Nevertheless, the term "acid-hydrolyzable phosphate" is preferred over "condensed phosphate" for this technic.

The phosphate fractions which are converted to orthophosphate only by oxidative destruction of the organic matter present are considered "organic" or "organically bound" phosphate. The severity of the oxidation required for this conversion depends upon the form —and to some extent upon the amount —of the organic phosphate present. Like the orthophosphates and acid-hydrolyzable phosphates, the organic phosphates occur both in the filtrable (dissolved) and in the particulate fractions.

The resulting classification of phosphates into three chemical types and two physical states is summarized in Table 223(1).

2. *Selection of Procedure*

Subdividing the phosphates according to Table 223(1) makes it possible to report a number of different phosphate fractions. If each of the fractions were determined separately, this could lead to a very complicated procedure. In practice, even when the concentration of every fraction is reported, several are calculated by difference. The analytical scheme for phosphate differentiation can be summarized as follows:

a. Total dissolved and suspended phosphate: Digestion of the whole sample is followed by orthophosphate determination. Difficulties may be encountered with highly saline samples when using digestion technics that drastically reduce the volume of the sample, because of the precipitation of large quantities of salt. If it is necessary to carry out total phosphate analyses on such samples, direct determination of total filtrable phosphate (*e*) and total particulate phosphate (*i*) is recommended, followed by addition of the results.

b. Total dissolved and suspended orthophosphate: Colorimetric method

TABLE 223(1): CLASSIFICATION OF PHOSPHATE FRACTIONS

Chemical Types	Physical States		
	Total	Filtrable (Dissolved)	Particulate
Total	*a.* Total dissolved and suspended phosphate	*e.* Total filtrable (dissolved) phosphate	*i.* Total particulate phosphate
Ortho	*b.* Total dissolved and suspended orthophosphate	*f.* Filtrable (dissolved) orthophosphate	*j.* Particulate orthophosphate
Acid-hydrolyzable	*c.* Total dissolved and suspended acid-hydrolyzable phosphate	*g.* Filtrable (dissolved) acid-hydrolyzable phosphate	*k.* Particulate acid-hydrolyzable phosphate
Organic	*d.* Total dissolved and suspended organic phosphate	*h.* Filtrable (dissolved) organic phosphate	*l.* Particulate organic phosphate

D, E or F is applied without preliminary filtration, hydrolysis or digestion of the sample. Anomalous results may be obtained on samples containing large amounts of suspended sediments through a time-dependent desorption of orthophosphate from the suspended particles. Very often the result depends largely on the degree of agitation and mixing to which the sample is subjected during analysis.

c. Total dissolved and suspended acid-hydrolyzable phosphate: The unfiltered sample is treated by mild acid hydrolysis, followed by orthophosphate determination. The result includes dissolved and suspended orthophosphates and acid-hydrolyzable phosphates originally present in the sample. The concentration of dissolved and suspended acid-hydrolyzable phosphate is obtained by subtracting the dissolved and suspended orthophosphate (*b*).

d. Total dissolved and suspended organic phosphate: The concentration is calculated by subtracting from the total dissolved and suspended phosphate (*a*) the concentration of dissolved and suspended orthophosphate (*b*), and acid-hydrolyzable phosphate (*c*).

e. Total filtrable (dissolved) phosphate: Filtration of the sample through a 0.45-μ membrane filter is followed by digestion of the filtrate and orthophosphate determination. Persulfate digestion is usually suitable for filtered samples.

f. Filtrable (dissolved) orthophosphate: Filtration of the sample through a 0.45-μ membrane filter is followed by orthophosphate determination on the filtrate.

g. Filtrable (dissolved) acid-hydrolyzable phosphate: Filtration of the sample through a 0.45-μ membrane filter is followed by mild acid hydrolysis of the filtrate and orthophosphate determination. The result includes the filtrable (dissolved) orthophosphate and acid-hydrolyzable phosphate of the original sample, and the concentration of filtrable acid-hydrolyzable phosphate is obtained by subtracting the filtrable (dissolved) orthophosphate (*f*).

h. Filtrable (dissolved) organic phosphate: The concentration is calculated by subtracting from the total filtrable (dissolved) phosphate (*e*) the concentration of filtrable orthophosphate (*f*) and acid-hydrolyzable phosphate (*g*).

i. Total particulate phosphate: The concentration may be obtained either by difference or by direct determination. To calculate total particulate phosphate by difference, the concentration of total filtrable (dissolved) phosphate (*e*) is subtracted from the total dissolved and suspended phosphate (*a*). For a direct determination, the membrane filter containing the particulate matter collected from the sample is treated by digestion with nitric acid and then perchloric acid, followed by colorimetric determination. The latter technic is suggested for use with saline samples (see ¶ *a*). It also makes possible the determination of small amounts of particulate phosphate with greater precision than that obtained in the calculation by difference, since the particles can be derived from a large sample volume.

j. Particulate orthophosphate: The concentration is usually calculated by subtracting the filtrable (dissolved) orthophosphate (*f*) from the total dissolved and suspended orthophosphate (*b*).

k. Particulate acid-hydrolyzable phosphate: The concentration usually is calculated by subtracting the filtrable (dissolved) acid-hydrolyzable phosphate (*g*) from the total dissolved and suspended acid-hydrolyzable phosphate (*c*).

l. Particulate organic phosphate: The concentration usually is calculated by subtracting the filtrable (dissolved) organic phosphate (*h*) from the total dissolved and suspended organic phosphate (*d*).

In many cases, it is unnecessary to determine or report all the various phosphate fractions given in Table 223 (1). The analyst should select appropriate procedures to provide the information which is required.

3. Selection of Method

a. Digestion Methods: Since phosphorus may occur in suspension and in combination with organic matter, a digestion method to determine total phosphate must be able to effectively oxidize organic matter, rupturing both C-P and C-O-P bonds, and to solubilize suspended material to release the phosphorus as soluble orthophosphate.

Three digestion methods are given. The perchloric acid method, the most drastic and time-consuming method, is recommended only for particularly difficult samples such as sediments. The nitric acid-sulfuric acid method is recommended for most samples. By far the simplest method is the persulfate oxidation technic. It is recommended that this method be checked against one or more of the more drastic digestion technics and be adopted if identical recoveries are obtained.

b. Colorimetric Methods: Three methods of orthophosphate determination are described. Selection depends largely on the concentration range of orthophosphate. Thus, the vanadomolybdic acid method (*D*) is most useful for routine analyses in the range of 0.2–18 mg P/l. The stannous chloride method (*E*) or the ascorbic acid method (*F*) is more suited for the range of 0.01–6 mg P/l. With the stannous chloride method, an extraction step is recommended for the lower levels of this range and when interferences need to be overcome.

4. Sampling and Storage

If a differentiation of phosphorus forms is to be made, it is recommended that filtration be carried out immediately upon sample collection and that samples be preserved by freezing (at or below −10 C) either in the presence or absence of 40 mg $HgCl_2$/l. The addition of the mercury preservative is especially recommended when samples are to be stored for long periods. *Preservation with acid or chloroform should be avoided.* If total phosphorus alone is to be determined, preservation is not necessary. Samples containing low concentrations of phosphorus should not be stored in plastic bottles because it is suspected that adsorption of phosphate onto the walls of the bottles takes place. All glass containers should be rinsed with hot dilute HCl followed by several rinses in distilled water. The use of commercial detergents containing phosphate for cleansing of glassware used in phosphate analyses should be avoided.

223 A. Preliminary Filtration Step

Samples for the determination of filtrable (dissolved) orthophosphate, filtrable (dissolved) acid-hydrolyzable phosphate, and total filtrable (dissolved) phosphate should be filtered through membrane filters of 0.45-μ pore size. If the specified pore size is unavailable, any size from 0.4 to 0.6 may be used. However, for reproducible separations, consistent use of a given pore size is often important. Unless the standard 0.45-μ filters are used, the pore size should be reported with the results of the analyses.

Membrane filters should be washed by soaking in distilled water prior to use in separations, since they may contribute significant amounts of phosphorus to samples containing low concentrations of phosphate. Two washing technics are suggested: (a) Soak filters (50 per 2 liters) in distilled water for 24 hr; (b) soak filters (50 per 2 liters) in distilled water for 1 hr, change the distilled water, and soak the filters an additional 3 hr.

After the membrane filters have been properly washed, insert in a suitable filter holder connected to a suction flask and vacuum source and collect a sufficient volume of filtrate for the required determinations.

223 B. Preliminary Acid Hydrolysis Step for Condensed Phosphates

1. Discussion

The acid-hydrolyzable phosphate content of the sample is operationally defined as the difference between the orthophosphate as measured in the untreated sample and the phosphate found after mild acid hydrolysis. Generally, it includes the condensed phosphates such as pyro-, tripoly-, and higher-molecular-weight species like hexametaphosphate. In addition, some natural waters contain organic phosphate compounds that are hydrolyzed to orthophosphate under the conditions of this test. Polyphosphates generally do not respond to the orthophosphate tests but can be hydrolyzed to orthophosphate by boiling with acid.

Following hydrolysis, orthophosphate is determined by colorimetric method D, E or F. The degree of interference, precision, accuracy and sensitivity will depend on the colorimetric method employed.

2. Apparatus

a. Autoclave or pressure cooker, capable of operating at 15–20 psig.

3. Reagents

a. Phenolphthalein indicator solution.

b. Strong acid solution: Slowly add 300 ml conc H_2SO_4 to about 600 ml distilled water. When cool, add 4.0 ml conc HNO_3 and dilute to 1 liter.

c. Sodium hydroxide, 6N.

4. Procedure

a. To 100 ml sample or an aliquot diluted to 100 ml, add 1 drop (0.05 ml) phenolphthalein indicator solution. If a red color develops, add strong acid solution dropwise, to just discharge the color. Then add 1 ml in excess.

b. Boil gently for at least 90 min, adding distilled water to keep the volume between 25 and 50 ml. Alternatively, heat for 30 min in an autoclave or pressure cooker at 15–20 psi. Cool, neutralize to a faint pink color with sodium hydroxide solution, and restore to the original 100-ml volume with distilled water.

c. Prepare a calibration curve by carrying a series of standards containing orthophosphate (see colorimetric method D, E or F) through the hydrolysis step. Do not use orthophosphate standards without hydrolysis, since the salts added in hydrolysis cause an increase in the color intensity in some methods.

d. Determine the orthophosphate content of the treated portions, using colorimetric method D, E or F. This gives the sum of polyphosphate and orthophosphate in the sample. To calculate its content of acid-hydrolyzable phosphate, determine orthophosphate in a portion of the sample which has not been hydrolyzed, using the same colorimetric method as that for the treated sample, and subtract.

223 C. Preliminary Digestion Steps for Total Phosphorus

The total phosphorus content of the sample includes all of the orthophosphates and condensed phosphates, both soluble and insoluble, and organic and inorganic species. To release phosphate from combination with organic matter, a digestion or oxidation technic is called for. The rigor of the digestion required depends on the type of sample. The three digestion technics presented, in order of decreasing rigor, are perchloric acid digestion, sulfuric acid-nitric acid digestion, and persulfate digestion. It is recommended that the digestion technics be compared as to phosphorus recovery on the specific type of samples being tested, and if it is found that the less tedious persulfate method gives good phosphorus recovery, this is the method that should be adopted.

Following digestion, the liberated orthophosphate is determined by colorimetric method D, E or F. The colorimetric method used, rather than the digestion procedure, governs in matters of interference and minimum detectable concentration.

I—PERCHLORIC ACID DIGESTION

1. Apparatus

a. Hot plate: A 30 × 50 cm heating surface is adequate.

b. Safety shield.

c. Safety goggles.

d. Conical flasks, 125-ml, which have been acid-washed followed by distilled water rinses.

e. Porcelain evaporating dishes, acid-washed and rinsed in distilled water.

2. Reagents

a. Nitric acid, concentrated, reagent grade.

b. Perchloric acid, $HClO_4 \cdot 2H_2O$; purchased as 70–72% $HClO_4$, reagent grade.

c. Sodium hydroxide, 6N.

d. Methyl orange indicator solution.

3. Procedure

a. CAUTION—Heated mixtures of concentrated perchloric acid and organic matter may explode violently. Avoid this hazard by taking the following precautions: (1) Do not add perchloric acid to a hot solution that may contain organic matter. (2) Always pretreat samples containing organic matter with HNO_3 prior to addition of $HClO_4$. (3) Use a mixture of nitric and perchloric acids in starting the digestion step. (4) Avoid repeated fumings with perchloric acid in ordinary hoods. For routine operations, use hoods of all-stone or asbestos-cement. For occasional work with perchloric acid, connect a water pump to a glass fume eradicator.*

b. Measure out a sample containing the desired amount of phosphate (this will be determined by whether Method D, E or F is to be used for the colorimetric finish). Acidify to methyl orange with conc HNO_3, add another 5 ml conc HNO_3, and evaporate on a steam bath or hot plate to 15–20 ml, covering the vessel with a watch glass when necessary to avoid loss of material by spattering. Place an infrared lamp over the sample to hasten evaporation if desired.

c. Transfer the evaporated sample to a 125-ml conical flask using 5 ml conc nitric acid to rinse the evaporating dish, cool, and add 5 ml HNO_3 and 10 ml 70–72% $HClO_4$. After adding a few boiling chips, heat on a hot plate and evaporate gently until dense white fumes of $HClO_4$ just appear. If the solution is not clear at this point, cover the neck of the flask with a watch glass and keep the solution just barely boiling until it clears. If necessary, add 10 ml more HNO_3 to aid the oxidation.

d. Cool the digested solution and add 1 drop aqueous phenolphthalein solution. Neutralize with 6*N* NaOH solution. If necessary, filter the neutralized solution, washing the filter liberally with distilled water. Make up the filtrate to 100 ml with distilled water.

e. Determine the orthophosphate of the treated sample using colorimetric method D, E or F.

f. Prepare a calibration curve by carrying a series of standards containing orthophosphate (see colorimetric method D, E or F) through the digestion step. Do not use orthophosphate standards without treatment, since the salts added in digestion cause an increase in the color intensity in some methods.

* Such as those obtainable from G. F. Smith Chemical Company, Columbus, Ohio.

II—SULFURIC ACID-NITRIC ACID DIGESTION

1. Apparatus

a. Digestion rack: An electrically or gas-heated digestion rack with a provision for withdrawal of fumes is recommended. Digestion racks typical of those used for microkjeldahl digestions are suitable.

b. Microkjeldahl flasks.

2. Reagents

a. Sulfuric acid, conc.
b. Nitric acid, conc.
c. Phenolphthalein indicator solution.
d. Sodium hydroxide, 1*N*.

3. Procedure

a. Measure out a sample into a microkjeldahl flask, containing the desired amount of phosphate (this is determined by the method used for the colorimetric finish). Add 1 ml conc H_2SO_4 and 5 ml conc HNO_3.

b. Digest the sample to a volume of 1 ml and then continue the digestion until the solution becomes colorless in order to remove HNO_3.

c. Cool and add approximately 20 ml distilled water, 1 drop phenolphthalein indicator, and as much 1*N* NaOH solution as required to produce a faint pink tinge in the solution. Transfer the neutralized solution, filtering if necessary to remove particulate material or turbidity, into a 100-ml volumetric flask. Add the filter washings to the flask and adjust the sample volume to 100 ml with distilled water.

d. Determine the phosphorus present using colorimetric method D, E or F, for which a separate calibration curve has been constructed by carrying standards through the acid digestion procedure described above.

III—PERSULFATE DIGESTION METHOD

1. Apparatus

a. Hot plate: A 30 × 50 cm heating surface is adequate.

b. Autoclave: An autoclave or pressure cooker capable of developing 15–20 psi may be used in place of a hot plate.

2. Reagents

a. Phenolphthalein indicator solution.

b. Sulfuric acid solution: Carefully add 300 ml conc H_2SO_4 to approximately 600 ml distilled water and then dilute to 1 liter with distilled water.

c. Potassium persulfate solution: Dissolve 5 g $K_2S_2O_8$ in 100 ml distilled water. Prepare daily.

d. Sodium hydroxide, 1*N*.

3. Procedure

a. Take 100 ml or a suitable aliquot of thoroughly mixed sample. To each 100-ml sample or aliquot diluted to 100 ml, add 1 drop (0.05 ml) phenolphthalein indicator solution. If a red color develops, add sulfuric acid solution dropwise to just discharge the color. Then add 1 ml sulfuric acid solution and 15 ml potassium persulfate solution.

b. Boil gently for at least 90 min, adding distilled water to keep the volume between 25 and 50 ml. Alternatively, heat for 30 min in an autoclave or pressure cooker at 15–20 psi. Cool, add 1 drop (0.05 ml) phenolphthalein indicator solution, and neutralize to a faint pink color with sodium hydroxide solution. Restore the volume to 100 ml with distilled water. Determine the phosphorus present by means of colorimetric method D, E or F, for which a separate calibration curve has been constructed by carrying the standards through the persulfate digestion procedure.

223 D. Vanadomolybdophosphoric Acid Colorimetric Method

1. General Discussion

a. Principle: In a dilute orthophosphate solution, ammonium molybdate reacts under acid conditions to form a heteropoly acid, molybdophosphoric acid. In the presence of vanadium the vanadomolybdophosphoric yellow color is formed. The intensity of the yellow color is proportional to the phosphate concentration in the solution.

b. Interference: Positive interference is caused by silica and arsenic only if the sample is heated. Negative interferences are caused by arsenate, fluoride, thorium, bismuth, sulfide, thiosulfate, thiocyanate, or excess molybdate. Blue color is caused by ferrous iron but this does not affect results if the Fe(II) is less than 100 mg/l. Sulfide interference may be removed by oxidation with bromine water. Ions that do not interfere in concentrations up to 1,000 mg/l are Al, Fe(III), Mg, Ca, Ba, Sr, Li, Na, K, NH_4^+, Cd, Mn, Pb, Hg(I), Hg(II), Sn(II), Cu, Ni, Ag, U, Zr, AsO_3^-, Br^-, $CO_3^=$, ClO_4^-, CN^-, IO_3^-, SiO_4, NO_3^-, NO_2^-, $SO_4^=$, $SO_3^=$, pyrophosphate, molybdate, tetraborate, selenate, benzoate, citrate, oxalate, lactate, tartrate, formate and salicylate. If nitric acid is used in the test, chloride interferes at 75 mg/l.

c. Minimum detectable concentration: The minimum detectable concentration is 0.2 mg/l P in 1-cm spectrophotometer cells.

2. Apparatus

a. Colorimetric equipment: Visual comparison in nessler tubes is not recommended because the sensitivity of the method is dependent on the wavelength used. One of the following is required:

1) SPECTROPHOTOMETER, for use at approximately 400–490 mμ.

2) FILTER PHOTOMETER, provided with a blue or violet filter exhibiting maximum transmittance between 400 and 490 mμ.

The wavelength at which color intensity is measured depends on the sensitivity desired, since the sensitivity varies tenfold with wavelengths from 400 to 490 mμ. Ferric iron causes interference at low wavelengths, particularly at 400 mμ. A wavelength of 470 mμ is generally employed. Concentration ranges for different wavelengths are:

Range mg/l P	Wavelength mμ
0.75–5.5	400
2.0 –15	440
4 –17	470
7 –20	490

b. Acid-washed glassware may be of great importance, particularly when determining low concentrations of phosphate. Phosphate contamination is common due to its adsorption on glass surfaces. *Commercial detergents containing phosphate should be avoided.* All glassware should be cleansed with hot dilute HCl and rinsed well with distilled water. Alternatively, the glassware should be filled with conc H_2SO_4, allowed to stand overnight, and then rinsed thoroughly. Preferably, the glassware should be reserved only for the determination of phosphate, and after use it should be washed and kept filled with water until needed. If this is done, the acid treatment is only required occasionally.

3. Reagents

a. Phenolphthalein indicator solution.

b. Hydrochloric acid, conc.

c. Activated carbon.

d. Vanadate-molybdate reagent:

1) SOLUTION A: Dissolve 25 g ammonium molybdate, $(NH_4)_6Mo_7O_{24} \cdot 4H_2O$, in 400 ml distilled water.

2) SOLUTION B: Dissolve 1.25 g ammonium metavanadate, NH_4VO_3, by heating to boiling in 300 ml distilled water. Cool and add 330 ml conc HCl (see note).

Cool solution B to room temperature, pour solution A into solution B, and dilute the mixture to 1 liter.

NOTE: H_2SO_4, $HClO_4$ or HNO_3 may be substituted for HCl. The acid concentration in the determination is not critical but a final sample concentration of 0.5*N* is recommended.

e. Standard phosphate solution: Dissolve in distilled water 219.5 mg anhydrous potassium dihydrogen phosphate, KH_2PO_4, and dilute to 1,000 ml; 1.00 ml = 50.0 μg $PO_4 - P$.

4. Procedure

a. Sample pH adjustment: If the pH of the sample is between 4 and 10, no adjustment is necessary. If the pH is less than 4, dilute 50 ml to 100 ml in a volumetric flask with distilled water and mix thoroughly. Use this diluted sample in the following steps. If the pH is greater than 10, add 1 drop phenolphthalein indicator to 50.0 ml sample and discharge the red color with conc HCl before diluting to 100 ml. [Dilution is also useful when concentrations greater than 15 mg $PO_4 - P/l$ are present. When dilutions are made, the correct interpretation of "ml sample" in the calculation below must be made; it refers to the volume of original (undiluted) sample contained in the aliquot taken for the color development step, ¶ c below.]

b. Color removal from sample: Remove any excessive color present in the sample by shaking about 50 ml sample with 200 mg activated carbon (Darco G60 or equivalent quality) in an erlenmeyer flask for 5 min, followed by filtering the sample through filter paper (Whatman No. 42 or equivalent) to remove the carbon. Check each batch of carbon for phosphate, since some batches produce high reagent blanks.

c. Color development in sample: Place 35 ml or less of the sample, containing 50 to 1,000 μg P, in a 50-ml volumetric flask. Add 10 ml vanadate-molybdate reagent and dilute to the mark with distilled water. Prepare a blank in which 35 ml distilled water is substituted for the sample solution. After 10 min from the time of adding the vanadate-molybdate reagent, measure the transmittance of the sample versus the blank at a wavelength of 400–490 mμ, depending on the sensitivity desired (see ¶ 2a above). The color is stable for days and its intensity is unaffected by variations in room temperature.

d. Preparation of calibration graph: Prepare a calibration curve by using suitable volumes of standard phosphate solution and proceeding as in ¶ 4c. When ferric ion is low enough not to interfere, a convenient practice is to plot a family of calibration curves of one series of standard solutions for various wavelengths. This permits a wide latitude of concentrations in one series of determinations. At least one standard should be analyzed with each set of samples.

5. Calculation

$$mg/l\ P = \frac{mg\ P \times 1{,}000}{ml\ sample}$$

6. Precision and Accuracy

Three synthetic unknown samples containing phosphorus compounds and other constituents dissolved in distilled water were examined for orthophosphate by the vanadomolybdate, stannous chloride, and ascorbic acid methods. The samples were also hydrolyzed for determination of the polyphosphate fraction; and digested with persulfate, perchloric acid, or sulfuric and nitric acids for the determination of total phosphorus content. The color was developed by the vanadomolybdate and stannous chloride methods after the hydrolysis and digestion treatments. Results of the participating laboratories are summarized in Table 223(2).

TABLE 223(2): PRECISION AND ACCURACY DATA FOR PHOSPHORUS METHODS

Method	Phosphorus Concentration			No. of Laboratories	Relative Standard Deviation %	Relative Error %
	Ortho-phosphorus phosphate µg/l	Poly-phosphate µg/l	Total µg/l			
D. Vanadomolybdate	100			45	75.2	21.6
	600			43	19.6	10.8
	7,000			44	8.6	5.4
E. Stannous chloride	100			45	25.5	28.7
	600			44	14.2	8.0
	7,000			45	7.6	4.3
F. Ascorbic acid	100			3	9.1	10.0
	600			3	4.0	4.4
	7,000			3	5.2	4.9
Hydrolysis + vanadomolybdate		80		37	106.8	7.4
		300		38	66.5	14.0
		3,000		37	36.1	23.5
Hydrolysis + stannous chloride		80		39	60.1	12.5
		300		36	47.6	21.7
		3,000		38	37.4	22.8
Persulfate + vanadomolybdate			210	32	55.8	1.6
			990	32	23.9	2.3
			10,230	31	6.5	0.3
Sulfuric-nitric acids + vanadomolybdate			210	23	65.6	20.9
			990	22	47.3	0.6
			10,230	20	7.0	0.4
Perchloric acid + vanadomolybdate			210	4	33.5	45.2
			990	5	20.3	2.6
			10,230	6	11.7	2.2
Persulfate + stannous chloride			210	29	28.1	9.2
			990	30	14.9	12.3
			10,230	29	11.5	4.3
Sulfuric-nitric acids + stannous chloride			210	20	20.8	1.2
			990	17	8.8	3.2
			10,230	19	7.5	0.4

SAMPLE 1 contained the following components: 100 μg/l orthophosphate phosphorus, 80 μg/l polyphosphate phosphorus added as sodium hexametaphosphate, 30 μg/l organic phosphorus in the form of adenylic acid, 1.50 mg/l ammonia nitrogen, 500 μg/l nitrate nitrogen, and 400 mg/l chloride.

SAMPLE 2 contained 600 μg/l orthophosphate phosphorus, 300 μg/l polyphosphate phosphorus added as sodium hexametaphosphate, 90 μg/l organic phosphorus in the form of adenylic acid, 800 μg/l ammonia nitrogen, 5.00 mg/l nitrate nitrogen, and 400 mg/l chloride.

SAMPLE 3 contained 7.00 mg/l orthophosphate phosphorus, 3.00 mg/l polyphosphate phosphorus added as sodium hexametaphosphate, 230 μg/l organic phosphorus in the form of adenylic acid, 200 μg/l ammonia nitrogen, 50 μg/l nitrate nitrogen, and 400 mg/l chloride.

223 E. Stannous Chloride Method

1. General Discussion

a. Principle: The principle of this method involves the formation of molybdophosphoric acid, which is reduced to the intensely colored complex, molybdenum blue, by stannous chloride. This method greatly increases sensitivity, as compared with Method D, and makes an extraction step feasible, which increases reliability of the method at concentrations below 0.1 mg P/l and lessens interference.

b. Interference: The occurrence of interferences is an important consideration, particularly in wastewater and polluted water samples. For a discussion of the problem, see Section 223D.1b.

c. Minimum detectable concentration: The minimum detectable concentration is about 3 μg/l P. The sensitivity at 50% transmittance is about 10 μg/l for 1% change in transmittance.

2. Apparatus

The same apparatus is required as for Method D, except when the extraction step is employed, in which case a safety aspirator is required. The spectrophotometer will be used at 625 mμ in the measurement of the benzene-isobutanol extracts, and at 690 mμ for the aqueous solutions. A wavelength of 650 mμ may be used for the aqueous solutions, with somewhat reduced sensitivity and precision if the instrument available is not equipped to read at 690 mμ.

3. Reagents

a. Phenolphthalein indicator solution.

b. Strong-acid solution: Prepare as directed in Method B, ¶ 3b above.

c. Ammonium molybdate reagent (I): Dissolve 25 g $(NH_4)_6Mo_7O_{24} \cdot 4H_2O$ in 175 ml distilled water. Cautiously add 280 ml conc H_2SO_4 to 400 ml distilled water. Cool, add the molybdate solution, and dilute to 1 liter.

d. Stannous chloride reagent (I): Dissolve 2.5 g of a fresh supply of $SnCl_2 \cdot 2H_2O$ in 100 ml glycerol. Heat in a water bath and stir with a glass rod to hasten dissolution. This reagent is stable and requires neither preservatives nor special storage.

e. Standard phosphate solution: Prepare as directed in Method D, ¶ 3e.

f. Reagents for extraction:

1) BENZENE-ISOBUTANOL SOLVENT—Mix equal volumes of benzene and isobutyl alcohol. (CAUTION—*This solvent is highly flammable.*)

2) AMMONIUM MOLYBDATE REAGENT *(II)*—Dissolve 40.1 g $(NH_4)_6Mo_7O_{24} \cdot 4H_2O$ in approximately 500 ml distilled water. Slowly add 396 ml molybdate reagent (I). Cool and dilute to 1 liter.

3) ALCOHOLIC SULFURIC ACID SOLUTION—Cautiously add 20 ml conc H_2SO_4 to 980 ml methyl alcohol with continuous mixing.

4) DILUTE STANNOUS CHLORIDE REAGENT *(II)*—Mix 8 ml stannous chloride reagent (I) with 50 ml glycerol. This reagent is stable for at least 6 months.

4. Procedure

a. Preliminary sample treatment: To a 100-ml sample containing not more than 0.2 mg P, and free from color and turbidity, add 1 drop (0.05 ml) phenolphthalein indicator. If the sample turns pink, add strong acid solution, dropwise, to discharge the color. If more than 5 drops are required, take a smaller sample and dilute to 100 ml with distilled water after first discharging the pink color with acid.

b. Color development: Add, with thorough mixing after each addition, 4.0 ml molybdate reagent (I) and 0.5 ml (10 drops) stannous chloride reagent (I). The rate of color development and the intensity of color depend on the temperature of the final solution, each 1°C increase producing about 1% increase in color. Hence, samples, standards and reagents should be within 2 C of one another and at a temperature between 20 and 30 C.

c. Color measurement: After 10 min, but before 12 min, employing the same specific interval for all determinations, measure the color photometrically at 690 mμ and compare with a calibration curve, using a distilled water blank. Light path lengths suitable for various concentration ranges are as follows:

Approximate P Range *μg/l*	Light Path *cm*
0.3–2	0.5
0.1–1	2
0.007–0.2	10

Always run a blank on the reagents and distilled water. Inasmuch as the color at first develops progressively and later fades, maintain equal timing conditions for samples as for standards. Prepare at least one standard with each set of samples, or once each day that tests are made. The calibration curve may deviate from a straight line at the upper concentrations of the 300–2,000 μg/l range.

d. Extraction: When increased sensitivity is desired or interferences need to be overcome, extract the phosphate as follows: Pipet a suitable aliquot of sample into a 100-ml graduated extraction cylinder and dilute, if necessary, to 40 ml with distilled water. Add 50.0 ml benzene-isobutanol solvent and 15.0 ml molybdate reagent (II). Close container at once and shake vigorously for exactly 15 sec. Any delay increases the amount of polyphosphate, if present, which will be included in the orthophosphate value. Remove the stopper and withdraw 25.0 ml of separated organic layer, using a pipet and a safety aspirator. Transfer to a 50-ml volumetric flask, add 15 to 16 ml alcoholic sulfuric acid solution, swirl, add 10 drops (0.50 ml) dilute stannous chloride reagent (II), swirl, and dilute to the mark with alcoholic sulfuric acid. Mix thoroughly; after 10 min, but before 30 min, read against the blank at 625 mμ. Prepare the blank by carrying 40 ml distilled water through the same procedure as the sample. Read the PO_4 concentration from a calibration curve prepared by taking known phosphate standards through the same procedural steps as the samples.

5. Calculation

The results from the direct and the extraction procedures can be calculated by the following equation:

$$\text{mg/l P} = \frac{\text{mg P} \times 1{,}000}{\text{ml sample}}$$

6. Precision and Accuracy

See Section 223D.6 preceding.

223 F. *Ascorbic Acid Method (TENTATIVE)*

1. General Discussion

a. Principle: Ammonium molybdate and potassium antimonyl tartrate react in an acid medium with dilute solutions of orthophosphate to form a heteropoly acid — phosphomolybdic acid—which is reduced to the intensely colored molybdenum blue by ascorbic acid.

b. Interference: Arsenates react with the molybdate reagent to produce a blue color similar to that formed with phosphate. Concentrations as low as 0.10 mg/l arsenic interfere with the phosphate determination. Hexavalent chromium and nitrite interfere to give results about 3% low at concentrations of 1.0 mg/l and 10–15% low at concentrations of 10 mg/l chromium and nitrite. Sulfide (Na_2S) and silicate do not interfere in concentrations of 1.0 and 10.0 mg/l.

c. Minimum detectable concentration: Approximately 30 μg P/l. See Table 223(3).

TABLE 223(3): RELATIONSHIP OF LIGHT PATH LENGTHS TO PHOSPHATE RANGES

Approximate P Range *μg/l*	Light Path Length *cm*
0.30–2.0	0.5
0.15–1.30	1.0
0.03–0.25	5.0

2. Apparatus

a. Colorimetric equipment: One of the following is required—

1) SPECTROPHOTOMETER, with infrared phototube for use at 880 mμ, providing a light path of 0.5 cm or longer.

2) FILTER PHOTOMETER, equipped with a red color filter and a light path of 0.5 cm or longer.

b. Acid-washed glassware: See Method D, ¶ 2b above.

3. Reagents

a. Alcohol, ethyl (95%) or isopropyl.

b. Sulfuric acid solution, 5N: Dilute 70 ml conc H_2SO_4 with distilled water to 500 ml.

c. Antimony potassium tartrate: Dissolve 4.3888 g $K(SbO)C_4H_4O_6 \cdot \frac{1}{2}H_2O$ in 200 ml distilled water. Store in a dark bottle at 4 C.

d. Ammonium molybdate solution: Dissolve 20 g $(NH_4)_6Mo_7O_{24} \cdot 4H_2O$ in 500 ml distilled water. Store in a plastic bottle at 4 C.

e. Ascorbic acid, 0.1*M:* Dissolve 1.76 g ascorbic acid in 100 ml distilled water. The solution is stable for about a week if stored at 4 C.

f. Combined reagent: Mix the above reagents in the following proportions for 100 ml combined reagent: 50 ml 5*N* sulfuric acid, 5 ml antimony potassium tartrate, 15 ml ammonium molybdate solution, and 30 ml ascorbic acid solution. Allow all reagents to reach room temperature before they are mixed, and mix in the order given. If turbidity forms in the combined reagent after the addition of antimony potassium tartrate or ammonium molybdate, shake the combined reagent and let it stand for a few minutes until the turbidity disappears before proceeding. The reagent is stable for at least 1 week if stored at 4 C.

g. Stock phosphate solution: See Method D, ¶ 3e.

h. Standard phosphate solution: Dilute 50.0 ml stock phosphate solution to 1,000 ml with distilled water to form a solution containing 2.00 μg P per 1.00 ml.

4. Procedure

a. Treatment of sample: Pipet 20.0 ml clear sample into a clean, dry test tube or a 125-ml erlenmeyer flask. Add 1 ml ethyl or isopropyl alcohol. Mix thoroughly. Because curves prepared with ethyl alcohol are slightly different from those prepared with isopropyl alcohol, use the same alcohol in treating samples and standards. Add 1 ml combined reagent. Mix thoroughly and allow to stand 10 min for color development before reading in a spectrophotometer at a wavelength of 880 mμ or a filter photometer equipped with a red color filter.

b. Correction for turbidity or interfering color: Natural color of water generally does not interfere at the high wavelength used. In the case of highly colored or turbid waters, prepare a blank by adding all the reagents except ascorbic acid and antimony potassium tartrate to the sample. Subtract the absorbance of the blank from the absorbance of each of the unknown samples.

c. Preparation of calibration curve: Prepare individual calibration graphs from a series of six standards within the phosphate ranges indicated in Table 223(3). Use a distilled water blank with the combined reagent to make the photometric readings for the calibration curve. Plot absorbance vs. phosphate concentration, which should form a straight line passing through the origin. Test at least one phosphate standard with each set of samples.

5. Calculation

$$\text{mg/l P} = \frac{\text{mg P} \times 1{,}000}{\text{ml sample}}$$

If phosphate as PO_4 is desired, multiply the result as phosphorus by 3.06.

6. Precision and Accuracy

a. See Section 223D.6 preceding.

b. Standard deviation: The standard

deviation of the absorbances based on 20 replicate samples containing 1.00 mg/l of phosphate phosphorus was ±0.0034, which is 0.51% of the mean absorbance. This is equivalent to 1.00 ±.005 mg/l.

223 G. Bibliography

BOLTZ, D. F. & M. G. MELLON. 1947. Determination of phosphorus, germanium, silicon, and arsenic by the heteropoly blue method. *Ind. Eng. Chem.*, Anal. Ed. 19:873.

GREENBERG, A. E., L. W. WEINBERGER & C. N. SAWYER. 1950. Control of nitrite interference in colorimetric determination of phosphorus. *Anal. Chem.* 22: 499.

YOUNG, R. S. & A. GOLLEDGE. 1950. Determination of hexametaphosphate in water after threshold treatment. *Ind. Chemist* 26:13.

GRISWOLD, B. L., F. L. HUMOLLER & A. R. MCINTYRE. 1951. Inorganic phosphates and phosphate esters in tissue extracts. *Anal. Chem.* 23:192.

BOLTZ, D. F., Ed. 1958. *Colorimetric Determination of Nonmetals.* Interscience Publishers, New York, pp. 29–40.

AMERICAN WATER WORKS ASSOCIATION. 1958. Committee Report. Determination of orthophosphate, hydrolyzable phosphate, and total phosphate in surface waters. *JAWWA* 50:1563.

JACKSON, M. L. 1958. *Soil Chemical Analysis.* Prentice-Hall, Englewood Cliffs, N.J.

SLETTEN, O. & C. M. BACH. 1961. Modified stannous chloride reagent for orthophosphate determination. *JAWWA* 53: 1031.

STRICKLAND, J. D. H. & T. R. PARSONS. 1965. *A Manual of Sea Water Analysis* (2nd ed.). Fisheries Reserve Board, Ottawa, Canada.

BLACK, C. A., D. D. EVANS, J. L. WHITE, L. E. ENSMINGER & F. E. CLARK, Eds. 1965. *Methods of Soil Analysis, Part 2. Chemical and Microbiological Properties.* American Society for Agronomy, Madison, Wisc.

EDWARDS, G. P., A. H. MOLOF & R. W. SCHNEEMAN. 1965. Determination of orthophosphate in fresh and saline waters. *JAWWA* 57:917.

LEE, G. F., N. L. CLESCERI & G. P. FITZGERALD. 1965. Studies on the analysis of phosphates in algal cultures. *J. Air & Water Poll.* 9:715.

JENKINS, D. 1965. A study of methods suitable for the analysis and preservation of phosphorus forms in an estuarine environment. *SERL Report No. 65–18.* Sanitation Engineering Research Laboratory, Univ. of California, Berkeley.

SHANNON, J. E. & G. F. LEE. 1966. Hydrolysis of condensed phosphates in natural waters. *J. Air & Water Poll.* 10:735.

GALES, M. E., JR., E. C. JULIAN & R. C. KRONER. 1966. Method for quantitative determination of total phosphorus in water. *JAWWA* 58:1363.

LEE, G. F. 1967. Analytical chemistry of plant nutrients. *Proc. Int. Conf. Eutrophication,* Madison, Wisc.

FITZGERALD, G. P. & S. L. FAUST. 1967. Effect of water sample preservation methods on the release of phosphorus from algae. *Limnol. & Oceanogr.* 12: 332.

POTASSIUM: See Metals (Groups I and II), Section 210.

224 RESIDUE

Tests for the various forms of residue do not determine specific chemical substances, but rather classes of material which have similar physical properties and similar responses to ignition. The tests are therefore basically empirical in nature and the constituents of each form of residue are defined largely by the procedures employed. For this reason, the realization of reproducible or comparable results requires close attention to the constancy of such procedural details as drying time, ignition time, temperatures, and filter characteristics.

In some cases, analyses performed for a special purpose may demand deviation from the stated procedures in order to include with the measured residue some unusual ingredient of the sample. Whenever such variations of technic are introduced, they must be recorded and presented with the results.

The results for total, volatile and fixed residues are subject to considerable error through losses of volatile compounds during evaporation and of carbon dioxide and volatile minerals during ignition, and also because of the presence of calcium oxide in the ash. Results for residues high in oil or grease content may be of questionable value owing to the difficulty of drying to constant weight in a reasonable time. By definition, results will not include materials in the sample which are volatile under the conditions of the procedure.

In the interpretation of results, these possible sources of error must be recognized.

Methods A through F are intended for use with wastewaters, effluents and polluted waters. Use Method G for sludges, muds, and other solid or semisolid samples.

224 A. Total Residue on Evaporation

1. General Discussion

The determination of residue by evaporation may be of limited value for estimating the effect of an effluent on a receiving water, but it may be useful as a control in plant operation. A large number of solids crystallize as hydrates, which lose water at various temperatures and form decomposition products before all their water of hydration is given off. This also is true of various colloidal suspensions. In addition, volatile compounds are lost during evaporation and ignition. It is essential for the analyst to understand that the procedure given for residue on evaporation is quite arbitrary and the results generally will not represent the weight of actual dissolved and suspended solids. Because of the organic content of sewage, samples should be dried at 103 C. A more complete discussion of the temperature for drying residues may be found in Section 148, Residue.

2. Apparatus

a. Evaporating dish.

b. Steam bath or infrared lamp.

c. Drying oven.
d. Desiccator.
e. Analytical balance.

3. Reagent

a. Sodium hydroxide, 1*N.*

4. Procedure

Evaporate 100 ml of sample in an ignited and tared dish, dry to constant weight at 103 C, cool in a desiccator, and weigh. Drying for 1 hr at 103 C is usually sufficient. On samples with a pH below 4.3, NaOH is added and a pH of 4.3 maintained during evaporation. The weight of Na added is subtracted from the weight of residue.

5. Calculation

$$\text{mg/l residue on evaporation} = \frac{\text{mg residue} \times 1{,}000}{\text{ml sample}}$$

6. Precision and Accuracy

The accuracy of all the solids determinations in sewage and industrial wastes is not measurable because there is no universal standard of comparison. When the residue from a 50–100 ml sample of raw sewage was weighed, the standard deviation of the weighing was found to be 1.9 mg ($n = 3$; 60×10), but the data are considered statistically unreliable because of sampling errors. On settled effluents, a standard deviation of 0.9 mg ($n = 1$; 5×20) was found and is statistically reliable.

224 B. Total Volatile and Fixed Residue

1. Apparatus

a. Muffle furnace.

2. Procedure

Determine total volatile and fixed solids by igniting the residue on evaporation (Method A) at 550 C in an electric muffle furnace to constant weight. (It has been found that wastewater and effluent residues usually attain constant weight in 15 to 20 min ignition.) Report the loss of weight on ignition as mg/l volatile solids and the residue as mg/l fixed solids. Calculate as in Method A, ¶ 5.

3. Precision and Accuracy

Using this procedure, the standard deviation of the weighing was found to be 1.5 mg ($n = 2$; 50×10), but these data are considered statistically unreliable because of sampling errors.

224 C. Total Suspended Matter (Nonfiltrable Residue)

1. General Discussion

The amount of suspended matter removed by a filter varies with the porosity of the filter. A number of the common filters used in water analysis will be found suitable for this purpose. Inasmuch as wastewater treatment plant operations demand less than complete particle removal, the glass filter disk is empirically specified for the determination of suspended matter in wastewater, effluents and polluted water.

In unusual cases, such as special-purpose analyses of certain industrial wastewaters, variations in the procedure may be necessary. For example, if it is desired to exclude material such as oil, the oil may be extracted from the suspended matter on the filter. Any such variations from the standard procedure should be reported with the results.

2. Apparatus

a. Glass fiber filter disks, 5.5 cm * (see also ¶ 3c below).

b. Filter holder: Membrane filter holder, Hirsch funnel, or Buchner funnel. Alternatively, Gooch crucibles may be used (see ¶ 3c).

c. Suction apparatus.

d. Drying oven, for use at 103 C.

e. Muffle furnace, for use at 550 C.

f. Desiccator.

g. Analytical balance.

3. Procedure

a. Preparation of filter disk: Place a glass fiber filter disk in a membrane filter holder, Hirsch funnel or Buchner funnel, with the wrinkled surface of the disk facing upward. Apply vacuum to the assembled filtration apparatus to seat the filter disk. With vacuum applied, wash the disk with distilled water. After the water has filtered through, disconnect the vacuum, remove the filter disk from the apparatus, and dry it in an oven at 103 C for 1 hr (30 min in a mechanical convection oven). If volatile matter is not to be determined, cool the filter disk to room temperature in a desiccator and weigh. If volatile matter is to be determined, transfer the disk to a muffle furnace and ignite at 550 C for 15 min. Remove the disk from the furnace, place it in a desiccator until cooled to room temperature, and then weigh.

b. Treatment of sample: Except for samples containing a very high concentration of suspended matter, or which filter very slowly, select a sample volume which equals 14 ml or more per sq cm of filter area.

Place the prepared filter disk in the membrane filter holder, Hirsch funnel or Buchner funnel, with the wrinkled surface upward. With the vacuum applied, wet the disk with distilled water to seat it against the holder or funnel. Measure out the selected volume of well-mixed sample with a wide-tip pipet, volumetric flask, or graduated cylinder. Filter the sample through the disk, using suction. Leaving the suction on, wash the apparatus three times with 10-ml portions of distilled water, allowing complete drainage between

* Whatman GF/C, or equivalent.

washings. Discontinue suction, remove the filter disk, and dry it at 103 C for 1 hr in an oven (30 min in a mechanical convection oven). After drying, cool the disk to room temperature in a desiccator before weighing on an analytical balance.

c. Filtration with Gooch crucibles: Alternatively, use glass-fiber filter disks of suitable diameter (usually 2.1 or 2.4 cm) with Gooch crucibles, making certain that the disk lies flat in the bottom of the crucible and completely covers the perforations.

Prepare the disk and treat the sample as described in ¶s 3a and b above, except that the Gooch crucible is usually dried, ignited and weighed along with the disk, rather than removing the disk for separate handling.

4. Calculation

$$\text{mg/l total suspended matter} = \frac{A \times 1{,}000}{B}$$

where A = mg suspended solids and B = ml sample.

5. Precision and Accuracy

The precision of the determination varies directly with the concentration of suspended matter in the sample. The standard deviation was ±5.2 mg/l (coefficient of variation 33%) at 15 mg/l, ±24 mg/l (10%) at 242 mg/l, and ±13 mg/l (7.6%) at 1,707 mg/l ($n = 2$; 4×10). There is no satisfactory procedure for obtaining the accuracy of the method on wastewater samples, since the true concentration of suspended matter is unknown.

224 D. Volatile and Fixed Suspended Matter

1. General Discussion

The volatilization of organic matter in wastewater solids is subject to a number of errors. It should be done in a muffle furnace at 550 C.

2. Apparatus

The same as that listed for Total Suspended Matter (Method C above).

3. Procedure

a. Prepare the filter disk, filter the sample portion selected, and dry and weigh the solids as directed in Method C for Total Suspended Matter, or proceed using the filter disk upon completion of the step as outlined for the method.

b. Ignite the filter disk with its suspended matter for 15 min at 550 C, transfer the disk to a desiccator, allow to cool to room temperature, and weigh. Report the weight loss on ignition as mg/l volatile suspended matter and the weight of ash remaining as mg/l fixed suspended matter.

4. Precision and Accuracy

The standard deviation of the volatile matter determination was ±11 mg/l at 170 mg/l (coefficient of variation 6.5%) ($n = 3$; 4×10). As in the case of suspended matter, the accuracy of the determination cannot be evaluated. The principal sources of error are failure to obtain a representative sample and inadequate temperature control.

224 E. Dissolved Matter (Filtrable Residue)

Dissolved matter may be obtained by difference between the residue on evaporation (*A*) and total suspended matter (*C*) or by evaporating a filtered sample as directed for residue on evaporation (Method A, ¶ 4, preceding).

224 F. Settleable Matter

Settleable matter may be determined and reported on either a volume (ml/l) or a weight (mg/l) basis, as given in the following procedure.

1. Procedure

a. By volume: Fill an Imhoff cone to the liter mark with a thoroughly mixed sample. Settle for 45 min, gently stir the sides of the cone with a rod or by spinning, settle 15 min longer, and record the volume of settleable matter in the cone as ml/l.

b. By weight: This technic defines settleable matter as that matter in sewage which will not stay in suspension during the settling period but either settles to the bottom or floats to the top.

1) Determine the suspended matter (in mg/l) in a sample of the sewage under investigation, as in Method C, preceding.

2) Pour a well-mixed sample of the sewage into a glass vessel not less than 9 cm in diameter, using a quantity of sample not less than 1 liter and sufficient to insure a depth of 20 cm. A glass vessel of greater diameter and a larger volume of sample may be used. Allow to stand quiescent for 1 hr and, without disturbing the settled material or that which may be floating, siphon 250 ml of sample from the center of the container at a point halfway between the surface of the settled sludge and the liquid surface. Determine the suspended matter (in mg/l) in all or in an aliquot portion of this supernatant liquor as directed under Method C. This is the nonsettling matter.

2. Calculation

mg/l settleable matter
= mg/l suspended matter
− mg/l nonsettleable matter.

224 G. Method for Solid and Semisolid Samples

1. Discussion

These modifications are recommended for use with samples of materials such as river and lake sediments, sludges separated from wastewater treatment processes, and sludge cakes from vacuum filtration, centrifugation or other dewatering treatment of wastewater sludges. In such samples it is difficult and usually unnecessary to distinguish between filtrable and nonfiltrable residue. Ordinarily, only the total residue on evaporation and its fixed and volatile fractions are determined.

The determination of both total and volatile residue in these materials is subject to error due to the loss of ammonium carbonate and volatile organic matter while drying, making the results lower than they should be. Although this is also the case with wastewater samples, the effect tends to be more pronounced with sediments, and especially with sludges and sludge cakes.

The mass of organic matter usually recovered from sludge and sediment samples requires a period of ignition longer than that specified for the residue from wastewaters, effluents or polluted waters. The specified ignition time and temperature must be carefully observed in order to control losses of volatile inorganic salts.

All weighings must be performed quickly. Wet samples tend to lose weight by evaporation. After drying or ignition, the residues are often very hygroscopic and rapidly absorb moisture from the air.

2. Apparatus

a. Evaporating dishes.
b. Oven, for use at 103 C.
c. Muffle furnace, for use at 550 C.
d. Desiccators.
e. Balance, accurate to 0.01 g.

3. Procedure

a. Total residue and moisture:

1) PREPARATION OF EVAPORATING DISH—Ignite evaporating dishes at least 60 min at a temperature of at least 550 C, then cool in a desiccator, weigh to the nearest 10 mg, and keep in the desiccator until ready for use.

2) FLUID SAMPLES—If the sample contains enough moisture to flow more or less readily, stir to homogenize, then place 25–50 g in a prepared evaporating dish and weigh to the nearest 10 mg. Evaporate to dryness on a water bath, dry at 103 C for 1 hr, cool in an individual desiccator containing fresh desiccant, and weigh.

3) SOLID SAMPLES—If the sample consists of discrete pieces of solid material (dewatered sludge, for example), take cores from each piece with a No. 7 cork borer, or pulverize the entire sample coarsely on a clean surface by hand, using rubber gloves. Place 25–50 g in a prepared evaporating dish and weigh to the nearest 10 mg. Place in an oven at 103 C overnight. Cool in an individual desiccator containing fresh desiccant and weigh. Heating for this prolonged period may result in a loss of volatile organic matter and ammonium carbonate, but it is usually necessary in order to realize thorough drying of samples of this kind.

b. Volatile residue: Determine volatile residue, which includes organic matter and volatile inorganic salts, on the total residue obtained in step 3a by igniting it in an electric muffle furnace at 550 C for 60 min, avoiding loss of solids by decrepitation. Cool in a desiccator and reweigh. Report results as percent ash and volatile solids.

4. Calculations

$$\text{Total residue (\%)} = \frac{A \times 100}{B}$$

$$\text{Volatile residue (\%)} = \frac{A - C}{A} \times 100$$

$$\text{Fixed residue (\%)} = \frac{C \times 100}{A}$$

where A = weight of dried solids, B =

weight of wet sample, and C = weight of ash.

5. Precision and Accuracy

On digested sludge (42% ash) the standard deviation was found to be 0.2% ash ($n = 1$; 13×10). On elutriated sludge (29% ash) the standard deviation was found to be 0.2% ash ($n = 1$; 4×10).

224 H. Bibliography

Methods A–D

SYMONS, G. E. & B. MOREY. 1941. The effect of drying time on the determination of solids in sewage and sewage sludges. *Sewage Works J.* 13:936.

DEGEN, J. & F. E. NUSSBERGER. 1956. Notes on the determination of suspended solids. *Sewage & Ind. Wastes* 28:237.

CHANIN, G., E. H. CHOW, R. B. ALEXANDER & J. POWERS. 1958. Use of glass fiber filter medium in the suspended solids determination. *Sewage & Ind. Wastes* 30:1062.

NUSBAUM, I. 1958. New method for determination of suspended solids. *Sewage & Ind. Wastes* 30:1066.

SMITH, A. L. & A. E. GREENBERG. 1963. Evaluation of methods for determining suspended solids in wastewater. *JWPCF* 35:940.

WYCKOFF, B. M. 1964. Rapid solids determination using glass fiber filters. *Water & Sewage Works* 111:277.

Methods E–G

THERIAULT, E. J. & H. H. WAGENHALS. 1923. Studies of representative sewage plants. *Pub. Health Bull.* No. 132.

SYMONS, G. E. & B. MOREY. 1941. The effect of drying time on the determination of solids in sewage and sewage sludges. *Sewage Works J.* 13:936.

FISCHER, A. J. & G. E. SYMONS. 1944. The determination of settleable sewage solids by weight. *Water Works & Sew.* 91:37.

DEGEN, J. & F. E. NUSSBERGER. 1956. Notes on the determination of suspended solids. *Sewage & Ind. Wastes* 28:237.

GOODMAN, B. L. 1964. Processing thickened sludge with chemical conditioners. In *Sludge Concentration, Filtration and Incineration.* University of Michigan Continued Education Series No. 113, Ann Arbor, page 78.

SETTLED VOLUME OF ACTIVATED SLUDGE:
See Tests on Activated Sludge, Section 230.

225 SLUDGE DIGESTER GAS

Gas produced during the anaerobic decomposition of wastes contains methane and carbon dioxide as the major components, and varying quantities of hydrogen, hydrogen sulfide, nitrogen, oxygen, and water vapor. It is common practice to analyze the gases produced to determine their fuel value, and in some cases to check on the behavior of the treatment process. The relative proportions of carbon dioxide, methane and nitrogen present are normally of most concern and the easiest to determine because of the relatively high percentages of each usually present. It is sometimes of interest to evaluate the quantities of hydrogen, hydrogen sulfide and oxygen present, but these occur in smaller, less readily measured amounts.

1. Selection of Method

Two different procedures are described for gas analysis, (*A*) the Volumetric Method, and (*B*) the Gas Chromatographic Method. The volumetric analysis is suitable for the determination of carbon dioxide, hydrogen, methane and oxygen. Nitrogen is indirectly estimated by difference. Although the method is time-consuming, the equipment is relatively simple. Since no calibration is needed before use, the procedure is particularly adaptable when analyses are conducted on an infrequent basis.

The principal advantage of the chromatographic procedure is speed. In order to obtain this advantage, however, the instrument must have been previously calibrated for each gas of interest, the oven must have reached a constant temperature, and the detector must yield a stable response. Thus, this procedure is most suitable for routine measurements where analyses are made several times a week. It is possible to separate and measure carbon dioxide, hydrogen, hydrogen sulfide, methane, nitrogen and oxygen by gas chromatography, but not with a single instrument employing only a single column and detector. Also, the quantities of hydrogen and hydrogen sulfide present are normally too small for accurate detection. The main value of gas chromatography is for routine analysis to determine the relative proportions of "air" (nitrogen plus oxygen), carbon dioxide, and methane.

2. Sample Collection

When the source of gas is some distance from the apparatus used for analysis, samples must be collected in sealed containers and brought to the instrument for introduction. Displacement collectors offer the most suitable means by which this may be done. Long glass tubes with three-way glass stopcocks at each end as indicated in Figure 45 are particularly suitable for

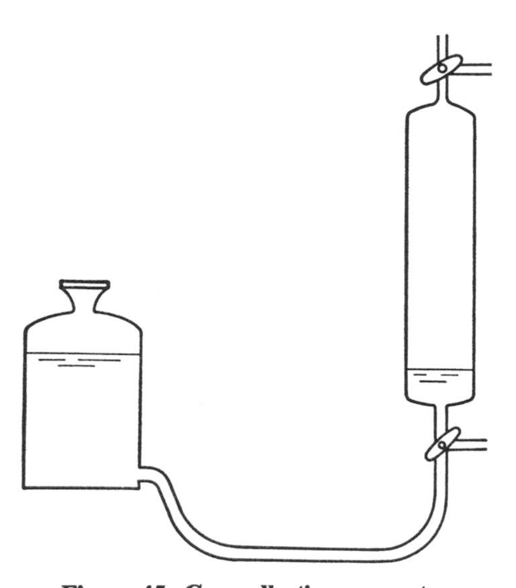

Figure 45. Gas collection apparatus.

this purpose. These are also available with centrally located ports provided with septa for syringe transfer of samples. One end of the collector is connected to the gas source and the three-way stopcock is vented to the atmosphere. The line is cleared of air by passing 10 to 15 volumes of gas through the vent, and then the stopcock is turned to admit the sample. If large quantities of gas are available, the air can be swept away by passing 10 to 15 volumes of the gas through the tube. However, if the gas supply is more limited, the tube should be filled with a liquid and the liquid displaced with the gas. Either mercury or an aqueous solution containing 200 g sodium sulfate and 50 g conc sulfuric acid per 800 ml of water should be used. The latter solution is easier and less expensive to use, but dissolves gases somewhat. Therefore, when it is used, the collection tube should be completely filled with the gas being collected and should be sealed off from any contact with the confining fluid during temporary storage. When transferring gas to the gas-analyzing apparatus, caution should be taken not to transfer the confining fluid into the instrument.

225 A. Volumetric Method (TENTATIVE)

1. General Discussion

a. Principle: This method may be used for the analysis either of digester gas or of methane in water (see Section 130, Methane). A measured volume of gas is passed first through a solution of potassium hydroxide to remove carbon dioxide, next through a solution of alkaline pyrogallol to remove oxygen, and then over heated cupric oxide, which removes hydrogen by oxidation to water. After each of the above steps, the volume of gas remaining is measured, the decrease which results being an indication of the relative percentage by volume of each component in the mixture. Finally, methane is determined by conversion to carbon dioxide and water in a slow-combustion pipet or a catalytic oxidation assembly. The volume of carbon dioxide formed during the combustion is then measured to determine the fraction of methane originally present. Nitrogen is estimated by assuming that it represents the only gas remaining. The percentage of nitrogen by volume is taken as equal to the difference between 100% and the summation of the measured percentages of the other components.

2. Apparatus

a. Orsat-type gas-analysis apparatus, consisting of at least: (1) a water jacketed gas buret with leveling bulb; (2) a carbon dioxide-absorption pipet; (3) an oxygen-absorption pipet; (4) a cupric oxide-hydrogen oxidation assembly; (5) a catalytic methane-oxidation assembly or a slow-combustion pipet; and (6) a leveling bulb. If the slow-combustion pipet is used, a controlled source of current should be available to heat the platinum filament electrically. Mercury is recommended as the confining liquid. The aqueous sodium sulfate-sulfuric acid solution for the sample collection container has also been used successfully. Any of the commercially available gas analyzers having these units may be used.

3. Reagents

a. Potassium hydroxide solution: Dissolve 500 g KOH in distilled water and dilute to 1 liter.

b. Alkaline pyrogallol reagent: Dissolve 30 g pyrogallol (also called pyrogallic acid) in distilled water and make up to 100 ml. Add 500 ml potassium hydroxide solution.

c. Oxygen gas: Approximately 100 ml needed for each gas sample analyzed.

4. Procedure

a. Sample introduction: Transfer 5–10 ml of the gas sample into the gas buret through a capillary-tube connection to the sample collector. Expel this portion of the sample to the atmosphere to purge the system. Transfer up to 100 ml of gas sample to the buret. As the sample is withdrawn from the collection vessel, replace with water or sulfate-sulfuric acid solution. Bring the sample in the buret to atmospheric or reference pressure by adjusting the leveling bulb. Measure the volume accurately and record as V_1.

b. Carbon dioxide absorption: Remove the carbon dioxide from the sample by passing it through the carbon dioxide-absorption pipet charged with the potassium hydroxide solution. Pass back and forth until the sample volume remains constant. Before opening the stopcocks between the buret and any absorption pipet, make sure that the gas in the buret is under a slight positive pressure. This precaution will prevent the reagent in the pipet from contaminating the stopcock or manifold. After absorption of carbon dioxide, transfer the sample to the buret and measure its volume. Record as V_2.

c. Oxygen absorption: Remove the oxygen by passing the sample through the oxygen-absorption pipet charged with alkaline pyrogallol reagent, until the volume of the sample remains constant. Measure the volume accurately and record as V_3. In the case of a digester gas sample, continue as directed in ¶ 4e below.

d. Special handling of methane in water sample: Store the gas from the water sample in the carbon dioxide pipet and proceed to ¶ 4f below.

e. Hydrogen oxidation: Remove the hydrogen by passing the sample through the cupric oxide assembly which should be maintained at a temperature in the range of 290 to 300 C. When a constant volume has been obtained, transfer the sample back to the buret and measure its volume accurately. Record as V_4.

Waste to the atmosphere all but 20–25 ml of the remaining gas. Measure the remaining volume accurately and record as V_5. Transfer this sample for temporary storage into the carbon dioxide-absorption pipet.

f. Methane oxidation: Purge the inlet connections to the buret with oxygen by drawing 5–10 ml into the buret and expelling to the atmosphere. Oxidize the methane by either (1) the catalytic oxidation process for digester gas and the gas phase of the water samples, or (2) the slow-combustion process for the gas phase of the water samples.

1) THE CATALYTIC OXIDATION PROCESS—For catalytic oxidation of digester gas and the gas phase of the water samples, transfer 65–70 ml of oxygen to the buret and measure accurately. Record this volume as V_6. Pass the oxygen into the carbon dioxide-absorption pipet so that it will mix with the sample stored there. Bring

this mixture back to the buret and measure its volume accurately. Record as V_7. This volume should closely equal V_5 plus V_6. Pass the oxygen-sample mixture through the catalytic oxidation assembly, which should be heated in accordance with directions from the manufacturer. The rate of passage should not exceed about 30 ml/min. After the first pass, transfer the mixture back and forth through the assembly between the buret and the reservoir at a rate not greater than 60 ml/min until a constant residual volume is obtained. Record as V_8.

2) THE SLOW-COMBUSTION PROCESS —For slow combustion of the gas phase of the water samples, transfer 35–40 ml of oxygen to the buret and measure accurately. Record this volume as V_6. Transfer the oxygen to the slow-combustion pipet and then transfer the sample from the carbon dioxide-absorption pipet to the buret. Heat the platinum coil in the combustion pipet to yellow heat, controlling the temperature by adjusting the current passing through the coil. Reduce the pressure of the oxygen in the pipet to somewhat less than atmospheric pressure by means of the leveling bulb attached to the pipet. Pass the sample into the slow-combustion pipet at the rate of approximately 10 ml/min. After the first pass, transfer the sample and oxygen mixture back and forth between the pipet and buret several times at a faster rate, allowing the mercury in the pipet to rise to a point just below the heated coil. Collect the sample in the combustion pipet, turn off the coil, and cool pipet and sample with a jet of compressed air. Transfer the sample to the buret and measure its volume. Record as V_8.

g. Measurement of carbon dioxide produced: Determine the amount of carbon dioxide formed in the reaction by passing the sample through the carbon dioxide-absorption pipet until the volume remains constant. Record the volume after this step as V_9.

A further check on the accuracy of the determination may be made by absorbing the residual oxygen from the sample. After this absorption, record the final volume as V_{10}.

5. Calculation

a. Methane and hydrogen are usually the only combustible gases present in sludge digester gas. When this is the case, the percentage by volume of each gas can be determined as follows:

$$\%\ CO_2 = \frac{(V_1 - V_2) \times 100}{V_1}$$

$$\%\ O_2 = \frac{(V_2 - V_3) \times 100}{V_1}$$

$$\%\ H_2 = \frac{(V_3 - V_4) \times 100}{V_1}$$

$$\%\ CH_4 = \frac{V_4 \times (V_8 - V_9) \times 100}{V_1 \times V_5}$$

$$\%\ N_2 = 100 - (\%\ CO_2 + \%\ O_2 + \%\ H_2 + \%\ CH_4)$$

b. Methane may be calculated by either of two additional equations as follows:

$$\%\ CH_4 = \frac{V_4 \times (V_6 + V_{10} - V_9) \times 100}{2 \times V_1 \times V_5}$$

$$\text{or } \%\ CH_4 = \frac{V_4 \times (V_7 - V_8) \times 100}{2 \times V_1 \times V_5}$$

Results from the calculations for methane by the three equations should be in reasonable agreement. If not, the analysis should be repeated after the apparatus has been thoroughly checked for sources of error, such as leaky stopcocks or connections. The presence of other combustible gases, such as ethane, butane or pentane, would cause a lack of agreement among the calculations. However, the possibility that the digester gas contains a significant amount of any of these is remote.

6. Precision and Accuracy

A gas buret can measure gas volume with a precision of 0.05 ml and a probable accuracy of 0.1 ml. With the large fractions of carbon dioxide and methane normally present in digester gas, the overall error for their determination can be made less than ±1%. The error in the determination of oxygen and hydrogen, however, can be considerable because of the small concentrations normally present. For a concentration of 1%, an error as large as ±20% can be expected. When nitrogen is present in a similar low-volume percentage, the error in its determination would be even greater, since errors in each of the other determinations would be reflected in the calculation for nitrogen.

225 B. Gas Chromatographic Method (TENTATIVE)

1. General Discussion

a. Principle: Gas chromatography is a method by which a gas mixture is separated into its various components so that they can be individually identified and quantitatively measured. The separation is obtained by passing the mixture through a column containing either a solid material or a liquid solvent coated over an inert solid support, providing a large surface for adsorption. The solid absorbent or liquid solvent is considered the stationary phase. The sample is transported through the column by a carrier gas, which is considered the mobile phase. In a properly selected column, the stationary phase selectively retards the components of the sample, causing their movement through the column at different effective rates. The various components therefore tend to segregate into separate zones or bands, which are detected and measured quantitatively by a thermal conductivity cell at the exit of the column.

b. Interference: The selection of a suitable column is all-important in obtaining proper separation of the gas components. With some columns, the separation obtained between methane, oxygen and nitrogen may be adequate when oxygen and nitrogen are present in low concentrations. However, when the concentration of either of these components is unusually high (more than 50%, by volume, of either component), interference with the determination of methane may occur. This interference may be eliminated by the selection of a longer column or of a column with a different packing.

2. Apparatus

a. Gas chromatograph: Any commercially available instrument with a temperature range up to about 130 C and equipped with a thermal conductivity detector can be used.

b. Recorder: A 10-mV full-span recorder for the gas chromatograph should be adequate for general usage, although a 1-mV full-span recorder is more desirable where minor components such as hydrogen and hydrogen sulfide are to be detected.

c. Column packing: Several columns are available commercially for the separation of carbon dioxide and methane from air (nitrogen plus oxygen). A 10-ft-long silica gel or a 2-ft-long activated-carbon column can carry out this separation quite adequately. With such columns, however, H_2S is adsorbed irreversibly and N_2, O_2 and H_2 are not separated. Other individual columns or a combination of columns may be used to separate these latter gases.[1, 2]

d. Sample introduction apparatus: Introduction of gas samples is best performed on instruments equipped with gas-sampling valves specially designed to permit automatic injection of a specific volume of sample into the chromatograph. If such an instrument is not available, then introduction may be performed with a 2-ml syringe fitted with a hypodermic needle (usually 27-gauge). Escape of gas can be reduced by greasing the plunger lightly with mineral oil, or by using a special gas-tight syringe.

3. Reagents

a. Carrier gas: Helium is the most commonly used carrier gas for separation of digester gases. However, for some separations, nitrogen or argon may be more appropriate.

b. Pure gases for calibration: Pure samples of methane, carbon dioxide and nitrogen, or mixtures of known composition, are required for calibration. Samples of oxygen, hydrogen and hydrogen sulfide are also required if analysis for these components is to be made.

4. Procedures

a. Preparation of gas chromatograph: Install the column in the oven of the gas chromatograph. Open the valve of the carrier gas tank and adjust the pressure gauge to maintain a constant gas flow rate, usually in the range of 60–80 ml/min. Turn on the column oven heater and the detector current, and adjust them to the desired values. The column oven temperature is best maintained at about 100 C when an activated-carbon or silica gel column is used.

Turn on the recorder approximately 30 min after the carrier gas flow has started. Adjust the base line on the recorder chart to zero. Inject a 0.5- to 2.0-ml sample of gas with a syringe or through the gas-sampling valve after a stable base line is obtained on the recorder.

b. Calibration: For accurate results, prepare calibration curves for each gas to be measured, since different gas components do not give equivalent detector responses on either a weight or a molar basis. Calibrate with synthetic mixtures or with pure gases.

1) SYNTHETIC MIXTURES—Use either synthetically prepared or commercially purchased gas mixtures of known composition. Inject a standard volume of each mixture into the gas chromatograph and note the response for each gas. Compute the detector response, either as the area under a

peak or as the height of the peak, after appropriate correction is made for attenuation. Peak heights can be read easily and accurately and can be correlated with the concentration of the component in the sample if operating parameters are reproduced exactly from one analysis to the next. If sufficient reproducibility cannot be obtained by this procedure, use peak areas for calibration. Prepare the calibration curve by plotting either peak area or peak height against volume percent for each component.

2) PURE GASES—Introduce pure gases into the chromatograph individually with a syringe. Inject sample volumes of 0.25, 0.5, 1.0 ml, etc., and plot the detector response, corrected for attenuation, against the gas volume.

c. Sample analysis: If samples are to be injected with a syringe, equip the sample collection container with a port closed by a rubber or silicone septum. To take a sample for analysis, expel air from the barrel of the syringe by depressing the plunger and force the needle through the septum. Withdraw the plunger to take the volume of gas desired, pull the needle from the collection container, and inject the sample rapidly into the chromatograph.

When samples are to be injected through a gas-sampling valve, connect the sample collection container to the inlet tube. Permit gas to flow from the collection tube through the valve to purge the dead air space and fill the sample tube. About 15 ml are normally sufficient to clear the lines and to provide a sample of 1 to 2 ml. Transfer the sample from the loop into the carrier gas stream by turning the knob of the valve in the direction indicated for the particular instrument.

When calibration curves have been prepared by the method using synthetic mixtures, take the same sample volume as that used during calibration. When calibration curves are prepared by the procedure using varying volumes of pure gases, then any convenient gas sample volume up to about 2 ml may be injected into the chromatograph.

5. Calculation

a. When calibration curves have been prepared by the method using synthetic mixtures, and the volume of the sample analyzed is the same as that used in calibration, read the volume percent of each component directly from the calibration curve after the detector response for that component is computed.

b. When calibration curves are prepared by the procedure using varying volumes of pure gases, read the partial volume of each component from the calibration curve after the detector response for that component is computed. Calculate the percentage of each gas in the mixture as follows:

$$\text{Volume \%} = \frac{A}{B} \times 100$$

where A = partial volume of the component (read from calibration curve) and B = volume of sample injected.

6. Precision and Accuracy

The precision and accuracy attainable will depend on the instrument employed and the technics of operation. With proper care, a precision of 2% can generally be achieved. With digester gas the summation of the methane, carbon dioxide and nitrogen percentages should total close to 100%. If it does not, then errors in collection, handling, storage, and injection of gas, or in instrumental operation or calibration might be suspected.

225 C. References

1. W. N. GRUNE & C. F. CHUEH. 1960. Gas chromatography for waste treatment control. *JWPCF* 32:942.
2. ———. Sludge gas analysis using gas chromatography. *Water & Sewage Works* 109:486 (1962); 110:43, 110:77, 110:102, 110:127, 110:171, 110:220, and 110:254 (1963).

225 D. Bibliography

Volumetric Method

YANT, W. P. & L. B. BERGER. 1936. Sampling of mine gases and the use of the Bureau of Mines portable Orsat apparatus in their analysis. Miner's Circular No. 34, U. S. Bureau of Mines, Washington, D.C.

MULLEN, P. W. 1955. *Modern Gas Analysis.* Interscience Publishers, New York.

Chromatographic Method

CHMIELOWSKI, J., J. R. SIMPSON & P. C. ISAAC. 1959. Use of gas chromatography in sludge digestion. *Sewage & Ind. Wastes* 31:1237.

SHEA, T. G., W. A. PRETORIUS & E. A. PEARSON. 1967. *Notes on Chromatographic Analysis of Digester Gases.* Sanitary Engineering Research Laboratory, Univ. of California, Richmond Field Station, Richmond, Calif.

ANDREWS, J. F. 1968. Chromatographic analysis of gaseous products and reactants for biological processes. *Water & Sewage Works* 115:54.

SLUDGE VOLUME AND DENSITY INDEXES: See Tests on Activated Sludge, Section 230.

SODIUM: See Metals (Groups I and II), Section 210.

226 SPECIFIC CONDUCTANCE

The specific electrical conductance of industrial wastewater, treatment plant effluents, and polluted water may give useful indications of the total concentration of ionic solutes. In some types of waste, all or nearly all of the dissolved material is ionic.

Methods and equipment required for determining specific conductance are described in Section 154 and are directly applicable to most wastewaters. Special attention may be required to obtain representative samples and to prevent fouling of electrode surfaces.

It seems likely that the most useful application of specific conductance measurements to wastewater will be through monitoring equipment, which is commercially available. These instruments provide essentially continuous records or indications of the conductance of flowing streams.

Specific conductance can be recorded either by single-parameter instruments or by more elaborate monitors which also measure and record other variables such as dissolved oxygen, pH and temperature of the stream. The sensor (or cell) may be placed in a tank through which water is pumped continuously, or placed directly in the flowing stream, depending on conditions at the monitor site.

In order to obtain reliable results, these instruments must be carefully maintained and frequently checked. Procedures for doing so will depend on the nature of the effluents being monitored and the characteristics of the instruments, and cannot be prescribed here in detail. Periodic checks of the indicated conductance using another cell and bridge suitable for field measurements, and checking by means of sampling and laboratory determinations, as discussed in Section 154, will show how frequently the sensor and intake must be cleaned. Most problems in obtaining good records with monitoring equipment are related to electrode fouling and to inadequate circulation of solutions being measured.

227 SPECIFIC GRAVITY

Specific gravity is determined by comparing the weight of a volume of the sample of mud, sludge or industrial waste with that of an equal volume of distilled water.

Weigh to the nearest 0.1 g an empty wide-mouth flask or bottle of about 250-ml capacity. Fill completely with distilled water and weigh again.

If the sample flows readily, fill the flask completely with the sample, weigh, and calculate the result:

$$\text{sp gr} = \frac{\text{weight of sample}}{\text{weight of distilled water}}$$

If the sample does not flow readily, add as much of it to the bottle as possible, without exerting pressure, and weigh. Fill the bottle containing the sample with water and weigh again, making sure that all entrained air bubbles have escaped. Determine the weight of added water by difference. Then:

$$\text{sp gr} = \frac{A}{B - C}$$

where A = weight of sample, B = weight of water to fill bottle, and C = weight of water added to sample.

STRONTIUM: See Metals (Groups I and II), Section 210.

228 SULFIDE

1. *General Discussion*

Sulfide may be found in water, wastewater and sludge as a result of microbial action on organic matter under anaerobic conditions and from certain industrial operations. Concentrations of a few tenths of a milligram per liter cause an objectionable rotten egg odor.

"Crown" corrosion of concrete sewers is often caused indirectly by the hydrogen sulfide liberated from slow-flowing sewage and wastewaters. Hydrogen sulfide-oxidizing bacteria are common in nature and frequently infect the walls and crowns of sewers. These bacteria produce sulfuric acid in the oxidation of H_2S; the sulfuric acid attacks the exposed concrete, sometimes leading to collapse of the pipe. High concentrations of soluble sulfides (over 200 mg/l) produce toxic effects in anaerobic treatment processes.

In analyses of sewage and wastewaters, three forms of sulfide are significant:

a. Total sulfide includes the dissolved H_2S and HS^-, as well as *acid-soluble* metallic sulfides present in the suspended matter. The $S^=$ ion is generally not present in significant amounts below a pH of 13. Acid-insoluble sulfides are not detected by the tests given here. Copper sulfide is the only common sulfide in this class.

b. Dissolved sulfide is that remaining after the suspended solids have been removed by flocculation and settling or centrifugation.

c. Un-ionized hydrogen sulfide may be calculated from the concentration of dissolved sulfide and the pH of the sample.

2. *Selection of Method*

Qualitatively, odors indicating hydrogen sulfide can be confirmed with lead acetate test paper, which becomes blackened on exposure to the vapor from a slightly acidified sample.

All three forms of sulfide may be

determined by any of the following methods: (*A*) titrimetric, using iodine, (*B*) methylene blue color-matching technic, and (*C*) the methylene blue colorimetric procedure adapted to the use of a spectrophotometer or filter photometer.

METHOD A, the iodometric procedure, is more accurate than B or C but cannot be carried out directly in sewage or certain wastewaters because of interfering substances. It is necessary to evolve the sulfide in a stream of inert gas and to collect it in zinc acetate before titration. Method A is suitable for the determination of sulfide in concentrations above 1 mg/l.

METHOD B, a drop-counting, color-matching methylene blue method, is designed for convenience rather than maximum accuracy. It is applicable to sulfide concentrations of 0.05–20 mg/l.

METHOD C is also a methylene blue procedure, but a spectrophotometer or filter photometer is used to measure the color. It is applicable to samples containing from 0.02 to 20 mg/l of sulfide; higher concentrations are determined by dilution of the sample with boiled and cooled distilled water before the color reaction.

3. Sampling and Storage

Samples must be taken with a minimum of aeration, for not only is sulfide volatilized by aeration, but also any oxygen which is taken up destroys it by chemical action. Samples to be used only for total sulfide determination may be preserved by adding zinc acetate solution at the rate of 2 ml per liter. This precipitates sulfide as inert ZnS, and it also prevents further sulfide generation. Determinations of dissolved sulfide, and analyses of samples not preserved with zinc acetate, must be commenced within 3 min of the time of sampling.

Samples to be used for determination of total sulfide must contain a representative proportion of suspended solids.

228 A. Titrimetric (Iodine) Method

1. General Discussion

a. Principle: Sulfides are stripped from the acidified sample with an inert gas and collected in zinc acetate solution. Excess iodine solution added to the zinc sulfide suspension reacts with the sulfide under acidic conditions. Thiosulfate is used to measure unreacted iodine to indicate the quantity of iodine consumed by sulfide.

b. Interferences: Reduced sulfur compounds, such as sulfite, thiosulfate and hydrosulfite, which decompose in acid, may yield erratic results. Volatile iodine-consuming substances will give high results.

2. Apparatus

a. Reaction flask: Wide-mouth bottle, 1-liter capacity, with a 2-hole stopper, fitted with a fritted gas-diffusion tube (plastic, ceramic or glass) and a gas outlet tube. Equivalent apparatus may be used.

b. Absorption flasks, erlenmeyer, 250-ml capacity, two, with 2-hole stoppers fitted with glass tubes and suitable connections to pass gas through in series.

3. Reagents

a. Zinc acetate solution, 2*N:* Dissolve 220 g $Zn(C_2H_3O_2)_2 \cdot 2H_2O$ in 870 ml water; this makes 1 liter of solution.

b. Inert gas: A cylinder of nitrogen or CO_2 or a CO_2 generator can be used.

c. Sulfuric acid, conc.

d. Standard iodine solution, 0.0250*N:* Dissolve 20–25 g potassium iodide, KI, in a little water and add 3.175 g iodine. After the iodine has dissolved, dilute to 1,000 ml and standardize against 0.0250*N* sodium thiosulfate, using starch solution as indicator. Standard iodine solution, exactly 0.0250*N*, is equivalent to 400 mg S per 1.00 ml.

e. Hydrochloric acid, conc.

f. Standard sodium thiosulfate titrant, 0.0250*N:* Prepare as directed in Dissolved Oxygen, Azide Modification (Section 218B.2e).

g. Starch: Prepare as directed in Dissolved Oxygen, Azide Modification (Section 218B.2d).

h. Aluminum chloride solution, 6*N:* Because of the hygroscopic and caking tendencies of this chemical, it will be convenient to purchase 100-g or ¼-lb bottles of the hexahydrate, $AlCl_3 \cdot 6H_2O$. Dissolve the contents of a previously unopened 100-g bottle of this salt in 144 ml water, or the contents of a ¼-lb bottle in 164 ml water.

i. Sodium hydroxide, 6*N.*

4. Procedure

a. Total sulfide:

1) Measure 5 ml zinc acetate and 95 ml distilled water into each of the two absorption flasks. Connect the reaction flask and two absorption flasks in series and purge the system with CO_2 or N_2 for 2 min. Measure 500 ml well-mixed sample into the reaction flask.

2) Acidify the sample with 10 ml conc H_2SO_4 and replace the prepared 2-hole stopper tightly; pass N_2 or CO_2 (not air or oxygen) through the sample for 1 hr or until tests show no more sulfide coming over. To each of the absorption flasks then add iodine solution well in excess of the amount necessary to react with the collected sulfide. Add 2.5 ml conc HCl to each flask, stopper, and shake to mix thoroughly. Transfer contents of both flasks to a 500-ml beaker or flask and back-titrate with 0.025*N* sodium thiosulfate titrant, using starch solution as indicator. For accurate results a blank should be run on the reagents, especially if the sulfide content is low.

b. Dissolved sulfide: Dissolved sulfide is determined on a sample from which the suspended solids have been removed by flocculating and settling.

1) Fill a 1-liter bottle with sample, flowing the liquid through the bottle after the manner of sampling for dissolved oxygen, in order to secure a sample which has had the least possible contact with air. Add 2 ml aluminum chloride solution and 2 ml NaOH solution and stopper, with no air bubbles under the stopper. Rotate back and forth about a transverse axis as vigorously as possible for at least 1 min in order to flocculate the contents thoroughly. The volumes of these chemicals may be varied according to experience, the aim being to get good clarification without using excessively large amounts. Always use equal amounts of the two reagents.

2) Allow to settle 15 min, or until the supernatant liquid is reasonably clear. Alternatively, remove the suspended matter by centrifugation of tightly stoppered sample bottles or tubes.

3) Proceed as for total sulfide [¶ 4a(2)] after siphoning 500 ml sample into the reaction flask.

c. Un-ionized hydrogen sulfide: Determine the pH of the original sample. Determine dissolved sulfide as given in ¶ 4b et seq above. Calculate the concentration of un-ionized H_2S by multiplying the concentration of dissolved sulfide by a suitable factor as given in Table 228(1). These factors are applicable at a temperature of 25 C. Apply suitable corrections for temperatures below 20 C or above 30 C, or for samples having a mineral solids content exceeding 2,000 mg/l. Refer to Figure 46 for dilutions of sea water and for other samples containing similar proportions of the various ions.

TABLE 228(1): HYDROGEN SULFIDE FACTORS *

pH	Factor
5.0	0.99
5.4	0.97
5.8	0.92
6.0	0.89
6.2	0.83
6.4	0.76
6.5	0.71
6.6	0.66
6.7	0.61
6.8	0.55
6.9	0.49
7.0	0.44
7.1	0.38
7.2	0.33
7.3	0.28
7.4	0.24
7.5	0.20
7.6	0.16
7.7	0.13
7.8	0.11
7.9	0.089
8.0	0.072
8.2	0.046
8.4	0.030
8.8	0.012
9.2	0.0049
9.6	0.0019

* Revised 1968. Based on: $K_1 = 1.1 \times 10^{-7}$ (25 C); ionic strength, $\mu = 0.02$.

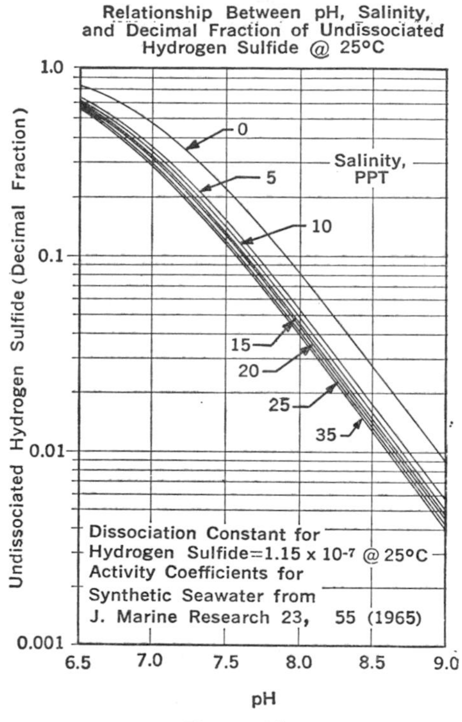

Figure 46

5. Calculation

$$\text{mg/l S} = \frac{(\text{ml iodine} - \text{ml } Na_2S_2O_3) \times 400}{\text{ml sample}}$$

6. Precision and Accuracy

Precision and accuracy have not been determined, but it is known that the iodometric titration of zinc sulfide is quite accurate. The principal chance of error of the method is in the gaseous transfer of sulfide to the zinc acetate receiving solution. The analyst should check his technic for this by preparing a zinc sulfide suspension as directed in Method B, ¶ 4a, then determining the sulfide concentration by titrating one sample directly and another sample after gaseous transfer. Recovery should not be less than 95%.

228 B. Methylene Blue Visual Color-Matching Method

1. General Discussion

a. Principle: The colorimetric method is based on the reaction which takes place, under suitable conditions, between paraaminodimethylaniline, ferric chloride and sulfide ion, resulting in the formation of methylene blue. Ammonium phosphate is added before color comparison to remove the color due to the presence of ferric ion.

b. Interference: Some strong reducing agents prevent the formation of the color or diminish its intensity. High sulfide concentrations—several hundred milligrams per liter—may completely inhibit the reaction, but dilution of the sample prior to analysis eliminates this problem. Sulfide up to 10 mg/l SO_2 has no effect, although higher concentrations retard the reaction. Thiosulfate concentrations below 10 mg/l do not interfere seriously, but higher concentrations prevent color formation unless the thiosulfate is oxidized. The interference of sulfite and thiosulfate up to 40 mg/l of SO_2 or S_2O_3 can be eliminated by increasing the amount of $FeCl_3$ solution added from 2 to 6 drops, and extending the reaction time to 5 min. If present, sodium hydrosulfite, $Na_2S_2O_4$, will interfere by releasing some sulfide when the sample is acidified. Nitrite gives a pale yellow color at concentrations as low as 0.5 mg/l NO_2, but nitrite and sulfide are not likely to be found together, so that this possible interference is of little practical importance. To eliminate a slight interfering color due to the reagent, which may be noticeable at sulfide concentrations below 0.1 mg/l, a dilute amine-sulfuric acid test solution is specified for concentrations of that order.

c. Minimum detectable concentration: 50 μg/l sulfide.

2. Apparatus

a. Matched test tubes, approximately 125 mm long and 15 mm O.D., are most convenient for field use; 50-ml nessler tubes, with a corresponding increase in the amounts of sample and reagents, may also be used to give an increased depth of colored solutions, and therefore an increased sensitivity.

b. Droppers, delivering 20 drops per milliliter of the methylene blue solutions. In order to secure accurate results when measuring by drops, it is essential to hold the dropper in a vertical position and to allow the drops to form slowly, so that the outside of the dropper is thoroughly drained before the drop falls.

c. Glass-stoppered bottles, capacity 100–300 ml. A BOD incubation bottle is recommended because its stopper is ground in such a way that it minimizes the possibility of entrapping air, and its specially designed lip provides a water seal.

3. Reagents

a. Zinc acetate solution: Prepare as directed in Method A, ¶ 3a.

b. Sodium carbonate solution: Dissolve 5.0 g Na_2CO_3 in distilled water and dilute to 100 ml.

c. Amine-sulfuric acid stock reagent: Dissolve 26.6 g N,N-dimethyl-*p*-phenylenediamine oxalate * (also called *p*-aminodimethylaniline oxalate) in a cold mixture of 50 ml conc sulfuric acid and 20 ml distilled water; cool, then dilute to 100 ml with distilled water. Store in a dark glass bottle. This stock solution may discolor on aging, but its usefulness is unimpaired.

d. Amine-sulfuric acid reagent: Dilute 25 ml amine-sulfuric acid stock solution with 975 ml 1 + 1 H_2SO_4. Store in a dark glass bottle.

e. Ferric chloride solution: Dissolve 100 g $FeCl_3 \cdot 6H_2O$ in 39 ml water; this makes 100 ml of solution.

f. Sulfuric acid solution, 1 + 1: Add, cautiously, 500 ml conc H_2SO_4 to 500 ml distilled water with continuous mixing. Cool the solution before using.

g. Diammonium hydrogen phosphate solution: Dissolve 40 g $(NH_4)_2HPO_4$ in distilled water and dilute to 100 ml.

h. Stock sulfide solution: Dissolve 4.10 g sodium sulfide trihydrate ($Na_2S \cdot 3H_2O$) † in boiled, cooled distilled water. Weigh the sodium sulfide from a well-stoppered weighing bottle. Dilute to 1 liter in a volumetric flask to form a solution containing 1.0 mg S per 1.0 ml. If the weight of $Na_2S \cdot 3H_2O$ used is other than that recommended, calculate the sulfide concentration as follows:

$$\text{mg/l } S^{=} = 242.8 \times B$$

where B = grams $Na_2S \cdot 3H_2O$ per liter. Prepare the stock solution daily.

i. Standard sulfide solution: Take 20.0 ml stock solution or an appropriate aliquot which contains 20.0 mg sulfide and dilute to 1 liter with boiled, cooled distilled water. Because of its instability, prepare this solution as needed. Standardize by pipetting 100 ml solution into an erlenmeyer flask and immediately add 10.00 ml standard 0.0250*N* iodine solution (prepared and standardized as described in Method A, ¶ 3d) and add 2 drops conc HCl. Titrate the residual iodine with standard 0.0250*N* $Na_2S_2O_3$ titrant [prepared and standardized as described in Oxygen (Dissolved), Section 218B.2e], using starch indicator [prepared as directed in Oxygen (Dissolved) Section 218B. 2d] at the end point. Run a blank on the reagents. Calculate the sulfide concentration, which should be approximately 20 mg/l S or 1 ml = 20 μg, as follows:

$$\text{mg/l } S^{=} = (10.00 - C - D) \times 4$$

where C = ml 0.0250*N* $Na_2S_2O_3$ titrant required for titration and D = ml 0.0250*N* iodine solution used for reagent blank.

j. Methylene blue solution (I): Use the USP grade of the dye, or one certified by the Biological Stain Commission. The percentage of actual dye content should be reported on the label and should be 84% or more. Dissolve 1.0 g methylene blue powder in water

* Eastman catalog No. 5672 has been found satisfactory for this purpose.

† Sodium sulfide, technical flakes, $Na_2S \cdot 3H_2O$ (60% Na_2S), Mallinckrodt No. 8032, has been found satisfactory for this purpose.

and make up to 1 liter. This solution will be approximately the correct strength, but because of variation between different lots of the dye, it must be standardized against sulfide solutions of known strength and its concentration adjusted so that 1 drop (0.05 ml) of solution will be equivalent to 1.0 mg/l of sulfide.

STANDARDIZATION—Determine the number of drops of methylene blue solution which will produce a color equivalent to that obtained with a measured aliquot of the standard sulfide solution in accordance with Method B, starting at ¶ 4a(2) below. After making this analysis, adjust the methylene blue solution either by diluting with water or by adding more dye so that 1 drop is equivalent to 1.0 mg/l of sulfide. After making an adjustment, repeat the colorimetric determination to check the adjusted solution. The methylene blue solution is stable for a year if kept in the dark and tightly stoppered.

k. Methylene blue solution (II): Dilute 10.00 ml of the adjusted methylene blue solution (I) to 100 ml, making 1 drop (0.05 ml) equivalent to 0.1 mg/l sulfide.

l. Sodium hydroxide 6*N*.

4. Procedure

a. Total sulfide:

1) SAMPLE PRETREATMENT—Add 3 or 4 drops zinc acetate solution to 100 ml sample and follow with a few drops of Na_2CO_3 solution. Allow the precipitated ZnS to settle, and then decant the clear liquid. Add sufficient water to the precipitated slurry to restore the volume to 100 ml. When interferences are known to be absent, the pretreatment may be omitted.

2) COLOR DEVELOPMENT—Fill two color comparison tubes to the 7.5 ml mark with sample. Add to one tube 0.5 ml amine-sulfuric acid reagent and 3 drops (0.15 ml) $FeCl_3$ solution; stopper and mix the contents immediately by inverting the tube slowly, only once. Add to the other tube 0.5 ml 1 + 1 H_2SO_4 and 3 drops (0.15 ml) $FeCl_3$ solution; stopper and mix the contents immediately by inverting the tube slowly, only once.

The presence of sulfide ion will be indicated by the immediate appearance of blue color in the first tube. Complete color development requires about 1 min. One to 5 min after the color first appears (see ¶ 1b above), add 1.6 ml $(NH_4)_2HPO_4$ solution to each tube.

3) VISUAL COLOR ESTIMATION—Add methylene blue solution I or II, depending on the sulfide concentration and the desired accuracy of the test, dropwise, to the contents of the second tube, until the color imparted by the methylene blue matches that developed in the first tube. Record the total number of drops of methylene blue solution added to the contents of the second tube.

b. Dissolved sulfide: Fill a glass-stoppered BOD bottle with sample and eliminate air bubbles. Add 0.5 ml $AlCl_3$ solution (Method A, ¶ 3h) and 0.5 ml 6*N* NaOH (Method A, ¶ 3i, preceding). Stopper the bottle and flocculate the precipitate by rotating the bottle back and forth about a transverse axis. Allow the floc to settle. Proceed with the clear supernatant liquid as directed in ¶ 4a(2) above.

c. Un-ionized hydrogen sulfide: Calculate the un-ionized hydrogen sulfide according to ¶ 4c of Method A (above). Be sure to use, in this calculation, the pH of the original sample—

not the pH after adding any reagents.

d. Very low sulfide concentrations: Determine very low sulfide concentrations by the method for such concentrations given in Section 157.

5. Calculation

With methylene blue solution (I), adjusted so that 1 drop (0.05 ml) corresponds to 1.0 mg/l sulfide when 7.5 ml of sample are used:

$$\text{mg/l sulfide} = \text{No. drops} = \text{ml} \times 20$$

With methylene blue solution (II), adjusted so that 1 drop (0.05 ml) corresponds to 0.1 mg/l sulfide when 7.5 ml of sample are used:

$$\text{mg/l sulfide} = \text{No. drops} \times 0.1 = \text{ml} \times 2$$

If dilution is necessary, multiply the result by the appropriate factor.

6. Precision and Accuracy

With care, the accuracy is about ± 10%. The standard deviation has not been determined.

228 C. *Methylene Blue Photometric Method (TENTATIVE)*

1. Apparatus

a. Colorimetric equipment—One of the following is required:

1) SPECTROPHOTOMETER, for use at 600 mμ, providing a light path of 1 cm or longer.

2) FILTER PHOTOMETER, providing a light path of 1 cm or longer and equipped with a red filter exhibiting maximum transmittance near 600 mμ.

b. Graduated cylinders or flasks, 50-ml capacity.

2. Reagents

All the reagents listed for Method B (Section 228B.3a-l) are required except the standard methylene blue solutions.

3. Procedure

a. Preparation of standard curve:

1) Add to separate 50-ml graduated cylinders or flasks the following volumes of standard sulfide solution (1.0 ml = 20 μg): 0 (reagent blank), 0.5, 1.0, 2.0, 3.0, 4.0 and 5.0 ml, in order to prepare a sulfide series containing 0, 10, 20, 40, 60, 80 and 100 μg, respectively. Dilute with boiled and cooled distilled water to 50 ml.

2) Add 0.5 ml amine-sulfuric acid reagent and mix; then add 2 drops (0.10 ml) $FeCl_3$ solution and mix again. After 1 min add 1.5 ml diammonium hydrogen phosphate solution and mix. Measure the absorbance against the reagent blank (usually colorless) at a wavelength of 600 mμ. Plot absorbance against μg S.

b. Total sulfide: See Method B (Section 228B.4a). When interference is absent, omit this step. Measure 50 ml distilled water and 50 ml sample (or a suitable aliquot diluted to 50 ml) into separate graduated cylinders or flasks. Complete the determination as directed in ¶ 4a et seq and refer to the standard curve for the sulfide concentration.

c. Dissolved sulfide: Remove the suspended matter in the sample as directed in Method B, ¶ 4b. Complete the determination as described in ¶s 4c and d.

4. Calculation

$$\text{mg/l S} = \frac{\mu g\ S}{\text{ml sample}}$$

5. Precision and Accuracy

Results by the photometric method are estimated to be equal to, or perhaps more reliable than, those obtained by the visual comparison method.

228 D. Bibliography

POMEROY, R. D. 1936. The determination of sulfides in sewage. *Sewage Works J.* 8:572.

———. 1941. Hydrogen sulfides in sewage. *Sewage Works J.* 13:498.

NUSBAUM, I. 1953. Determination of phenols by the *p*-nitrosodimethylaniline method—A discussion. *Sewage & Ind. Wastes* 25:312.

CAMP, T. R. 1963. *Water and Its Impurities.* Reinhold Publishing Corporation, New York, pp. 63–64.

NUSBAUM, I. 1965. Determining sulfides in water and waste water. *Water & Sewage Works* 112:113.

PLATFORD, R. F. 1965. The activity coefficient of sodium chloride in seawater. *J. Marine Research* 23:55.

LAWRENCE, A. W., P. L. MCCARTY & F. J. A. GUERIN. 1966. The effects of sulfides on anaerobic treatment. *Int. J. Air & Water Poll.* 10:207.

229 SURFACTANTS (ANIONIC)

So many substances normally found in wastewaters, effluents and polluted waters interfere with determination of the surfactant component of synthetic detergents that it is very difficult to obtain an accurate value. An estimate of the concentration of anionic surfactants may be made using the methods given in Section 159.

SUSPENDED MATTER IN ACTIVATED SLUDGE: See Tests on Activated Sludge, Section 230.

TEMPERATURE: See Temperature, Section 162.

230 TESTS ON ACTIVATED SLUDGE

The activated-sludge process of sewage treatment is dependent on laboratory control through use of the procedures given below. These methods are presented as a group, because the sludge volume index (SVI) and the sludge density index (SDI) are calculated from suspended solids and the 30-min settled volume test.

230 A. Suspended Matter

Determine suspended matter in sludges and aeration-tank mixed liquors by gravimetric methods (Residue, Section 224C).

230 B. Settled Volume

Determine the settled volume of activated sludge by collecting a 1-liter sample at the outlet of the aeration tank in a 1,000-ml graduated cylinder, or by transferring it quickly to such a cylinder, and allowing the activated sludge to settle at the same temperature as that of the aeration tank. The volume occupied by the sludge may be recorded at such time intervals as 5, 10, 15, 20, 30, 45 and 60 minutes. For plant control, a 30-min settled volume or the ratio of the 15-min to the 30-min settled volume is generally used. Although many types of activated sludge give consistent results, there are some types that will show a great variation if such factors as temperature, agitation, and the time between sampling and the start of the determination are allowed to vary. In order to obtain consistent results, follow exactly the same procedure each time the determination is made.

When a sample of activated sludge is settled, if the suspended-solids concentration is low enough, the phenomena observed are discrete settling and compaction. If the suspended-solids concentration is in an intermediate range, the phenomena observed are hindered settling followed by compaction, but the hindered settling is usually completed in less than 10 min. If the suspended-solids concentration is high enough, the only phenomenon observed is compaction. The settled volume test is used mostly by plant operators to determine when to increase or decrease the returned-sludge rate and when to waste sludge. The need to change the returned-sludge rate depends upon how well the sludge compacts, not upon how well it settles. The use of the 30-min settled volume for calculation of the sludge volume index gives a control parameter for the process which has no basis in solid-liquid separation theory but which has been found empirically to be of considerable value.

230 C. Sludge Volume Index

The sludge volume index (SVI) is the volume in milliliters occupied by 1 g of activated sludge after settling the aerated liquor for 30 min. Collect a 1-liter sample at the outlet of the aeration tanks and settle for 30 min in a 1,000-ml graduated cylinder; report the volume occupied by the sludge as percent or milliliters. Thoroughly mix the sample, or take a new sample, determine the suspended solids, and report in percent by weight or mg/l.

$$\text{SVI} = \frac{\%\ \text{settling by volume}}{\%\ \text{suspended matter}}$$

$$\text{SVI} = \frac{\text{ml settled sludge} \times 1{,}000}{\text{mg/l suspended matter}}$$

The standard deviation of the sludge volume index was determined as 1.69 on an average index of 72—a coefficient of variation of 2.35% ($n = 1$; 10×10).

230 D. Sludge Density Index

The sludge density index (SDI) is the reciprocal of the sludge volume index (SVI) multiplied by 100. Calculate from the data determined by the methods described above.

$$\text{SDI} = \frac{\%\ \text{suspended matter} \times 100}{\%\ \text{settling by volume}}$$

$$= \frac{\text{mg/l suspended matter}}{\text{ml settled sludge} \times 10}$$

$$= \frac{100}{\text{SVI}}$$

The standard deviation of the sludge density index was found to be 0.033 on an average index of 1.40—a coefficient of variation of 2.35% ($n = 1$; 10×10).

230 E. Bibliography

DONALDSON, W. 1932. Some notes on the operation of sewage treatment works. *Sewage Works J.* 4:48.

MOHLMAN, F. W. 1934. Editorial. *Sewage Works J.* 6:119.

RUDOLFS, W. & I. O. LACY. 1934. Settling and compacting of activated sludge. *Sewage Works J.* 6:647.

FINCH, J. & H. IVES. 1950. Settleability indexes for activated sludge. *Sewage & Ind. Wastes* 22:883.

ISENBERG, E. & H. HEUKELEKIAN. 1959. Sludge volume index. *Water & Sewage Works* 106:525.

231 TOXICITY TO FISH

1. General Principles and Selection of Method

a. Introduction: Bioassays are conducted to evaluate the toxicity of effluents or other materials, determine permissible effluent discharge rates, establish the relative sensitivity of various fish species, and identify effects of physical and chemical variables such as temperature and pH on toxicity. Bioassays can be used to judge compliance with water quality standards established by water pollution control authorities. In a bioassay, experimental organisms are subjected to a series of concentrations of a known or suspected toxicant under adequately controlled conditions. The methods described here essentially derive from and correspond to those presented in a committee report by Doudoroff *et al*,[1] in which additional details and explanations can be found.

b. Measures of toxicity: Bioassay results using fish shall be expressed in terms of tolerance limits (TL).* Along with the symbol TL, the time of exposure and the percentage of fish surviving are indicated. For example, a 96-hr TL_{50} of a toxic substance is that concentration in which 50% of the fish survive for 96 hr. The TL_{50} is equivalent to the median tolerance limit (TL_m). The use of TL with the percentage subscript allows the designation of percentages of survival other than 50%; for example, one can determine a TL_{10} and a TL_{90}. However, the TL_{50} is the standard measure of toxicity and must always be determined.

c. Selection of method: Tolerance limits can be determined by static bioassays or by continuous-flow bioassays.

1) Static bioassays are suitable to detect and evaluate toxicity that is not associated with excessive oxygen demand and that is due to relatively stable substances. When dissolved oxygen (DO) in the diluent is insufficient, or when surface oxygen absorption does not maintain a DO level adequate for the test organisms, oxygen may be supplied by initial oxygenation of the diluent, controlled artificial oxygenation of test solutions, or periodic renewal of test solutions. The last-named modification of the static bioassay may also be employed whenever there is evidence or expectation of a rapid change of toxicity of the test solution. Such a change is indicated when the survival time of test animals in a fresh solution is significantly shorter than the survival time in a corresponding 2-day-old solution, provided adequate DO is present throughout both tests.

2) Continuous-flow bioassays are used mainly to test industrial effluents and chemicals that have high biochemical oxygen demands, are unstable or volatile, or are removed appreciably from solution by precipitation or the test fish. The continuous-flow bioassay is preferable to the static bioassay and

* The expressions "lethal dose" (LD) and "lethal concentration" (LC) have also been frequently used, the term "lethal dose" often incorrectly. The expression "lethal dose" is not appropriate when designating a certain concentration in an external medium, inasmuch as a dose, strictly speaking, is a measured quantity administered. Unlike "lethal dose" and "lethal concentration," the term "tolerance limit" is universally applicable in designating a level of any measurable lethal agent, including high and low temperatures, pH, and the like. The expression "effective concentration" (EC) applies to concentrations only and is generally used in connection with effects other than death.

its modifications when such substances are being tested. Continuous-flow bioassays provide for well-oxygenated test solutions, nonfluctuating concentrations of the toxicant, and removal of metabolic products of the fish. These bioassays duplicate the natural conditions of receiving streams, not far downstream from waste outfalls, more precisely than do static bioassays, and they permit extended exposures to determine chronic toxicity or safe concentrations of the toxicant under consideration.

2. *Selection and Preparation of Test Materials*

a. Selection of test fish: Experimental fish should be those species adaptable to laboratory conditions and those of which adequate numbers of a usable size can be maintained.

For the determination of permissible effluent discharge rates, sensitive species important in the receiving water should be the test species. When circumstances necessitate the use of some other species, comparative tests using the effluents of concern should be performed to relate the sensitivity of the selected species to the most sensitive of locally important game and food fishes. It is recommended that the advice of the responsible water pollution control authority on the selection of species, size of test fish, and test conditions be sought, especially when effluents are discharged directly into a salt water environment.

Species of the important freshwater families Centrarchidae (sunfishes and basses), Salmonidae (trouts and salmons), and Cyprinidae (minnows) are commonly used as test fish. The officially accepted species name should be used in the bioassay report.[2]

Test fish should be obtained from a common source for any one series of bioassays. Any known unusual condition to which fish were exposed before use (e.g., pesticides or chemotherapeutic agents) should be reported. Small fish, not more than 7.5 cm in length, are generally the most convenient. The length of the largest individual should be no more than 1.5 times the length of the smallest.

b. Preparation of test fish: Fish stocks may be kept in small ponds, live-boxes, screened pens, and glass or other aquaria, in water of a quantity and quality such that they will remain in good condition. Care and feeding of stock fish are discussed by Doudoroff *et al.*[1] Fish selected for testing should be acclimatized to the test temperature and the experimental dilution water for at least 10 and preferably 30 days. For acclimatization, they are held in aquaria which are placed in a constant-temperature room or are equipped with thermostatic devices that will not contaminate the water with harmful metals such as copper, zinc or cadmium. Adequate aeration of the water with oil-free air * released from dispersers located near the bottom of the aquaria is essential unless the water is renewed continuously by the introduction of sufficient well-aerated water. The fish should be fed daily or at least three times per week regularly, but they should not be fed for 2 days before testing when short-term or static tests are used. Incidence of disease or death among acclimatized fish within a period of 4 days immediately preceding the test must be less than 5%. Test specimens must show no symptoms of

* Air compressors must be water-sealed and located where the intake air is not contaminated.

disease or abnormalities of appearance or behavior at the time of their transfer to the test containers. They should be selected or graded according to size some time in advance to avoid unnecessary handling just before use in the bioassays.

c. Selection and preparation of experimental water (diluent): To determine permissible effluent discharge rates, the experimental water must be obtained from the receiving stream or water body outside the zone of influence of the effluent. When effluent discharge is to a flowing stream, the source for the experimental water should be just upstream from the point of discharge. The water must not be subjected to treatment, such as aeration, that may change its quality, and it should be stored no longer than absolutely necessary before initiation of the bioassay. A water other than that prescribed above may be used only when a different water has been specified or accepted by the responsible water pollution control authority as being suitable or more appropriate. A description of the source and history of the experimental water should be included in the test report.

When the purpose of the bioassay is other than that specified above, the experimental water should be an unpolluted natural water or a synthetic dilution water of a constant and reproducible quality and one that is capable of supporting aquatic life. In many instances groundwaters meet these requirements after aeration. A carbon-filtered tap water also may prove satisfactory. Synthetic dilution waters of a constant and reproducible quality capable of supporting aquatic life may be prepared by the addition of appropriate chemicals to distilled water or deionized water. Synthetic waters that have proved satisfactory for some purposes have been described.[3, 4] Inasmuch as the test fish will be kept and observed in the experimental water for 10 to 30 days during acclimatization, their ability to live in this water will have been established before the bioassays are initiated.

d. Sampling and storage of test materials: When the composition of an effluent varies, samples should be collected and tested periodically to determine the range in toxicity and the maximal toxicity of the effluent. Evaluation of the average toxicity by testing composite samples collected over an extended time period is not usually sufficiently instructive.

Test liquids or effluents should be stored in chemically clean, completely filled, stoppered glass bottles at 4 C. If it is known that storage under some other conditions will result in less change in toxicity, then such storage should be provided for and reported. Duration of storage prior to testing should be kept to a minimum and reported.

3. General Test Conditions and Procedures for Bioassays

a. Temperature: The range of temperatures for test solutions must not exceed 4 C and must be appropriate to the species of fish used. The test temperature should be selected with consideration of the usual and maximum temperatures of problem waters to which the bioassay results are to apply. Temperatures selected for tests to determine permissible effluent discharge rates must be within the range of temperatures of the receiving water; low temperatures within this range usually should be avoided, as should temperatures very near the upper limits of thermal tolerance of the test animals. When there is no good reason, relating to problems under investigation, for selecting other temperatures for bioassays with freshwater fishes, test temperatures of 25 ± 2 C and 15 ± 2 C are recommended for warm water and cold water species, respectively.

b. Dissolved oxygen content and aeration of test solutions: The dissolved oxygen content of test solutions must not fall below 4 mg/l when warm water fish are used as test animals, or 5 mg/l when cold water fish are used. However, aeration of test solutions, with finely dispersed compressed air or otherwise, is not permissible when it will cause material reduction of toxicity of the solutions during tests by accelerating loss of volatile components.

c. Concentrations of toxicants tested: Concentrations of dilutions of liquid industrial wastes (aqueous solutions, suspensions, and emulsions of complex or unknown composition) are expressed as percent by volume. For example, a 10% dilution equals 1 volume of wastewater in 9 volumes of diluent water. Concentrations of nonaqueous wastes and of individual chemicals (solids, liquids or gases) are expressed in terms of milligrams per liter (mg/l) or micrograms per liter (μg/l). The inclusion of any water of hydration as part of the weight of the solute (e.g., $CuSo_4 \cdot 5H_2O$) should be clearly indicated. Likewise, when an impure chemical is tested, especially a formulation containing added inert ingredients, the report must indicate the chemical composition by weight, and whether a concentration of total material or a concentration of active ingredient is represented by the TL value reported.

Although a TL_{50} may be determined by testing any appropriate series of concentrations of the substance or waste assayed, the geometric series of concentration values given in Table 231(1) is often most convenient and has been widely used. These values can represent concentrations expressed as percent by volume or as milligrams per liter, etc.; they may all be multiplied or divided, as necessary, by any power of 10. For example, the two values in the first column may be 10.0 and 1.0 as shown, or they may be 100 and 10, or 1.0 and 0.1, with the values in the other columns changed accordingly. The values of the series 10.0, 5.6, 3.2, 1.8, and 1.0 (i.e., Cols. 1–3), or 10.0, 7.5, 5.6, 4.2, 3.2, etc. (Cols. 1 through 4), are evenly spaced when plotted on a logarithmic scale. The values in the first three columns are often sufficient, but precision can often be increased by

TABLE 231(1): GUIDE TO SELECTION OF EXPERIMENTAL CONCENTRATIONS, BASED ON PROGRESSIVE BISECTION OF INTERVALS ON LOGARITHMIC SCALE

Col. 1	Col. 2	Col. 3	Col. 4	Col. 5
10.0				
				8.7
			7.5	
				6.5
		5.6		
				4.9
			4.2	
				3.7
	3.2			
				2.8
			2.4	
				2.1
		1.8		
				1.55
			1.35	
				1.15
1.0				

including values from Col. 4 in the test concentration series—initially or by performing additional tests. Values in Col. 5 are not often used.

Some investigators prefer other, similar series of concentrations [Table 231(2)]. The values in Col. 1 only may be used and are often sufficient; those in Col. 2 are also used when it is deemed advisable to reduce the intervals between test concentrations. The reason for the selection of these concentration values will be apparent when their logarithms, given in the right-hand column, are considered. Successive dilution whereby the concentration of a solution is reduced stepwise by a constant factor—for example, 0.5—is a simple way to obtain a geometric series of concentrations, such as 8, 4, 2, 1 and 0.5%.

TABLE 231(2): GUIDE TO SELECTION OF EXPERIMENTAL CONCENTRATIONS, BASED ON DECILOG INTERVALS

Concentrations		Log of Concentration
Col. 1	Col. 2	
10.0		1.00
	7.94 (or 7.9)	0.90
6.31 (or 6.3)		0.80
	5.01 (or 5.0)	0.70
3.98 (or 4.0)		0.60
	3.16 (or 3.15)	0.50
2.51 (or 2.5)		0.40
	1.99 (or 2.0)	0.30
1.58 (or 1.6)		0.20
	1.26 (or 1.25)	0.10
1.00		0.00

The magnitude of suitable intervals between concentrations tested to establish a TL_{50} by interpolation depends on the required degree of precision and on the nature of the experimental data. When two test concentrations bracketing the TL_{50} (i.e., one above and one below the TL_{50}) have proved lethal to at least 20% and not to all the test fish, determination of survival percentages at intermediate concentrations usually is not very advantageous, although greater precision may be attainable by testing these additional concentrations. If the difference or interval between the two test concentrations bracketing the TL_{50} is not much more than 25% of the higher concentration value, an estimate of the TL_{50} sufficiently precise for most practical purposes can be obtained even when the observed survival percentages at these concentrations are 0 and 100%. At least one concentration higher and one lower than these bracketing concentrations should always be included in the series tested to obtain confirmatory data.

When testing materials of unknown toxicity, much time and effort can be saved by conducting small-scale exploratory bioassays to determine the range of concentrations that should be tested in full-scale tests. In these tests, solutions are prepared over a wide range of concentrations; for example, 100, 10, 1 and 0.1% of the effluent by volume and two or three fish are placed in each test solution. Usually the full-scale test range falls between the highest concentrations at which all fish survive for 24 hr and the lowest concentration at which all or most fish die in the same period.

When the range in concentrations to be covered by the full-scale tests has been determined by exploratory bioassays, toxicity is measured by testing a series of concentrations, usually five or six, to make possible more precise estimation of the TL_{50}.

For the preparation of test solutions

with highly toxic substances, it may not be feasible or convenient to add measured quantities of the toxicants directly to the dilution water in test containers. Table 231(3) can be useful in determining volumes of suitable stock solutions or dilutions to add.

TABLE 231(3): DILUTIONS FOR VARIOUS TEST SOLUTION CONCENTRATIONS

Test Solution Concentration Desired			Strength of Stock Solution—*g/l*				
			100	10	1	0.1	0.01
Percent	*mg/l*	*µg/l*	Volume (*ml*) to Be Diluted to 1 Liter				
1.0	10,000		100				
0.56	5,600		56				
0.32	3,200		32				
0.18	1,800		18				
0.10	1,000		10	100			
0.056	560		5.6	56			
0.032	320		3.2	32			
0.018	180		1.8	18			
0.010	100		1.0	10	100		
0.0056	56			5.6	56		
0.0032	32			3.2	32		
0.0018	18			1.8	18		
0.0010	10			1.0	10	100	
0.00056	5.6				5.6	56	
0.00032	3.2				3.2	32	
0.00018	1.8				1.8	18	
0.00010	1.0	1,000			1.0	10	100
0.000056	0.56	560				5.6	56
0.000032	0.32	320				3.2	32
0.000018	0.18	180				1.8	18
0.000010	0.10	100				1.0	10
0.0000056	0.056	56					5.6
0.0000032	0.032	32					3.2
0.0000018	0.018	18					1.8
0.0000010	0.010	10					1.0

d. Controls: With each test or each series of simultaneous tests of different solutions, a concurrent control test must be performed in exactly the same manner as the other tests and under the conditions prescribed or selected for those tests. The experimental water or diluent alone is used as the medium in which the control fish are held. There must be no more than 10% mortality among the control fish during the course of any valid test and at least 90% must remain apparently healthy.

When an organic solvent or other dispersing agent is used to prepare test solutions, suspensions or emulsions of toxicants that are insoluble or only slightly soluble in water, a different control test usually must be performed in addition to the ordinary control test. In this control test, the fish are exposed to the maximal concentration of the solvent or dispersant to which fish in the other test solutions are exposed, this material being added alone to the experimental water or diluent.

e. Number of test fish: At least 10 fish will be used to test each experimental concentration of the substance assayed. Usually the fish should be divided equally among two or more test containers with solutions or waste dilutions of the same concentration. Fewer than 10 fish (usually 2 or 3) may be used only in exploratory tests to determine what concentrations should be tested in the full-scale tests.

f. Transfer of fish: Fish should be transferred from the acclimatizing aquaria to the test containers only with small-mesh dip nets of soft material or wet hands, and must not rest on any dry surface. They must not be held out of the water longer than necessary. Any specimen accidentally dropped or otherwise mishandled during transfer must be discarded. These fish usually should be transferred to the test solutions within 30 min or less after preparation of the solutions.

g. Feeding of fish during tests: Fish should not be fed during tests of limited duration (96 hr or less), thus avoiding large fluctuations in their metabolic rate and fouling of test solutions with metabolic waste products and uneaten food. During tests of longer duration, food should be provided. However, the fish should be trained to accept the food before the tests are begun. Use of the continuous-flow bioassay in this case will avoid the problems of feeding usually associated with the static bioassay.

h. Test duration and observations: The duration of all tests should be at least 48 hr, and 96-hr tests are usually preferable. When more than half of the test fish survive for 48 hr at the highest possible test concentration, the test must be continued for a total of 96 hr. Whenever some test animals are still alive but are dying or evidently affected after a 48-hr or longer exposure to some tested concentrations of a toxic material, it is advisable to prolong the tests further.

The number of dead fish in each test container must be observed and recorded at the end of each 24-hr period after introduction of the fish. The number of live fish that show pronounced symptoms of intoxication and distress, such as loss of equilibrium and other markedly abnormal behavior, should be recorded. Fish reactions during the first 8 hr of each test give an indication of the nature of the toxicant and can be useful in interpreting test results. Fish are considered dead upon cessation of respiratory and all other overt movements, whether spontaneous or in response to mild mechanical prodding. Dead fish must be removed as soon as observed.

i. Physical and chemical determinations: Determinations of the temperature, DO and pH of test solutions and determinations of measurable toxicant concentrations normally are made before introducing the fish and again as soon as possible after the death of all or most of the fish, or at the end of a test where fish are still alive. At regular time intervals or when fish are dying, additional determinations, especially of temperature, DO and pH, may be needed for proper control of test conditions and to facilitate interpretation and application of the bioassay results. Determinations of the chemical properties or dissolved mineral content of the experimental water (diluent) should be made not long before the test solutions are prepared, unless the composition of the water is known to be constant. The salinity or total dissolved-solids content, total alkalinity, pH of the water, and the concentrations of calcium and magnesium ions should be determined and reported. This should be done also for any other constituents of the water that are known to be present in unusual amounts or which markedly influence the toxicity of the material under test. A rather complete mineral analysis of the water is advisable.

4. *Special Test Conditions and Procedures for Static Bioassays*

a. Testing laboratory: An ordinary heated or air-conditioned laboratory room with thermostatic controls suitable to maintain prescribed test temperatures will suffice generally to conduct static bioassays with warm water fishes. However, a specially insulated constant-temperature room or a large water bath equipped for precise temperature control and adequate circulation of air and water is usually preferable, and such a facility may be necessary to conduct bioassays with cold water fishes. Henderson and Tarzwell [5] and Lennon and Walker [6] have described a satisfactory design for a bioassay laboratory.

b. Test containers: The size and shape of the test containers have not been standardized. Size depends on the required volume of test solution, which in turn depends on the number and size of fish used in each test. The depth of the vessels, however, should be more than 15 cm. Test containers should be of glass, except when other more convenient materials have been conclusively shown to be nontoxic to the test fish and nonreactive with the tested material. For tests with fish of convenient size, 5 to 7.5 cm in length, the test containers may be wide-mouth glass jars 25 to 30 cm in diameter, 30 cm or more high, with a capacity of about 20 liters.

Test containers must be cleaned thoroughly after use to remove all toxic residues. Soap and hot water cleaning followed by acid and/or solvent rinsing (the choice being dependent on the toxicant) and final rinsing with distilled or demineralized water may be necessary. Hesselberg and Burress [7] have discussed labor-saving devices useful when large numbers of bioassays are performed routinely.

c. Preparation and depth of test solutions: All solutions required for a single toxicity bioassay must be prepared from the same sample of waste. Any undissolved material present in a waste sample is uniformly dispersed by agitation before a measured portion of the sample is withdrawn for addition to a measured quantity of water in a test container. The material to be tested is then mixed thoroughly with the diluent by gentle stirring to insure good dispersion and solution of any undissolved soluble matter. Unnecessary exposure of the waste samples and dilutions to the atmosphere, through violent agitation or otherwise, must be carefully avoided. Average depth of the liquid in the test containers must be uniform in all parallel tests and must not be less than 15 cm.

d. Total fish weight and liquid volume: The weight of all fish in a test container must not exceed 1 g per liter of test solution. When the test container is too small to accommodate properly all the fish that are to be exposed to one test concentration, the fish must be divided equally among two or more test containers for each concentration. Sometimes the weight of fish that can be held successfully in a given volume of liquid may be further restricted by the available oxygen supply and related requirements.

e. Modifications of the static bioassay: Controlled artificial oxygenation of test solutions may be employed when excessive biochemical or other oxygen demand of the tested material is found to interfere with the evaluation of its toxicity by ordinary static bioassays. Uncontrolled or vigorous aeration is unsatisfactory because of the rapid losses of toxicity that often result. In many instances, the addition of pure oxygen in the form of large bubbles at a slow rate (30 to 180 bubbles per min) to the open test containers is satisfactory to maintain DO concentrations without excessive loss of volatile materials or toxicity beyond that which occurs normally in the static bioassay. An oxygen cylinder, a pressure-reduction valve, necessary tubing, and three-way air valves described by Henderson and Tarzwell [5] are suitable for this purpose. Careful regulation is necessary to maintain adequate DO and to avoid any considerable supersaturation. A method for maintaining controlled oxygenation without accelerating the rate of escape of volatile substances has been described in detail by Doudoroff *et al.*[1] Another method of oxygenating test solutions in open test jars has been described by Hart *et al.*[8]

Initial oxygenation of the diluent before addition of the material to be tested can be undertaken to satisfy an immediate oxygen demand or to avoid an initial deficiency of dissolved oxygen in a dilution of a liquid waste. Oxygen supersaturation of the test solution must be avoided, however.

Another modification of the static bioassay involves renewal of test solutions for the purpose of maintaining more or less uniform concentrations of any volatile or unstable toxic material and an adequate DO content. Periodic renewal can be accomplished by transferring the test animals quickly, by means of a dip net, to test containers with fresh solutions. Test solutions must be renewed every 24 hr or less. Exploratory tests with periodic renewal every 8, 12 and 24 hr are recommended to ascertain the frequency of renewal necessary in the full-scale tests to determine TL values.

5. Special Test Conditions and Procedures for Continuous-flow Bioassays

a. Testing facilities and apparatus: There are two basic ways to perform continuous-flow bioassays. One is simply the adjustment of paired flows of the material being tested and the diluent water that are combined to provide a series of concentrations predetermined on the basis of exploratory static bioassays. The other is the automatic intermittent introduction of the test material and the diluent water into the test containers.

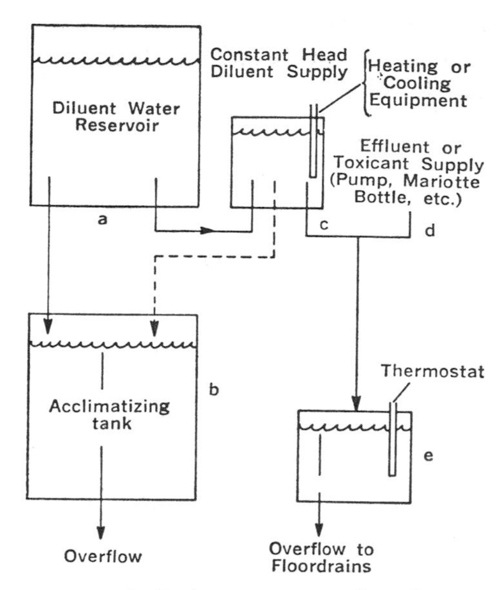

Figure 47. Basic components of continuous-flow bioassay system.

Figure 47 shows the basic components of any continuous-flow bioassay system that are needed in addition to the testing laboratory described for the static bioassay. A much greater volume of control water or diluent water is required for continuous-flow bioassays than for static bioassays. This normally necessitates a large, elevated diluent-water reservoir (a) of sufficient volume to provide water for at least 5 days, usually about 5,000 liters. When experimental water is being added to this reservoir continuously (by a float-controlled valve system such as a roof-tank float valve) or intermittently (by a pump-up system), a reservoir of lesser capacity is preferable. The diluent water flows by gravity from this tank to a much smaller constant-head diluent-supply head box through a nonmetallic, float-controlled valve or other device, then to the testing apparatus at a constant rate. The head box (c) should have the necessary heating or cooling equipment to maintain a constant temperature controlled by a thermostat in the test container (e). Test containers must have an overflow system (to remove the test solutions) that is designed to prevent fish from entering outlets. Such containers have been described by Lemke.[9] Cleaning of the test containers will be the same as for static bioassay test containers. Water from the diluent water reservoir can flow by gravity to the acclimatizing tank (b). When the resultant temperature in the acclimatizing tank is not in the acceptable range, water may be provided from the temperature-controlled constant-head diluent supply.

The constant-head effluent or toxicant supply, which can be a Mariotte bottle or other device (d), should contain conveniently a 5-day supply of the material to be tested. However, if this material is not stable for that period of time, it may be necessary to provide a fresh supply daily. When chemical metering pumps are used, the toxicant supply system need not maintain a constant pressure.

Jackson and Brungs[10] have described a device to supply materials of relatively low toxicity with a simple valve control system to regulate the flow rates of the diluent and toxicant solution. For more toxic materials, less volume of toxicant is required and a Mariotte bottle that delivers a very slow but constant flow is useful.[11] The assembly and operation of a Mariotte bottle has been described by Burrows.[12] Chemical metering pumps[13, 14] may supply the effluent or toxicant at constant flow rates. Metering pumps, or any other means of introducing the toxicant or waste, operating independently of the diluent water flow have the basic shortcoming of continuing to deliver the toxicant when the flow of diluent water ceases for one reason or another. This results in increased solution concentrations and often in total mortality of the test fish.

A basically different kind of facility for continuous-flow bioassays utilizes the serial-dilution apparatus [15] or the proportional diluter.[16] These dilution systems were designed so that when the diluent water flow ceases, the toxicant or waste does not continue to flow into the test containers. The proportional diluter is generally the more useful and is easier to construct, calibrate, and operate, but the serial dilution apparatus is more applicable when the desired dilution factor (i.e., the value by which a concentration is multiplied in order to obtain the next lower concentration) is less than 0.50. The proportional diluter has been modified to provide a very narrow range of concentrations, with a dilution factor of 0.90.[17]

A proportional diluter [16] has been described that can deliver 5 toxicant dilutions and water for a control test at any desired flow rate up to 400 ml/min for each concentration, with dilution factors ranging from 0.75 to 0.50. Metering cells can be exchanged to provide dilution factors outside this range. Proportional diluters have been used that deliver up to 2,000 ml/min and can be made even larger. Some examples of the precision of the proportional diluter are available in the literature.[17, 18]

b. Test dilutions: All continuous-flow technics discussed previously except that involving use of a large volume of waste or effluent of relatively low toxicity [10] require a stock solution of the toxicant. After proper calibration of the chemical metering apparatus, the toxicant stock can be made to the appropriate concentration. The toxicant stock solution should be insulated against rapid temperature fluctuations to reduce variations of flow resulting from pressure changes. A constant-head device that is open to the atmosphere need not be insulated. When water-soluble materials are tested, aqueous solutions are best for the toxicant stock solution. For organic compounds (e.g., many pesticides) that are only slightly soluble in water, a more appropriate solvent is used.

The test fish are not put in the test containers until the desired toxicant concentrations have been established. This can be done by waiting until the containers have been filled with test water from the continuous-flow apparatus or by filling the test containers with diluent water and adding sufficient amounts of the toxicant stock solution to each container to produce the desired concentrations.

c. Total fish weight and liquid volume: The total weight of fish that can be held in the test containers is determined by the temperature, DO and flow-through volume of the test solution. In these continuous-flow studies, the volume of flow must be sufficient to maintain adequate or desired DO and toxicant concentrations. The availability of diluent water and the toxicant will limit the weight of fish that can be utilized. In determining this amount, an average oxygen consumption rate of 0.2 mg oxygen per gram of fish per hour may be used.[19]

This value is based on the wet weight of the fish at room temperature.

The test container should be of such size that the test fish will not be crowded and aggressive behavior will be minimized. The depth of solution should not be less than 15 cm.

d. Flow rates: The constant flow rate of the test solutions should be such that the volume of solution introduced into each test container every 6 hr will be at least equal to the volume of solution in the test container. When a high oxygen demand of the substance tested and oxygen consumption by the fish result in unsatisfactory DO levels, the flow rate must be increased until satisfactory DO levels are maintained. The flow rate must also be increased if the waste or other material is known to be volatile or unstable, or is for other reasons likely to decrease in concentration.

e. Measurement of toxicant concentrations: When the toxicant is known and analytical determinations are possible, it is highly recommended that the toxicant concentration be measured in each test container at frequent intervals. The TL_{50} values should be based on the measured concentrations and reported accordingly.

6. *Calculation, Reporting and Significance of Bioassay Results*

a. Calculations: A TL_{50} is a concentration at which 50% of the experimental animals survived, or it is an interpolated value, based on percentages of fish surviving at two or more concentrations, at which less than half and more than half survived. Estimation of the TL_{50} by interpolation involves merely the plotting of the data on semilogarithmic coordinate paper with concentrations on the logarithmic, and percentage survival on the arithmetic, axis or scale. A straight line is drawn between two points representing survival at the two successive concentrations that were lethal to more than half and to less than half of the fish. The concentration at which this line crosses the 50% survival line is the TL_{50} value. Figure 48 illustrates this procedure, which is commonly referred to as straight-line graphical interpolation. Hypothetical results used in developing the graph are given in the table. The TL_{50} values for 48 and 96 hr are 6.7 and 4.4%, respectively.

There are other widely accepted and often more satisfactory procedures: (1) graphical methods that involve fitting a smooth sigmoid curve by eye to data plotted in the manner described above, (2) fitting a straight line to data plotted on logarithmic-probability graph paper,[20] and (3) the more refined methods of probits, logits or angles.[21] These latter methods are especially useful when survival percentages are found to change little or erratically with progressive increases of tested concentrations. By these latter methods, TL values other than the TL_{50} value can be determined to test the statistical significance of small differences in results of any comparative toxicity bioassays.

b. Precision and accuracy: The precision of a toxicity bioassay is limited by the normal biological variation among individuals of a species. A precision within about 10% is sometimes attainable, but better precision is not to be expected even under favorable circumstances when 10 fish are tested at each concentration of a toxicant.

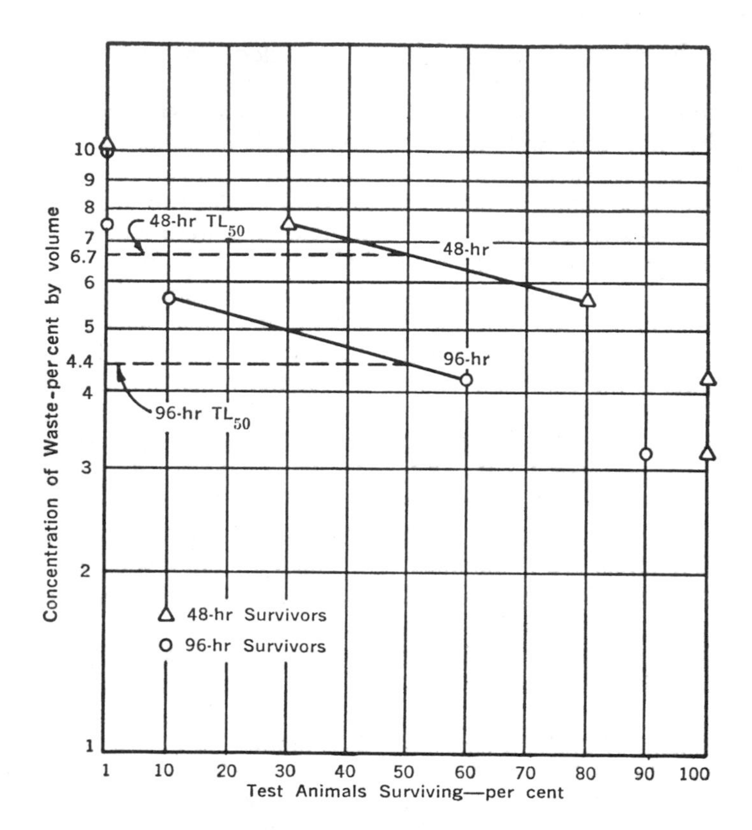

Experimental Data (Hypothetical) Plotted Above

Concentration of Waste *% by vol.*	No. of Test Animals	No. of Test Animals Surviving	
		After 48-Hr	After 96-Hr
10.0	10	0	0
7.5	10	3	0
5.6	10	8	1
4.2	10	10	6
3.2	10	10	9

Figure 48. Estimation of 50% tolerance limits by straight-line graphical interpolation.

Toxicity studies with a randomly selected species cannot be expected to give accurate information on the toxicity of that material to other species and life stages or to an entire biota. A toxicity bioassay with one species yields an accurate estimate of the toxicity of the material in question only to others of that species of similar size, age and physiological condition and in water with the same or similar characteristics and under similar test conditions.

c. Reporting: Descriptions of the tested material and its storage, the source of the experimental water or diluent, its determined physical and chemical properties and those of the test solutions, and the volume, depth and frequency or rate of renewal (if any) of the solutions are all given in the bioassay report. Any pronounced turbidity of the experimental water or the test solutions, and the known or possible presence in the water of any unusual natural constituents or any contaminants should be noted. Also included in the test report are the species of fish used, the source, size and condition of the fish, data on any known treatment of the fish for disease or infestation with parasites prior to their use, and any observations on the behavior of the fish during tests. In addition to the calculated TL_{50} values, data used to make the calculations (i.e., the number of fish tested and the percent survival at the end of each day of exposure at each concentration of toxicant) must be reported.

d. Interpretation and application of bioassay results: The 48-hr and 96-hr TL_{50} values provide useful measures of the relative acute lethal toxicity of tested substances to fish under certain experimental conditions; but these values do not represent concentrations that are safe in fish habitats. Long-term exposure to much lower concentrations may be lethal to fishes and other organisms, and still lower concentrations may cause nonlethal impairment of their functions or performance, such as swimming ability, appetite and growth, resistance to disease, reproductive capacity or ability to compete with other species in the biota. A review article [22] on the water quality requirements of fish serves as a general introduction to physiological, toxicological and ecological fundamentals.

Formulas for the estimation of permissible discharge rates or dilution ratios for industrial effluents and other water pollutants on the basis of evaluations of the acute toxicity have been tentatively proposed and their derivation has been discussed elsewhere.[23–27] The use of fractional "application factors" by which TL values are multiplied to arrive at permissible or presumably safe concentrations of toxic wastes or chemicals has recently been widely favored. Mount and Stephan [28] and Mount [29] have derived experimentally some tentative application factors, and these studies have demonstrated much variation, depending on the toxicant. Available data indicate that these factors must be variable according to the toxicant in question if they are to be reasonable and equitable as well as effective. It is quite evident that no single application factor can be equally appropriate to all toxic materials. Recognizing this fact, as well as our present lack of knowledge and the pressing need to use all available knowledge and experience, the National Technical Advisory Committee on Water Quality Requirements for Aquatic Life has tentatively grouped toxicants into three main categories according to their persistence, and has recommended three general application factors for these groups of toxicants.[30] In all approaches to this problem, possible synergism or antagonism should be taken into consideration as well as the effects of the presence of two or more toxicants in the water being tested.

7. References

1. P. DOUDOROFF et al. 1951. Bioassay methods for the evaluation of acute toxicity of industrial wastes to fish. *Sewage & Ind. Wastes* 23:1380.
2. R. M. BAILEY et al. 1960. *A List of Common and Scientific Names of Fishes from the United States and Canada* (2nd ed.). Special Pub. No. 2, American Fisheries Society,
3. J. CAIRNS, JR. & A. SCHEIER. 1963. Environmental effects upon cyanide toxicity to fish. *Notulae Naturae* No. 361 (July 30).
4. L. L. MARKING & J. W. HOGAN. 1967. Investigations in fish control. 19. Toxicity of Bayer 73 to fish. Bureau of Sport Fisheries and Wildlife Resource Pub. No. 36.
5. C. HENDERSON & C. M. TARZWELL. 1957. Bioassays for control of industrial effluents. *Sewage & Ind. Wastes* 29:1002.
6. R. E. LENNON & C. R. WALKER. 1964. Investigations in fish control. I. Laboratories and methods for screening fish control chemicals. Bureau of Sport Fisheries and Wildlife Circular 185.
7. R. J. HESSELBERG & R. M. BURRESS. 1967. Investigations in fish control. 21. Labor-saving devices for bioassay laboratories. Bureau of Sport Fisheries and Wildlife Resource Pub. No. 38.
8. W. B. HART, R. F. WESTON & J. G. DEMANN. 1948. An apparatus for oxygenating test solutions in which fish are used as test animals for evaluating toxicity. *Trans. Amer. Fisheries Soc.* 75: 225.
9. A. E. LEMKE. 1964. A new design for constant-flow test chambers. *Prog. Fish Culturist* 26:136.
10. H. W. JACKSON & W. A. BRUNGS. 1966. Biomonitoring of industrial effluents. *Proc. 21st Ind. Waste Conf.* (Purdue Univ.)., Engineering Extension Bulletin No. 121, page 117.
11. E. W. SURBER & T. O. THATCHER. 1963. Laboratory studies of the effects of alkyl benzene sulfonate (ABS) on aquatic invertebrates. *Trans. Amer. Fisheries Soc.* 92:152.
12. R. E. BURROWS. 1949. Prophylactic treatment for control of fungus (*Saprolegnia parasitica*). *Prog. Fish Culturist* 11(2):97 (April).
13. A. E. LEMKE & D. I. MOUNT. 1963. Some effects of alkyl benzene sulfonate on the bluegill, *Lepomis macrochirus*. *Trans. Amer. Fisheries Soc.* 92:372.
14. J. M. SYMONS. 1963. Simple, continuous-flow, low and variable rate pump. *JWPCF* 35:1480.
15. D. I. MOUNT & R. E. WARNER. 1965. A serial dilution apparatus for continuous delivery of various concentrations of materials in water. PHS Pub. No. 999–WP–23, U. S. Department of Health, Education & Welfare, Washington, D. C.
16. D. I. MOUNT & W. A. BRUNGS. 1967. A simplified dosing apparatus for fish toxicology studies. *Water Res.* 1:21.
17. T. O. THATCHER & J. F. SANTNER. 1966. Acute toxicity of LAS to various fish species. *Proc. 21st Ind. Waste Conf.* (Purdue Univ.), Engineering Extension Bulletin No. 121, page 996.
18. W. A. BRUNGS & G. W. BAILEY. 1966. Influence of suspended solids on the acute toxicity of endrin to fathead minnows. *Proc. 21st Ind. Waste Conf.* (Purdue Univ.), Engineering Extension Bulletin No. 121, page 4.
19. W. A. SPOOR. 1959. The state of our knowledge of the oxygen consumption of fish. *Anatomical Rec.* 134:643.
20. J. T. LITCHFIELD & F. WILCOXON. 1949. A simplified method of evaluating dose-effect experiments. *J. Pharmacol. Exper. Therap.* 96:99.
21. D. J. FINNEY. 1952. *Statistical Method in Biological Assay*. Hafner Publishing Co., New York.
22. P. DOUDOROFF. 1957. Water quality requirements of fishes and effects of toxic substances. In *The Physiology of Fishes* (M. E. Brown, Ed.). Academic Press, New York, Vol. 2, pp. 403–430.
23. W. B. HART, P. DOUDOROFF & J. GREENBANK. 1945. The evaluation of the toxicity of industrial wastes, chemicals, and other substances to fresh-water fishes. Waste Control Laboratory, Atlantic Refining Co., Philadelphia.
24. P. DOUDOROFF. 1951. Biological observations of industrial waste disposal. *Proc. 6th Ind. Waste Conf.* (Purdue Univ.), Engineering Extension Bulletin No. 76, page 88.
25. Committee Report. 1955. Aquatic life water quality criteria. *Sewage & Ind. Wastes* 27:321.

26. C. HENDERSON. 1957. Application factors to be applied to bioassays for the safe disposal of toxic wastes. In *Biological Problems in Water Pollution* (C. M. Tarzwell, Ed.). Robert A. Taft Sanitary Engineering Center, Cincinnati, pp. 31–37.
27. C. E. WARREN & P. DOUDOROFF. 1958. The development of methods for using bioassays in the control of pulp mill waste disposal. *TAPPI* 41:8, 211A.
28. D. I. MOUNT & C. STEPHAN. 1967. A method for establishing acceptable toxicant limits for fish—Malathion and the butoxyethanol ester of 2,4-D. *Trans. Amer. Fisheries Soc.* 96:185.
29. D. I. MOUNT. 1968. Chronic toxicity of copper to fathead minnows. (*Pimephales promelas, Rafinesque*). *Water Res.* 2: 215.
30. FEDERAL WATER POLLUTION CONTROL ADMINISTRATION. 1968. *Report of the Committee on Water Quality Criteria.* Section 3, Fish, other aquatic life and wildlife. pp. 27–110. Govt. Ptg. Off., Washington, D. C.

232 TURBIDITY

Turbidity is an expression of an optical property of the fine suspended matter in a sample. Measurement is based on comparison of interference in the passage of light rays through a sample with that in standard samples.

Turbidity may be determined by using a candle turbidimeter, provided the suspended matter is finely divided. The procedure to be followed is given in Section 163. Turbidity may also be measured by a photometer or nephelometer that has been calibrated against prepared turbidity standards which, in turn, have been calibrated against a candle turbidimeter. Such determinations are subject to the limitations discussed in Section 163.

Report the type of instrument used, since no other instrument yet developed agrees perfectly with the standard candle turbidimeter over a wide range of particle concentrations, sizes and compositions.

233 VOLATILE ACIDS (TOTAL ORGANIC ACIDS)

223 A. Column-Partition Chromatographic Method (TENTATIVE)

1. General Discussion

a. Principle: Chromatographic columns are capable of a dynamic partition or distribution of dissolved or dispersed substances between two immiscible phases, one of which is moving past the other. If an acidified aqueous sample containing organic acids is adsorbed on a column of inert granular material and an appropriate organic solvent is passed through the column, the organic acids can be extracted from the aqueous sample. Silicic acid is used as the adsorbent column, acidified aqueous solution as the stationary phase, and normal butanol in chloroform as the mobile phase.

By controlling the relative concentrations of butanol and chloroform in the solvent system, organic acids may be selectively eluted from the column, collected and measured by titration with a standard base. All of the short-chain 1- to 6-carbon organic or volatile acids are eluted with the solvent system used in the method and are reported collectively as total organic acids.

b. Interference: The chloroform-butanol solvent system employed in the method is capable of eluting organic acids other than the volatile acids and some synthetic detergents as well. Crotonic, adipic, pyruvic, phthalic, fumaric, lactic, succinic, malonic, gallic, aconitic and oxalic acids, alkyl sulfates, and alkyl-aryl sulfonates are all adsorbed by silicic acid and eluted when present. Fortunately, these nonvolatile components are generally present in very low concentration and constitute only an insignificant fraction of the total organic content of most sludge samples so analyzed.

c. Precautions: The normalities of basic alcohol solutions decrease with time, particularly when subjected to repeated exposure to the atmosphere. These decreases usually are accompanied by the appearance of a white precipitate in the reagent. The magnitudes of such changes are not normally significant in ordinary process control if the tests are performed within a few days of standardization. To minimize this effect, the standard sodium hydroxide titrant should be stored in a tightly stoppered pyrex glass bottle and protected from atmospheric CO_2 by attaching a tube of carbon dioxide-absorbing material, as described in the General Introduction, Section 000A. For more precise analyses, the titrant should be standardized or freshly prepared before each analysis.

Although the procedure is adequate for routine analysis of most sludge samples, volatile-acids concentrations in excess of 5,000 mg/l may require an increased amount of organic solvent for quantitative recovery. Elution with a second portion of solvent and subsequent titration will reveal possible incomplete recoveries.

2. Apparatus

a. Centrifuge or filtering assembly.

b. Crucibles, Gooch or fritted-glass, with filtering flask and vacuum source.

c. Separatory funnel, 1,000-ml.

3. Reagents

a. Silicic acid, specially prepared for chromatography, 50–200 mesh: Remove fines by slurrying the acid in distilled water and decanting the supernatant after settling for 15 min. Repeat the process several times. Dry the washed acid in an oven at 103 C until *absolutely dry,* then store in a desiccator prior to use.

b. Chloroform-butanol reagent, CB_{25}: Mix 300 ml reagent-grade chloroform, 100 ml *n*-butanol, and 80 ml 0.5*N* H_2SO_4 in a separatory funnel and allow the water and organic layers to separate. Drain off the lower organic CB_{25} layer through a fluted filter paper into a dry bottle.

c. Thymol blue indicator solution: Dissolve 80 mg thymol blue in 100 ml absolute methanol.

d. Phenolphthalein indicator solution: Dissolve 80 mg phenolphthalein in 100 ml absolute methanol.

e. Sulfuric acid: Conc, reagent-grade H_2SO_4.

f. Standard sodium hydroxide titrant, 0.02*N:* Dilute 20 ml 1.0*N* NaOH stock solution to 1 liter with absolute methanol. The stock is prepared in water and standardized in accordance with the methods outlined in Acidity, Section 101.3c.

4. Procedure

a. Pretreatment of sample: Centrifuge or vacuum-filter enough sludge to obtain 10–15 ml clear sample in a small test tube or beaker. Add a few drops of thymol blue indicator solution, then conc H_2SO_4, dropwise until definitely red to thymol blue (pH = 1.0–1.2).

b. Column chromatography: Place 12 g silicic acid in a Gooch or fritted-glass crucible and apply suction to pack the column. With a pipet, distribute 5.0 ml of the acidified sample as uniformly as possible over the surface of the column. Apply suction momentarily to draw the sample into the silicic acid, releasing the vacuum as soon as the last portion of the sample has entered the column. Quickly add 65 ml CB_{25} reagent to the column and apply suction. Discontinue the suction just before the last of the reagent enters the column. Use a new column for each sample to be analyzed.

c. Titration: Remove the filter flask and purge the eluted sample with nitrogen gas or CO_2-free air immediately before titration. (CO_2-free air may be obtained by passing air through Ascarite or equivalent.)

Titrate the sample with standard 0.02*N* NaOH reagent to the phenolphthalein end point, taking care to avoid aeration of the sample. Nitrogen gas or CO_2-free air delivered through a small glass tube may be used to purge and mix the sample and to prevent contact with atmospheric CO_2 during titration.

d. Blank: Prepare a blank composed of 5.0 ml acidified (H_2SO_4) distilled water, place on column, extract with 65 ml of CB_{25} reagent, and titrate in a similar manner.

5. Calculation

$$\text{Total organic acids (mg/l as acetic acid)} = \frac{(a - b) \times N \times 60{,}000}{\text{ml sample}}$$

where a = ml of NaOH titrant used for sample, b = ml of NaOH titrant used for blank, and *N* = normality of NaOH titrant.

6. Precision

The method consistently yields average recovery efficiencies of about 95% for volatile acid concentrations in excess of 200 mg/l as acetic acid. Individual tests generally vary from the average by no more than 3% if the tests are performed with reasonable care. A greater variation results when lower concentrations of volatile acids are present in the sample. Titration precision expressed as the standard deviation is about ± 0.1 ml, or approximately 24 mg/l as acetic acid.

233 B. Bibliography

MUELLER, H. F., A. M. BUSWELL & T. E. LARSON. 1956. Chromatographic determination of volatile acids. *Sewage & Ind. Wastes* 28:255.

MUELLER, H. F., T. E. LARSON & M. FERRETTI. 1960. Chromatographic separation and identification of organic acids. *Anal. Chem.* 32:687.

WESTERHOLD, A. F. 1963. Organic acids in digester liquor by chromatography. *JWPCF* 35:1431.

POHLAND, F. G. & B. H. DICKSON, JR. 1964. Organic acids by column chromatography. *Water Works & Wastes Eng.* 1:54.

HATTINGH, W. H. J. & F. V. HAYWARD. 1964. An improved chromatographic method for the determination of total volatile fatty acid content in anaerobic digester liquors. *Int. J. Air & Water Poll.* 8:411.

ZINC: See Metals (Heavy), Sections 211 (II) K and (III) B.

PART 300

EXAMINATION OF WATER AND WASTEWATER FOR RADIOACTIVITY

300 INTRODUCTION

The radioactivity in water and wastewater originates from natural and artificial or man-made sources. The natural or background radioactivity generally contributes less than picocurie quantities of alpha activity and tens of picocuries of beta activity in each liter of surface water. Gamma activity is also associated with alpha and beta emissions. Artificial sources of radioactivity originate from fission, fusion or particle acceleration, giving rise largely to alpha, beta and gamma radioactivity. The development of nuclear science and its application to power development, industrial operations, and industrial uses require that attention be given to the formulation of technics to assess the resulting degree of environmental radioactive contamination. It is important to provide adequate warning of unsafe conditions so that proper precautions can be taken. It is of nearly equal importance to assure that conditions are indeed safe when they are, in fact, safe.

In either event it is necessary to establish base lines as to the kinds and amount of radionuclides that are present naturally and to measure man-made additions to this background. In this way, measurements may be made to provide information for sound judgments regarding the hazardous or nonhazardous nature of increased concentrations.

Measurement technics are not difficult to devise because radiation counting equipment of high sensitivity, selectivity and stability is fairly commonplace. Furthermore, the guides provided by the Federal Radiation Council [1] on the permissible daily intake of some radionuclides, the recommendations on radionuclide concentrations in water made by the National Council on Radiation Protection and Measurements (NCRP),[2] those made by the International Commission on Radiation Protection (ICRP),[3] and the Public Health Service Drinking Water Standards [4] are, with few exceptions, at concentrations which are readily measured by current methods and instruments.

Meaningful measurements do require the careful application of good scientific technics. Gross alpha and gross beta measurements are relatively inexpensive and serve a useful purpose for screening samples. Samples sufficiently low in radioactivity do not require further analyses. Samples at intermediate concentrations may be composited for the more complete and expensive analysis of specific radionuclides. To be effective, a gross screening technic must be based on knowledge of the relationship between the gross measurements and the radionuclides of greatest concern.

Both natural and artificial sources of radiation from samples emitting alpha, beta or gamma activity are included in the examination (to the exclusion of radiation external to the sample—i.e., cosmic, gamma, X-ray, and hard beta radiation in the environment). Because the rate of decay and the energy of radiation are unique characteristics of each radioelement, strict adherence to a standard procedure is essential to the proper interpretation of a radioactivity examination. Frequently the procedure may have rigid timing requirements to discriminate between radioelements. For example, the rapid alpha analysis of airborne particulates usually consists of the measurement of radon daughter products (largely ^{218}Po and ^{214}Po) from which the equilibrium parent radon concentration and each of its descendent products may be estimated. Subsequent alpha-counting of the same sample could be designed to measure thoron daughter activity or long-lived alpha emitters. The beta activity of fresh rain a few minutes to several hours after collection includes significant contamination by radon daughter products. If the analysis is postponed for 6 hr, the radon daughters will disappear, along with some short-lived artificial radionuclides. The loss of activity resulting from delayed counting can be estimated by the extrapolation of decay data. During the concentration of water samples by evaporation, radionuclides such as elemental iodine or hydrogen iodide (in acid solution) may be lost by volatilization at temperatures below 105 C. If the sample is ignited, the chance of volatilization is even greater. Radioactive substances such as carbon 14 and tritium may be present as volatile chemicals for the procedure of sample preparation used. Groundwater generally contains nuclides of the uranium and thorium series. Special care in sampling and analyses is necessary because members of these series are often not in secular equilibrium. This is particularly true of gaseous radon, thoron and their daughter products, which may be present far in excess of the equilibrium concentration from radium in solution.

300 A. Collection of Samples

The principles of representative sampling of water (see Section 100A.3) and sampling of sewage and wastes (Section 200A) apply to sampling for radioactivity examinations.

Because a radioactive element is often present in submicrogram quantities, a significant fraction of it may be readily lost by adsorption on the surface of containers or glassware used in the examination. Similarly, a radionuclide may be largely or wholly adsorbed on the surface of suspended particles.

1. Sample Containers

When radioactive industrial wastes or comparable materials are sampled, consideration should be given to the deposition of radioactivity on the walls and surfaces of glassware, plastic containers and equipment. This may cause a loss of radioactivity and the possible contamination of subsequent samples due to reuse of inadequately cleansed containers.

2. Preservation of Samples

The comments in Part 200 are particularly appropriate for all types of samples in this Part. Inasmuch as preservatives may alter the distribution of radioactivity in a sample, they should not be used until after the sample is separated into suspended and dissolved fractions. Formaldehyde or ethyl alcohol is suggested as a preservative for highly perishable samples such as food or foodlike samples. Preservatives and reagents should be tested for their radioactive content.

300 B. Counting Room

The design and construction of the counting room may vary widely, according to the work to be accomplished. The room should be free of dust and fumes, which may affect the electrical stability of instruments. The background can be stabilized and lowered considerably by making the walls, floor and ceiling out of several inches of concrete. Some shales, granites and sands may contain sufficient natural activity to affect instrument background if used in the construction of a counting room.

A modern chemical laboratory can be used for processing routine environmental samples. It is generally better to segregate monitoring work from other laboratory operations when possible.

The need for air-conditioning and humidity control depends on the number of instruments to be used and the prevailing climatic conditions. Generally, electronic instruments perform best when the temperature remains constant within 3 C and does not exceed 30 C. The temperature inside the chassis of the instrument should be kept below that specified by the manufacturer.

Humidity affects instrument performance to an even greater extent than extremes of temperature because of moisture buildup on critical components. This causes leakage and arcing, and shortens the life of these components. A humidity of between 30 and 80% is usually satisfactory.

Most scalers are supplied with constant-voltage regulators suitable for controlling the usual minor fluctuations in line voltage. For unusual fluctuations, an auxiliary voltage regulation transformer should be used. A manually reset voltage-sensitive device in series with a voltage regulator placed in the main power line to instruments is suggested to protect them in case of power failure or a fluctuating line voltage.

Samples containing appreciable activity should be stored at a distance so as not to affect instrument background counting rate.

Floors and desk tops should be covered with a material that can be cleaned easily or replaced if necessary.

300 C. Counting Instruments

The operating principle of Geiger-Mueller and proportional counters is that the expenditure of energy by a radiation event causes ionization of counter gas and electron collection at the anode of the counting chamber. Through gas or electronic amplification, or both, the ion-collection event triggers an electronic scaler recorder.

The principle of scintillation counters is similar in that quanta of light caused by the interaction of a radiation event and the detection phosphor are seen by a photomultiplier tube. The tube converts the light pulse into an amplified electrical pulse, which is recorded by an electronic scaler. Thallium-activated sodium iodide crystals and silver-activated zinc sulfide screens form useful scintillation detectors for counting gamma and alpha radioactivity, respectively.

Characteristic of most counters is a background or instrument counting rate usually due to cosmic radiation, to radioactive contaminants of instrument parts and counting room construction material, and to the nearness of radioactive sources such as samples, fallout dust, and X-ray machines. In general, the background is roughly proportional to the size or mass of the counting chamber or detector, but it can be reduced by metal shielding, such as several inches of lead.

Instrument "noise" or the false recording of radiation events may be caused by faulty circuitry, too sensitive a gain setting, effects of high humidity, and variable line voltage or transients. This problem is controlled by constant-voltage transformers with transient filters, proper adjustment of gain setting as specified by the manufacturer, and air-conditioning of the counting room.

The internal proportional counter accepts counting pans within the counting chamber and thus, at the beta operating voltage, records all alpha, all beta, and a little gamma radiation emitted into the counting gas. Theoretically, half of the radiation is emitted in the direction of the counting pan. Some of the beta radiation, but only 1 to 2% of the alpha radiation, is backscattered into the counting gas by sample solids, the counting pan, or the walls of the counting chamber, so that, for substantially weightless samples, considerably more than 50% of the beta radiation and slightly more than 50% of the alpha radiation is counted. However, considerable care must be taken in sample preparation to prevent the sample or counting pan from distorting the electrical field of the counter and thus depressing the counting rate. Nonconducting surfaces, airborne dusts, and vapor from moisture or solvents in particular interfere with counting.

The end-window Geiger-Mueller counting tubes are rugged and stable counting detectors. Usually the samples are mounted 5 to 15 mm from the window. Under these conditions, most alpha and weak beta radiations are completely stopped by the air gap and mica window and are not counted. Counting efficiencies for mixed fission products are frequently less than 10% for substantially weightless samples having an area less than that of the window. Because most Geiger-Mueller tubes have diameters of about 2.5 cm, the pan size—and, as a consequence, the water sample volume—must be restricted. Under these conditions, the detectability is low and uncertain, particularly for unknown sources of radiation. On the other hand, the Geiger-Mueller tubes are excellent for counting samples of tracers or purified radionuclides. Usually, standard sample mounts can be prepared which yield reproducible counting efficiencies, and counting is not affected by the electrical conductance of sample pans.

Thin-window (Mylar less than 250 μg/sq cm) tubes approximately 5 cm in diameter provide counting efficiencies intermediate between conventional Geiger-Mueller tubes and internal counters. The counting of alpha activity in these thin-window counters is satisfactory.

The chamber diameter may be in excess of 60 mm, and sample mount diameters may be greater than 50 mm. The counting chambers have operational stability and less interference from nonconducting surfaces and moisture vapors than internal proportional counters. These counters are superior to the more conventional small-diameter mica window counters.

1. Internal Proportional Counters

a. Uses: Internal proportional counters are suitable for determining alpha activity at the alpha operating plateau and alpha-plus-beta activity at the beta operating plateau. The alpha or beta activity, or both, can refer to a single or to several radionuclides.

The instruments usually consist of a counting chamber, a preamplifier, and a scaler with high-voltage power supply, timer, and register. Each instrument requires the use of a specified type of counting gas and accessories, the making of adjustments for sensitivity, and the carrying out of prescribed operating instructions.

b. Plateau (alpha or beta): It is necessary to find the operating voltage where the counting rate is constant—i.e., varies less than 5% over a 150-V change in anode voltage.

1) With the instrument in operating order, place the alpha or beta standard (see Section 300D.3) in the chamber, close, and flush the chamber with counter gas for 2–5 min.

2) Using the manufacturer's recommended operating voltage, count for a convenient time equal to an acceptable coefficient of variation, preferably 2%. Repeat the test at voltages higher and lower than the suggested operating voltage in increments of 50 V. (CAUTION: *Instrument damage will result from prolonged continuous discharge at too high a voltage.*)

3) Plot the relative counting rate (ordinate) against anode voltage (abscissa). A plateau of at least 150 V in length, with a slope of 5% or less, should result (see Figure 49). Select an anode voltage near the center of this plateau for the operating voltage.

c. Counter stability: Check instrument stability at the operating voltage by counting the plateau source daily (see Section 300D.3 below). If the instrument reproduces the source count within two standard deviations of the count rate, proceed as in the paragraph following. If the source count is not so reproduced, repeat the test. If stability

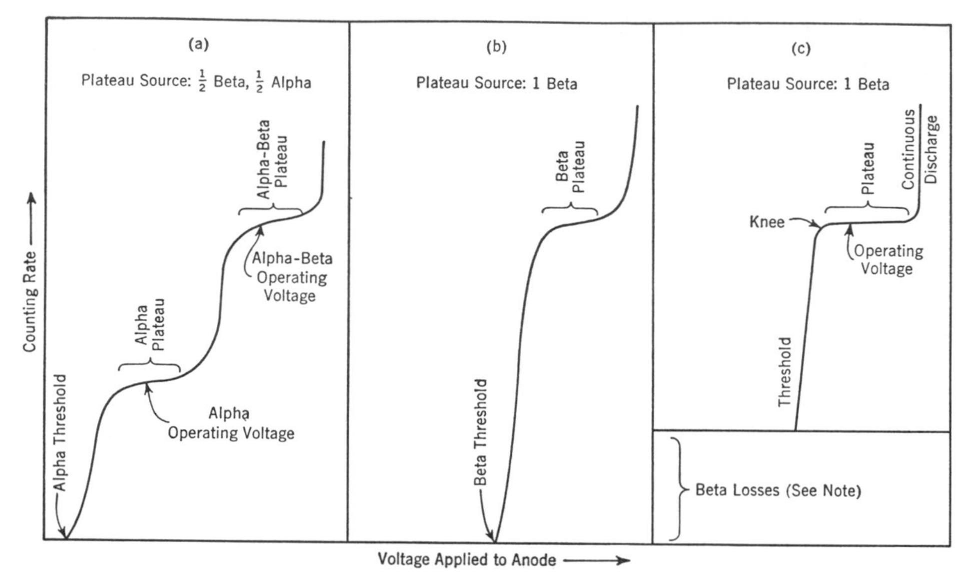

Figure 49. Shape of counting rate—anode voltage curves. *Key: (a) and (b) are for internal proportional counter with P-10 gas; (c) is for end-window Geiger-Mueller counter with Geiger gas (Note: Beta losses are dependent on energy of radiation and thickness of window and air path).*

is not attained, service the instrument.

d. Background: Determine the background (with an empty counting pan in the counting chamber). The background counting time should be as long as the longest sample counting time. Control charts are useful for stability testing.

e. Sample counting: Place the sample in the counting chamber. Be sure it is dry and adequately grounded to the chamber piston. (Thin aluminum metal pans can be grounded by impaling the pan wall on a pin mounted in the piston; heavier pans are self-grounded.) Flush with counter gas and count for a preset time, or preset count, to give the desired counting precision (see Section 300F).

f. Calibration of overall counter efficiency: It is necessary to correct the observed counting rate for the factors affecting efficiency: geometry, backscatter and self-absorption (sample absorption).

Although it is useful to know the variation in these factors, the overall efficiency can be determined for a fixed standard procedure by preparing standard sample sources and unknowns.

1) For measuring mixed fission products or beta radioactivity of unknown composition, use a standard solution of cesium 137 * for calibration of overall counter efficiency.

Prepare a standard (known disintegration rate) in an aqueous solution of sample solids similar in composition to that present in the unknown samples. Dispense increasing increments of solution in tared pans and evaporate. Make a series of samples having a

* For calibration standards and certification see *The Isotope Index,* J. S. Sommerville, Ed. Scientific Equipment Co., P.O. Box 19086, Indianapolis, Indiana.

solids thickness of 1 to 10 mg/sq cm of bottom area in the counting pan. Use care in evaporation to obtain uniform solids deposition. Dry (103–105 C), weigh, and count. Calculate the ratio of counts per minute to disintegrations per minute (efficiency) for different weights of sample solids. Plot the efficiency as a function of sample thickness and use the resulting calibration curve to convert counts per minute (cpm) to disintegrations per minute (dpm).

2) If other radionuclides are to be tested, repeat the above procedure, using certified solutions of each radionuclide. Unequal distribution of sample solids, particularly in the 0–3 mg/sq cm range, should be avoided in both calibration and unknown sample preparation; otherwise, inconsistent results will occasionally be obtained.

3) For alpha calibration, proceed as above, using a standard solution of natural uranium salt (avoid the use of depleted uranium).

2. *End-Window Counters*

End-window counters may be used for beta-gamma and absorption examinations. Most alpha and soft beta radiations are stopped by the air gap and window. The sample pan should have a diameter less than that of the window and, for maximum efficiency, should be placed as close to the window as possible. Housing the detector inside a 5-cm-thick lead shield will improve sensitivity of counting by decreasing the background by about 50%. Associated equipment generally consists of a scaler having a timer, a register, and a high-voltage power supply.

The operation and calibration of these counters are performed as described in Section 300C.1a–f, with modifications as applicable to the specific instrument.

COINCIDENCE CORRECTION: Geiger-Mueller counters commonly have resolving times of 100 to 400 microseconds; therefore, data on samples of high counting rate must be corrected for loss in counts.

3. *Thin-Window Proportional Counter*

The thin-window proportional counter has application for counting moderate to high levels and for counting residues which adhere poorly to the counting pan. The counters detect alpha and low-energy beta emitters. They are about one-half as sensitive as internal counters because the geometry of counting is not as great and absorption losses (air path and window) are greater. However, since the sample is on the outside, the counter is less affected than the internal counter by conditions such as contamination from loose residues and losses due to residue moisture and poor electrical conductance. The operation and calibration of these counters are as described in Section 300C.1a–f, with modifications applicable to the specific instrument.

4. *Low-Background Beta Counter*

The low-background beta counter is useful primarily for measurements as low as 0.1 and as high as 50 pCi per sample. Higher activity levels, to about 1,000 pCi, can be counted if other beta detectors are not available. The counters are designed primarily for beta emitters having a maximum beta energy above 0.3 MeV.

Usually the detector window thickness is less than 1.0 mg/sq cm, so that the attenuation of high-energy beta rays is relatively minor. The diameter of sample pans should be less than that of the window. The counting efficiencies for weightless samples vary from 30 to 55% for beta radiation of moderate energy.

The detectors of instruments with a background counting rate of 1 count per minute (cpm) or less normally have a lead or steel shield and an anticoincidence device of one or more guard detectors with the electronics needed to prevent counting in the sample detectors when a count is recorded in the guard. Some instruments have automatic sample changers. Most counters of this type use helium-isobutane or similar gases that operate in the Geiger region. Instruments using proportional counting gas are available. Geiger-Mueller counters commonly have resolving times of 100 to 400 microseconds; therefore, data on samples of high counting rate must be corrected for loss of counts.

5. *Multichannel Gamma Spectrum Analysis*

An attractive feature of gamma spectrum analysis is that an analysis is made with minimum sample preparation. Only when a complex spectrum results from a mixture of radionuclides whose primary photopeaks overlap with those of others is it necessary to perform chemical separations followed by gamma analysis for quantitative measurements on each fraction of the sample. An important limitation of the method is that nongamma-emitting radionuclides are excluded from consideration and those having photon energies of less than 0.1 MeV are usually measured with considerable uncertainty.

Details on the operation and calibration of multichannel gamma spectrum analysis may be found in the literature.[5–8]

a. The principle of a gamma spectrometer is that gamma photons from a sample enter a sensitive detector and interact with the detector atoms. The interaction gives rise to pulses of light. The light pulses are proportional in intensity to the gamma photon energy transferred to the detector. The light pulses enter a photomultiplier tube and are converted to electrical voltage pulses proportional to the light intensity. The pulses are stored in sequence into finite energy increments (such as 0.02 MeV) over the entire spectrum range (such as 0.1 to 2.0 MeV), depending on instrument capabilities and operator's choice.

After the sample is counted, the accumulated counts in each energy increment of the entire spectrum are analyzed for the number and energy of photopeaks (a qualitative test) or the number of pulses associated with each photopeak, with correction for background counts and interference from other gamma emitters (a quantitative test). Since each gamma-emitting radionuclide usually has several photopeaks, one of which yields the greatest abundance of pulses, the number of radionuclides in the sample to be analyzed is limited by the probability that overlapping photopeaks will cause errors in a quantitative estimation. Analysis of four to eight components is practical. For more complex mixtures, chemical separations followed by a gamma spectrum analysis of each fraction will be necessary.

b. A gamma spectrometer consists of a scintillation detector system, a pulse-height analyzer system, and a data readout system. The scintillation detector system is a detector enclosed in a shield and connected to a preamplifier and a high-voltage power supply. A common detector for gamma spectrometric analysis of environmental samples is a 4-in. diameter by 4-in. thick sodium iodide crystal (thallium-activated) enclosed in a hermetically sealed can coupled to a photomultiplier tube. The crystal and sample are placed in a metal shield (4 to 8 in. of steel or equivalent) to reduce external gamma radiation.

The pulse-height analyzer system consists of a linear amplifier, a pulse-height analyzer, a memory storage, and a logic control mechanism. The logic control capability permits storage of data in various modes and the displaying or recalling of data for visual display or use.

The data readout system contains one or more of the following devices: an oscilloscope for visual display, a readout indicator, an electric typewriter, a digital printer, a paper-tape perforator, a magnetic tape recorder, a strip chart recorder, and an x-y recorder. The oscilloscope is useful in aligning the instrument with standards such as ^{60}Co, ^{137}Cs and ^{207}Bi.

The digital printer records the number of pulses accumulated in each pulse-height range covering the spectrum range set by the mode of operation.

6. *Single-Channel Gamma Spectrum Analysis*

A single-channel gamma spectrum analyzer is similar to a multichannel analyzer but is limited to the examination of a single energy range at a time. The instrument is best used for situations such as the continuous monitoring of waste having fixed radionuclide composition, making gross gamma measurements, or measuring a single gamma-emitting radionuclide in a sample. The single-channel gamma analyzer is similar to the multichannel analyzer, except that the design is inexpensive compared with that of a multichannel analyzer.

a. The instrument consists of a sodium iodide (thallium-activated) crystal detector; a high-voltage supply; a photomultiplier tube; an amplifier; a pulse-height discriminator which can be set to obtain anything within a narrow to a broad energy range of the gamma spectrum; a scaler; and a shield to reduce the external gamma background.

Operations of the single-channel analyzer are detailed in the literature.[5–8]

7. *Alpha Scintillation Counter*

When an alpha particle bombards an impure crystal of zinc sulfide, a portion of the kinetic energy is transformed into visible light. The sulfide scintillates more efficiently when it contains silver impurities and when the duration of the light pulse is shortened by the presence of nickel ions.

The alpha scintillation counter consists of a phosphor detector coupled to a photomultiplier, a high-voltage supply, an amplifier-discriminator, and a scaler. Generally the photomultiplier tube should have a window diameter greater than the diameter of the sample unless the phosphor is coupled to a light-focusing optical system.

The silver-activated and nickel-quenched zinc sulfide phosphor is placed near, or in contact with, the alpha-emitting sample and is so arranged that a photomultiplier tube observes the light pulses, which are amplified and recorded on the scaler.

a. Solid samples should be mounted in a thin layer (less than 3 mg/sq cm) on a planchet. The phosphor is located between the sample and the photomultiplier tube. The sample and detector are enclosed in a light-tight chamber 3 to 5 mm from the phototube window. Under these conditions the counting efficiency is from 35 to 40%.

b. Gaseous samples contained in a dome-shaped cell coated with zinc sulfide "paint" are more efficiently observed than solid samples. Details of one such system are described under the determinations of radium 226 by radon (Section 305).

8. Liquid Beta Scintillation Counter

The principle of liquid scintillation counters is that the sample having radionuclides is mixed with an organic liquid scintillator, resulting in the production of light. The flashes of light are detected and amplified by one or more photomultiplier tubes.

a. Liquid scintillation counters are particularly well suited for counting low-energy beta emitters such as tritium or carbon 14 because self-absorption losses are eliminated. Counting efficiencies can approach 100% for high-energy betas, but for tritium the efficiency is much lower because the low beta pulses are not detected. These weak pulses are at the level of the "dark current" pulses from the photomultiplier tube and are discriminated against to reduce background. Some liquid scintillation instruments use two photomultipliers in coincidence as a means of reducing the background from "dark current." Most liquid scintillation counter systems incorporate at least a two-channel analyzer, which enables more than one beta emitter to be counted at the same time if their respective E's (maximum beta energies) differ by at least a factor of three.

Usually in a liquid scintillation counter the samples are dissolved or suspended in a scintillator solvent such as toluene, xylene or 1-4-dioxane. The samples are placed in a transparent bottle to enable the light flashes to be transmitted to the phototube. As in any other counter, the calibration standard must contain the same radionuclide prepared in the same medium. Background is determined by putting a bottle containing both solvent and scintillator into the counter, since this mixture is the sensor and a slight amount of activity may be present in the material itself. Background should be taken at least once daily.

300 D. Laboratory Reagents and Apparatus

See Section 000A for basic standards applying to laboratory reagents and apparatus. The following special instructions are pertinent.

1. Reagents and Distilled Water

Make periodic checks on the background radioactivity of all solutions and reagents used in an examination.

Discard those having a radioactivity which significantly interferes with the test.

2. *Apparatus*

Before reuse, thoroughly decontaminate apparatus and glassware with detergents and complexing agents, followed, if necessary, by acid and distilled-water rinses. Segregate equipment and glassware for storage and reuse on samples of comparable activity—i.e., keep apparatus for background and low-level studies separate from higher-level studies by the use of distinctive markings and different storage cabinets or laboratories. It is wise to adopt single-use counting pans, planchets and auxiliary supplies. Slightly radiocontaminated glassware may be entirely satisfactory for use in chemical tests but is unsatisfactory for radioanalysis.

3. *Radioactivity Sources*

a. Solutions: Employ standard solutions whose calibration is traceable to sources of radioactivity certified by the National Bureau of Standards.

b. Plateau sources:

1) ALPHA—Uranium oxide (U_3O_8), plated, not less than 45 mm in diameter, having an alpha activity of about 10,000 cpm. Plutonium may also be plated as a weightless alpha standard source.

2) BETA—Uranium oxide (U_3O_8), plated as described above, is covered with 8–10 mg/sq cm of aluminum foil. Cesium 137 will also provide an excellent beta standard source.

300 E. Expression of Results

Results of radioactivity analyses are reported preferably in terms of picocuries per liter (pCi/l) at 20 C or, for samples of specific gravity significantly different from 1.00, picocuries per gram, where 1 picocurie = 10^{-12} curies = 2.22 dpm. For samples normally containing 1,000 to 1,000,000 pCi per unit volume or weight, the nanocurie (nCi) unit is preferred (1 nCi = 10^{-9} curies = 1,000 pCi). If the values are higher than 1,000 nCi, the microcurie (μCi) unit is preferred. Ordinarily, the liter, kilogram and square meter are preferred units of volume, weight and area, respectively.

It is important to report results in such a way that they will not imply greater or less accuracy than can be obtained by the method used. This matter is discussed in Section 000B.2 (General Introduction, Significant Figures).

"Gross alpha" implies unknown alpha sources in which natural uranium salts have been used to determine self-absorption and efficiency factors.

"Gross beta" implies unknown sources of beta, including some gamma radiation, and calibration with ^{137}Cs as in Section 300C.1f above.

300 F. Statistics

Section 000C.1 of this manual discusses the statistics of analytical problems as applied to chemical parameters. These remarks are also generally applicable to radioactivity examinations.

The variability of any measurement is measured by the standard deviation, which can be obtained from replicate determinations by well-known methods. There is an inherent variability in radioactivity measurements because the disintegrations occur in a random manner described by the Poisson distribution. This distribution is characterized by the property that the standard deviation of a large number of events, N, is equal to its square root, or:

$$\sigma(N) = N^{1/2} \quad (1)$$

For ease in mathematical application, the normal (Gaussian) approximation to the Poisson distribution is ordinarily used. This approximation, which is generally valid at $N \geqq 20$, is the particular normal distribution whose mean is N and whose standard deviation is $N^{1/2}$.

Generally, the concern is not with the standard deviation of the number of counts but rather with the deviation in the rate (number of counts per unit time):

$$R' = \frac{N}{t} \quad (2)$$

where t is the time of observation, which is assumed to be known with such high precision that its error may be neglected. The standard deviation in the counting rate, $\sigma(R')$, can be calculated by the usual methods for propagation of error:

$$\sigma(R') = \frac{N^{1/2}}{t} = \left(\frac{R'}{t}\right)^{1/2} \quad (3)$$

In practice, all counting instruments have a background counting rate, B, when no sample is present. When a sample is present, the counting rate increases to R_0. The counting rate R due to the sample then is:

$$R = R_o - B \quad (4)$$

By propagation-of-error methods, the standard deviation of R can be calculated as follows:

$$\sigma(R) = \left(\frac{R_o}{t_1} + \frac{B}{t_2}\right)^{1/2} \quad (5)$$

where t_1 and t_2 are the times at which the gross sample and background counting rates were measured, respectively. Practical counting times are often 30 min, or 2,500 total counts above background, whichever takes less time. It is desirable to divide the counting time into two equal periods, so as to check constancy of the observed counting rate. For low-level counting, t_2 should be about the same as t_1. *The error thus calculated includes only the error caused by inherent variability of the radioactive disintegration process and should be reported as the "counting error."*

A confidence level of 95%, or 1.96 standard deviations, should preferably be selected and reported as the counting error.

300 G. References

1. FEDERAL RADIATION COUNCIL. 1961. Background material for the development of radiation protection standards. Report No. 2 (Sept.). Govt. Ptg. Off., Washington, D. C.
2. NATIONAL COMMITTEE ON RADIATION PROTECTION AND MEASUREMENTS. 1959. Maximum permissible body burdens and maximum permissible concentrations of radionuclides in air and water for occupational exposure. NBS Handbook No. 69, pp. 1, 17, 37, 38 and 93.
3. Recommendation of the International Commission on Radiological Protection (rev. Dec. 1, 1954). 1960. *Health Physics* 3:1.
4. U. S. PUBLIC HEALTH SERVICE. 1962. Public Health Service Drinking Water Standards, 1962. PHS Pub. No. 956. Govt. Ptg. Off., Washington, D. C.
5. R. L. HEATH. 1964. *Scintillation Spectrometry, Gamma Ray Spectrum* IDO-16880. Technical Information Division, U. S. Atomic Energy Commission, Washington, D. C., Vols. 1 and 2.
6. C. E. CROUTHAMEL, Ed. 1960. *Applied Gamma-Ray Spectrometry*. Pergamon Press, New York, Vol. II.
7. NATIONAL CENTER FOR RADIOLOGICAL HEALTH. 1967. Radioassay procedures for environmental samples. PHS Pub. No. 999-RH-27. U. S. Department of Health, Education & Welfare, Washington, D. C.
8. INTERLABORATORY TECHNICAL ADVISORY COMMITTEE. 1968. Report No. 2: Common laboratory instruments for measurement of radioactivity. PHS Pub. No. 999-RH-32. National Center for Radiological Health, U. S. Department of Health, Education & Welfare, Washington, D. C.

300 H. Bibliography

JARRETT, A. A. 1946. Statistical methods used in the measurement of radioactivity (some useful graphs). U. S. Atomic Energy Commission Document No. AECU-262 (June 17). AEC, Washington, D. C.

CORYELL, C. D. & N. SUGARMAN, Eds. 1951. *Radiochemical Studies: The Fission Products*. McGraw-Hill Book Co., New York.

NADER, J. S., G. R. HAGEE & L. R. SETTER. 1954. Evaluating the performance of the internal counter. *Nucleonics* 12:6, 29.

COMAR, C. I. 1955. *Radioisotopes in Biology and Agriculture*. McGraw-Hill Book Co., New York.

JOHNSON, N. F., E. EICHLER & G. O. O'KELLEY. 1963. Nuclear chemistry. Vol. II of *Technique of Inorganic Chemistry*. Interscience Publishers, New York.

FRIEDLANDER, G., J. W. KENNEDY & J. M. MILLER. 1964. *Nuclear and Radiochemistry* (2nd ed.). John Wiley & Sons, New York.

LEDERER, C. M., J. M. HOLLANDER & I. PERLMANN. 1967. *Table of Isotopes* (6th ed.). John Wiley & Sons, New York.

LOS ALAMOS SCIENTIFIC LABORATORY, Radiochemistry Group J-11. 1967. Collected radiochemical procedures. *U. S. Atomic Energy Comm. Rep.* No. LA-1721 (3rd ed.). AEC, Washington, D. C.

HARLEY, JOHN R., Ed. 1967 (Reissue). *Manual of Standard Procedures*. AEC Document No. NYO-4700, 1957. Health & Safety Laboratory, USAEC, New York.

301 RADIOACTIVITY IN WASTEWATER

1. Discussion

Factors considered in sampling and sample preservation and the behavior of radioactive species are of great significance in the analysis of wastewater. Usually wastewater contains larger amounts of nonradioactive suspended and dissolved solids than does water, and often a preponderance of the radioactivity is in the solid phase. Generally, the use of carriers in the analysis is ineffective without first converting the solid phase to the soluble phase; even then the high fixed solids may interfere with radioanalytical procedures. Table 301(1) shows the usual solubility characteristics of common radioelements in wastewater.

TABLE 301(1): THE USUAL DISTRIBUTION OF COMMON RADIOELEMENTS BETWEEN THE SOLID AND LIQUID PHASES OF WASTEWATER

In Solution	In Suspension
HCO_3	Ce
Co	Cs
Cr	Mn
Cs	Nb
H	P
I	Pm
K	Pu
Ra	Ra
Rn	Sc
Ru	Th
Sb	U
Sr	Y
	Zn
	Zr

Moreover, the radioelements may exhibit unusual chemical characteristics due to the presence of complexing agents or to the method of waste production. For example, tritium may be combined in an organic compound when used in the manufacture of luminous articles; radioiodine from hospitals may occur as complex organic compounds, compared to elemental and iodide forms found in fission products from the processing of spent nuclear fuels; uranium and thorium daughter products often exist as inorganic complexes other than oxides after processing in uranium mills; and strontium 90 titanate waste from a radioisotope heat source would be quite insoluble compared to most other strontium wastes.

Valuable information on the chemical composition of wastes, the behavior of radioelements, and the quantity of radioisotopes in use appears in the literature.[1, 2] Radionuclides having or likely to have a public health significance are here emphasized. Methods are provided for radionuclides of high radiotoxicity. Some of these are beta emitters. The levels of most gamma emitters which have public health significance can be measured by gamma spectrometry without chemical separation. This is usually true for ^{106}Ru, ^{137}Cs, ^{131}I and ^{60}Co.

Information on the determination of radioactivity in wastes, as well as other environmental samples, may be found, for example, in manuals on Radioassay Procedures of the Public Health Service,[3, 4] the AEC manual,[5] and the American Society for Testing and Materials' *Book of Standards*.[6] General information on the behavior of the radioelements and on analytical methods are found in the monographs of the National Research Council.[7]

Radionuclide standards for those elements commonly encountered in wastewater are available from one or more of the following: The National Bureau of Standards and Amersham/Searle Corporation in the United States, the Radiochemical Centre, Amersham, England, the International Atomic Energy Agency, Vienna, Austria, and CEA-Saclay, France. General information on radionuclide standards is available in American publications.[8, 9]

For data on half-lives and decay schemes, the most authoritative sources are the publications of the Oak Ridge [10] and California [11] groups. The Public Health Service through its Analytical Quality Control Service of the Bureau of Radiological Health * assists laboratories in achieving radioanalytical proficiency.

It is not generally feasible to perform collaborative (interlaboratory) analyses of wastewater samples due to the variable composition of elements and solids from one facility to the next, but the methods which follow have been evaluated by use of homogeneous samples and could be useful for nonhomogeneous samples after sample preparation (wet or dry oxidation and/or fusion and solution) resulting in homogeneity. A potential problem or characteristic of reference samples used for collaborative testing is that they may be deficient in radioelements exhibiting interferences due to decay during shipment of short half-life radionuclides. Generally, however, analytical steps have been incorporated into the methods to eliminate these interferences, even though they may not be necessary for the reference samples under study.

* Analytical Quality Control Service, Northeast Radiological Health Laboratory, Bureau of Radiological Health, ECA, CPEHS, U.S. Department of Health, Education & Welfare, 109 Holton Street, Winchester, Mass. 01890.

2. References

1. INTERNATIONAL ATOMIC ENERGY AGENCY. 1960. *Disposal of Radioactive Wastes.* IAEA, Vienna, Austria.
2. N. L. NEMEROW. 1963. *Industrial Waste Treatment.* Addison-Wesley, Reading, Mass.
3. G. S. DOUGLAS, Ed. 1967. Radioassay procedures for environmental samples. PHS Pub. No. 999-RH-27. U. S. Department of Health, Education & Welfare, Washington, D. C.
4. INTERLABORATORY TECHNICAL ADVISORY COMMITTEE. 1968. Common laboratory instruments for measurement of radioactivity. PHS Pub. No. 999-RH-32. National Center for Radiological Health, Department of Health, Education & Welfare, Washington, D. C.
5. J. H. HARLEY, Ed. 1967. *Manual of Standard Procedures.* U. S. Atomic Energy Commission Document No. NYO-4700 (2nd ed.). Clearinghouse, Springfield, Va.
6. AMERICAN SOCIETY FOR TESTING AND MATERIALS. *1968 Book of ASTM Standards.* ASTM, Philadelphia, Pa., Part 23.
7. NAS-NRC. 1960 to date. *Radiochemistry of the Elements.* Rep. Nos. NAS-NS-3001 et seq., and *Radiochemical Techniques.* Rep. Nos. 3101 et seq. Clearinghouse, Springfield, Va.
8. W. B. MANN & H. H. SELIGER. 1958. Preparation, maintenance, and application of standards of radioactivity. NBS Circular No. 594. U. S. Department of Commerce, Washington, D. C.
9. H. F. BEEGHLY, J. P. CALI & W. W. MEINKE, Eds. 1968. *Nuclear Stan-*

dards for Chemistry and Technology. NBS Special Pub. 310 (Dec.). U. S. Department of Commerce, Washington, D. C.

10. K. WAY, Ed. 1966. *Nuclear Data Sheets;* and *Journal Nuclear Data,* Part B. Academic Press, New York.
11. C. M. LEDERER, J. M. HOLLANDER & I. PERLMAN. 1967. *Table of Isotopes.* John Wiley & Sons, New York.

3. Bibliography

GARFINKEL, S. B., A. P. BAERG & P. E. ZIGMAN. 1966. *Certificates of Radioactivity Standards.* National Academy of Sciences, Washington, D. C.

KAHN, B., C. R. CHOPPIN & J. G. V. TAYLOR. 1967. *User's Guide for Radioactivity Standards.* National Academy of Sciences, Washington, D. C.

302 GROSS ALPHA AND GROSS BETA RADIOACTIVITY IN WATER (TOTAL, SUSPENDED AND DISSOLVED)

1. General Discussion

a. Natural radioactivity: Uranium, thorium and radium are naturally occurring radioactive elements that have a long series of radioactive daughters which emit alpha or beta and gamma radiations until a stable end-element is produced. These naturally occurring elements, through their radioactive daughter gases, radon and thoron, cause an appreciable airborne particulate activity and contribute to the radioactivity of rain and groundwaters. Additional naturally radioactive elements include potassium 40, rubidium 87, samarium 147, lutetium 176, and rhenium 187.

b. Artificial radioactivity: With the development and operation of nuclear reactors and other atom-smashing machines, large quantities of radioactive elements are being produced. These include almost all the elements in the periodic table.

c. Significance of gross alpha and gross beta concentrations in water: The 1962 Public Health Service Drinking Water Standards recommend limits for the concentration of radium 226 (3 pCi/l) and strontium 90 (10 pCi/l) in water. Furthermore, if alpha emitters and strontium 90 are known to be a negligible fraction of the above-specified limits, the water supply would usually be regarded as radiologically acceptable, provided that the gross beta concentration does not exceed 1,000 pCi/l.

By using the simpler technics for routine measurement of gross beta activity, the presence of contamination may be determined in a matter of minutes, whereas hours or even days may be required to conduct the radiochemical analyses necessary to identify the particular radionuclides that are present in the sample.

Regular measurements of gross alpha and gross beta activity in water may be invaluable for early detection of radioactive contamination and indicate the need for supplemental data on the concentrations of the more hazardous radionuclides.

d. Preferred counting instrument and calibration standard: The internal proportional counter is the recommended instrument for counting gross beta radioactivity because of its superior operating characteristics. These include a high sensitivity to detect and count a wide range of low- to high-energy beta radiation and a high geometry (2π) due to the introduction of the sample into the counting chamber. In this case the system of assay is calibrated by adding standard nuclide portions to media comparable to the samples and preparing, mounting and counting the standards identical to that of the samples.

Thin-window proportional or Geiger counters may be used for this determination, although they have lower counting efficiencies than the internal proportional counter. When a Geiger counter is used, the alpha activity cannot be determined separately. Alpha counting efficiency in end-window counters may be very low because of absorption in the air and the window.

When assaying gross beta activity in samples containing mixtures of naturally radioactive elements and fission products, the choice of a calibration standard may significantly influence the beta results because self-absorption factors and counting chamber characteristics are beta energy dependent.

A standard solution of cesium 137, which is certified by the National Bureau of Standards * or is traceable to a certified source, is recommended for calibration of counter efficiency and self-absorption for gross beta determinations. The half-life of cesium 137 is about 30 years. The daughter products after beta decay of cesium 137 are stable barium 137 and metastable barium 137, which in turn disintegrates by gamma emission. For this reason, the standardization of cesium 137 solutions may be stated in terms of the gamma emission rate per milliliter or per gram. To convert gamma rate to equivalent beta disintegration rate, multiply the calibrated gamma emission rate by 1.33.

e. Radiation lost by self-absorption: The radiation from alpha emitters having an energy of 8 MeV and from beta emitters having an energy of 60 KeV will not escape from the sample if they are covered by a sample thickness of 5.5 mg/sq cm. The radiation from a weak alpha emitter will be stopped if covered by only 4 mg/sq cm of sample solids. Consequently, for low-level counting it is imperative to evaporate all moisture and preferable to destroy organic matter before depositing a thin film of sample solids from which radiation may readily enter the counter. In counting water samples for gross beta radioactivity, a solids thickness of 10 mg/sq cm or less on the bottom area of the counting pan is recommended. For the most accurate results, the self-absorption factor should be determined as outlined in Section 300C.1f.

2. Apparatus

a. Counting pans, of metal resistant to corrosion from sample solids or reagents, about 50 mm in diameter, 6–10 mm in height, and thick enough to be serviceable for one-time use. Stainless steel or aluminum pans are satisfactory, depending on the kind of sample and reagents added.

b. Internal proportional counting chambers, capable of receiving and maintaining good electrical contact with counting pans, complete with preamplifier, scaler, timer, register, constant-voltage supply, counting gas equipment, and counting gas.

---

* For calibration standards and certification see *The Isotope Index,* J. S. Sommerville, Ed. Scientific Equipment Co., P.O. Box 19086, Indianapolis, Indiana.

c. Alternate counters: Other beta counters are thin end-window proportional and Geiger counters.

d. Membrane filter,† 0.45-μ pore size.

e. Gooch crucibles.

3. Reagents

a. Methyl orange indicator solution: Dissolve 0.5 g methyl orange in 1 liter distilled water.

b. Hydrochloric acid, 1*N* (1 + 11).

c. Nitric acid, 1*N:* Dilute 64 ml conc HNO_3 to 1 liter with distilled water.

d. Lucite solution: Dissolve 50 mg Lucite in 100 ml acetone.

e. Ethyl alcohol, 95%.

f. Conducting fluid: Anstac AC.‡ or equivalent; prepare according to manufacturer's directions.

g. Standard certified cesium 137 solution.

h. Reagents for wet-combustion procedure:

(1) *Nitric acid,* 6*N:* Dilute 380 ml conc HNO_3 to 1 liter with distilled water.

(2) *Hydrogen peroxide solution:* Dilute 30% H_2O_2 with an equal volume of water.

4a. Procedure for Gross Alpha and Gross Beta Activity

1) For each 20 sq cm of counting pan area, take a volume of sample containing not more than 200 mg of residue for beta examination and not more than 100 mg of residue for alpha examination. The specific conductance test helps to select the appropriate sample volume.

2) Evaporate by either of the following technics:

(a) Add the sample directly to a tared counting pan in small increments, with evaporation just below boiling temperature.

(b) Place the sample in a pyrex beaker or evaporating dish, add a few drops of methyl orange indicator solution, add 1*N* HCl or 1*N* HNO_3 dropwise to pH 4–6, and evaporate on a hot plate or steam bath to near dryness. Avoid baking solids on the evaporation vessel. Transfer the residue to a tared counting pan with the aid of a rubber policeman and distilled water from a wash bottle. Thoroughly wet the walls of the evaporating vessel with a few drops of acid by means of a rubber policeman and transfer the acid washings to the counting pan. (Excess alkalinity or mineral acidity is corrosive to aluminum counting pans.)

3) Complete the drying in an oven at 103–105 C, cool in a desiccator, weigh, and keep the sample dry until counted.

4) Sample residues having particles that tend to be airborne, which are to be counted in internal counters, should be treated with a few drops of Lucite solution, then air- and oven-dried and weighed. The Lucite acts as a binder to prevent counter contamination by such particles.

5) For an internal counter, count the alpha activity at the alpha plateau and count the beta-gamma activity at the beta plateau.

6) Store sample in a desiccator and count for decay if necessary. Avoid heat treatment if ingrowth of gaseous daughter products is suspected.

† Type HA (Millipore Filter Corp., Bedford, Mass.) or equivalent.

‡ Chemical Development Corporation, Danvers, Mass.

4b. Procedure for Gross Alpha and Gross Beta of Dissolved Matter

1) Proceed as in ¶ 4a(1) above with a sample volume containing the requisite maximum weight of dissolved matter.

2) Filter through a Gooch crucible or, if the suspended matter is to be examined, a membrane filter.

3) Process the filtrate as described in ¶s 4a(2)–(6) above, and report the dissolved alpha activity and dissolved beta activity by Gooch or by membrane filtration as the case may be.

4c. Procedure for Gross Alpha and Gross Beta of Suspended Matter

1) For each 10 sq cm of membrane filter area, take a volume of sample not to exceed 50 mg of suspended matter for alpha assay and not to exceed 100 mg for beta assay.

2) Filter sample through the membrane filter with suction; then wash sides of filter funnel with a few milliliters of distilled water.

3) Transfer filter to a tared counting pan and oven-dry.

4) If the sample is to be counted in an internal counter, saturate the membrane with alcohol and ignite (when counting beta or alpha activity with other counters, ignition is not necessary provided that the sample is dry and flat). When burning has stopped, direct the flame of a Meker burner down on the partially ignited sample to fix the sample to the pan and obtain more complete ignition.

5) Cool, weigh, and count at the alpha and the beta plateaus.

6) If sample particles tend to be airborne, treat the sample with a few drops of Lucite solution, air-dry, and count.

7) An alternate method of preparing membrane filters for counting in internal counters consists of wetting the filters with conducting fluid, drying, weighing, and counting. (The weight of the membrane filter is then included in the tare.)

4d. Alternate Procedure for Gross Alpha and Gross Beta of Suspended Matter

It is impractical to filter some sewage, highly polluted waters, and industrial wastes through membrane filters. In such cases it is necessary to proceed as follows:

1) Determine the total and dissolved activity by the procedures given in ¶s 4a and 4b and estimate the suspended activity by difference.

2) Filter the sample through an ashless mat or filter paper of stated porosity. Dry, ignite and weigh the suspended fixed residue. Transfer and fix a thin uniform layer of sample residue to a tared counting pan with a few drops of Lucite solution. Dry, weigh and count in an internal counter for alpha and beta, or count the beta with a thin end-window counter and the alpha with an alpha scintillation counter.

4e. Procedure for Gross Alpha and Gross Beta of Nonfatty Semisolid Samples

The following procedure is applicable to samples of sludge, vegetation, soil and the like:

1) Determine the total residue and fixed residue of representative samples according to Sections 224A and B or 148D.

2) Reduce fixed residue of a granular nature to a fine powder with pestle and mortar.

3) Transfer a maximum of 100 mg fixed residue for alpha assay and 200 mg fixed residue for beta assay for each 20 sq cm of counting pan area (see Note below).

4) Distribute the residue to uniform thickness in a tared counting pan by (a) spreading a thick aqueous cream of residue which is weighed after oven-drying, or (b) dispensing dry residue of known weight which is spread with acetone and a few drops of Lucite solution.

5) Oven-dry at 103–105 C, weigh and count.

NOTE: The fixed residue of vegetation and similar samples is usually corrosive to aluminum counting pans. To avoid difficulty, use stainless steel pans or treat a weighed amount of fixed residue with HCl or HNO_3 in the presence of methyl orange indicator to pH 4–6, transfer to an aluminum counting pan, dry at 103–105 C, reweigh, and count.

4f. Alternate Wet-Combustion Procedure for Biologic Samples

Some samples, such as fatty animal tissues, are difficult to process according to Section 4e above. An alternate procedure consists of acid digestion. Because the procedure creates a highly acid and oxidizing state, volatile radionuclides would be lost under these conditions.

1) To 2–10 g sample in a tared silica dish or equivalent, add 20–50 ml 6*N* HNO_3 and 1 ml 15% H_2O_2 and digest at room temperature for a few hours or overnight. Heat gently and, when frothing subsides, heat more vigorously but without spattering, until near dryness. Add two more 6*N* HNO_3 aliquots of 10–20 ml each, heat to near boiling, and continue gentle treatment until the sample is dry.

2) Ignite the sample in a muffle furnace for 30 min at 600 C, cool in a desiccator, and weigh.

3) Continue the test as described in ¶s 4e(3)–(5) above.

5. Calculation and Reporting

a. Counting error: Determine the counting error, *E* (in picocuries per sample), at the 95% confidence level from:

$$E = \frac{1.96\ \sigma(R)}{2.22e}$$

where $\sigma(R)$ is calculated from Eq 5 (Section 300F), using $t_1 = t_2$ (in minutes); and *e,* the counter efficiency, is defined and calculated as in Section 300C.1f preceding.

b. Alpha activity of water, biologic samples, or silts: Report the alpha activity of water, in pCi/l, by the equation

$$\text{Alpha} = \frac{\text{net cpm} \times 1{,}000}{2.22\ e\ v}$$

where:

e = calibrated overall counter efficiency (see Section 300C.1f), and
v = volume of sample counted, in ml.

The counting error must also be expressed in terms of picocuries per liter by dividing the picocuries per sample by the sample volume in liters. Similarly, calculate and report the alpha activity in picocuries or nanocuries per kilogram of moist biologic material or per kilogram of moist and per kilogram of dry silt.

c. Gross beta activity when alpha activity is insignificant: For samples having an alpha activity less than one-half the beta counting error, calculate and report the gross beta activity and counting error in picocuries or nanocuries per liter of water or fluid, per kilogram of moist (live weight) biologic material, or per kilogram of moist and per kilogram of dry silt, according to ¶s a and b above, disregarding the slight amount of alpha activity.

For calculation of the picocuries per liter of beta activity, the value of *e* in the above equation is determined as described in Section 300C.1f preceding.

d. Beta activity when alpha activity is significant: In samples containing an alpha activity (in cpm) which exceeds one-half the beta error (in cpm), deduct the net alpha cpm from the net beta cpm to give the net corrected beta cpm. Proceed as in ¶ c above to calculate and report the beta radioactivity in picocuries or nanocuries per liter of water, per kilogram of moist biologic sample, or per kilogram of moist and per kilogram of dry silt. When the count of alpha activity at the beta plateau represents a small fraction of the activity, a rough approximation of the beta counting error consists of the gross beta counting error. Where greater precision is desired—for example, when the count of alpha activity at the beta plateau is a substantial fraction of the net cpm of gross beta activity—the beta counting error equals $(E_a^2 + E_b^2)^{1/2}$, where E_a is the alpha counting error and E_b the gross beta counting error.

e. Miscellaneous information to be reported: In reporting radioactivity data, it is important to identify adequately the sample, sampling station, date of collection, volume of sample, type of test, type of activity, type of counting equipment, standard calibration solutions used (particularly when standards other than natural uranium for alpha or cesium 137 for beta were used), time of counting (particularly if short-lived isotopes are involved), weight of sample solids, and kind and amount of radioactivity. So far as possible, the data should be tabulated for ease of interpretation and repetitious items should be incorporated in the table heading or in footnotes. Unless especially inconvenient, quantity units should not change within a given table. For low-level assays, where the counting error represents a significant fraction of the measurement, it should be reported to assist in the interpretation of results.

6. Precision and Accuracy

In a collaborative study of two sets of paired water samples containing known additions of radionuclides, 15 laboratories determined the gross alpha activity and 16 analyzed the gross beta activity. The water samples contained simulated water minerals of approximately 350 mg fixed solids per liter. The alpha results of one laboratory were rejected as outliers.

The average recoveries of added gross alpha activity were 86, 87, 84 and 82%. The precision (random error) at the 95% confidence level was 20 and 24% for the two sets of paired samples. The method was biased low, but not seriously.

The average recoveries of added gross beta activity were 99, 100, 100 and 100%. The precision (random error) at the 95% confidence level was

12 and 18% for the two sets of paired samples. The method showed no bias.

7. Bibliography

BURTT, B. P. 1949. Absolute beta counting. *Nucleonics* 5:8, 28.

GOLDIN, A. S., J. S. NADER & L. R. SETTER. 1953. The detectability of low-level radioactivity in water. *JAWWA* 45:73.

SETTER, L. R., A. S. GOLDIN & J. S. NADER. 1954. Radioactivity assay of water and industrial wastes with internal proportional counter. *Anal. Chem.* 26:1304.

SETTER, L. R. 1964. Reliability of measurements of gross beta radioactivity in water. *JAWWA* 56:228.

NATIONAL CENTER FOR RADIOLOGICAL HEALTH. 1967. Radioassay procedures for environmental samples. PHS Pub. No. 999-RH-27 (Jan.). U. S. Department of Health, Education & Welfare, Washington, D. C.

303 TOTAL RADIOACTIVE STRONTIUM AND STRONTIUM 90 IN WATER

The important radioactive nuclides of strontium produced in nuclear fission are ^{89}Sr and ^{90}Sr. Strontium 90 is one of the most hazardous of all fission products. It decays slowly, with a half-life of 28 years. Upon ingestion, the strontium is concentrated in the bone; 10% of the occupational maximum permissible concentration for ^{90}Sr in water is 100 pCi/l, as compared to 10,000 pCi/l for ^{89}Sr which has a half-life of only 50.5 days. The Federal Radiation Council intake guides for ^{90}Sr in ranges I, II and III are 0–20, 20–200 and 200–2,000 pCi per day per person, respectively, and for ^{89}Sr in ranges I, II and III the intake guides are 0–200, 200–2,000 and 2,000–20,000 pCi per day per person, respectively. The 1962 Public Health Service Drinking Water Standards limit the concentration of ^{90}Sr in water to 10 pCi/l when other sources of intake are not considered.

1. General Discussion

a. Principle: The following method is designed to measure total radioactive strontium (^{89}Sr and ^{90}Sr) or ^{90}Sr alone in drinking water or in filtered raw water. It is applicable to sewage and industrial wastes, provided that steps are taken to destroy organic matter and eliminate other interfering ions. In this analysis, a known amount of inactive strontium ions, in the form of strontium nitrate, is added as a "carrier." The carrier, alkaline earths and rare earths are precipitated as the carbonate to concentrate the radiostrontium. The carrier, along with the radionuclides of strontium, is separated from other radioactive elements and inactive sample solids by precipitation as strontium nitrate from fuming nitric acid solution. The strontium carrier, together with the radionuclides of strontium, is finally precipitated as strontium carbonate, which is dried, weighed to determine recovery of carrier, and then measured for radioactivity. The activity in the final precipitate is due to radioactive strontium only, because all other radioactive elements have been removed. A correction is applied to compensate for losses of carrier and activity during the various purification steps. A delay in the count will give an increased counting rate due to the ingrowth of ^{90}Y.

b. Concentration technics: Because of the very low amount of radioactivity, a large sample must be taken and the activity concentrated by precipitation. Strontium nitrate and barium nitrate carriers are added to the sample. Sodium carbonate is then added to concentrate radiostrontium by precipitation of alkaline earth carbonates along with other radioactive elements. The supernate is discarded. The precipitate is dissolved and reprecipitated to remove interfering radionuclides.

c. Interference: Radioactive barium (^{140}Ba, ^{140}La) interferes in the determination of radioactive strontium inasmuch as it precipitates along with the radioactive strontium. This interference is eliminated by adding inactive barium nitrate carrier and separating this from the strontium by precipitating barium chromate in acetate buffer solution. Radium isotopes are also eliminated by this treatment.

In hard water, some calcium nitrate may be coprecipitated with strontium nitrate and can cause errors in measuring activity and recovery in the final precipitate. This interference is eliminated by repeated precipitations of strontium as the nitrate followed by leaching the $Sr(NO_3)_2$ with acetone (CAUTION).

For total radiostrontium, the precipitate should be counted within 3–4 hr after the final separation and before ingrowth of ^{90}Y.

d. Determination of ^{90}Sr: Since it is impossible to separate the isotopes ^{89}Sr and ^{90}Sr by any chemical procedure, the amount of ^{90}Sr is determined by separating and measuring the activity of ^{90}Y, its daughter. After equilibrium is reached, the activity of ^{90}Y is exactly equal to the activity of ^{90}Sr. Two alternate procedures are given for the separation of ^{90}Y. In the first method, ^{90}Y is separated by extraction into tributyl phosphate from concentrated nitric acid solution. It is back-extracted into dilute nitric acid and evaporated to dryness for beta counting. The second method consists of adding yttrium carrier, separating by precipitation as yttrium hydroxide, and finally precipitating yttrium oxalate for counting.

2. Apparatus

a. Counting instruments: One of the following is required: an internal proportional counter, gas-flow, with scaler, timer and register; or a thin end-window (Mylar) proportional or G-M counting chamber with scaler, timer, register amplifier and preferably having an anticoincident system (low background).

b. Filter paper, Whatman No. 42, 2.4 cm in diameter; or glass fiber filters, 2.4 cm in diameter.

c. Two-piece filtering apparatus for 2.4-cm filters such as teflon filter holder *; stainless steel filter holder †; or equivalent.

d. Stainless steel pans, about 50 mm in diameter and 7 mm deep, for counting solids deposited on pan bottom. For counting precipitates on 2.4-cm filters, use nylon disk with ring ‡ on which the filter samples are mounted and covered by 0.25 mil Mylar film.§

---

* Flurolon Laboratory, Box 305, Caldwell, New Jersey.

† Catalog No. E-8B, Tracerlab, Inc., Waltham, Massachusetts.

‡ Control Molding Corp., Staten Island, New York.

§ E. I. du Pont de Nemours, Wilmington, Delaware.

3. Reagents

a. Strontium carrier (10 mg Sr^{2+} per ml) standardized: Carefully add 24.16 g $Sr(NO_3)_2$ to a 1-liter volumetric flask and dilute with distilled water to the mark. For standardization, pipet three 10.0-ml portions of strontium carrier solution into 40-ml centrifuge tubes and add 15 ml of 2*N* Na_2CO_3 solution. Stir, heat in a boiling water bath for 15 min, and cool. Filter the $SrCO_3$ precipitate through a tared fine-porosity sintered-glass crucible of 15-ml size. Wash the precipitate with three 5-ml portions of water and then with three 5-ml portions of absolute ethanol (or acetone). Wipe the crucible with absorbent tissue and dry to constant weight in an oven at 110 C (20 min). Cool in a desiccator and weigh.

$$\text{Sr, mg/ml} = \frac{(\text{mg SrCO}_3)\ (0.5935)}{10}$$

b. Barium carrier (10 mg Ba^{2+} per ml): Dissolve 19.0 g $Ba(NO_3)_2$ in distilled water and dilute to 1 liter.

c. Rare earth carrier, mixed: Dissolve 12.8 g cerous nitrate hexahydrate, $Ce(NO_3)_3 \cdot 6H_2O$, 14 g zirconyl chloride octahydrate, $ZrOCl_2 \cdot 8H_2O$, and 25 g ferric chloride hexahydrate, $FeCl_3 \cdot 6H_2O$, in 600 ml distilled water containing 10 ml conc HCl, and dilute to 1 liter.

d. Yttrium carrier: Dissolve 12.7 g yttrium oxide,* Y_2O_3, in 30 ml conc HNO_3 by stirring and warming. Add an additional 20 ml of conc HNO_3 and dilute to 1 liter with distilled water; 1 ml is equivalent to 10 mg Y, or approximately 34 mg $Y_2(C_2O_4)_3 \cdot 9H_2O$. Determine the exact equivalence by precipitating yttrium carrier in acid solution according to Section 303.4c (2)–(8) or by extracting yttrium carrier in acid solution according to Section 303.4b(3)–(11) following.

e. Acetate buffer solution: Dissolve 154 g ammonium acetate, $NH_4C_2H_3O_2$, in 700 ml distilled water, add 57 ml conc acetic acid, adjust pH to 5.5 by dropwise addition of conc acetic acid or 6*N* NH_4OH as necessary, and dilute to 1 liter.

f. Acetic acid, 6*N*.

g. Acetone, anhydrous.

h. Ammonium hydroxide, 6*N*.

i. Hydrochloric acid, 6*N*.

j. Methyl red indicator, 0.1%: Dissolve 0.1 g methyl red in 100 ml distilled water.

k. Nitric acid, fuming (90%), conc, 14*N*, 6*N* and 0.1*N*.

l. Oxalic acid, saturated solution: Approximately 11 g $H_2C_2O_4 \cdot 2H_2O$ in 100 ml distilled water.

m. Sodium carbonate solution, 2*N*: Dissolve 124 g sodium carbonate monohydrate, $Na_2CO_3 \cdot H_2O$, in distilled water and dilute to 1 liter.

n. Sodium chromate solution, 0.5*M*: Dissolve 117 g sodium chromate tetrahydrate, $Na_2CrO_4 \cdot 4H_2O$, in distilled water and dilute to 1 liter.

o. Sodium hydroxide, 6*N*: Dissolve 240 g NaOH in distilled water and dilute to 1 liter.

p. Tributyl phosphate, reagent grade: Shake with an equal volume of 14*N* nitric acid to equilibrate. Separate and discard the nitric acid washings.

4a. Procedure for Total Radiostrontium

1) To 1 liter of drinking water, or a filtered sample of raw water in a

* Yttrium oxide, Code 1118, American Potash and Chemical Corp., West Chicago, Illinois, or equivalent. Yttrium oxide of purity less than Code 1118 may require purification due to radioactivity contamination.

beaker, add 2.0 ml of conc HNO_3 and mix. Add 2.0 ml each of strontium and barium carriers and mix well. (A precipitate of $BaSO_4$ may form if the water is high in sulfate ion but this will cause no difficulties.) A smaller sample may be used if it contains at least 25 pCi of strontium. The suspended matter that has been filtered off may be digested [see Gross Alpha and Gross Beta Radioactivity, 302.4f(1)], diluted, and analyzed separately.

2) Heat the solution to boiling, then add 20 ml 6*N* NaOH and 20 ml 2*N* sodium carbonate. Stir and allow to simmer at 90–95 C for about 1 hr.

3) Set beaker aside until the precipitate has settled (about 1–3 hr).

4) Decant and discard the clear supernate. Transfer the precipitate to a 40-ml centrifuge tube and centrifuge. Discard the supernate.

5) Add, dropwise (CAUTION—effervescence), 4 ml conc HNO_3 to the precipitate. Heat to boiling, stir, then cool under running water.

6) Add 20 ml fuming HNO_3, cool 5–10 min in ice bath, stir, and centrifuge. Discard the supernate.

7) Add 4 ml of water to the residue, stir and heat to boiling to dissolve the strontium. Centrifuge while hot to remove remaining insolubles and decant supernate to a clean centrifuge tube. Add 2 ml 6*N* nitric acid to the residue, heat to boiling, centrifuge while hot, and combine the supernate with the aqueous supernate. Discard the insoluble residue of SiO_2, $BaSO_4$, and so on.

8) Cool combined supernates, then add 20 ml fuming HNO_3, cool 5–10 min in ice bath, stir, centrifuge, and discard the supernate.

9) Add 4 ml water to the precipitate and dissolve by heating. Repeat step (8) preceding.

10) Repeat step (9) preceding if more than 200 mg Ca were present in the water sample.

11) After the last HNO_3 precipitation, invert tube in a beaker for about 10 min to drain off most of the excess HNO_3 and then add 20 ml anhydrous acetone to the precipitate. Stir thoroughly, cool, and centrifuge. Discard the supernate (CAUTION).

12) Dissolve the precipitate of $Sr(NO_3)_2 + Ba(NO_3)_2$ in 10 ml distilled water and boil for 30 sec to remove any remaining acetone.

13) Add 0.25 ml (5 drops) mixed rare earth carrier and precipitate rare earth hydroxides by making the solution basic with 6*N* NH_4OH. Digest in a boiling water bath for 10 min. Cool, centrifuge, and decant the supernate to a clean tube. Discard the precipitate.

14) Repeat step (13) preceding.

Note the time of rare earth precipitation, which marks the beginning of the ^{90}Y ingrowth period. Do not delay the procedure more than a few hours after the separation; otherwise, false results will be obtained owing to the ingrowth of ^{90}Y.

15) Add 2 drops methyl red indicator and then add 6*N* acetic acid dropwise with stirring until the indicator changes from yellow to red.

16) Add 5 ml acetate buffer solution, heat to boiling, and add dropwise, with stirring, 2 ml sodium chromate solution. Digest in a boiling water bath for 5 min. Cool, centrifuge, and decant the supernate to a clean tube. Discard the residue.

17) Add 2 ml 6*N* NaOH to the supernate and then add 5 ml 2*N* sodium carbonate solution and heat to boiling. Cool in an ice bath (about 5 min) and centrifuge. Discard supernate.

18) Add 15 ml distilled water to the precipitate, stir, centrifuge, and discard the wash water.

19) Repeat step (18) and proceed either as in step (20a) or (20b) below. *Be sure to save this precipitate* if a determination of ^{90}Sr is required.

20a) Slurry the precipitate with a small volume of distilled H_2O and transfer to a tared stainless steel pan. Dry under an infrared lamp, cool, weigh and count * the precipitate of $SrCO_3$.†

20b) Transfer the precipitate to a tared paper or glass filter mounted in a 2-piece funnel. Allow gravity settling for uniform deposition and then apply suction. Wash precipitate with three 5-ml portions of water, three 5-ml portions of 95% alcohol, and three 5-ml portions of ethyl ether or acetone. Dry in an oven at 110 to 125 C for 15–30 min, cool, weigh,† mount on a nylon disk and ring with Mylar cover, and count.

21) Calculation:

$$\text{Total Sr activity in pCi/1} = \frac{h}{adf \times 2.22}$$

where:

a = beta counter efficiency [see step (22) below]

$$d = \frac{\text{mg final } SrCO_3 \text{ ppt}}{\text{mg } SrCO_3 \text{ in 2 ml of carrier}}$$
= Correction for carrier recovery [see step (23) below],

f = sample volume, in liters,

h = beta activity, in net counts per minute = $(i/t) - k$,

i = total counts accumulated,

t = time of counting, in minutes, and

k = background, in counts per minute.

22) Counting efficiency: As a first estimate, when mounting sample according to step (20a) convert counts per minute to disintegrations per minute, based on the beta activity of cesium 137 standard solutions having a sample thickness equivalent to the $SrCO_3$ precipitate. More precise measurements may follow a second count after substantial ingrowth of ^{90}Y from ^{90}Sr, but this precision is not warranted for the usual total radiostrontium determination. When mounting samples according to step (20b), self-absorption curves are determined by separately precipitating standard solutions of ^{89}Sr and ^{90}Sr as the carbonate (see Section on Gross Beta).

* Strontium 90 in thick samples is counted with low efficiency; hence, a first count within hours favors ^{89}Sr counting, and a recount after 3 to 6 days which exceeds the first count provides a rough estimate of the ^{90}Y ingrowth—see Figure 50 and R. J. Velten (1966) below.

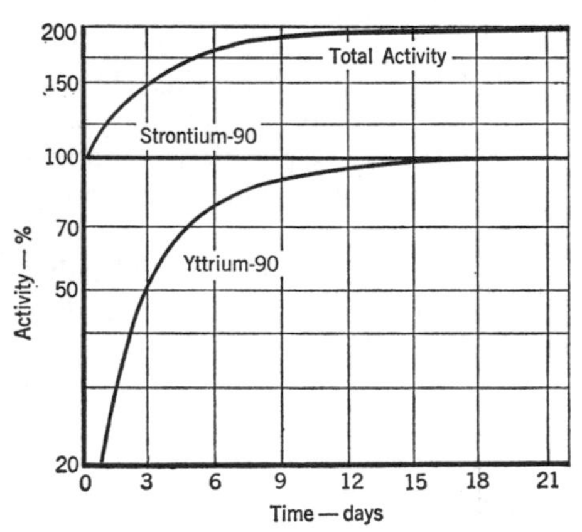

Figure 50. Yttrium 90 vs. strontium 90 activity as a function of time.

† When a determination of total strontium is not required, weigh the precipitate [step (20a) or (20b)] for carrier recovery but do not count. Then proceed with ^{90}Sr determination according to Section 303.4b following.

23) Correction for carrier recovery: 20 mg Sr are equivalent to 33.7 mg $SrCO_3$. Should more than traces of stable strontium be present in the water sample, it would act as carrier; hence its determination, as by flame photometry, would be required.

4b. Procedure for Strontium 90 * (by Extraction of Yttrium 90)

Store the strontium carbonate precipitate, as in ¶ 4a (20), for at least 2 weeks to allow ingrowth of ^{90}Y and then proceed as given in this section or in an alternate procedure in Section 303.4c following.

1a) Place a small funnel upright into the mouth of a 60-ml separatory funnel; then place pan with precipitate, as in step (20a), in funnel and add, dropwise, 1 ml 6*N* HNO_3. (CAUTION—effervescence.) Tilt pan to empty into funnel and rinse pan twice with 2-ml portions of 6*N* HNO_3.

1b) Uncover precipitate from filter, as in step (20b), and transfer filter with forceps to upright funnel in mouth of 60-ml separatory funnel as in ¶ 1a above. Dislodge bulk of precipitate into funnel stem. Dropwise, add with caution 1 ml 6*N* HNO_3 to filter, which removes residual precipitate and dissolves bulk precipitate. Rinse filter and funnel twice with 2-ml portions of 6*N* HNO_3.

2) Remove filter or pan and add 10 ml fuming HNO_3 to separatory funnel through the upright funnel.

3) Remove upright funnel and add 1 ml yttrium carrier to solution in a separatory funnel.

4) Add 5.0 ml tributyl phosphate reagent, shake thoroughly for 3–5 min, allow the phases to separate, and transfer the aqueous layer to a second 60-ml separatory funnel.

5) Add 5.0 ml tributyl phosphate reagent, shake 5 min, allow the phases to separate, and transfer the aqueous layer to a third 60-ml separatory funnel.

6) Combine the organic extractants in the first and second funnels into one funnel and wash the organic phase twice with 5-ml portions of 14*N* HNO_3. Record the time as the beginning of ^{90}Y decay (combine acid washings with aqueous phase in the third funnel if a second ingrowth of ^{90}Y is desired).

7) Back-extract ^{90}Y from the combined organic phases with 10 ml of 0.1*N* HNO_3 for 5 min.

8) Continue as given in Section 303.4c, steps (6)–(8) below or transfer the aqueous phase from step (7) immediately above into a 50-ml beaker and evaporate on a hot plate to 5–10 ml.

9) Repeat step (7) above and transfer the aqueous phase to the beaker in step (8) preceding; evaporate to 5–10 ml.

10) Transfer residual solution in beaker to a tared stainless steel counting pan and evaporate.

11) Rinse beaker twice with 2-ml portions of 0.1*N* HNO_3; add rinsings to counting pan, evaporate to dryness, and weigh.

12) Count in an internal proportional or end-window counter and calculate ^{90}Sr as given in Section 4c(9) following.

* See footnote to step (20a) when a determination for only ^{90}Sr is required.

4c. Alternate Procedure for Strontium 90 (Oxalate Precipitation of Yttrium 90) *

1) Quantitatively transfer the $SrCO_3$ precipitate to a 40-ml centrifuge tube with 2 ml of 6*N* HNO_3. Add acid dropwise during dissolution. (CAUTION—effervescence.) Use 0.1*N* HNO_3 for rinsing purposes.

2) Add 1 ml yttrium carrier, 2 drops methyl red indicator and, *dropwise,* add conc NH_4OH to the methyl red end point.

3) Add an additional 5 ml conc NH_4OH and *record the time,* which is the end of ^{90}Y ingrowth and the beginning of decay; centrifuge, and decant supernate to a beaker (save supernate and washings for a second ingrowth if desired).

4) Wash the precipitate twice with 20-ml portions of hot distilled water.

5) Add 5–10 drops of 6*N* HNO_3, stir to dissolve precipitate, add 25 ml distilled water, and heat in a water bath at 90 C.

6) Gradually add 15–20 drops of saturated oxalic acid reagent with stirring and adjust the pH to 1.5–2.0 (pH meter or indicator paper) by adding conc NH_4OH dropwise. Digest the precipitate for 5 min and then cool in an ice bath, with occasional stirring.

7) Transfer the precipitate to a tared glass fiber filter in a 2-piece funnel. Allow the precipitate to settle by gravity (for uniform deposition) and then apply suction. Wash precipitate in sequence with 10–15 ml hot distilled water and then 3 times with 95% ethyl alcohol and 3 times with diethyl ether.

* See footnote to step (20a) above when a determination for only ^{90}Sr is required.

8) Air-dry the precipitate with suction for 2 min, weigh, mount on a nylon disk and ring with Mylar cover, count, and calculate ^{90}Sr as follows.

9) Calculation:

$$^{90}\text{Sr pCi/l} = \frac{\text{net cpm}}{a\ b\ c\ d\ f\ g \times 2.22}$$

where

a = counting efficiency for ^{90}Y,
b = chemical yield of extracting or precipitating ^{90}Y,
c = ingrowth correction factor if not in secular equilibrium,
d = chemical yield of strontium determined gravimetrically or by flame photometry,
f = volume, in liters, of original sample,
g = ^{90}Y decay factor, $e^{-\lambda t}$, and
e = base of natural logarithms,
$\lambda = 0.693/T_{1/2}$, where $T_{1/2}$ for ^{90}Y is 64.2 hr, and
t = time, in hours, between separation and counting.

5. Precision and Accuracy

In a collaborative study of two sets of paired, moderately hard water samples containing known additions of radionuclides, 12 laboratories determined the total radiostrontium and 10 laboratories determined ^{90}Sr. The results of one sample from one laboratory were rejected as an outlier.

The average recoveries of added total radiostrontium from the four samples were 99, 99, 96 and 93%. The precision (random error) at the 95% confidence level was 10 and 12% for the two sets of paired samples. The method was biased on the low side, but not seriously biased.

The average recoveries of added ^{90}Sr from the four samples were 90, 96, 80 and 94%. The precision (random error) at the 95% confidence level was 14 and 28% for the two sets of paired samples. The method was biased toward the low side, but not seriously biased.

6. Bibliography

HAHN, R. B. & C. P. STRAUB. 1955. Determination of radioactive strontium and barium in water. *JAWWA* 47:335.

GOLDIN, A. S., R. J. VELTEN & G. W. FRISHKORN. 1959. Determination of radioactive strontium. *Anal. Chem.* 31:1490.

GOLDIN, A. S. & R. J. VELTEN. 1961. Application of tributyl phosphate extraction to the determination of strontium 90. *Anal. Chem.* 33:149.

VELTEN, R. J. 1966. Resolution of Sr-89 and Sr-90 in environmental media by an instrumental technique. *Nuclear Instrument Methods* 42:169.

304 RADIUM IN WATER BY PRECIPITATION

The determination of radium by precipitation is a screening technic applicable in particular to drinking water. As long as the concentration of radium is less than the ^{226}Ra drinking water standard, the need for examination by a more specific method is minimal.

There are four naturally occurring radium isotopes—11.6-day radium 223, 3.6-day radium 224, 1,600-year radium 226, and 5.75-year radium 228. Radium 223 is a member of the uranium 235 series, radium 224 and radium 228 are members of the thorium series, and radium 226 is a member of the uranium 238 series. The contribution of radium 228 (a beta emitter) to the total radium alpha activity is negligible because of the 1.9-year half-life of its first alpha-emitting daughter product, thorium 228. The other three radium isotopes are alpha emitters; each gives rise to a series of relatively short-lived daughter products, including three more alpha emitters. Because of the difference in half-lives of the nuclides in these series, the isotopes of radium can be identified by the rate of ingrowth and decay of their daughters in a barium sulfate precipitate.[1-3] The ingrowth of alpha activity from radium 226 increases at a rate governed primarily by the 3.8-day half-life of radon 222. The ingrowth of alpha activity in radium 223 is complete by the time a radium-barium precipitate can be prepared for counting. The ingrowths of the first two alpha-emitting daughters of radium 224 are complete within a few minutes and the third alpha daughter activity increases at a rate which is governed by the 10.6-hour lead 212. The activity of the radium 224 itself, with a 3.6-day half-life, is also decreasing, leading to a rather complicated ingrowth and decay curve.

The Federal Radiation Council has provided guidance for federal agencies conducting activities designed to limit exposure of people to radiation from radionuclides deposited in the body as a result of their occurrence in the environment. The recommended radiation protection guides (RPG) for radium 226 transient rates of intake are 0-2, 2-20 and 20-200 picocuries per person per day for the ranges I, II and III, respectively. Range III calls for the application of control measures to reduce the intake to within Range II or below.

Inasmuch as these guides apply to

total intake (from air, food and water), the Public Health Service Advisory Committee on the 1962 Drinking Water Standards recommended a limit of 3 pCi/l for radium 226. The standard specifies radium 226 in particular, because other radium isotopes are much less important in causing internal radiation exposure.

The principles of the two common methods for measuring radium are (a) the alpha-counting of a barium-radium sulfate precipitate which has been isolated from the sample and purified, and (b) the measurement of the radon 222 produced from the radium 226 in a sample or in a soluble concentrate isolated from the sample. The former technic includes all alpha-emitting radium isotopes present in the sample, whereas the latter (emanation) technic is quite, but not absolutely, specific for radium 226. At concentrations of total radium above the drinking water standard, the total alpha activity isolated by the precipitation technics requires further examination, such as a measurement of its rate of decay, to determine the radium 226 content. Preferably, the radium 226 content should be determined by the emanation technic, using either a new aliquot of the original sample or a solution of the barium-radium sulfate precipitate.

1. General Discussion

a. Principle: The following method is designed to measure radium in clear water. It is applicable to sewage and industrial wastes, provided that steps are taken to destroy organic matter and eliminate other interfering ions. (See Gross Alpha and Gross Beta Radioactivity, 302.4f.) However, ignition of sample ash should be avoided, or a fusion will be necessary. Radium carried by barium sulfate is determined by alpha-counting. Lead and barium carriers are added to the sample containing alkaline citrate, then sulfuric acid is added to precipitate radium, barium and lead as sulfates. The precipitate is purified by washing with nitric acid, dissolving in alkaline EDTA, and reprecipitating as radium-barium sulfate after adjusting the pH to 4.5. This slightly acidic EDTA keeps other naturally occurring alpha emitters and the lead carrier in solution.

2. Apparatus

a. COUNTING INSTRUMENTS—One of the following is required:

1) Internal proportional counter, gas-flow, with scaler and register.

2) Alpha scintillation counter, silver-activated zinc sulfide phosphor deposited on thin plastic (Mylar), with photomultiplier tube, scaler, timer and register; or

3) Proportional counter, thin end-window, gas-flow, with scaler and register.

b. MEMBRANE FILTER HOLDER, or stainless steel (or teflon) filter funnels (Tracerlab), with Fisher filtrator or an equivalent vacuum source.

c. MEMBRANE FILTERS (Millipore, type HAWP), or glass fiber filters.*

3. Reagents

a. Citric acid 1M: Dissolve 210 g citric acid, $H_3C_6H_5O_7 \cdot H_2O$, in distilled water and dilute to 1 liter.

b. Ammonium hydroxide, conc and 5*N:* The strength of old 5*N* ammonium hydroxide solution must be verified before use.

* No. 934-AH, diameter 2.4 cm, H. Reeve Angel and Co.

c. Lead nitrate carrier: Dissolve 160 g lead nitrate, $Pb(NO_3)_2$, in distilled water and dilute to 1 liter; 1 ml = 100 mg Pb.

d. Stock barium chloride solution: Dissolve 17.79 g barium chloride, $BaCl_2 \cdot 2H_2O$, in distilled water and dilute to 1 liter in a volumetric flask; 1 ml = 10 mg Ba.

e. Barium chloride carrier: To a 100-ml volumetric flask, add 20.00 ml of stock barium chloride solution using a transfer pipet, add distilled water to the mark, and mix; 1 ml = 2.00 mg Ba.

f. Methyl orange indicator solution: Dissolve 0.5 g methyl orange in 1 liter distilled water.

g. Phenolphthalein indicator solution: Dissolve 0.5 g phenolphthalein in 50 ml 95% ethyl alcohol, add 50 ml distilled water, and mix.

h. Bromcresol green indicator solution: Dissolve 0.1 g bromcresol green sodium salt in 100 ml distilled water.

i. Sulfuric acid, 18*N*.

j. Nitric acid, conc.

k. EDTA reagent, 0.25*M*: Add 93 g disodium ethylenediaminetetraacetate dihydrate to distilled water, dilute to 1 liter, and mix.

l. Acetic acid, conc.

m. Ethyl alcohol, 95%.

n. Acetone.

o. Lucite solution: Dissolve 50 mg Lucite in 100 ml acetone.

p. Standard radium 226 solution: Prepare as directed in method for radium 226 by radon 222, Section 305. 3d-f below, except that in ¶ f (standard radium 226 solution), add 0.50 ml of barium chloride stock solution (Section 305.3d, method for total radium) prior to adding the ^{226}Ra solution; 1 ml final standard radium solution so prepared contains 2.00 mg Ba per ml and approximately 3 pCi ^{226}Ra per ml after the necessary correcting factors are applied.

4. Procedure for Radium in Drinking Water and for Dissolved Radium

a. To 1 liter drinking water or filtered raw water in a 1,500-ml beaker, add 5 ml 1*M* citric acid, 2.5 ml conc NH_4OH, 2 ml lead nitrate carrier, and 3.00 ml barium chloride carrier. In each batch of samples include a blank consisting of distilled water.

b. Heat to boiling and add 10 drops methyl orange indicator.

c. While stirring, slowly add 18*N* H_2SO_4 to obtain a permanent pink color; then add 0.25 ml acid in excess.

d. Boil gently 5 to 10 min.

e. Set the beaker aside and let stand until the precipitate has settled (3 to 5 hr or more).*

f. Decant and discard the clear supernate. Transfer the precipitate to a 40-ml or larger centrifuge tube, centrifuge, decant, and discard the supernate.

g. Rinse the wall of the centrifuge tube with a 10-ml portion of conc HNO_3, stir precipitate with a glass rod, centrifuge, and discard supernate. Repeat the rinsing and washing two more times.

---

* If original concentrations of isotopes of radium other than ^{226}Ra are of interest, the date and time of this original precipitation should be noted as the separation of the isotopes from their parents; the settling time should be minimal; and the procedure should be completed through ¶ j without delay. Assuming the presence of and separation of parents, decay of ^{228}Ra and ^{224}Ra begins at the time of the first precipitation, but ingrowth of decay products is timed from the second precipitation (¶ i). The time of the first precipitation is not needed if the objective is to check the final precipitate for its ^{226}Ra content only.

h. To the precipitate in the centrifuge tube, add 10 ml water and 1 to 2 drops phenolphthalein indicator solution. Stir and loosen precipitate from bottom of tube (using a glass rod if necessary) and add 5*N* NH_4OH, dropwise, until the solution is definitely alkaline (red). Add 10 ml EDTA reagent and 3 ml 5*N* NH_4OH. Stir occasionally for 2 min. Most of the precipitate should dissolve, but a slight turbidity may remain.

i. Warm in a steam bath to clear solution (about 10 min), but do not heat for an unnecessarily long period.† Add conc acetic acid, dropwise, until the red color disappears; add 2 or 3 drops bromcresol green indicator solution and continue to add conc acetic acid dropwise, while stirring with a glass rod, until the indicator turns green (aqua).‡ Barium sulfate will precipitate. Note date and time of precipitation as zero time for ingrowth of alpha activity. Digest in a steam bath for 5 to 10 min, cool and centrifuge. Discard supernate. The final pH should be about 4.5, which is sufficiently low to destroy the Ba-EDTA complex, but not the Pb-EDTA. A pH much below 4.5 will cause the precipitation of $PbSO_4$.

j. Wash the Ba-Ra sulfate precipitate with distilled water and mount in a manner suitable for counting as given in ¶s k, l or m following.

k. Transfer the Ba-Ra sulfate precipitate to a tared stainless steel planchet with a minimum of 95% ethyl alcohol and evaporate under an infrared lamp. Add 2 ml acetone, 2 drops Lucite solution, disperse the precipitate evenly, and evaporate under an infrared lamp. Dry in oven at 110 C, weigh, and determine the alpha activity, preferably with an internal proportional counter. Calculate the net cpm and the weight of precipitate.

l. Weigh a membrane filter, a counting dish, and a weight (glass ring) as a unit. Transfer precipitate to the tared membrane filter in a holder and wash with 15–25 ml distilled water. Place membrane filter in the dish, add the glass ring, and dry at 110 C. Weigh and count in one of the counters mentioned under ¶ 2a above. Calculate net cpm and weight of the precipitate.

m. Add 20 ml distilled water to the Ba-Ra sulfate precipitate, allow to settle in a steam bath, cool, and filter using a special funnel * with a tared glass fiber filter. Dry the precipitate in the oven at 110 C to constant weight, cool and weigh. Mount the precipitate on a nylon disk and ring with an alpha phosphor on Mylar,[4] and count in an alpha scintillation counter without a ZnS phosphor. Calculate net cpm and weight of the precipitate.

n. If the isotopic composition of the precipitate is to be estimated, additional counting will be required, as mentioned in the calculation below.

o. Determination of combined efficiency and self-absorption factor: Prepare standards from 1 liter distilled water and the standard radium 226 solution (¶ 3p preceding). At least one blank should be included. The barium content will impose an upper limit of 3.0 ml on the volume of the standard

---

† If solution does not clear in 10 min, cool, add another ml of 5*N* NH_4OH, let stand 2 min, and heat for another 10-min period.

‡ The end point is most easily determined by comparison with a solution of similar composition which has been adjusted to pH 4.5 using a pH meter.

* Tracerlab stainless steel 2-piece funnel or equivalent.

radium 226 solution which can be used. If x is the ml of standard radium 226 solution added, then add $(3.00 - x)$ ml of barium chloride carrier (¶ 3e above). Analyze standards like samples beginning with ¶ 4a, but omitting the 3.00-ml barium chloride carrier.

From the observed net count rate, calculate the combined factor, bc, from the formula:

$$bc = \frac{\text{net cpm}}{ad \times 2.22 \times \text{pCi radium 226}} \dagger$$

If all chemical yields on samples and standards are not essentially equal, the factor bc will not be a constant. In this event, it will be necessary to construct a curve relating the factor bc to varying weights of recovered barium sulfate.

5. Calculation

$$\text{Radium, pCi/l} = \frac{\text{net cpm}}{a\ b\ c\ d\ e \times 2.22}$$

where

a = ingrowth factor (as shown in the following tabulation):

Ingrowth (hr)	Alpha Activity from ^{226}Ra
0	1.000
1	1.016
2	1.036
3	1.058
4	1.080
5	1.102
6	1.124
24	1.489
48	1.905
72	2.253

b = efficiency factor for alpha counting,
c = self-absorption factor,
d = chemical yield, and
e = sample volume in liters.

† See calculation which follows.

The calculations are based on the assumption that the radium is radium 226. If the observed concentration approaches 3 pCi/l, it may be desirable to follow the rate of ingrowth and estimate the isotopic content[2, 3] or, preferably, to determine radium 226 by radon 222.

The optimum ingrowth periods can be selected only if the ratios and identities of the radium isotopes are known. The number of observed count rates at different ages must be equal to or greater than the number of radium isotopes present in a mixture. In the general case, suitable ages for counting are 3 to 18 hr for the first count and, for isotopic analysis, additional counting at 7, 14 or 28 days is suggested, depending on the number of isotopes in mixture. The amounts of the various radium isotopes can be determined by solving a set of simultaneous equations.[4] This approach is most satisfactory when radium 226 is the predominant isotope; in other situations, the approach suffers on the basis of statistical counting errors.

6. Precision and Accuracy

In a collaborative study, 20 laboratories analyzed four water samples for total (dissolved) radium. The radionuclide composition of these reference samples is shown in Table 304(1). It should be noted that Samples C and D had a ^{224}Ra concentration equal to that of ^{226}Ra.

The four results from each of two laboratories and two results from a third laboratory were rejected as outliers. The average recoveries of radium 226 from the remaining A, B, C and D samples were 97.5, 98.7, 94.9 and 99.4%, respectively. At the 95%

TABLE 304(1): CHEMICAL AND RADIOCHEMICAL COMPOSITION OF SAMPLES USED TO DETERMINE ACCURACY AND PRECISION OF RADIUM 226 METHOD

Radionuclide Composition	Samples			
	Pair 1		Pair 2	
	A	B	C	D
Radium 226,* pCi/l	12.12	8.96	25.53	18.84
Thorium 228,* pCi/l	none	none	25.90	19.12
Uranium, natural, pCi/l	105	77.9	27.7	20.5
Lead 210,* pCi/l	11.5	8.5	23.7	17.5
Strontium 90,* pCi/l	49.1	36.3	13.9	10.2
Cesium 137, pCi/l	50.3	37.2	12.7	9.5
NaCl, mg/l	60	60	300	300
$CaSO_4$, mg/l	30	30	150	150
$MgCl_2 \cdot 6H_2O$, mg/l	30	30	150	150
KCl, mg/l	5	5	10	10

* Daughter products were in substantial secular equilibrium.

confidence level, the precision (random error) was 28% and 30% for the two sets of paired samples. The method is biased low for radium 226, but not seriously. The method appears satisfactory for radium 226 alone or in the presence of an equal activity of radium 224 when correction for radium 224 interference is made from a second count.

For the determination of ^{224}Ra in samples C and D, the results of two laboratories were excluded. Hence the average recoveries were 51 and 45% for samples C and D, respectively. At the 95% confidence level, the precision was 46% for this pair of samples. The results indicated that the method for ^{224}Ra is seriously biased low. When the recoveries for radium 224 did not agree with those for radium 226, a search revealed that this may have been due, in part, to incomplete instructions given in the method to account for the transitory nature of ^{224}Ra activity. The method now contains footnotes calling attention to the importance of the time of counting. Still uncertain is the degree of separation of radium 224 from its parent, thorium 228, in ¶s 4a through g above.

Radium 223 and ^{224}Ra analysis by this method may be satisfactory, but special refinements and further investigations are required.

7. References

1. H. W. KIRBY. 1954. Decay and growth tables for naturally occurring radioactive series. *Anal. Chem.* 26:1063.
2. C. SILL. 1960. Determination of radium-226, thorium-230, and thorium-232. *U. S. Atomic Energy Comm. Rep.* No. TID 7616 (Oct.). USAEC, Washington, D. C.
3. A. S. GOLDIN. 1961. Determination of dissolved radium. *Anal. Chem.* 33:406.
4. N. A. HALLDEN & J. H. HARLEY. 1960. An improved alpha-counting technique. *Anal. Chem.* 32:1961.

305 RADIUM 226 BY RADON IN WATER (SOLUBLE, SUSPENDED AND TOTAL)

1. General Discussion

a. Introduction: The discussion of radium, particularly in drinking water, presented in Section 304 preceding, is also pertinent to the determination of radium 226 by radon 222. In this method, *total* radium 226 means the sum of suspended and dissolved radium 226. Radon means radon 222 unless otherwise specified.

b. Principle: The radium in water is concentrated and separated from sample solids by coprecipitation with a relatively large amount of barium as the sulfate. The precipitate is treated to remove silicates, if present, and to decompose insoluble radium compounds, fumed with phosphoric acid to remove SO_3 and dissolved in HCl. The completely dissolved radium is placed in a bubbler, which is then closed and stored for a period of several days to 4 weeks for ingrowth of radon. The bubbler is connected to an evacuated system and the radon gas is removed from the liquid by aeration, dried with a desiccant, and collected in a counting chamber. The counting chamber consists of a dome-topped scintillation cell coated inside with silver-activated zinc sulfide phosphor; a transparent window forms thc bottom (Figure 51). The chamber rests on a photomultiplier tube during counting. About 4 hr after radon collection, the alpha-counting rate of radon and decay products is at equilibrium, and a count is obtained and related to radium 226 standards similarly treated.

The counting gas used to purge radon from the liquid to the counting chamber may be helium, nitrogen or air. The gas should be freed of radon by aging. Although all these gases are satisfactory, the yield and pulse heights of scintillations are improved if helium is used.

A variety of radium 226 by radon (emanation) technics are available. Some employ a minimum of chemistry, but require high dilution of the sample solution and large chambers for counting of the radon 222.[1] Others involve more chemical separation, concentration, and purification of radium 226

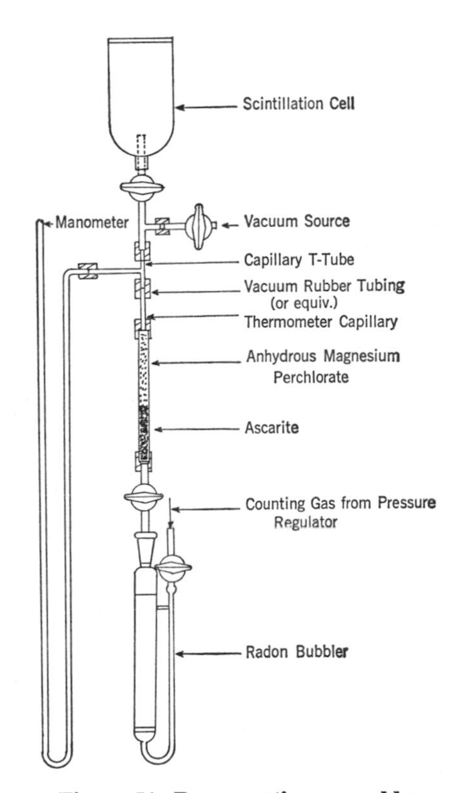

Figure 51. De-emanation assembly.

prior to de-emanation into counting cells of either the ionization or alpha scintillation types.

The selected method [2] requires a moderate amount of chemistry coupled with a sensitive alpha scintillation count of radon 222 plus daughter products in a small chamber.[3]

c. Concentration technics: The chemical properties of barium and radium are similar; therefore, because barium does not interfere with de-emanation, as much as 100 mg may be used to aid in coprecipitating radium from a sample, to be placed in a single radon bubbler. However, since some radium 226 is present in barium salts, reagent tests are necessary in order to account for radium 226 introduced in this way.

d. Interferences: Only the gaseous alpha-emitting radionuclides, radon 219 (actinon) and radon 220 (thoron), can interfere with the test. Interference from these radionuclides would be expected to be very rare in water not contaminated by industrial wastes, such as uranium mill effluents.[2] The half-lives of these nuclides are only 3.92 and 54.5 sec, respectively, so that it is only their alpha-emitting decay products which interfere.

Interference from stable chemicals is limited. Small amounts of lead, calcium and strontium, which are collected by the barium sulfate, do not interfere. However, lead may deteriorate the platinum ware. Calcium at a concentration of 300 mg/l and other dissolved solids (in brines) at 269,000 mg/l cause no difficulty.[4]

The formation of precipitates in excess of a few milligrams during the radon 222 ingrowth period is a warning that modifications [2] may be necessary because radon 222 recovery may be impaired.

e. Minimum detectable concentration: The minimum detectable concentration depends upon counter characteristics, background-counting rate of scintillation cell, length of counting period, and contamination of apparatus and environment by radium 226. Without reagent purification, the overall reagent blank (excluding background) should be between 0.03 and 0.05 pCi radium 226, which may be considered the minimum detectable amount under routine conditions.

2. Apparatus

a. Scintillation counter assembly, with a photomultiplier (PM) tube 2 in. or more in diameter, normally mounted, face up, in a light-tight housing: The photomultiplier tube, preamplifier, high-voltage supply, and scaler may be contained in one chassis; or the PM tube and the preamplifier may be used as an accessory with a proportional counter or a separate scaler. A high-voltage safety switch should open automatically when the light cover is removed, to avoid damage to the photomultiplier tube.

The preamplifier should incorporate a variable gain adjustment. The counter should be equipped with a flexible ground wire which is attached to the chassis and to the neck of the scintillation cell by means of an alligator clip or similar device. The operating voltage is ascertained by determining a plateau using ^{222}Rn in the scintillation cell as the alpha source. The slope of the plateau should not exceed 2% per hundred volts. The counter and scintillation cell should be calibrated and used as a unit when more than one counter is available. The background-counting rate for the counter assembly without the scintillation cell in place should be of the order of 0.00 to 0.03 cpm.

b. Scintillation cells,[2, 3] Lucas-type, preferably having a volume of 95–140 ml, made in the laboratory, or commercially available.*

c. Radon bubblers, capacity 18–25 ml, as shown in Figure 51.† The glass stopcocks must be gastight and the fritted glass disk must be the equivalent of Corning's medium porosity. One bubbler is used for a standard ^{226}Ra solution and one for each sample and blank in a batch.[2]

d. Manometer, open-end capillary tube or vacuum gauge having volume which is small compared to volume of scintillation cell, 0–760 mm Hg.

e. Gas purification tube, 7–8 mm O.D. standard-wall glass tubing, 100–120 mm long, constricted at lower end to hold glass wool plug (Figure 51); thermometer capillary tubing.

f. Sample bottles, polyethylene, 2- to 4-liter capacity.

g. Membrane filters.‡

h. Gas supply: Helium, nitrogen or air aged in high-pressure cylinder with two-stage pressure regulator and needle valve.

* William H. Johnston Laboratories, 3617 Woodland Ave., Baltimore, Maryland 21215.

† Available from Corning Glass Works, Special Sales Section, Corning, New York 14830.

‡ Type HAWP (Millipore Filter Corp., Bedford, Massachusetts), or equivalent.

i. Silicone grease, high-vacuum.

j. Sealing wax, "Pyseal" § (or equivalent), low-melting.

k. Laboratory glassware: Excepting bubblers, all glassware must be decontaminated before and between uses by heating for 1 hr in EDTA decontaminating solution at 90–100 C, then rinsed in water, 1*N* HCl, and again in distilled water to dissolve $Ba(Ra)SO_4$.

The removal of previous samples from bubblers and rinsing is described in Section 305.4b(17). More extensive cleaning of bubblers requires removal of the wax from joints, silicone grease from stopcocks, and the last traces of barium-radium compounds.

l. Platinum ware: Crucibles (20–30 ml) or dishes (50–75 ml), large dish (for flux preparation), and platinum-tipped tongs (preferably Blair type). Platinum ware is cleaned by immersion and rotation in a molten bath of potassium pyrosulfate, removing, cooling, rinsing in hot tap water, digesting in hot 6*N* HCl, rinsing in distilled water, and finally flaming over a burner.

3. Reagents

a. Stock barium chloride solution: Dissolve 17.79 g barium chloride, $BaCl_2 \cdot 2H_2O$, in distilled water and dilute to 1 liter; 1 ml = 10 mg Ba.

b. Dilute barium chloride solution: Dilute 200.0 ml stock barium chloride solution to 1,000 ml in a volumetric flask, as needed; 1 ml = 2.00 mg Ba. Allow to stand 24 hr and filter through a membrane filter.

Optionally, approximately 40,000

§ Available from Fisher Scientific Co., Pittsburgh, Pa.

dpm of ^{133}Ba may be added to this solution before dilution in the volumetric flask. Account must be taken of the stable barium carrier added with the ^{133}Ba and with the diluting solution, so that the final barium concentration is near 2 mg per ml. (The use of ^{133}Ba provides a convenient means of checking on the recovery of ^{226}Ra from the sample (Section 305.6). The $BaCl_2$ solution containing ^{133}Ba is used in Sections 305.4b(3), 4c(8) and 4d(3) and must be measured accurately from a pipet or buret. It is *not* used in ¶ d below; instead, a separate dilution of the stock barium chloride solution is used for preparing the ^{226}Ra standard solutions.

c. Acid barium chloride solution: To 20 ml conc HCl in a 1-liter volumetric flask, add dilute barium chloride solution to the mark and mix.

d. Stock radium 226 solution: Take every precaution to avoid unnecessary contamination of the working area, equipment and glassware, preferably by preparing the ^{226}Ra standards in a separate area or room reserved for this purpose. Obtain a National Bureau of Standards gamma ray standard containing 0.1 g ^{226}Ra as of the date of standardization. Using a heavy glass rod, cautiously break the neck of the ampul, which is submerged in 300 ml acid barium chloride solution in a 600-ml beaker. Chip the ampul until it is thoroughly broken or until the hole is large enough to obtain complete mixing. Transfer the solution to a 1-liter volumetric flask, rinse the beaker with acid barium chloride solution, dilute to the mark with the same solution, and mix; 1 ml = approximately 100 pg ^{226}Ra.

Determine the time in years since the NBS standardization of the original ^{226}Ra solution and multiply the time by 4.3×10^{-4}. Subtract the product from one; the resulting factor is multiplied by 100 pg per ml to correct the concentration of ^{226}Ra for decay. Multiply the last result by 0.990 ± 0.004 to convert pg ^{226}Ra to pCi ^{226}Ra.

e. Intermediate radium 226 solution: Add 100 ml stock radium 226 solution to a 1-liter volumetric flask and dilute to the mark with acid barium chloride solution; 1 ml = approximately 10 pCi ^{226}Ra.

f. Standard radium 226 solution: Add 30.0 ml intermediate radium 226 solution to a 100-ml volumetric flask and dilute to the mark with acid barium chloride solution; 1 ml = approximately 3 pCi ^{226}Ra and contains about 2 mg Ba. See ¶ d et seq above for correction factors.

g. Hydrochloric acid, conc, 6*N*, 1*N*, and 0.1*N*.

h. Sulfuric acid, conc and 0.1*N*.

i. Hydrofluoric acid, 48%, in a plastic dropping bottle. (CAUTION.)

j. Ammonium sulfate solution: Dissolve 10 g ammonium sulfate, $(NH_4)_2SO_4$, in distilled water and dilute to 100 ml in a graduated cylinder.

k. Phosphoric acid, 85%.

l. Ascarite, 8–20 mesh.

m. Magnesium perchlorate, anhydrous desiccant.

n. EDTA decontaminating solution: Dissolve 10 g disodium ethylenediaminetetraacetate dihydrate [also called (ethylenedinitrilo) tetraacetic acid sodium salt] and 10 g sodium carbonate in distilled water and dilute to 1 liter in a graduated cylinder.

o. Special reagents for total and suspended radium:

1) FLUX—Add 30 mg barium sulfate, $BaSO_4$, 65.8 g potassium carbonate, K_2CO_3, 50.5 g sodium carbonate, Na_2CO_3, and 33.7 g sodium tetraborate decahydrate, $Na_2B_4O_7 \cdot 10H_2O$, to a large platinum dish (500-ml capacity). Mix thoroughly and heat cautiously to expel water, then fuse and mix thoroughly by swirling. Cool the flux, grind in a porcelain mortar to pass a 10- to 12-mesh (or finer) screen, and store in an airtight bottle.

2) DILUTE HYDROGEN PEROXIDE SOLUTION—Dilute 10 ml 30% H_2O_2 to 100 ml in a graduated cylinder. Prepare daily.

4a. Calibration of Scintillation Counter Assembly

1) Test bubblers by placing about 10 ml distilled water in them and passing air through them at the rate of 3 to 5 ml (free volume) per min. Air should form many fine bubbles rather than a few large ones; the latter condition indicates nonuniform pores. Bubblers requiring excessive pressure to initiate bubbling should not be used. Corning's "medium-porosity" fritted-glass disks are usually satisfactory. Reject unsatisfactory bubblers.

2) Apply silicone grease to stopcocks of a bubbler and, with gas inlet stopcock closed, add 1 ml stock barium chloride solution, 10 ml (30 pCi) standard radium 226 solution, and fill the bubbler two-thirds to three-fourths full with additional acid barium chloride solution.

3) With the bubbler in a clamp or rack, dry the joint with lintfree paper or cloth, warm the separate parts of the joint, apply sealing wax sparingly to the male part of the joint, and make the connection with a twisting motion to spread the wax uniformly in the ground joint. Allow joint to cool. Establish zero ingrowth time by purging liquid with counting gas for 15–20 min according to ¶ 4a(10) below and adjusting inlet pressure to produce a froth a few mm thick. Close stopcocks, record date and time, and store bubbler, preferably for 3 weeks or more (with most samples) before collecting and counting the ^{222}Rn. A much shorter ingrowth period of 16 to 24 hr is convenient for a standard bubbler. An estimate of the ^{222}Rn present at any time may be obtained from the B columns in Table 305(1).

4) Attach scintillation cell as shown in Figure 51 *; substitute a glass tube with a stopcock for the bubbler so that the compressed gas can be turned on or off conveniently. Open stopcock on scintillation cell, close stopcock to gas, and gradually open stopcock to vacuum source to evacuate cell. Close stopcock to vacuum source and check manometer reading for 2 min to test system, especially the scintillation cell, for leaks.

5) Open stopcock to counting gas and cautiously admit gas to scintillation

* The system as described and shown in Figure 51 is considered minimal. In routine work, the use of manifold systems and additional, more precise needle valves is warranted. An occasional drop of solution will escape from the bubbler; there should be enough free space beyond the outlet stopcock to accommodate this liquid, thus preventing its entrance into the gas-purifying train.

TABLE 305(1): FACTORS FOR DECAY OF RADON 222, GROWTH OF RADON 222 FROM RADIUM 226, AND CORRECTION OF RADON 222 ACTIVITY FOR DECAY DURING COUNTING

Time	Factor for Decay of Radon 222		Factor for Growth of Radon 222 from Radium 226		Factor for Correction of Radon 222 Activity for Decay during Counting
	$A = e^{-\lambda t}$		$B = 1 - e^{-\lambda t}$		$C = \lambda t/(1-e^{-\lambda t})$
	Hours	Days	Hours	Days	Hours
0.0	1.0000		0.000 00		1.000
0.2	0.9985		0.001 51		1.001
0.4	0.9970		0.003 01		1.001
0.6	0.9955		0.004 52		1.002
0.8	0.9940		0.006 02		1.003
1	0.9925	0.8343	0.007 52	0.1657	1.004
2	0.9850	0.6960	0.014 99	0.3040	1.008
3	0.9776	0.5807	0.022 40	0.4193	1.011
4	0.9703	0.4844	0.029 75	0.5156	1.015
5	0.9630	0.4041	0.037 05	0.5959	1.019
6	0.9557	0.3372	0.044 29	0.6628	1.023
7	0.9485	0.2813	0.051 48	0.7187	1.027
8	0.9414	0.2347	0.058 61	0.7653	1.031
9	0.9343	0.1958	0.065 69	0.8042	1.034
10	0.9273	0.1633	0.072 72	0.8367	1.038
11	0.9203	0.1363	0.079 69	0.8637	1.042
12	0.9134	0.1137	0.086 62	0.8863	1.046
13	0.9065	0.0948	0.093 49	0.9052	1.050
14	0.8997	0.0791	0.100 31	0.9209	1.054
15	0.8929	0.0660	0.107 07	0.9340	1.058
16	0.8862	0.0551	0.1138	0.9449	1.062
17	0.8795	0.0459	0.1205	0.9541	1.066
18	0.8729	0.0383	0.1271	0.9617	1.069
19	0.8664	0.0320	0.1336	0.9680	1.073
20	0.8598	0.0267	0.1402	0.9733	1.077
21	0.8534	0.0223	0.1466	0.9777	1.081
22	0.8470	0.0186	0.1530	0.9814	1.085
23	0.8406	0.0155	0.1594	0.9845	1.089
24	0.8343	0.0129	0.1657	0.9871	1.093
25	0.8280	0.0108	0.1720	0.9892	1.097

TABLE 305(1): FACTORS FOR DECAY OF RADON 222, GROWTH OF RADON 222 FROM RADIUM 226, AND CORRECTION OF RADON 222 ACTIVITY FOR DECAY DURING COUNTING—*Continued*

Time	Factor for Decay of Radon 222		Factor for Growth of Radon 222 from Radium 226		Factor for Correction of Radon 222 Activity for Decay during Counting
	$A = e^{-\lambda t}$		$B = 1 - e^{-\lambda t}$		$C = \lambda t/(1-e^{-\lambda t})$
	Hours	Days	Hours	Days	Hours
26	0.8218	0.0090	0.1782	0.9910	1.101
27	0.8156	0.0075	0.1844	0.9925	1.105
28	0.8095	0.0063	0.1905	0.9937	1.109
29	0.8034	0.0052	0.1966	0.9948	1.113
30	0.7973	0.0044	0.2027	0.9956	1.118
31	0.7913	0.0036	0.2087	0.9964	1.122
32	0.7854	0.0030	0.2146	0.9970	1.126
33	0.7795	0.0025	0.2205	0.9975	1.130
34	0.7736	0.0021	0.2264	0.9979	1.134
35	0.7678	0.0018	0.2322	0.9982	1.138
36	0.7620	0.0015	0.2380	0.9985	1.142
37	0.7563	0.0012	0.2437	0.9988	1.146
38	0.7506	0.0010	0.2494	0.9990	1.150
39	0.7449	0.0009	0.2551	0.9991	1.154
40	0.7393	0.0007	0.2607	0.9993	1.159
41	0.7338	0.0006	0.2662	0.9994	1.163
42	0.7283	0.0005	0.2717	0.9995	1.167
43	0.7228	0.0004	0.2772	0.9996	1.171
44	0.7173	0.0003	0.2827	0.9997	1.175
45	0.7120	0.0003	0.2880	0.9997	1.179
46	0.7066	0.0002	0.2934	0.9998	1.184
47	0.7013	0.0002	0.2987	0.9998	1.188
48	0.6960	0.0002	0.3040	0.9998	1.192
49	0.6908	0.0001	0.3092	0.9999	1.196
50	0.6856	0.0001	0.3144	0.9999	1.201
51	0.6804	0.0001	0.3196	0.9999	1.205
52	0.6753	0.0001	0.3247	0.9999	1.209
53	0.6702	0.0001	0.3298	0.9999	1.213
54	0.6652	0.0001	0.3348	0.9999	1.218
55	0.6602	0.0000	0.3398	1.0000	1.222
56	0.6552	0.0000	0.3448	1.0000	1.226
57	0.6503	0.0000	0.3497	1.0000	1.231
58	0.6454	0.0000	0.3546	1.0000	1.235
59	0.6405	0.0000	0.3595	1.0000	1.239
60	0.6357	0.0000	0.3643	1.0000	1.244

cell until atmospheric pressure is reached.

6) Center scintillation cell on photomultiplier tube, cover with light-tight hood and, after 10 min, obtain a background counting rate (preferably over a 100- to 1,000-min period, depending on concentration of ^{226}Ra in unknown samples). *Phototube must not be exposed to external light with the high voltage applied.*

7) Repeat steps (4)–(6) above for each scintillation cell.

8) If the leakage test and background are satisfactory, continue calibration.

9) With scintillation cell and standard bubbler [¶ 4a(3)] on vacuum train, open stopcock on scintillation cell and evacuate scintillation cell and purification system (Figure 51) by opening the stopcock to vacuum source. Close stopcock to vacuum source. Check system for leaks as in step (4) above.

10) Adjust gas regulator (diaphragm) valve so that a very slow stream of gas will flow with the needle valve open. Attach gas supply to inlet of bubbler.

11) Note time as beginning of approximately a 20-min de-emanation period. Very cautiously open bubbler outlet stopcock to equalize pressure and transfer all or most of the fluid in the inlet side arm to the bubbler chamber.

12) Close outlet stopcock and very cautiously open inlet stopcock to flush remaining fluid from side arm and fritted disk. Close inlet stopcock.

13) Repeat steps (11) and (12) above, four or five times, to obtain more nearly equal pressures on the two sides of the bubbler.

14) With outlet stopcock fully open, cautiously open inlet stopcock so that the flow of gas produces a froth a few mm thick at the surface of bubbler solution. Maintain flow rate by gradually increasing pressure with regulator valve and continue de-emanation until the pressure in the cell reaches atmospheric pressure. The total elapsed time for the de-emanation should be 15 to 25 min.

15) Close stopcocks to scintillation cell, close bubbler inlet and outlet, shut off and disconnect gas supply, and record the date and time as the ends of the ^{222}Rn ingrowth and de-emanation periods and as the beginnings of decay of ^{222}Rn and ingrowth of decay products.

16) Store the bubbler for another ^{222}Rn ingrowth in the event a subsequent de-emanation is desired [Table 305(1)]. The standard bubbler may be kept indefinitely.

17) Four hours after de-emanation, when daughter products are in virtual transient equilibrium with ^{222}Rn, place scintillation cell on photomultiplier tube, cover with light-tight hood, let stand for at least 10 min, then begin counting. Record date and time counting was started and finished.

18) Correct the net counting rate for ^{222}Rn decay [Table 305(1)] and relate it to the pCi of ^{226}Ra in standard bubbler [see Section 305.5(1)]. Unless the scintillation cell is physically damaged, the calibration will remain essentially unchanged for years. Occasional calibration is recommended.

19) Repeat steps (8) through (18) above on each scintillation cell.

20) To remove ^{222}Rn and prepare scintillation cell for reuse, evacuate and cautiously refill with the counting gas. Routinely, repeat evacuation and refilling twice, and repeat process more times if the cells have contained a high activity of ^{222}Rn. (Decay products with a half-life of approximately 30 min will remain in the cell. Background on cells should not be checked until the activity of decay products has had time to decay to insignificance.)

4b. Procedure for Soluble Radium 226

1) Using a membrane filter, filter at least 1 liter of sample or a volume containing up to 30 pCi ^{226}Ra and transfer to a polyethylene bottle as soon after sampling as possible. Save the suspended matter for determination by the procedure described in Section 305.4c immediately following. Record volume of sample actually filtered if suspended solids are to be analyzed as in the procedure for ^{226}Ra in suspended matter.

2) Add 20 ml conc HCl per liter of filtrate and continue analysis when convenient.

3) Add 50 ml dilute barium chloride solution, with vigorous stirring, to 1,020 ml of acidified filtrate [Section 305.4b(2) preceding] in a 1,500-ml beaker. In each batch of samples include a reagent blank consisting of distilled water plus 20 ml conc HCl.

4) Cautiously, with vigorous stirring, add 20 ml conc H_2SO_4. Cover beaker and allow overnight precipitation.

5) Filter supernate through a membrane filter, using 0.1*N* H_2SO_4 to transfer Ba-Ra precipitate to filter, and wash precipitate twice with 0.1*N* H_2SO_4.

6) Place filter with precipitate in a platinum crucible or dish, add 0.5 ml HF and 3 drops (0.15 ml) ammonium sulfate solution, and evaporate to dryness.

7) Carefully ignite filter and residue over a small flame until carbon is burned off; cool. (After charring filter, a Meker burner may be used.)

8) Add 1 ml H_3PO_4 with a calibrated dropper and heat on hot plate at about 200 C. Gradually raise temperature and maintain it at about 300–400 C for 30 min.

9) Swirl vessel over a low Bunsen flame, adjusted to avoid spattering, while covering the walls with hot H_3PO_4. Continue to heat for a minute after precipitate fuses into a clear melt (just below redness) to insure complete removal of SO_3.

10) Fill cooled vessel one-half full with 6*N* HCl, heat on steam bath, then gradually add distilled water to within 2 mm of the top of the vessel.

11) Evaporate on boiling steam bath until there are no more vapors of HCl.

12) Add 6 ml 1*N* HCl, swirl, and warm to dissolve $BaCl_2$ crystals.

13) Close gas inlet stopcock, add a drop of water to the fritted disk of the fully greased and tested radon bubbler, and transfer sample from platinum vessel to bubbler by means of a medicine dropper. Use dropper to rinse the vessel with at least three 2-ml portions of distilled water. Add distilled water until bubbler is two-thirds to three-fourths full.

14) Dry, wax if necessary, and seal the joint. Establish zero ingrowth time as instructed in Section 305.4a(3) preceding.

15) Close stopcocks, record date and time, and store bubbler for ^{222}Rn ingrowth, preferably for 3 weeks for low concentrations of radium 226.

16) De-emanate and count ^{222}Rn as instructed for calibrations in ¶s 4a (9) through (18), with unknown sample replacing the standard bubbler.

17) The sample in the bubbler may

be stored for a second ingrowth or discarded and the bubbler cleaned for reuse. [A bubbler is readily cleaned while in an inverted position by attaching a tube from a beaker containing 100 ml 0.1*N* HCl to the inlet and attaching another tube from outlet to a suction flask. By alternately opening and closing outlet and inlet stopcocks, the acid rinse water is sequentially passed through the fritted disk, accumulated in the bubbler, and flushed into the suction flask. Drain bubbler with the aid of vacuum, heat the ground joint gently to melt the wax, and separate the joint. More extensive cleaning, as indicated in Section 305.2k above, may be necessary if the bubbler contained more than 10 pCi ^{226}Ra.]

4c. Procedure for Radium 226 in Suspended Matter

1) Suspended matter in water usually contains siliceous materials which require fusion with an alkaline flux to insure recovery of radium. The suspended matter of the sample (up to 1,000 mg of inorganic material) retained on the membrane filter specified in ¶4b(1) above from a known volume of water is dried in a tared platinum crucible and ignited as in ¶4b(7).

2) Weigh crucible to estimate residue.

3) Add 8 g flux for each gram of residue, but not less than 2 g flux, and mix with a glass rod.

4) Heat over a Meker burner until melting begins, being careful to prevent spattering. Continue heating for 20 min after bubbling stops, with an occasional swirl of the crucible to mix the contents and achieve a uniform melt. A clear melt is usually obtained only when the suspended solids are present in small amount or have a high silica content.

5) Remove crucible from burner and rotate as melt cools to distribute it in a thin layer on crucible wall.

6) When cool, place crucible in a covered beaker containing 120 ml distilled water, 20 ml conc H_2SO_4, and 5 ml dilute H_2O_2 solution for each 8 g of flux. (Reduce acid and H_2O_2 in proportion to flux used.) Rotate crucible to dissolve melt if necessary.

7) When melt is dissolved, remove and rinse crucible into beaker. Save crucible for step (10) below.

8) Heat solution and slowly add 50 ml dilute $BaCl_2$ solution with vigorous stirring. Cover beaker and let stand overnight for precipitation. (Precipitation with cool sample solution is also satisfactory.)

9) Add about 1 ml dilute H_2O_2 and, if yellow color (from titanium) deepens, add additional H_2O_2 until there is no further color change.

10) Continue analysis according to Section 305.4b(5) through (16).

11) Calculate result as directed in Section 305.5(1) and (2), taking into account that the suspended solids possibly were contained in a sample volume of other than 1 liter of sample [see Section 305.4b(1)].

4d. Procedure for Total Radium 226

1) Total ^{226}Ra in water is the sum of soluble and suspended ^{226}Ra as determined in Sections 4b and 4c preceding, or it may be determined directly by examining the original water sample which has been acidified with 20 ml conc HCl for each liter of sample and stored in a polyethylene bottle.

2) Thoroughly mix the acidified sample and take 1,020 ml or a measured volume containing not more than 1,000 mg inorganic suspended solids.

3) Add 50 ml dilute $BaCl_2$ solution and slowly, with vigorous stirring, add 20 ml conc H_2SO_4 per liter of sample. Cover and allow to precipitate overnight.

4) Filter supernate through membrane filter and transfer solids to filter as in ¶ 4b(5) preceding.

5) Place filter and precipitate in tared platinum crucible and proceed as in ¶s 4c(2) through (10) above but with the following changes in the procedure given in ¶ 4c(8): Omit the addition of dilute $BaCl_2$ solution, digest for 1 hr on a steam bath, and filter immediately after digestion without stirring up $BaSO_4$. (If these changes are not made, filtration will be very slow.)

6) Calculate total radium 226 concentration as directed in Sections 305.5 (1) and (2) immediately following.

5. Calculations

1) The ^{226}Ra in a bubbler, including reagent blank, is calculated as follows:

$$^{226}\text{Ra in pCi} = \frac{R_s - R_b}{R_c} \times \frac{1}{1-e^{-\lambda t_1}} \times \frac{1}{e^{-\lambda t_2}} \times \frac{\lambda t_3}{1-e^{-\lambda t_3}}$$

where

λ = decay constant for ^{222}Rn 0.0755/hr;
t_1 = time interval allowed for ingrowth of ^{222}Rn, in hours;
t_2 = time interval between de-emanation and counting, in hours;
t_3 = time interval of counting, in hours;
R_s = observed counting rate of sample in scintillation cell, counts per hour;
R_b = (previously) observed background counting rate of scintillation cell with counting gas, counts per hour;
R_c = calibration constant for scintillation cell (i.e., observed net counts per hour, corrected by use of ingrowth and decay factors (C/AB from below) per picocurie of Ra in standard);

or:

$$\text{Ra in pCi} = \frac{(R_s - R_b)}{R_c} \times \frac{C}{AB}$$

where

A = factor for decay of ^{222}Rn [see Table 305(1)];
B = factor for growth of ^{222}Rn from ^{226}Ra [see Table 305(1); and
C = factor for correction of ^{222}Rn activity for decay during counting [see Table 305(1)].

For nontabulated times, decay factors for ^{222}Rn are obtained by multiplying together the appropriate tabulated "day" and "hour" decay factors, interpolating for less than 0.2 hr if indicated by the precision desired. Radon 222 growth factors for nontabulated times are obtained most accurately, especially for short periods (e.g., in calibrations), by calculation from ^{222}Rn decay factors given in Column A and using formula given in heading for Column B [of Table 305(1)]. Linear interpolations are satisfactory for routine samples. The decay-during-counting factors are obtained by linear interpolation for all nontabulated times.

In calculating cell calibration constants, the same equation is used, but the pCi of ^{226}Ra is known and R_c is the unknown.

2) Convert the activity into pCi/l of soluble, suspended or total ^{226}Ra by the following equation:

$$^{226}\text{Ra, pCi/l} = \frac{(D - E) \times 1{,}000}{\text{ml sample}}$$

where

D = pCi ^{226}Ra found in sample and
E = pCi ^{226}Ra found in reagent blank.

6. Recovery of Barium (Radium 226) (Optional)

If ^{133}Ba was added in reagent *b,* the recovery of Ba can be checked by removing the solution of sample from the bubbler, adjusting its volume appropriately, gamma-counting it under standardized conditions, and comparing the result with the count obtained from a 50-ml aliquot (evaporated if necessary to reduce volume) of the dilute barium solution also counted under standardized conditions; 1 ml H_3PO_4 should be added to the latter aliquot before counting. The assumption that the Ba and ^{226}Ra are recovered to the same extent is valid in the method described.

It should be noted that ^{226}Ra and its decay products interfere slightly even if a gamma spectrometer is used. The technic works best when the ratio of ^{133}Ba to ^{226}Ra is high.

Determinations of recovery are particularly helpful with irreplaceable samples, both in gaining experience with the method and in applying the general method to unfamiliar media.

7. Precision and Accuracy

In a collaborative study, seven laboratories analyzed four water samples for dissolved radium 226 using the method. No result was rejected as an outlier. The average recoveries of added radium 226 from samples A, B, C and D (below) were 97.1, 97.3, 97.6 and 98.0%, respectively. At the 95% confidence level, the precision (random error) was 6% and 8% for the two sets of paired samples. Because of the small number of participating laboratories and the low values for random and total errors, there was no evidence of laboratory systematic errors. Neither radium 224 at an activity equal to that of the radium 226 nor dissolved solids up to 610 mg per liter produced a detectable error in the results.

Test samples consisted of two pairs of simulated moderately hard and hard water samples containing known amounts of added radium 226 and other radionuclides. The composition of the samples with respect to nonradioactive substances was the same for a pair of samples but varied for the two pairs. The radiochemical composition of the samples is given in Table 304(1).

8. References

1. J. B. HURSH. 1954. Radium-226 in water supplies of the U. S. *JAWWA* 46:43.
2. D. E. RUSHING, W. J. GARCIA & D. A. CLARK. 1964. The analysis of effluents and environmental samples from uranium mills and of biological samples for radium, polonium, and uranium. In *Radiological Health and Safety in Mining and Milling of Nuclear Materials.* International Atomic Energy Agency, Vienna, Austria, Vol. II, page 187.
3. H. F. LUCAS. 1957. Improved low-level alpha scintillation counter for radon. *Rev. Sci. Instr.* 28:680.
4. D. E. RUSHING. 1967. Determination of dissolved radium-226 in water. *JAWWA* 59:593.

306 TRITIUM IN WATER *

The Association appreciates the permission granted to publish a revision of the method adopted by the Food and Agriculture Organization, the International Atomic Energy Agency, the World Health Organization, and the Association of Official Analytical Chemists.

1. Discussion

Tritium exists fairly uniformly in the environment as a result of natural production by cosmic radiation[3] and residual fallout from nuclear weapons tests. This background level is gradually being increased by the use of nuclear reactors to generate electricity. Current tritium from the nuclear power industry comprises a small proportion of environmental tritium in comparison with that from nuclear weapons fallout and naturally produced tritium. Nuclear reactors and fuel-processing plants do, however, provide localized sources of tritium as a result of discharges during normal operation. This industry is expected to become the major source of environmental tritium contamination some time after the year 2000 if present growth trends continue and nuclear explosions in the atmosphere are not resumed. Tritium is produced in light-water nuclear reactors by ternary fission, neutron capture in coolant additives, control rods and plates, and activation of deuterium.[4] About 1% of the tritium in the primary coolant is released in gaseous form to the atmosphere[5]; the remainder is eventually released in liquid waste discharges.[6] Most of the tritium produced in reactors remains in the fuel and is released when the fuel is reprocessed.

Naturally occurring tritium is most abundant in precipitation such as rain and lowest in aged water due to its physical decay by beta emission to helium. The maximum beta energy of tritium is 0.018 MeV and its half-life is 12.26 years.

a. Exposure criteria: The guidance given by both the NCRP[7] and the ICRP[8] on the maximum permissible concentrations of tritium in water for an individual in the general population sets a level of 3 microcuries per liter or, for the average of a suitable sample of the population, 1 microcurie (1,000 nanocuries) per liter.

b. Principle: A sample of water or waste is distilled to remove quenching materials and nonvolatile radioactivity. Complete transfer of tritiated water is assured by distillation to dryness. A subsample of distillate is mixed with scintillation solution and the beta activity is counted on a coincidence-type liquid scintillation spectrometer. The scintillation solution consists of 1,4-dioxane, naphthalene, POPOP † and PPO.[9] The spectrometer is calibrated with standard solutions of tritiated water and background and unknown samples are prepared and counted alternately, thus nullifying errors which could result from instrument drift or from the aging of scintillation solution.

* This method is recommended by the Food and Agriculture Organization, the International Atomic Energy Agency and the World Health Organization[1]; collaboratively tested by a committee and adopted as Official First Action by the Association of Official Analytical Chemists[2]; and revised to conform to APHA format.

† POPOP = 1,4-di-2-(5-phenyloxazolyl) benzene; PPO = (2,5-diphenyloxazole).

c. Interferences: Distillation of natural waters is effective in removing nonvolatile radioactivity and the usual quenching materials. For waters containing volatile organic or radioactive materials, additional precautions and measures are necessary. Steps should be taken to remove interference from quenching due to volatile organic material, by wet oxidation (Section 215) or by alkaline permanganate distillation (Albuminoid Nitrogen, Section 131). Distillation at a pH about 8.5 may be required to hold back volatile radionuclides such as iodides and bicarbonates. Double distillation with an appropriate delay (10 half-lives) between distillations may be required to circumvent interference from the volatile daughters of radium isotopes. Some clear-water samples collected in the vicinity of nuclear facilities may be satisfactorily monitored for tritium without distillation, especially when the monitoring instrument is capable of discriminating against beta radiation energies higher than those in the tritium range.

2. Apparatus

a. Liquid scintillation spectrometer, coincidence-type.*

b. Liquid scintillation vial: 20-ml; low-K glass, polyethylene, nylon, or equivalent bottles, available from manufacturers of liquid scintillation spectrometers.

3. Reagents

a. Scintillation solution: Thoroughly mix 4 g PPO (2,5-diphenyloxazole), 0.05 g POPOP [1,4-di-2-(5-phenyloxazolyl) benzene], and 120 g solid naphthalene in 1 liter spectroquality 1,4-dioxane (available from manufacturers of liquid scintillation spectrometers). Store in dark bottles. Solution is stable for 2 months.

b. Standard solution of tritium: Pipet 4 ml H_2O of known ^3H activity and 16 ml scintillation solution into scintillation vial, cover vial tightly with screw cap, and mix thoroughly by shaking.

c. Background solution: Mix 4 ml distilled H_2O (free of ^3H activity to be measured in samples) with 16 ml scintillation solution as in paragraph preceding.

4. Procedure

a. Distill 20–30 ml sample to near dryness. Mix 4 ml sample distillate with 16 ml reagent (¶ 3a above) in vial with stopper.

b. Dilute known quantities of tritium standard solution to 4 ml with background water in vials and mix with 16 ml of reagent (¶ 3a above).

c. Keep samples in the dark until the counting rate is constant (within the counting error). Dark adaptation requires about 3 hr unless the samples have been exposed to sunlight. When using a freezer unit, cool all vials from steps *a* and *b* preceding to a temperature of about 4 C. When using an ambient-temperature liquid scintillation spectrometer, dark-adapt all vials

---

* Various manufacturers have one or more models of liquid scintillation spectrometers with features of merit, depending on specific needs—for example, Beckman Instruments, Inc., 2400 Harbor Boulevard, Fullerton, California 92634; Nuclear-Chicago Corporation, 333 East Howard Avenue, Des Plaines, Illinois 60018; Packard Instrument Co., 2200 Warrenville Road, Downers Grove, Illinois 60515; and others.

from steps *a* and *b* for about 3 hr at ambient temperature. Count samples and standards.

5. Calculations and Reporting

a. Calculate and report the tritium, ^3H, in picocuries per milliliter (pCi/ml) or its equivalent, nanocuries per liter (nCi/l) based on the formula:

$$^3H = (C - B)/(E \times 4 \times 2.22)$$

where

$(S - B)/D$ = counting efficiency, E,
B = cpm rate for background count,
$C - B$ = net cpm for sample,
$S - B$ = net cpm for standard solution, and
D = disintegrations per minute (dpm) of tritium activity in standard sample.

b. Calculate the counting error of the sample at the 95% confidence level based on equation 5, Section 300F (Statistics). A total count of 40,000 within 1 hr for a background count of about 50 cpm gives a counting error slightly in excess of 1% at the 95% confidence level.

6. Precision and Accuracy

In a collaborative study,[2] 12 samples of tap water containing tritium additions, a stock standard solution of tritium, and a background sample of tap water were supplied to seven collaborators, who reported results from the use of the above method. Two subsamples each of six stock preparations to which had been added, respectively, 1.2, 2.9, 6.8, 17.1, 42.9 and 115.8 nCi tritium per liter were furnished each collaborator. The theoretical minimum detectable activity was 0.2 to 0.5 pCi/ml based on a 99% confidence level with a 100-min counting time over a range of background counts from 9 to 67 cpm. However, the result for a practical detectable limit is about 1 to 2 pCi/ml, since the sample containing 1.2 pCi tritium per ml varied from 0 to 4.8 pCi/ml. Over the concentration range 2.9 to 116 pCi/ml, the minimum, maximum and average recovery of tritium for the seven sets of samples are given in the following tabulation:

Tritium Taken (pCi/ml)	Recovery of Added Tritium		
	Minimum %	Maximum %	Average %
2.9	72	224	109
6.8	63	117	99
17.1	64	108	93
42.9	91	107	99
115.6	92	104	96
2.9	86	110	98[a]
6.8	89	117	101[b]
17.1	92	108	96[c]

[a] = four outlier results omitted.
[b] = one outlier result omitted.
[c] = two outlier results omitted.

At the 2.9 nCi/l level, which is roughly 0.1% of the maximum permissible concentration in water for an individual of the population, the test, based on all results, is not very precise. When outlier results are omitted,[10] the method produces satisfactory results, particularly from a public health standpoint.

7. References

1. FAO, IAEA & WHO. 1966. Methods of radiochemical analysis. World Health Organization, Geneva.
2. V. J. SODD & K. L. SCHOLZ. 1969. Analysis of tritium in water; a collaborative study. *JAOAC* 52:1.

3. W. F. LIBBY. 1946. Atmospheric helium-3 and radiocarbon from cosmic radiation. *Phys. Rev.* 69:671.
4. H. T. J. PETERSON, J. E. MARTIN, C. L. WEAVER & E. D. HARWARD. 1969. Environmental tritium contamination from increasing utilization of nuclear energy sources. Presented at the Seminar on Agricultural and Public Health Aspects of Environmental Contamination by Radioactive Materials, IAEA, Vienna, Austria, March 24–28, 1969. (Scheduled for publication in the *Proceedings* of the Seminar by the IAEA.)
5. J. M. SMITH. 1967. The significance of tritium in water reactors. General Electric Co., San Jose, Calif. (Sept. 19).
6. C. L. WEAVER, E. D. HARWARD & H. T. PETERSON. 1969. Tritium in the environment from nuclear power plants. *Pub. Health Rep.* 84,4:363.
7. NATIONAL COUNCIL ON RADIATION PROTECTION, Subcommittee on Permissible Internal Dose. 1959. Maximum permissible body burdens and maximum permissible concentrations of radionuclides in air and in water for occupational exposure. NBS Handbook 69 (June). National Bureau of Standards, Washington, D. C.
8. INTERNATIONAL COMMISSION ON RADIATION PROTECTION. 1960. Report of Committee II on Permissible Dose for Internal Radiation, 1959. *Health Physics* 3:41 (June).
9. F. E. BUTLER. 1961. Determination of tritium in water and urine. *Anal. Chem.* 33:409.
10. W. J. YOUDEN. 1967. Statistical techniques for collaborative tests. AOAC, Box 540, Benjamin Franklin Sta., Washington, D. C. 20044.

PART 400

BACTERIOLOGICAL EXAMINATION OF WATER TO DETERMINE ITS SANITARY QUALITY

400 INTRODUCTION

The following sections describe the procedures to be employed in making bacteriologic examinations of samples of water to determine sanitary quality and suitability for general use. The methods are intended to indicate the degree of contamination of the water with wastes from human or animal sources. They are the best currently available technics; however, their limitations must be thoroughly understood.

Traditionally, use has been made of tests for the detection and enumeration of indicator organisms rather than of pathogens. The coliform group of bacteria, as herein defined below, has been the principal indicator of the suitability of a particular water for domestic, dietetic or other uses. The cultural reactions and characteristics of this group of bacteria have been studied extensively and can be found described in many texts on bacteriology, particularly on the bacteriology of water and sanitation.

Experience has established the significance of coliform group densities as criteria of the degree of pollution and thus of the sanitary quality of the sample under examination. Developments in bacteriologic technics and culture media have increased the sensitivity of the historically older multiple-tube fermentation test, resulting in acceptance of this test as a standard method. The significance of the tests and the interpretations of the results are well authenticated and have been used as a basis for standards of bacteriologic quality of water supplies.

The membrane filter technic, which provides a direct plating for the detection and estimation of coliform densities, is an equally effective but newer method for the detection of bacteria of the coliform group. Modification of the details of this method, particularly of the culture medium, has made the results of this test comparable with those given by the multiple-tube fermentation procedure. Although there are limitations in the application of the membrane filter technic for the examination of all types of water, it can, when used with strict adherence to these limitations and to the specified technical details, be considered a method equivalent to the multiple-tube fermentation procedure. It is presented as an additional standard method for the detection of bacteria of the coliform group.

It has become the custom to report the results of the coliform test by the multiple-tube fermentation procedure as a Most Probable Number (MPN) index. It should be realized that this is merely an index of the number of coliform bacteria which, more probably than any other number, would give the results shown by the laboratory examination. It is not an actual enumeration of the coliform bacteria. By contrast, direct plating methods such as the membrane filter procedure permit a direct count of coliform colonies. In both procedures coliform density is reported conventionally as the MPN or membrane filter count per 100 milliliters. Either procedure may serve as a valuable tool for appraising the sanitary quality of water and the effectiveness of treatment processes.

Increasing attention to the potential value of fecal streptococci as indicators of significant pollution of water has prompted the inclusion of methods for the detection and enumeration of such microorganisms. Improvements in the technical details of these procedures, based on current research, have been incorporated. A tentative pour plate method has been added to the standard multiple-tube and membrane filter methods previously described.

Past editions of this volume have not given additional standard methods for the differentiation of that segment of the coliform group designated as fecal coliforms. Such differentiation has in the past been considered of limited value in assessing the quality of water for human consumption because the presence of either type of coliform bacteria renders the water potentially unsatisfactory and unsafe. Recent investigations strongly indicate that the portion of the coliform group which is present in the gut and feces of warm-blooded animals generally includes organisms which are capable of producing gas from lactose in a suitable culture medium at 44.5 ± 0.2 C. Inasmuch as coliform organisms from other sources cannot generally produce gas under these conditions, this criterion may be used to define the fecal component of the coliform group. Both the multiple-tube dilution technic and the membrane filter procedure have been modified to incorporate incubation in confirmatory tests at 44.5 C in order to provide estimates of the density of fecal organisms, as defined. The investigations cited suggest that this differentiation will yield valuable information concerning the possible source of pollution in water, and especially the remoteness of this pollution, inasmuch as the *nonfecal* members of the coliform group may be expected to survive longer than the *fecal* members in the unfavorable environment provided by the water.

Methods for determination of the standard plate count in water are retained as optional procedures because experience indicates that an approximate enumeration of total numbers of bacteria multiplying at temperatures of 35 C and 20 C may yield useful information about the quality of the water and may provide supporting data on the significance of coliform test results. The Standard Plate Count is useful in judging the efficiency in operation of various water treatment processes and may have its greatest application as an in-plant control test.

Experience accumulated during recent years in the shipment of uniced samples by mail indicates that changes in type or numbers of bacteria during such shipment for limited periods of time are not negligible. Therefore, requirements for storage and shipment of samples to a laboratory for bacteriological examination, which were set forth in previous (11th and 12th) editions, no longer apply and are not given in this edition. Refrigeration during transportation is recommended.

Tentative procedures for the isolation of certain pathogenic bacteria are presented in this edition for the first time. These procedures are generally tedious and complicated and are not recommended for routine use.

Although methods have been proposed for the detection of enteric viruses in water, to date such methods have not been studied sufficiently to warrant their detailed inclusion in this edition, even as tentative procedures. By the time subsequent editions have been prepared, these technics will doubtless be sufficiently well established to permit their inclusion, although their routine use is not advocated at the present time.

The results of the examination of routine bacteriologic samples of water cannot be regarded as providing complete or final information concerning the quality of the water. Bacteriologic results must be considered in the light of information available concerning the sanitary conditions surrounding the source of any particular sample. Precise evaluation of the quality of a water supply can be made only when the results of laboratory examinations of the water are interpreted in the light of such sanitary survey data.

In particular, the results of the examination of a single sample from a given source can only be considered inadequate. When possible, evaluation of the quality of a water supply must be based on the examination of a series of samples collected over a known and protracted period of time.

The rapidly increasing attention being given pollution problems of tidal estuaries and other bodies of saline water has focused attention on necessary modification of existing bacteriologic technics in order that they may be used effectively in the examination of samples from such sources. In the following section, application of the specific technics to saline water has not been discussed because available experience suggests that the methods used for fresh waters also can be used satisfactorily with saline waters.

Methods for examination of the waters of swimming pools and other bathing places have been restored to this edition. The standard procedures for the total count, total coliform group, fecal coliforms, and fecal streptococci are identical with those used for other waters. Procedures for *Staphylococcus aureus* and *Pseudomonas aeruginosa*, organisms commonly associated with the upper respiratory tract or the skin, have been added on a tentative basis. Further study of these tests will be necessary before their acceptability as standard procedures can be established.

The various bacteriological methods outlined in Part 400, developed primarily to permit the prompt and rapid examination of samples of water, have frequently been considered to apply only to routine examinations. These same methods, however, are the basic technics required for research investigations in problems of sanitary bacteriology and water treatment. Their value in routine studies must not be allowed to overshadow or limit their even greater value in research studies. Similarly, all these technics should be the subject of experimental investigations to establish their specificity, improve their procedural details, and expand their application to the measurement of the sanitary quality of water supplies or polluted waters.

401 USPHS STANDARDS OF DRINKING WATER QUALITY

In the United States the quality of public water supplies is generally judged in terms of the 1962 U. S. Public Health Service Drinking Water Standards, which are prescribed for water supplies to be certified for use on carriers subject to federal quarantine regulations. These standards provide for a minimum number of samples to be examined per month and also establish the maximum number of coliform organisms allowable per 100 milliliters of finished water.

1. Sampling

Bacteriologic examinations should be carried out on samples collected at representative points throughout the distribution system. The frequency of sampling and the location of sampling points should be such as to insure accurate determination of the bacteriologic quality of the treated water supply, which may be controlled in part by the known quality of the untreated water and thus by the need for treatment. The minimum number of samples to be collected and examined each month should be based on the population served by the supply. It is important to examine repetitive samples from a designated point, as well as samples from a number of widely distributed sampling points. Daily samples collected after an unsatisfactory sample has been taken should be considered special samples and should not be counted when totaling the number of samples examined monthly.

2. Application

The maximum number of allowable coliform organisms is prescribed in terms of standard portion volume (10 ml or 100 ml) and the number of portions examined. The absence of gas in all tubes, when five 10-ml portions are examined by the fermentation tube method (less than 2.2 coliforms per 100 ml), is generally interpreted to indicate that the single sample meets the standards. A positive Confirmed Test for coliform organisms in three or more tubes (10-ml portions), or the presence of 4 or more coliform organisms in 100-ml samples established by membrane filter tests, indicates the need for immediate remedial action and additional examinations. Daily samples from the sampling point should be collected and examined promptly until the results obtained from at least two consecutive samples show the water to be of satisfactory quality.

These standards also specify limiting concentrations of chemical and physical constituents of water as related to its safety and potability.

The World Health Organization has established International Standards of Drinking Water Quality. These are similar to the U. S. Public Health Service Drinking Water Standards, but they have been modified and liberalized to apply to water supply conditions in all parts of the world.

3. Bibliography

World Health Organization. 1963. *International Standards for Drinking-Water.* WHO, c/o American Public Health Association, 1740 Broadway, New York, N.Y. 10019. (206 pp.)

U. S. Public Health Service. 1962. Public Health Service Drinking Water Standards, 1962. PHS Pub. No. 956. Department of Health, Education & Welfare, Washington, D. C.

402 LABORATORY APPARATUS

1. Incubators

Incubators must maintain a uniform and constant temperature at all times in all areas, that is, they must not vary more than ±0.5 C in the areas used. Such accuracy can be accomplished by the use of a water-jacketed or anhydric type of incubator with thermostatically controlled low-temperature electric heating units properly insulated and located in or adjacent to the walls or floor of the chamber and preferably equipped with mechanical means of circulating air.

Incubators equipped with high-temperature heating units are unsatisfactory, because such sources of heat, when improperly placed, frequently cause localized overheating and excessive drying of the media, with consequent inhibition of bacterial growth. Incubators so heated may be operated satisfactorily by replacing the high-temperature units with suitable wiring arranged to operate at a lower temperature and by installation of mechanical air-circulation devices. It is desirable, where ordinary room temperatures vary excessively, that laboratory incubators be kept in special rooms maintained at a few degrees below the recommended incubator temperature.

Special incubating rooms, well insulated and equipped with properly distributed heating units, and with forced-air circulation, may be used provided that they conform to desired temperature limits. When such rooms are used, the daily range in temperature in areas where plates or tubes are incubated shall be recorded. Incubators shall be provided with shelves so spaced as to assure uniformity of temperature throughout the chamber. A 1-in. space shall be provided between walls and stacks of dishes or baskets of tubes.

An accurate thermometer (checked against one certified by the National Bureau of Standards) with the bulb continuously immersed in liquid (glycerine, water, or mineral oil) shall be maintained on each shelf within the incubator and daily readings of the temperature recorded. It is desirable, in addition, to maintain a maximum and minimum registering thermometer within the incubator on the middle shelf to record the gross range in temperature variations over a 24-hr period. Temperature variations within the incubator when filled to maximum capacity should be determined at intervals. It is recommended that a recording thermometer be installed in every incubator whenever possible, so that a permanent record of temperature variations within the incubating chamber may be maintained.

Adequate temperature control of an air incubator operated at 44.5 C is not ordinarily possible. To obtain this temperature and to maintain a variation within ±0.2 C, a water bath incubator should be used. Most water baths equipped with a gabled cover to reduce water and heat loss are adequate. The water depth in the incubator should be sufficient to immerse tubes to the upper level of the media. In the event that satisfactory temperature control is not achieved, water recirculation should be provided.

2. Hot-Air Sterilizing Ovens

Hot-air sterilizing ovens shall be of sufficient size to prevent internal crowding; constructed to give uniform and adequate sterilizing temperatures; and equipped with suitable thermometers capable of registering accurately in the range 160–180 C. The use of a temperature-recording instrument is optional.

3. *Autoclaves*

Autoclaves shall be of sufficient size to prevent internal crowding; constructed to provide uniform temperatures within the chambers (up to and including the sterilizing temperature of 121 C); equipped with an accurate thermometer the bulb of which is located properly on the exhaust line so as to register minimum temperature within the sterilizing chambers (temperature-recording instrument is optional); having pressure gauge and properly adjusted safety valves connected directly with saturated-steam power lines or directly to a suitable special steam generator (steam from a boiler treated with amines for corrosion control should not be used); and capable of reaching the desired temperature within 30 min.

A pressure cooker may be substituted for an autoclave, provided that it is equipped with an efficient pressure gauge and with a thermometer the bulb of which is 1 in. above the water level.

4. *Gas Sterilizers*

The sterilizers shall be equipped with automatic controls capable of carrying out a complete sterilization cycle. Ethylene oxide diluted to 10–12% with an inert gas shall be used. The automatic control cycle shall consist of evacuation of the sterilizing chamber to at least 25 in. of vacuum, which shall be held for 30 min; adjustment of humidity and temperature; charging with the ethylene oxide mixture to a pressure dependent on the mixture used; holding such pressure for at least 4 hr; venting of the gas; again, evacuation to 25 in. of vacuum; and finally bringing to atmospheric pressure with sterile air. The humidity, temperature, pressure and time of the sterilizing cycle depend on the gas mixture used.

If sample bottles packaged for shipment are sterilized by gas, they shall be stored overnight before being shipped, to allow the last traces of the gas mixture to dissipate. If media are sterilized by gas, they shall be incubated overnight to insure dissipation of the gas.

In general, mixtures of ethylene oxide with chlorinated hydrocarbons such as freon are deleterious to plastics, although with temperatures below 130 F, gas pressure not over 5 psi, and time of sterilization less than 6 hr, the effect is minimal. Carbon dioxide as a diluent of the ethylene oxide is preferable for plastic, but the exposure time and pressure required are greater, depending on the temperature and humidity that can be used.

The proper cycle and gas mixture shall be determined for the particular objects to be sterilized and confirmed by sterility tests of the object.

5. *Colony Counters*

Standard apparatus shall be used, such as a Quebec colony counter, darkfield model preferred, or one providing equivalent magnification (1.5 diameters) and satisfactory visibility.

6. *pH Equipment*

Electrometric pH meters, accurate to at least 0.1 pH units, shall be used for determination of pH values of media.

7. *Balances*

Balances shall provide a sensitivity of at least 0.1 g at a load of 150 g, with appropriate weights. An analytical balance having a sensitivity of 1 mg under a load of 10 g shall be used for weighing small quantities (less than 2 g) of materials. Single-pan rapid-weigh balances are most convenient.

8. *Media Preparation Utensils*

Borosilicate glass shall be used, or other suitable noncorrosive equipment such as stainless steel. Glassware must be clean and free from foreign residues or dried particles of agar and also from toxic or foreign materials that may contaminate media, such as chlorine, copper, zinc, antimony, chromium or detergents.

9. *Pipets and Graduated Cylinders*

Pipets may be of any convenient size, provided that they deliver accurately and quickly the required amount. The error of calibration for a given manufacturer's lot must not exceed 2.5%. Pipets shall have graduations distinctly marked and have unbroken tips. For satisfactory work relating to enforcement of water quality regulations, bacteriologic transfer pipets may be required that are calibrated and marked. Pipets conforming to the APHA standards given in the latest edition of *Standard Methods for the Examination of Dairy Products* may be used. It is recommended that the mouth end of all pipets be protected—e.g., by a cotton plug—to eliminate hazards to the worker or possible contamination by saliva of the sample being pipetted.

Graduated cylinders meeting ASTM Standards (D-86 and D-216) and with accuracy limits established by the National Bureau of Standards may be used where appropriate.

10. *Pipet Containers*

Boxes shall be of aluminum or stainless steel, end measurement 2–3 in., cylindrical or rectangular, and length about 16 in. When these are not available, paper wrappings may be substituted. To avoid excessive charring during sterilization, best-quality sulfate pulp (kraft) paper should be used. *Copper or copper alloy cans or boxes should not be used as pipet containers.*

11. *Dilution Bottles or Tubes*

Bottles or tubes shall be of resistant glass, preferably borosilicate glass, closed with glass stoppers or screw caps equipped with liners that do not produce toxic or bacteriostatic compounds on sterilization. Cotton plugs must not be used as closures. Graduation levels shall be indelibly marked on the side of the dilution bottle or tube. Plastic bottles constructed of nontoxic materials and of acceptable size may be substituted for glass provided that they can be sterilized properly.

12. *Petri Dishes*

For making the Standard Plate Count, petri dishes shall be about 100 mm in diameter, with the side wall of the bottom at least 15 mm high, and with glass or porous tops as preferred. The bottom of the dish shall be free from bubbles and scratches and shall be flat so that the medium will be of uniform thickness throughout the plate. Plastic dishes about 60 × 15 mm are convenient for use in the membrane filter technic. Plastic petri dishes, when found to be satisfactory and when presterilized by the manufacturer, may be substituted for glass dishes for single use only. Petri dishes may be sterilized and stored in metal cans (aluminum or stainless steel, but not copper), or they may be wrapped in paper—preferably best-quality sulfate pulp (kraft)—prior to sterilization.

13. Fermentation Tubes and Vials

Fermentation tubes of any type may be used, if their design permits conformance to the requirements for concentration of nutritive ingredients as described subsequently. Where tubes are to be used for a test of gas production, a shell vial, inverted, shall be enclosed. The sizes of the tube and the vial shall be such that the vial is completely filled with medium and at least partly submerged in the tube.

14. Inoculating Equipment

Wire loops shall be made of 22- or 24-gauge Chromel, nichrome, or platinum-iridium where flame sterilization is used. Single-service transfer loops of aluminum or stainless steel are satisfactory. The diameter of all loops shall be at least 3 mm. Dry heat or steam may be used for sterilization. Single-service hardwood applicators may also be used. They should be $\frac{1}{12}$ to $\frac{1}{8}$ in. in diameter and at least 1 in. longer than the fermentation tube, and should be sterilized by dry heat and stored in glass or other nontoxic containers.

15. Sample Bottles

Bottles of glass or other material resistant to the solvent action of water, capable of being sterilized, and of any suitable size and shape may be used for samples intended for bacteriologic examination. Bottles shall hold a sufficient volume of sample for all the required tests, permit proper washing, and maintain the samples uncontaminated until the examinations are completed. Ground-glass-stoppered bottles, preferably wide mouthed and of resistant glass, are recommended. Plastic bottles of suitable size, wide mouthed, and manufactured of nontoxic materials have been found satisfactory as sample containers and eliminate hazards due to breakage during shipment.

Metal or plastic screw-cap closures may be used on sample bottles provided that no volatile compounds are produced on sterilization and provided also that they are equipped with liners which do not produce toxic or bacteriostatic compounds on sterilization.

The tops and necks of sample bottles with glass closures shall be covered, before sterilization, with metal foil, rubberized cloth, heavy impermeable paper, or milk bottle cover caps.

Many plastic sample bottles are commercially available. These should not be used for repetitive sampling unless it has been demonstrated that they can be sterilized. Some types may be autoclaved once or twice at 121 C for 10 min, but only a few do not distort and leak when autoclaved repeatedly. Generally the neck of the bottle shrinks faster than the thicker cap, so that the threads no longer make a watertight seal. Resistance to distortion not only depends on the type of plastic used, but also is markedly affected by the method of molding. Polypropylene has been found a satisfactory material.

16. Bibliography

COLLINS, W. D. & H. B. RIFFENBURG. 1923. Contamination of water samples with material dissolved from glass containers. *Ind. Eng. Chem.* 15:48.

CLARK, W. M. 1928. *The Determination of Hydrogen Ion Concentration* (3rd ed.). Williams & Wilkins, Baltimore, Md.

ARCHAMBAULT, J., J. CUROT & M. H. MCCRADY. 1937. The need of uniformity of conditions for counting plates (with suggestions for a standard colony counter). *AJPH* 27:809.

RICHARDS, O. W. & P. C. HEIJN. 1945. An improved dark-field Quebec colony counter. *J. Milk Tech.* 8:253.

COHEN, B. 1957. The measurement of pH, titratable acidity, and oxidation-reduction potentials. In *Manual of Microbiological Methods.* Society of American Bacteriologists. McGraw-Hill Book Co., New York.

MCGUIRE, O. E. 1964. Wood applicators for the confirmatory test in the bacteriological analysis of water. *Pub. Health Rep.* 79:812.

AMERICAN PUBLIC HEALTH ASSOCIATION. 1967. *Standard Methods for the Examination of Dairy Products* (12th ed.). APHA, New York.

403 WASHING AND STERILIZATION

All glassware must be thoroughly cleansed, using a suitable detergent and hot water; rinsed with hot water to remove all traces of residual washing compound, and finally rinsed with distilled water.

1. Inhibitory Residues on Glassware

Certain wetting agents or detergents used in washing glassware may contain bacteriostatic or inhibiting substances which require 6 to 12 successive rinsings to remove all traces from the glass surface and insure freedom from residual bacteriostatic action. The following test procedure is recommended for the biological examination of glassware where bacteriostatic or inhibitory residues may be present.

a. PROCEDURE FOR TEST

1) Wash six petri dishes according to usual laboratory practice and designate as group A.

2) Wash six petri dishes as above, rinsing 12 times with successive portions of distilled water, and designate as group B.

3) Rinse six petri dishes with the detergent wash water (in use concentration), dry without further rinsing, and designate as group C.

4) Sterilize the dishes in groups A, B and C by the usual procedure.

5) Add a water sample yielding 20 to 60 colonies, pour plates in triplicate, and proceed according to the procedure described for the Standard Plate Count.

b. INTERPRETATION OF RESULTS

1) Difference in average number of colonies of less than 15% on plates of groups A, B and C indicates that the detergent has no toxicity or inhibitory characteristics.

2) Difference in colony count of 15% or more between groups A and B demonstrates inhibitory residue left on supplies and equipment by routine washing procedure.

3) Disagreement in averages of less than 15% between groups A and B and greater than 15% between groups

A and C indicates that the cleaning detergent has inhibitory properties which are eliminated during routine washing.

2. *Sterilization*

Glassware, except when in metal containers, shall be sterilized for not less than 60 min at a temperature of 170 C, unless it is known from recording thermometers that oven temperatures are uniform, under which exceptional condition 160 C will suffice. Glassware in metal containers should be heated to a temperature of 170 C for not less than 2 hr.

Sample bottles other than of plastic may be sterilized as above or in an autoclave at 121 C for 15 min.

For those plastic bottles that distort on autoclaving, low-temperature ethylene oxide gas sterilization should be used.

404 PREPARATION OF CULTURE MEDIA

404 A. General Procedures

1. *Storage of Culture Media*

The dehydrated media (powders) shall be stored in tightly closed bottles in the dark at less than 30 C in an atmosphere of low humidity and shall not be used if they discolor or become caked so as to lose their free-flowing power. It is advisable to purchase dehydrated media in small quantities that will be used within 6 months after opening.

Culture media should be prepared in batches of such size that the entire batch will be used in less than 1 week.

Liquid media in fermentation tubes, if stored at refrigeration or even moderately low temperatures, may dissolve sufficient air to produce, upon incubation at 35 C, a bubble of air in the tube. It is therefore imperative that fermentation tubes which have been stored at a low temperature be incubated overnight before use and that those tubes containing air be discarded.

Fermentation tubes may be stored at approximately 25 C; but because evaporation may proceed rapidly under these conditions—resulting in marked changes in concentration of the ingredient—storage at this temperature should not exceed a period of 1 week.

2. *Adjustment of Reaction*

The reaction of culture media should be stated in terms of hydrogen ion concentration, expressed as pH.

The increase in the hydrogen ion concentration (decrease in pH) during sterilization will vary slightly with the individual sterilizer in use, and the initial reaction required to obtain the correct final reaction will have to be determined. The decrease in the pH reading will usually be 0.1 to 0.2 but may occasionally be as great as 0.4. When buffering salts such as phosphates are present in the media, the decrease in pH value as determined will be negligible.

a. POTENTIOMETRIC METHOD: Tests to control the adjustment to the required hydrogen ion concentration shall be made with a pH meter. Measure the pH of the prepared medium as directed in pH Value, Glass Electrode Method (Section 144A). Titrate a known volume of the medium with a solution of NaOH to the desired pH. Calculate the amount of NaOH solution which must be added to the bulk of the medium to reach this reaction. After addition and thorough mixing, check the reaction and adjust if necessary. The required final pH is given in the directions for preparing each medium. If a specific pH is not prescribed, adjustment will be unnecessary.

The pH of reconstituted dehydrated media will seldom require adjustment if made according to directions. Such factors as errors in weighing the dehydrated medium or overheating of the reconstituted medium may produce an unacceptable final pH. Measurement of pH should be made regularly to insure quality control.

3. *Sterilization*

All media, except sugar broths or broths with other specifications, must be sterilized in an autoclave at 121 C for 15 min after the temperature has reached 121 C. When the pressure reaches zero, the medium must be removed from the autoclave and cooled quickly to avoid decomposition of sugars by prolonged exposure to heat. To permit uniform heating and rapid cooling, materials should be packed loosely and in small containers. The maximum elapsed time for exposure of sugar broths to any heat (from the time of closing the loaded autoclave to unloading) is 45 min. Preheating the autoclave before loading can reduce total needed heating time to within the 45-min limit.

404 B. Materials

i—Water Characteristics

Only distilled or demineralized water which has been tested and found free from traces of dissolved metals and bactericidal or inhibitory compounds may be used for preparation of culture media and reagents. Toxicity in distilled water may be derived from fluoridated water high in silica. Other sources of toxicity are silver, lead, and various unidentified organic complexes. Where condensate return is used as feed for a still, toxic amines or other boiler compounds may be present in the distilled water. Residual chlorine or chloramines may also be found in distilled water prepared from chlorinated water supplies. If chlorine compounds are found in the distilled water, they should be neutralized by addition of an equivalent amount of sodium thiosulfate or sodium sulfite.

Distilled water should also be free of contaminating nutrients. Such contamination may be derived from flashover of organics during distillation; continued use of exhausted carbon filter beds; deionizing columns in need of recharging; solder flux residues in new piping; dust and chemical fumes; and storage of water in unclean bottles. Distilled water preferably should be stored out of direct sunlight so as to prevent growth of algae. Good housekeeping practices will usually eliminate nutrient contamination.

ii—Test for bactericidal properties of distilled water

1. Principle

The test is based on the growth of *Aerobacter aerogenes* in a chemically defined minimal growth medium. The presence of a toxic agent or a growth-promoting substance will alter the 24-hr population by an increase or decrease of 20% or more when compared to a control.

2. Apparatus and Materials

a. Glassware: All glassware used in this procedure should be borosilicate and must receive a final rinse in water freshly redistilled from a glass still prior to dry heat sterilization. Steam sterilization will recontaminate these specially cleaned glassware items. The sensitivity and reproducibility of the test depend in part upon the cleanliness of the sample containers, flasks, tubes and pipets. It is often convenient to use new glassware, which is then used exclusively for this test.

b. Culture: Any strain of coliform IMViC type −−++ (*A. aerogenes*). This can be obtained easily from any polluted river or sewage sample.

3. Reagents

Use only reagents of the highest purity. Some brands of potassium dihydrogen phosphate, KH_2PO_4, contain large amounts of impurities. Sensitivity of the test is controlled in part by the purity of the reagents employed. Reagents should be made in water freshly redistilled from a glass still.

a. Sodium citrate solution: Dissolve 0.29 g sodium citrate, $Na_3C_6H_5O_7 \cdot 2H_2O$, in 500 ml redistilled water.

b. Ammonium sulfate solution: Dissolve 0.60 g ammonium sulfate, $(NH_4)_2SO_4$, in 500 ml redistilled water.

c. Salt mixture solution: Dissolve 0.26 g magnesium sulfate, $MgSO_4 \cdot 7H_2O$, 0.17 g calcium chloride, $CaCl_2 \cdot 2H_2O$, 0.23 g ferrous sulfate, $FeSO_4 \cdot 7H_2O$, and 2.50 g sodium chloride, NaCl, in 500 ml redistilled water.

d. Phosphate buffer solution: Stock phosphate buffer solution, Media Specifications, Section 404C, following, diluted 1:25 in redistilled water.

e. Sterilization of reagents: All reagent solutions must be boiled 1 to 2 min to kill vegetative cells. These solutions may be stored in sterilized glass-stoppered bottles in the dark at 5 C for a period not exceeding 2 weeks to avoid any significant contamination from volatile materials in the air. The salt-mixture solution will develop a slight turbidity within 3 to 5 days as the ferrous salt converts to the ferric state. Solutions with a heavy turbidity should be discarded and a new solution prepared. Bacterial contamination may cause turbidity in the phosphate buffer solution, which should be discarded if this occurs.

f. Preparation of unknown distilled water sample: Collect 150–200 ml water sample in a sterile borosilicate glass flask and boil for 1 to 2 min to kill any vegetative cells present. Longer boiling should be avoided to prevent chemical changes in the sample.

4. *Procedure*

a) Label 5 flasks or tubes, A, B, C, D and E. Add water samples and redistilled water to each flask as indicated in the following protocol:

Media Reagents	Control Test (ml)		Optional Tests (ml)		
	Control A	Unknown Distilled Water B	Food Available C	Nitrogen Source D	Carbon Source E
Sodium citrate solution	2.5	2.5	–	2.5	–
Ammonium sulfate solution	2.5	2.5	–	–	2.5
Salt-mixture solution	2.5	2.5	2.5	2.5	2.5
Phosphate buffer (7.3 ± 0.1)	1.5	1.5	1.5	1.5	1.5
Unknown water	–	21.0	21.0	21.0	21.0
Redistilled water	21.0	–	5.0	2.5	2.5
Total volume	30.0	30.0	30.0	30.0	30.0

b) Add a suspension of *Aerobacter aerogenes* (IMViC type −−++) of such density that each flask will contain 30–80 cells per milliliter. Cell densities below this range result in ratios which are not consistent, while densities above 100 cells per ml result in decreased sensitivity to nutrients in the test water. Make an initial bacterial count by plating triplicate 1-ml portions from each culture flask in plate count agar. Incubate tests A–E at 35 C for 24 ±2 hr. Prepare final plate counts from each flask, using dilutions of 1, 0.1, 0.01, 0.001 and 0.0001 ml.

5. *Preparation of Bacterial Suspension*

a. Bacterial growth: On the day before performing the distilled-water suitability test, inoculate a strain of *Aerobacter aerogenes* onto a nutrient agar slant with a slope of approximately 2½ in. length contained in a 125 × 16 mm screw-cap tube. Streak the entire agar surface to develop a continuous-growth film and incubate 18–24 hr at 35 C.

b. Harvesting of viable cells: Pipet 1–2 ml sterile dilution water from a 99-ml water blank onto the 18–24 hr culture. Emulsify the growth on the slant by gently rubbing the bacterial film with the pipet, being careful not to tear the agar; then pipet the suspension back into the original 99-ml water blank.

c. Dilution of bacterial suspension: Make a 1:100 dilution of the original bottle into a 2nd water blank, and a further 1:100 dilution of the 2nd bottle into a 3rd water blank, shaking vigorously after each transfer. Then pipet 0.1 ml of the 3rd dilution (1:1,000,000) into each of the flasks A, B, C, D and E. This procedure should result in a final dilution of the organisms to a range of 30–80 viable cells for each ml of test solution.

d. Verification of bacterial density: Variations among strains of the same organism, different organisms, media and surface area of agar slopes will possibly necessitate adjustment of the dilution procedure in order to arrive at a specific density range between 30 and 80 viable cells. To establish the growth range numerically for a specific organism and medium, make a series of plate counts from the 3rd dilution to determine the bacterial density. Then choose the proper volume from this 3rd dilution, which, when diluted by the 30 ml in flasks A, B, C, D and E, will contain 30–80 viable cells per ml. If the procedures are standardized as to surface area of the slant and laboratory technic, it is possible to reproduce results on repeated experiments with the same strain of microorganism.

e. Procedural difficulties:

1) Storage of unknown distilled water sample in soft-glass containers or in glass containers without liners for metal caps.

2) Use of chemicals in preparation of reagents not of analytical-reagent grade or not of recent manufacture.

3) Contamination of reagent by distilled water with a bacterial background. The initial colony count before flask incubation is made to rule out gross contamination of the sample.

4) Failure to obtain desired initial bacterial concentration or incorrect choice of dilution used to obtain 24-hr plate count.

5) Prolongation of incubation time beyond 26-hr limit, resulting in desensitized growth response.

f. Calculation:

(*1*) For growth-inhibiting substances:

$$\text{Ratio} = \frac{\text{colony count per ml flask B}}{\text{colony count per ml flask A}}$$

A ratio of 0.8–1.2 (inclusive) shows no toxic substances; a ratio of less than 0.8 shows growth-inhibiting substances in the water sample.

(*2*) For nitrogen and carbon sources that promote growth:

$$\text{Ratio} = \frac{\text{colony count per ml flask C}}{\text{colony count per ml flask A}}$$

(*3*) For nitrogen sources that promote growth:

$$\text{Ratio} = \frac{\text{colony count per ml flask D}}{\text{colony count per ml flask A}}$$

(*4*) For carbon sources that promote bacterial growth:

$$\text{Ratio} = \frac{\text{colony count per ml flask E}}{\text{colony count per ml flask A}}$$

Do not calculate ratios (2), (3) or (4) when ratio (1) indicates a toxic reaction. For ratios (2), (3) or (4), a value in excess of 1.2 indicates an available source for bacterial growth.

6. Interpretation of Results

a. The colony count from flask A after 20–24 hr at 35 C will depend on the number of organisms initially planted in flask A and on the strain of *A. aerogenes* used in the test procedures. This is the reason the control, flask A, must be run for each individual series of tests. However, for a given strain of *A. aerogenes* under identical environmental conditions, the terminal count should be reasonably constant when the initial plant is the same. The difference in the initial plant of 30 and 80 will be about 3-fold larger for the 80 organisms initially planted in flask A, providing the growth rate remains constant. Thus, it is essential that the initial colony counts on flask A and flask B be approximately equal to secure accurate data.

b. When the ratio exceeds 1.2, it may be assumed that growth-stimulating substances are present. However, this procedure is extremely sensitive and ratios up to 3.0 would have little significance in actual practice. Therefore, when the ratio is between 1.2 and 3.0, Tests C, D and E do not appear to be necessary except in special circumstances.

c. Usually flask C will be very low and flasks D and E will have a ratio of less than 1.2 when the ratio of flask B to flask A is between 0.8 and 1.2. The limiting factors of growth in flask A are the nitrogen and organic carbon present. An extremely large amount of ammonia nitrogen with no organic carbon could increase the ratio in flask D above 1.2, or the absence of nitrogen with high carbon concentration could give ratios above 1.2 in flask E, with a B/A ratio between 0.8 and 1.2.

d. A ratio below 0.8 indicates that the water contains toxic substances, and this ratio includes all allowable tolerances. As indicated in ¶ *b* preceding, the ratio could go as high as 3.0 from 1.2 without any undesirable consequences.

e. Specific corrective measures cannot be recommended in specific instances of defective distillation apparatus. However, careful inspection of the distillation equipment and a review of the production and handling of the distilled water should enable local laboratory personnel to correct the cause of the difficulty.

Feedwater to a still is often passed through a deionizing column and a carbon filter. If these columns are well maintained, most inorganic and organic contaminants will be removed. If maintenance is poor, the input water may be degraded to a quality lower than that of the raw tap water.

The best distillation system is made of stainless steel. Quartz, Vycor, or pyrex glass, in that order of preference, is also acceptable. Tin-lined hardware is least desirable because maintenance is difficult. All connecting plumbing should be of stainless steel, pyrex, or special plastic pipes made of polyvinyl chloride (PVC). Storage reservoirs should be of stainless steel and should be protected from dust.

7. Test Sensitivity

Taking copper as one relative measurement of distilled water toxicity, maximum sensitivity of the test will be 0.05 mg of copper per liter in a distilled water sample.

404 C. Media Specifications

The need for uniformity dictates the use of dehydrated media. Media shall not be prepared from the basic ingredients when suitable dehydrated media are available. The manufacturer's directions for rehydration and sterilization should be followed.

NOTE—The term "percent solution" as used in these directions is to be understood to mean "grams of solute per 100 milliliters of solution."

1. *Dilution Water*

a. BUFFERED WATER: To prepare stock phosphate buffer solution, dissolve 34.0 g potassium dihydrogen phosphate, KH_2PO_4, in 500 ml distilled water, adjust to pH 7.2 with 1*N* NaOH, and dilute to 1 liter with distilled water.

Add 1.25 ml stock phosphate buffer solution to 1 liter distilled water. Dispense in amounts that will provide 99 ±2.0 ml or 9 ±0.2 ml after autoclaving for 15 min.

b. PEPTONE DILUTION WATER: Prepare a 10% solution of peptone in distilled water. Dilute a measured volume to provide a final 0.5% solution.

Dispense in amounts to provide 99 ±2.0 ml or 9 ±0.2 ml after autoclaving for 15 min.

2. *Nutrient Broth*

Beef extract .... 3.0 g
Peptone .... 5.0 g
Distilled water .... 1 liter

pH should be between 6.8 and 7.0 after sterilization.

3. *Lactose Broth*

Beef extract .... 3.0 g
Peptone .... 5.0 g
Lactose .... 5.0 g
Distilled water .... 1 liter

pH should be between 6.8 and 7.0, but preferably 6.9 after sterilization. Prior to sterilization, dispense in fermentation tubes of such dimensions that the liquid in the inoculated tube will cover the inverted vial at least partially after sterilization.

When fermentation tubes or other containers are prepared for the examination of 10-ml or 100-ml portions of sample, the lactose broth medium must be of such strength that the addition of that volume of sample to the medium in the fermentation tube will not reduce the concentration of ingredients in the mixture below that in the standard medium. Where dehydrated medium is used, the proper concentration of ingredients may be obtained by consulting the following tabulation:

Inoculum *ml*	Amount of Medium in Tube *ml*	Volume of Medium + Inoculum *ml*	Dehydrated Lactose Broth Required *g/l*
1	10 or more	11 or more	13.0
10	10	20	26.0
10	20	30	19.5
100	50	150	39.0
100	35	135	50.1
100	20	120	78.0

4. Lauryl Tryptose Broth

Tryptose	20.0 g
Lactose	5.0 g
Dipotassium hydrogen phosphate, K_2HPO_4	2.75g
Potassium dihydrogen phosphate, KH_2PO_4	2.75g
Sodium chloride, NaCl	5.0 g
Sodium lauryl sulfate	0.1 g
Distilled water	1 liter

pH should be approximately 6.8 after sterilization. Prior to sterilization, dispense in fermentation tubes of such dimensions that the liquid in the inoculated tube will cover the inverted vial at least partially after sterilization.

As with lactose broth, the lauryl tryptose broth must be of such strength that the addition of 100-ml or 10-ml portions of the sample to the medium will not reduce the concentrations of the various ingredients below those of the standard medium. When the dehydrated material is used, prepare in accordance with the following tabulation:

Inoculum *ml*	Amount of Medium in Tube *ml*	Volume of Medium + Inoculum *ml*	Dehydrated Lauryl Tryptose Broth Required *g/l*
1	10 or more	11 or more	35.6
10	10	20	71.2
10	20	30	53.4
100	50	150	106.8
100	35	135	137.1
100	20	120	213.6

5. Tryptone Glucose Extract Agar

Beef extract	3.0 g
Tryptone	5.0 g
Glucose	1.0 g
Agar	15.0 g
Distilled water	1 liter

pH should be between 6.8 and 7.0 after sterilization.

6. Plate Count Agar (Tryptone Glucose Yeast Agar)

Peptone-tryptone	5.0 g
Yeast extract	2.5 g
Glucose	1.0 g
Agar	15.0 g
Distilled water	1 liter

pH should be 7.0 ± 0.1 after sterilization.

7. Endo Agar

Peptone	10.0 g
Lactose	10.0 g
Dipotassium hydrogen phosphate, K_2HPO_4	3.5 g
Agar	15.0 g
Sodium sulfite	2.5 g
Basic fuchsin	0.5 g
Distilled water	1 liter

pH should be 7.4 after sterilization. The medium should be light pink when hot and almost colorless when cool.

8. Eosin Methylene Blue (EMB) Agar

Peptone	10.0 g
Lactose	10.0 g
Dipotassium hydrogen phosphate, K_2HPO_4	2.0 g
Agar	15.0 g
Eosin Y	0.4 g
Methylene blue	0.065g
Distilled water	1 liter

pH should be 7.1 after sterilization. Decolorization of the medium occurs during sterilization, but the color returns after cooling.

9. Brilliant Green Lactose Bile Broth

Peptone	10.0 g
Lactose	10.0 g
Oxgall	20.0 g
Brilliant green	0.0133g
Distilled water	1 liter

pH should be 7.2 after sterilization. Prior to sterilization, dispense in fermentation tubes with sufficient medium to cover the inverted vial at least partially after sterilization.

10. EC Medium

Tryptose or trypticase	20.0 g
Lactose	5.0 g
Bile salts mixture or bile salts No. 3	1.5 g
Dipotassium hydrogen phosphate, K_2HPO_4	4.0 g
Potassium dihydrogen phosphate, KH_2PO_4	1.5 g
Sodium chloride, NaCl	5.0 g
Distilled water	1 liter

pH should be 6.9 after sterilization. Prior to sterilization, dispense in fermentation tubes with sufficient medium to cover the inverted vial at least partially after sterilization.

11. Boric Acid Lactose Broth

Proteose peptone	10.0 g
Lactose	5.0 g
Dipotassium hydrogen phosphate, K_2HPO_4	12.2 g
Potassium dihydrogen phosphate, KH_2PO_4	4.1 g
Boric acid	3.5 g
Distilled water	1 liter

pH should be 7.0 after sterilization. Prior to sterilization, dispense in fermentation tubes with sufficient medium to cover the inverted vial at least partially after sterilization.

12. M-FC Broth *

Tryptose or biosate	10.0 g
Proteose peptone No. 3 or polypeptone	5.0 g
Yeast extract	3.0 g
Sodium chloride	5.0 g
Lactose	12.5 g
Bile salts No. 3 or bile salts mixture	1.5 g
Aniline blue	0.1 g
Distilled water	1 liter

Rehydrate in the distilled water containing 10 ml of 1% rosolic acid in 0.2*N* NaOH.† Heat the medium to the boiling point, promptly remove from heat and cool to below 45 C. Do not sterilize by autoclaving. Final pH should be 7.4.

The finished media should be stored at 2–10 C and any unused medium discarded after 96 hr.

13. M-Endo Medium

M-Endo broth contains the following ingredients per liter:

	g
Tryptone or polypeptone	10.0
Thiopeptone or thiotone	5.0
Casitone or trypticase	5.0
Yeast extract	1.5
Lactose	12.5
Sodium chloride	5.0
Dipotassium hydrogen phosphate	4.375
Potassium dihydrogen phosphate	1.375
Sodium lauryl sulfate	0.050
Sodium desoxycholate	0.10
Sodium sulfite	2.10
Basic fuchsin	1.05

---

* Dehydrated Difco M-FC Broth Base (No. 0883), dehydrated BBL m-FC Broth (No. 01-757), or equivalent may be used.

† Rosolic acid reagent will decompose if sterilized by autoclaving. The stock solution should be stored in the dark at 2–10 C and discarded after 2 weeks, or sooner if its color changes from dark red to muddy brown.

Rehydrate in 1 liter of distilled water containing 20 ml of 95% ethanol. Heat the medium to the boiling point, promptly remove from heat, and cool to below 45 C. Do not sterilize by autoclaving. Final pH should be between 7.1 and 7.3.

The finished medium should be stored in the dark at 2–10 C and any unused medium discarded after 96 hr.

14. LES MF Holding Medium, Coliform

Tryptone	3.0	g
M-Endo broth MF	3.0	g
Dipotassium hydrogen phosphate	3.0	g
Sodium benzoate	1.0	g
Sulfanilamide	1.0	g
Paraaminobenzoic acid	1.2	g
Cycloheximide	0.5	g
Distilled water	1	liter

Rehydrate in the distilled water without heating. Final pH should be 7.1 ±0.1

15. LES Endo Agar

Yeast extract	1.2	g
Casitone or trypticase	3.7	g
Thiopeptone or thiotone	3.7	g
Tryptose	7.5	g
Lactose	9.4	g
Dipotassium hydrogen phosphate	3.3	g
Potassium dihydrogen phosphate	1.0	g
Sodium chloride	3.7	g
Sodium desoxycholate	0.1	g
Sodium lauryl sulfate	0.05	g
Sodium sulfite	1.6	g
Basic fuchsin	0.8	g
Agar	15.0	g
Distilled water	1	liter

Rehydrate in the distilled water containing 20 ml 95% ethanol. Bring to a boil, cool to 45–50 C and dispense in 4-ml quantities into the lower section of 60-mm glass or plastic petri dishes. If dishes of any other size are used, adjust the quantity to give an equivalent depth. Plates may be stored in the dark up to 2 weeks when held at 2–10 C. Do not expose to direct sunlight.

16. Azide Dextrose Broth

Beef extract	4.5	g
Tryptone or polypeptone	15.0	g
Glucose	7.5	g
Sodium chloride, NaCl	7.5	g
Sodium azide, NaN_3	0.2	g
Distilled water	1	liter

pH should be about 7.2 after sterilization.

17. Ethyl Violet Azide Broth

Tryptone or biosate	20.0	g
Glucose	5.0	g
Sodium chloride	5.0	g
Dipotassium hydrogen phosphate, K_2HPO_4	2.7	g
Potassium dihydrogen phosphate, KH_2PO_4	2.7	g
Sodium azide, NaN_3	0.4	g
Ethyl violet	0.00083	g
Distilled water	1	liter

pH should be about 7.0 after sterilization.

18. M-Enterococcus Agar *

Tryptose	20.0	g
Yeast extract	5.0	g
Glucose	2.0	g
Dipotassium hydrogen phosphate	4.0	g
Sodium azide	0.4	g
Agar	10.0	g
2,3,5-triphenyltetrazolium chloride	0.1	g
Distilled water	1	liter

After rehydrating in the distilled water, sterilize by bringing to a boil. The pH

* Dehydrated Difco m-Enterococcus Agar (No. 0746), dehydrated BBL M-Enterococcus Agar (No. 01-533), or equivalent, may be used.

should be 7.2 after heating. Poured plates may be stored in the dark up to 30 days when held at 2–10 C.

19. KF Streptococcus Agar †

Proteose peptone No. 3 or polypeptone	10.0	g
Yeast extract	10.0	g
Sodium chloride	5.0	g
Sodium glycerophosphate	10.0	g
Maltose	20.0	g
Lactose	1.0	g
Sodium azide	0.4	g
Bromcresol purple	0.015	g
Agar	20.0	g
Distilled water	1	liter

Mix 7.64 g of dehydrated medium with 100 ml of sterile distilled water in a sterile flask. Heat in a boiling water bath to dissolve the agar. After solution is complete heat for an additional 5 min. Cool to 50–60 C and add 1 ml sterile aqueous 1% solution of 2,3,5-triphenyltetrazolium chloride per 100 ml. Adjust pH to 7.2 with 10% Na_2CO_3 if necessary. The medium may be held at 45–50 C for up to 4 hr before pouring plates. Poured plates may be stored in the dark up to 30 days when held at 2–10 C.

20. Brain-Heart Infusion

Infusion of calf brains	200	g
Infusion of beef heart	250	g
Proteose peptone	10.0	g
Glucose	2.0	g
Sodium chloride, NaCl	5.0	g
Disodium hydrogen phosphate, Na_2HPO_4	2.5	g
Distilled water	1	liter

pH should be 7.4 after sterilization.

† Dehydrated Difco KF Streptococcus Agar (No. 0496), dehydrated BBL KF Streptococcal Agar (No. 01-690), or equivalent, may be used.

21. Brain-Heart Infusion Agar

Brain-heart infusion agar contains the same ingredients as brain-heart infusion except that 15.0 g agar are added. The pH should be 7.4 after sterilization. Tube for slants.

22. Tryptophane Broth

Tryptophane broth contains 10.0 g tryptone or trypticase per liter of distilled water. Dispense in 5-ml portions in test tubes. Sterilize by autoclaving at 121 C for 15 min.

23. Buffered Glucose Broth

Proteose peptone or equivalent peptone	5.0	g
Glucose	5.0	g
Dipotassium hydrogen phosphate, K_2HPO_4	5.0	g
Distilled water	1	liter

Dispense in 5-ml portions in test tubes and sterilize in an autoclave at 121 C for 12–15 min, making sure that the total time of exposure to heat is not longer than 30 min.

24. Salt Peptone Glucose Broth

Polypetone or proteose peptone	10.0	g
Sodium chloride, NaCl	5.0	g
Glucose	10.0	g
Distilled water	1	liter

pH should be 7.0 to 7.2 before sterilization. Dispense in 5-ml portions in test tubes and sterilize in an autoclave at 121 C for 12–15 min, making sure that the total time of exposure to heat is not longer than 30 min.

25. Koser's Citrate Broth

Sodium ammonium hydrogen phosphate, $NaNH_4HPO_4 \cdot 4H_2O$	1.5	g

Dipotassium hydrogen phosphate, K_2HPO_4 ... 1.0 g
Magnesium sulfate heptahydrate, $MgSO_4 \cdot 7H_2O$ .... 0.2 g
Sodium citrate dihydrate, crystals ... 3.0 g
Distilled water .... 1 liter

Dispense in 5-ml portions in test tubes. Sterilize by autoclaving at 121 C for 15 min.

26. *Simmons' Citrate Agar*

Magnesium sulfate heptahydrate, $MgSO_4 \cdot 7H_2O$ .... 0.2 g
Ammonium dihydrogen phosphate, $NH_4H_2PO_4$. 1.0 g
Dipotassium hydrogen phosphate, K_2HPO_4 ... 1.0 g
Sodium citrate dihydrate 2.0 g
Sodium chloride, NaCl .. 5.0 g
Agar ....15.0 g
Bromthymol blue 0.08g
Distilled water .... 1 liter

Tube for long slants and sterilize by autoclaving at 121 C for 15 min.

27. *M-Staphylococcus Broth*

Tryptone or polypeptone ....10.0 g
Yeast extract .... 2.5 g
Lactose .... 2.0 g
Mannitol ....10.0 g
Dipotassium hydrogen phosphate, K_2HPO_4 ... 5.0 g
Sodium chloride, NaCl..75.0 g
Distilled water .... 1 liter

pH should be 7.0 after sterilization.

28. *Heart Infusion Broth*

Infusion of beef heart...375 g
Thiotone or tryptose.... 10.0g
Sodium chloride, NaCl.. 0.5g
Distilled water .... 1 liter

pH should be 7.2 to 7.4 after sterilization.

29. *Asparagine Enrichment Broth*

Asparagine .... 2.0 g
Anhydrous dipotassium hydrogen phosphate, K_2HPO_4 .... 1.0 g
Anhydrous potassium dihydrogen phosphate, KH_2PO_4 ......10.0 g
Magnesium sulfate, $MgSO_4 \cdot 7H_2O$ .... 0.5 g
Glycerol .... 8.0 ml
Distilled water .... 1 liter

pH should be adjusted to 6.9–7.2 before sterilization.

30. *Acetamide Broth*

Acetamide ....10.0 g
Sodium chloride, NaCl.. 5.0 g
Anhydrous dipotassium hydrogen phosphate, K_2HPO_4 ... 1.39 g
Anhydrous potassium dihydrogen phosphate, KH_2PO_4 ... 0.73 g
Phenol red 0.012g
Distilled water .... 1 liter

pH should be adjusted to 6.9–7.2 before sterilization.

31. *Tech Medium*

Peptone or gelysate.....20.0 g
Anhydrous magnesium chloride, $MgCl_2$...... 1.4 g
Anhydrous potassium sulfate, K_2SO_4.......10.0 g
Hexadecyltrimethyl ammonium bromide.. 0.5 g
Glycerol ....10 ml
Distilled water .... 1 liter

404 D. Bibliography

LEVINE, M. 1918. Differentiation of *B. coli* and *B. aerogenes* on a simplified eosine methylene blue agar. *J. Infect. Dis.* 23:43.

———. 1918. A simplified fuchsin sulphite (Endo) agar. *AJPH* 8:864.

———. 1921. Further observations on the eosine methylene blue agar. *JAWWA* 8:151.

———. 1921. Bacteria fermenting lactose and their significance in water analysis. *Iowa State Coll. Agr. Mech. Arts Bull.* 62:117.

BUNKER, G. C. & H. SCHUBER. 1922. The reaction of culture media. *JAWWA* 9:63.

JORDAN, H. E. 1932. Brilliant green bile for *Coli-Aerogenes* group determinations. *JAWWA* 24:1027.

RUCHHOFT, C. C. 1935. Comparative studies of media for the determination of the *Coli-Aerogenes* group in water analysis. *JAWWA* 27:1732.

RUCHHOFT, C. C. & J. F. NORTON. 1935. Study of selective media for *Coli-Aerogenes* isolations. *JAWWA* 27:1134.

MCCRADY, M. H. 1937. A practical study of procedures for the detection of the presence of coliform organisms in water. *AJPH* 27:1243.

DARBY, C. W. & W. L. MALLMANN. 1939. Studies on media for coliform organisms. *JAWWA* 31:689.

KELLY, C. B. 1940. Brilliant green lactose bile and the *Standard Methods* completed test in isolation of coliform organisms. *AJPH* 30:1034.

RICHEY, D. 1941. Relative value of 2 per cent and 5 per cent brilliant green bile confirmatory media. *JAWWA* 33:649.

HOWARD, N. J., A. G. LOCHHEAD & M. H. MCCRADY. 1941. A study of methods for the detection of the presence of coliform organisms in water. *Can. Pub. Health J.* 32:29.

MALLMANN, W. L. & C. W. DARBY. 1941. Uses of a lauryl sulphate tryptose broth for the detection of coliform organisms. *AJPH* 31:127.

MALLMANN, W. L. & R. S. BREED. 1941. A comparative study of standard agars for determining bacterial counts in water. *AJPH* 31:341.

HOWARD, N. J., A. G. LOCHHEAD & M. H. MCCRADY. 1942. Report of the Committee on Bacteriological Examination of Water and Sewage. *Can. Pub. Health J.* 33:49.

ARCHAMBAULT, J. & M. H. MCCRADY. 1942. Dissolved air as a source of error in fermentation tube results. *AJPH* 32:1164.

WATTIE, E. 1943. Coliform confirmation from raw and chlorinated waters with brilliant green bile lactose broth. *Pub. Health Rep.* 58:377.

MCCRADY, M. H. 1943. A practical study of lauryl sulfate tryptose broth for detection of the presence of coliform organisms in water. *AJPH* 33:1199.

LEVINE, M. 1944. The effect of concentration of dyes on differentiation of enteric bacteria on eosin methylene blue agar. *J. Bact.* 45:471.

MALLMANN, W. L. & E. B. SELIGMANN. 1950. A comparative study of media for the detection of streptococci in water and sewage. *AJPH* 40:286.

VAUGHN, R. H., M. LEVINE & H. A. SMITH. 1951. A buffered boric acid lactose medium for enrichment and presumptive identification of *Escherichia coli*. *Food Res.* 16:10.

LITSKY, W., W. L. MALLMANN & C. W. FIFIELD. 1955. Comparison of the most probable numbers of *Escherichia coli* and enterococci in river waters. *AJPH* 45:1049.

SLANETZ, L. W. & C. H. BARTLEY. 1957. Numbers of enterococci in water, sewage, and feces determined by the membrane filter technique, with an improved medium. *J. Bact.* 74:591.

FIFIELD, C. W. & C. P. SCHAUFUS. 1958. Improved membrane filter medium for the detection of coliform organisms. *JAWWA* 50:193.

KENNER, B. A., H. F. CLARK & P. W. KABLER. 1961. Fecal streptococci. I. Cultivation and enumeration of streptococci in surface waters. *Applied Microbiol.* 9:15.

MCCARTHY, J. A., J. E. DELANEY & R. J. GRASSO. 1961. Measuring coliforms in water. *Water & Sewage Works* 108:238.

DELANEY, J. E., J. A. MCCARTHY & R. J. GRASSO. 1962. Measurement of *E. coli*

Type I by the membrane filter. *Water & Sewage Works* 109:289.
GELDREICH, E. E., H. F. CLARK, C. B. HUFF & L. C. BEST. 1965. Fecal coliform-organism medium for the membrane filter technique. *JAWWA* 57:208.
GELDREICH, E. E. & H. F. CLARK. 1965. Distilled water suitability for microbiological applications. *J. Milk & Food Tech.* 28:351.
AMERICAN PUBLIC HEALTH ASSOCIATION. 1967. *Standard Methods for the Examination of Dairy Products* (12th ed.). APHA, New York.

405 SAMPLES

1. Collection

a. CONTAINERS: Samples for bacteriologic examination must be collected in bottles which have been cleansed and rinsed with great care, given a final rinse with distilled water, and sterilized as directed in Section 402, Laboratory Apparatus, and Section 403, Washing and Sterilization.

b. DECHLORINATION: A dechlorinating agent should be added to bottles intended for the collection of water containing residual chlorine unless they contain broth for direct planting of the sample therein. Sodium thiosulfate is a satisfactory dechlorinating agent. Its presence at the instant of collection of a sample from a chlorinated supply will neutralize any residual chlorine and will prevent a continuation of the bactericidal action of the chlorine during the time the sample is in transit to the laboratory. The bacteriologic examination will then indicate more probably the true bacterial content of the water at the time of sampling.

The sodium thiosulfate should be added to the clean sample bottle before sterilization in an amount sufficient to provide an approximate concentration of 100 mg per liter in the sample. This can be accomplished by adding to a 4-oz bottle 0.1 ml of a 10% solution of sodium thiosulfate (this will neutralize a sample containing about 15 mg of residual chlorine per liter). The bottle is then stoppered, capped and sterilized by either dry or moist heat, as directed previously.

c. SAMPLING PROCEDURES: When the sample is collected, ample air space shall be left in the bottle to facilitate mixing of the sample by shaking, preparatory to examination. Care must be exercised to take samples that will be representative of the water being tested and to avoid contamination of the sample at the time of collection or in the period prior to examination.

The sampling bottle shall be kept unopened until the moment it is to be filled. The stopper and hood or cap shall be removed as a unit, with care taken to avoid soiling. During sampling the stopper or cap and neck of the bottle shall not be handled and shall be protected from contamination. The bottle shall be held near the base, filled without rinsing, the stopper or cap replaced immediately, and the hood secured around the neck of the bottle.

If the sample of water is to be taken from a distribution-system tap without attachments, it should be ascertained that the tap chosen is supplying water from a service pipe directly connected with the main, and is not, for example, served from a cistern or storage tank. The tap should be opened fully and the water allowed to run to waste for 2 or 3 min, or for a time sufficient to permit clearing of the service line. The flow from the tap should then be restricted to one that will permit filling the bottle without splashing. Leaking taps which allow water to flow over the outside of the tap must be avoided as sampling points.

In collecting samples directly from a river, stream, lake, reservoir, spring or shallow well, the aim must be to obtain a sample that is representative of the water which will be the source of supply to consumers. It is therefore undesirable to take samples too near the bank or too far from the point of drawoff, or at a depth above or below the point of drawoff.

The location of sampling sites and the frequency of sampling are critical factors in obtaining reliable information about bacterial pollution in any body of water. Single or unscheduled grab samples from a river, stream or lake can often be collected for control data or to satisfy regulatory requirements. A grab sample can be taken near the surface.

For extensive stream studies whereby the source and extent of pollution are to be determined, more representative samples must be taken, with consideration of the site, the method, and the time of sampling. In many instances, the number of sampling sites may represent a compromise based on the physical limitations of the laboratory, detection of pollution peaks, and frequency of sample collection. The number of samples to be processed is dependent on whether the survey objective is to measure cycles of immediate pollution, the duration of peak pollution, or the probable average pollution. Sites for measuring cyclic pollution and its duration are immediately below the pollution source. Sampling should be done as frequently as possible.

The site designated to measure estimated average pollution conditions should be far enough downstream to insure complete mixing of the pollutant and the water. Sampling at such points does not eliminate all the variations that may occur but will minimize any sharp fluctuations in quality. Downstream site sampling need not be done as frequently as cyclic pollution sampling.

Samples may be collected one-quarter, one-half or three-quarters the width of the stream at each site or at other distances, depending on the objectives of the survey. Areas of relative stagnation should be avoided. Often only one sample in the channel of the stream may be collected, which is usually taken near the surface.

Samples of bathing beach water should be collected at locations and times of the greatest bather load, and in natural bathing places, following periods of storm water runoff during the bathing season.

Samples from a river, stream, lake or reservoir can often be taken by holding the bottle near its base in the hand and plunging it, neck downward, below the surface. The bottle should then be turned until the neck points slightly upward, the mouth being directed toward the current. If there is no current, as in the case of a reservoir, a current should be artificially created by pushing the bottle horizontally forward in a direction away from the hand. When sampling from a boat, samples should be obtained from the upstream side of the boat. If it is not possible to collect samples from these situations in this way, a weight may be attached to the base of the bottle, which can then be lowered into the water. In any case care must be taken to avoid damage to the bank or stream bed; otherwise, fouling of the water may occur.

Special apparatus which permits mechanical removal of the bottle stopper below the water surface is required to collect samples from the depths of a lake or reservoir. Various types of deep sampling devices are available. The most common of these is the ZoBell J-Z sampler. This sampler utilizes a sterile 350-ml bottle and a rubber stopper through which a piece of glass tubing has been passed. This tubing is connected to another piece of glass tubing by a rubber connecting hose. The unit is mounted on a metal frame containing a cable and a messenger. When the messenger is released, it strikes the glass tubing at a point which has been slightly weakened by a file mark. The glass tube is broken by the messenger and the tension set up by the rubber connecting hose is released and the tubing swings to the side. Water is sucked into the bottle as a consequence of the partial vacuum created by sealing of the unit at the time of autoclaving. Commercial adaptations of this sampler and of others are available.

If the sample is to be taken from a well fitted with a hand pump, water should be pumped to waste for about 5 min before the sample is collected. If the well is equipped with a mechanical pump, the sample should be collected from a tap on the discharge. If there is no pumping machinery, a sample can be collected directly from the well by means of a sterilized bottle fitted with a weight at the base; in this case care should be taken to avoid contaminating samples by any surface scum.

d. Size of sample: The volume of a sample should be sufficient to carry out all the tests required, preferably not less than 100 ml of water for samples intended for bacteriologic examination.

e. Identifying data: All samples should be accompanied by complete and accurate identifying and descriptive data. Samples not so identified should not be accepted for examination.

2. *Preservation and Storage*

The bacteriological examination of a water sample should be started promptly after collection to avoid unpredictable changes. If samples cannot be processed within 1 hr following collection, the use of iced coolers for storage of water samples during transport to the laboratory is recommended.

The temperature of all stream pollution samples should be held below 10 C during a maximum transport time of 6 hr. Such samples should be refrigerated upon receipt in the laboratory and processed within 2 hr. When local conditions necessitate delays in delivery of samples longer than 6 hr, consideration should be given to field examinations by the use of field laboratory facilities located at the site of collection or by use of the tentative delayed-incubation total coliform procedure.

Since these requirements are seldom realistic in the case of individual potable water samples sent to the laboratory by mail service, the time elapsing between collection and examination should in no case exceed 30 hr. Where refrigeration of individual water samples sent by mail is not possible, the use of a thermos-type insulated sample bottle which can be sterilized is recommended as an option. The time and temperature of storage of all samples should be recorded and should be considered in the interpretation of data.

3. Bibliography

CALDWELL, E. L. & L. W. PARR. 1933. Present status of handling water samples—Comparison of bacteriological analyses under varying temperatures and holding conditions, with special reference to the direct method. *AJPH*. 23:467.

ZOBELL, C. E. 1941. Apparatus for collecting water samples from different depths for bacteriological analysis. *J. Marine Res.* 4:173.

COX, K. E. & F. B. CLAIBORNE. 1949. Effect of age and storage temperature on bacteriological water samples. *JAWWA* 41:948.

PUBLIC HEALTH LABORATORY SERVICE WATER SUB-COMMITTEE. 1952. The effect of storage on the coliform and *Bacterium coli* counts of water samples. Overnight storage at room and refrigerator temperatures. *J. Hygiene* 50:107.

———. 1953. The effect of storage on the coliform and *Bacterium coli* counts of water samples. Storage for six hours at room and refrigerator temperatures. *J. Hygiene* 51:559.

———. 1953. The effect of sodium thiosulphate on the coliform and *Bacterium coli* counts of non-chlorinated water samples. *J. Hygiene* 51:572.

MCCARTHY, J. A. 1957. Storage of water sample for bacteriological examinations. *AJPH* 47:971.

HOATHER, R. C. 1961. The bacteriological examination of water. *J. Inst. Water Eng.* 61:426.

LONSANE, B. K., N. M. PARHAD & N. U. RAO. 1967. Effect of storage temperature and time on the coliform in water samples. *Water Res.* (Britain) 1:309.

LUCKING, H. E. 1967. Death rate of coliform bacteria in stored Montana water samples. *J. Environ. Health* 29:576.

406 STANDARD PLATE COUNT

1. Introduction

The Standard Plate Count is a highly empirical technic for determining the bacterial density of waters. Bacteria occur singly, in pairs, chains, clusters or packets; consequently, the number of colonies which develop per milliliter of sample may be lower than the actual number of individual cells present. Moreover, the requirements of some bacteria for special nutrients, variable oxygen requirements, specific incubation temperatures, or other factors may cause fewer organisms to be visible on the plate, under the conditions employed in the standard procedure, than the number actually present. Because the Standard Plate Count is an empirical method, the competence and accuracy of the analyst are critical for the validity of test results.

2. Preparation and Dilution

The sample bottle shall be shaken vigorously 25 times and the required portion shall be withdrawn at once, with a standard sterile pipet, to the petri dish, dilution bottle or tube. If dilutions are made, the dilution bottle likewise shall be shaken 25 times before portions are removed.

The water used for dilution must be prepared as directed in Media Specifications, Section 404C.1a or b. Tap or plain distilled water shall not be used.

3. *Plating*

A 1-ml, 0.1-ml, or other suitable volume of the sample or dilution to be used for plating should be placed in the petri dish first. It is recommended that dilutions be used in preparing volumes of less than 1 ml; in the examination of sewage or turbid water, a 0.1-ml inoculum of the original sample shall not be measured but an appropriate dilution should be prepared.

Not less than 10 ml of liquefied agar medium at a temperature of 43 to 45 C should be added to the water in the petri dish. The agar may be stored in a melted condition at the proper temperature for no longer than 3 hr and shall not be remelted.

Tryptone glucose extract agar or plate count agar shall be used.

The cover of the dish should be lifted just enough for the introduction of the pipet or the culture medium. The agar and the sample shall be thoroughly mixed and uniformly spread over the bottom of the dish by tilting and rotating the dish.

The plates shall be solidified as rapidly as possible after pouring and placed immediately in an appropriate incubator. Not more than 20 min should elapse between plating and pouring.

4. *Incubation*

Incubation for the Standard Plate Count shall be at a temperature of 35 ± 0.5 C for 24 ± 2 hr, or at 20 ± 0.5C for 48 ± 3 hr. In the examination of chlorinated water supplies, where chlorination has not been effective and where the chlorine in the sample has been neutralized by the addition of sodium thiosulfate, bacteria may not develop sufficiently to be detected in 24 hr, although in 48 hr the count may be appreciable. Glass-covered dishes and plastic dishes shall be inverted in the incubator. Plates are to be packed as directed under Laboratory Apparatus, Section 402, without crowding in the incubator. Any deviation from this method must be stated in the report of examination.

5. *Counting*

In preparing plates, such amounts of water should be planted as will give from 30 to 300 colonies on a plate. The aim should be always to have at least two plates that will give colony numbers between these limits, except as provided below.

Ordinarily, it is not desirable to plant more than 1.0 ml of water in a plate; therefore, when the total number of colonies developing from 1.0 ml is less than 30, it is obviously necessary to disregard the rule above and to record the result as observed. With this exception, only plates showing 30 to 300 colonies should be considered in determining the Standard Plate Count. The result as reported shall be the average of all plates falling within these limits.

Counting shall be done with an approved counting aid such as the Quebec colony counter. If such equipment is not available, counting may be done with any other counter providing equivalent magnification and illumination.

To avoid fictitious accuracy and yet to express the numerical results by a method consistent with the precision of the technic employed, the recorded number of colonies per ml shall not include more than two significant figures.

For example, a count of 142 is recorded as 140, and a count of 155 as 160, whereas a count of 35 is recorded as 35.

When colonies per plate in the highest dilution exceed 300, record the result as greater than 300 times the appropriate dilution factor. If no chosen dilution has colonies, record the value as less than 1 colony per lowest dilution and report the result as a "less than" number per milliliter.

Counts shall be designated as "standard plate count at 35 C," or "standard plate count at 20 C."

6. Bibliography

BUTTERFIELD, C. T. 1933. The selection of a dilution water for bacteriological examinations. *J. Bact.* 23:355; *Pub. Health Rep.* 48:681.

ARCHAMBAULT, J., J. CUROT & M. H. MCCRADY. 1937. The need of uniformity of conditions for counting plates (with suggestions for a standard colony counter). *AJPH* 27:809.

RICHARDS, O. W. & P. C. HEIJN. 1945. An improved darkfield Quebec colony counter. *J. Milk Tech.* 8:253.

AMERICAN PUBLIC HEALTH ASSOCIATION. 1967. *Standard Methods for the Examination of Dairy Products* (12th ed.). APHA, New York.

407 MULTIPLE-TUBE FERMENTATION TECHNIC FOR MEMBERS OF THE COLIFORM GROUP

The coliform group comprises all of the aerobic and facultative anaerobic, gram-negative, nonspore-forming, rod-shaped bacteria which ferment lactose with gas formation within 48 hr at 35 C.*

The standard test for the coliform group may be carried out either by the multiple-tube fermentation technic (presumptive test, confirmed test, or completed test) described herein or by the membrane filter technic described under a separate heading, each technic being applicable within the limitations specified and with due consideration of the purpose of the examination.

As applied to the membrane filter technic, the coliform group may be redefined as comprising all the aerobic and facultative anaerobic, gram-negative, nonspore-forming, rod-shaped bacteria which produce a dark colony with a metallic sheen within 24 hr on an Endo-type medium containing lactose.

It has been adequately demonstrated that, even after the prescribed shaking, the distribution of bacteria in water is irregular. It is entirely possible to divide a given volume of water into portions and after testing find that the number of organisms in any portion may be none, or at least less than the arithmetic average based on examination of the total volume might indicate. It is also quite probable that the growth in a fermentation tube may result not from one organism but from many organisms. It is reasonable, however, to assume that growth develops from a single individual.

It is convenient to express the results of the examination of replicate tubes and dilutions in terms of the

* The "coliform group" as defined above is equivalent to the "*B. coli* group" as used in the third, fourth and fifth editions of this manual, and to the "*coli-aerogenes* group" as used through the eighth edition.

Most Probable Number (MPN). This term is actually an estimate based on certain probability formulas. Theoretical considerations and large-scale replicate determinations indicate that this estimate tends to be greater than the actual number and that the disparity tends to diminish with increasing numbers of tubes in each dilution examined.

The accuracy of any single test will depend, then, on the number of tubes used. The most satisfactory information will be obtained when the largest portion examined shows gas in some or all of the tubes and the smallest portion shows no gas in all or a majority of the tubes. The numerical value of the estimation of the bacterial content is largely determined by that dilution which shows both positive and negative results. The number of portions scheduled, especially in the critical dilution, will be governed by the desired accuracy of the result. The increased interest in the multiple-tube technic, the numerous investigations into its precision, and the expression of test results as MPNs should not lead the analyst to regard this method as a statistical exercise rather than a means of estimating the coliform density of a water and thereby an aid to establishing its sanitary quality. The best assessment of the sanitary quality of a water still must depend on the interpretation of results of the multiple-tube technic —or of other methods, possibly more precise—and of all other information regarding a water which may be obtained by surveys or otherwise.

1. *Water of Drinking Water Quality*

When examining water for evidence of quality that meets the standards of the U. S. Public Health Service, it is necessary to use a minimum of five fermentation tubes of the presumptive medium, each containing 10 ml or 100 ml of the water sample. Practical considerations generally militate against the use of larger portions. The Confirmed Test or the Completed Test shall be the test of choice.

For water examined frequently, or even daily, the common practice of inoculating five 10-ml or five 100-ml portions generally provides sufficient definite information. In the examination of other waters presumed to be of drinking-water quality, the use of at least five tubes in each of at least three dilutions is desirable to provide acceptable precision and reasonably satisfactory information; in no case should less than three tubes per dilution be used.

For the routine examination of most potable water supplies, particularly those that are disinfected, the object of the test is to determine the presence or absence of coliform organisms as a measure of either the efficiency of operation or the presence of bacterial contamination. The safety of the water is generally judged by a knowledge of the sanitary condition of the supply and monitored by the number of samples yielding positive or negative results. It is expected that greater than 95% of all samples examined yield negative results. An occasional positive result, unless repeated from the same sampling point, or unless it is one yielding three or more positive tubes when five tubes are inoculated, is generally of limited significance. What is important is an increase in the number of positive samples over a period of time or an abrupt increase in a short period of time. Either increase indicates a change in the quality of the water, the significance of which should be studied, with correction made as necessary.

2. *Water of Other than Drinking Water Quality*

In the examination of waters of other than drinking water quality, a series of lactose broth or lauryl tryptose broth tubes should be inoculated with decimal quantities of the water, the selection of portion sizes depending on the probable coliform density as indicated by the experience of the analyst and how much is known about the character of the water. The object of the examination of nonpotable water is generally to estimate the density of bacterial contamination or determine a source of pollution. Either objective requires a numerical value for reporting results. The multiple-tube fermentation technic may be used; however, to obtain statistically valid MPN values, a minimum series of three, but preferably five, tubes—each inoculated with decimal quantities of sample—should be run. A sufficient number of samples must be examined to yield representative results for the sampling station. Generally, the log average or median value of the results of a number of samples will yield a value in which the effect of individual extreme values is minimized. The membrane filter technic may prove the better procedure to accomplish this objective.

407 A. Standard Total Coliform MPN Tests

1. *Presumptive Test*

Lactose broth or lauryl tryptose broth may be used in the Presumptive Test.

a. PROCEDURE:

1) Inoculate a series of fermentation tubes ("primary" fermentation tubes) with appropriate graduated quantities (multiples and submultiples of 1 ml) of the water to be tested. Bottles to contain 100-ml sample portions should be prewarmed in a water bath at 35 C. The concentration of nutritive ingredients in the mixture of medium and added portion of sample must conform to the requirements given in Section 404C, Media Specifications, Media 3 and 4. The portions of the water sample used for inoculating the lactose or lauryl tryptose broth fermentation tubes will vary in size and number with the character of the water under examination, but in general should be decimal multiples and submultiples of 1 ml. These should be selected in accordance with the discussion of the multiple-tube test above.

2) Incubate the inoculated fermentation tubes at 35 ± 0.5 C. After shaking gently, examine each tube at the end of 24 ± 2 hr and, if no gas has formed and been trapped in the inverted vial, again at the end of 48 ± 3 hr. Record the presence or absence of gas formation at each examination of the tubes, regardless of the amount.

b. INTERPRETATION:

Formation within 48 ± 3 hr of gas in any amount in the inner fermentation tubes or vials constitutes a positive Presumptive Test.

The appearance of an air bubble must not be confused with actual gas production. If the gas is formed as a result of fermentation, the broth medium will become cloudy. Active fermentation may be shown by the continued appearance of small bubbles of gas throughout the medium outside the inner vial when the fermentation tube is shaken gently.

The absence of gas formation at the end of 48 ± 3 hr of incubation constitutes a negative test. An arbitrary limit of 48 hr for observation doubtless excludes from consideration occasional members of the coliform group which form gas very slowly and are generally of limited sanitary significance; for the purpose of a standard test based on the definition of the coliform group, exclusion of these occasional slow gas-forming organisms does not compromise the value of the test.

2. *Confirmed Test*

The use of confirmatory brilliant green lactose bile broth fermentation tubes or of Endo or eosin methylene blue agar plates is permitted, although the use of a solid confirmatory medium is not recommended.

a. PROCEDURE: Submit all primary fermentation tubes showing any amount of gas at the end of 24 hr of incubation to the confirmed test. If active fermentation appears in the primary fermentation tube before expiration of the 24-hr period of incubation, it is preferable to transfer to the confirmatory medium without waiting for the full 24-hr period to elapse. If additional primary fermentation tubes show gas production at the end of 48-hr incubation, these too shall be submitted to the confirmed test.

b. ALTERNATIVE PROCEDURE: Where three or more multiple portions of a series of three or more decimal dilutions of a given sample are planted, submit to the Confirmed Test all tubes of the two highest dilutions (smallest volumes) of the original samples showing gas formation in 24 hr.

All tubes producing gas in 24 hr that have not been submitted to the Confirmed Test must be recorded as containing organisms of the coliform group—that is, as positive—even though all the confirmed tests actually performed yield negative results.

Submit to the Confirmed Test all tubes of all dilutions of the original sample in which gas is produced only at the end of 48 hr.

If less than three portions of any dilution (volume), or if a series of less than three decimal dilutions of the original sample are planted, submit all tubes producing gas at 24 or 48 hr to the confirmed test.

c. PROCEDURE WITH BRILLIANT GREEN LACTOSE BILE BROTH:

1) Metal loop—Gently shake or rotate primary fermentation tube showing gas and with a sterile metal loop, 3 mm in diameter, transfer one to three loopfuls of medium to a fermentation tube containing brilliant green lactose bile broth, or

2) Wood applicator—Gently shake or rotate primary fermentation tube showing gas and insert a sterile wood applicator at least 1 in. into the medium. Promptly remove and plunge applicator to bottom of fermentation tube containing brilliant green lactose bile broth. Remove and discard applicator.

3) Incubation—Incubate the inoculated brilliant green lactose bile broth tube for 48 ± 3 hr at 35 ± 0.5 C.

4) Interpretation—The formation of gas in any amount in the inverted vial of the brilliant green lactose bile broth fermentation tube at any time within 48 ± 3 hr constitutes a positive Confirmed Test.

d. PROCEDURE WITH ENDO OR EOSIN METHYLENE BLUE AGAR PLATES:

1)—Streak one or more plates from each of the selected primary fermentation tubes showing gas formation; it is essential that the plates be so streaked as to insure the presence of some discrete colonies, separated by at least 0.5 cm from one another. Careful attention to the following details when streaking plates will result in a high proportion of successful isolations if coliform organisms are present: *(a)* Employ an inoculating needle slightly curved at the tip; *(b)* tap and incline the primary fermentation tube to avoid picking up any membrane or scum on the needle; *(c)* insert the end of the needle into the liquid in the tube to a depth of approximately 5.0 mm; *(d)* streak the plate by bringing only the curved section of the needle in contact with the agar surface so that the latter will not be scratched or torn.

2)—Incubate the plate (inverted, if with glass or plastic cover) at 35 ± 0.5 C for 24 ± 2 hr.

3)—The colonies developing on Endo or eosin methylene blue agar may be described as *typical* (nucleated, with or without metallic sheen); *atypical* (opaque, unnucleated, mucoid, pink after 24-hr incubation), or *negative* (all others).

If typical coliform colonies have developed on the plate within the incubation period of 24 ± 2 hr, the result of the Confirmed Test may be considered positive.

If only atypical colonies have developed within 24 ± 2 hr, the result cannot yet be considered definitely negative because many coliform organisms fail to form typical colonies on Endo or eosin methylene blue plates, or because the colonies develop slowly. In such a case it is always necessary to complete the test as directed in Section 3 below.

If no colonies, or only noncoliform-type colonies, have developed within 24 ± 2 hr, the results of the confirmed test may be considered negative.

3. *Completed Test*

The Completed Test is used as the next step following the Confirmed Test. It may be applied to the brilliant green lactose bile broth fermentation tubes showing gas in the Confirmed Test, or to typical or atypical colonies found on the plates of solid differential medium used for the Confirmed Test.

a. PROCEDURE:

1) If the brilliant green lactose bile broth tubes used for the Confirmed Test are to be employed for the Completed Test, streak one or more Endo or eosin methylene blue plates from each tube showing gas, as soon as possible after the appearance of gas. Incubate the plates at 35 ± 0.5 C for 24 ± 2 hr.

2) From each of these plates, or from each of the plates used for the Confirmed Test (Section 407A.2d above), fish one or more typical well-isolated coliform colonies or, if no typical colonies are present, fish two or more colonies considered most likely to consist of organisms of the coliform group, transferring each fishing to a lactose broth or a lauryl tryptose broth fermentation tube and to a nutrient agar slant.

The use of a colony counter is recommended to provide optimum magnification when fishing colonies from the plates of selective medium.

If possible, when transferring colonies, take care to choose well-isolated colonies separated by at least 0.5 cm from other colonies and barely to touch the surface of the colony with a flame-sterilized, air-cooled transfer needle, so as to minimize the danger of transferring a mixed culture.

The agar slants and secondary broth tubes are incubated at 35 ± 0.5 C for 24 ± 2 or 48 ± 3 hr if gas is not produced in 24 hr. Gram-stained preparations (see Section 407A.4 below) from those agar slant cultures corresponding to the secondary lactose broth tubes that show gas are examined microscopically.

b. INTERPRETATION:

The formation of gas in the secondary lactose broth tube and the demonstration of gram-negative nonspore-forming rod-shaped bacteria in the agar culture may be considered a satisfactory Completed Test, demonstrating the presence of a member of the coliform group in the volume of sample examined.

If, after 48 ± 3 hr, gas is produced in the lactose and no spores or gram-positive rods are found on the slant, the test may be considered completed and the presence of coliform organisms demonstrated.

4. Gram-Stain Technic

The Completed Test for coliform-group organisms requires the determination of gram-stain characteristics of the organisms isolated, as discussed above.

There are a large variety of modifications of the Gram stain, many of which have been listed by Hucker and Conn (Section 407E). The following modification by Hucker is valuable for staining smears of pure culture. It is desirable to use a gram-positive and a gram-negative culture as controls for the staining process.

a. REAGENTS:

1) Ammonium oxalate-crystal violet—Dissolve 2 g crystal violet (85% dye content) in 20 ml 95% ethyl alcohol; dissolve 0.2 g of ammonium oxalate monohydrate in 20 ml distilled water; mix the two solutions, ordinarily in equal parts. It is sometimes found, however, that this proportion gives so concentrated a stain that gram-negative organisms are not properly decolorized. To avoid this difficulty, the crystal violet solution may be diluted as much as 10 times and the diluted solution mixed with an equal quantity of ammonium oxalate solution.

2) Lugol's solution, Gram's modification—Dissolve 1 g iodine crystals and 2 g potassium iodide in 300 ml distilled water.

3) Counterstain—Dissolve 2.5 g safranin dye in 100 ml of 95% ethyl alcohol. Add 10 ml of the alcoholic solution of safranin to 100 ml of distilled water.

4) Ethyl alcohol, 95%.

b. PROCEDURE:

Prepare a smear on a glass slide of the bacterial growth on an agar slant. Air-dry, fix by passing the slide through a flame, and stain for 1 min with the ammonium oxalate-crystal violet solution. Wash the slide in water; immerse in Lugol's solution for 1 min.

Wash the stained slide in water; blot dry. Decolorize with ethyl alcohol for 30 sec using gentle agitation. Blot and cover with counterstain for 10 sec; then wash, dry and examine.

Cells which decolorize and accept the safranin stain are pink in color and defined as gram-negative in reaction. Cells which do not decolorize but retain the crystal violet stain are deep blue in color and are defined as gram-positive.

407 B. Application of Tests to Routine Examinations

The following basic considerations apply to the selection of the Presumptive Test, the Confirmed Test, or the Completed Test in the examination of any given sample of water or wastewater.

1. Presumptive Test

The Presumptive Test without confirmation may be applied to the examination of:

a. Any sample of waste, sewage, sewage effluent (except chlorinated effluent), or water known to be heavily polluted, the fitness of which for drinking water is not under consideration.

b. Any routine sample of raw water in a treatment plant, provided records indicate that the Presumptive Test is not too inclusive for the development of pertinent data.

2. Confirmed Test

The Confirmed Test should be applied in the examination of:

a. Any water to which the Presumptive Test is known, from previous records, to be inapplicable.

b. Routine samples of drinking water, water in process of treatment, and finished waters.

c. Chlorinated sewage effluents.

d. Bathing waters.

3. Completed Test

The Completed Test should be applied in the examination of water samples where the results are to be used for the control of the quality of raw or finished waters; or if not applied to all samples, then to such a proportion of them as to establish beyond reasonable doubt the value of the Confirmed Test in determining the sanitary quality of such water supplies.

NOTE: Schematic outlines of the Presumptive, Confirmed, and Completed Tests are shown in Figures 52a and b.

407 C. Fecal Coliform MPN Procedure

Elevated temperature tests for the separation of organisms of the coliform group into those of fecal origin and those derived from nonfecal sources have been used in many parts of the world and with various modifications. Recent modifications in technical procedures, standardization of methods, and detailed studies of members of the coliform group found in the feces of various warm-blooded animals compared with those from other environmental sources have established the value of a fecal coliform determination. The test may be performed either by multiple-tube procedures as described here or by a membrane filter method as described in the section on the membrane filter technic. The following two procedures yield adequate information as to the source of the coliform group (fecal or nonfecal) when used as a *confirmatory* test procedure. These multiple-tube procedures cannot be used for direct isolation of coliforms from water but require prior enrichment in a Presumptive Test medium for optimum recovery of fecal coliforms.

The fecal coliform test is applicable to investigations of stream pollution, raw water sources, sewage treatment systems, bathing waters, sea waters, and general water-quality monitoring. The procedure is not recommended as a substitute for the coliform test in the examination of potable waters, since no coliform bacteria of any kind should be tolerated in a treated water.

1. Fecal Coliform Test (EC Medium)

The fecal coliform test, when executed as described, may be expected to differentiate between coliforms of fecal origin (intestines of warm-blooded animals) and coliforms from other sources. Use EC medium as described in Section 404C, Media Specifications, No. 10, preceding.

a. Procedure—Transfers should be made from all positive presumptive tubes to EC medium. This examination may be performed simultaneously with the confirmatory procedure using brilliant green lactose bile broth. Use a sterile metal loop with a minimum 3-mm diameter or a sterile wooden applicator to transfer from the positive fermentation tube to EC medium. When making such transfers, first gently shake the presumptive tube or mix by rotating. Inoculated tubes are incubated in a water bath at 44.5 ± 0.2 C for 24 ± 2 hr. All EC tubes must be placed in the water bath within 30 min after planting. The water depth in the incubator should be sufficient to immerse tubes to the upper level of the medium.

b. Interpretation—Gas production in a fermentation tube within 24 hr or less is considered a positive reaction indicating fecal origin. Failure to produce gas (growth sometimes occurs) constitutes a negative reaction indicating a source other than the intestinal tract of warm-blooded animals. Fecal coliform densities are calculated as described under Estimation of Bacterial Density (Section 407D below).

2. Fecal Coliform Test (Boric Acid Lactose Broth)

This broth has essentially the same selectivity and sensitivity as the EC medium; however, the incubation temper-

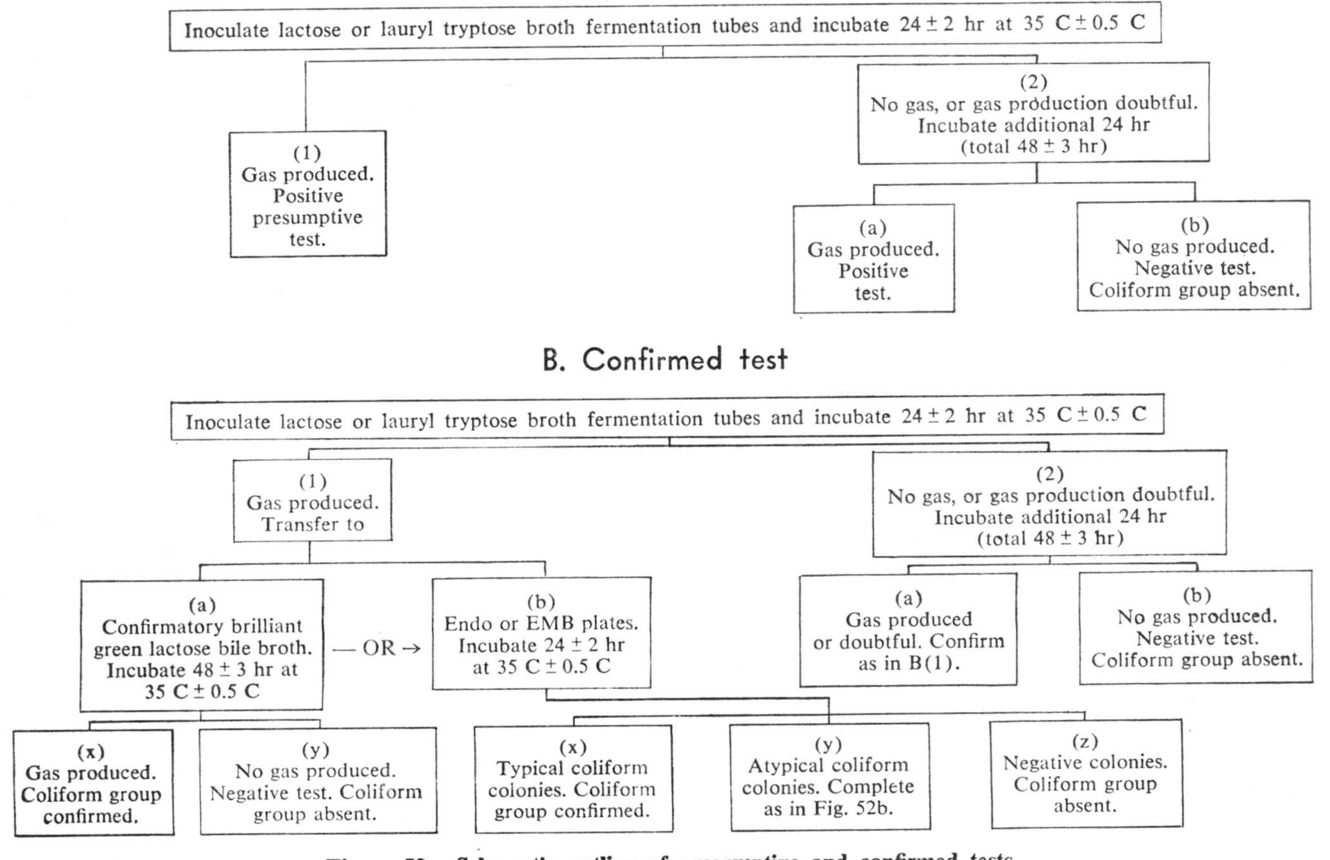

Figure 52a. Schematic outline of presumptive and confirmed tests.

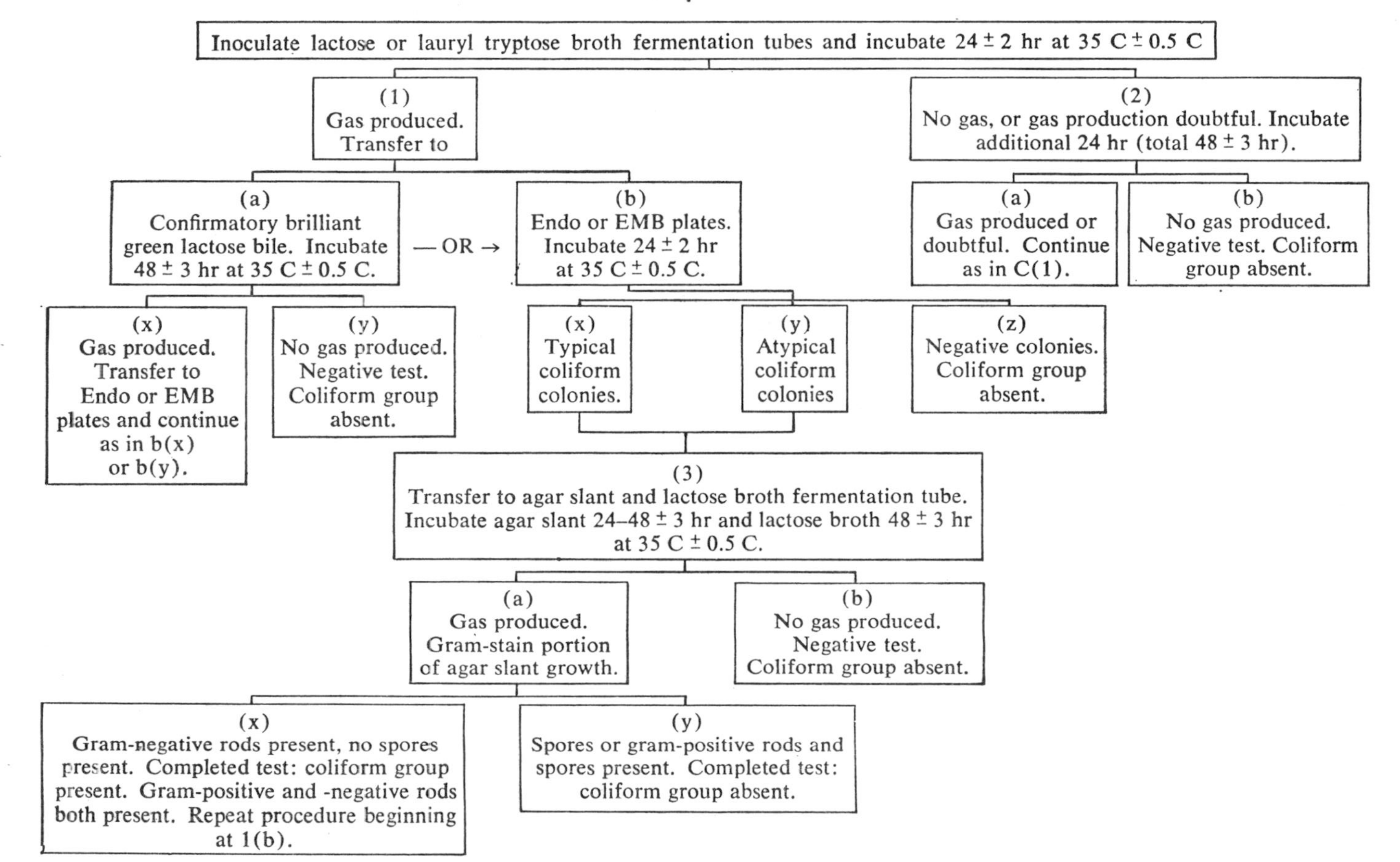

Figure 52b. Schematic outline of completed test.

ature is 43 ± 0.2 C and the incubation time is 48 ± 3 hr. Use boric acid lactose broth as described under Media Specifications (No. 11) and follow the procedure for the fecal coliform test (EC medium) as given above.

407 D. Estimation of Bacterial Density

1. Precision of Fermentation Tube Test

It is desirable to bear in mind that unless a large number of portions of sample are examined, the precision of the fermentation tube test is rather low. For example, even when the sample contains 1 coliform organism per milliliter, about 37% of 1-ml tubes may be expected to yield negative results because of irregular distribution of the bacteria in the sample. When five tubes, each with 1 ml of sample are employed under these conditions, a completely negative result may be expected less than 1% of the time.

Even when five fermentation tubes are employed, the precision of the results obtained is not of a high order. Consequently, great caution must be exercised when interpreting, in terms of sanitary significance, the coliform results obtained from the use of a few tubes with each dilution of sample, especially when the number of samples from a given sampling point is limited.

2. Computing and Recording of MPN

The number of positive findings of coliform group organisms (either presumptive, confirmed or completed) resulting from multiple-portion decimal-dilution plantings should be computed as the combination of positives and recorded in terms of the Most Probable Number (MPN). The MPN, for a variety of planting series and results, is given in Tables 407(1) through (6). Included in these tables are the 95% confidence limits for each MPN value determined.

The quantities indicated at the heads of the columns relate more specifically to finished waters. The values may be used in computing the MPN in larger

TABLE 407(1): MPN INDEX AND 95% CONFIDENCE LIMITS FOR VARIOUS COMBINATIONS OF POSITIVE AND NEGATIVE RESULTS WHEN FIVE 10-ML PORTIONS ARE USED

No. of Tubes Giving Positive Reaction out of 5 of 10 ml Each	MPN Index per 100 ml	95% Confidence Limits	
		Lower	Upper
0	<2.2	0	6.0
1	2.2	0.1	12.6
2	5.1	0.5	19.2
3	9.2	1.6	29.4
4	16.	3.3	52.9
5	>16.	8.0	Infinite

TABLE 407(2): MPN INDEX AND 95% CONFIDENCE LIMITS FOR VARIOUS COMBINATIONS OF POSITIVE AND NEGATIVE RESULTS WHEN FIVE 10-ML PORTIONS, FIVE 1-ML PORTIONS AND FIVE 0.1-ML PORTIONS ARE USED

No. of Tubes Giving Positive Reaction out of			MPN Index per 100 ml	95% Confidence Limits	
5 of 10 ml Each	5 of 1 ml Each	5 of 0.1 ml Each		Lower	Upper
0	0	0	<2		
0	0	1	2	<0.5	7
0	1	0	2	<0.5	7
0	2	0	4	<0.5	11
1	0	0	2	<0.5	7
1	0	1	4	<0.5	11
1	1	0	4	<0.5	11
1	1	1	6	<0.5	15
1	2	0	6	<0.5	15
2	0	0	5	<0.5	13
2	0	1	7	1	17
2	1	0	7	1	17
2	1	1	9	2	21
2	2	0	9	2	21
2	3	0	12	3	28
3	0	0	8	1	19
3	0	1	11	2	25
3	1	0	11	2	25
3	1	1	14	4	34
3	2	0	14	4	34
3	2	1	17	5	46
3	3	0	17	5	46
4	0	0	13	3	31
4	0	1	17	5	46
4	1	0	17	5	46
4	1	1	21	7	63
4	1	2	26	9	78
4	2	0	22	7	67
4	2	1	26	9	78
4	3	0	27	9	80
4	3	1	33	11	93
4	4	0	34	12	93
5	0	0	23	7	70
5	0	1	31	11	89
5	0	2	43	15	110
5	1	0	33	11	93
5	1	1	46	16	120
5	1	2	63	21	150
5	2	0	49	17	130
5	2	1	70	23	170
5	2	2	94	28	220
5	3	0	79	25	190
5	3	1	110	31	250
5	3	2	140	37	340
5	3	3	180	44	500
5	4	0	130	35	300
5	4	1	170	43	490
5	4	2	220	57	700
5	4	3	280	90	850
5	4	4	350	120	1,000
5	5	0	240	68	750
5	5	1	350	120	1,000
5	5	2	540	180	1,400
5	5	3	920	300	3,200
5	5	4	1600	640	5,800
5	5	5	≥2400		

or smaller portion plantings in the following manner: If, instead of portions of 10, 1.0 and 0.1 ml, a combination of portions of 100, 10 and 1 ml is used, the MPN is recorded as 0.1 times the value given in the applicable table.

If, on the other hand, a combination of corresponding portions at 1.0, 0.1 and 0.01 ml is planted, record 10 times the value shown in the table; if a combination of portions of 0.1, 0.01 and 0.001 ml is planted, record 100 times the value shown in the table; and so on for other combinations.

When more than three dilutions are employed in a decimal series of dilutions, the results from only three of these are used in computing the MPN. To select the three dilutions to be employed in determining the MPN index,

TABLE 407(3): MPN INDEX AND 95% CONFIDENCE LIMITS FOR VARIOUS COMBINATIONS OF POSITIVE AND NEGATIVE RESULTS WHEN ONE 50-ML PORTION, FIVE 10-ML PORTIONS AND FIVE 1-ML PORTIONS ARE USED

No. of Tubes Giving Positive Reaction out of			MPN Index per 100 ml	95% Confidence Limits		No. of Tubes Giving Positive Reaction out of			MPN Index per 100 ml	95% Confidence Limits	
1 of 50 ml Each	5 of 10 ml Each	5 of 1 ml Each		Lower	Upper	1 of 50 ml Each	5 of 10 ml Each	5 of 1 ml Each		Lower	Upper
0	0	0	<1								
0	0	1	1	<0.5	4	1	2	1	7	1	17
0	0	2	2	<0.5	6	1	2	2	10	3	23
0	1	0	1	<0.5	4	1	2	3	12	3	28
0	1	1	2	<0.5	6	1	3	0	8	2	19
0	1	2	3	<0.5	8	1	3	1	11	3	26
0	2	0	2	<0.5	6	1	3	2	14	4	34
0	2	1	3	<0.5	8	1	3	3	18	5	53
0	2	2	4	<0.5	11	1	3	4	21	6	66
0	3	0	3	<0.5	8	1	4	0	13	4	31
0	3	1	5	<0.5	13	1	4	1	17	5	47
0	4	0	5	<0.5	13	1	4	2	22	7	69
1	0	0	1	<0.5	4	1	4	3	28	9	85
1	0	1	3	<0.5	8	1	4	4	35	12	100
1	0	2	4	<0.5	11	1	4	5	43	15	120
1	0	3	6	<0.5	15	1	5	0	24	8	75
1	1	0	3	<0.5	8	1	5	1	35	12	100
1	1	1	5	<0.5	13	1	5	2	54	18	140
1	1	2	7	1	17	1	5	3	92	27	220
1	1	3	9	2	21	1	5	4	160	39	450
1	2	0	5	<0.5	13	1	5	5	≧240		

taking the system of five tubes of each dilution as an example, the highest dilution which gives positive results in all five portions tested (no lower dilution giving any negative results) and the two next succeeding higher dilutions should be chosen. The results at these three volumes should then be used in computing the MPN index. In the examples given below, the significant dilution results are shown in boldface. The number in the numerator represents positive tubes; that in the denominator, the total tubes planted; the combination of positives simply represents the total number of positive tubes per dilution:

Example	*1 ml*	*0.1 ml*	*0.01 ml*	*0.001 ml*	*Combination of positives*
(*a*)	5/5	**5/5**	**2/5**	**0/5**	5–2–0
(*b*)	**5/5**	**4/5**	**2/5**	0/5	5–4–2
(*c*)	**0/5**	**1/5**	**0/5**	0/5	0–1–0

TABLE 407(4): MPN INDEX AND 95% CONFIDENCE LIMITS FOR VARIOUS COMBINATIONS OF POSITIVE AND NEGATIVE RESULTS WHEN FIVE 50-ML PORTIONS, FIVE 10-ML PORTIONS AND FIVE 1-ML PORTIONS ARE USED

No. of Tubes Giving Positive Reaction out of			MPN Index per 100 ml	95% Confidence Limits	
5 of 50 ml Each	5 of 10 ml Each	5 of 1 ml Each		Lower	Upper
0	0	0	<1		
0	0	1	1	<0.5	2
0	1	0	1	<0.5	2
0	1	1	1	<0.5	2
0	2	0	1	<0.5	2
0	3	0	1	<0.5	2
1	0	0	1	<0.5	2
1	0	1	1	<0.5	2
1	1	0	1	<0.5	2
1	1	1	1	<0.5	2
1	2	0	1	<0.5	2
1	2	1	2	<0.5	4
1	3	0	2	<0.5	4
2	0	0	1	<0.5	2
2	0	1	1	<0.5	2
2	1	0	1	<0.5	2
2	1	1	2	<0.5	4
2	2	0	2	<0.5	4
2	2	1	2	<0.5	4
2	3	0	2	<0.5	4
2	3	1	3	1	7
2	4	0	3	1	7
3	0	0	2	<0.5	4
3	0	1	2	<0.5	4
3	1	0	2	<0.5	4
3	1	1	2	<0.5	4
3	1	2	3	1	7
3	2	0	3	1	7
3	2	1	3	1	7
3	2	2	4	1	9
3	3	0	3	1	7
3	3	1	4	1	9
3	4	0	4	1	9
3	4	1	4	1	9
4	0	0	2	<0.5	4
4	0	1	3	1	7
4	0	2	3	1	7
4	1	0	3	1	7
4	1	1	4	1	9
4	1	2	4	1	9
4	2	0	4	1	9
4	2	1	4	1	9
4	2	2	5	2	12
4	3	0	5	2	12
4	3	1	5	2	12
4	3	2	6	2	14
4	4	0	6	2	14
4	4	1	7	3	17
4	5	0	7	3	17
4	5	1	8	3	19
5	0	0	4	1	9
5	0	1	4	1	9
5	0	2	6	2	14
5	1	0	5	2	12
5	1	1	6	2	14
5	1	2	7	3	17
5	2	0	6	2	14
5	2	1	8	3	19
5	2	2	10	4	23
5	2	3	12	4	28
5	3	0	9	3	21
5	3	1	11	4	26
5	3	2	14	5	34
5	3	3	18	6	53
5	4	0	13	6	31
5	4	1	17	6	47
5	4	2	22	7	70
5	4	3	28	9	85
5	4	4	35	11	100
5	5	0	24	8	75
5	5	1	35	11	100
5	5	2	54	18	140
5	5	3	92	27	220
5	5	4	160	39	420
5	5	5	≧240		

TABLE 407(5): MPN INDEX AND 95% CONFIDENCE LIMITS FOR VARIOUS COMBINATIONS OF POSITIVE AND NEGATIVE RESULTS WHEN THREE 10-ML PORTIONS, THREE 1-ML PORTIONS AND THREE 0.1-ML PORTIONS ARE USED

No. of Tubes Giving Positive Reaction out of			MPN Index per 100 ml	95% Confidence Limits	
3 of 10 ml Each	3 of 1 ml Each	3 of 0.1 ml Each		Lower	Upper
0	0	0	<3		
0	0	1	3	<0.5	9
0	1	0	3	<0.5	13
1	0	0	4	<0.5	20
1	0	1	7	1	21
1	1	0	7	1	23
1	1	1	11	3	36
1	2	0	11	3	36
2	0	0	9	1	36
2	0	1	14	3	37
2	1	0	15	3	44
2	1	1	20	7	89
2	2	0	21	4	47
2	2	1	28	10	150
3	0	0	23	4	120
3	0	1	39	7	130
3	0	2	64	15	380
3	1	0	43	7	210
3	1	1	75	14	230
3	1	2	120	30	380
3	2	0	93	15	380
3	2	1	150	30	440
3	2	2	210	35	470
3	3	0	240	36	1,300
3	3	1	460	71	2,400
3	3	2	1,100	150	4,800
3	3	3	≥2,400		

In c, the first three dilutions should be taken, so as to throw the positive result in the middle dilution.

When a case such as shown below in line *d* arises, where a positive occurs in a dilution higher than the three chosen according to the rule, it should be incorporated in the result for the highest chosen dilution, as in *e*:

Example	*1 ml*	*0.1 ml*	*0.01 ml*	*0.001 ml*	*Combination of positives*
(*d*)	**5/5**	**3/5**	**1/5**	1/5	5–3–2
(*e*)	**5/5**	**3/5**	**2/5**	0/5	

When it is desired to summarize with a single MPN value the results from a series of samples, the geometric mean, the arithmetic mean, or the median may be used.

TABLE 407(6): MPN INDEX AND 95% CONFIDENCE LIMITS FOR VARIOUS COMBINATIONS OF POSITIVE AND NEGATIVE RESULTS WHEN FIVE 10-ML PORTIONS, ONE 1-ML PORTION AND ONE 0.1-ML PORTION ARE USED

No. of Tubes Giving Positive Reaction out of*			MPN Index per 100 ml	95% Confidence Limits	
5 of 10 ml Each	1 of 1 ml Each	1 of 0.1 ml Each		Lower	Upper
0	0	0	<2	0	5.9
0	1	0	2	0.050	13
1	0	0	2.2	0.050	13
1	1	0	4.4	0.52	14
2	0	0	5	0.54	19
2	1	0	7.6	1.5	19
3	0	0	8.8	1.6	29
3	1	0	12	3.1	30
4	0	0	15	3.3	46
4	0	1	20	5.9	48
4	1	0	21	6.0	53
5	0	0	38	6.4	330
5	0	1	96	12	370
5	1	0	240	12	3,700
5	1	1	≥240		

* Includes only 15 of the 24 combinations of positive tubes. The other 9 are inherently unlikely to occur with any degree of frequency. If they occur in more than 1% of the tests, it is an indication that technic is faulty or that the assumptions underlying the MPN estimate are not being fulfilled.

407 E. Bibliography

Standard Tests

MEYER, E. M. 1918. An aerobic spore-forming bacillus giving gas in lactose broth isolated in routine water examination. *J. Bact.* 3:9.

HUCKER, G. J. & H. J. CONN. 1923. Methods of gram staining. *N. Y. State Agr. Exp. Station Tech. Bull.* No. 93.

NORTON, J. F. & J. J. WEIGHT. 1924. Aerobic spore-forming lactose fermenting organisms and their significance in water analysis. *AJPH* 14:1019.

HUCKER, G. J. & H. J. CONN. 1927. Further studies on the methods of gram staining. *N. Y. State Agr. Exp. Station Tech. Bull.* No. 128.

PORTER, R., C. S. MCCLESKEY & M. LEVINE. 1937. The facultative sporulating bacteria producing gas from lactose. *J. Bact.* 33:163.

COWLES, P. B. 1939. A modified fermentation tube. *J. Bact.* 38:677.

Manual of Methods for Pure Culture Study of Bacteria. 1946. Society of American Bacteriologists, Geneva, New York, Leaflet No. 4.

BREED, R. S., E. G. D. MURRAY & N. R. SMITH. 1957. *Bergey's Manual of Determinative Bacteriology* (7th ed.). Williams & Wilkins, Baltimore, Md.

Fecal Coliform Tests

PERRY, C. A. & A. A. HAJNA. 1933. A modified Eijkman medium. *J. Bact.* 25:419.

———. 1944. Further evaluation of EC medium for the isolation of coliform bacteria and *Escherichia coli. AJPH* 34:735.

VAUGHN, R. H. et al. 1951. A buffered boric acid lactose medium for enrichment and presumptive identification of *Escherichia coli. Food Research* 16:10.

LEVINE, M., R. H. TANIMOTO, H. MINETTE, J. ARAKAKI & G. FERNANDES. 1955. Simultaneous determination of coliform and *Escherichia coli* indices. *Applied Microbiol.* 3:310.

CLARK, H. F., E. E. GELDREICH, P. W. KABLER, R. H. BORDNER & C. B. HUFF. 1957. The coliform group. I. The boric acid lactose broth reaction of coliform IMViC types. *Applied Microbiol.* 5:396.

GELDREICH, E. E., H. F. CLARK, P. W. KABLER, C. B. HUFF & R. H. BORDNER. 1958. The coliform group. II. Reactions in EC medium at 45 C. *Applied Microbiol.* 6:347.

GELDREICH, E. E., R. H. BORDNER, C. B. HUFF, H. F. CLARK & P. W. KABLER. 1962. Type distribution of coliform bacteria in the feces of warm-blooded animals. *JWPCF* 34:295.

GELDREICH, E. E. 1966. Sanitary significance of fecal coliforms in the environment. FWPCA Pub. WP-20-3 (Nov.). U. S. Department of the Interior, Washington, D. C.

Numerical Interpretation

MCCRADY, M. H. 1915. The numerical interpretation of fermentation tube results. *J. Infect. Dis.* 17:183.

GREENWOOD, M. & G. U. YULE. 1917. On the statistical interpretation of some bacteriological methods employed in water analysis. *J. Hygiene* 16:36.

WOLMAN, A. & H. L. WEAVER. 1917. A modification of the McCrady method of the numerical interpretation of fermentation tube results. *J. Infect. Dis.* 21:287.

MCCRADY, M. H. 1918. Tables for rapid interpretation of fermentation tube results. *Can. Pub. Health J.* 9:201.

REED, L. J. 1925. *B. coli* densities as determined from various types of samples. *Pub. Health Rep.* 40:704 (Reprint 1029).

HOSKINS, J. K. 1933. The most probable number of *B. coli* in water analysis. *JAWWA* 25:867.

———. 1934. Most Probable Numbers for evaluation of *Coli-Aerogenes* tests by fermentation tube method. *Pub. Health Rep.* 49:393 (Reprint 1621).

HOSKINS, J. K. & C. T. BUTTERFIELD. 1935. Determining the bacteriological quality of drinking water. *JAWWA* 27:1101.

HALVORSON, H. O. & N. R. ZIEGLER. 1933–35. Application of statistics to problems in bacteriology. *J. Bact.* 25:101; 26:331, 559; 29:609.

SWAROOP, S. 1938. Numerical estimation of *B. coli* by dilution method. *Indian J. Med. Research* 26:353.

DALLA VALLE, J. M. 1941. Notes on the most probable number index as used in bacteriology. *Pub. Health Rep.* 56:229.

THOMAS, H. A., JR. 1942. Bacterial densities from fermentation tube tests. *JAWWA* 34:572.

U. S. PUBLIC HEALTH SERVICE. 1946. Public Health Service Drinking Water Standards, 1946. *Pub. Health Rep.* 61:371 (Reprint 2697).

APHA, AWWA, & FSIWA. 1955. *Standard Methods for the Examination of Water, Sewage, and Industrial Wastes* (10th ed.). APHA, New York.

WOODWARD, R. L. 1957. How probable is the Most Probable Number? *JAWWA* 49:1060.

MCCARTHY, J. A., H. A. THOMAS & J. E. DELANEY. 1958. Evaluation of reliability of coliform density tests. *AJPH* 48:12.

408 MEMBRANE FILTER TECHNIC FOR MEMBERS OF THE COLIFORM GROUP

The membrane filter technic was presented as a tentative procedure in the 10th Edition of this work. The information obtained by subsequent use of this technic led to its adoption as a standard procedure in the 11th Edition, with the proviso that it be used for determining the potability of drinking waters only after parallel testing had shown that it would afford information equivalent to that obtainable by the standard multiple-tube test. Certain limitations were noted, especially with regard to its effectiveness for testing waters high in turbidity and in noncoliform bacteria.

Since publication of the 11th Edition, widespread use of the technic has confirmed its value, especially its high degree of reproducibility, the possibility of testing relatively larger volumes of sample, and its ability to yield definite results more rapidly than the standard tube procedure. The method has proved particularly valuable in the routine analysis of a given water after its applicability has been established. The U. S. Public Health Service has approved its use for certain water supplies. The membrane filter technic has also been shown to be extremely useful in emergencies and in the examination of waters not used for drinking. However, it is still desirable to conduct parallel tests in order to demonstrate applicability and to familiarize the worker with the procedures involved.

It must be recognized that turbidity due to the presence of algae or other interfering material may not permit testing of a sample volume sufficient to yield significant results and that low coliform estimates may be caused by the presence of high numbers of noncoliforms or of substances toxic to the procedure. Experience indicates that the membrane filter technic is applicable to the examination of saline waters, but not chlorinated wastewaters.

408 A. Standard Total Coliform Membrane Filter Procedure

1. Laboratory Apparatus

All glassware and other apparatus required for bacteriologic analyses using the membrane filter should be composed of material free from agents having unfavorable effects on bacterial growth. Any deviations from the recommendations presented below must be carefully noted, and quantitative tests to demonstrate that such deviations have not introduced agents or factors resulting in conditions less favorable for growth will be necessary.

Glassware should be sterilized as in Washing and Sterilization, Section 403, preceding.

a. Sample bottles should be of the type described in Laboratory Apparatus, Section 402.15.

b. Dilution bottles should be of the type described in Laboratory Apparatus, Section 402.11.

c. Pipets and graduated cylinders may be of any convenient size or shape provided they meet the requirements described in Laboratory Apparatus, Section 402.9.

The opening of graduated cylinders should be covered, prior to sterilization, with metal foil or a suitable paper substitute.

d. Containers for culture medium should be of clean borosilicate glass, presterilized to reduce bacterial contamination. Although they may be of any size or shape, erlenmeyer flasks with metal caps, metal foil covers or screw caps are recommended for ease of mixing adequately the medium contained and for convenience of storage.

e. Culture dishes of the petri dish type, 60 × 15 mm, should be used. The bottom of the dish should be flat and should be 5 to 6 cm in diameter so that the absorbent pad for the culture nutrient will lie flat. The glass should be borosilicate or equivalent grade. Clean culture dishes may be wrapped, prior to sterilization, singly or in convenient numbers, in metal foil or suitable paper substitute. If glass petri dishes are used, precautions must be taken (1) to prevent possible loss of medium by evaporation, with resultant change in medium concentration, since covers for such dishes are loose-fitting; and (2) to maintain a humid environment for optimum colony development.

Disposable plastic dishes that are tight fitting and meet the specifications noted above may also be used for routine laboratory analyses. Suitable sterile plastic dishes are available commercially. If reuse is necessary, these culture dishes should be treated by exposure of the opened dishes to immersion in 70% ethanol for 30 min, air-dried on a sterile towel, protected from dust, and reassembled. Ultraviolet radiation or other appropriate chemical or physical agents may be used for sterilization purposes. Choice of means of sterilization should be governed not only by convenience but also by actual tests demonstrating the effectiveness of such methods. Freedom of the culture containers from residual growth-suppressive effects of the particular method used must be demonstrated. After sterilization and removal of the sterilizing agent, the containers should be closed, employing sterile technics, and stored in a dustproof container until needed.

f. Filtration units: The filter-holding assembly should consist of a seamless funnel which fastens to a receptacle bearing a porous plate for support of the filter membrane. Assembly parts should be so designed that the funnel unit can be attached to the receptacle by means of a convenient locking device. The construction should be such that the membrane filter will be securely held on the porous plate of the receptacle without mechanical damage and all the fluid will pass through the membrane during filtration of the sample. The filter-holding assembly may be constructed of glass, porcelain or any noncorrosive, bacteriologically inert metal. It is recommended that the two parts of the assembly be wrapped separately in heavy wrapping paper for sterilization and storage until use. Sterilization may be done by boiling, autoclaving, or ultraviolet radiation.

For filtration, the receptacle of the filter-holding assembly is mounted in a 1-liter filtering flask with a side tube or other suitable device such that a pressure differential can be exerted on the filter membrane. The filter flask should be connected by the side arm to an electric vacuum pump, a filter pump operating on water pressure, a hand aspirator, or other means of securing a pressure differential. An additional flask may be connected between the filtering flask and the vacuum source to trap carry-over water.

g. Filter membranes: Only those filter membranes may be employed which have been found, through complete laboratory tests certified by the manufacturer, to provide full bacterial retention, stability in use, freedom from chemicals inimical to the growth and development of bacteria, and satisfactory speed of filtration. They should preferably be grid-marked in such a manner that bacterial growth is neither inhibited nor stimulated along the grid lines. Several different brands of membrane filters meeting these specifications can be obtained from manufacturers and suppliers of laboratory equipment.

Filter membranes must be sterilized prior to use, preferably by autoclave. The paper separators—but not the absorbent paper pads—should be removed from the packaged filters. The filters should be divided into groups of 10–12, or other convenient units, and placed in 10-cm petri dishes or wrapped in heavy wrapping paper. The membranes are then autoclaved for 10 min at 121 C (15 psi). At the end of the sterilization period, the steam is allowed to escape rapidly to minimize the accumulation of water of condensation on the filters. Suitable packaged filters designed for autoclave sterilization—or if desired, presterilized—can be purchased.

h. Absorbent pads for nutrients should consist of disks of filter paper or other material known to be of high quality and free of sulfites or other substances that could inhibit bacterial growth. These should be approximately 48 mm in diameter and of a thickness sufficient to absorb 1.8–2.2 ml of nutrient. Presterilized absorbent pads or pads subsequently sterilized in the laboratory should release less than 1 milligram of total acidity (calculated as $CaCO_3$) when titrated to the phenolphthalein end point, pH 8.3, using 0.02 *N* NaOH. The pads may be simultaneously sterilized with membrane filters available in resealable kraft envelopes, or separately in other suitable containers. They must be free of visible moisture prior to use, a qualification best insured by the sterilization procedure described for membrane filters.

i. Forceps should be round-tipped,

without corrugations on the inner sides of the tips. They may be sterilized before use by dipping in 95% ethyl or absolute methyl alcohol and then igniting the fluid.

j. Incubators: Facilities for incubation of membrane filter cultures must provide a temperature of 35 ± 0.5 C and maintain a high level of humidity (approximately 90% relative humidity).

k. Microscope and light source: Membrane filter colonies are best counted with a magnification of 10–15 diameters and the light source adjusted to give maximum sheen. A binocular wide-field dissecting microscope is recommended as the best optical system. However, a small fluorescent lamp with magnifier is acceptable. Colony differentiation is best made with diffused daylight developed from cool white fluorescent lamps. The use of a microscope illuminator with optical system for light concentration from an incandescent light source is specifically unsatisfactory for coliform colony identification on Endo-type media.

2. *Materials and Culture Media*

Refer to Preparation of Culture Media, Sections 404A, B and C.

3. *Samples*

Samples should be collected and stored as directed previously under Samples, Sections 405.1 and 2.

4. *Definition*

All organisms which produce a colony with a golden green metallic sheen within 24 hr of incubation are considered members of the coliform group. The sheen may cover the entire colony or may appear only in a central area or on the periphery. The coliform group thus defined is not necessarily the same as the group defined as the "coliform group" and described in the multiple-tube fermentation technic, but it probably has the same sanitary significance, particularly if suitable studies have been conducted to establish the relationship between the results obtained by the filter and those obtained by the standard tube dilution procedure.

Coliform organisms may occasionally produce colonies which are atypical. If only atypical forms are found, their identity as coliform bacteria should be verified by transfer of doubtful colonies to tubes of lactose or lauryl tryptose broth, followed by transfer of positives to brilliant green lactose bile broth. Gas formation in the confirmatory medium within 48 hr of incubation at 35 ± 0.5 C is deemed evidence of coliform colonies.

5. *Procedures*

Generally speaking, an enrichment procedure will give the best assessment of the quality of drinking waters. However, this step may be eliminated in the routine examination of drinking water where repeated determinations have shown that adequate results are obtained by a single-step technic. Enrichment is generally not necessary in the examination of nonpotable waters or sewages.

In the following sections, methods are offered with and without enrichment that provide for use of the agar-based medium or the M-Endo medium without agar. In the report of results, it is advisable to state the method followed.

a. Selection of sample size: Size of the sample will be governed by the expected bacterial density, which in finished-water samples will be limited only by the degree of turbidity. An ideal quantity will result in the growth of about 50 coliform colonies and not more than 200 colonies of all types. Finished waters may be examined by the filtration of duplicate portions of the same volume, such as 100 to 500 ml or more, or by filtration of two aliquot volumes. All other waters should be examined by the filtration of three aliquot volumes, depending on the expected bacterial density. When less than 20 ml of sample (diluted or undiluted) is to be filtered, a small amount of sterile dilution water should be added to the funnel before filtration. This increase in water volume aids in uniform dispersion of the bacterial suspension over the entire effective filtering surface.

b. Filtration of sample: Using sterile forceps, place a sterile filter over the porous plate of the apparatus, grid side up. Carefully place the matched funnel unit over the receptacle and lock it in place. Filtration is then accomplished by passing the sample through the filter under partial vacuum. The filter may be rinsed by the filtration of three 20–30 ml portions of sterile buffered water between samples. Unlock and remove the funnel, immediately remove the filter with sterile forceps, and place it on the sterile pad or agar with a rolling motion to avoid the entrapment of air.

Filtration units should be sterile at the beginning of each filtration series as a minimum precaution to avoid accidental contamination. A filtration series is considered to be interrupted when an interval of 30 min or longer elapses between sample filtrations. After such interruption, any further sample filtration is treated as a new filtration series which requires resterilization of all membrane filter holders in use. Rapid decontamination of this equipment between successive filtrations may be accomplished by use of an ultraviolet (UV) sterilizer, flowing steam, or boiling water. In the UV sterilization procedure, a 2-min exposure of the filtration unit to UV radiation is sufficient. Do not subject membrane-filter culture preparations to any random UV radiation leaks that might emanate from the sterilization cabinet. Some measure of eye protection is recommended. Either safety glasses or prescription-ground glasses afford adequate eye protection against stray radiation from a UV sterilization cabinet that is not light-tight during the exposure interval.

c. Enrichment technic: Place a sterile absorbent pad in the upper half of a sterile culture dish and pipet enough enrichment medium (1.8–2.0 ml lauryl tryptose broth) to saturate the pad. Carefully remove any surplus liquid. Aseptically place the filter through which the sample has been passed on the pad. Incubate the filter, without inverting the dish, for 1½–2 hr at 35 ± 0.5 C in an atmosphere of at least 90% relative humidity.

If the agar-based medium is used, the final culture dish is prepared as directed under Preparation of Culture Media, Section 404C, No. 15. The enrichment culture is removed from the incubator and the filter is stripped from the enrichment pad and rolled onto the surface of the agar. Incorrect placement of the filter is at once obvious, because patches of unstained membrane indicate entrapment of air. Where such patches occur, the filter must be carefully realigned. The used pad may be transferred to the dish (by exchanging covers) to aid in maintaining humidity.

If the liquid medium is used, the final culture is prepared by removing the enrichment culture from the incubator and separating the dish halves. A fresh sterile pad is placed in the bottom half of the dish and saturated with 1.8–2.0 ml of the final M-Endo medium (Section 404C, No. 13). The filter is transferred, observing the same precautions as above, to the new pad. The used pad may be discarded.

With either the agar or the liquid medium, invert the dish and incubate for 20–22 hr at 35 ± 0.5 C. Proceed to Counting, ¶ e below.

d. Alternative single-step direct technic: If the agar-based medium is used, the prepared filter is placed directly on the agar as described in the preceding section. The filter is incubated for 22–24 hr at 35 ± 0.5 C.

If the liquid medium is used, a pad is placed in the culture dish and saturated with 1.8–2.0 ml of M-Endo medium. The prepared filter is placed directly on the pad and incubated for 22–24 hr at 35 ± 0.5 C.

e. Counting: The typical coliform colony has a pink to dark red color with a metallic surface sheen. The sheen area may vary in size from a small pinhead to complete coverage of the colony surface. The count is best made with the aid of a low-power (10–15 magnifications) binocular wide-field dissecting microscope or other optical device, using a daylight fluorescent light source above and approximately perpendicular to the plane of the filter. A total count on Endo-type media has no relation to the total number of bacteria present in the original sample and, so far as is known, no significance can be inferred or correlation made with the pollution or purity of the water sample.

6. Calculation of Coliform Density

The calculated coliform density is reported in terms of (total) coliforms per 100 ml. The computation is derived from the membrane filter count within the 20–80 coliform colony range and is made by use of the following equation:

$$\text{(Total) coliform colonies/100 ml} = \frac{\text{coliform colonies counted} \times 100}{\text{ml sample filtered}}$$

If the membrane filter counts are individually less than 20, all such counts should be totaled and the value based on the total volume of sample examined. For example, if duplicate 50-ml portions contained 5 and 3 coliform colonies, the count would be reported as 8 coliforms per 100 ml. However, if 10, 1.0 and 0.1 ml portions were examined with, respectively, 19, 3 and <1 coliform(s), the result would be reported as 200 coliforms per 100 ml. The number of coliforms should not be recorded with more than two significant figures per 100 ml.

When there are excessive colonies on the membrane filter, the report should be TNTC (Too Numerous To Count); if there is growth without well-defined colonies, the report should be "confluent." In either case a new sample should be requested and more appropriate volumes selected for filtration.

408 B. Fecal Coliform Membrane Filter Procedure

Determination of fecal-coliform bacterial densities may be made either by multiple-tube procedures or by a membrane filter technic. The choice of method should be governed by the methodology employed for total coliform enumeration. The following procedure gives 93% accuracy for differentiating between coliforms of warm-blooded animals and coliforms from other sources. The membrane filter procedure calls for an enriched lactose medium that depends on an incubation temperature of 44.5 ± 0.2 C for its selectivity. Since incubation temperature is critical, membrane filter cultures must be placed in watertight plastic bags and submerged in a water bath for incubation at the elevated temperature. Areas of application for this method are stated in the introduction to the multiple-tube fecal-coliform procedures.

1. Materials and Culture Medium

a. M-FC medium: Prepare as described in Media Specifications, Section 404C, No. 12.

b. Culture dishes: Tight-fitting plastic dishes are essential because these membrane-filter cultures must be submerged in a water bath during incubation. Enclosing groups of fecal coliform cultures in plastic bags is recommended to reduce further the occurrence of leakage during submersion. Specifications for plastic culture dishes are described in Section 408A.1e above.

c. Incubator: The specificity of the fecal coliform test is directly related to the incubation temperature. Air incubation is undesirable because of heat layering within the chamber and the slow recovery of temperature each time the incubator is opened during daily operations. Therefore the need for greater temperature control must be met with a water bath. A temperature tolerance of 44.5 ± 0.2 C can be obtained with most types of water baths that also are equipped with a gable-top for the reduction of water and heat losses. A circulating water bath is excellent but may not be essential to this test if the maximum permissible variation of ± 0.2 C in temperature can be maintained with existing equipment.

2. Procedure

a. Selection of sample size: The volume of water sample to be examined by the membrane filter technic must receive careful consideration before filtration is started. When the bacterial density of the sample is totally unknown, it is necessary to filter several decimal quantities of sample to establish the true coliform density. The best method is to estimate the ideal quantity expected to yield a countable membrane and select two additional quantities representing one-tenth and ten times this quantity, respectively. Sample quantities that will yield counts between 20 and 60 fecal coliform colonies result in greater accuracy of density determination.

b. Filtration of sample: Observe the same procedure and precautions as prescribed under Section 408A.5b above.

c. Preparation of culture dish: Place a sterile absorbent pad in each culture dish and pipet approximately 2 ml of M-FC medium, prepared as directed under Media Specifications (Section 404C) to saturate the pad. Carefully remove any surplus liquid from the culture dish. The prepared filter is then placed on the medium-impregnated pad as described under Section 408A above.

d. Incubation: The prepared cultures are placed in waterproof plastic bags for protection during submersion in the water bath for the 24-hr incubation period at 44.5 ± 0.2 C. These dishes must be anchored below the water surface during incubation to maintain critical temperature requirements. All prepared cultures should be placed in the water bath within 30 min after filtration.

e. Counting: Colonies produced by fecal coliform bacteria are blue in color. The nonfecal coliform colonies are gray to cream-colored. Background color on the membrane filter will vary from a yellowish cream to faint blue, depending on the age of the rosolic acid salt reagent. Normally, few nonfecal coliform colonies will be observed on M-FC medium because of the selective action of the elevated temperature and addition of the rosolic acid salt reagent. The colony count is best made with the aid of a low-power (10–15 magnifications) binocular wide-field dissecting microscope or other optical device.

3. *Calculation of Fecal Coliform Density*

The density is computed from the sample quantities that produced membrane filter counts within the desired 20–60 fecal coliform colony range. This colony density range is more restrictive than the 20–80 total coliform range because of larger colony growth on M-FC medium. Proceed with the calculation as stated under Section 408A.6 above. Record densities as fecal coliforms per 100 ml.

408 C. Delayed-Incubation Total Coliform Procedure (TENTATIVE)

Modification of the standard membrane filter technic permits shipment or transport of the membrane after filtration to a distant laboratory for incubation and completion of the test. This delayed-incubation test may be used where it is impractical to apply conventional procedures. It may be employed where it is not possible to maintain the desired sample temperature during transport; when the elapsed time between sample collection and analysis would exceed the approved time limit; where the sampling location is remote from laboratory services; when it is necessary to monitor streams for water quality or pollution control activities by a standardized procedure; or for other reasons which prevent analysis of the sample at or near the sample site.

Data secured by the delayed-incubation test have yielded results consistent with those from the immediate standard test in independent studies of samples from both fresh and salt waters. The applicability of the delayed-incubation test for a specific water source can be determined by comparison with results of test procedures using conventional methods.

The delayed-incubation test consists

of filtering the sample in the field immediately after collection, placing the filter on the transport medium, and shipping to the laboratory. The coliform determination is completed in the laboratory by transferring the membrane to a growth medium, incubating at 35 ± 0.5 C for the stipulated time, and counting the typical coliform colonies so developed. The transport media are designed to keep the coliform organisms viable and generally do not permit visible growth during the time of transit. Bacteriostatic agents suppress growth of microorganisms en route but allow normal coliform growth after transfer to a fresh growth medium.

The delayed-incubation test follows the methods outlined for the Total Coliform Membrane Filter Procedure, except as indicated below. Two alternative methods are given, using either the M-Endo preservative medium (No. 13) or the LES MF holding medium (No. 14).

1. Apparatus

a. Culture dishes: Disposable, sterile, moisture-tight plastic petri dishes (50 × 12 mm) are recommended for use during shipping and also during incubation where a high humidity is not otherwise available. Such containers are light in weight and are less likely to break in transit. In an emergency, sterile glass petri dishes wrapped in plastic film or similar material may be used. Specifications for culture dishes are described in Section 408A.1e preceding.

2. Materials and Transport Media

a. M-ENDO METHODS

1) *M-Endo preservative medium:* Prepare as described in Media Specifications, No. 13. Add 3.84 g per liter of sodium benzoate (USP grade) or 3.2 ml of a 12% sodium benzoate solution per 100 ml of M-Endo medium.

2) *Sodium benzoate solution:* Dissolve 12 g sodium benzoate in sufficient distilled water to make 100 ml. This solution may be sterilized by autoclaving or filtration. Discard the solution after 6 months.

3) *Cycloheximide:* * The addition to M-Endo preservative medium of cycloheximide is optional. It may be used for samples which previously have shown overgrowth of molds or fungi. Add 500 mg per liter. A cycloheximide solution must be stored in the refrigerator and discarded after 6 months. Cycloheximide is a powerful skin irritant and should be handled with caution according to the manufacturer's directions.

b. LES METHOD

1) *LES MF holding medium, coliform:* Prepare as in Media Specifications, No. 14.

3. Procedure

a. *Sample preservation and shipment:* Place an absorbent pad in the bottom of a sterile petri dish and saturate with the selected coliform holding medium in accordance with the procedures given in Section 408A.5c above. Remove the membrane filter from the filtration unit with sterile forceps and roll it, grid side up, onto the surface of the absorbent pad that has been saturated with the transport medium. Protect the membrane from moisture loss. High humidity is main-

* Actidione, manufactured by the Upjohn Company, Kalamazoo, Michigan, or equivalent.

tained by tight closure of the plastic petri dish. While it is important to see that the membrane does not become dehydrated during transit, an excess of liquid in the dish is also undesirable. Place the culture dish containing the membrane in an appropriate shipping container and send to the laboratory for completion of the examination. The sample can be held without visible growth for a maximum of 72 hr on the transport medium, which allows use of the U. S. mails and common carriers. Visible growth is occasionally initiated on the transport medium when high temperatures are encountered.

b. *Transfer:* At the laboratory, transfer the membrane from the plastic dish in which it was shipped to a second sterile petri dish containing the growth medium. Another culture dish is used in this step to avoid any residues of sodium benzoate.

c. *Incubation:*

1) M-ENDO METHOD—Transfer the membrane from M-Endo preservative medium to a pad and petri dish containing M-Endo medium without the growth-suppressing reagents (Media Specifications, No. 13) and incubate at 35 ± 0.5 C for 20–22 hr.

2) LES METHOD—Transfer the membrane from the LES MF holding medium to LES Endo agar (Media Specifications, No. 15) and incubate at 35 ± 0.5 C for 20–22 hr. If distinct colonies are observable without the aid of magnification at time of transfer, it is recommended that the petri dish containing the transferred membrane be refrigerated until such time that it can be incubated at 35 ± 0.5 C for a 16–18 hr period. This manipulation of incubation time will permit the analyst a measure of control over the problems of overgrowth and sheen dissipation, which interfere with the coliform colony count.

4. *Estimation of Coliform Density*

Proceed as in Section 408A.6 above. Record times of collection, filtration, and laboratory examination and calculate the elapsed time.

408 D. Bibliography

CLARK, H. F., E. E. GELDREICH, H. L. JETER & P. W. KABLER. 1951. The membrane filter in sanitary bacteriology. *Pub. Health Rep.* 66:951.

GOETZ, A. & N. TSUNEISHI. 1951. Application of molecular filter membranes to bacteriological analysis of water. *JAWWA* 43:943.

VELS, C. J. 1951. Graphical approach to statistics. IV. Evaluation of bacterial density. *Water & Sewage Works* 98:66.

TASK GROUP REPORT. 1953. Technic of bacterial examination of water. *JAWWA* 45:1196.

TAYLOR, E. W., N. P. BURMAN & C. W. OLIVER. 1953. Use of the membrane filter in the bacteriological examination of water. *J. Applied Chem.* (London) 3:233.

KABLER, P. W. 1954. Water examinations by membrane filter and MPN procedures. *AJPH* 44:379.

GELDREICH, E. E., P. W. KABLER, H. L. JETER & H. F. CLARK. 1955. A delayed incubation membrane filter test for coliform bacteria in water. *AJPH* 45:1462.

THOMAS, H. A. & R. L. WOODWARD. 1956. Use of molecular filter membranes for water potability control. *JAWWA* 48: 1391.

CLARK, H. F., P. W. KABLER & E. E. GELDREICH. 1957. Advantages and limitations of the membrane filter procedure. *Water & Sewage Works* 104: 385.

FIFIELD, C. W. & C. P. SCHAUFUS. 1958. Improved membrane filter medium for the detection of coliform organisms. *JAWWA* 50:193.

MCCARTHY, J. A. & J. E. DELANEY. 1958. Membrane filter media studies. *Water & Sewage Works* 105:292.

MCKEE, J. E., R. T. MCLAUGHLIN & P. LESGOURGUES. 1958. Application of molecular filter technics to the bacterial assay of sewage. III. Effects of physical and chemical disinfection. *Sewage & Ind. Wastes* 30:245.

MCCARTHY, J. A., J. E. DELANEY & R. J. GRASSO. 1961. Measuring coliforms in water. *Water & Sewage Works* 108:238.

RHINES, C. E. & W. P. CHEEVERS. 1965. Decontamination of membrane filter holders by ultraviolet light. *JAWWA* 57:500.

GELDREICH, E. E., H. F. CLARK, C. B. HUFF & L. C. BEST. 1965. Fecal-coliform-organism medium for the membrane filter technic. *JAWWA* 57:208.

PANEZAI, A. K., T. J. MACKLIN & H. G. COLES. 1965. *Coli-Aerogenes* and *Escherichia coli* counts on water samples by means of transported membranes. *Proc. Soc. Water Treatment & Exam.* 14:179.

MCCARTHY, J. A. & J. E. DELANEY. 1965. Methods for measuring the coliform content of water. Sec. III. Delayed holding procedure for coliform bacteria. PHS Research Grant WP 00202 NIH Report (Nov. 26).

GELDREICH, E. E., H. L. JETER & J. A. WINTER. 1967. Technical considerations in applying the membrane filter procedure. *Health Lab. Sci.* 4:113.

BREZENSKI, F. T. & J. A. WINTER. 1968. Use of the delayed incubation membrane filter test for determining coliform bacteria in sea water. North Atlantic Water Quality Management Center (FWPCA, DI), Edison, N. J. In preparation.

409 TESTS FOR THE FECAL STREPTOCOCCAL GROUP

The terms "fecal streptococcus" and "enterococcus" have been used somewhat synonymously by many authors in recent years and there have been varying opinions as to what species, varieties or biotypes of streptococci are included when these terms are employed.

On the basis of newer concepts of speciation of the fecal streptococci it is suggested that the terms "fecal streptococcus" and "Lancefield's Group D Streptococcus" be considered as synonymous and that the use of these terms be restricted to denote the following species, or their varieties, used as indicators of fecal contamination: *S. faecalis, S. faecalis* var. *liquefaciens, S. faecalis* var. *zymogenes, S. durans, S. faecium, S. bovis* and *S. equinus*. Other varieties or biotypes of *S. faecalis* and *S. faecium* have been reported, but their nomenclature and taxonomic position in the fecal streptococcal group must await further investigation. The term "enterococcus" refers to a more restrictive group, including all the above species except *S. bovis* and *S. equinus;* its use is not recommended.

The streptococci in the fecal streptococcal group are indicators of fecal pollution of water, inasmuch as the normal habitat of these organisms is generally the intestine of man and animals. Therefore, fecal streptococcal determinations may be of particular value for stream pollution surveys and for determining the sanitary quality of waters from shallow lakes, bathing areas, and wells. Because recent studies indicate that streptococci similar to organisms in the fecal streptococcal group may be found on certain plants or plant products, it is possible that wastes from food-processing industries discharged into a body of water constitute the source of some of these bacteria.

Standard multiple-tube and membrane filter technics are available as well as a tentative plate count method.

409 A. Multiple-Tube Technic

1. Presumptive Test

a. *Procedure:*

1) Inoculate a series of tubes of azide dextrose broth (Media Specifications, No. 16) with appropriate graduated quantities of the water to be tested. Use 10 ml single-strength broth for inocula of 1 ml or less and 10 ml double-strength broth for 10-ml inocula. The portions of the water sample used will necessarily vary in size and number with the character of the water and should be decimal multiples of 1 ml. Refer to the section on tests for the presence of members of the coliform group (Section 407) for suggestions concerning suitable amounts of inocula in order to have some negative tubes in the higher dilution.

2) Incubate inoculated tubes at 35 ± 0.5 C. Examine each tube for the presence of turbidity at the end of 24 ± 2 hr. If no definite turbidity is present, reincubate and read again at the end of 48 ± 3 hr.

2. Confirmed Test

All azide dextrose broth tubes showing turbidity after 24- or 48-hr incubation must be subjected to the Confirmed Test.

a. *Procedure:*

1) Transfer 3 loopfuls of growth or use a wood applicator to transfer growth from each azide dextrose broth tube to a tube containing 10 ml ethyl violet azide broth (Media Specifications, No. 17). The wire loop should have a minimum diameter of 3 mm. A single inoculating wire, fashioned to have three individual 3-mm loops in a row, may be used to eliminate need for 3 separate loopfuls. Do not discard positive tubes but hold in the incubator.

2) Incubate the inoculated tubes for 24 hr at 35 ± 0.5 C. The presence of fecal streptococci is indicated by the formation of a purple button at the bottom of the tube, or occasionally by a dense turbidity. Record all positive results and discard those tubes. If no growth occurs in ethyl violet azide broth in 24 hr, reinoculate the tubes with an additional 3 loopfuls from the original positive azide broth cultures and reincubate for a second 24-hr period. Record results as final.

3. Computing and Recording of MPN

Refer to Tables 407(1) through 407(6) and to Section 407D, Estimation of Bacterial Density.

409 B. Membrane Filter Technic

1. *Laboratory Apparatus*

Refer to membrane filter assembly and laboratory apparatus given in Standard Total Coliform Membrane Filter Procedure, Section 408A.1 preceding.

2. *Materials and Culture Media*

a. Culture media: Refer to Preparation of Culture Media, Sections 404A and B, and Media Specifications Nos. 18 and 19, for M-Enterococcus agar and KF Streptococcus agar formulations.

b. Culture dish preparation: Pour or pipet 4–5 ml liquefied medium into culture dishes (60 × 15 mm); flame the surface if necessary to eliminate bubbles. If tight-fitting plastic dishes are used, a stock of prepared dishes may be made in advance and stored at 4–10 C for use within a 4-week period.

3. *Procedure*

a. Selection of sample size and filtration: Filter samples of water through the sterile membrane to attain 20 to 100 colonies on the membrane surface. Amounts varying from 100 to 10, 1, 0.1 or 0.01 ml may be necessary, depending on the amount of pollution in the water sample (refer to Section 408A.5a, Standard Total Coliform Membrane Filter Procedure). Transfer the filter directly to the agar medium in the petri dishes, avoiding air bubbles.

b. Incubation: Invert culture plates and incubate at 35 ± 0.5 C for 48 hr.

c. Counting: Colonies produced by fecal streptococci are dark red to pink in color. The count is best made with the aid of a low-power (10–15 magnifications) binocular wide-field dissecting microscope or equivalent optical device.

4. *Calculation of Fecal Streptococcal Density*

The density is computed from the sample quantities that produce membrane filter counts within the desired 20–100 fecal streptococcus colony range. This colony density range is greater than the 20–80 total coliform range because of the increased selectivity of fecal streptococci media. Proceed with the calculation as given under Standard Total Coliform Membrane Filter Procedure, Section 408A.6. Record densities as fecal streptococci per 100 ml.

5. *Confirmed Test*

In the examination of samples of water from sources other than swimming pools, results reported to date indicate that practically 100% of the red and pink colonies that grow on filters placed on M-Enterococcus or KF agar are fecal streptococci. If further confirmation or subgroup identification is indicated, the following procedure is recommended:

a. Fish selected typical colonies from membrane and inoculate onto a brain-heart infusion agar slant (Media Specifications, No. 21). Incubate at 35 ± 0.5 C for 24–48 hr. When growth is detected continue as in ¶s *b* and *c*.

b. Transfer a loopful of growth from the brain-heart infusion agar slant to a clean glass slide and add a few drops of freshly tested 3% hydrogen peroxide to the smear. The absence of bubbles constitutes a negative catalase test indicating a probable streptococcus culture, and confirmation should be continued as stated in the following paragraphs. The presence of bubbles constitutes a positive catalase test, which indicates the presence of nonstreptococcal species, and confirmation need not be continued.

c. Transfer a loopful of growth from the brain-heart infusion agar into brain-heart infusion broth and incubate at 45 C for 48 hr. Also transfer a loopful of growth into bile broth medium and incubate at 35 C for 3 days. This latter medium is prepared by adding 40 ml sterile 10% oxgall solution to 60 ml sterile brain-heart infusion broth.

d. Growth in the above media constitutes a positive test for fecal streptococci.

6. *Differentiation of Fecal Streptococcal Organisms*

Further identification of the distribution of fecal streptococcal types present within a given sample will require other biochemical tests over and above that described in Section 5 preceding. A minimum series of additional tests would include tests for growth in 6.5% NaCl, growth at both 45 C and 10 C, starch hydrolysis, and peptonization and acid development in litmus milk. The bibliography should be consulted for other selective tests as desired.

409 C. Fecal Streptococcal Plate Count (TENTATIVE)

Fecal streptococcal densities may also be determined by the pour-plate technic using M-Enterococcus or KF Streptococcus agar. This direct count procedure may be considered an alternative to the membrane filter technic and should be used preferentially for those samples known to contain significant turbidity and few fecal streptococci.

1. *Preparation and Dilution*

Refer to Standard Plate Count, Section 406.2.

2. *Plating*

Prepare M-Enterococcus or KF Streptococcus agar as stated in Preparation of Culture Media, Section 404C.18 or 19, and hold in a water bath at 45 C prior to making pour plates. Discard any liquid agar medium held over 4 hr.

A 1-ml, 0.1-ml, or other suitable volume of the sample or dilution to be used for plating should be placed in the culture dish first. It is recommended that dilutions be used in preparing volumes less than 1 ml; in the examination of sewage or turbid water, a 0.1-ml inoculum of the original sample shall not be measured but an appropriate dilution should be prepared. Not more than 20 min should elapse between making the dilution and pouring the plate.

Pour 12–15 ml liquefied agar medium into each culture dish containing the measured sample. The cover of the dish should be lifted just enough to permit introduction of the pipet or the culture medium. Thoroughly mix the agar and sample together for a uniform dispersion of organisms and medium over the bottom of the dish. This is best accomplished by gently tilting and rotating the dish, taking care not to splash the upper portion of the culture dish. The plates should be solidified as rapidly as possible after pouring and placed immediately, in inverted position, in the incubator.

3. *Incubation*

Incubate fecal streptococcal pour plates at a temperature of 35 ± 0.5 C for 48 ± 3 hr.

4. *Counting*

Surface and subsurface colonies produced by fecal streptococci are dark red to pink in color with entire edges. Subsurface colonies frequently are lens-shaped. Normally, few nonfecal streptococcus colonies will be observed on KF Streptococcus agar because of the selectivity of the medium. However, occasional stream samples may contain gram-positive soil organisms such as *Corynebacterium* species, which develop yellow or orange colonies on this medium. Infrequently, *Bacillus* species may produce fuzzy white colonies with or without minute red-dot centers.

Counting may be done with either a Quebec colony counter or a low-power (10–15 magnifications) binocular wide-field dissecting microscope and suitable light source—preferably cool white fluorescent lamps.

5. *Calculation of Fecal Streptococcal Density*

Refer to Standard Plate Count, Section 406.5.

409 D. Bibliography

SHERMAN, J. M. 1937. The streptococci. *Bact. Rev.* 1:3.

SKAUDHAUGE, K. 1950. *Studies on Enterococci, with Special Reference to the Serological Properties.* Einar Munksgaards, Copenhagen.

MALLMANN, W. L. & E. B. SELIGMANN. 1950. A comparative study of media for the detection of streptococci in water and sewage. *AJPH* 40:286.

LITSKY, W., W. L. MALLMANN & C. W. FIFIELD. 1953. A new medium for the detection of enterococci in water. *AJPH* 43:873.

———. 1955. Comparison of the Most Probable Number of *Escherichia coli* and enterococci in river waters. *AJPH* 45:1049.

SHATTOCK, P. M. F. 1955. The identification and classification of *Streptococcus faecalis* and some associated streptococci. *Ann. Inst. Pasteur* (Lille) 7:95.

COOPER, K. E. & F. M. RAMADAN. 1955. Studies in the differentiation between human and animal pollution by means of faecal streptococci. *J. Gen. Microbiol.* 12:180.

LAKE, D. E., R. H. DIEBEL & C. F. NIVEN, JR. 1957. The identity of *Streptococcus faecium. Bact. Proc.*, p. 13.

BARNES, E. M. 1957. Reduction as a means of differentiating *Streptococcus faecalis* from *Streptococcus faecium. J. Gen. Microbiol.* 14:57.

SLANETZ, L. W. & C. H. BARTLEY. 1957. Numbers of enterococci in water, sewage, and feces determined by the membrane filter technic with an improved medium. *J. Bact.* 74:591.

BREED, R. S., E. G. D. MURRAY & N. R.

SMITH. 1957. *Bergey's Manual of Determinative Bacteriology* (7th ed.). Williams & Wilkins, Baltimore, Md.
MORELIS, P. & L. COLOBERT. 1958. Un milieu selectif permettant l'identification et le denombrement rapides de *Streptococcus faecalis*. *Ann Inst. Pasteur* 95:667.
SUREAU, P. 1958. Isolation and enumeration of faecal streptococci in waters by means of filtering membranes. *Ann. Inst. Pasteur* 95:6.
MEDREK, T. F. & W. LITSKY. 1959. Comparative incidence of coliform bacteria and enterococci in undisturbed soil. *Applied Microbiol.* 8:60.
CROFT, C. C. 1959. A comparative study of media for detection of enterococci in water. *AJPH* 49:1379.
BARTLEY, C. H. & L. W. SLANETZ. 1960. Types and sanitary significance of fecal streptococci isolated from feces, sewage and water. *AJPH* 50:1545.
KENNER, B. A., H. F. CLARK & P. W. KABLER. 1960. Fecal streptococci. II. Quantification of streptococci in feces. *AJPH* 50:1553.
———. 1961. Fecal streptococci. I. Cultivation and enumeration of streptococci in surface waters. *Applied Microbiol.* 9:15.
NIVEN, C. F., JR. 1963. Microbial indices of food quality: Fecal streptococci. *Proc. Conf. Microbiol. Qual. Foods.* Academic Press, New York.
SHATTOCK, P. M. F. 1963. *Enterococci: Chemical and Biological Hazards in Food.* Iowa University Press, Des Moines, p. 303.
MUNDT, J. C. 1963. Occurrence of enterococci on plants in a wild environment. *Applied Microbiol.* 11:141.

410 DIFFERENTIATION OF COLIFORM GROUP OF ORGANISMS (TENTATIVE)

The methods previously given for the detection and estimation of the coliform group of bacteria provide full information on the pollution and sanitary quality of the water supply under examination. Differentiation of the fecal coliform organisms as a group has been described in the test procedures given in other sections herein.

Occasionally, it is of value to differentiate the coliform strains and identify them according to genera and species for research purposes or for special study. Tentative methods for such differentiation are presented.

410 A. Culture Purification

It is well known that the accuracy of the Completed Test and of differential tests is at times impaired by failure to purify cultures. It is essential that a pure culture be obtained. This may be accomplished by streaking the culture from the completed lactose broth tube to an eosin-methylene blue agar plate, which is then incubated at 35 ± 0.5 C for 24 hr. A single well-isolated colony fished to an agar slant is incubated at 35 ± 0.5 C for 24 hr and gram-stained to confirm the presence of gram-negative, nonspore-forming rods.

Variation in organisms of the coliform group, particularly the "unstable" variation characteristic of the *mutabile* type, is occasionally encountered. It is therefore advisable, when attempting purification of cultures, to be on the lookout for this phenomenon. An apparent mixture of organisms may, in reality, consist of a single strain that is showing variation. However, persistent plus-minus reactions may very well indicate inadequate purification of the culture.

410 B. Differential Tests

The differentiation of the coliform group into the *Escherichia coli, Aerobacter aerogenes,* and *Escherichia freundii* (or intermediate) species has been carried out on the basis of the results of four tests (indole, methyl red, Voges-Proskauer, and sodium citrate) often referred to collectively as the "IMViC tests." These tests are tentatively recommended for differential determination. If further tests are added to these, the real and apparent variety of strains within the coliform group may be correspondingly increased, as has been done in the classical systems of MacConkey, Clemesha, and Levine. Although such complete differentiation may be desirable from a research standpoint, it does not appear to be warranted in routine water work.

A simplified grouping of the reaction combinations is given in Table 410(1).

The significance of finding various types of coliform organisms in water samples has been and still is a subject of considerable study (see discussion under Fecal Coliform MPN Procedure, Section 407C). It must be remembered that all types of coliform organisms may occur in feces. Although *E. coli* will nearly always be found in fresh pollution derived from

TABLE 410(1): INTERPRETATION OF IMVIC REACTIONS

Organism	Indole	Methyl Red	Voges-Proskauer	Citrate
Escherichia coli				
Variety I	+	+	−	−
Variety II	−	+	−	−
Escherichia freundii (Intermediates)				
Variety I	−	+	−	±
Variety II	+	+	−	+
Aerobacter aerogenes				
Variety I	−	−	+	±
Variety II	±	−	+	+

warm-blooded animals, some other type or types of coliform organisms, not accompanied by *E. coli,* may occasionally be found in fresh pollution from a particular source.

It is well to keep in mind, however, the possibility of occasional multiplication of coliform organisms on leather washers, wood, swimming pool ropes, or jute packing, as well as in slime formation inside of pipes. In fact, differentiation of coliform types finds one of its most practical applications in the study of unexpected coliform densities that may be explained by multiplication on or in organic materials. The presence of a large number of coliform organisms of the same type in water from a well or spring—or from a single tap on a distribution system, for example—is quite suggestive of such multiplication.

1. Indole Test

a. Reagents:

1) MEDIUM—Use tryptophane broth as described under Media Specifications, No. 22.

2) TEST REAGENT—Dissolve 5 g paradimethylaminobenzaldehyde in 75 ml isoamyl (or normal amyl) alcohol, ACS grade, and add 25 ml conc HCl. Thc reagent should be yellow. Some brands of paradimethylaminobenzaldehyde are not satisfactory and some good brands become unsatisfactory on aging.

The amyl alcohol solution should have a pH value of less than 6.0. Both amyl alcohol and benzaldehyde compound should be purchased in as small amounts as will be consistent with the volume of work to be done.

b. Procedure: Inoculate 5-ml portions of medium from a pure culture and incubate at 35 ± 0.5 C for 24 ± 2 hr. Add 0.2–0.3 ml test reagent and shake. Let the tube stand for about 10 min and observe the results.

A dark red color in the amyl alcohol surface layer constitutes a positive indole test; the original color of the reagent, a negative test. An orange color probably indicates the presence of skatole and may be reported as a ± reaction.

2. Methyl Red Test

a. Reagents:

1) MEDIUM—Use buffered glucose broth as described under Media Specifications, Section 404C.23.

2) INDICATOR SOLUTION—Dissolve 0.1 g methyl red in 300 ml of 95% ethyl alcohol and dilute to 500 ml with distilled water.

b. Procedure: Inoculate 10-ml portions of medium from a pure culture. Incubate at 35 C for 5 days. To 5 ml of the culture add 5 drops methyl red indicator solution.

Record a distinct red color as methyl red-positive and a distinct yellow color as methyl red-negative. A mixed shade should be recorded as questionable and possibly indicative of incomplete culture purification.

3. Voges-Proskauer Test

a. Reagents:

1) MEDIA—This test may be carried out using the medium as described for the methyl red differential test or if desired, an alternative salt peptone glucose medium may be used as described under Media Specification, Section 404C.24.

2) NAPHTHOL SOLUTION—Dissolve 5 g purified α-naphthol (melting point 92.5 C or higher) in 100 ml absolute

ethyl alcohol. This solution should be prepared fresh each day.

3) POTASSIUM HYDROXIDE SOLUTION—Dissolve 40 g KOH in 100 ml distilled water.

b. Procedure: Inoculate 5 ml of either culture medium and incubate at 35 ± 0.5 C for 48 hr. To 1 ml of culture add 0.6 ml naphthol solution and 0.2 ml KOH solution. Development of a pink to crimson color in the mixture from 2 to 4 hr after adding the reagents constitutes a positive test. Results should not be read after this period of time.

4. Sodium Citrate Test

a. Alternate media: Use either Koser's citrate broth as described under Media Specification, No. 25, or Simmons' citrate agar as described under the same heading, No. 26.

b. Procedure:

1) Inoculation into the liquid medium may be made only with a straight needle, and it should a light inoculum. A pipet should never be used because of the danger of invalidating the result by the introduction of nutrient material with the transfer. Incubate at 35 ± 0.5 C for 72 to 96 hr. Record visible growth as positive, no growth as negative.

2) Inoculate the agar medium with a straight needle, using both a stab and a streak. Incubate 48 hr at 35 ± 0.5 C. Growth on the medium with (usually) a blue color constitutes a positive reaction; the absence of growth is recorded as negative.

410 C. Bibliography

CLARK, W. M. 1915. The final hydrogen ion concentrations of cultures of *Bacillus coli*. *Science* 42:71.

CLARK, W. M. & W. A. LUBS. 1915. The differentiation of bacteria of the colon-aerogenes family by the use of indicators. *J. Infect. Dis.* 17:160.

LEVINE, M. 1916. On the significance of the Voges-Proskauer reaction. *J. Bact.* 1:153.

———. 1921. Notes on *Bact. coli* and *Bact. aerogenes*. *AJPH* 11:21.

KOSER, S. A. 1924. Correlation of citrate utilization by members of the colon-aerogenes group with other differential characteristics and with habitat. *J. Bact.* 9:59.

SIMMONS, J. S. 1926. A culture medium for differentiating organisms of typhoid-colon-aerogenes groups and for isolation of certain fungi. *J. Infect. Dis.* 39:309.

KOVACS, N. 1928. A simplified method for detecting indol formation by bacteria. *Z. Immunitatsforsch.* 56:311; *Chem. Abstracts* 22:3425.

RUCHHOFT, C. C., J. G. KALLAS, B. CHINN & E. W. COULTER. 1930 and 1931. Coli-aerogenes differentiation in water analysis. *J. Bact.* 21:407; 22:125.

EPSTEIN, S. S. & R. H. VAUGHN. 1934. Differential reactions in the coli group of bacteria. *AJPH* 24:505.

BARRITT, M. W. 1936. The intensification of the Voges-Proskauer reaction by the addition of alpha-naphthol. *J. Pathol. & Bact.* 42:441.

VAUGHN, R., N. B. MITCHELL & M. LEVINE. 1939. The Voges-Proskauer and methyl red reactions in the coli-aerogenes group. *JAWWA* 31:993.

BORMAN, E. K., C. A. STUART & K. M. WHEELER. 1944. Taxonomy of the family Enterobacteriaceae. *J. Bact.* 48:351.

411 DETECTION OF PATHOGENIC MICROORGANISMS IN WATER AND WASTEWATER

The most common and important pathogenic microorganisms which can be demonstrated in wastewater and, under certain conditions, surface and groundwaters of the United States are *Salmonella, Shigella,* enteropathogenic *Escherichia coli, Leptospira,* and the enteric viruses. Organisms such as hookworm larva, the cysts of *Endamoeba histolytica,* and other animal parasites may on occasion find their way into poorly constructed wells, particularly in areas where the infections they cause are endemic. Other organisms not normally associated with the climate in this country might also be found in water because of extensive and rapid world travel. Perhaps the most important of these "foreign" organisms, as far as waterborne transmission is concerned, is *Vibrio cholerae.*

Routine examination of water and wastewater for pathogenic microorganisms cannot be recommended at this time. There is no single procedure which can be used to isolate and identify these microorganisms. Salmonellae are extremely common in the environment and are probably responsible for most recognized waterborne disease outbreaks. Unfortunately, isolation technics even for these ubiquitous organisms involve relatively complicated procedures that will exceed the capabilities of all but a few water laboratories. Certainly monitoring of water or wastewater for enteric viruses cannot be carried out except in very well-equipped laboratories and then usually as a special research study. Thus, a combination of factors—among them lack of facilities, lack of trained personnel, lack of laboratory time, high costs, and lack of adequate methods—makes the routine examination of water for pathogens impossible. In view of the foregoing, it is apparent that there is a strong need for intensive research in this area, research which should be encouraged at every opportunity.

Some suspicion has been cast on the validity of the coliform test as an indicator of the biological safety of water.[1-3] These reports suggest that under unusual circumstances pathogenic bacteria can be isolated from waters containing few if any coliform bacteria. *The circumstances surrounding these isolations are not at all clear and it should not be concluded that the coliform test is unreliable or even needs to be supplemented by routine examinations for pathogens at this time.* The coliform test has, over the years, clearly proven its value. The discussion of pathogen isolation procedures which follows is offered for the specialist who may wish to initiate a research study—for example, to obtain background data on the numbers, types and frequency of occurrence of pathogens in water as related to the coliform or fecal coliform index.

411 A. General Qualitative Isolation and Identification Procedures for *Salmonella and Shigella*

The recommended methods that are presented below for the isolation of *Salmonella* and *Shigella* from water or wastewater are not standardized and must be considered as research procedures which may need modification to fit a particular set of circumstances. The recovery efficiency of given lots of media should be checked by using several recently isolated strains of *Salmonella* or *Shigella*.[4, 5]

Rather than recommend a specific protocol for *Salmonella* and *Shigella* detection in water, a brief summary of suitable methods for recovery of these organisms from water is presented. This approach is necessitated by the fact that some critical areas of procedural details require further study in the research laboratory before a specific protocol can be established. However, methods currently available have been used in numerous field investigations to demonstrate *Salmonella* in both fresh and estuarine water environments. It is further recommended that the technics available be carefully evaluated for the development of a protocol which will yield optimum isolation of these organisms in a specific investigation. Finally, it must be remembered that the occurrence of *Salmonella* in water is highly variable and that there are limitations and variations in sensitivity and selectivity of accepted *Salmonella* isolation procedures for the detection of the 900 to 1,200 different *Salmonella* serotypes currently recognized. Thus, a negative result by any of these methods does not imply the absence of all salmonellae, nor does it imply the absence of other pathogens.

1. Concentration Technics for Waterborne Pathogens

Generally, it is necessary to examine a relatively large sample in order to isolate pathogenic organisms. These organisms are usually present in small numbers as compared to coliforms, because their sporadic occurrence is related to the incidence of disease or infection at a given period.

a. Swab technic: Swabs may be prepared from cheesecloth 9 in. wide, folded five times at 14-in. lengths and cut lengthwise to within 4 in. from the head, into strips that are 1¾ in. long. The uncut or folded end of the swab is then securely wrapped with 16-gauge wire and placed just below the surface of the stream, lake or estuary sampling location for from 3 to 5 days. Gauze pads of similar thickness—for example, maternity pads—may be substituted for cheesecloth swabs. During the period of sampling, particulate matter and microorganisms are concentrated from the water passing through or over the swab. After the exposure period, the swab is retrieved, placed in a plastic bag, iced, and sent to the laboratory. Maximum storage time allowable is 6 hr. At the laboratory, the sample water is expressed from the pad into suitable enrichment media, or the pad itself or portions of it may be placed in enrichment media.

b. Diatomaceous earth technic: The filtration capacity of diatomaceous earth is used to concentrate a relatively large proportion of the microorganisms present in a sample. This is accomplished by placing an absorbent pad (not a membrane filter) on a membrane filter funnel receptacle, assembling the funnel, then adding sufficient diatomaceous earth * to pack the funnel neck loosely. Two liters of sample are poured slowly through the diatomaceous earth filter and vacuum is applied. After filtration, the funnel is disassembled and the resulting "plug" of diatomaceous earth can be divided with a sterile spatula into portions which may be added to suitable enrichment media.

c. *Membrane filter technic:* In the examination of samples relatively free from turbidity, sample volumes of several liters may be passed through a sterile membrane filter (see Section 408, Membrane Filter Technic) which can be divided with sterile scissors into sections for inoculation into suitable enrichment media.

2. *Enrichment*

The concentrated sample must be selectively enriched in a growth medium that simultaneously suppresses the growth of coliform bacteria. Enrichment of the initial sample is essential, since the pathogens are generally present in low numbers and solid selective media for colony isolation are often somewhat toxic, even to the pathogens. There is no single enrichment medium that can be recommended to give optimum growth of both the *Salmonella* and the *Shigella* groups. Tetrathionate broth is excellent for primary enrichment of *Salmonella,* but it is very toxic to *Shigella* strains. Media containing selenite are strongly inhibitory to *Shigella flexneri* and, in lesser degree, to *Shigella sonnei. Shigella* enrichment has been found to be satisfactory only in media containing bile salts for coliform suppression.

a. *Dulcitol selenite broth* has the advantage of inhibiting the nonpathogenic colon bacilli during the early hours of incubation following inoculation, while allowing the *Salmonella* strains to multiply pretty rapidly. Optimum incubation time for maximum recovery of *Salmonella* is 24 hr. However, recovery of relatively slow-growing organisms like *S. montevideo, S. enteritidis* and *S. worthington* will necessitate longer incubation periods. Therefore, repeat streaking from the same inoculated medium after each 24-hr period may be necessary. Broth cultures which develop turbidity and any orange-red color resulting from selenite reduction are streaked onto suitable selective solid media.

b. *Tetrathionate broth* may yield more salmonellae than selenite broth. However, incubation should be extended beyond 48 hr, with repeat streaking from the same tube daily up to 5 days to insure recovery of all serotypes that may be present. Suppression of nonpathogenic organisms is improved by the addition of 1–100,000 brilliant green. Sensitivity is improved by the addition of 3 mg L-cystine per liter of tetrathionate broth.

c. *GN broth* has been found to permit good growth of various *Shigella* species and is recommended for those investigations of water pollution involving this pathogenic group. This medium will suppress not only the coliform group but also fecal streptococci, which may be numerous in polluted water. Incubation time should not be extended beyond 24 hr because longer incubation favors the growth of *Pseudomonas aeruginosa* and *Proteus* species.

* Johns-Mansville's "Celite" or equivalent.

3. Selective Growth

Further separation of pathogens from the surviving nonpathogenic bacterial population may be accomplished by the proper choice of incubation temperature for primary enrichment and secondary differentiation on selective solid media. These two factors—that is, temperature and choice of media—are interrelated. More *Salmonella* may be recovered at 37 C using bismuth sulfite agar than at other temperatures using other media. However, great skill at screening for these pathogens is necessary because of the competing growth of various nonpathogens. Using an incubation temperature of 41.5 C and brilliant green agar reduces the number of interfering organisms, but some *Salmonella* serotypes will not grow at this elevated temperature.

Solid media commonly used for enteric pathogen detection may be classed into three groups: (a) differential media with little or no inhibition toward nonpathogenic bacteria, such as EMB (containing sucrose) and MacConkey's agar; (b) selective media containing brilliant green dye, such as brilliant green agar or bismuth sulfite agar; and (c) selective media containing bile salts inhibitors such as desoxycholate citrate agar or xylose lysine desoxycholate agar (*Salmonella-Shigella,* SS, agar contains a combination of these two selective agents). Any medium selected must provide optimum suppression of coliforms while permitting good recovery of the pathogenic group. Since *Shigella* organisms are among the more fastidious enteric bacteria in their growth requirements, media suitable for *Salmonella* recovery may not be optimum for *Shigella.* Therefore, the protocol must include several selective media for optimum recovery of both *Salmonella* and *Shigella* from water. Streaking duplicate plates, one heavily and one lightly, often aids in the recognition of enteric pathogens in the presence of large numbers of interfering organisms.

a. Brilliant green agar: Typical well-isolated *Salmonella* colonies grown on this medium form a pinkish white colony with a red background. *Salmonella typhi* and a few other species of *Salmonella* grow poorly on this medium because of the brilliant green dye content. Those lactose fermenters whose growth is not suppressed will form greenish colonies, or they may at times produce other colorations. Occasionally, slow lactose fermenters (*Proteus, Citrobacter* and *Pseudomonas*) will produce colonies that resemble a pathogen. In some instances, *Proteus* has been observed to "swarm." This medium should be incubated a full 48 hr so as to permit any slow-growing or partially inhibited organisms to develop visible colonies. If no typical colonies are observed or if the streak plate is crowded, it may be necessary to transfer a few isolated colonies for further processing through the biochemical tests. Nonlactose-fermenting colonies may be masked by bordering lactose-fermenting colonies.

b. Bismuth sulfite agar: Luxuriant growth of many *Salmonella* species (including *S. typhi*) can be expected upon this medium after 48 hr of incubation. Typical colonies usually develop a black color, with or without a metallic sheen, and frequently this blackening extends beyond the colony to give a "halo" effect. A few species of *Salmonella* have been observed that develop a green coloration. Therefore, it may be necessary to isolate some of these colony types when the typical forms are absent. As with brilliant green agar, typical colony coloration may be masked by the presence of numerous bordering colonies. A black color is also developed by other hydrogen sulfide-producing colonies—for example, *Proteus* and certain coliforms.

c. Xylose lysine desoxycholate agar: This medium is recommended for isolation of *Shigella* species when used in conjunction with GN enrichment broth. Media containing brilliant green dye are unsuited to *Shigella* recovery. Sodium desoxycholate is far less toxic to *Shigella* and the fastidious *Salmonella.* Colonies of *Shigella* grown on this medium are red, while *Salmonella* and *Arizona* organisms produce black-centered red colonies. Coliform bacteria, *Citrobacter, Proteus,* and most paracolons produce yellow colonies. Optimum incubation time is 24 hr. If plates are incubated longer, there is an alkaline reversion and subsequent blackening by H_2S-positive nonpathogens (*Citrobacter, Proteus vulgaris,* and *P. mirabilis*).

4. Biochemical Reactions

Numerous enteric organisms of little or no pathogenicity have some major biochemical characteristics in common with the *Salmonella* and *Shigella.* The identification of pathogens by colony characteristics on selective media poses limitations inherent in the biological variations of certain organisms. Suspected colonies grown on selective solid media must be purified and further classified by biochemical reactions and finally verified by serological identification. Usually the number of cultures obtained from the screening procedure will be large. It is therefore recommended that a sequential pattern of biochemical testing be followed which will result in a great saving of media and time for laboratory personnel. The following schedule of testing is suggested:

PHASE 1: *Urea agar or urea broth*

Urea-positive cultures should be immediately discarded as indicative of the *Proteus* group or other nonpathogenic forms. The urea-negative cultures should be subjected to the biochemical tests of Phase 2. A 24-hr incubation period will be sufficient to indicate most positive cultures. Cultures negative after 24 hr also may be incubated for an additional 24 hr to detect the occasional slow urease producer.

PHASE 2: *Biochemical tests*

Medium	*Purpose of Test*
Decarboxylase media	Presence or absence of enzyme system
Citrate	Utilization of citrate as carbon source
TSI	Fermentation pattern; H_2S production
Lactose broth	Fermentation capability
Saccharose broth	Fermentation capability
Salicin broth	Fermentation capability
KCN broth	Growth capability in the presence of CN^- group
SIM	Production of indole, motility, H_2S production
Raffinose broth	Fermentation capability

Conformance to the typical biochemical patterns of the *Salmonella-Shigella* will determine whether the cultures are to be processed further (Phase 3). Aberrant cultures may be encountered which will not satisfy all the classical reactions attributed to each of the pathogenic groups. In all cases, therefore, it will be necessary to review all the reactions as a whole and not to discard cultures on the basis of a small number of apparent anomalies.

PHASE 3: *Fermentation reactions*

Fermentation reactions in dextrose broth, mannitol broth, maltose broth, dulcitol broth, xylose broth, rhamnose broth, and inositol broth are tested to characterize further the biochemical capabilities of the isolates. This additional sorting of the isolates will reduce the possible number of positive cultures that are to be processed for serological confirmation. If the testing laboratory is equipped for flagellar analysis, this series of biochemical tests may be eliminated.

5. *Identification by Serological Technics*

Serological identification of *Salmonella* or *Shigella* involves complex, highly specialized procedures which, if called for, should be carried out as described by Edwards and Ewing.[6]

411 B. Quantitative *Salmonella typhi* Procedure

A quantitative procedure for *Salmonella* is available only when *Salmonella typhi* is suspect. The method utilizes M-bismuth sulfite broth and the membrane filter procedure for bacterial concentration. This method of concentration can be used only with samples low in organic and particulate materials, since quantities of 100 ml or more are generally filtered. Following filtration (see Membrane Filter Technic, Section 408A.5), the filter is incubated on a pad containing M-bismuth sulfite broth for 18–20 hr at 35 C and transferred to a fresh pad saturated with M-bismuth sulfite broth. Incubation at 35 C is continued, to give a total of 30 hr. Suspected colonies (smooth glistening colonies with jet black centers surrounded by a thin clear white border) are transferred to triple sugar iron agar (TSI) for incubation at 35 C for 18 hr. Proceed with additional biochemical and serological procedures as described under qualitative methods.

411 C. Enteropathogenic *Escherichia coli*

Enteropathogenic *E. coli* has been isolated from tap water,[7] drinking water sources,[8] and mountain streams.[9] It is unlikely that *E. coli* organisms could initiate disease by transmission through a properly treated potable water. Additionally, at least in the United States, these organisms reportedly cause disease almost exclusively in infants. Since infants are normally given boiled or sterilized water, waterborne infections by enteropathogenic *E. coli* appear quite improbable. Isolation procedures for these organisms are the same as for any coliform. Identification procedures should be carried out as described by Edwards and Ewing.[6]

411 D. *Leptospira*, Vibrios, *Endamoeba histolytica* Cysts, Hookworm Larvae

Isolation and identification of these organisms require highly specialized procedures. Accordingly, if it is suspected that any of these organisms may be involved in waterborne disease, the services of a medical bacteriologist working in a state or local health department should be requested.

Infection of swimmers with *Leptospira* has been reported on several occasions [10] and isolation procedures have recently been described.[11]

411 E. References

1. Z. Ahmed, I. A. Poshni & M. A. Siddiqui. 1964. Bacteriological examination of drinking water of Karachi and isolation of enteric pathogens. *Pakistan J. Sci. & Ind. Research* 7:103.
2. R. Seligmann & R. Reitler. 1965. Enteropathogens in water with low *Esch. coli* titers. *JAWWA* 57:1572.
3. A. E. Greenberg & H. J. Ongerth. 1966. Salmonellosis in Riverside, California. *JAWWA* 58:1145.
4. R. B. Read & A. L. Reyes. 1968. Variation in plating efficiency of Salmonella on eight lots of brilliant green agar. *Applied Microbiol.* 16:746.
5. S. King & W. L. Metzger. 1968. A new medium for the isolation of enteric pathogens. I. Hektoen enteric agar. *Applied Microbiol.* 16:577.
6. P. R. Edwards & W. H. Ewing. 1962. *Identification of Enterobacteriaceae* (2nd ed.). Burgess Publishing Co., Minneapolis, Minn.
7. W. H. Ewing. 1962. Sources of *Escherichia coli* cultures that belong to O-antigen groups associated with infantile diarrheal disease. *J. Infect. Dis.* 110:114.
8. R. Seigneurin, R. Magnin & M. L. Achard. 1951. Types d'*Escherichia coli* isolés des eaux d'alimentation. *Ann. Inst. Pasteur* 89:473.
9. N. Petersen & J. R. Boring. 1960. A study of coliform densities and *Escherichia coli* serotypes in two mountain streams. *Amer. J. Hygiene* 71:134.
10. M. M. Galton, R. W. Menges, E. B. Shotts, A. J. Nahmias & C. W. Heath, Jr. 1962. Leptospirosis: Epidemiology, clinical manifestations in man and animals, and methods in laboratory diagnosis. PHS Pub. No. 951. Govt. Ptg. Off., Washington, D. C.
11. J. L. Braun, S. L. Diesch & W. F. McCulloch. 1968. A method for isolating leptospires from natural surface waters. *Can. J. Microbiol.* 14:1011.

411 F. Bibliography

CLARK, H. F., E. E. GELDREICH, H. L. JETER & P. W. KABLER. 1951. The membrane filter in sanitary bacteriology—Culture of *Salmonella typhosa* from water samples on a membrane filter. *Pub. Health Rep.* 66:951.

GREENBERG, A. E., R. W. WICKENDEN & T. W. LEE. 1957. Tracing typhoid carriers by means of sewage. *Sewage & Ind. Wastes* 29:1237.

KABLER, P. 1959. Removal of pathogenic microorganisms by sewage treatment processes. *Sewage & Ind. Wastes* 31: 1373.

MCCOY, J. H. 1962. Salmonella in crude sewage, sewage effluent, and sewage polluted natural waters. *Int. Conf. Water Poll. Research* (London), Vol. 1:205.

BREZENSKI, F. T., R. RUSSOMANNO & P. DEFALCO, JR. 1965. The occurrence of Salmonella and Shigella in post-chlorinated and nonchlorinated sewage effluents and receiving waters. *Health Lab. Sci.* 2:40.

TAYLOR, W. I. 1965. Isolation of Shigellae, I. Xylose-lysine agars; new media for isolation on enteric pathogens. *Amer. J. Clin. Path.* 44:471.

TAYLOR, W. I. & B. HARRIS. 1965. Isolation of Shigella, II. Comparison of plating media and enrichment broths. *Amer. J. Clin. Path.* 44:476.

RAJ, H. 1966. Enrichment medium for selection of Salmonella from fish homogenate. *Applied Microbiol.* 14:12.

SPINO, D. E. 1966. Elevated-temperature technique for the isolation of *Salmonella* from streams. *Applied Microbiol.* 14:591.

BREZENSKI, F. T. & R. RUSSOMANNO. 1968. The detection and use of Salmonella in studying polluted tidal estuaries: A correlation of coliform and fecal coliform indices with the presence of Salmonella in shellfish and overlying waters. Presented at the 41st Annual Conference, WPCF, Chicago, Ill. (Sept. 22–27).

GALTON, M. M., G. K. MORRIS & W. T. MARTIN. 1968. Salmonella in foods and feeds. Review of isolation methods and recommended procedures. PHS Bureau of Disease Prevention & Environmental Control, NCDC, Atlanta, Ga. (Jan.). 41 pp.

TAYLOR, W. I. & D. SCHELHART. 1968. Isolation of Shigella. V. Comparison of enrichment broths with stools. *Applied Microbiol.* 16:1383.

———. 1968. Isolation of Shigella. VI. Performance of media with stool specimens. *Applied Microbiol.* 16:1387.

412 DETECTION OF ENTERIC VIRUSES IN WATER AND WASTEWATER

1. Discussion

Certain viruses infect the gastrointestinal tracts of man and animals and are excreted with feces of infected individuals into domestic sewage which, after varying degrees of treatment, enters the waterways to become a part of the rivers and streams that serve as the source of water for most large communities. The viruses known to be excreted in relatively large numbers with feces are those of the enterovirus group [polioviruses, coxsackieviruses (Groups A and B), and echoviruses], the adenoviruses, reoviruses, and the virus(es) of infectious hepatitis. Other viruses may be present in human excretions, but not usually in large numbers.[1–5]

Most of these viruses, probably transmitted most frequently by the fecal-oral route, may be found in sewage predominantly during the warmer months of the year. Infectious hepatitis virus(es) may be an important exception because the incidence of the disease it produces increases in the colder months. No etiological agent of this disease has yet been isolated.

Viruses are not normal flora in the intestinal tract; they are excreted only by infected individuals, mostly young preschool and school-age children. Infection rates vary considerably from area to area, depending on sanitary and socioeconomic conditions. Viruses are usually excreted in numbers several orders of magnitude lower than those of coliform bacteria; because viruses multiply only within living susceptible cells, their numbers do not increase in sewage. Sewage treatment, dilution, natural die-off, and water treatment further reduce viral numbers by the time water is consumed for drinking purposes. Thus, although large outbreaks of waterborne viral disease may occur when massive sewage contamination of a water supply takes place,[6] transmission of viral infection and disease in technologically advanced nations depends on whether minimal quantities of viruses are capable of producing infections and, if so, whether they will produce infections when ingested with relatively large volumes of water. Ingestion of a virus in a large volume of water would reduce the opportunity for the virus to adsorb to a susceptible cell and initiate the infectious process. That very small amounts of virus can produce infection has been demonstrated.[7] However, the risk of infection incurred by the individual in a community with a water containing small amounts of viruses has not been determined.[3]

It has been argued that transmission of small numbers of viruses through water supplies may produce inapparent immunizing infections. However, the subsequent transmission of viruses from index infections to contacts probably involves large quantities of viruses and may result in a considerable amount of disease in the community epidemiologically consistent with contact and not with transmission from a common source.

Direct demonstration and quantitation of viruses in relatively clean waters is difficult because the numbers present are likely to be small; thus, large volumes of such waters must be sampled to increase the probability of detection. Quantitation of viruses in waste and natural waters is more difficult. The most commonly used method today for concentrating small amounts of viruses from large volumes of water is the gauze pad technic. Pads of gauze or sanitary napkins are suspended in flowing waters, usually for about 2 days, then placed in plastic bags. The pH of the absorbed water is adjusted to 8.0 (presumably to elute the virus from the gauze fibers), the water is expressed from the pads and centrifuged, first at low speed to sediment bacteria and particulate matter, then at high speed to sediment viruses which are subsequently assayed. The major deficiency of this method is that it is not quantitative. There is no way to determine how much water flows through the pad, how much virus in the water makes contact and adheres to the pad but is not eluted, or how much adsorbed virus becomes noninfective during the period in which the gauze is suspended.[8]

An older quantitative technic, grab sampling, has been made more practical by recent improvements in assay technology[9] but the amount of water that can be sampled by this technic is limited to a gallon or two, and even this is expensive. With this method, water to be sampled for viruses is used to prepare the media for nourishing the large number of cell cultures that serve as the assay system for the viruses. Viruses to which the cells are susceptible will infect the cells and destroy them. This cell destruction can be detected microscopically and the viruses can then be quantified by the MPN procedure. The limitation in the volume of sample that can be processed constitutes a major deficiency of this procedure and this is related directly to the cost of the large numbers of cell cultures required by the technic.

A polymer two-phase separation system has been described which is also useful for quantitatively detecting small amounts of viruses,[10] but the volume of water that can be tested by this method is also limited. Test water is mixed with polyethylene glycol and dextran sulfate and allowed to settle. The mixture separates into phases, with the viruses concentrated in the small dextran sulfate phase. The dextran is precipitated with KCl and the virus can be recovered from the supernatant by viral assay procedures.

At the moment, the most promising method for concentrating small quantities of viruses from large volumes of water is the membrane filter technic of Cliver.[11] Volumes of water, 100 gal and more, may be passed under suction or light pressure through membrane filters * (0.45μ-porosity) to which viruses adsorb. Adsorption of at least several of these viruses is best at pH 7 and in the presence of salt.[12, 13] Turbid waters can be cleared by filtration through coarse filters with relatively little loss of virus. Elution of the viruses is achieved by immersing the filters in 3% beef extract.[13] This technic, though the most quantitative presently available, suffers in that the beef extract is not a universal eluant, that is, a given lot of beef extract may elute 100% of one strain of virus but will elute only 50 or 60% of another virus or even another strain of the same virus. Moreover, a virus that can be completely eluted by one lot of beef extract may be eluted inefficiently by another lot. Efforts to determine the eluting component of beef extract have not yet been successful.

The membrane filter technic is the most quantitative method available within the limitations described. However, the gauze pad procedure permits the passage of huge volumes of water through its adsorbent fibers. Even if the efficiency of the gauze pad technic is low, the very large volumes that pass through the gauze may retain for this method a sensitivity not readily matched even by the efficiently adsorbing membrane filter.

At present, studies to determine the efficiency of the gauze pad procedure are in progress. Other methods for quantitative recovery of viruses also are under study.[14]

For those who must at this time determine quantitatively the virus content of waters, two procedures are recommended. The gauze pad procedure is recommended for qualitative studies on the assumption that this technic may be the most sensitive presently available. The membrane filter procedure, the most quantitative technic available, possesses also the ultimate potential of un-

* Cliver [11] reports that filters from Millipore Filter Corp. were used, since certain other types did not perform satisfactorily.

limited sampling volume and, with this, the greatest sensitivity. It is tentatively recommended for quantitative studies.

No routine examination of water or wastewater for enteric viruses is practical or necessarily meaningful at the present time. Only special circumstances, particularly in the context of wastewater reclamation, recreational water quality and disease incidence, or special research studies, may require virus testing.

2. *References*

1. N. A. CLARKE & S. L. CHANG. 1959. Enteric viruses in water. *JAWWA* 51: 1299.
2. N. A. CLARKE, G. BERG, P. W. KABLER & S. L. CHANG. 1962 and 1964. Human enteric viruses in water: Source, survival and removability. In *Proc. Int. Conf. Water Poll. Research* (London). Macmillan Co., New York; and Pergamon Press, Oxford, England, p. 523.
3. G. BERG. 1966. Virus transmission by the water vehicle. I. Viruses. *Health Lab. Sci.* 3:86.
4. ———. 1966. Virus transmission by the water vehicle. II. Virus removal by sewage treatment procedures. *Health Lab. Sci.* 3:90.
5. ———. 1966. Virus transmission by the water vehicle. III. Removal of viruses by water treatment procedures. *Health Lab. Sci.* 3:170.
6. R. VISWANATHAN. 1957. Epidemiology. *Indian J. Med. Research* 45:1 (supplementary number).
7. S. A. PLOTKIN & M. KATZ. 1967. Minimal infective doses of viruses for man by the oral route. In *Transmission of Viruses by the Water Route* (G. Berg, Ed.). Interscience Publishers, New York, p. 151.
8. G. BERG. 1967. Discussion. In *Transmission of Viruses by the Water Route* (G. Berg, Ed.). Interscience Publishers, New York, page 462.
9. G. BERG, D. BERMAN, S. L. CHANG & N. A. CLARKE. 1966. A sensitive quantitative method for detecting small quantities of virus in large volumes of water. *Amer. J. Epidemiol.* 83:196.
10. H. I. SHUVAL, S. CYMBALISTA, B. FATAL & N. GOLDBLUM. 1967. Concentration of enteric viruses in water by hydro-extraction and two-phase separation. In *Transmission of Viruses by the Water Route* (G. Berg, Ed.). Interscience Publishers, New York, p. 45.
11. D. O. CLIVER. 1967. Enterovirus detection by membrane chromatography. In *Transmission of Viruses by the Water Route* (G. Berg, Ed.). Interscience Publishers, New York, p. 139.
12. C. WALLIS & J. L. MELNICK. 1967. Concentration of enteroviruses on membrane filters. *J. Virol.* 1:472.
13. G. BERG, R. B. DEAN & D. R. DAHLING. 1968. Removal of poliovirus 1 from secondary effluents by lime flocculation and rapid sand filtration. *JAWWA* 60: 193.
14. G. BERG, Ed. 1967. *Transmission of Viruses by the Water Route.* Interscience Publishers, New York, pp. 45–143.

413 TESTS FOR SWIMMING POOL AND BATHING-PLACE WATERS

Historically, bathing waters have been examined for coliform bacteria and/or total viable bacteria (Standard Plate Count). It has been recognized that these procedures do not provide the most satisfactory information with which to evaluate water quality. Without discarding the conventional tests, tentative procedures are added below that will permit the enumeration of organisms which can provide more specific information of public health significance. However, it is unlikely that the newer test procedures will be used in the establishment of water quality standards until adequate information has been accumulated.

Staphylococcus aureus and *Pseudomonas aeruginosa* are the two indicator organisms proposed. The former is an inhabitant of the mucous membranes and the human skin, is commonly found in bathing waters, and can be enumerated simply by a membrane filter technic. Staphylococci are more resistant to halogen disinfectants than enteric organisms, so that if their absence can be demonstrated, effective disinfection is indicated.

Pseudomonas aeruginosa has been associated with human otitis externa and other infections. It should be absent from any well-operated and adequately disinfected pool.

1. Samples

a. Containers: Samples for bacteriologic examination of bathing waters should be collected as directed in Section 405.1 (Samples, Collection). All sample containers should contain a dechlorinating agent.

b. Sampling procedure: Standard sampling procedures should be followed. Ideally, samples should be collected directly from the pool, both when in use and after it has been free of bathers for some time. Information on the bathing load is helpful in subsequent interpretation of laboratory results. Care should be taken to avoid contamination of the sample by floating debris.

It is recommended that residual chlorine, or other halogen disinfectant, be determined at pool side, at the time of sample collection. Residual chlorine should be redetermined when the sample is brought to the laboratory to insure against the loss of the dechlorinating agent during sampling.

c. Sample storage: Samples should not be held for more than 6 hr if the Standard Plate Count is to be made. If analysis is not begun promptly after sample collection, the samples should be refrigerated.

2. Standard Plate Count

The total bacterial count should be determined as directed under Standard Plate Count, Section 406.

3. Tests for Members of the Coliform Group

Tests for members of the coliform group should be made as directed under the Multiple-Tube Fermentation Technic (Section 407) or the Membrane Filter Technic (Section 408).

4. Tests for Fecal Coliforms

The tests for fecal coliform bacteria should be made as directed under Multiple-Tube Fermentation Technic, Fecal Coliform Test (Section 407C); or the Membrane Filter Technic, Fecal Coliform Membrane Filter Procedure (Section 408B).

5. Tests for Fecal Streptococci

The tests for fecal streptococci should be made as directed under Tests for the Fecal Streptococcal Group (Section 409).

6. Tests for Other Body Organisms

See Sections A, B and C following.

413 A. *Membrane Filter Technic for* Staphylococcus aureus *(TENTATIVE)*

1. Laboratory Apparatus

Refer to membrane filter assembly and laboratory apparatus under Standard Total Coliform Membrane Filter Procedure (Section 408A).

2. Materials and Culture Media

a. Culture media: Refer to Media Specifications (M-Staphylococcus Broth), Section 404C.27.

b. Culture dish preparation: An absorbent sterile pad is placed in the bottom half of the culture dish and saturated with about 2 ml of M-Staphylococcus broth. Excess liquid is carefully removed.

3. Procedure

a. Selection of sample size and filtration: Filter samples of water through sterile membrane to attain 40–100 colonies on the membrane surface. Amounts varying from 100 to 10, 1, 0.1 or 0.01 ml may be necessary, depending on the number of organisms present. Transfer the filter directly to the broth-saturated pad in the petri dish, avoiding air bubbles.

b. Incubation: Invert culture plates and incubate at 35 ± 0.5 C for 48 hr. If no pigmented colonies develop, hold plates an additional 48 hr at room temperature before discarding as negative.

c. Counting: Colonies produced by *Staphylococcus aureus* are generally yellow-gold in color. The count is best made with the aid of a low-power (10–15 magnifications) binocular wide-field dissecting microscope or other optical device.

4. Calculation of Density

Density is computed from the sample quantities that produce membrane filter counts within the desired 40–100 colony range. Proceed with the calculation as stated under Section 408A.6 (Standard Total Coliform Membrane Filter Procedure). Record densities as yellow-gold colonies per 100 ml.

5. Confirmed Test

Typical yellow-gold colonies should be fished for staining and coagulase-testing.

a. Staining and coagulase-testing: Fish selected typical colonies and, on a clean microscope slide, emulsify the colony in a drop of distilled water. Do not spread emulsion. On a separate slide prepare a smear, gram-stain it, and examine as in Section 407A.4 (Multiple-Tube Fermentation Technic, Standard Total Coliform MPN Tests). Complete the coagulase test by adding a large loopful of coagulase plasma solution to the bacterial emulsion on the first slide. Avoid the use of excess plasma to prevent false-positive reactions. A positive reaction is indicated by rapid clumping of the emulsion. Plasma should be checked against a known coagulase-positive strain of *Staphylococcus* prior to use.

If verification of the slide test for coagulase is desired, the suspicious colony should be transferred to a tube of heart infusion broth and incubated at 35 ± 0.5 C for 18–24 hr. Place 0.5 ml of plasma in a 7-mm test tube and add 0.05 ml of the broth culture. Mix gently by rotation and place in a water bath at 37 ± 0.5 C. Examine for coagulation at half-hourly intervals. Any degree of clotting within 3–5 hr is considered positive, although some weak strains may require overnight incubation before coagulation may be observed.

b. Interpretation of results: A positive confirmed test for *S. aureus* requires the presence of gram-positive staphylococci and a positive coagulase test.

Consult Cowan and Steel's Manual (see Bibliography) if further confirmatory tests are desired.

413 B. Multiple-Tube Technic for Pseudomonas aeruginosa (TENTATIVE)

1. Presumptive Test

a. Procedure: Inoculate 5–10 ml samples into double-strength asparagine enrichment broth (Section 404C.29). Incubate inoculated tubes at 35 ± 0.5 C for 48 hr. Green or blue pigment production and/or turbidity constitute a positive presumptive test.

2. Confirmed Test

a. Confirmation: All positive presumptive tubes should be confirmed.

b. Procedure: Transfer a loopful of growth from each asparagine enrichment tube to a tube of acetamide broth (Section 404C. 30). Incubate at 35 ± 0.5 C for 48 hr. The presence of *Pseudomonas aeruginosa* is indicated by the development of a purple coloration.

3. Computing and Recording of MPN

Refer to Table 407(1) and to the section on estimation of bacterial density (407D).

413 C. Membrane Filter Qualitative Technic for Pseudomonas aeruginosa (TENTATIVE)

Use the general membrane filter technic described under Membrane Filter Technic (Section 408), with the following exceptions: Use "Tech" medium with 0.05% hexadecyltrimethyl ammonium bromide (Section 404C. 31); incubate at 35± 0.5 C for 24–48 hr; typical colonies are translucent and blue or blue-green, with a soluble diffused pigment.

This procedure is considered qualitative because it is not known that single cells will yield pigmented colonies within the specified incubation time. Furthermore, spread of the pigment may make counting impossible on more crowded membranes.

413 D. Bibliography

ROBINTON, ELIZABETH D., E. W. MOOD & LOUISE R. ELLIOTT. 1957. A study of bacterial flora in swimming pool water treated with high-free residual chlorine. *AJPH* 47:1101.

MALLMAN, W. L. 1962. Cocci test for detecting mouth and nose pollution of swimming pool waters. *AJPH* 52:2001.

McLEAN, D. M. 1963. Infection hazards in swimming pools. *Pediatrics* 31:811.

FAVERO, M. S., C. H. DRAKE & GEORGANNE B. RANDALL. 1964. Use of staphylococci as indicators of swimming pool pollution. *Pub. Health Rep.* 79:61.

BØE, J., C. O. SOLBERG, T. M. VOGELSANG & A. WORMNES. 1964. Perianal carriers of staphylococci. *Brit. Med. J.* 2:280.

FAVERO, M. S. & C. H. DRAKE. 1964. Comparative study of microbial flora of iodated and chlorinated pools. *Pub. Health Rep.* 79:251.

COWAN, S. T. & K. J. STEEL. 1965. *Manual for the Identification of Medical Bacteria.* Cambridge University Press, New York.

Report of a Working Party of the Public Health Laboratory Service. 1965. A bacteriological survey of swimming baths in primary schools. *Monthly Bull. Min. Health & Pub. Health Lab. Service* 24:116.

DRAKE, C. H. 1966. Evaluation of culture media for the isolation and enumeration of *Pseudomonas aeruginosa. Health Lab. Sci.* 3:10.

ROBINTON, ELIZABETH D. & E. W. MOOD. 1966. A quantitative and qualitative appraisal of microbial pollution of water by swimmers: A preliminary report. *J. Hygiene* 64:489.

———. 1967. An evaluation of the inhibitory influence of cyanuric acid upon swimming pool disinfection. *AJPH* 57:301.

PART 500

IDENTIFICATION OF IRON AND SULFUR BACTERIA

500 INTRODUCTION

This section deals with a group of nuisance organisms collectively designated as iron and sulfur bacteria. The group is neither morphologically nor physiologically homogeneous, yet it may be characterized by the ability to transform or deposit significant amounts of iron or sulfur, usually in the form of objectionable slimes. Iron and sulfur bacteria are not, however, the sole producers of bacterial slimes.

The organisms that are placed in this group may be filamentous or single celled, autotrophic or heterotrophic, aerobic or anaerobic. Following conventional bacterial classification, these organisms are assigned to a variety of orders, families and genera. They are studied as "iron and sulfur bacteria" because these elements and their transformations may be important in water treatment and distribution systems, and may be especially bothersome in waters for industrial use, as in cooling and boiler waters. Iron bacteria may cause fouling and plugging of wells and distribution systems, and sulfate-reducing bacteria may cause rusty water and tuberculation of pipes. These organisms may also cause odor, taste, frothing, color and increases in turbidity in waters.

The food supply of iron and sulfur bacteria may be wholly or partly inorganic and they may extract it, if attached or in a gelatinous substrate, from a low concentration in flowing water. This seems quite important in the case of certain sulfur bacteria utilizing small amounts of hydrogen sulfide, or in the case of organisms such as *Gallionella,* which obtain their energy from the oxidation of ferrous iron. Temperature, light, pH, and oxygen supply also affect the growth of these organisms. Under different environmental conditions some bacteria may appear either as iron or as sulfur bacteria.

501 IRON BACTERIA

1. General Characteristics

"Iron bacteria" are considered to be capable of withdrawing iron present in their aqueous habitat and of depositing it in the form of hydrated ferric hydroxide on or in their mucilaginous secretions. A somewhat similar mechanism is employed by bacteria utilizing manganese. The large amount of brown slime so produced will impart a reddish tinge and an unpleasant odor to drinking water which may render the supply unsuitable for domestic or industrial purposes. Such bacteria also may be the causative agents in the initiation of pitting and tuberculation of pipes. Bacteria of this type, to obtain energy, oxidize ferrous to ferric iron, which is precipitated as ferric hydrate. Iron may be obtained from the pipe itself or from the water being carried. The amount of ferric hydrate deposited is very large in comparison with the enclosed cells.

Some bacteria which do not oxidize ferrous iron may nevertheless indirectly cause it to be dissolved or deposited. In their growth, they either liberate iron by utilizing organic radicals to which the iron is attached or they alter environmental conditions to permit the solution or deposition of iron. In consequence, less ferric hydrate may be produced, but taste, odor and fouling may be encouraged.

2. Collection of Samples and Identification

Identification of nuisance iron bacteria has usually been made on the basis of microscopic examination of the suspected material. Bulked activated sludge, masses of microbial growth in

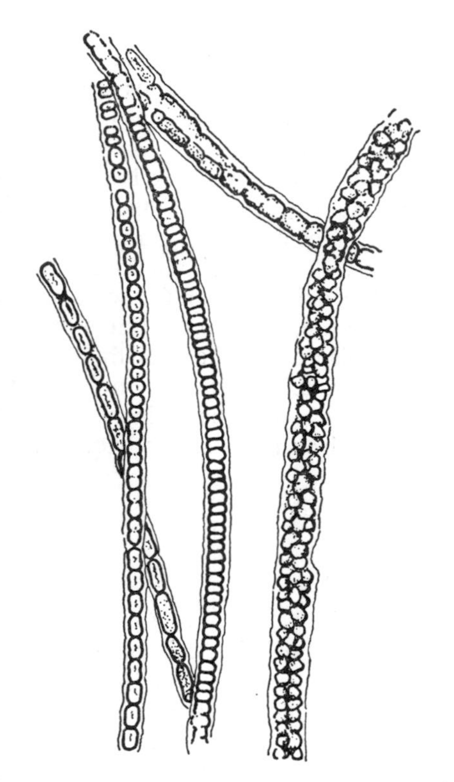

Figure 53. Filaments of *Crenothrix polyspora* showing variation of size and shape of cells within the sheath. Note especially the multiple small round cells, or "conidia," found in one of the filaments. This distinctive feature is the reason for the name *polyspora*. Young growing colonies are usually not encrusted with iron or manganese. Older colonies often exhibit empty sheaths that are heavily encrusted. Cells may vary considerably in size: Rod-shaped cells average 1.2–2.0 μ in width by 2.4–5.6 μ in length; coccoid cells or "conidia" average 0.6 μ in diameter.

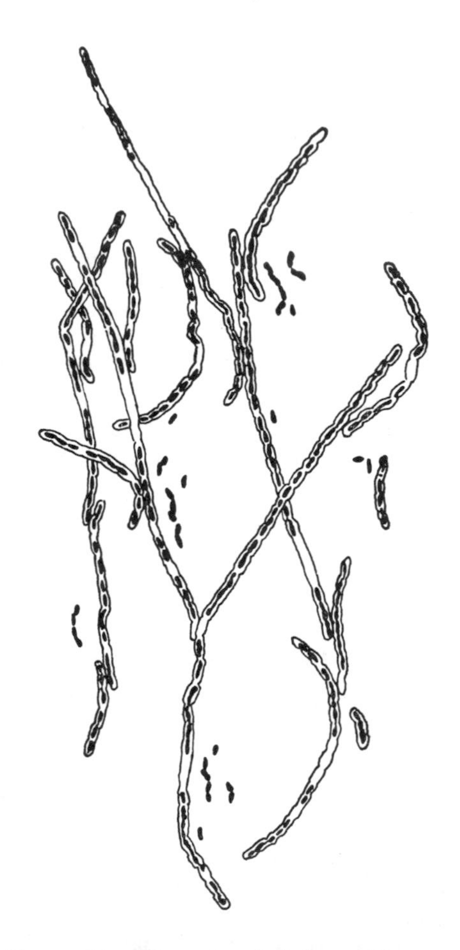

Figure 54. Filaments of *Sphaerotilus natans*, showing cells within the filaments and some free "swarmer" cells. Filaments show false branching and areas devoid of cells. Individual cells within the sheath may vary in size, averaging 0.6–2.4 μ in width by 1.0–12.0 μ in length; most strains are 1.1–1.6 μ wide by 2.0–4.0 μ long.

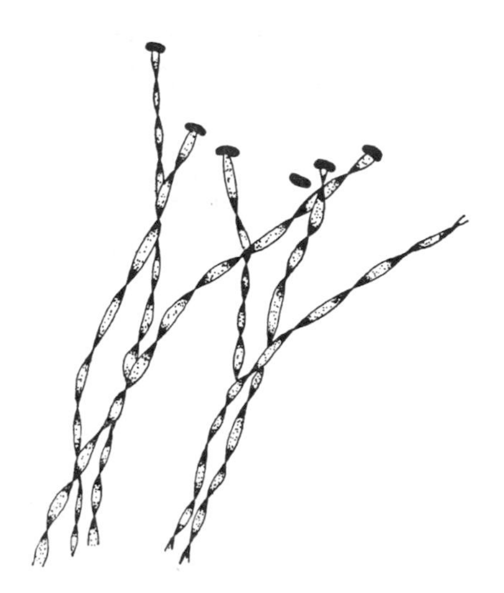

Figure 55. Laboratory culture of *Gallionella ferruginea,* showing cells, stalks excreted by cells, and branching of stalks where cells have divided. A precipitate of inorganic iron on and around the stalks often blurs the outlines. Cells at tip of stalk average 0.4–0.6 μ in width by 0.7–1.1 μ in length.

Figure 56. Mixture of fragments of stalks of *Gallionella ferruginea* and inorganic iron-manganese precipitate found in natural samples from wells. Fragmented stalks appear golden yellow to orange in color when examined under the microscope.

lakes, rivers and streams, and slime growths in coolant tower waters may be examined directly. Suspected development of iron bacteria in wells or in distribution systems may require special efforts to secure samples useful for identification. Continued heavy deposition of iron caused by the oxidation of ferrous iron by air, or by other environmental changes, often hides the sheaths or stalks of iron bacteria. The cells within the filaments often die and disintegrate and the filaments tend to be fragmented or crushed by the mass of the iron precipitate.

Samples of water drawn directly from wells should be allowed to settle and the sediment may be examined microscopically. The material trapped by filters placed in front of back-surge valves has often exhibited excellent specimens of iron bacteria. Water pumped from the well may be passed through a membrane filter and the filter can then be examined under the microscope.[1] Phase-contrast microscopes have made possible the examination of unstained cultural material. India ink or lactophenol cotton blue may be used for

Figure 57. Single-celled iron bacterium *Siderocapsa treubii.* Cells are surrounded by a deposit of ferric hydrate. Individual cells average 0.4–1.5 μ in width by 0.8–2.5 μ in length.

staining when microscopes are used that do not provide phase contrast. Reducing compounds such as sodium ascorbate mixed with the material on the slide will help remove some of the heaviest deposits of iron and allow cellular structure to be observed.

Identification is made by comparing the material with available drawings or photographs of iron bacteria.[2-11] A single-celled autotrophic bacterium, *Ferrobacillus ferrooxidans,* which contributes to the problems of acid mine drainage, may be quantitatively determined by the MPN procedure of Silverman and Lundgren.[12]

502 SULFUR BACTERIA

1. General Characteristics

The bacteria that oxidize or reduce significant amounts of inorganic sulfur compounds exhibit a wide diversity of morphological and biochemical characteristics. One group, the sulfate-reducing bacteria, consists of single-celled forms that grow anaerobically and reduce sulfate to hydrogen sulfide. A second group—the green photosynthetic and the sulfur purple bacteria—grows anaerobically in the light and uses hydrogen sulfide as a hydrogen donor for photosynthetic activity. The sulfide is oxidized to sulfur or sulfate. A third group, the aerobic sulfur oxidizers, oxidizes reduced sulfur compounds aerobically to obtain energy for chemoautotrophic growth.

The sulfur bacteria of most importance in the water and wastewater field are the sulfate-reducing bacteria and the single-celled aerobic sulfur oxidizers of the genus *Thiobacillus.* The sulfate-reducing bacteria contribute greatly to tuberculations and galvanic corrosion of water mains and to taste and odor problems in water. The *Thiobacillus,* by its production of sulfuric acid, has contributed to the destruction of concrete sewers and the acid corrosion of metals.

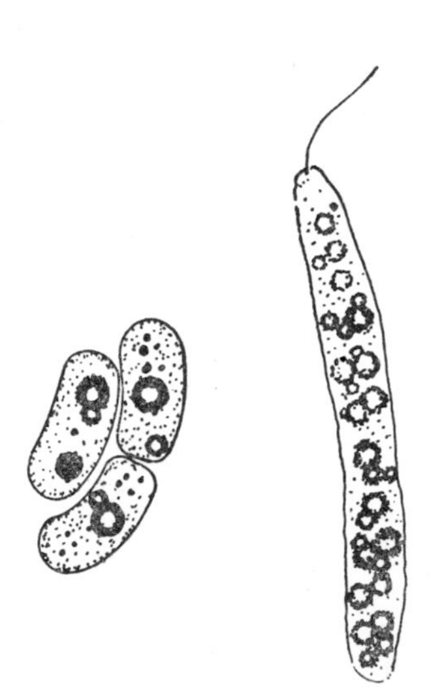

Figure 58. Photosynthetic sulfur purple bacteria: Large masses of cells have brown-orange to purple color—may appear chalky if there is a large amount of sulfur within the cells. Left: cells of *Chromatium okenii* (5.0–6.5 μ wide by 8–15 μ long) containing sulfur granules. Right: *Thiospirillum jenense* (3.5–4.5 μ wide by 30–40 μ long); cell contains sulfur granules, and polar flagellum is visible.

2. Collection of Samples and Identification

Identification of nuisance sulfur bacteria has usually been made on the basis of microscopic examination of the suspected material. Samples of slimes suspended in waters, scrapings from exposed surfaces, or sediments may be examined directly.

Three groups of sulfur bacteria may be recognized microscopically: green and purple sulfur bacteria; large, colorless filamentous sulfur bacteria; and large, colorless nonfilamentous sulfur bacteria. A fourth group cannot be identified by appearance alone.

a. Green and purple sulfur bacteria:

1) Green sulfur bacteria most frequently occur in waters high in hydrogen sulfide. They are small, ovoid to rod-shaped nonmotile organisms, generally less than 1 μ in diameter, and with a yellowish green color in masses. Sulfur globules are seldom if ever deposited within the cells.

2) Purple sulfur bacteria occur in waters containing hydrogen sulfide. They are large, generally stuffed with sulfur globules, and often so intensely pigmented as to make individual cells appear red. Large, dense highly colored masses are easily detected by the naked eye.

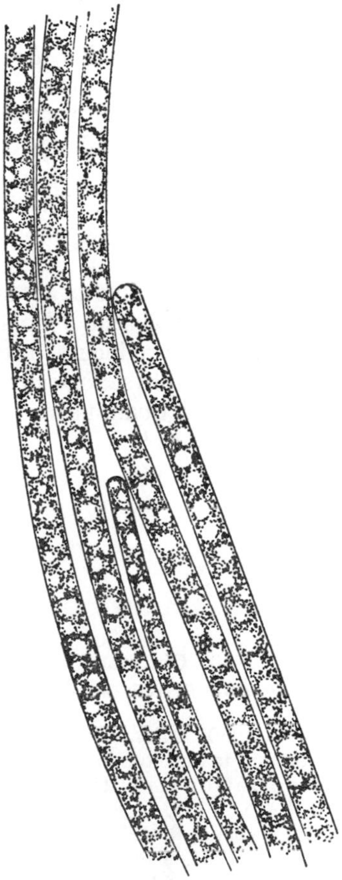

Figure 59. Colorless filamentous sulfur bacteria: *Beggiatoa alba* trichomes, containing granules of sulfur. Filaments are composed of a linear series of individual rod-shaped cells that may be visible when not obscured by light reflecting from sulfur granules. Trichomes are 2–15 μ in diameter and may be up to 1,500 μ long; individual cells, if visible, are 4.0–16.0 μ long.

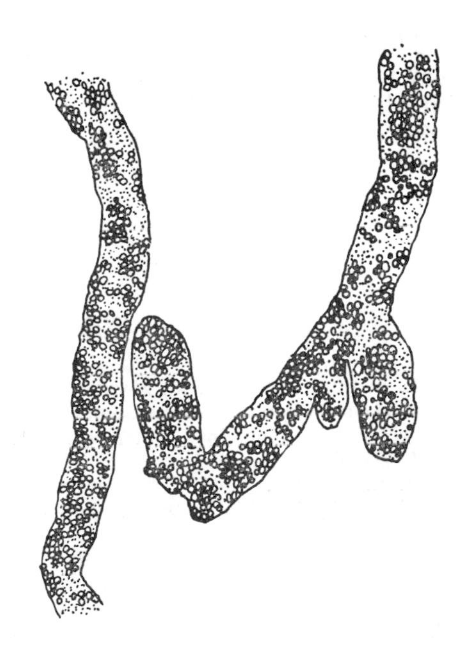

Figure 60. Colorless filamentous sulfur bacteria: portion of a colony of *Thiodendron mucosum,* showing branching of the mucoid filament. Individual cells (1.0–2.5 μ wide by 3–9 μ long) have been found within the jelly-like material of the filaments. The long axis of the cells runs parallel to the long axis of the filaments.

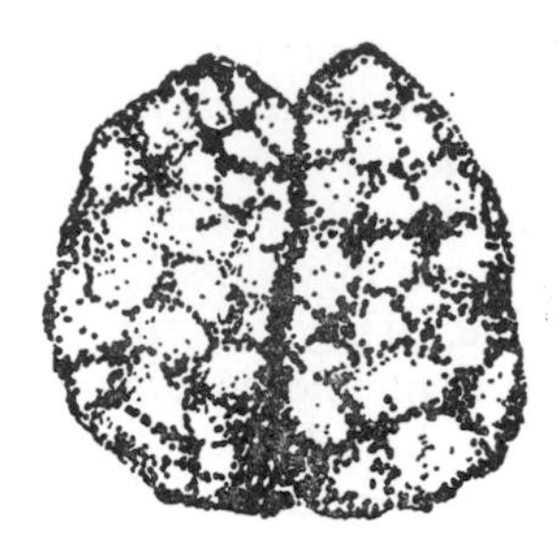

Figure 61. Colorless nonfilamentous sulfur bacteria: dividing cell of *Thiovolum majus,* containing sulfur granules. Cells may measure 9–17 μ in width by 11–18 μ in length and are generally found in nature in a marine littoral zone rich in organic matter and hydrogen sulfide.

b. Colorless filamentous sulfur bacteria: Colorless filamentous sulfur bacteria occur in waters where both oxygen and hydrogen sulfide are present. They may form mats with a slightly yellowish white appearance due to the deposition of internal sulfur globules. They are generally large and may be motile with a characteristic gliding movement. Identification may be made by comparing the material with available photographs.[13-15]

c. Colorless nonfilamentous sulfur bacteria: Colorless, nonfilamentous sulfur bacteria are usually associated with decaying algae. They are extremely motile, ovoid to rod-shaped with sulfur globules and possible calcium carbonate deposits. They are generally very large.

d. Colorless small sulfur bacteria and sulfate-reducing bacteria: The small single-celled sulfur bacteria, the *Thiobacilli,* and the sulfate-reducing bacteria cannot be identified by direct microscopic examination. *Thiobacillus* types are small, colorless, motile and rod-shaped and are found in an environment containing hydrogen sulfide. Sulfur globules are absent. *Thiobacillus* types and sulfate-reducing bacteria must be identified physiologically. Procedures for their quantitative estimation are available.[16, 17]

503 REFERENCES

1. L. A. Lueschow & K. M. Mackenthun. 1962. Detection and enumeration of iron bacteria in municipal water supplies. *JAWWA* 54:751.
2. R. L. Starkey. 1945. Transformations of iron by bacteria in water. *JAWWA* 37:963.
3. J. L. Stokes. 1954. Studies on the filamentous sheathed iron bacterium *Sphaerotilus natans. J. Bact.* 67:278.
4. S. Kucera & R. S. Wolfe. 1957. A selective enrichment method for *Gallionella ferruginea. J. Bact.* 74:344.
5. S. Waitz & J. B. Lackey. 1958. Morphological and biochemical studies on the organism *Sphaerotilus natans. Quart. J. Florida Acad. Sci.* 21:335.
6. R. S. Wolfe. 1958. Cultivation, morphology, and classification of the iron bacteria. *JAWWA* 50:1241.
7. ———. 1960. Observations and studies of *Crenothrix polyspora. JAWWA* 52:915.
8. ———. 1960. Microbial concentration of iron and manganese in water with low concentrations of these elements. *JAWWA* 52:1335.
9. N. C. Dondero, R. A. Philips & H. Heukelekian. 1961. Isolation and preservation of cultures of *Sphaerotilus. Applied Microbiol.* 9:219.
10. E. G. Mulder. 1964. Iron bacteria, particularly those of the *Sphaerotilus-Leptothrix* group, and industrial problems. *J. Applied Bact.* 27:151.
11. C. H. Drake. 1965. Occurrence of *Siderocapsa treubii* in certain waters of the Niederrhein. *Gewässer & Abwässer* 39/40:41.
12. M. P. Silverman & D. G. Lundgren.

1959. Studies on the chemosynthetic iron bacterium *Ferrobacillus ferrooxidans*. 1. An improved medium and a harvesting procedure for securing high yields. *J. Bact.* 77:642.

13. J. B. LACKEY & E. W. LACKEY. 1961. The habitat and description of a new genus of sulphur bacterium. *J. Gen. Microbiol.* 26:28.

14. L. FAUST & R. S. WOLFE. 1961. Enrichment and cultivation of *Beggiatoa alba*. *J. Bact.* 81:99.

15. G. B. MORGAN & J. B. LACKEY. 1965. Ecology of a sulfuretum in a semitropical environment. *Zeitsch. Allg. Mikrobiol.* 5:237.

16. R. L. STARKEY. 1956. Transformations of sulfur by microorganisms. *Ind. Eng. Chem.* 48:1429.

17. R. F. LEWIS. 1965. Control of sulfate-reducing bacteria. *JAWWA* 57:1011.

PART 600

BIOLOGICAL SAMPLING AND ANALYSIS

600 INTRODUCTION

Water quality in a stream or reservoir, ocean or estuary, is strongly influenced by the biological interactions that take place there. Field observations are indispensable to adequate biological interpretations, but there are many biological parameters which cannot be evaluated directly in the field. These must be examined as field data or field samples within the laboratory. Since no analytical result can be any better than the sample it represents, attention in this part is given to field methods as well as to laboratory procedures. In biological examinations field and laboratory personnel are often the same; if they are not, their activities must be closely coordinated.

The specific nature of a problem and the reasons for collecting samples will dictate those aquatic communities of organisms to be examined and these in turn will establish the sampling and analytical technics. The following communities and types of organisms are considered:

1. PLANKTON: A community of plants and animals usually swimming or suspended in water, nonmotile or insufficiently motile to overcome passive transport by currents. In freshwaters they are generally small or microscopic; in salt water, larger forms are more frequently observed.

2. PERIPHYTON, or "aufwuchs": A community of microorganisms associated with the surfaces of objects. Some are attached, some move about. Protozoa, numerous other minute invertebrates, and the smaller algae are found in both the plankton and the periphyton.

3. MACROINVERTEBRATES: The larger invertebrates or "macroinvertebrates" (herein defined as those retained by a U. S. Standard No. 30 sieve) are generally bottom-dwelling organisms (benthos).

4. MACROPHYTES: The macrophytes are the larger plants of all types. They are sometimes attached to the bottom (benthic), sometimes free-floating, and sometimes partly emergent. "Higher" types usually have true roots, stems and leaves; the algae are simpler in structure.

5. FISH: Fish may be found in nearly any type of aquatic habitat, and no single set of equipment will collect all kinds. Some of the basic fish-collecting devices, such as the trawl nets and traps described below, may be so designed as to catch either fish or certain macroinvertebrates—for example, shrimp or other crustaceans. The emphasis in this section, however, is on fish.

Information on all types of aquatic organisms is important in evaluating water quality and may serve one or more of the following purposes:

a. To explain the cause of color and turbidity and the presence of objectionable odors, tastes and visible particulates in water.

b. To aid in the interpretation of the various chemical analyses—as, for example, in relating the presence of biologic forms to oxygen deficiency or supersaturation in natural waters.

c. To identify the source of a water that is mixing with another water.

d. To explain the clogging of pipes, screens or filters and to aid in the design and operation of water and wastewater treatment plants.

e. To indicate the nature, extent and effects of pollution, as well as any adverse effects on aquatic life.

f. To indicate the progress of the self-purification of streams and other bodies of water.

g. To aid in explaining the mechanism of biologic sewage treatment methods or to serve as an index of the effectiveness of treatment.

h. To determine optimum times for the treatment of surface water with algicides and to check treatment effectiveness.

i. To determine the effectiveness of various treatment stages and to aid in determining effective chlorine dosage within the water treatment plant as such dosage is related to organic materials in water.

j. To aid in determining the condition and effectiveness of the various units in the wastewater treatment plant.

The methods described are valuable in the appraisal of water quality. Principal emphasis is on method and equipment, rather than on the interpretation or application of the results. Preference is given to procedures of value in assessing water quality rather than to those used in managing aquatic resources.

Each collection should be associated with a record of environmental conditions at the time and place of collection to insure proper interpretation and use. Whenever practical, a biologist should collect his own samples. Much of the value of an experienced biologist lies in his personal observations of conditions in the field and in his ability to recognize signs of environmental changes as reflected in the various aquatic communities.

Many specialized items of biological collecting equipment may not be available from the usual laboratory supply houses. The American Society of Limnology and Oceanography has compiled a list of manufacturers and distributors of such equipment entitled "Special Publication No. 1, Sources of Limnological Oceanographic Apparatus and Supplies," which is available on request from the secretary of the society (consult a current issue of *Limnology & Oceanography* for the current name and address).

601 PLANKTON

1. Station Selection

Sampling stations should correspond as nearly as possible to those selected for chemical and bacteriologic sampling to insure maximum correlation of findings.

In stream work, stations should be located upstream and downstream from suspected pollution sources, from major tributary streams, and at appropriate intervals throughout the reach under investigation. Some effects of pollution on plankton populations may not be apparent for a distance equal to 3 days of stream flow. Tributary streams suspected of being polluted should be investigated in a similar manner. Observations for each station should be compared with observations in an unpolluted area.

The sampling program for a lake or reservoir is aided by the use of transection lines. Collections from a transection can be taken from all major depth zones; however, a sufficient number of samples must be taken to make the data meaningful. A circular lake basin should be sampled at strategic points along a minimum of 2 perpendicular transections extending from shore to shore; the deepest point in the basin should be included. A long narrow basin is best sampled at several points along a minimum of 3 regularly spaced parallel transects that cross the long axis of the basin perpendicularly, beginning near the inlet and ending near the outlet. A large bay should be bisected by a transection originating near shore and extending to the lake proper.

Because of the large number of samples necessary to completely appraise the plankton population, it may be necessary to restrict sampling to strategic points, such as water intakes, sites near the dam in the forebay area or discharge, constrictions within the water body, and major bays that may influence the main basin. Plankton samples should be taken at various depths and at different times during the day, since populations fluctuate.

Plankton in tidal areas of freshwater streams, in saline reaches of tributaries and estuaries, and in marine waters should be collected in accordance with tidal oscillations at each preselected depth during the flood and ebb tides. Sampling should cover more than one tidal cycle. Data covering samples from these waters frequently are most meaningful when the samples have been collected near the termination or the beginning of both the flood and the ebb tides, rather than during the middle phases of the tides.

2. *Sample Collection*

Water samples for plankton examination are taken in much the same fashion as samples for chemical analyses. In most cases, a 1-liter volume of water is sufficient. The Kemmerer water bottle (Figure 62) is widely used in limnological investigations, but due to some flow inhibition leads to inaccuracies in depth sampling. In special studies it may be advantageous to use one of the specialized plankton samplers such as the Clarke-Bumpus sampler [1] or a Van Dorn-type sampler.[2] Care should be taken to obtain samples containing a typical dispersion of aquatic organisms free only of floating debris, mud or other extraneous materials.

The plankton population in many rivers can be ascertained by examining periodic samples collected at midstream 1 to 2 ft beneath the surface. Depending on the velocity of the water mass, the plankton in the sample is the resultant of factors affecting water quality at some point upstream rather than at the sampling site.

The sampling frequency will depend on objectives, facilities, weather conditions and personnel available. In special studies, samples are often collected daily or even periodically during a day. To measure plankton populations that may change rapidly, daily collections are desirable throughout the season of active biological growth. Where this is not possible, weekly, biweekly or

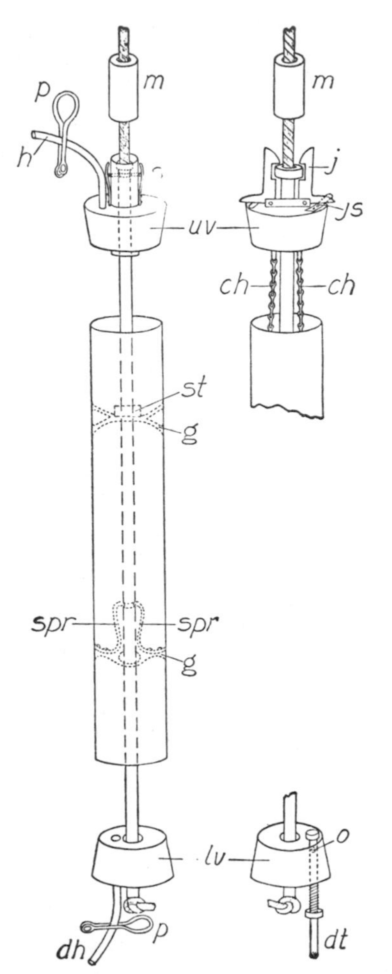

Figure 62. Modified Kemmerer sampler— Left: View of complete sampler with valves open. Top right: another type of construction of upper valve and tripping device. Bottom right: another type of construction of lower valve and drain tube. Key: ch—chain which anchors upper valve to upper interior guide; dh—rubber drain tube; dt—brass drain tube; g—interior guide fastened to inner surface of body of sampler; h—rubber tube; j—jaw of release; js—jaw spring; lv—lower valve; m—messenger; o—opening into interior of drain tube; p—pinchcock; s—upper release spring operating on horizontal pin, one end of which fits into groove on central rod; spr—spring fastened to lower internal guide and operating in groove on central rod to provide lower release; st—stop on central rod; uv—upper valve. SOURCE: P. S. Welch. 1948. *Limnological Methods.* Blakiston, Philadelphia.

monthly collections may still be useful to determine major population changes.

3. Sample Preservation and Storage

Live samples should occupy no more than one-half the volume of the container and should be examined within 2 or 3 hr after collection. For extended storage, the sample must be preserved and the container may be filled. Because colors fade rapidly, the preserved plankton must be stored in the dark. Under favorable conditions, although carotenes and xanthophyll are said to break down, chlorophyll retains its color rather well; it has been found that an expert can identify most organisms in a preserved sample even after several years of storage. For practical purposes a preserved sample has many advantages, but it should be remembered that the plankton organisms in a preserved concentrate have been subjected to sudden immersion in a fluid which often produces severe contraction and distortion of body form. No ideal preservative has yet been found. The microscopist, therefore, must always be on the alert for misleading effects produced by the preservative. Comparison with an occasional live sample from the same source will help the investigator to recognize forms that may be distorted in routine preserved samples.[3]

Preservation can be accomplished by the immediate addition of 40 ml formalin (a 37–42% aqueous solution of formaldehyde) per liter of sample. Alternatively, the 1-liter sample is mixed with 36 ml Merthiolate preservative. This preservative is prepared by dissolving in 1 liter of water: 1.0 g Merthiolate, 1.5 g sodium borate (borax), and 1.0 ml Lugol's solution (a saturated aqueous iodine-KI solution prepared by dissolving 60 g KI and 40 g iodine crystals in 1 liter distilled water). The Lugol's solution stains parts of the cells, making identification easier; it also aids in settling, since the iodine causes some plankters to lose gas and therefore buoyancy. This preservative has been found to be effective for at least 1 year.[4]

4. Sample Analysis

Innumerable methods have been employed to estimate plankton populations in a sample, and simplified procedures have been presented.[5] Statistical precision of results also has been given thoughtful treatment.[6, 7] The analyst should record precisely the procedure followed in both sample collection and examination.

Some waters contain sufficient phytoplankton to require that grab samples be diluted before counting; when sparse, phytoplankton may be concentrated. The phytoplankton in samples from most natural waters requires neither dilution nor concentration. Usually, zooplankton are not sufficiently abundant to be counted without concentration. The selection of methods and materials used in plankton enumeration depends on objectives of the study, density of plankters in the water being investigated, equipment available, and the experience of the investigator.

5. Plankton Concentration

If an investigator has been using a specific method of plankton concentration in a continuing study, that method should be continued to insure comparability of data. No completely satisfactory concentration procedure has yet been developed. Two acceptable methods are the membrane filter method and sedimentation.

601 A. Membrane Filter Concentration Technic

Application of the membrane filter method of plankton counting requires a vacuum source, filtering membranes, and experience in determining the proper amount of sample to be filtered. Plankton in samples from waters containing substantial quantities of suspended matter such as silt may be difficult to enumerate by this method, since, in the process of filtering, the suspended matter tends to crush the plankton or otherwise obscure them from view. However, the method has certain features that make it particularly adaptable for use on waters with a low phytoplankton and silt content. Primary among these features, the method permits the use of high magnification for enumeration of small plankters, provides relatively rapid processing of samples if the investigator is familiar with the procedure and the plankton, does not require counting of individual plankters to assemble enumeration data, and increases the probability of observing the less abundant forms.[8]

Filter the sample through a membrane filter 25 mm in diameter (with a pore size depending on its purpose). Let filter dry 5 min, remove, and place on top of 2 drops of immersion oil on a microscope slide. Add 2 drops of immersion oil on top of filter. Dry until clear (10–15 min in a low-temperature oven, up to 48 hr at room temperature); cover filter with cover slip prior to examination.

During microscopic examination the magnification and sampling field or quadrat must be of such size that the most abundant species will appear in at least 70 but not more than 90% of the microscopic quadrats examined (80% is optimum). Otherwise, the field size or the amount of sample concentrated must be altered. The occurrence of each species in 30 random microscopic fields is recorded. The results are reported as organisms per milliliter, calculated as follows:

$$\text{No. of organisms per ml} = \frac{\text{d} \times \text{number of quadrats per filter}}{\text{ml filtered} \times \text{dilution factor}}$$

where d is the density as obtained from Table 601(1) and the dilution factor is 0.96 for 4% formalin preservative.

TABLE 601(1): CONVERSION TABLE FOR MEMBRANE FILTER TECHNIC (Based on 30 Scored Fields)

Total Occurrence	F%	d
1	3.3	0.03
2	6.7	0.07
3	10.0	0.10
4	13.3	0.14
5	16.7	0.18
6	20.0	0.22
7	23.3	0.26
8	26.7	0.31
9	30.0	0.35
10	33.3	0.40
11	36.7	0.45
12	40.0	0.51
13	43.3	0.57
14	46.7	0.63
15	50.0	0.69
16	53.3	0.76
17	56.7	0.83
18	60.0	0.91
19	63.3	1.00
20	66.7	1.10
21	70.0	1.20
22	73.3	1.32
23	76.7	1.47
24	80.0	1.61
25	83.3	1.79
26	86.7	2.02
27	90.0	2.30
28	93.3	2.71
29	96.7	3.42
30	100.0	?

$$\text{Where F} = \frac{\text{total number of species occurrences} \times 100}{\text{total number of quadrats examined}}$$

601 B. Sedimentation Concentration Technic

Plankton samples may be concentrated by settling with the aid of a liquid detergent. To concentrate the phytoplankton, place 500 ml of a sample in a 1-liter glass cylinder and add 20 ml of commercial formalin or 18 ml of

Merthiolate preservative and 10 ml of a liquid household detergent. Sedimentation of the plankton is essentially complete within 24 hr. Carefully siphon the supernatant from the cylinder and wash the concentrate into 100-ml centrifuge tubes. Centrifuge at 2,000 rpm for 6 min. Decant the supernatant from the tubes, wash the concentrate into vials with 4% formalin or 3.6% Merthiolate preservative, and adjust the volume to the nearest 5 ml by adding preservative.

601 C. Microscopes and Calibration

1. Compound microscope: Although most workers prefer the binocular compound microscope, the monocular type can be used. Either type should be equipped with a mechanical stage capable of moving all parts of a counting cell past the aperture of the objective. Standard equipment should include 10× oculars (paired when a binocular microscope is used) and objectives in the following ranges (manufacturers differ slightly in exact specification):

Type of Objective	Approximate Overall Magnification with 10× Ocular
16 mm (low power, 10×)	100×
8 mm (medium power, 20×)	200×
4 mm (high power, dry 43×)	430×
1.8 mm (oil immersion, 90×)	900×

Unlike the higher powers, the medium-power or 8-mm objective with a working distance of approximately 1.6 mm can be used with a standard plankton-counting cell 1 mm deep.

2. Low-power stereoscopic microscope: Essentially, the stereoscopic microscope comprises two complete microscopes assembled into a binocular instrument to give a stereoscopic view and an erect rather than an inverted image. This microscope is indispensable for the study of organisms which occur in bottom sediments and for counting large organisms such as crustacea in plankton samples. The optical equipment of this microscope should include 9× or 10× and 12× or 15× paired oculars in combination with 1×, 4× and 8× objectives. This combination of lenses bridges the gap between the hand lens and the compound microscope, making available magnifications ranging from 9× to 120×.

3. Inverted compound microscope: In many laboratories, the inverted compound microscope is used routinely for plankton counting because it enables the technician to bypass time-consuming concentration technics.[9] This instrument is unique in that the objectives are below a movable stage and the illumination comes from above. Workers employing this instrument place their samples directly into a 10-, 15-, or 20-ml glass cylinder with a clear glass bottom. After a suitable period of settling, usually 6 hr, the preserved samples are examined and counted directly. If a 10-ml sample is used, the concentration is automatically 10:1.

This instrument is recommended for research investigations and for use in the larger water treatment plants.

4. Micrometers and microscope calibration: Calibration of microscopes is essential, since actual microscope magnification is not always exactly equal to theoretical magnification. The usual equipment for calibration is a Whipple ocular micrometer and a stage micrometer which has a standardized, accurately ruled scale on a glass slide.

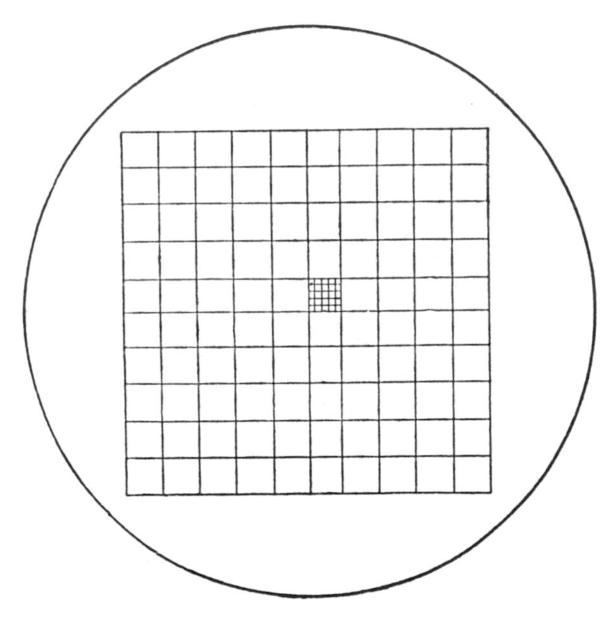

Figure 63. Ocular micrometer ruling. A Whipple micrometer reticule is illustrated.

The Whipple disk (Figure 63) most often is used in plankton studies. This micrometer, placed in an eyepiece of the microscope, is an accurately ruled grid which has been subdivided into 100 squares. One of the squares near the center is further subdivided into 25 smaller squares. The dimensions of the entire grid are such that with a 16-mm (10×) objective and a 10× ocular, the theoretical area delimited on the stage of the microscope represents 1 mm^2.

With the ocular and stage micrometers parallel and in part superimposed, the line at the left edge of the Whipple grid is matched with the zero mark on the stage micrometer scale. The width of the Whipple grid image then is determined to the nearest 0.01 mm from the stage micrometer scale. Should the outer limits of the Whipple grid cover exactly 1 mm^2 (1,000 μ^2), the larger squares will be 100 μ on a side and each of the smallest squares 20 μ.

Whipple ocular micrometers or similar devices in all microscopes must be calibrated carefully to enumerate plankton. When the microscope is calibrated at higher magnifications, the entire scale on the stage micrometer will not be seen (Figure 64) and measurements should be made to the nearest 0.001 mm. Additional details for calibration procedures are reported by Jackson and Williams [10] and by Welch.[1]

With a 10× eyepiece, magnification with the 10× objective lens (giving a total magnification of 10 × 10, or 100×) usually is not adequate for examination and enumeration of many plankters (individual plankton organisms), because they will appear as unidentifiable dots 10μ or less in diameter; a set of objective lenses with greater magnification such as 20× (or 8 mm) must be employed when minute forms are being investigated. When a 20× objective lens is used, each smallest

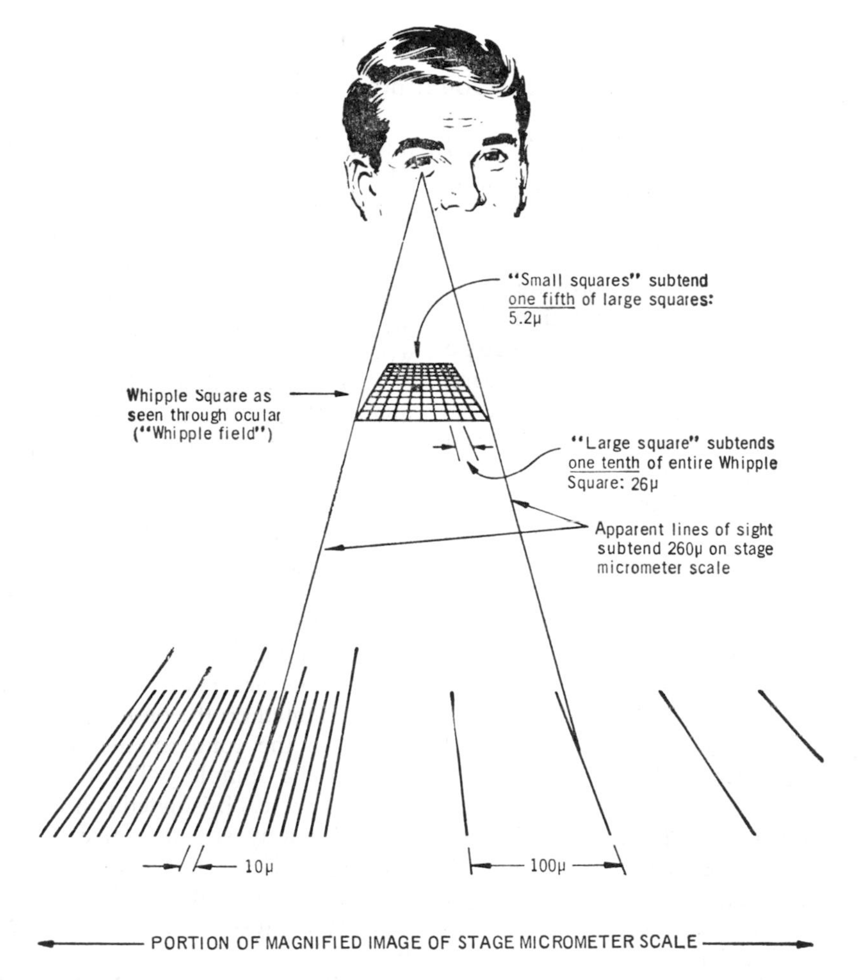

Figure 64. Calibration of Whipple Square, as seen with 10× ocular and 43× objective (approximately 430× total magnification).

square on the Whipple micrometer field is approximately 10×10 μ, or 100 μ^2. Conventional objective lenses with magnifications greater than 20× or 21× cannot be used to examine plankton in the Sedgwick-Rafter counting chamber discussed below because their working distance is less than 1 mm and they will break the cover slip on the chamber when in position. Microscopes with the "zoom" mechanism will afford the same visibility as a 20× or 21× objective. "Long working distance" 40× objectives, providing approximately 400× magnification with a 10× ocular, are available.

601 D. Counting Plankton

1. Sedgwick-Rafter (S-R) Counting Cell

The Sedgwick-Rafter (S-R) cell is the most commonly employed device for plankton counting because it is easily manipulated and provides reasonably reproducible information when used with a calibrated microscope equipped with an eyepiece measuring device such as the Whipple micrometer. The Sedgwick-Rafter cell is 50 mm long by 20 mm wide by 1 mm deep. The total area is 1,000 mm^2 and the total volume is 1×10^{12} cubic microns, or 1,000 mm^3 or 1 ml. The greatest disadvantage associated with the cell is that high magnification cannot be used unless the microscope is equipped with special devices such as adjustable zoom or objective lenses that provide sufficient magnification and clearance between objective lenses and the S-R cell.

a. Filling the cell: Before filling the S-R cell with the sample to be counted, the cover glass is placed diagonally across the cell and the sample transferred with a large-bore pipet (Figure 65). Placing the cover slip in this manner will prevent formation of air bubbles in the cell and eliminate errors. The cover slip often will rotate slowly and cover the inner portion of the S-R cell during filling, but it should not be allowed to float high on an overfilled cell, since this would yield a depth greater than 1 mm and an invalid count would result.

Before proceeding with the count, allow the S-R cell to stand for at least 15 min to permit settling of the plankton. Counts are made of the plankton on the bottom of the S-R cell. Some phytoplankton, notably some blue-green algae, may not settle but instead may rise to the underside of the cover slip. When this occurs, separate counts must be made of such organisms and these totals are added to the total of those counted on the bottom of the cell, to derive the total number of organisms in the sample. The units to be counted are each isolated cell and each natural colony (clump) of cells. One colony—like an isolated cell—is counted as one unit, and the total count is the summation of all units in the sample.

b. Strip counting: A "strip" the length of the cell constitutes a volume

50 mm long, 1 mm deep, and the width of the total Whipple field. When 10× eyepieces and 20× objectives are used and the width of the total Whipple field is calibrated to be 0.5 mm (500 μ), the volume of one strip is 25 mm^3, or $\frac{1}{40}$ (2.5%) the total volume of the cell. The total number of plankters in to derive the number of plankton in the S-R cell is:

$$\text{Enumeration factor} = \frac{1{,}000\ mm^3}{\text{Volume of "strips" counted, in } mm^3}$$

$$\text{No. per ml} = \text{Actual count} \times \text{enumeration factor}$$

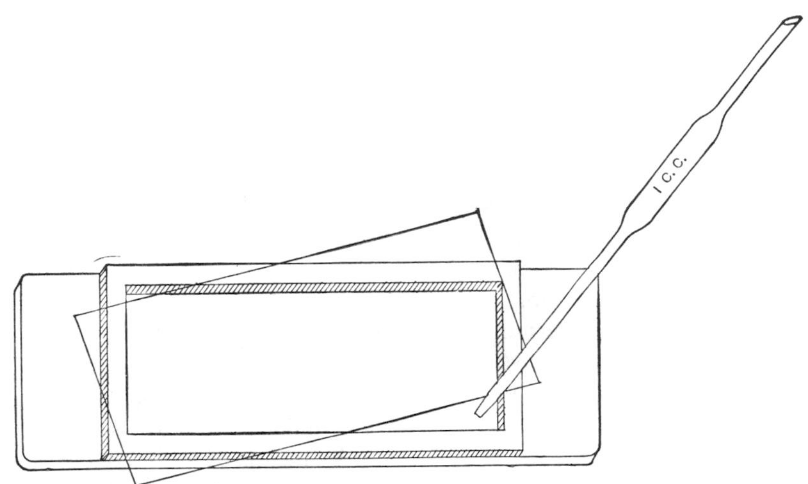

Figure 65. Counting cell (Sedgwick-Rafter), showing method of filling. SOURCE: G. C. Whipple, G. M. Fair & M. C. Whipple. 1927. *The Microscopy of Drinking Water.* John Wiley & Sons, New York.

the S-R cell is calculated by multiplying the actual count of plankton in the "strip" by the number (enumeration factor) representing the portion of the S-R cell counted.

Usually two or four strips are counted, depending on the density of the plankters; the fewer the plankton, the greater the number of strips to be counted. When 10× eyepieces and a 20× objective are used, the enumeration factor for plankton counted along two strips would be approximately 20 and for four strips it would be approximately 10, depending on the calibration. The arithmetic expression used

c. Field counting: As an alternative method, field counts rather than strip counts may be made. Field counts of plankton in the S-R cell are made by using the entire Whipple grid (outermost dimensions) on samples containing many plankton. Plankters should be counted in 10 or more random fields of the Whipple grid. The total area of the combined fields is multiplied by the enumeration factor to derive the total number of algae in the sample.

2. Special Methods

a. Volumetric analyses: Plankton abundance, as determined by counts, often requires much less time than volume determinations. In many instances, a conventional count of the total plankton and its components is sufficient for the practical problems involved and may be used without modification. Plankton data derived on a volume-per-volume basis are often more useful than data as numbers per milliliter. If necessary, the conventional count can be converted to volume units by assigning to each species a volumetric factor which for practical purposes represents the average volume of any organism within the species. Optical measurements with a calibrated microscope and ocular micrometer are made on 20 representative individuals of each major species encountered in the sample. The shape of the organisms determines the measurements made to derive their volume; the unit of measurement is the micron.

Wet algal volume (mm^3/l)
= No. of organisms/ml
× average species volume in microns$^3 \times 10^{-6}$

b. Diatoms: Diatoms constitute a significant portion of the phytoplankton in most waters. Identification of these plankters often requires special methods because distinguishing characteristics are obscured by protoplasm. Destroying the protoplasm by heat or chemicals enables recognition of taxonomic features. Destruction by heat requires no special glassware and reagents, causes no separation of the cell walls, reduces the risk of losing organisms during sample preparation, and decreases processing time. Chemical treatment usually causes cell wall separation and makes counting more difficult. Patrick and Reimer [11] discuss the reagents required and associated technics for chemical destruction of protoplasm and other carbonaceous matter in such samples.

When diatom data are needed, the organisms can be concentrated by settling-decanting or centrifuge-decanting technics that employ a 1 to 2% solution of household detergent to free organisms lodged on the walls of sample containers and in water-surface films. Samples containing dissolved materials, such as marine salts, formalin and detergents, that will leave carbonaceous or other residues which will interfere with identification must be well washed with distilled water prior to slide preparation.

Place a cover slip on a hot plate that is warmed sufficiently to increase the evaporation rate but does not boil the concentrated plankton sample. Transfer several drops of the washed concentrate sufficient to cover the entire cover slip by means of a disposable pipet or a large-bore dropper, and evaporate to dryness. Repeat the evaporation procedure on concentrates containing few diatoms until the entire sample has been transferred to the cover slip; exercise care to avoid a residue so dense that the organisms cannot be recognized. After evaporation, incinerate the residue on the cover slip on the hot plate at temperatures ranging from 300 to 550 C. This usually requires ⅓ to ¾ hr.

Place a drop of mounting medium in the center of the slide. Commercially available Hyrax (or equivalent *) microscopic mounting medium assures permanent, easily handled mounts for examination under oil immersion. Heat-

* For example, a product of Harleco, 60th Street & Woodland Avenue, Philadelphia, Pa.

ing of the slide to near 90 C for 1–2 min before application of the heated cover slip with its sample residue hastens evaporation of solvent in the mounting medium and reduces curing time to about 20 sec. After removing the slide to a cool surface, apply a firm but gentle pressure to the cover glass by means of a broad flat instrument during cooling (5–10 sec) to reduce the thickness of the mount.

Examination requires sufficient counting (a minimum of 250 cells) to provide data that adequately represent the original sample; usually at least one horizontal strip is counted, but random field counts would also provide adequate information. The number (N) of any given diatom species per milliliter is determined by the following relationship:

$$N = \%\ \text{in diatom count} \times \text{total diatom count per ml}$$

c. Other methods: For some plankton investigations, samples collected from waste stabilization ponds, shallow lakes and sluggish streams may require other specialized counting methods to solve specific problems associated with individual samples or groups of samples, or with the entire sampling program. In these cases the Sedgwick-Rafter method of plankton enumeration may not be expedient or practical. Specialized counting and sampling methods have been published by Mackenthun and Ingram [12] for the constable tube method and by Lackey [3] for the drop count method. Palmer and Maloney [13] devised a special method and associated apparatus for study of minute forms (nannoplankton). Methods used to evaluate chlorophyll content of phytoplankton have been published by Creitz and Richards,[14] Strickland and Parsons,[2] and Yentsch and Menzel.[15] (See section on Periphyton for details.)

3. *Reporting Results*

Data often are more useful and more easily reported when organisms are grouped on the basis of similarity of forms. For example, the numbers of counted algae may be placed in such categories as green, blue-green, diatoms and flagellated forms. Zooplankton may be grouped in categories such as nonflagellated protozoa, flagellated protozoa (exclusive of algae), rotifers, cladocera, copepods, and arthropod nauplii. Palmer and Ingram [16] and Palmer [17] have proposed similar groupings. Study objectives and the composition of plankton in the sample determine in part the selection of categories that will be used in reporting the data.

Plankton data derived on a volume-per-volume basis are more meaningful and more widely understood than data reported as numbers per milliliter. Such information should be grouped and reported much the same as for plankton numbers. Reporting of algae on a volume basis should also specify their numbers per milliliter.

601 E. Productivity Measured by Oxygen Method

The basic reactions in algal photosynthesis involve the uptake of inorganic carbon and the release of oxygen, summarized by the equation:

$$CO_2 + H_2O \rightarrow CH_2O + O_2.$$

Two well-established methods of measuring this reaction rate *in situ* are: (1) the oxygen method of Gaarder and Gran [18] and (2) the carbon 14 method of Steeman-Nielsen.[19] In both methods, clear (light) and darkened (dark) bottles are filled with water samples and suspended at regular depth intervals for an incubation period of several hours.

Chief advantages of the oxygen method are that it provides estimates of gross and net productivity and respiration and that analyses can be performed with inexpensive laboratory equipment and common reagents. The concentration of dissolved oxygen is determined at the beginning and at the end of the incubation period. Productivity is calculated on the assumption that one atom of carbon is assimilated for each molecule of oxygen released.

1. Apparatus

a. Numbered, 300-ml, clear pyrex or borosilicon BOD bottles with ground-glass stopper and flared mouth, for sample incubation. The bottles should be acid-cleaned and thoroughly rinsed with distilled water before use. Detergents containing phosphorus should not be used.

Suitable opaque bottles may not be commercially available. Clear BOD bottles can be made opaque by painting with black paint and wrapping with black cellulose tape. As a further precaution, the entire bottle should be wrapped in aluminum foil or placed in a light-tight container during incubation.

b. A supporting line or rack that does not shade the suspended bottles.

c. A nonmetallic opaque Lucite or Uscolite Van Dorn sampler or equivalent, of 3- to 5-liter capacity.[2]

d. Laboratory equipment and reagents for dissolved oxygen determinations (see Section 218).

2. Procedure

a. Determine the depth of the euphotic zone (the region that receives 1% or more of surface illumination) with a submarine photometer. Depth intervals for bottle placement are then selected. The photosynthesis-depth curve [20] will be closely approximated by placing samples at intervals equal to one-tenth the depth of the euphotic zone. Productivity in relatively shallow water may be adequately estimated using fewer depth intervals.

b. Introduce samples taken from each preselected depth into duplicate clear, darkened and initial-analysis bottles. Insert the delivery tube of the sampler to the bottom of the sample bottle and fill the bottle so that three volumes of water are allowed to overflow.[1] Slowly remove the tube and close the bottle. Water used to fill a "set" (one light, one dark, and one initial bottle) should come from the same grab sample.

c. Samples taken for the chemical determination of initial dissolved oxygen (see Dissolved Oxygen, Section 218) should be treated immediately (fixed) with manganous sulfate, alkaline iodide, and sulfuric acid. In samples fixed (or iced) and protected from direct sunlight, analyses may be delayed several hours if necessary.

d. Suspend the duplicate paired clear and darkened bottles at the depth from which the samples were taken and incubate. Usual incubation is from dawn until noon or noon until dusk, or for the entire photoperiod.

e. At the end of the exposure period, fix the samples immediately as described above and determine the dissolved oxygen. Average the results obtained from duplicates. The increase in oxygen concentration in the light bottle during incubation is a measure of net production which, because of the concurrent use of oxygen in respiration, is somewhat less than the total (or gross) production. The loss of oxygen in the dark bottles is used as an estimate of respiration. Thus:

$$\text{Net photosynthesis} = \text{Light bottle}_{DO} - \text{initial}_{DO}$$

$$\text{Respiration} = \text{Initial}_{DO} - \text{dark bottle}_{DO}$$

$$\text{Gross photosynthesis} = \text{Light bottle}_{DO} - \text{dark bottle}_{DO}$$

Productivity is defined as the rate of production and is generally reported in grams of carbon fixed per square meter per day.

3. Calculations

a. The gross or net production is calculated for each incubation depth and plotted.

$$\text{mg carbon fixed/m}^3 = \text{mg oxygen released/liter} \times 12/32 \times 1{,}000$$

b. The productivity of a vertical column of water one meter square is determined by plotting the value for each exposure depth and graphically integrating the area under the productivity curve.

c. The data are adjusted to represent production for the entire photoperiod. Since photosynthetic rates vary widely during the daily cycle,[20] conversion of data obtained from exposure periods other than those described may be difficult or completely impossible.

601 F. Productivity Measured by Carbon 14 Method

A solution of radioactive carbonate ($^{14}CO_3^{=}$) is added to light and dark bottles which have been filled with sample as described for the oxygen method. Following *in situ* incubation, the plankton is collected on a membrane filter, treated with hydrochloric acid fumes to remove inorganic carbon 14, and assayed for radioactivity. The quantity of carbon fixed is proportional to the fraction of radioactive carbon assimilated.

This procedure differs from the oxygen method in that it affords a direct measurement of carbon uptake and measures only net photosynthesis.[21] It is basically more sensitive than the oxygen method, but fails to account for the organic materials that leach from the cells[22, 23] during the incubation period.

1. Apparatus and Reagents

a. BOD bottles and supporting apparatus (see Oxygen Method, above).

b. Membrane-filtering device and 25-mm filters with pore diameters of 0.22, 0.30, 0.45, 0.80 and 1.2μ.

c. Counting equipment for measuring radioactivity: scaler with end-window tube, gas flow detector, or liquid scintillation counter (see Part 300).

d. Fuming chamber. A glass desiccator with ½ in. of conc HCl in the desiccant chamber serves well.

e. A 1-ml hypodermic syringe with 6-in. needle.

f. For chemical reagents, see the sections on carbon dioxide and alkalinity (Part 100).

g. Carrier-free radioactive carbonate solution containing approximately 5 μCi of carbon 14 per ml (commercially available in sealed 1-ml glass vials).

2. *Procedure*

a. Determine the depth intervals for sampling and incubation as described for the Oxygen Method, above.

b. Use duplicate light and dark bottles at each depth. Fill bottles with sample, add 1 ml of radioactive carbonate solution (using the syringe with needle) to the bottom of each bottle, and mix thoroughly by inversion. The concentration of carbon 14 in the sample should be approximately 10 μCi per liter. Duplicate samples are taken at each depth to determine the initial concentration of inorganic carbon (CO_2, HCO_3^- and $CO_3^=$) available for photosynthesis (see Carbon Dioxide, Section 111C).

c. Incubate as described for the oxygen method.

d. At the end of incubation remove sample bottles and immediately place in the dark or preserve by adding 40 ml formalin per liter. Unpreserved samples should be filtered without delay.

e. Filter an aliquot of each sample through a membrane filter, making sure that the largest pore size is consistent with quantitative retention of the plankton. Although the 0.45-μ pore filter is usually adequate,[21] the efficiency of sample retention should be determined using a wide range of pore sizes.[24, 25] Apply approximately 0.3 atmosphere of vacuum during filtration. Excess vacuum may cause extensive cell rupture and loss of radioactivity through the membrane.[21, 26] The sample aliquot should be the maximum size consistent with rapid filtration (1–2 min).

f. After filtration, place the membranes in HCl fumes for 20 min. Dried filters may be stored indefinitely.

g. Radioactivity is determined by counting with an end-window tube, windowless gas flow detector, or liquid scintillation counter. The efficiency of the counting methods is approximately as follows: thin-window, 3%; windowless gas flow, 50%; liquid scintillation, 40%. The thin-window tube is the least expensive detector and, when used with a small scaler, provides acceptable data at a modest cost.

h. Determination of counting geometry in planchets: [27] Prepare in triplicate, using 3 ampuls of carbon 14, a series of $BaCO_3$ precipitates on tared 0.45-μ membrane filters, each precipitate containing the same amount of carbon 14 activity but varying in thickness from 0.5 to 6.0 mg/cm^2. Dilute each ampul to 500 ml with a solution of 1.36 g Na_2CO_3/l of CO_2-free distilled water. Pipet 0.5-ml aliquots of this solution into each of seven conical flasks containing 0, 0.5, 1.5, 2.5, 3.5, 4.5 and 5.5 ml, respectively, of a solution of 1.36 g Na_2CO_3/l of CO_2-free distilled water. Add, respectively, 0.3, 0.6, 1.2, 1.8, 2.4, 3.0 and 3.6 ml of 1.04% $BaCl_2$ solution. Allow the $BaCO_3$ precipitate to stand 2 hr with gentle swirling every half hour. Collect each precipitate on a filter (using an apparatus with a filtration area of 2.5 cm^2), suck the filters dry without washing, place in a desiccator for 24 hr, weigh, and count. The counting rate increases exponentially with decreasing precipitate thickness and is extrapolated graphically (or mathematically) to zero precipitate thickness. Multiply the zero-thickness counting rate by 1,000 to correct for ampul dilution. This represents the amount of activity added to each sample bottle and is used to determine the fraction of carbon 14 taken up in the light and dark bottles.

3. *Calculations*

a. Subtract the dark-bottle sample counts from the light-bottle counts for each replicate pair.

b. Calculate the total dissolved inorganic carbon available for photosynthesis as described under Total Carbon Dioxide (Section 111C).

c. Determine the quantity of carbon fixed by using the following relationship:

$$\text{mg carbon fixed/l} = \frac{\text{counting rate of filtered sample}}{\text{total activity added to sample}} \times \frac{300}{\text{volume filtered}} \times \text{mg/l initial inorganic carbon} \times 1.064^{*}$$

d. If the samples were incubated for less than the full photoperiod, a correction factor is applied to the data.

e. The productivity is integrated for the entire depth of the euphotic zone and is expressed as grams of carbon fixed per square meter per day (see Oxygen Method, Section 601E preceding).

* Correction for isotope effect.

601 G. References

1. P. S. Welch. 1948. *Limnological Methods.* Blakiston Company, Philadelphia.
2. J. D. H. Strickland & T. R. Parsons. 1968. *A Practical Manual of Sea Water Analysis.* Fisheries Res. Board of Canada Bull. No. 167. Queens Printer, Ottawa, Ontario, Canada.
3. J. B. Lackey. 1938. The manipulation and counting of river plankton and changes in some organisms due to formalin preservation. *Pub. Health Rep.* 53:2080.
4. C. I. Weber. 1968. The preservation of phytoplankton grab samples. *Tr. Amer. Microscop. Soc.* 87:70.
5. W. M. Ingram & C. M. Palmer. 1952. Simplified procedures for collecting, examining, and recording plankton in water. *JAWWA* 44:617.
6. E. W. Moore. 1952. The precision of microscopic counts of plankton in water. *JAWWA* 44:208.
7. J. H. Kutkuhn. 1958. Notes on the precision of numerical and volumetric

plankton estimates from small-sample concentrates. *Limnol. & Oceanog.* 3:69.
8. C. D. McNabb. 1960. Enumeration of freshwater phytoplankton concentrated on the membrane filter. *Limnol. & Oceanog.* 5:57.
9. J. W. G. Lund, C. Kipling & E. D. LeCren. 1958. The inverted microscope method of estimating algal numbers and the statistical basis of estimations by counting. *Hydrobiologia* 11:143.
10. H. W. Jackson & L. G. Williams. 1962. Calibration and use of certain plankton counting equipment. *Tr. Amer. Microscop. Soc.* 81:96.
11. R. Patrick & C. W. Reimer. 1967. *The Diatoms of the United States.* Vol. I. *Fragilariaceae, Eunotiaceae, Naviculaceae.* Monogr. 13, Philadelphia Academy of Natural Sciences.
12. K. M. Mackenthun & W. M. Ingram. 1967. *Biological Associated Problems in Freshwater Environments, Their Identification, Investigation and Control.* Federal Water Pollution Control Administration, Washington, D. C.
13. C. M. Palmer & T. E. Maloney. 1954. *A New Counting Slide for Nannoplankton.* Special Publication No. 21, American Society for Limnology & Oceanography,
14. G. I. Creitz & F. A. Richards. 1955. The estimation and characterization of plankton populations by pigment analysis. III. A note on the use of "Millipore" membrane filters in the estimation of plankton pigments. *J. Marine Res.* (Sears Foundation) 14:211.
15. C. S. Yentsch & D. W. Menzel. 1963. A method for the determination of phytoplankton chlorophyll and phaeophytin by fluorescence. *Deep Sea Res.* 10:221.
16. C. M. Palmer & W. M. Ingram. 1955. Suggested classification of algae and protozoa in sanitary science. *Sewage & Ind. Wastes* 27:1183.
17. C. M. Palmer. 1963. The effect of pollution on river algae. *Bull. New York Acad. Sci.* 108:389.
18. T. Gaarder & H. H. Gran. 1927. Investigations of the production of plankton in the Oslo Fjord. *Rapp. et Proc. Verb., J. Cons. Int. Explor. Mer.* 42:1.
19. E. Steeman-Nielsen. 1952. The use of radioactive carbon (C-14) for measuring organic production in the sea. *J. Cons. Int. Explor. Mer.* 18:117.
20. J. H. Ryther. 1956. Photosynthesis in the ocean as a function of light intensity. *Limnol. & Oceanog.* 1:61.
21. E. Steeman-Nielsen. 1964. Recent advances in measuring and understanding marine primary production. *J. Ecol.* 52 (Suppl.):119.
22. M. B. Allen. 1956. Excretion of organic compounds by *Chlamydomonas. Arch. Mikrobiol.* 24:163.
23. G. E. Fogg & W. D. Watt. 1965. The kinetics of release of extracellular products of photosynthesis by phytoplankton. In *Primary Productivity in Aquatic Environments,* C. R. Goldman, Ed. Mem. Inst. Ital. Idrobiol. (18 Suppl.), University of California Press, Berkeley.
24. R. Lasker & R. W. Holmes. 1957. Variability in retention of marine phytoplankton by membrane filters. *Nature* (London) 180:1295.
25. R. W. Holmes & G. C. Anderson. 1963. Size fractionation of C^{14}-labeled natural phytoplankton communities. In *Symposium on Marine Microbiology,* C. H. Oppenheimer, Ed. Charles C Thomas, Springfield, Illinois.
26. C. R. Arthur & F. H. Rigler. 1967. A possible source of error in the ^{14}C method of measuring primary productivity. *Limnol. & Oceanog.* 12:121.
27. H. R. Jitts & B. D. Scott. 1961. The determination of zero-thickness activity in Geiger counting of C^{14} solutions used in marine productivity studies. *Limnol. & Oceanog.* 6:116.

602 PERIPHYTON

Communities of microorganisms growing on stones, sticks, aquatic macrophytes, and other submerged surfaces are greatly influenced by water quality and are very useful in assessing the effects of pollutants on lakes and streams. Included in this group of organisms, here designated periphyton,[1, 2] are the zoogleal and filamentous bacteria, attached protozoa, rotifers and algae, and also the free-living microorganisms found swimming, creeping or lodged among the attached forms.

Unlike the plankton, which often do not respond fully to the influence of pollution in rivers for a considerable distance downstream, the periphyton show dramatic effects immediately below pollution sources. Examples are the beds of *Sphaerotilus* and other "slime organisms" commonly observed in streams below discharges of organic wastes. Since the abundance and composition of the periphyton at a given location are governed by the water quality at that point, observations of their condition generally are very useful in assessing conditions in streams.

The use of periphyton in determining water quality is often hindered by the lack of suitable natural substrates at the desired sampling station. Furthermore, it is often difficult to collect quantitative samples from these surfaces. As a result, a number of artificial substrates have been used which can be located at will and which provide a uniform, controlled surface-type area, and orientation.[3]

1. Station Selection

In rivers, stations should be located a short distance upstream and at one or more points downstream from the pollution source. Since the effects of a pollutant depend on the carrying capacity of the stream and on the nature of the pollutant, progressive changes in water quality downstream from the pollution source may be due entirely to dilution and cooling—as in the case of nutrients, toxic industrial wastes, and thermal pollution—or to gradual mineralization of degradable organics. In the case of domestic and some industrial wastes, cursory examination of shoreline and bottom periphyton growths downstream from the outfall may disclose conspicuous zones of biological response to water quality which will be useful in determining appropriate locations for the sampling stations. In this manner, the boundaries of various zones of pollution can be delineated and the length of the affected reach determined. Where an intensive sampling program is not feasible, a minimum of two sampling stations will provide data on both the periphyton community at a control point above the pollution source and changes in the periphyton induced by the wastes in the zone downstream from the outfall, where complete mixing with the receiving water has occurred.

In lakes, reservoirs and other standing-water bodies where the zones of pollution may be concentrically arranged, stations should be located in an area adjacent to the waste outfall and in a control (unaffected) area.

2. Sample Collection

a. NATURAL SUBSTRATES—Qualitative samples may be taken by scraping submerged stones, sticks, pilings and other substrates available at the station. Although many devices have been developed for the collection of quantitative samples from irregular surfaces, success is rarely achieved.

b. ARTIFICIAL SUBSTRATES—The most widely used artificial substrate is the standard (plain) 1×3 in. glass microscope slide, but other materials such as Plexiglas are also suitable. In small, shallow streams and in the littoral regions of lakes, slides may be attached to bricks or stones with adhesive or placed in frames anchored to the bottom (Figure 66). In large, deep streams or standing-water bodies where turbidity varies widely, the slides are best placed at the surface in a floating rack (Figure 66). Where siltation is a problem, the slides should be placed vertically. Several slides should be exposed for each type of analysis to assure the collection of sufficient material and to reduce the variability in results due to normal differences in the colonization of individual slides. It must also be recognized that, in addition to the effects of the pollutants, the length of substrate exposure and seasonal changes in temperature and other natural environmental conditions may have a profound effect on the composition of the samples collected.

c. EXPOSURE PERIOD—Colonization of clean slides proceeds at an exponential rate for the first week or two and then slows. Because exposures of less than 2 weeks may result in very sparse collections, this period generally constitutes the minimum practical sampling interval. Sampling at this frequency, however, will preclude collection of the adult thalli of the larger, slow-growing filamentous algae such as *Cladophora* and *Stigeoclonium.*

3. Sample Analysis

a. Sedgwick-Rafter counts: Samples that are taken for counting and identification may be preserved in 5% formalin or other suitable material. Solvents which remove the chlorophylls and other cell pigments should be avoided.

The periphyton is easily removed from the slides with a razor blade and rubber policeman. Disperse the scrapings in the preservative (*i.e.,* 100 ml)

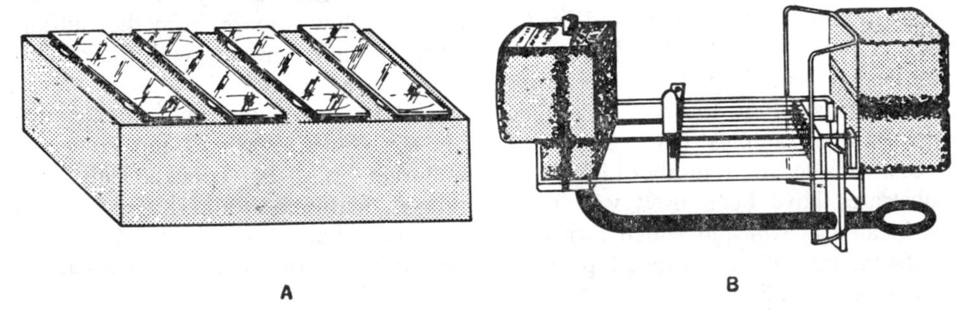

Figure 66. Periphyton Samplers. Left: Slides fastened to a brick with Plasti-tab adhesive. Used in small shallow streams. Right: Floating slide rack constructed of Plexiglas and styrofoam. (SOURCE: Patrick, Hohn & Wallace. 1954. *Bull. Philadelphia Acad. Nat. Sci.* 259:1.) Used in streams and lakes.

with vigorous shaking, transfer a 1-ml aliquot to a Sedgwick-Rafter cell, and make a strip count as described in Section 601D.1. If the material in the Sedgwick-Rafter cell is too dense to count directly, discard, and replace with a diluted aliquot.

The counts are expressed as cells per square millimeter (mm^2) of substrate area, calculated as follows:

(1) Cells/ml of suspended scrapings

$$= \frac{\text{actual count/strip}}{\text{volume of 1 strip (ml)}}$$

(2) Cells/mm^2 of slide surface

$$= \text{cells/ml suspended scrapings} \times \frac{\text{total volume of scrapings}}{\text{area of slide or slides } (mm^2)}$$

b. Diatom species proportional counts: The preparation of permanent diatom mounts from periphyton samples usually requires somewhat different treatment than mounts from plankton samples because of the presence of large amounts of extracellular organic matter (such as the gelatinous attachment materials and formalin) which, if not removed, will lay down a thick brown or black carbonaceous deposit on the cover glass when the sample is incinerated. The organic substances can be decomposed by oxidation with ammonium persulfate before mounting the sample. Oxidation and cleanup are carried out as follows:

Place approximately 5 ml sample in a disposable 10-ml vial. Let stand 24 hr, withdraw supernatant liquid by aspiration, replace with a 5% solution of ammonium persulfate, and mix thoroughly. A total volume of 8 ml should not be exceeded. Heat vial to approximately 90 C for 30 min. Let stand 24 hr, withdraw supernatant liquid, and replace with distilled water. After three changes of distilled water, transfer a drop of the diatom suspension to a cover glass with a disposable pipet, evaporate the water by warming, and prepare and count a mount as described in the Plankton Section (601).

c. Dry and ash-free weight: Several replicate slides are collected for weight determinations.[4] The slides may be air-dried in the field and can be stored indefinitely if protected from abrasion and dust. The material is removed from the slides, dried, and ashed. The data are usually reported as dry weight and ash-free weight per square meter of exposed substrate.

I. EQUIPMENT—

1) Analytical balance, with a sensitivity of 0.1 mg.

2) Drying oven, double-wall, thermostatically controlled to within ± 1C.

3) Electric muffle furnace, with automatic temperature control.

4) Crucibles, porcelain, 30-ml capacity.

5) Single-edge razor blades or rubber policeman.

II. PROCEDURE—

1) Rewet the dried material with distilled water and remove from slides with a razor blade or rubber policeman. Place scrapings from each slide in a separate crucible, dry to constant weight at 105 C, and ignite for 1 hr at 500 C.

2) Rewet the ash with distilled water and dry to constant weight at 105 C. This step is taken to reintroduce the water of hydration of the clay (and other minerals), which is not driven off at 105 C but is lost during ashing. If not corrected for, this water loss will be recorded as volatile organic matter.[5]

3) Calculate the mean weight from the several slides and report as grams dry weight and ash-free weight per square meter of exposed surface. If 1 × 3-in. slides (25 mm × 75 mm) are used, then

$$g/m^2 = \frac{\text{g per slide (average)}}{0.00375}$$

602 A. Trichromatic Method for Chlorophyll

The chlorophyll content of attached communities is a useful index of the biomass of the phytoperiphyton. Because quantitative chlorophyll determinations require the collection of periphyton from a known surface area, artificial substrates are well suited for this purpose. The pigments are extracted with aqueous acetone and the optical density of the extract is determined with a spectrophotometer. When immediate pigment extraction is not possible, the samples may be stored frozen for as long as 30 days if kept in the dark.[6] The ease with which the chlorophylls are removed from the cells varies considerably with different algae. To achieve complete extraction of the pigments it is usually necessary to disrupt the cells mechanically with a grinder, blender or sonic disintegrator, or by freezing. Grinding is the most rigorous and effective of these methods.

1. *Equipment and Reagents*

a. Spectrophotometer, preferably a narrow-band (0.5–5 mμ) instrument. A wide-band (20 mμ) spectrophotometer is also acceptable but is less accurate.

b. Clinical centrifuge.

c. Tissue grinder, sonic disintegrator, or other equipment for cell disruption.

d. Centrifuge tubes, 15-ml, screw-cap.

e. Aqueous acetone solution: Mix 90 parts acetone (reagent grade, BP 56 C) with 10 parts water (v/v).

2. *Procedure*

a. Place the individual glass microscope slides used as substrates directly into 100 ml acetone solution in a wide-mouth bottle.

NOTE.—Plexiglas is a material that is soluble in acetone. If used as the substrate, the periphyton must be scraped from it before solvent extraction.

b. If extraction cannot be carried out immediately, freeze samples in the field and keep frozen until processed.

c. Steep periphyton in the acetone for 24 hr in the dark, at or near 4 C.

d. If extraction appears incomplete at the end of 24 hr, rupture the cells by grinding or sonification and reextract. If difficulty in extraction is encountered regularly, freezing or mechanical disruption should be practiced routinely. Use solvent sparingly and avoid excessive dilution of pigments. Determine the total volume of extract and clarify a 10- to 15-ml aliquot by centrifuging in a closed tube for 10 min at 500 *g*.

e. Transfer the clear extract to a cuvette and determine the optical density (OD) at 750, 665, 645 and 630 mμ. If the OD at any wavelength setting is greater than 0.5, dilute the extract or use a shorter light path to bring the reading between 0.20 and 0.50. If the OD reading is less than 0.05, select longer cuvettes (and avoid excessive dilution of the extract). Narrow-band spectrophotometers provide the maximum precision in OD determinations for the trichromatic equations used to calculate chlorophyll concentrations. Wide-band instruments are widely used but are less accurate because of spectral overlap.

3. *Calculations*

The optical density readings at 665, 645 and 630 mμ are used for the determination of chlorophyll *a, b* and *c*, respectively. The OD reading at 750 mμ serves as a correction for turbidity. This reading must be subtracted from each of the pigment OD values before they are used in the equations. It should be noted that the OD of the extract at 750 mμ is very sensitive to changes in the acetone-to-water proportions. It is therefore essential that the operator adhere rigidly to the 90 parts acetone:10 parts water (v/v) formula for pigment extraction. Use of the 750-mμ reading may be avoided if the pigment solution is cleared by centrifuging for 10 min at 500 *g* and the light path is limited to 1 cm.

a. The concentrations of the chlorophylls are calculated by inserting the (corrected) optical densities in the following equations.[7, 8]

(1) $$C_a = 11.6D_{665} - 0.14D_{630} - 1.31D_{645}$$

(2) $$C_b = 20.7D_{645} - 4.34D_{665} - 4.42D_{630}$$

(3) $$C_c = 55D_{630} - 16.3D_{645} - 4.64D_{665}$$

where C_a, C_b and C_c are the concentrations, in mg/l, of chlorophyll *a, b* and *c*, respectively, in the extract; and D_{665}, D_{645} and D_{630} are the optical densities (with a 1-cm light path) at the respective wavelengths.

b. When the concentration of pigment in the extract has been determined, the amount of pigment per unit surface area of sample is calculated as follows:

$$\text{mg Chl } a/\text{m}^2 = \frac{C_a \times \text{volume of extract (liters)}}{\text{area of substrate (m}^2\text{)}}$$

c. A simple alternative method for the determination of chlorophyll *a* that involves measurement of the optical density of the acetone extract at only one wavelength is:[9]

$C_a = 13.4\ D_{665}$ (narrow band-pass instrument)

or

$C_a = 14.3\ D_{665}$ (wide band-pass instrument)

where C_a is the concentration (mg/l) of chlorophyll *a* in the extract.

602 B. *Chlorophyll c Method (TENTATIVE)*

An independent method for the determination of chlorophyll *c*[10] involves reading the optical density of the extract at 450 mμ before and after acidification. Acidification results in the loss of magnesium from the chlorophyll *c* molecule and a shift in the "blue" absorption peak from 450 mμ to 430 mμ.

This method is highly specific for

chlorophyll *c* and is approximately four times more sensitive than the trichromatic method.

1. *Equipment and Reagents*

a. Separatory funnel, 50-ml.
b. Sodium chloride solution, 0.05%.
c. Hexane.
d. Hydrochloric acid, conc.

NOTE—See trichromatic method (602A preceding) for other equipment and reagents.

2. *Procedure*

a. Transfer 10 ml pigment extract (E_1, prepared as in the trichromatic method, Section 602A.2d) to a 50-ml separatory funnel. Drain but do not rinse tube.

b. Add 3.5 ml 0.05% NaCl solution and 13.5 ml hexane. Shake flask to partition pigments (and precipitate the membrane filter if one was used to concentrate the sample).

c. Drain off 8.5 ml of the lower phase to a 15-ml graduated centrifuge tube, add undiluted acetone to bring volume to 10.0 ml (E_2), and mix well.

d. Transfer the solution to a cuvette of 10.0-cm light path which holds slightly less than 10 ml of fluid. Read optical density at 450 mμ. If OD exceeds 1.0, remove extract from cuvette and add an additional 18.3 ml of undiluted acetone. Mix well and again read the OD at 450 μ.[11]

e. Add a small drop (about 0.02 ml) of concentrated HCl to the cuvette, stopper, and invert several times.

f. Reread OD at 450 mμ within 1 min.

3. *Calculations*

a. The amount of chlorophyll *c* in the *original* 10 ml of acetone extract (E_1) is determined by multiplying the difference in optical density of E_2 before (OD_1) and after (OD_2) acidification by 17.5 (or by 49.5 if the extract is diluted to 28.3 ml).

b. If $E_2 = 10$ ml, then

$$\mu g \text{ chlorophyll } c/10 \text{ ml extract } (E_1) = 17.5\,(OD_1 - OD_2)$$

c. If $E_2 = 28.3$ ml, then

$$\mu g \text{ chlorophyll } c/10 \text{ ml extract } (E_1) = 49.5\,(OD_1 - OD_2)$$

and

$$\mu g \text{ chlorophyll } c/m^2 = \mu g \text{ chlorophyll } c/10 \text{ ml extract}$$

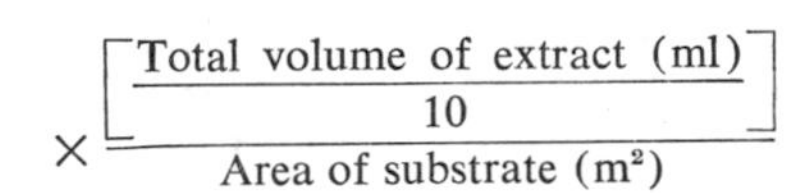

$$\times \frac{\left[\dfrac{\text{Total volume of extract (ml)}}{10}\right]}{\text{Area of substrate } (m^2)}$$

602 C. *Determination of Chlorophyll a in the Presence of Pheophytin a (TENTATIVE)*

Acetone extracts of periphyton samples may contain significant quantities of physiologically inactive green pigments such as pheophytins, pheophorbides and chlorophyllides,[12–15] which have absorption peaks in the same regions of the spectrum as the chlorophylls. If ignored, these may cause serious errors in chlorophyll data and in estimates of algal biomass.

The proportion of chlorophyll degradation products is determined by reading the optical density of the extract before and after acidification. The addition of acid causes a lowering of the optical density of the extract in the 630–665 mμ region, which is generally used for chlorophyll determinations.[8] Since acidification of a solution of pure chlorophyll *a* results in a 40% reduction in optical density at 665 mμ, yielding an OD ratio ($665_b/665_a$) of 1.70,[14] field samples with a $665_b/665_a$ ratio of 1.70 are considered to contain little if any pheophytin *a* and to be in excellent physiological condition. Solutions of pure pheophytin show no reduction in OD_{665} upon acidification and have a $665_b/665_a$ ratio of 1.0. Thus, mixtures of chlorophyll *a* and pheophytin *a* have OD_{665} ratios ranging between 1.0 and 1.7.

1. Procedure

a. Extract the pigment with 90% acetone (v/v) and clarify by centrifuging, as described in Section 602A.2.

b. Adjust the solvent volume so that the optical density falls between 0.2 and 0.5. Avoid unnecessary dilution.

c. Read the OD at 665 and 750 mμ before and after acidifying with 0.02 ml of concentrated HCl.

d. Subtract the 750 mμ values from the 665 mμ readings in each pair.

e. The corrected 665 mμ readings are then used to calculate the ratio and concentration of chlorophyll and pheophytin in the sample.

2. Calculations

a. The chlorophyll *a* (C) and pheophytin *a* (P) per square meter are calculated as follows: [14]

(1) C (mg/m²)

$$= \frac{26.73\,(665_b - 665_a) \times V}{A}$$

(2) P (mg/m²)

$$= \frac{26.73\,[1.7\,(665_a) - 665_b] \times V}{A}$$

where 665_b and 665_a are the optical densities of the 90% acetone extract before and after acidification, using a 1-cm light path; V = volume of the extract in liters; and A = substrate area in square meters.

602 D. Productivity Measured by Biomass Accumulation (TENTATIVE)

The productivity of periphyton communities is a function of water quality, substrate, and seasonal patterns in temperature and solar illumination. It may be estimated from temporal changes in standing crop (biomass) or from the rate of oxygen evolution or carbon uptake.

The rate of accumulation of organic matter on artificial substrates by the attachment, growth and reproduction of colonizing organisms has been widely used to estimate the productivity of streams and reservoirs.[6, 16, 17] In the application of this method, several replicate clean substrates are exposed for a predetermined period and the accumulated material is scraped from the slides and ashed as described previously.

$$P = \frac{\text{mg ash-free weight/slide}}{TA}$$

where P is the productivity in mg ash-free weight per square meter per day, T is the exposure time in days, and A is the area of a slide in square meters.

Estimates of the seasonal changes in the standing crop of established communities are obtained by placing many replicate substrates at a sampling point and then retrieving a few at a time at regular intervals, such as every 2 weeks or every month, over the period of a year or longer.[16] The gain in ash-free weight per unit area from one collection period to the next is a measure of net production.

602 E. Standing Water Productivity Measured by Oxygen Method (TENTATIVE)

Hourly and daily rates of oxygen evolution and carbon uptake by periphyton growing in standing water can be studied by confining them briefly in bottles, bell jars or other chambers. In contrast, the metabolism of organisms in flowing water is highly dependent on current velocity and cannot be determined accurately under static conditions. The measurement of productivity in flowing as opposed to standing waters presents somewhat different problems for each kind of water; therefore, procedures will be separated accordingly.

The productivity and respiration of the epilithic and epipelic periphyton in the littoral regions of lakes and ponds can be determined by inserting transparent and opaque bell jars or open-ended plastic chambers into the substratum along transects perpendicular to the shoreline.[18, 19] The chambers are left in place for one-half the photoperiod. The concentration of dissolved oxygen in the chamber is determined at the beginning and end of the exposure period. The gross productivity is the sum of the net gain in dissolved oxygen in the transparent chamber and the oxygen used in respiration. The values obtained are doubled to determine the productivity for the entire photoperiod.

Failure to account for changes in dissolved oxygen in the chambers due to the photosynthesis and respiration of the plankton may be the cause of serious errors in the estimates of periphyton metabolism. It is therefore essential that these values be obtained at the time the periphyton is studied. This can be done using the light and dark bottle method discussed in Section 601 for plankton.

1. Equipment and Reagents

a. Clear and darkened glass or Plexiglas chambers, approximately 20 cm in diameter and 30 cm high, with a median lateral port, sealed with a serum bottle stopper for removal of small samples of water for dissolved oxygen analyses or for the insertion of an oxygen probe. The chamber should be fitted with a small, manually operated, propeller-shaped stirring paddle.

b. Dissolved oxygen probe, or equipment and reagents required for Winkler dissolved oxygen determinations (see Section 218).

2. Procedure

a. At each station place a transparent and opaque chamber over the substrate at sunrise or noon and leave in place for one-half the photoperiod. Determine the concentration of dissolved oxygen at the beginning of the incubation period.

b. At the end of the exposure period, carefully mix the water in the chambers and determine the concentration of dissolved oxygen.

3. Calculations

$$P_g = \frac{2\,[(L_F - L_I) + (D_I - D_F)]}{A} \quad (1)$$

where the exposure period is one-half day, P_g is the gross production in mg $O_2/m^2/day$, L_F and L_I are the final and initial concentrations, respectively, of dissolved oxygen in the clear chamber, D_I and D_F are the initial and final concentrations, respectively, of dissolved oxygen in the opaque chamber, and A is the substrate area in square meters.

The net production rate (mg $O_2/m^2/$ day) is determined by calculating the 24 hr uptake of oxygen in respiration and subtracting it from the gross production:

$$P_n = P_g - \frac{24}{hr}\;\frac{(D_I - D_F)}{A} \quad (2)$$

where P_n is the net production in milligrams of oxygen per square meter per day and hr is the length of exposure in hours.

602 F. Standing Water Productivity Measured by Carbon 14 Method (TENTATIVE)

The approach is generally similar to that described above for the oxygen method. Transparent and opaque chambers are placed over the substrate. Carbon 14-labeled sodium carbonate is injected into the chamber by syringe, mixed well, and allowed to incubate with the periphyton for ½ the photoperiod. The concentration of dissolved inorganic carbon available for photosynthesis is determined by titration. At the end of the incubation period, the periphyton is removed from the substrate and assayed for carbon 14.[18, 20]

1. Equipment and Reagents

a. Incubation chamber: See above under Oxygen Method, Section 602E.1.

b. Special equipment and reagents: See Section 601F.1.

c. Carbon 14-labeled solution of sodium carbonate, having a specific activity of approximately 10 μCi per ml.

d. Other equipment and reagents: See Section 111 on carbon dioxide.

2. Procedure

a. At each station place a transparent and opaque chamber over the substrate and add approximately 10 μCi carbon 14 per liter of chamber volume. Mix water in the chambers well, taking care to avoid disturbing the periphyton. Determine the concentration of dissolved inorganic carbon as described in Section 102, Total Alkalinity.

b. At end of exposure period, remove surface centimeter of periphyton enclosed in the chamber, freeze, and store frozen in a vacuum desiccator.

c. Immediately before the analysis, expose sample to fumes of HCl for 10–15 min to drive off all inorganic carbon 14 retained in the periphyton.

d. Combust sample (or an aliquot) by the Van Slyke method [20] and assay the radioactivity by one of the following methods: The carbon dioxide produced by combustion is flushed into a gas-flow counter or electrometer; or is taken up in a 0.1*N* solution of sodium carbonate, precipitated as barium carbonate on a membrane filter, and counted with an end-window tube; or is assayed as the sodium carbonate solution by the liquid scintillation technic.

3. Calculations

$$P_n = \frac{(\text{activity in sample})}{(\text{activity added})} \times \frac{(\text{dissolved inorganic carbon})}{(\text{area of substrate})} \times 1.064$$

where P_n is the net productivity for the exposure period and the factor 1.064 is a correction for the isotope effect.

602 G. Flowing Water Productivity Measured by Oxygen Method (TENTATIVE)

Diurnal changes in the concentration of dissolved oxygen are the result of the integrated effects of the respiration and photosynthesis of the periphyton and plankton, water velocity and turbulence, turbidity, depth, organic waste loads, and accrual of ground water and surface drainage. Daily fluctuations in the photosynthetic production of oxygen are imposed on the relatively steady oxygen demand of respiratory activity. Respiration rates may also vary diurnally under certain conditions, but the factors involved are not well understood. The effects of plankton photosynthesis and respiration on the overall oxygen balance can be estimated by the light and dark bottle method.

The rate of change in the concentration of dissolved oxygen (q) in grams per cubic meter is the algebraic sum of the rates of photosynthesis (p), respiration (r), diffusion (d), and accrual in groundwater inflow and surface runoff (a).[21]

$$q = p - r + d_{in.} + a \quad (1)$$

If the equation is multiplied through by the depth in meters (z), the resulting values are in grams per square meter.

$$zq = Q = P - R + D_{in.} + A \quad (2)$$

The rate of diffusion of oxygen into the water (D) is a product of the gas transfer coefficient (K) and the percent saturation deficit (S).

$$D = KS \quad (3)$$

where D is the diffusion rate per area (i.e., $g/m^2/hr$) and K is based on the diffusion rate at zero percent saturation.

1. *Equipment and Reagents*

a. BOD bottles, for light and dark bottle measurements. See sections on plankton productivity (601E and F).

b. DO probe, where applicable.

c. Bottom chamber, 60 × 20 × 10 cm, with 32-cm lengthwise dividing baffle, rheostat-controlled submersible pump, temperature thermistor and DO probe or glass tube for removing water in oxygen determinations.[22]

d. Plastic dome, Plexiglas, approximately 22 cm in diameter, with float, temperature thermistor and rubber-sealed port for removal of gas samples.[23]

2. *Procedure*

Hourly or continuous measurements are made of the concentration of dissolved oxygen at one or two stations, depending upon stream conditions, precision desired, and availability of equipment. If similar conditions have obtained for some distance upstream from the reach to be studied, diurnal measurements of dissolved oxygen at a single station are sufficient to determine productivity. However, where upstream conditions are significantly different from the reach to be studied, measurements should be taken at the upstream and downstream limits of the reach.

a. Measure plankton photosynthesis and respiration rates by the light and dark bottle method described under plankton productivity (Section 601E).

b. Determine the gas transfer coefficient (K):

1) SINGLE-STATION METHOD—The K value can be determined from the measurements of dissolved oxygen taken shortly after sunset and just before sunrise. At sunset

$$q_e = \frac{K\,S_e}{z} - r$$

where q_e is the evening rate of change in dissolved oxygen and S_e is the saturation deficit. At sunrise

$$q_m = \frac{K\,S_m}{z} - r$$

where q_m is the morning rate of change in dissolved oxygen and S_m is the saturation deficit. Subtracting the two equations results in the following relationship:

$$K = z\,\frac{(q_m - q_e)}{S_m - S_e}$$

2) TWO-STATION METHOD—If the accrual is negligible, the diffusion rate (D) for a given saturation deficit can be determined by subtracting the respiration rate (R) from the upstream-

downstream change in dissolved oxygen.

(1) $$D = KS = z(C_1 - C_2) - R$$

(2) $$K = \frac{z(C_1 - C_2) - R}{S}$$

where C_1 and C_2 are the concentration of dissolved oxygen at the upstream and downstream stations, respectively.

3) PLASTIC DOME METHOD—Diffusion rate is determined directly by measuring the nighttime loss of oxygen from a plastic dome in contact with the water surface.[23] The dome, with a diameter of approximately 22 cm and a volume of 2.5 liters, is filled with atmospheric gases and floated on the water. Every 2–3 hr, 5-ml samples of gas are removed from the dome and analyzed for oxygen content. The concentration of dissolved oxygen in the water is determined.

c. Determination of periphyton respiration:

1) SINGLE-STATION METHOD—If the diffusion rate is known, the respiration rate is determined by subtracting the diffusion rate from the nighttime rate of change in oxygen concentration.

2) TWO-STATION METHOD—Nighttime upstream-downstream changes in dissolved oxygen (DO) observed at the time of 100% saturation are due to respiration.

3) CHAMBER METHOD (Thomas-O'Connell chamber) [22]—This chamber may be considered a modification of the bell jar. Current velocity of the stream is measured with a meter and duplicated inside the chamber with the aid of a pump. This is the only chamber method expected to yield accurate estimates of periphyton respiration at all current velocities.

3. *Calculations*

a. Hourly rates of change in stream DO are determined by subtracting successive pairs of DO measurements.

b. The percent oxygen saturation and diffusion rates D are calculated for each sample and the average value is determined for each sampling interval (if the plastic dome method is used, the D values are obtained directly).

c. The q and r values are corrected for phytoplankton photosynthesis and respiration and are plotted on the same axes. The area between the two curves is determined graphically and represents the gross productivity of the periphyton.[24]

d. The daily productivity per square meter of surface is determined by multiplying the daily productivity per cubic meter by the discharge in cubic meters and dividing by the average depth in meters.

602 H. Flowing Water Productivity Measured by Carbon 14 Method (TENTATIVE)

The use of carbon 14 to measure periphyton photosynthesis in flowing waters is restricted to closed chambers with forced circulation. In this case, periphyton grown on natural or artificial substrates may be transferred to the chamber, which rests on the bottom of the stream, or a chamber which is open at the bottom is placed over a section of undisturbed stream bed. Labeled sodium carbonate is introduced into the chamber and the water in the chamber is circulated mechanically to provide a current velocity comparable to that in the stream. The sample is incubated for one-half the photoperiod, removed, and analyzed as described previously. (See Section 601 F preceding.)

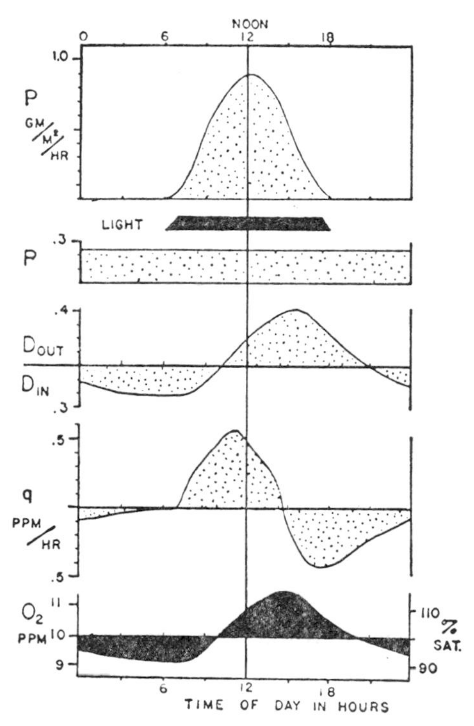

Figure 67. Component processes in the oxygen metabolism of a section of a hypothetical stream during the course of a cloudless day. Production (P), respiration (R), and diffusion (D) are given on an areal basis. The combined effect of these rate processes for a stream 1 meter deep is given in ppm/hr (q). The actual oxygen values that would result in a stream with a long homogeneous community are given in the lowermost curve. SOURCE: H. T. Odum. 1956. Primary production in flowing waters. *Limnol. & Oceanog.* 1:102.

602 I. Reporting Results

Although a number of systems have been developed to organize and interpret periphyton data, no single method has received universal acceptance. The methods may be qualitative or quantitative. The qualitative methods attempt to relate the taxonomic composition of the communities to zones of pollution, whereas the quantitative methods deal with numerical indices of saprobity or community diversity.

1. Qualitative Methods (Indicator Species and Communities)

The saprobity system developed by Kolkwitz and Marsson is probably the most widely used method of interpreting periphyton data. This scheme divides the polluted reaches of streams into polysaprobic, α and β mesosaprobic, and oligosaprobic zones, and lists the characteristic species found in each. The system has been refined [25, 26] and recently has been enlarged by Fjerdingstad [27, 28] to include eight zones of pollution by (a) adding a zone for undiluted sewage (coprozoic zone) and (b) dividing the polysaprobic and mesosaprobic zones into three regions. Two new zones were established for industrial pollution. Fjerdingstad [27, 28] rejects the use of indicator species and numerical indices of pollution, basing his revised system entirely on the community (biocenosis) concept.

2. *Quantitative Methods*

These methods incorporate the use of cell counts per unit area of substrate and numerical indices of pollution or water quality. Considerable data on cell densities and species composition of periphyton collected on glass slides in polluted rivers in England are available.[29] Other indices include those based on the saprobity system,[30] where code numbers assigned for the saprobial value and the abundance of individual species are used to calculate a Mean Saprobial Index; the truncated-log normal distribution of diatom species [31]; and indices of community diversity derived from information theory equations.[32]

602 J. References

1. H. ROLL. 1939. Zur terminologie des periphytons. *Arch. Hydrobiol.* 35:59.
2. O. W. YOUNG. 1945. A limnological investigation of periphyton in Douglas Lake, Michigan. *Tr. Amer. Microscop. Soc.* 64:1.
3. A. SLADECKOVA. 1962. Limnological investigation methods for the periphyton community. *Botan. Rev.* 28:286.
4. C. L. NEWCOMBE. 1950. A quantitative study of attachment materials in Sodon Lake, Michigan. *Ecology* 31:204.
5. D. J. NELSON & D. C. SCOTT. 1962. Role of detritus in the productivity of a rock outcrop community in a piedmont stream. *Limnol. & Oceanog.* 7:396.
6. A. R. GRZENDA & M. L. BREHMER. 1960. A quantitative method for the collection and measurement of stream periphyton. *Limnol. & Oceanog.* 5:190.
7. T. R. PARSONS & J. D. H. STRICKLAND. 1963. Discussion of spectrophotometric determination of marine-plant pigments, with revised equations for ascertaining chlorophylls and carotenoids. *J. Marine Res.* 21:155.
8. J. D. H. STRICKLAND & T. R. PARSONS. 1968. *A Practical Manual of Seawater Analysis.* Bull. 167, Fisheries Res. Board of Canada. Queens Printer, Ottawa, Ontario, Canada.
9. H. T. ODUM, W. T. MCCONNELL & W. ABBOTT. 1958. The chlorophyll "A" of communities. *Pub. Inst. Marine Sci.* (Texas) 5:65.
10. T. R. PARSONS. 1963. A new method for the microdetermination of chlorophyll "C" in sea water. *J. Marine Res.* 21:164.
11. T. R. RICKETTS. 1967. A note on the estimation of chlorophyll *c*. *Phytochemistry* 6:1353.
12. J. PATTERSON & T. R. PARSONS. 1963. Distribution of chlorophyll *a* and degradation products in various marine materials. *Limnol. & Oceanog.* 8:355.
13. B. MOSS. 1967. A note on the estimation of chlorophyll *a* in freshwater algal communities. *Limnol. & Oceanog.* 12:340.

14. C. J. LORENZEN. 1967. Determination of chlorophyll and pheopigments: Spectrophotometric equations. *Limnol. & Oceanog.* 12:343.
15. L. P. VERNON. 1960. Spectrophotometric determinations of chlorophylls and phaeophytins in plant extracts. *Anal. Chem.* 32:1144.
16. V. SLADECEK & A. SLADECKOVA. 1964. Determination of periphyton production by means of the glass slide method. *Hydrobiologia* 23:125.
17. D. L. KING & R. C. BALL. 1966. A qualitative and quantitative measure of aufwuchs production. *Tr. Amer. Microscop. Soc.* 82:232.
18. R. G. WETZEL. 1963. Primary productivity of periphyton. *Nature* 197:1026.
19. ———. 1964. A comparative study of the primary productivity of higher aquatic plants, periphyton, and phytoplankton in a large shallow lake. *Int. Rev. Hydrobiol.* 49:1.
20. S. ARONOFF. 1956. *Techniques in Radiobiochemistry.* Iowa State College Press, Ames.
21. H. T. ODUM. 1956. Primary production in flowing waters. *Limnol. & Oceanog.* 1:102.
22. N. A. THOMAS & R. L. O'CONNELL. 1966. A method for measuring primary production by stream benthos. *Limnol. & Oceanog.* 11:386.
23. B. J. COPELAND & W. R. DUFFER. 1964. Use of a clear plastic dome to measure gaseous diffusion rates in natural waters. *Limnol. & Oceanog.* 9:494.
24. H. T. ODUM & C. M. HOSKIN. 1958. Comparative studies of the metabolism of marine water. *Pub. Inst. Marine Sci.* (Texas) 4:115.
25. R. KOLKWITZ. 1950. Oekologie der Saprobien. *Ver. Wasser-, Boden, Lufthyg. Schriftenreihe* (Berlin) 4:1.
26. H. LIEBMANN. 1951. *Handbuch der Frischwasser und Abwasserbiologie.* Bd. I. Oldenbourg, Munchen.
27. E. FJERDINGSTAD. 1964. Pollution of streams estimated by benthal phytomicroorganisms. I. A saprobic system based on communities of organisms and ecological factors. *Int. Rev. Hydrobiol.* 49:63.
28. ———. 1965. Taxonomy and saprobic valency of benthic phytomicroorganisms. *Hydrobiologia* 50:475.
29. R. W. BUTCHER. 1946. Studies in the ecology of rivers. VI. The algal growth in certain highly calcareous streams. *J. Ecol.* 33:268.
30. R. PANTLE & H. BUCK. 1955. Die biologische uberwachung der Gewasser und der Darstellung der Ergebnisse. *Gas- und Wasserfach* 96:604.
31. R. PATRICK, M. H. HOHN & J. H. WALLACE. 1954. A new method for determining the pattern of the diatom flora. *Bull. Philadelphia Acad. Nat. Sci.* 259:1.
32. R. MARGALEF. 1956. Information y Diversidad Espicifia en las Comunidades de Organismos. *Inv. Pesq.* 3:99.

602 K. Bibliography

KOLKWITZ, R. & M. MARSSON. 1908. Okologie der pflanzlichen Saprobien. *Berl. Deut. Botan. Ges.* 26(a):118.

FRITSCH, F. E. 1929. The encrusting algal communities of certain fast-flowing streams. *New Phytologist* 28:166.

BUTCHER, R. W. 1931. An apparatus for studying the growth of epiphytic algae with special relation to the river Tees. *Tr. North Nat. Union* 1:1.

———. 1932. Studies in the ecology of rivers. II. The microflora of rivers, with special reference to the algae on the river bed. *Ann. Botany* 46:813.

———. 1947. Studies in the ecology of rivers. VII. The algae of organically enriched waters. *J. Ecol.* 35:186.

MARGALEF, R. 1948. A new limnological method for the investigation of thin-layered epilithic communities. *Tr. Amer. Microscop. Soc.* 67:153.

FJERDINGSTAD, E. 1950. The microflora of the River Mølleaa, with special reference to the relation of the benthal algae to pollution. *Folia Limnol. Scandinav.* 5:1.

YOUNT, J. L. 1956. Factors that control species numbers in Silver Springs, Florida. *Limnol. & Oceanog.* 1:286.

BLUM, J. L. 1956. The ecology of river algae. *Botan. Rev.* 22:291.

COOKE, W. B. 1956. Colonization of artificial bare areas by microorganisms. *Botan. Rev.* 22:613.

BUTCHER, R. W. 1959. Biological assessment of river pollution. *Proc. Linn. Soc.* (London) 170:159.

HOHN, M. H. 1959. The use of diatom populations as a measure of water quality in selected areas of Galveston and Chocolate Bay, Texas. *Pub. Inst. Marine Sci.* (Texas) 5:206.

POMEROY, L. R. 1959. Algal productivity in salt marshes. *Limnol. & Oceanog.* 4:386.

CASTENHOLZ, R. W. 1961. An evaluation of a submerged glass method of estimating production of attached algae. *Verh. Inter. Ver. Limnol.* 14:155.

HOHN, M. H. 1961. Determining the pattern of the diatom flora. *JWPCF* 33:48.

PATRICK, R. 1963. The structure of diatom communities under varying ecological conditions. *Ann. New York Acad. Sci.* 108:359.

WHITFORD, L. A. & G. J. SCHUMACHER. 1964. Effect of a current on respiration and mineral uptake in *Spirogyra* and *Oedogonium*. *Ecology* 45:168.

DUFFER, W. R. & T. C. DORRIS. 1966. Primary productivity in a southern Great Plains stream. *Limnol. & Oceanog.* 11:143.

EATON, J. W. & B. MOSS. 1966. The estimation of numbers and pigment content in epipelic algal populations. *Limnol. & Oceanog.* 11:584.

KEVERN, N. R., J. L. WILHM & G. M. VAN DYNE. 1966. Use of artificial substrata to estimate the productivity of periphyton communities. *Limnol. & Oceanog.* 11:499.

MCINTIRE, C. D. 1966. Some factors affecting respiration of periphyton communities in lotic environments. *Ecology* 47:918.

603 MACROPHYTON

The macrophyton group comprises the aquatic photosynthetic plants except for the algae. A large number of these are flowering plants, generally with a vascular system, although aquatic forms of mosses, liverworts and ferns are also included. The species commonly encountered in water number about 100. All are macroscopic, ranging in size from the tiny watermeal (*Wolffia*), about the size of a pinhead, to plants such as the cattail (*Typha*), up to 4 meters in height, and the water lily (*Nymphaea*), with large floating leaves. Often the higher aquatic plants are found clustered in large numbers and covering extensive areas. A few of the larger algae, among them *Chara* and *Cladophora* resemble the higher plants in size, form and habitat.

Three types of macrophyton are recognized: floating, submersed and emersed. The floating plants are not rooted; their principal foliage or crown floats on the water surface. All or most of the foliage of the submersed plants grows beneath the water surface, and they may or may not have roots. The emersed plants are erect or spreading, with their principal foliage in the air above the water surface; they are attached by roots to the bottom mud. In some cases the same species may grow as either a floating or an emersed type, depending upon the water level.

603 A. Genera

Identification of the plants makes it possible to report growth in terms of common names, genera or species. For this purpose, references giving keys, descriptions, illustrations, and geographical distribution are needed. Identified specimens, either fresh or dried, are also helpful for comparison.

Some of the more common aquatics are listed in the accompanying tabulation grouped according to growth types.

Common Name	Genus Name
Floating:	
1. Duckweed	*Lemna*
2. Floating fern	*Ceratopteris*
3. Great (giant) duckweed	*Spirodela*
4. Small duckweed	*Wolffiella*
5. Thallose liverwort	*Riccia* and *Ricciocarpus*
6. Water hyacinth	*Eichhornia*
7. Watermeal	*Wolffia*
8. Water pennywort	*Hydrocotyle*
9. Water velvet	*Azolla*
10. Water fern	*Salvinia*
Submersed:	
1. Bladderwort	*Utricularia*
2. Coontail	*Ceratophyllum*
3. Eelgrass	*Vallisneria*
4. Fanwort	*Cabomba*
5. Horned pondweed	*Zannichellia*
6. Naiad	*Naias*
7. Pondweed	*Potamogeton*
8. Water buttercup	*Ranunculus*
9. Water milfoil	*Myriophyllum*
10. Water star grass	*Heteranthera*
11. Elodea	*Elodea, Egeria, Hydrilla*

Common Name	Genus Name
Emersed:	
1. Alligator weed	*Alternanthera*
2. American lotus	*Nelumbo*
3. Arrowhead	*Sagittaria*
4. Bulrush	*Scirpus*
5. Bur reed	*Sparganium*
6. Cattail	*Typha*
7. Cut-grass	*Leersia*
8. Ditch (giant) reed	*Phragmites*
9. Pickerelweed	*Pontederia*
10. Sedge	*Carex*
11. Smartweed	*Polygonum*
12. Spatterdock	*Nuphar*
13. Spike rush	*Eleocharis*
14. Sweet flag	*Acorus*
15. Water chestnut	*Trapa*
16. Watercress	*Nasturtium*
17. Water lily	*Nymphaea*
18. Water shield	*Brasenia*
19. Water willow	*Justicia*
20. Wild rice	*Zizania*

1. Extent of growth (coverage)—Coverage may be reported either as marginal, occurring in patches, or extending continuously over all or a significant part of a body of water. Words often employed to describe the growth coverage are: *dense* (abundant, excessive, heavy, profuse) when there is continuous coverage of the area being considered; *medium* (common to fairly common) when the growth covers approximately half the area; and *sparse* (rare) when the growth is seldom observed.

Particularly when growth is dense, its magnitude of coverage for lakes is reported as hectares covered or as percentage of lake surface covered. For canals, ditches and streams, coverage may be recorded as kilometers of the watercourse infested.

2. *Depth of growth*—Depth of growth is commonly reported as depth in meters. Actual measurements may range from 1 centimeter to 3–5 meters or greater.

3. *Amount of growth*—Although seldom used as a measure, the volume of growth may be reported in terms of the number of cubic meters of water involved. From harvested representative samples, the wet or dry weight of the growth may be estimated.

4. *Differential record*—The area under study should be checked for the number of species or kinds of aquatic plants present. The plant crop may be restricted to a single species or it may represent a mixed growth. If the latter, the percentage of coverage (of the total growth) by each species should be reported.

5. *Preliminary area survey*—Subdivide the area of interest into a number of distinguishable geographic sections and plot on a map. During the period of maximum growth, conduct a reconnaissance by boat of the area to be surveyed. Record on the map the predominant genera or species of aquatic vegetation for each subarea and assign to each such genus or species a symbol of relative abundance. Later, determine the extent of plant growth by planimetering the areas. Aerial photographs, especially with infrared film, are a valuable aid to supplement observations by boat.

603 B. Bibliography

MUENSCHER, W. C. 1944. *Aquatic Plants of the United States.* Comstock Pub. Co., Ithaca, N. Y.

MASON, H. L. 1957. *A Flora of the Marshes of California.* Univ. of California Press, Berkeley.

FASSETT, N. C. 1960. *A Manual of Aquatic Plants* (with a revised appendix by E. C. Ogden). Univ. of Wisconsin Press, Madison.

ARBER, A. 1963. *Water Plants, A Study of Aquatic Angiosperms.* Hafner Pub. Co., N. Y.

EYLES, D. E. & J. L. ROBERTSON, JR. 1963. A guide and key to the aquatic plants of the southeastern United States. U.S. Fish & Wildlife Service Circular 158.

KLUSSMAN, W. G. & F. G. LOWMAN. 1964. *Common Aquatic Plants: Identification, Control.* Texas A. & M. Univ., College Station, Texas B-1018.

HOTCHKISS, N. 1964. Bulrushes and bulrushlike plants of eastern North America. U.S. Fish & Wildlife Service Circular 221.

LAWRENCE, J. M. & L. W. WELDON. 1965. Identification of aquatic weeds. *Hyacinth Control J.* 4:5.

OTTO, N. E. & T. R. BARTLEY. 1965. *Aquatic Pests on Irrigation Systems.* U.S. Dept. Interior, Bureau of Reclamation, *Water Resources Tech. Pub.*

WINTERRINGER, G. S. & A. C. LOPINOT. 1966. *Aquatic Plants of Illinois.* Illinois State Museum Popular Science Series Vol. 6.

HOTCHKISS, N. 1967. *Underwater and floating-leaved plants of the United States and Canada.* U.S. Fish & Wildlife Service Res. Pub. 44.

MACKENTHUN, K. E. & W. M. INGRAM. 1967. "Recognizing Some Common

Higher Aquatic Plants." In *Biological Associated Problems in Freshwater Environments.* Federal Water Pollution Control Administration, Washington, D. C.

SCULTHORPE, C. D. 1967. *The Biology of Aquatic Vascular Plants.* St. Martins Press, N. Y.

WELDON, L. W., R. D. BLACKBURN & D. S. HARRISON. 1969. *Common Aquatic Weeds.* U.S. Dept. Agr. Handbook No. 352.

604 MACROINVERTEBRATES

Macroinvertebrates are animals inhabiting the stream bottom or attached to stones or other objects in the stream. Although immature forms may be very small, by definition, organisms collected for study are those which are retained on a U. S. Standard No. 30 sieve (0.589-mm spaces). Macroinvertebrate communities are sampled to observe the occurrence of organisms or changes in predominance among species or groups. A body of water of good quality usually supports a diverse benthic fauna with no overabundance of any one group. Organic pollution may restrict the variety of organisms in the water; it may also favor the development of large numbers of organisms which tolerate the pollution-associated physical and chemical conditions. On the other hand, toxic pollution may eliminate almost all macroinvertebrates.

Quantitative and qualitative samplers have been designed to collect organisms from stream and lake bottoms. The most common quantitative sampling devices are the Petersen and Ekman dredges and the Surber or square-foot stream bottom sampler. Of these, the Petersen dredge is capable of sampling the widest variety of substrates. The Ekman dredge should be used for sampling fine-textured and soft substrates in quiescent waters. The Surber sampler is designed for work in shallow riffle areas. Sampling qualitatively, the collector finds as many different organisms as possible. Samples can be taken by any method that will capture representative species.

604 A. Quantitative Sampling Devices

1. The Petersen dredge (Figure 68) is used widely for sampling hard bottoms such as sand, gravel, marl and clay in swift currents and deep water. It is an iron, clam-type dredge manufactured in various sizes that will sample an area of 0.6 to 1.0 sq ft (0.06 to 0.09 m^2). Therefore, each dredge must be measured to determine its exact sampling area. It weighs approxi-

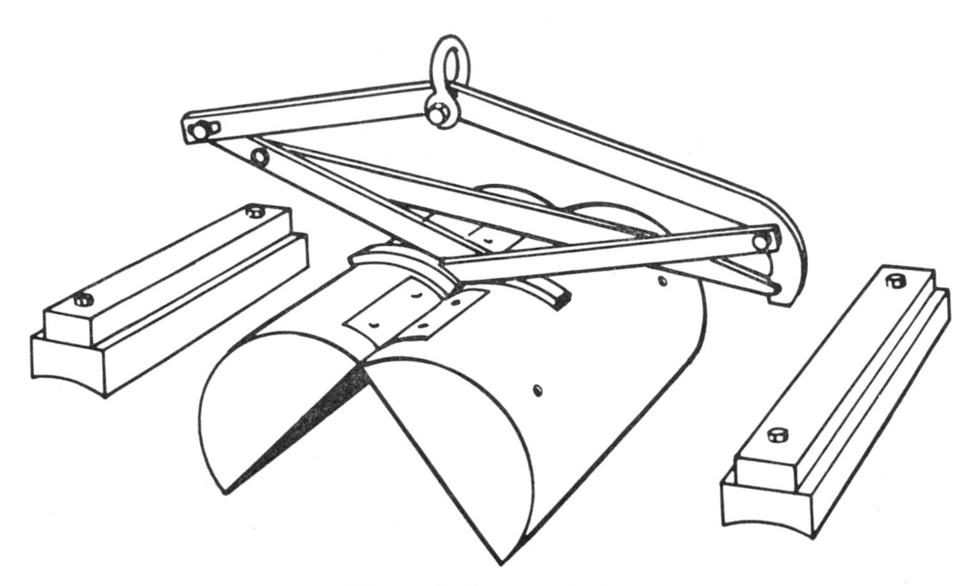

Figure 68. Petersen dredge.

mately 30 lb (13.7 kg), but may weigh as much as 70 lb (31.8 kg) when auxiliary weights are bolted to its sides. Primary purposes of the extra weights are to make the dredge stable in swift currents and to give additional cutting force in fibrous or firm bottom materials.

The dredge is set and lowered slowly to the bottom to avoid disturbing lighter bottom materials. Rope tension is eased to release the catch. As the dredge is raised, the lever system closes the jaws.

2. *The Ekman dredge* (Figure 69) is useful when sampling silt, muck and sludge in water with little current. It should not be used on rocky or sandy bottoms, as small pebbles or grit may prevent proper closing of the jaws. The dredge is made of 12- to 20-gauge brass or stainless steel and weighs approximately 7 lb (3.2 kg). The box-like part holding the sample has spring-operated jaws on the bottom that must be manually cocked (caution should be exercised in cocking and handling the dredge, which can cause injury if accidentally released). At the top of the dredge are two hinged overlapping lids that are held partially open during descent by water passing through the sample compartment. These lids are held shut by water pressure when the sampler is being retrieved.

The dredge is made in three sizes, 6 in. × 6 in. (15 cm × 15 cm), 9 in. × 9 in. (23 cm × 23 cm), and 12 in. × 12 in. (30 cm × 30 cm), but the smallest size is usually adequate. The soft fine-textured substrates sampled by this device are relatively uniform; therefore, use of the larger sizes does not usually result in a significant increase in faunal variety within individual samples.

3. *The Surber or square-foot stream bottom sampler* (Figure 70) is a lightweight device for procuring samples in water depths up to 2 ft in fast-flowing

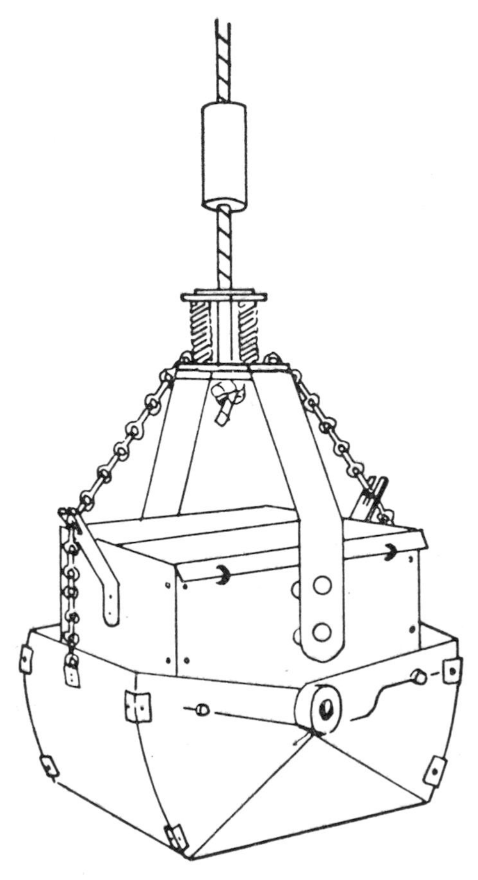

Figure 69. Ekman dredge.

streams. It consists of a strong close-woven fabric approximately 27 in. (69 cm) long. This net is held open by a square-foot metal frame (30.5 × 30.5 cm) hinged at one side to another frame of equal size.

In operation, the frame which supports the net is in a vertical position, while the other frame is locked into a horizontal position against the bottom. Triangular cloth sides fill half the side spaces between the horizontal and vertical frames. The net opening is placed facing upstream, utilizing the current to hold the net open. The horizontal frame is pushed into the stream bottom material. Within the framed areas, rocks and other bottom deposits are dug up by hand or with a tool to a depth of at least 2 in. The organisms dislodged drift into the open net.

4. Other quantitative sampling devices: In addition to those discussed above, many other quantitative samplers are available. Some of these have definite advantages for the sampling of particular habitats or macroinvertebrates. Welch,[1] Pennak,[2] and Barnes [3] have assembled information on several such samplers.

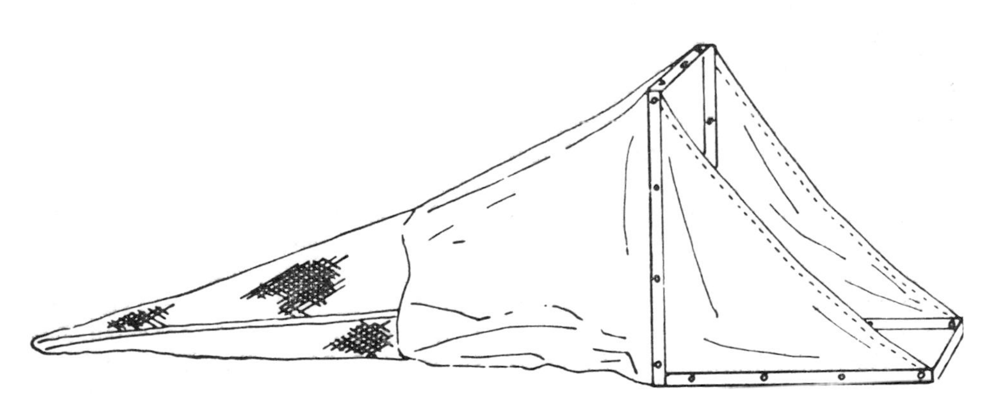

Figure 70. Surber or square-foot sampler.

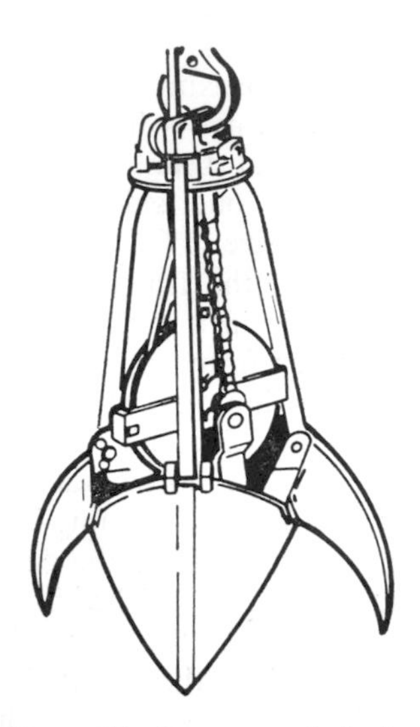

Figure 71. Orange peel dredge.

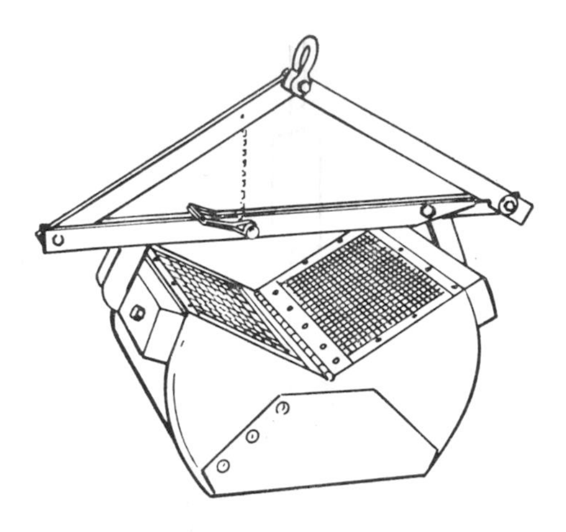

Figure 72. Ponar dredge.

a. The orange-peel dredge (Figure 71) is a multijawed round dredge with a canvas closure at the top serving as a portion of the sample compartment. The 100-cu-in. size is generally used, although larger sizes are available. The area sampled and the volume of material collected are dependent on the depth of penetration.[4] This dredge is suited to marine waters and deep lakes, where it has advantages over other tools when sampling sandy substrates.

b. The Ponar dredge (Figure 72) is increasingly used in deep lakes.[5] In size, weight, lever system and sample compartment it is similar to the Petersen dredge, but it has side plates and a screen on the top of the sample compartment. With one set of weights, the sampler weighs 46 lb. The modifications noted have been made to prevent loss of sample during closure.

c. The Smith-McIntyre dredge (Figure 73) has the heavy steel construction of the Petersen, but its jaws are closed by strong coil springs.[6] Chief advantages are its stability and easier control in rough water. Its bulk and heavy weight require operation from a large boat equipped with a winch. The 100-lb dredge (45.4 kg) can sample an area of 2.15 sq ft (0.20 m^2).

d. The Shipek dredge (Figure 74) is designed to take a sample 0.04 m^2 (approximately 8 in. × 8 in.) in surface area and approximately 10 cm (4 in.) deep at the center. The sample compartment is composed of two concentric half cylinders. When the dredge touches bottom, inertia from a self-contained weight releases a catch and helical springs rotate the inner half cylinder 180°. The sample bucket may be disengaged from the upper semicylinder by release of two retaining latches. This dredge is used primarily in marine waters and large bodies of inland water.

e. Core samplers are used to sample sediments in depth. The area collected at the mud-water interface is small, 2–4 sq in. (13–26 cm^2). Their efficient use as surface samplers calls for dense animal populations. Core samplers

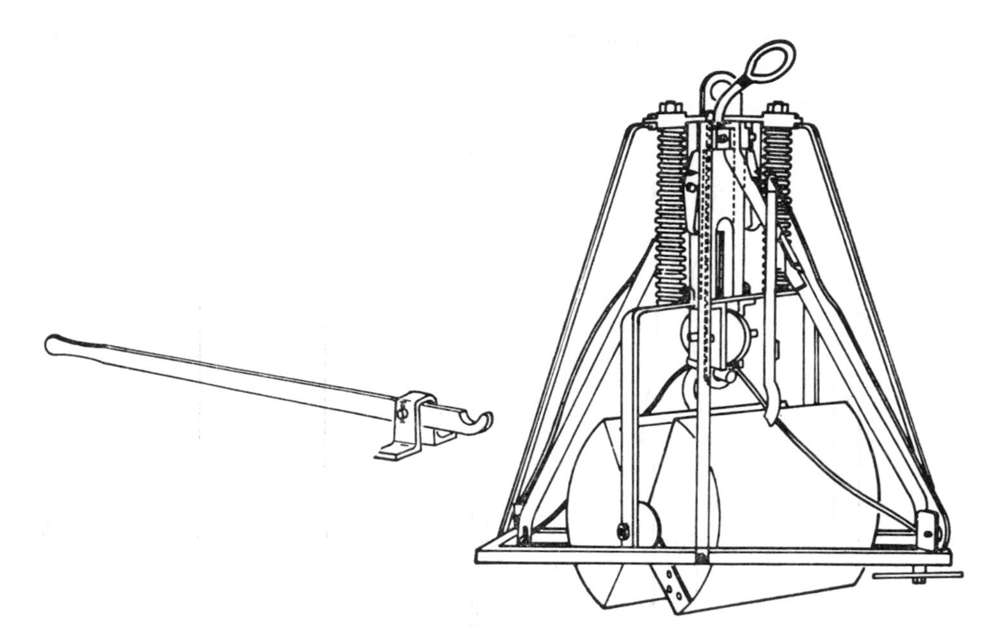

Figure 73. Smith-McIntyre dredge.

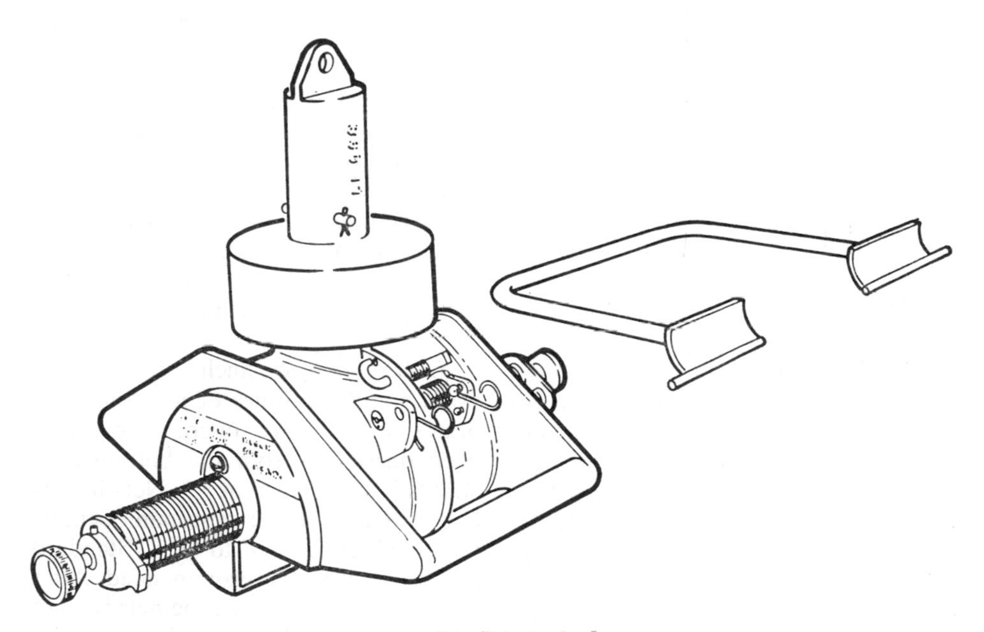

Figure 74. Shipek dredge.

vary from hand-pushed tubes to explosive-driven and automatic-surfacing models.[3] The Phleger type (Figure 75)

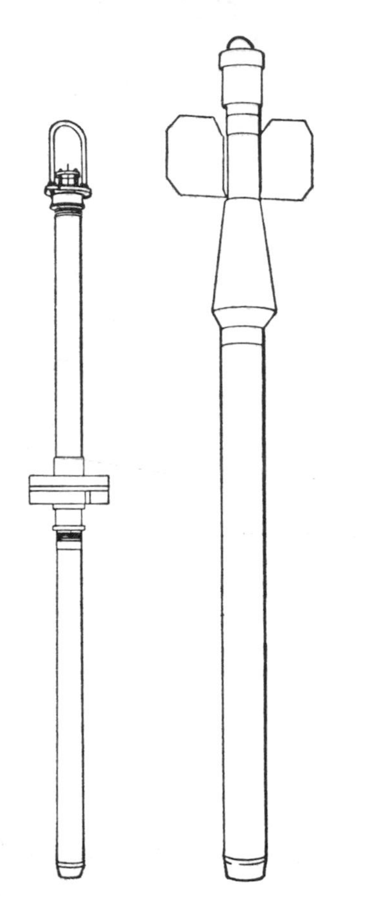

Figure 75. Phleger core sampler.

is widely used in water quality studies. It operates on the gravity principle. Styles and weights vary among manufacturers, some employing interchangeable weights that allow variations between 17 and 77 lb (7.7 to 35.0 kg), while others, with fixed weights, weigh 90 lb (41.0 kg) or more. Length of the core taken will vary with substrate texture, but such cores are adequate for most physical, chemical, or fossil examinations to delineate recent environmental changes.

f. The Wilding or stovepipe sampler (Figure 76) is made in various sizes

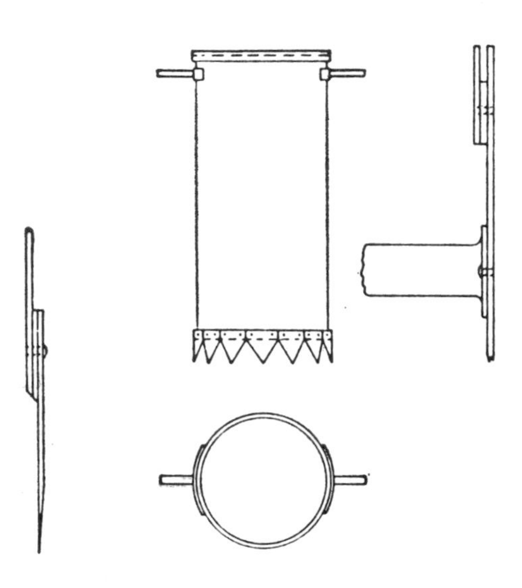

Figure 76. Wilding or stovepipe sampler.

and with many modifications. It is especially useful for quantitatively sampling a bottom with dense vascular plant growth. It may be used to sample the vegetation or the mud-water interface sediment, or both. Large volumes of vegetation, when sampled in this way, may require much time for laboratory processing.

5. *Drift nets* are anchored in flowing water for the capture of macroinvertebrates which have migrated or have been dislodged from the bottom substrates into the current.[7, 8] Nets having a 1 sq ft (929 cm^2) upstream opening, and mesh equivalent to U. S. Standard No. 30 screen, are recommended. After placement in the water, the nets require frequent removal of organisms and de-

bris to prevent clogging and subsequent diversion of water at the net opening. A sample comprises the total material collected over a 24-hr period in a single net. Drift net studies have proved useful in pesticide-related studies, since exposed animals become weakened and are swept into the nets by the current.

604 B. Qualitative Sampling Devices

1. Tow nets or trawls range from simple sled-mounted nets to complicated devices incorporating teeth that dig into the bottom. Some models feature special apparatus to hold the net open during towing and to close the net during descent and retrieval. Barnes,[3] Welch,[1] and Usinger [9] discuss some of the styles available.

2. Dip nets are practical devices for sweeping animals from vegetation or other substrates near the shore. The size and shape of the net and the length of the pole may be selected to best suit requirements of a particular sampling situation.

a. Hand screens may be constructed of ordinary window screen, approximately 1 yard square, and attached on two parallel sides to wooden poles. They are useful for catching organisms in currents and near the shoreline. The poles permit holding or manipulating the screen.

b. Miscellaneous devices such as garden rakes, pocket knives, buckets, or sieves are useful for collecting macroinvertebrates in a variety of situations. The extent of their use is determined by the type of substrate to be sampled and the collector's imagination.

604 C. Artificial Substrate Samplers

1. The multiple-plate sampler [10] is constructed of eight large tempered hardboard plates separated by seven small plates exposing slightly more than 1 sq ft (929 cm^2) of surface for the attachment of organisms. A hole is bored through the center of each plate. The larger plates are 3 inches square (7.6 × 7.6 cm) and ⅛ in. (3.2 mm) thick; the smaller plates are 1 inch square (2.5 × 2.5 cm) and ¼ in. (6.4 mm) thick. The plates are placed alternately on an eyebolt or long threaded rod and held together by two nuts (Figure 77). Instead of an iron or galvanized bolt, which may rust, a nylon cord may be looped through the plates to hold them together. The sampler may be used in streams or lakes, supported by any method that will hold it in the desired place. Depth and exposure should be consistent in a given study.

The collection procedure begins by

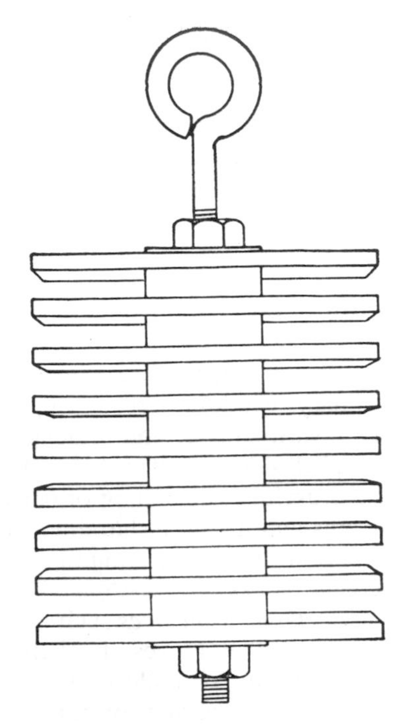

Figure 77. Multiple-plate or Hester-Dendy sampler.

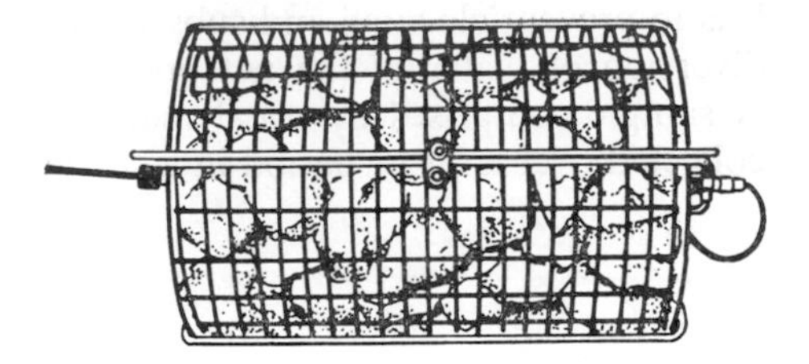

Figure 78. Basket sampler.

carefully placing a plastic bag or dip net under the sampler. The sample may be collected in the field by disassembling the plates and scraping the organisms into a container or the entire sampler in the plastic bag can be taken to the laboratory for processing. The collected material should be preserved in 5% formalin or 70% ethanol.

2. *The basket sampler* [11] was developed for the collection of macroinvertebrates in large rivers and lakes. The sampler (Figure 78) consists of a cylindrical chromium-plated basket 7 in. (18 cm) in diameter and 11 in. (28 cm) long which is filled with 30 rocks 2 to 3 in. (5 to 7.5 cm) in diameter. It weighs approximately 17 lb (7.8 kg). The basket is sturdy, inexpensive, and generally available.

The sampler preferably should be suspended within the euphotic zone (upper zone where light penetration permits growth of green plants) from stationary or floating structures at an approximate depth of 5 ft (1.5 m) for a 6-week exposure period. If these conditions cannot be met, it is important that the depth and exposure period be standard in any given study. The sampler collects immature insects, bryozoans, coelenterates, and other macroinvertebrates often not collected from the bottom sediments by dredge and trawl.

The collection procedure begins by emptying the rocks into a tub partially filled with water. Each rock is brushed with a stiff-bristle brush to remove the attached organisms and replaced in the basket for another exposure period. The sample is concentrated in a U. S. Standard No. 30 sieve and preserved.

604 D. Sample Analysis

After collecting a bottom sample containing sand or organic material, empty it into a tub, dilute with water, and swirl the mixture. Pour this slurry through a U. S. Standard No. 30 sieve. Slurries that clog the screen require removal of the screened material. A series of one or two coarser screens (e.g., 1-cm and 0.5-cm mesh) will hold back leaves, sticks, etc., while permitting the smaller organisms to pass through to the No. 30 sieve. Rocks, sticks and other artifacts must be carefully checked for clinging organisms before being discarded. Wash the screened material into a container and preserve in 5% formalin or 70% ethanol. (If ethanol is used, the screened material should not exceed one-half the volume of the container.) Label with the location, date, type of sampler used, name of collector, and other pertinent information. Some macroinvertebrates such as oligochaetes, leeches, and turbellarians are more easily identified if they are relaxed to prevent constriction during preservation.[2]

For qualitative samples hand-picked in the field, it is often desirable to place rocks, sticks, and other objects in a white pan partially filled with water. Many of the animals will float free from these objects and can be removed with forceps.

The samples are assigned identification numbers either in the field or at the laboratory and information from the labels is transcribed to a permanent ledger. The ledger provides a convenient reference in identifying the number of samples collected at various places, time of sampling, and characteristics of the water.

Whether the organisms are sorted from the sample detritus in the field or at the laboratory, the same procedures should be followed consistently. Before processing a sample, transfer information from the label to a data sheet that provides space for scientific names and the number of individuals. Place the sample directly in a shallow white tray with water for sorting. One method used to facilitate sorting organisms from detritus[12] is to stain the organisms red with a concentration of 200 mg/l of Rose Bengal in the formalin or ethanol preservative. Examine the entire sample and separate organisms unless they occur in very large numbers. If an aliquot sample is sorted, care must be taken to be certain that rare forms are not excluded. As the organisms are picked from the sample (a 2× scanning lens is useful), major taxonomic categories (e.g., Odonata, Coleoptera and Ephemeroptera) are enumerated on the data sheet. Place the animals in separate vials according to category and fill with 5% formalin or 70% ethanol. Label with sample number, date, sampling location, name of organisms, etc.

The animals in each vial are identified with the aid of stereoscopic and compound microscopes, according to the needs, experience and resources of the analyst. Additional references useful for laboratory technics and the identification of macroinvertebrates are included at the end of this section.

604 E. References

1. P. S. WELCH. 1948. *Limnological Methods.* Blakiston Co., Philadelphia.
2. R. W. PENNAK. 1953. *Fresh-water Invertebrates of the United States.* Ronald Press, New York.
3. H. BARNES. 1959. *Oceanographic and Marine Biology.* George Allen and Unwin, Ltd., London, England.
4. J. W. MERNA. 1962. Quantitative sampling with the orange peel dredge. *Limnol. & Oceanog.* 7:432.
5. C. F. POWERS & A. ROBERTSON. 1967. *Design and Evaluation of an All-Purpose Benthos Sampler.* Special Report No. 30. Great Lakes Research Division, Univ. of Michigan, Ann Arbor.
6. W. SMITH & A. D. MCINTYRE. 1954. A spring-loaded bottom sampler. *J. Marine Biol. Assoc.* (U. K.) 33:257.
7. T. F. WATERS. 1961. Standing crop and drift of stream bottom organisms. *Ecology* 42:532.
8. J. B. DIMOND. 1967. *Pesticides and Stream Insects.* Bull. No. 2. Maine Forest Service, Augusta, and the Conservation Foundation, Washington, D. C.
9. R. L. USINGER. 1956. *Aquatic Insects of California, with Keys to North American Genera and California Species.* Univ. of California Press, Berkeley.
10. F. E. HESTER & J. B. DENDY. 1962. A multiple-plate sampler for aquatic macroinvertebrates. *Tr. Amer. Fisheries Soc.* 91:420.
11. J. B. ANDERSON & W. T. MASON, JR. 1968. A comparison of benthic macroinvertebrates collected by dredge and basket sampler. *JWPCF* 40:252.
12. W. T. MASON, JR. & P. P. YEVICH. 1967. The use of phloxine B and rose bengal stains to facilitate sorting benthic samples. *Tr. Amer. Microscop. Soc.* 86:221.

604 F. Bibliography

BAKER, F. C. 1928. The freshwater mollusca of Wisconsin. *Wisc. Acad. Sci. Bull.* Part I: Gastropoda 70:1; Part II: Pelecypoda 70:1.

FRISON, T. H. 1935. The stoneflies or Plecoptera of Illinois. *Bull. Illinois Nat. Hist. Surv.* 20:281.

NEEDHAM, J. G. & P. R. NEEDHAM. 1941. *A Guide to the Study of Freshwater Biology.* Comstock Pub. Co., Ithaca, N. Y.

ROSS, H. H. 1944. The caddisflies, or Trichoptera, of Illinois. *Bull. Illinois Nat. Hist. Surv.* 23:1.

CHU, H. F. 1949. *How To Know the Immature Insects.* William C. Brown Co., Dubuque, Iowa.

BERNER, L. 1950. *The Mayflies of Florida.* Univ. of Florida Studies in Biological Sciences Series 4:1.

PRATT, H. W. 1951. *A Manual of the Common Invertebrate Animals Exclusive of Insects.* The Blakiston Co., Philadelphia.

PENNAK, R. W. 1953. *Freshwater Invertebrates of the United States.* The Ronald Press, New York.

BURKS, B. D. 1953. The mayflies or Ephemeroptera of Illinois. *Bull. Illinois Nat. Hist. Surv.* 26:1.

NEEDHAM, J. G. & M. J. WESTFALL, JR. 1954. *Dragonflies of North America.* Univ. of California Press, Berkeley.

HUTCHINSON, G. E. 1957. *A Treatise on Limnology.* John Wiley & Sons, N. Y.

ODUM, E. P. 1957. *Fundamentals of Ecology.* Saunders Pub. Co., Philadelphia, Pa.

ROBACK, S. S. 1957. *The Immature Tendipedids of the Philadelphia Area.* Philadelphia Academy of Natural Sciences Monogr. No. 9.

WALKER, E. M. 1958. *The Odonata of Canada and Alaska.* Univ. of Toronto Press, Toronto, Vols. 1 and 2.

BOUSFIELD, E. L. 1958. I. Freshwater amphipod crustaceans of glaciated North America. *Canad. Field Nat.* 72:55.

EDMONDSON, W. T., Ed. 1959. *Ward and Whipple's Freshwater Biology* (2nd ed.). John Wiley & Sons, Inc., N. Y.

EDDY, SAMUEL & A. C. HODSON. 1961. *Taxonomic Keys to the Common Animals of the North Central States* (3rd ed.). Burgess Pub. Co., Minneapolis, Minn.

HYNES, H. B. N. 1963. *The Biology of Polluted Waters.* Liverpool Univ. Press, England.

MACAN, T. T. 1963. *Freshwater Ecology.* John Wiley & Sons, New York.

BRINKHURST, R. O. 1964. Studies on the North American aquatic oligochaeta. Part I. *Proc. Acad. Sci. Phila.* 116:195.

SINCLAIR, R. M. 1964. Water quality requirements for elmid beetles. Tenn. Dept. Public Health, Nashville, Tenn.

BRINKHURST, R. O. 1965. Studies on the North American aquatic oligochaeta. Part II. *Proc. Acad. Sci. Phila.* 117:117.

SUBLETTE, J. E., and M. S. SUBLETTE. 1965. Family Chironomidae (Tendipedidae). A catalog of diptera of America north of Mexico. *Bull. U. S. Dept. Agr.* 276: 143.

RUTTNER, F. 1966. *Fundamentals of Limnology.* Univ. of Toronto Press, Canada.

HEARD, W. H. & J. BURCH. 1966. Keys to the genera of freshwater pelecypods of Michigan. Univ. of Michigan Museum of Zoology Circular No. 4.

BECK, W. M., JR. & E. C. BECK. 1966. Chironomidae (Diptera) of Florida. I. Pentaneurini (Tanypodinae). *Bull. Fla. State Museum* 10:305.

INGRAM, W., K. M. MACKENTHUN & A. F. BARTSCH. 1966. *Biological Field Investigative Data for Water Pollution Surveys.* U. S. Dept. Interior, FWPCA U. S. Govt. Ptg. Off., Washington, D. C.

MACKENTHUN, K. M. & W. M. INGRAM. 1967. *Biological Associated Problems in Freshwater Environments.* FWPCA, Washington, D. C.

MASON, W. T., JR. 1968. *An Introduction to the Identification of Chironomid Larvae.* Div. Poll. Surveillance, FWPCA, Cincinnati, O.

JACKSON, H. W. 1970. A controlled-depth volumetric bottom sampler. *Prog. Fish Culturist* Vol. 32, No. 2.

LARIMORE, R. W. 1970. Two shallow-water bottom samplers. *Prog. Fish Culturist* Vol. 32, No. 2.

605 FISHES

The size and nature of the community of fishes is a valuable method for assessing the quality of a body of water. Fishes occupy the peak of the aquatic food chain (barring predation by higher vertebrates); hence their condition constitutes a summation of the condition of lower biological forms and is a resultant of the total quality of the water. Water quality factors which alter the ecological balance of the periphyton, plankton and macroinvertebrate populations likewise can alter the fish population. Because fish and invertebrates have differing susceptibilities to certain toxicants, the fish might be affected by certain pollutants that do not cause a demonstrable change in the invertebrate-plant communities. It becomes important to sample fish populations as the final or climax product of the aquatic community. Since fish as aquatic organisms are already well known and also have economic value, they are to the general public the most intelligible symbol of water quality and must be ranked high for public relations purposes as well as for technical interpretations.

Only a summary of the equipment and procedures available specifically for the collection and sampling of fishes is provided below. Where commercial fisheries exist locally, the chartering of commercial fishermen and equipment should be considered, especially for studies of relatively short duration. Commercial catch data may also be useful in detecting certain long-term changes in water quality.

605 A. Station Selection

Fish may be collected by a variety of methods such as seining, trapping, gill- or trawlnetting, electrofishing, or with chemicals. A fishery survey should secure information as to the kinds of fish present and their relative abundance. To obtain a representative sample, sampling should be conducted in the obscure and unlikely areas as well as in obvious locations. Early life stages (eggs and larvae) of many species may be found in the plankton. Waterway bottoms should be trawled for bottom fish; both riffles and pools of streams should be seined; free-swimming open water types may be fished with various nets; migrating or roving types may best be taken with traps or gillnets. All depths should be sampled, not just surface and bottom. Brush, rock, and other types of obstructions are sometimes best sampled using chemicals or by electrofishing.

Visual observations by a trained individual are also very useful. Various methods of fish sampling such as electrofishing, trapping and gillnetting are best undertaken at night because so many species of fish are sedentary during daylight hours.

605 B. Sample Collection

A one-time study can provide information on the species of fish present in a given body of water. This may be sufficient, for example, when one is attempting to determine the possible devastating effect of a certain waste. In many rivers and lakes, the changes in fish populations are subtle and should be determined through long-range studies. Fishes should be identified as to species. In reports for nonfisheries personnel, the use of common names adopted by the American Fisheries Society is recommended.[1]

Fish collection for official purposes is subject to varying state regulations, which should be checked carefully when field operations are being planned. Scientific collecting permits issued by state fish and game agencies cover authorization requirements for most procedures. If the use of piscicidal chemicals is contemplated, however, a thorough check must be made of Food and Drug Administration, Federal Water Pollution Control Administration, and state regulations, since the introduction of toxic substances into any water is stringently controlled.

1. *Haul seines* are used to collect small fish from shallow water. Shoreline seining of lakes and large rivers is usually most effective using a bag seine. There are two common sizes of bag seines: One is 25 ft (7.5 m) long and 6 ft (1.8 m) deep, with the main portion constructed of ½-in. (12.6 mm) square-mesh netting. The center 6-ft (1.8 m) long bag is made of ¼-in. (6 mm) mesh netting. The second size, often used for larger fish, is 100 ft (30 m) long and 6 or 8 ft (1.8 or 2.4 m) deep, with 1–2 in. (2.5 to 5 cm) square-mesh netting in the main body and ½ to 1 in. (12 to 25 mm) netting in the center bag. A water free from snags is essential to successful seining. In small streams, seining is usually done with "straight" seines of various lengths, 4 ft (1.2 m) or longer, with square-mesh sizes of ⅛, ¼ or ½ in. (3, 6 or 12 mm). Results are expressed as number of fish per unit area seined. Quantitative seining is very difficult, however. The procedure is more useful in determining the variety of fish inhabiting the water than the numbers that may be expected.

2. *Gillnets* (Figure 79A) are designed to capture larger fish and are used in estuaries, lakes, reservoirs, or large rivers where fish movement can be expected. The most versatile experimental gillnet is 125 ft (38 m) long; there are five 25-ft (7.5 m) sections with mesh sizes ranging from ¾ in. (19 mm) to 2½ in. (62 mm) square. Results are expressed as number or weight of fish taken per length of net per day.

3. *Trammel nets* (Figure 79B) have a layer of large mesh netting on each side of loosely hung smaller gillnetting. Small fish are captured in the gillnetting and the larger fish are captured in a "bag" of the gillnetting that is formed in the larger mesh netting. Results are usually expressed as number or weight of fish captured per length of netting per day.

4. *Traps* range in size from small containers (minnow traps) with inverted cone entrances to semipermanent structures (weirs) (Figure 79C). Traps and weir nets are used mainly in rivers and estuaries.

Trap nets, when properly located to intercept fish movements, may be used effectively to sample fish populations in lakes during certain seasons. The trap net most used in fishery studies is the square or round hoop net. This net may have leads or wings attached to the first frame.[2] The second and third frames can each hold tunnel throats, which prevent the escape of fishes entering each section in turn. The opposite (closed) end of the net may be tied with a slip cord to facilitate fish removal. Results are expressed as fish per net-day. Most fish can be sampled when trap nets of varying mesh sizes are set in a variety of habitats.

5. *Trawls* are specialized gear used in large open water areas of reservoirs, lakes, large rivers, estuaries and offshore marine areas (Figure 79D). They are best used to gain information on a particular species of fish rather than on the overall fish population. Trawls are of three basic types: the fry trawl, with a permanent opening; the otter trawl, used to capture near-bottom

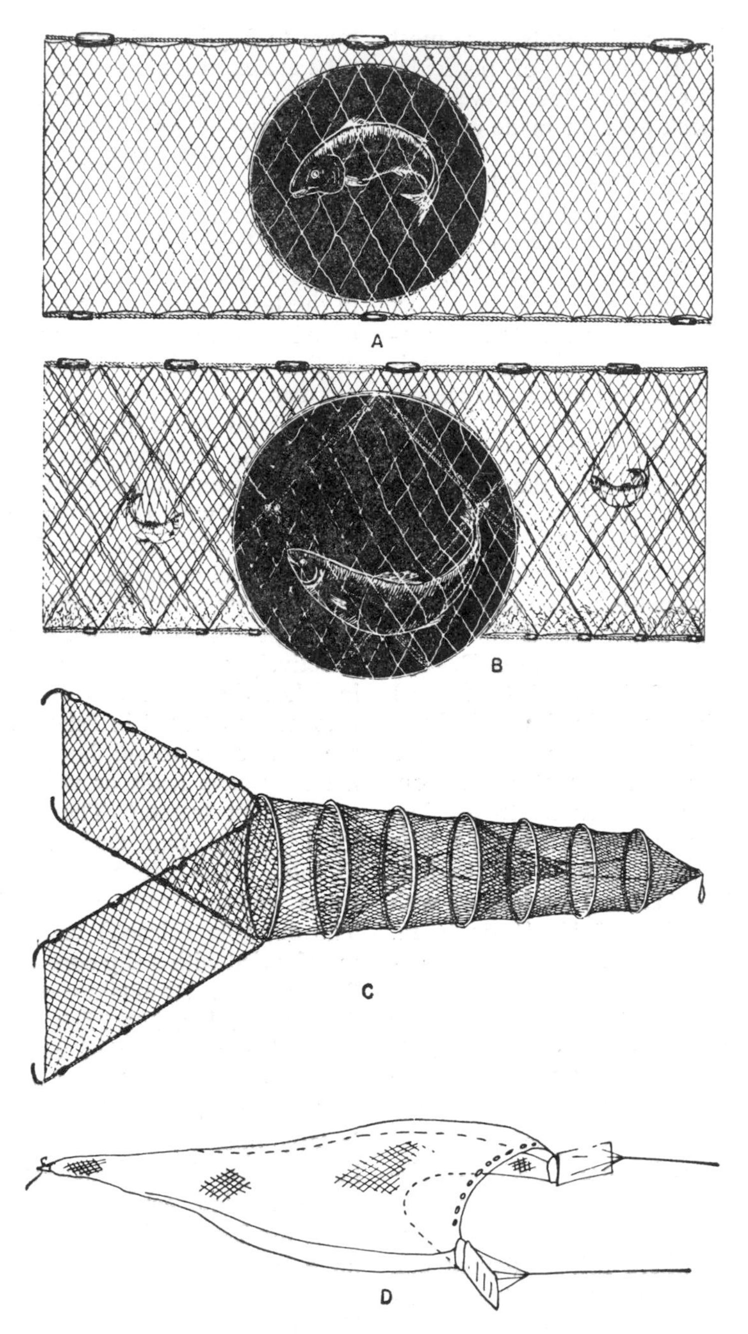

Figure 79. Some types of nests: A—gillnet; B—trammel net; C—Fyke or hoop net; D—otter trawl.

and bottom fishes [3]; and the mid-water trawl, used to collect schooling fish at various depths.

6. *Electrofishing devices* are effective in collecting most sizes and species of fish from many different environments. These devices vary in size and complexity. Small streams can be surveyed by two men, one using a backpack shocker, the other dipping fish. In large rivers and lakes, a generator and electrical control equipment are required to achieve satisfactory results. The survey of a large river may call for several men, but electrofishing does offer the advantage of surveying a reach of water in a short time and does not entail leaving unattended expensive and pilferable equipment such as nets. Shockers have been constructed on boats for sampling waters that cannot be effectively waded.[4] Electrofishing may be limited by water conductance, turbidity and depth. Sampling is more efficient at night, when underwater lights may be used. Block nets may be used to delineate the sampling area as well as to prevent the escape of fish from the electrical field.

7. *Chemicals* are often used to collect fish from a restricted area. This technic of sampling is usually employed on a spot basis—for example, a short reach of a river or an embayment of a lake. Results are expressed as fish per unit of surface area sampled.

8. *Trotlines* (or long lines) can be used to sample a limited segment of the fish population. These are used mainly to sample fish feeding at night. A trotline consists of a series of short drop lines with baited hooks attached to a long main line.

9. *Suction tubes* or hoses are often effective for the removal of eggs and fry from bottom nests. The study of fish egg viability is important because the egg stage is a most critical stage in the life cycle of the fish.

10. *Observations* by experienced personnel can provide much information on fish habitats and populations. Such observations can often be enhanced through the use of such equipment as underwater television or photographic cameras, underwater breathing equipment, or submersible vessels.

605 C. Laboratory Analysis for Sublethal or Chronic Effects of Pollution

The general health and well-being of a fish influences its response to pollution; likewise, sublethal levels of pollution may affect the health of the fish and its ability to resist disease. Natural epidemics and debilities of many types are known to occur among fishes as among all groups of organisms. Fish should be examined early in any water quality survey for their general condition, parasites, and other factors that might accentuate or mask the effects of pollution.

Parasites, particularly the larger attached external parasites like copepods or leeches, can usually be detected by examining the surface of live or freshly killed fish under a wide-field dissecting microscope. Examination, using greater magnification, of slime scraped from the body surface or from areas of accumulation around the gills may reveal smaller external parasites. Scars from lamprey attacks may appear as round fresh red lesions or older healed areas up to 2 cm or more in diameter. Inflamed areas, swellings, frayed or eroded fins, or other gross indications of disability may be visible externally and should be reported. Internal parasites and other pathologies may be revealed by appropriate microtechnics. For the critical identification of pathological conditions, an established laboratory specializing in this field should be contacted.

When chronic toxicity is suspected or when a general weakness or poor condition of the fish is noted, a program of histological, physiological, and/or biochemical testing should be established (see Section 231).

So-called "condition" factors—coefficients of condition—length/weight factors, etc., can be calculated for different species and are often useful in evaluating the overall health of a population.[5] Most fish scales, when magnified, reveal concentric lines of growth, or circuli. The spacing of certain rings (annuli) indicates seasonal effects and can be used to estimate the age and the rate of growth. The sex and degree of maturity of the individual fish must also be associated with the data for each scale sample. When properly prepared, the cross section of catfish spines and other suitable structures may also be utilized in a like manner.

Fish flesh is often unpalatable because of chemicals present in the water. Many of these taste-producing substances are from municipal or industrial wastes, although natural sources are also known to contribute.[6] Taste panels have been the most successful method for detecting tainted fish flesh. Test fish may be native fish from the stream, uncontaminated fish held in cages in the test area, or uncontaminated fish held in tanks, with the suspect chemical added. The taste panel should be trained in fish tasting and should be given acceptable samples for comparison.

605 D. Production and Productivity

Fish production in a given body of water is highly indicative of the quality of that water. The species composition of the entire fish community must be considered as well as the relative quantities of each. Productivity in a fishery context includes the following concepts:

—*Productivity:* the amount (usually by weight) of fish that a given body of water is capable of producing in a given period of time (usually a year).

—*Production:* the actual amount produced in a unit of time under existing conditions.

—*Standing crop:* the quantity (usually by weight) of fish present at any given time. This quantity may be reported as the total for all species or may be broken down into the relative quantities of each.

—*Harvest or yield:* the quantity of fish actually removed per unit of time or effort.

605 E. Investigation of Fish Kills

Fish kills vary as to cause—from the individual fish that dies of old age to the catastrophic kill—from partial to complete, and from natural to man-caused. No single investigative procedure can be appropriate for all situations. The following brief description may serve as an aid in investigating kills. Too much emphasis cannot be given the importance of getting to the scene promptly before the evidence has decomposed or drifted away. If surveillance of a particular body of water or area is involved, preset plans and equipment should be available on a standby basis.[7, 8]

Two information record forms are strongly recommended for fish kill investigation, an initial contact form and a field investigation form.

Fish kills may be due to such natural causes as acute temperature change, storms, ice and snow cover, decomposition of natural materials, salinity change, spawning mortalities, parasites, and bacterial and viral epidemics. Man-caused fish kills may be attributed to municipal or industrial wastes, agricultural activities, and water control activities.

One dead fish in a stream may be called a fish kill; however, in a practical sense some minimal range in the number of dead fish observed, plus additional qualifications, should be adopted in reporting and classifying fish kills. Any fish kill is of significance if it affects fish of sport or commercial value; results from a suspected negligent discharge or malfunctioning waste treatment facility; or causes widespread environmental damage. The following definitions, based on a stream about 200 ft (60 m) wide and 6 ft (2 m) deep, are suggested as guidelines. For other size streams, adjustments should be made.

1. MINOR KILL—1–100 dead or dying fish confined to a small area or stream stretch. If recurrent, it could be significant and should be investigated.

2. MODERATE KILL—100–1,000 dead or dying fish of various species in a mile or so of stream or equivalent area of a lake or estuary.

3. MAJOR KILL—1,000 or more dead or dying fish of many species over up to a 10-mile (16-km) or greater reach of stream or equivalent area of a lake or estuary.

In preparation for a field investigation, area maps should be studied. The kill area and access to it should be determined. Waste dischargers should be identified. Contact should be made with participating laboratories to make preliminary estimates of the number and size of samples that will be submitted, the types of analyses required, the dates of sample receipt, the method of sample shipment, the date results are needed, and to whom the results are to be reported.

Certain field equipment should be taken on all fish kill investigations: thermometer, dissolved oxygen test kit, conductivity meter and pH meter; or a general chemical kit, sample bottles and other specimen containers. The investigating team preferably should include one person who is experienced in investigating fish kills.[9]

The field investigation consists of visual observations, fish, water and biota sampling, and physical measurements of the environment. The first local observer of the kill makes a useful guide to the area, which should be reconnoitered initially to establish that a fish kill has actually occurred.

If a fish kill has taken place, fish sampling should be initiated immediately, since the collection of dying or recently dead fish is critical. For purposes of comparison, healthy fish from an unaffected area should also be collected. Individual fish are placed in well-labeled plastic bags and preserved by freezing until examined in a laboratory. Dying or dead fish are bled at collection time so as to obtain at least 1 gram of blood. The blood sample should be collected in a chemically clean, solvent-washed glass bottle with a teflon-lined screw cap.

Dead fish should be identified and counted. In a large river an observer may count dead fish from a fixed station such as a bridge during a fixed period of time. Extrapolations may then be made to the total time involved. Alternatively, in a large river or lake, a shore count may be made and projected to the entire area of the kill. In smaller bodies of water the entire area may be traversed for enumeration of dead fish.

Water samples representative of unpolluted and polluted areas should be collected in accordance with the instruction given in the plankton section (601.1). As a minimum, measurements of temperature, pH, dissolved oxygen, and specific conductance should be made. Additional tests may be performed, depending on suspected causes of the fish kill. Samples for the examination of plankton, periphyton, macrophyton and macroinvertebrates should also be taken.[10–12]

Observations on water appearance, streamflow and weather conditions should be made. Color photographs are valuable in recording conditions.

More specific recommendations are made in a recent publication of the U. S. Department of the Interior.[12]

605 F. References

1. American Fisheries Society. 1960. AFS Special Pub. No. 1, Ann Arbor, Mich.
2. G. A. Rounsefell & W. H. Everhart. 1953. *Fishery Science—Its Methods and Applications*. John Wiley & Sons, N. Y.
3. M. E. Stansby. 1963. *Industrial Fishery Technology*. Reinhold Pub. Co., N. Y.
4. K. F. Lagler. 1956. *Freshwater Fishery Biology*. Wm. C. Brown Co., Dubuque, Iowa.
5. K. D. Carlander. 1953. *Handbook of Freshwater Fishery Biology, with the First Supplement*. Wm. C. Brown Co., Dubuque, Iowa.

6. *Water Quality Criteria.* 1968. Report of the National Technical Advisory Commission. FWPCA, Washington, D. C.
7. G. E. BURDICK. 1965. "Some Problems in the Determination of the Cause of Fish Kills." In *Biological Problems in Water Pollution.* USPHS Pub. No. 999-WP-25.
8. *Pollution Caused Fish Kills 1967.* 1968. U. S. Dept. Interior, FWPCA Pub. No. CWA-7.
9. L. L. SMITH, JR. et al. 1956. *Procedures for Investigation of Fish Kills* (a guide for field reconnaissance and data collection). ORSANCO, Cincinnati, Ohio.
10. W. INGRAM & G. W. PRESCOTT. 1954. Toxic fresh-water algae. *Amer. Mid. Nat.* 52:75.
11. G. A. ROUNSEFELL & W. R. NELSON. 1966. *Red-Tide Research Summarized to 1964, Including an Annotated Bibliography.* U. S. Dept. Interior Special Science Reports, Fisheries No. 535.
12. *Investigating Fish Mortalities.* 1970. U. S. Dept. Interior, FWPCA Pub. No. CWT-5 (also available from U. S. Govt. Ptg. Off. as No. 0-380-257).

606 IDENTIFICATION OF TYPES OF AQUATIC ORGANISMS

Professional aquatic biologists will be familiar with most of the types of organisms illustrated in the black and white Plates 1–37, and will seldom need the assistance of a technical key in order to identify organisms to the level illustrated. Since these plates are not intended for critical identification, specific (species) names are not cited. Types most likely to be observed are illustrated in this group. For the convenience of those less familiar with the organisms referred to in preceding sections, a series of short keys is presented which should make possible the identification of most unknown organisms encountered with respect to a general type as illustrated by the plates.

In conformity with preceding sections, organisms are arbitrarily divided into microscopic and macroscopic, depending on whether or not they pass through a U. S. Standard No. 30 sieve. For the study of microscopic forms, a compound microscope is needed. For examination of the smaller macroscopic organisms and to resolve the finer structures of larger forms, a wide-field stereoscopic microscope will be required.

606 A. Procedure in Identification

Critical identification of an unknown specimen is often time-consuming, even for the experienced biologist. Before looking at any key or other aid to identification, allow from one to several minutes for carefully studying the specimen. If necessary, find other examples and compare them with the unknown.

It is often important to know where or under what conditions the subject organism lived before attempting to identify it. For example, did it come from fresh water—a lake or a stream? Is it marine—from the open ocean, shoreline or estuary? Was it a free swimmer or floater in the water? Was it a bottom organism, attached, crawling or burrowing? Finally, turn to the following key to major groups.

Only the more common types of aquatic organisms are illustrated here, with special attention to those most frequently employed in water quality evaluation. When specimens do not fit obviously into one of the types listed, consult a professional biologist, a microbiologist for the bacteria and fungi, or some of the references provided. Descriptions of color and movement refer to freshly collected or living specimens, or, in the case of microscopic forms, to those preserved with Merthiolate as described in Section 601 (Plankton).

Sizes of the organisms illustrated in the black and white plates (1–37) are given in metric terms and shown in parenthesis in the legend. These are intended to represent *common* sizes, not absolute maxima or minima. Exceptional individuals and even whole localized populations may be encountered that are considerably larger than the sizes cited and, of course, immature forms or dwarfed individuals of smaller size may be found.

606 B. Key to Major Groups of Aquatic Organisms, (Plates 1–37)

Beginning with couplet 1a and 1b of the Keys compare the descriptions given with the subject specimen. A choice must be made between statement "a" and statement "b." Proceed to the couplet number indicated at the right and repeat the process. Continue until the name of a type of organism or a plate number is cited instead of another couplet number. Additional information is provided in many of the plate legends.

	Refer to Couplet No.
1a. Macroscopic: The organism, mass or colony is visible to the naked eye	13
1b. Microscopic: Not readily visible to the naked eye	2

I. Key to Microscopic Organisms

2a. Specimen a single living cell or a mass or colony of relatively independent cells (shapeless, rounded or threadlike)	3
2b. Specimen a many-celled, highly organized plant or animal	7
3a. Cells contain one or more pigments, including chlorophyll *a* (overall color may range through various shades of green, blue, red, brown or yellow). ALGAE (for details, see Section 606C following, "Key for Identification of Freshwater Algae")	4
3b. Cells typically colorless, lacking chlorophyll *a*	12
4a. Nuclei present; pigment confined to chloroplasts	5
4b. Nuclei, plastids or vacuoles absent (pseudovacuoles may be present in certain filamentous forms). Pigment generally diffused throughout cytoplasm. BLUE-GREEN ALGAE, Plates 1 and 2.	

	Refer to Couplet No.
5a. Cell wall permanently rigid, composed of SiO_2, geometrical in appearance, and with regular patterns of fine markings; composed of two essentially similar halves, one placed over the other as a cover. Golden brown to greenish in color. DIATOMS, Plates 5 and 6.	
5b. Cell wall, if present, capable of sagging or bending, rigidity depending on internal pressure of cell contents. Cell walls usually of one piece	6
6a. Cells or colonies nonmotile. Usually some shade of green in color. NONMOTILE GREEN ALGAE, Plates 3 and 4.	
6b. Cells or colony move by means of relatively long whiplike "flagella." PIGMENTED FLAGELLATES, Plates 11 and 12.	
7a. Body with cilia (hairlike structures used for locomotion)	8
7b. Body without cilia	9
8a. Body generally covered with cilia, usually somewhat elongate or wormlike, bilaterally symmetrical. Minute FLATWORMS (Platyhelminthes), relatives of *Planaria,* Plate 19.	
8b. Cilia confined to one or two crowns at anterior end which often present the illusion of rotating wheels. Internal jaws present. ROTIFERS (Rotifera), Plate 17.	
9a. Long slender unsegmented worms that move by sinuous crawling or thrashing motion. ROUNDWORMS (Nemathelminthes), Plate 18.	
9b. Possess external skeleton and jointed appendages	10
10a. Crawl about or swim by means of jointed appendages thrust out from between two clamlike shells. All appendages can be withdrawn entirely within shells when disturbed. OSTRACODS (Ostracoda), Plate 21.	
10b. Swim rapidly by means of a pair of enlarged jointed appendages (antennae) which cannot be withdrawn inside carapace or shell	11
11a. Locomotor appendages (antennae) branched. Microcrustacea, CLADOCERA (Cladocera), Plate 20.	
11b. Locomotor appendages (antennae) unbranched; body tapers toward rear. Microcrustacea, COPEPODS (Copepoda), Plate 21.	
12a. Ingest and digest food internally (ingested food of various colors may be visible through body wall). Single-celled or colonial, attached or free-living. PROTOZOANS (Protozoa), Plates 13, 14 and 15.	
12b. Digest food externally and adsorb products through cell wall. Often secrete masses of slime. BACTERIA and FUNGI, Plate 37.	

2. Key to Macroscopic Organisms

13a. Specimen a mass of filaments or a glob of gelatinous or semisolid material containing many tiny units, requiring microscopic examination to determine details of structure	2
13b. Specimen a well-organized unit or colony	14
14a. Organism plantlike; flowerlike structures, if present, do not respond when touched, generally are colored some shade of green, brown or red	16
14b. Organism animal-like; usually responds rapidly when touched, whether attached or free-living	15
15a. Internal backbone present (vertebrates)	17
15b. No internal backbone present (macroinvertebrates)*	18

* Invertebrates retained on a U. S. Standard No. 30 sieve.

Refer to Couplet No.

16a. Plant structure relatively simple. Attachment structures may be present, but no true roots or fibrous tissue. Larger ALGAE, Plate 7 and Color Plates A (*Nitella*) and F (*Chara* and *Batrachospermum*).

16b. Plant structure usually includes true roots, stems and leaves. Fibers or vascular tissue usually present; flowers or seeds may be observed. (One atypical group, "watermeal," consists only of tiny roundish masses, 0.5 to 1 mm in diameter, often misidentified as algae.) HIGHER PLANTS. Plates 8, 9 and 10.

17a. Side appendages, if present, are flat fins. FISHES, Plate 35.

17b. Side appendages, if present, are footlike, with separate digits. AMPHIBIANS, Plate 36.

3. Key to Macroinvertebrates

18a. Body bilaterally symmetrical (with right and left sides, but may be superficially coiled into a spiral); animal not attached but may live inside an attached cocoon or case, or crawl about; usually solitary.................. 23

18b. Symmetry not bilateral 19

19a. Body typically radially symmetrical 21

19b. Body or colony nonsymmetrical 20

20a. Body mass generally porous; not a colony, sometimes finger- or antler-like. Freshwater representatives are generally fragile, colored green or brown; marine forms tougher, various colors. SPONGES (Porifera), Plate 16.

20b. Body mass otherwise 22

21a. Animals with soft smooth bodies and tentacles around a mouth; no anus. Solitary or colonial. Larger colonies usually have rigid limy skeleton of massive, branched or fan-shaped form. HYDRAS, SEA ANEMONES, JELLYFISHES, CORALS, etc. (Coelenterata), Plate 34A, B.

21b. Body covering usually spiny, soft or rigid, flattened or elongate, typically having five radii, with or without spines or arms; anus present. Solitary. Marine only. STARFISHES and relatives (Echinodermata), Plate 33.

22a. Colony a jellylike mass, a network of branching tubes, a plantlike tuft, or a lacy limy crust or mass. MOSS ANIMALS (Bryozoa), Plate 16.

22b. Exclusively marine. Surface of body or colony relatively smooth but tough. Solitary forms, sac-like, with two external openings. Exhibit all degrees of colonialism. Compound forms range from thin slimy masses, with organisms arranged in tiny radial patterns to huge shapeless masses resembling tough frozen gelatin. SEA SQUIRTS, SEA PORK (Ascidiacea, Urochorda, Chordata), not illustrated.

23a. Animal living within a hard limy shell, soft body (Mollusca) 29

23b. Animal without a limy shell... 24

24a. Jointed legs present (may not be functional). Body may be hard or soft.... 30

24b. Jointed legs absent, body covering mostly soft, animal pliable (a hardened head capsule may be present) 25

25a. Body girded by annulations or creases at regular intervals, dividing it into many small segments much wider than long.. 26

25b. Segments present or absent; if present, not much wider than they are long...... 27

26a. Body with suction disk at one or both ends, in length usually less than 10 times its width. LEECHES (Annelida, Hirudinea), Plate 19.

26b. Body without suction disks, in length usually more than 10 times its width; hairs or bristles often evident. SEGMENTED WORMS (Annelida), Plate 19.

27a. Body unsegmented, long and slender, appearing smooth, evenly tapered to a fine point at one end. ROUNDWORMS (Nematoda), Plate 18.

27b. Body otherwise 28

Refer to Couplet No.

28a. Body flat, elongate or oblong, unsegmented head is spade-shaped. Pigmented spots on top of head often give the animal a cross-eyed appearance. FLATWORMS (Turbellaria), Plate 19.

28b. Body segmented, cylindrical, oblong or capsule-like; may or may not have a head capsule and thick fleshy knobs on underside. Larvae of TWO-WINGED FLIES (Diptera), Plate 28 30

29a. Shell consisting of two hinged halves. BIVALVES (Pelecypoda), Plate 32.

29b. Shell entire, usually spiral but may be "coolie hat"-shaped. SNAILS (Gastropoda), Plate 31.

30a. Body with functional legs 31

30b. Body without functional legs, mummy- or capsule-like, living in a cocoon. PUPAE (Insecta), none illustrated 38

31a. Body with three pairs of legs. Larvae, nymphs and some adults (Insecta) 42

31b. Body with more than three pairs of legs 32

32a. Body compact, spider-like, with four conspicuous pairs of legs (two other pairs of appendages present). WATER MITES (Acari), Plate 34.

32b. Body with at least five conspicuous pairs of legs. CRUSTACEANS (Crustacea) 33

4. Key to Crustaceans

33a. Sides of body compressed 34

33b. Body flattened horizontally 36

34a. Eyes on stalks 35

34b. Eyes, if present, only seen as spots on sides of head. SCUDS (Amphipoda), Plate 21.

35a. Pincers on first pair of legs strong and large; other legs stout, cylindrical and used for walking. CRAYFISH, also marine lobster (Decapoda), Plate 21.

35b. Pincers on first pair of legs weak and small; other legs, thin and flattened, are used for swimming. SHRIMPS (Mysidea and others), Plate 21.

36a. Eyes on stalks, shells generally broad, various shapes (marine and brackish water). CRABS (Decapoda), not illustrated.

36b. Eyes not on stalks 37

37a. Body covering hard; divided into broad head, truncate body and sharp tail sections (marine). HORSESHOE CRABS (Arthropoda), Plate 34.

37b. Body with three or more joints. SOWBUGS (Isopoda), Plate 21.

5. Key to Insect Pupae

38a. Back of pupa with small, paired hook-bearing plates. CADDISFLIES (Trichoptera), Plate 26.

38b. Back without paired hook-bearing plates but may have knobs or bristles 39

39a. Developing wings (pads) held free from body. BEETLES (Coleoptera), Plate 29.

39b. Wing pads closely appressed to body, mummy-like, or appendages not evident 40

40a. With one closely appressed pair of wing pads, but not fused to body; or capsule-like, appendages not evident. TWO-WINGED FLIES (Diptera), Plate 27.

40b. Two pairs of wing pads 41

41a. First two or three abdominal segments with spiracles (holes for breathing) on each side; body without numerous projections. AQUATIC MOTHS (Lepidoptera), not illustrated.

41b. Body differing from above, may have numerous knobs or other projections on back. HELLGRAMMITES (Neuroptera and Megaloptera), Plate 25.

Refer to Couplet No.

6. Key to Insect Larvae, Nymphs, and Some Adults

42a. Animal flea-like, with a bifid projecting appendage on the underside. SPRINGTAILS (Collembola), Plate 34.
42b. Animal otherwise 43
43a. Body ending in long segmented filaments 44
43b. Long filaments absent or, if present, not segmented 45
44a. Two tail filaments, legs ending in two claws. STONEFLIES (Plecoptera), Plate 22.
44b. Three tail filaments (with few exceptions); middle filament may be slightly smaller than laterals, legs ending in one claw. MAYFLIES (Ephemeroptera), Plate 23.
45a. Back of body covered with two hard wing covers, a pair of membranous wings underneath the covers. Adult BEETLES (Coleoptera), Plate 29.
45b. Back without hard wing covers 46
46a. Body with exposed membranous wings or wing pads on back 47
46b. Body without membranous wings or wing pads (larvae) 49
47a. Membranous wings present; held flat and in a V-shape on back. Mouth parts formed into a long sharply pointed beak folded underneath body. TRUE BUGS (Hemiptera), Plate 30.
47b. Membranous wings absent, wing pads present. Mouth parts formed into an extendable, scoop-like mask which covers face. (Odonata) 48
48a. Body ending in three oblong, fan-like plates. DAMSELFLIES (Zygoptera), Plate 24.
48b. Fan-like plates absent. DRAGONFLIES (Anisoptera), Plate 24.
49a. Mouth parts formed into slender curved rods which are nearly half as long as body (less than 10 mm). SPONGILLA FLIES (Neuroptera), not illustrated.
49b. Mouth parts adapted for biting or chewing 50
50a. Body with five paired knobs on underside of abdominal segments, legs on first three segments short and stubby. Often found on lily pads. AQUATIC MOTHS (Lepidoptera), not illustrated.
50b. Body without paired knobs on underside of abdomen 51
51a. Sides of each abdominal segment with a slender, tapering process 52
51b. Sides of each abdominal segment without a tapering process, but may have hair-like or tubular processes 53
52a. Body ending in a pair of hook-bearing fleshy legs or in a single tapering filament. HELLGRAMMITES and relatives (Megaloptera), Plate 25.
52b. Body otherwise. BEETLES (Coleoptera), Plate 29.
53a. Body covering mostly hard; knobs, hairlike processes, or other special ornamentation may be present on back, or else body is entirely soft except for a hardened head capsule. BEETLES (Coleoptera), Plate 29.
53b. Most of body soft except for a hardened head capsule and with one to three hard plates on the back of first body segments; tubular processes may be present on sides of the body in various arrangements. Body may end in a pair of hook-bearing legs, most larvae living in portable cases made of bits of sticks, leaves or sand or in attached fibrous cases. CADDISFLIES (Trichoptera), Plate 26.

606 C. List of Common Types of Aquatic Organisms (Plates 1–37), by Trophic Level

Plate No.

1. Producers (plants)

2. Consumers (animals)

3. Reducers (bacteria and fungi)

ACKNOWLEDGMENTS

Plates 1–37, which follow on succeeding pages, present over 200 aquatic organisms commonly found in natural, polluted and treated waters. These plates were drawn especially for the Thirteenth Edition of this work by Eugene Schunk of the Cincinnati Art Service, Inc. In a number of instances, it would have been impossible to illustrate a certain organism for the purposes of this manual were it not for the courtesy of other publishers, who permitted illustrations from their publications to be incorporated as valuable components of this presentation. The following organisms were so reproduced:

Plate

5: B—*Diatoma,*
F—*Achnanthes,*
G—*Gomphonema*
H—*Cymbella,* and
K—*Surirella,* courtesy of Veb Gustav Fischer Verlag, Jena. Source: *Die Susswasser-Flora Mitteleuropas,* Heft 10, by F. Hustedt, 1930. [A second edition of this work is scheduled for publication some time in 1970.]

6: C—*Coscinodiscus,* and
D—*Melosira,* courtesy of E. Schweizerbart'sche Verlagsbuchhandlung, Stuttgart. Source: *Das Phytoplankton des Susswassers, Die Binnengewasser,* Band XVI, Teil II, Halfte II, by G. Huber-Pestalozzi and F. Hustedt, 1942. Plates CVIII–CXVI and CXXIII.
F—*Skeletonema*
Courtesy of Academische Verlagsgesellschaft, Leipzig. Source: "Die Kieselalgen," by F. Hustedt. In: L. Rabenhorst, *Kryptogamen-Flora von Deutschland, Osterreich und der Schweiz,* Band VII, 1930.

16: E—*Membranipora monostachys*
Reprinted by permission of G. P. Putnam's Sons, Inc., New York. Source: *Field Book of Seashore Life,* by R. W. Miner. Copyright 1950 by the author. Plate 236, page 817.

17: I—*Notholca*
Robert W. Pennak, *Fresh-Water Invertebrates of the United States.* Copyright © 1953, The Ronald Press Company, New York. Figure 116*N,* page 190, adapted for Figure 17I, courtesy of The Ronald Press.

21: A—*Asellus* (sowbug),
C—*Mysis* (shrimp),
D—*Diaptomus* (copepod),
E—*Cypridopsis* (ostracod),
F—*Cyclops* (copepod), and
G—*Cambarus* (crayfish, crawdad), courtesy of Holden-Day, Inc., San Francisco, California. Source: Needham & Needham's *Guide to the Study of Freshwater Biology,* 1951. Figures 1 and 10, Plate 14, page 37; Figures 16, 18 and 20, Plate 24, page 61; and Figure 9, Plate 14, page 37.

Plate

31: A—*Pomacea* (apple snail),
B—*Marisa,*
E—*Tarebia,*
I—*Lymnaea* (pond snail),
J—*Helisoma* (orb snail), and
M—*Lanx* (limpet) courtesy of John Wiley & Sons, Inc., New York. Source: Ward & Whipple, *Fresh Water Biology* (2nd ed.), W. T. Edmondson, Editor, 1959. Figures 43.31A (A), 43.31B (B), 43.62B (E), 43.13 (I), 43.20 (J) and 43.14 (M).
C—*Campeloma,*
D—*Bithynia* (faucet snail),
F—*Pleurocera* (river snail),
G—*Valvata,*
H—*Littorina* (periwinkle),
K—*Nassa* (mud snail),
L—*Ferrissia* (limpet), and
N—*Physa* courtesy of R. M. Sinclair, *Advisor* for Biological Sampling and Analysis (American Public Health Association), 13th ed.

33: A—*Ophionereis* and *Ophiothrix*
Courtesy of Naturegraph Books, Healdsburg, California. Source: Hedgpeth's *Common Seashore Life of Southern California,* 1961. Figure 28A, page 16.
B—*Asterias* (starfish), and
C—*Solaster* (starfish), courtesy of Western Publishing Company, Inc., Golden Press Division, Racine, Wisconsin. Source: *Seashores,* a Golden Nature Guide, 1955. Figure 6, page 62 and Figure 4, page 62.
D—*Echinarachnius*
Reprinted by permission of G. P. Putnam's Sons, New York. Source: *Field Book of Seashore Life,* by R. W. Miner. Copyright 1950 by the author. Plate 222, page 769.
F—*Thyone*
Used by permission of McGraw-Hill Book Company, New York. Source: *The Invertebrates,* Vol. 14 (Echinodermata), by L. H. Hyman. Copyright © 1955 by McGraw-Hill, Inc. Figure 51A, page 129.

34: C—*Limulus* (horseshoe crab)
Courtesy of Western Publishing Company, Inc., Golden Press Division, Racine, Wisconsin. Source: *Seashores,* a Golden Nature Guide, 1955. Page 79.

36: C—*Ambystoma* (terrestrial adult)
Courtesy of Dover Publications, Inc., New York. Source: *Biology of the Amphibia,* by G. K. Noble, 1931. Figure 147C, page 471.
D—*Ambystoma* (aquatic larva)
Courtesy of the New York State Museum and Science Service, Albany, New York. Source: *The Salamanders of New York,* by Sherman C. Bishop, 1941. Figure 33b, page 166. [Bulletin 324, New York State Museum, Albany.]
E—*Necturus*
Courtesy of Dover Publications, Inc., New York. Source: *Biology of the Amphibia,* by G. K. Noble, 1931. Figure 35B, page 99.

G—*Siren intermedia* (siren)
Reprinted from Sherman Bishop: *Handbook of Salamanders.* Copyright 1943 by Comstock Publishing Company, Inc. Used by permission of Cornell University Press.

37: A—(a) micrococcus, (b) streptococcus, (c) sarcina, (d) bacillus, (e) vibrio, (f) spirillum
Courtesy of John Wiley & Sons, Inc., New York. Source: Ward & Whipple, *Fresh Water Biology* (2nd ed.), W. T. Edmondson, Editor, 1959. Figure 3.1.

(k) actinomycete growth form
Selman A. Waksman, *The Actinomycetes.* Copyright © 1957, The Ronald Press Company, New York. Figure 2–6, page 18, adapted for Figure 37A(k), courtesy The Ronald Press.

B—(b) *Tetracladium* and (e)(f), *Achlya*
Courtesy of John Wiley & Sons, Inc., New York. Source: Ward & Whipple, *Fresh Water Biology* (2nd ed.), W. T. Edmondson, Editor, 1959. Figures 4.119 and 4.79.

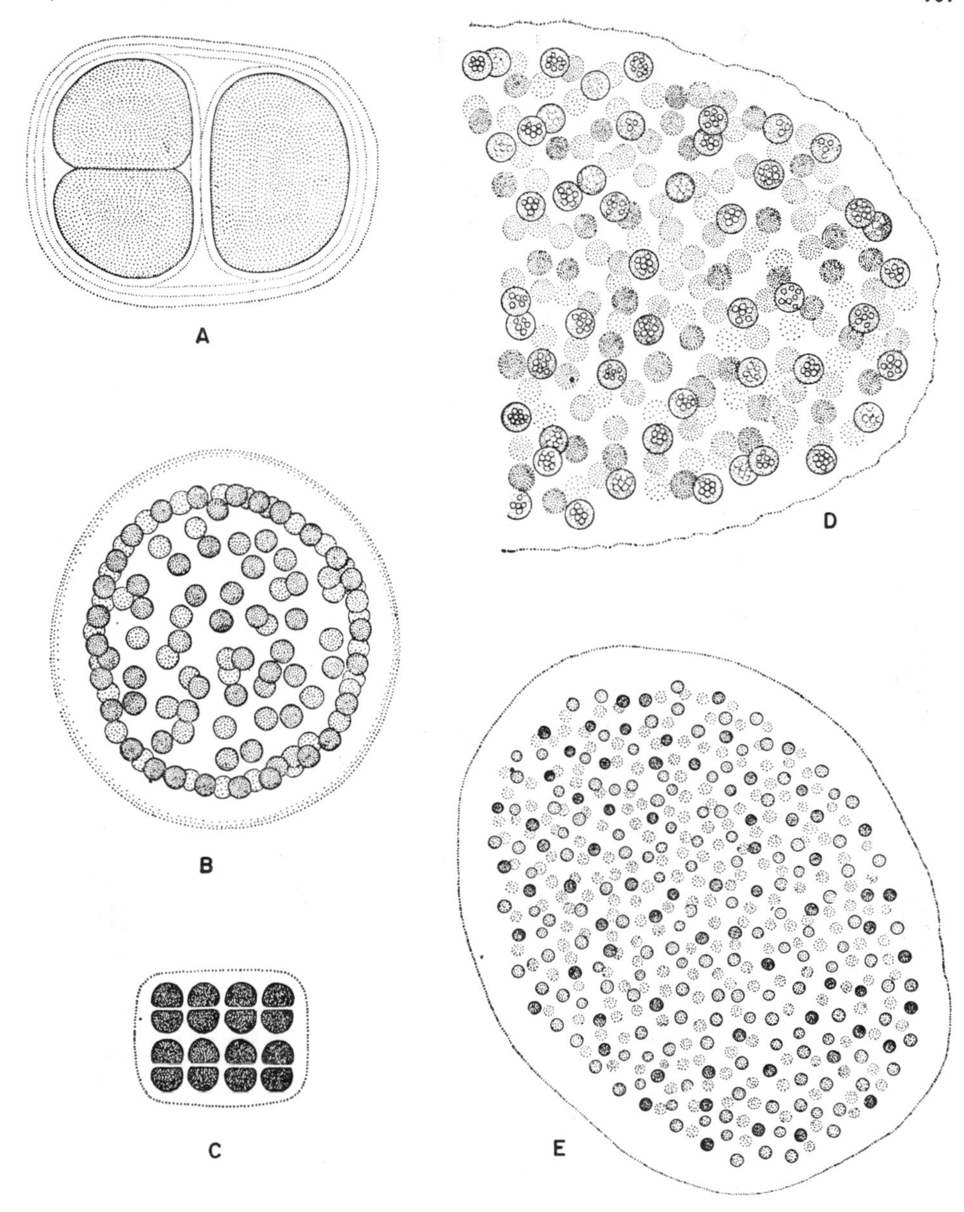

Plate 1. Blue-green algae: Coccoid (Phylum Cyanophyta). Dimensions refer to individual cells.

A—*Anacystis*	(4–20 μ)	D—*Anacystis* sp.	(4–6 μ)
B—*Gomphosphaeria*	(3–6 μ)	E—*Anacystis* sp.	(3–4 μ)
C—*Agmenellum*	(2–6 μ)		

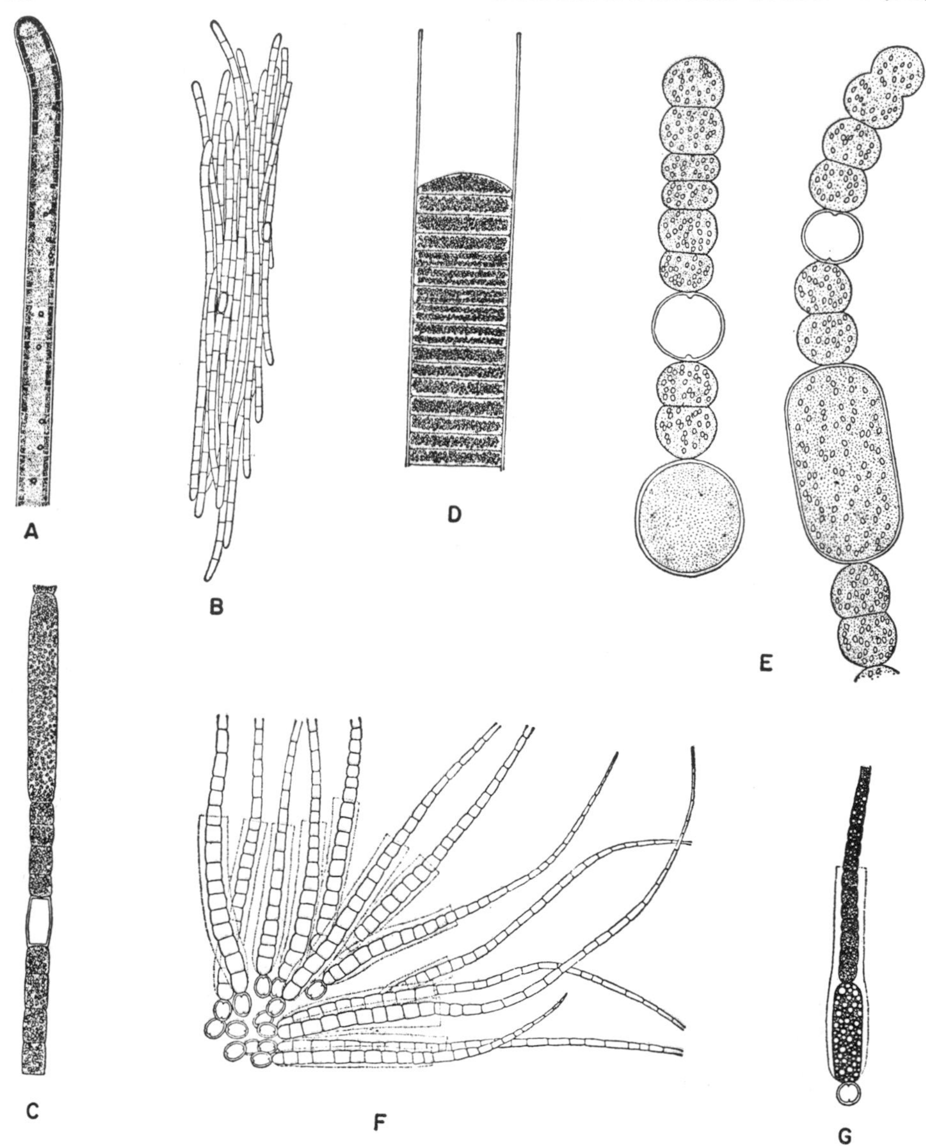

Plate 2. Blue-green algae: Filamentous (Phylum Cyanophyta). Most dimensions refer to diameter of individual filaments.

A—*Oscillatoria*	(4–20 μ)	E—*Anabaena*	(5–12 μ)
B—*Aphanizomenon*, aggregate of filaments	(5–6 μ)	F—*Gleotrichia*, portion of colony	(Cells 7–9 μ diameter near akinete)
C—*Aphanizomenon*, detail			
D—*Lyngbya*	(4–20 μ)	G—*Gleotrichia*, detail	

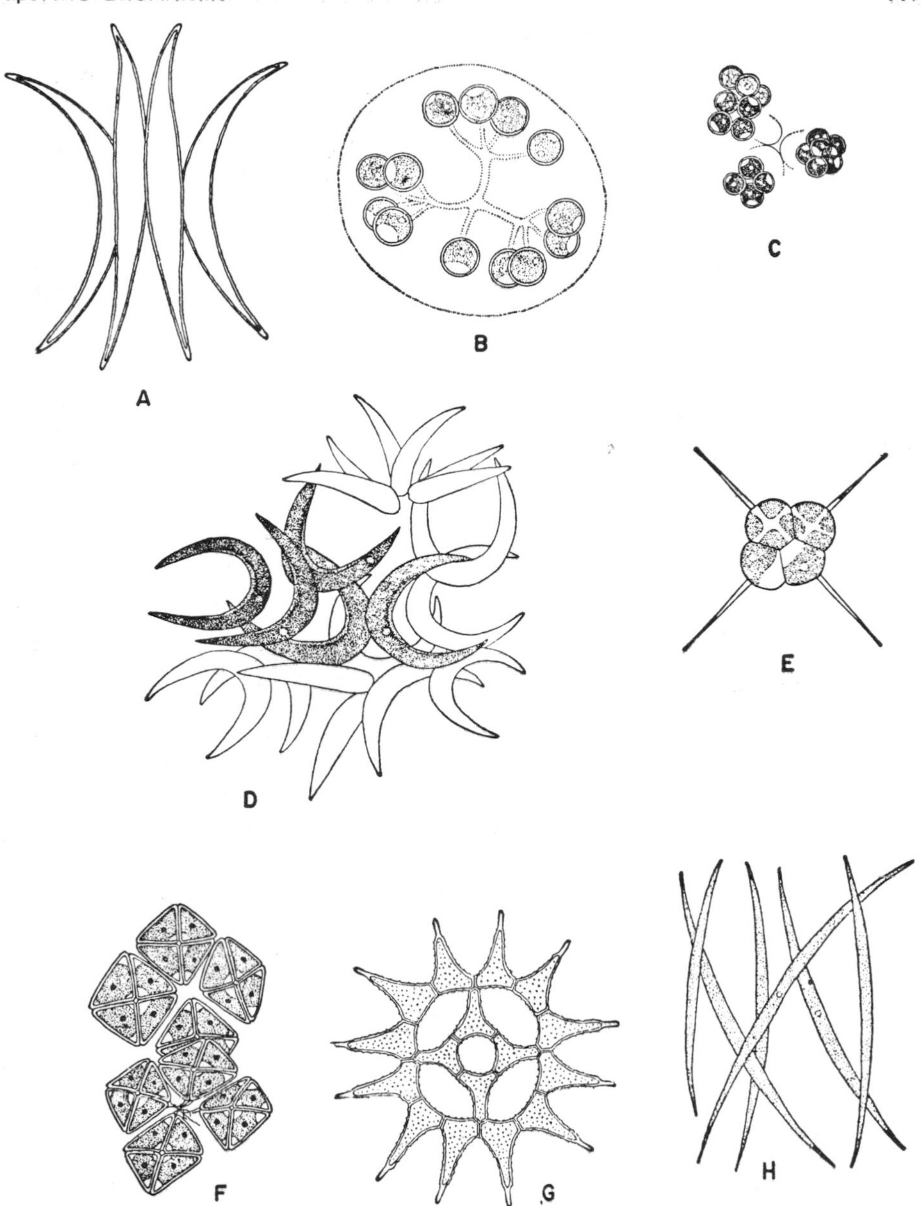

Plate 3. Nonmotile green algae: Coccoid (Phylum Chlorophyta). Dimensions refer to individual cells.

A—*Scenedesmus*	(4–6 μ diameter)	E—*Tetrastrum*	(5–9 μ)
B—*Dictyosphaerium*	(8–14 μ)	F—*Crucigenia*	(5–8 μ)
C—*Westella*	(5–7 μ)	G—*Pediastrum*	(10–20 μ)
D—*Selenastrum*	(6–7 μ)	H—*Ankistrodesmus*	(2–3 μ)

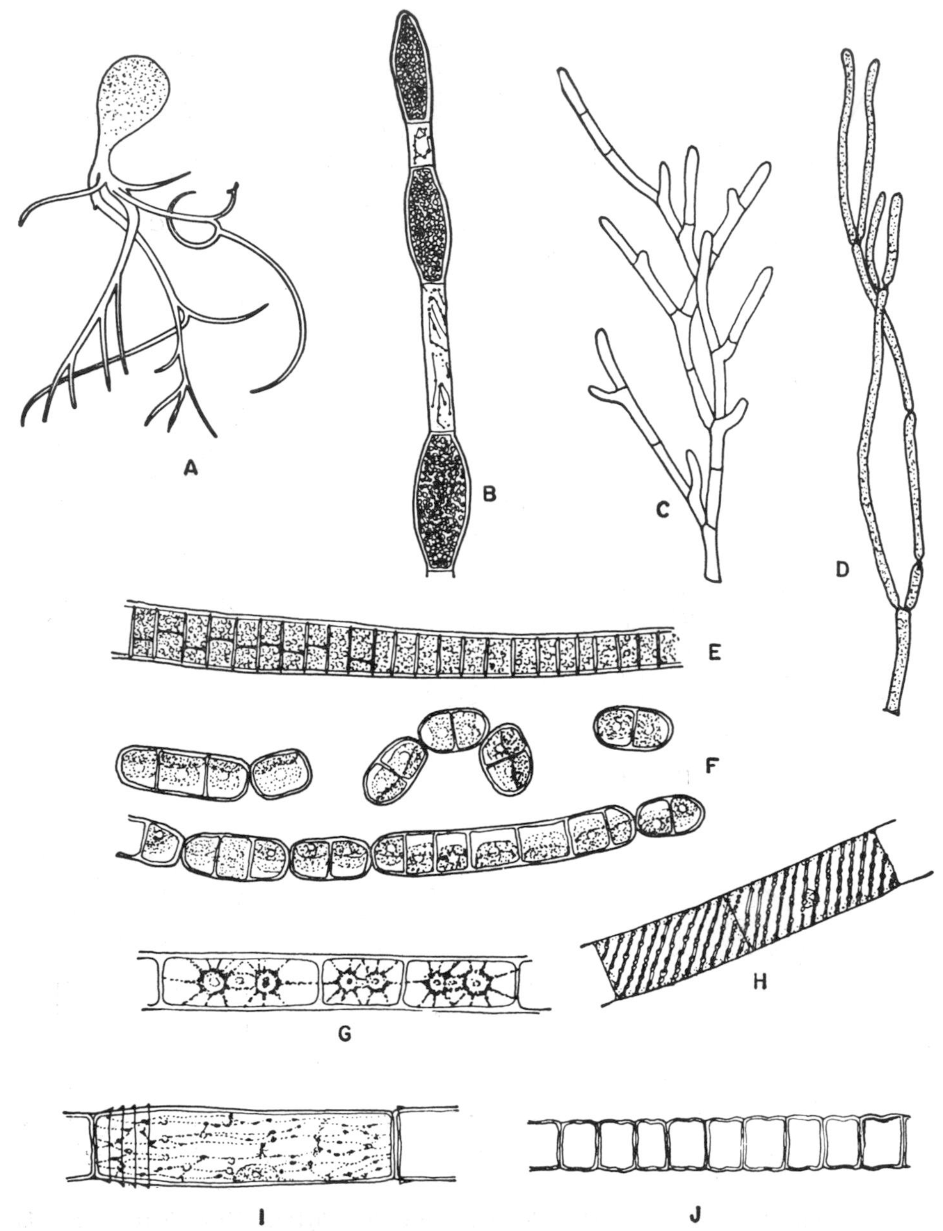

Plate 4. Nonmotile green algae: Filamentous (Phylum Chlorophyta). Dimensions refer to diameters of filaments or to mass.

A—*Botrydium*	(1000–2000 μ)	F—*Stichococcus*	(3 μ)
B—*Pithophora*	(50–100 μ)	G—*Zygnema*	(20–35 μ)
C—*Microthamnion*	(2–4 u)	H—*Spirogyra*	(15–100 μ)
D—*Dichotomosiphon*	(50–100 μ)	I—*Oedogonium*	(6–40 μ)
E—*Schizomeris*	(12–18 μ)	J—*Hyalotheca*	(12–30 μ)

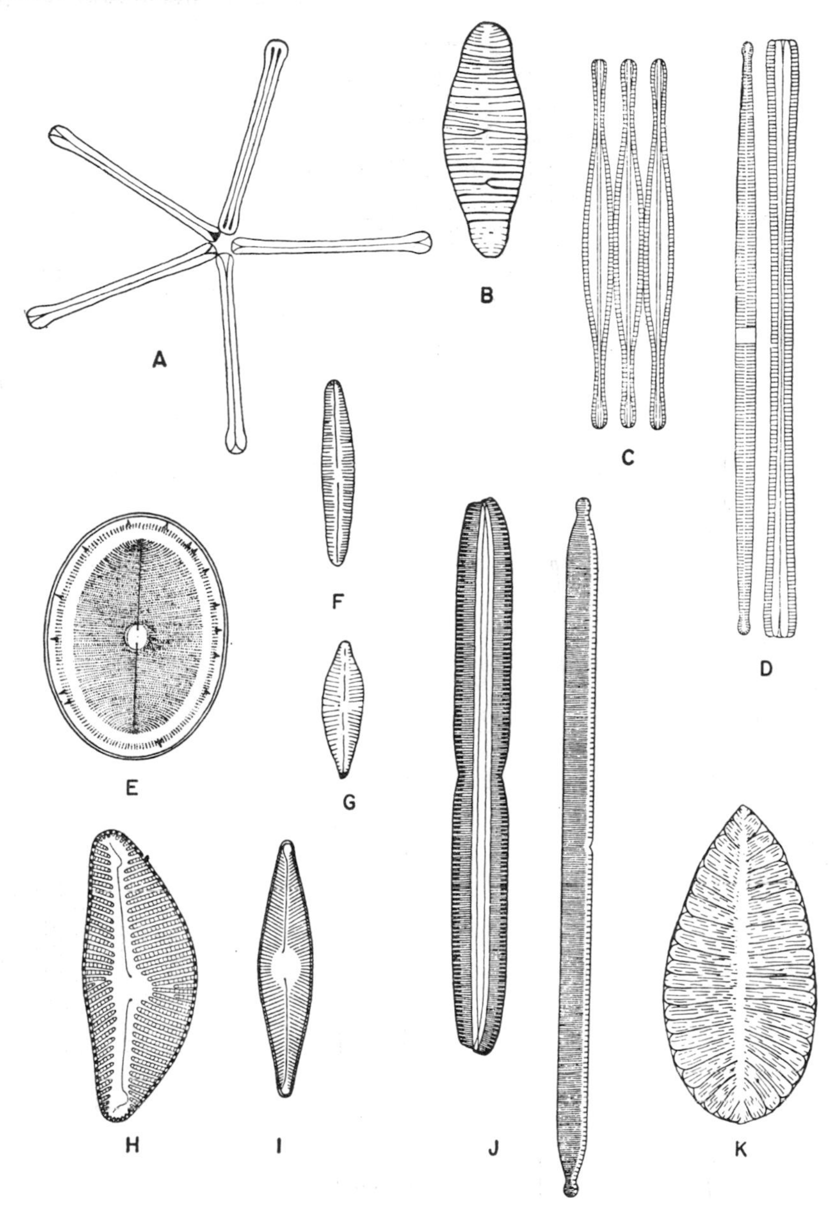

Plate 5. Diatoms: Pennate (Phylum Chrysophyta, Class Bacillariophyceae). Dimensions refer to length of cells unless otherwise specified.

A—*Asterionella*	(300 μ, entire colony)
B—*Diatoma*	(20 μ)
C—*Fragilaria*	(100 μ)
D—*Synedra*	(200 μ)
E—*Cocconeis*	(10 μ)
F—*Achnanthes*	(10 μ)
G—*Gomphonema*	(20 μ)
H—*Cymbella*	(15 μ)
I—*Navicula*	(30 μ)
J—*Nitzschia*	(100 μ)
K—*Surirella*	(20 μ)

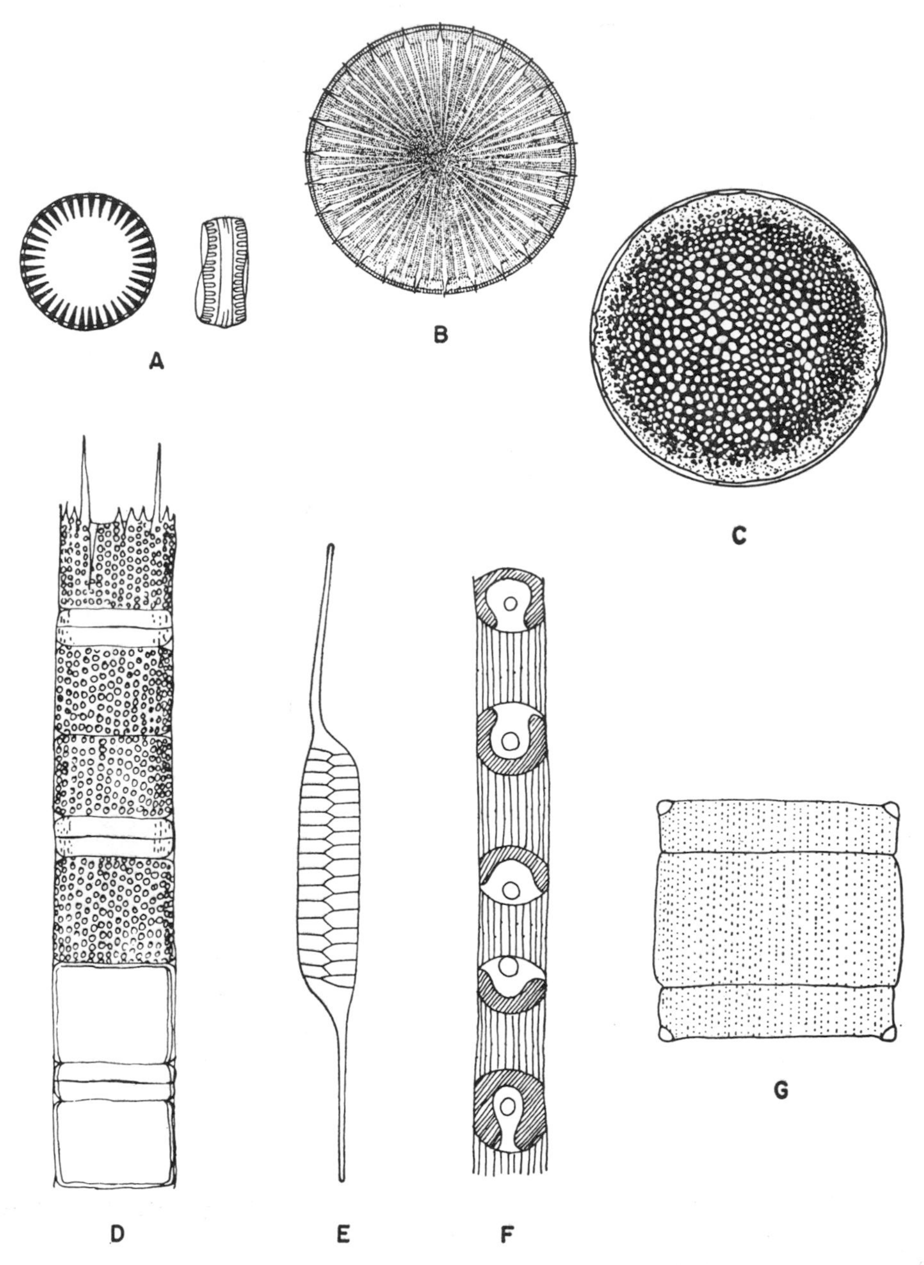

Plate 6. Diatoms: Centric (Phylum Chrysophyta, Class Bacillariophyceae). Dimensions refer to diameter.

A—*Cyclotella*	(10 μ)	E—*Rhizosolenia*	(5–15 μ)
B—*Stephanodiscus*	(30 μ)	F—*Skeletonema*	(3–18 μ)
C—*Coscinodiscus*	(20 μ)	G—*Biddulphia*	(100 μ)
D—*Melosira*	(3–12 μ)		

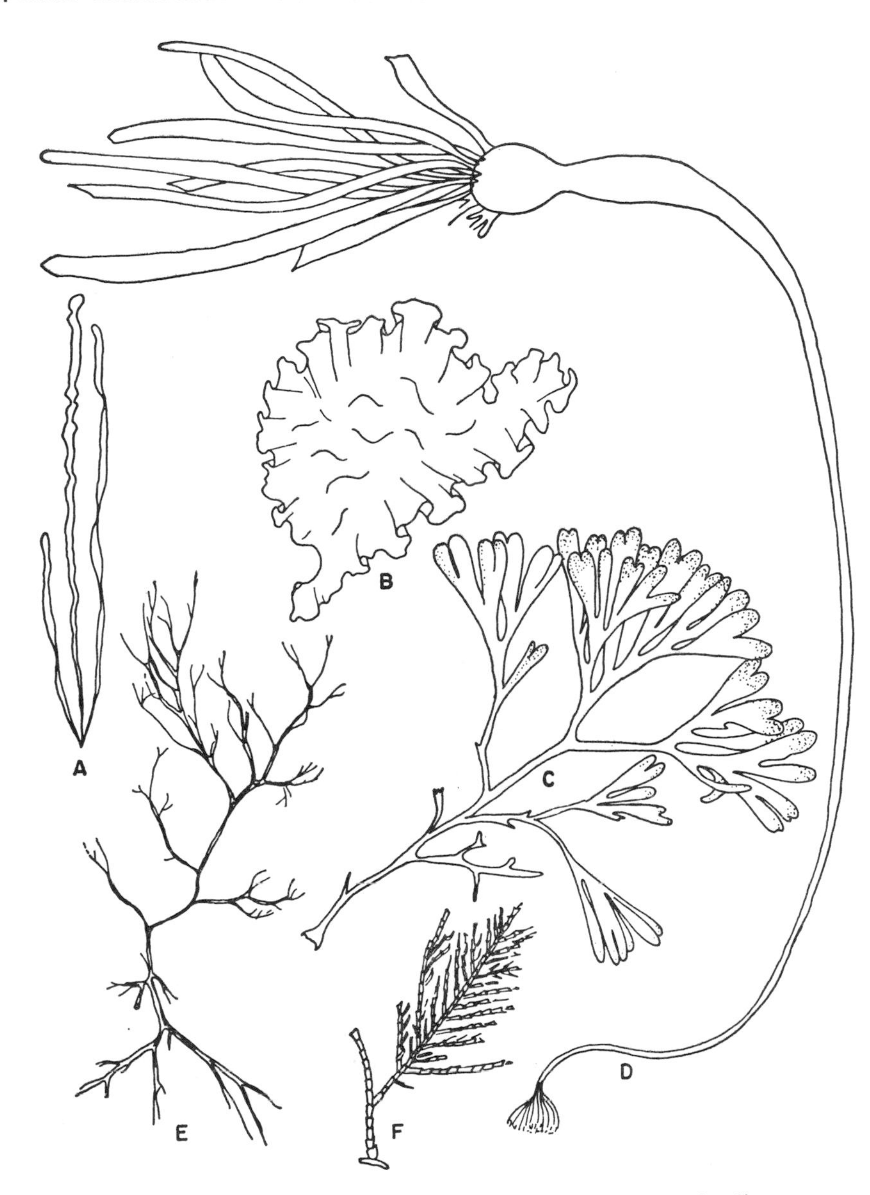

Plate 7. Types of larger marine algae (green, brown and red).

Green algae (Phylum Chlorophyta):
A—*Enteromorpha* (40 cm)
B—Sea lettuce, *Ulva* (20 cm)

Brown algae (Phylum Phaeophyta):
C—Rockweed, *Fucus* (75 cm)
D—Giant kelp, *Nereocystis* (20 m)

Red algae (Phylum Rhodophyta):
E—*Gracilaria* (50 cm)
F—*Corallina* (4 cm)

Plate 8. Higher plants: Floating plants.

A—Great duckweed, *Spirodela* (Phylum Spermatophyta, 8 mm)
B—Water velvet, *Azolla* (Phylum Pteridophyta, 1 cm)
C—Water hyacinth, *Eichhornia* (Phylum Spermatophyta, 22 cm)
D—Lesser duckweed, *Lemna* (Phylum Spermatophyta, 5 mm)
E—Water fern, *Salvinia* (Phylum Pteridophyta, 4 cm)
F—Watermeal, *Wolffia* (Phylum Spermatophyta, 1–1.5 mm)

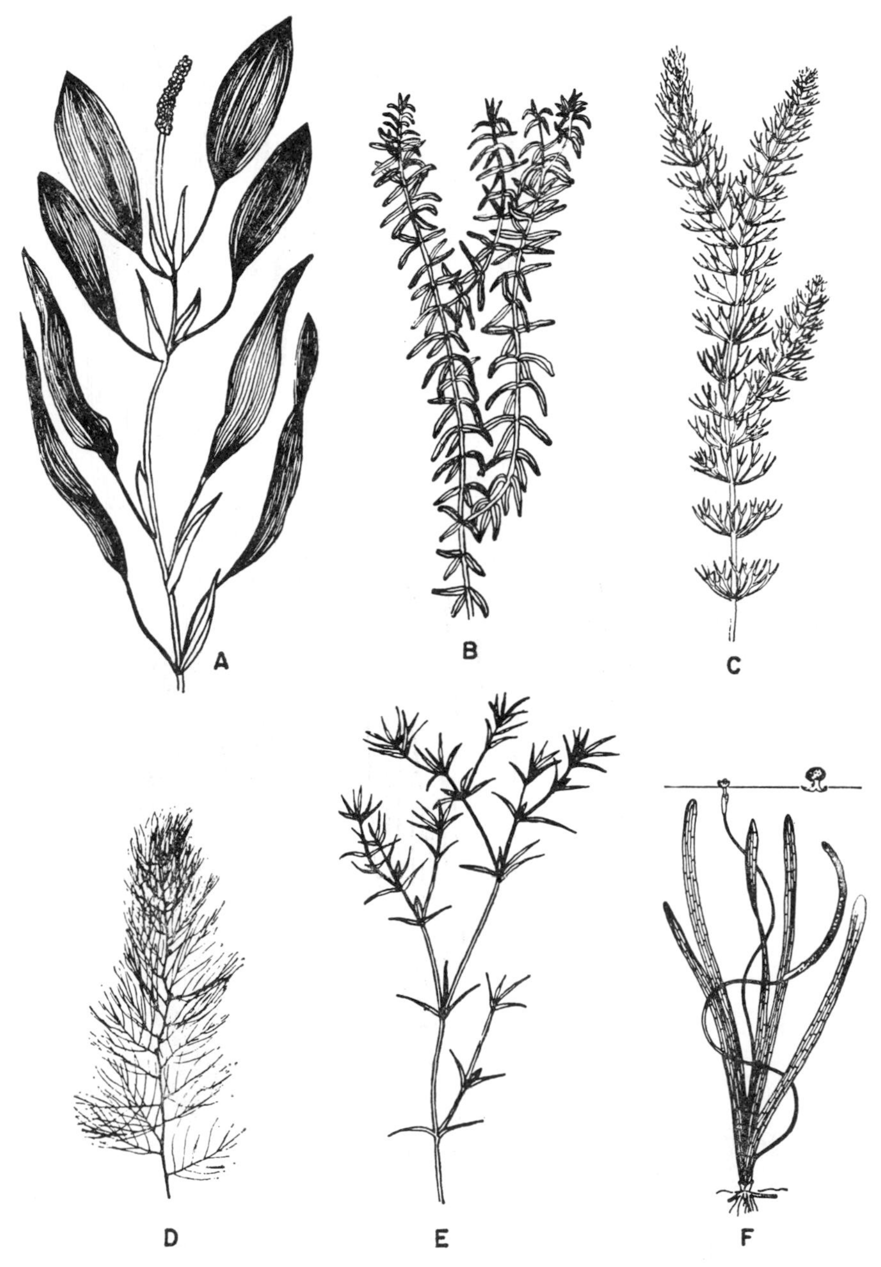

Plate 9. Higher plants: Submersed (all forms illustrated are Spermatophytes).

A—Pondweed, *Potamogeton* (30–60 cm)
B—Waterweed, *Elodea* (15 cm)
C—Coontail, *Ceratophyllum* (30 cm)
D—Water milfoil, *Myriophyllum* (30 cm)
E—Naiad, *Najas* (60 cm)
F—Eelgrass, *Vullisneria* (45 cm)

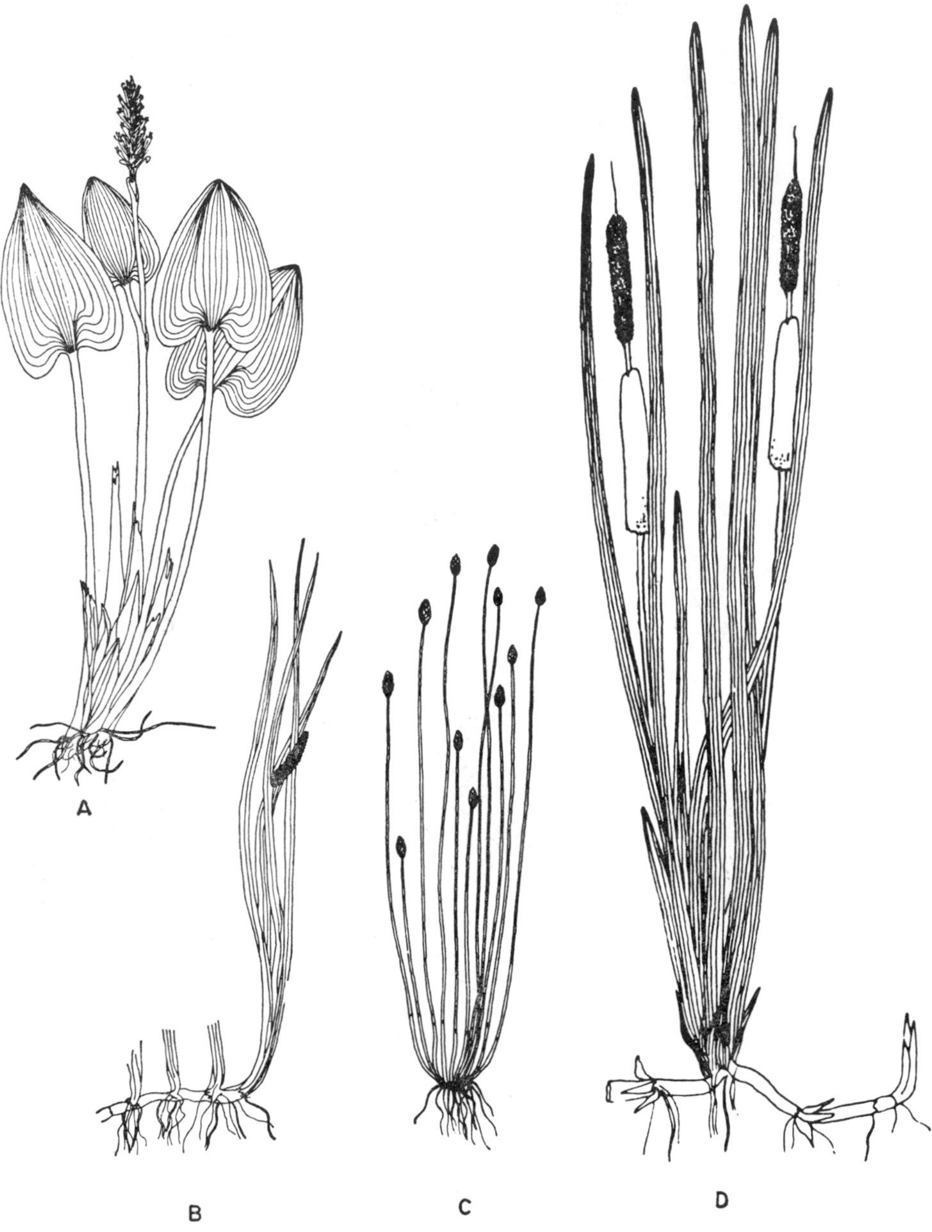

Plate 10. Higher plants: Emersed (all forms illustrated are Spermatophytes).

A—Pickerelweed, *Pontederia* (60 cm)
B—Sweetflag, *Acorus* (30 cm)
C—Spike rush, *Eleocharis* (30 cm)
D—Cattail, *Typha* (1–2 m)

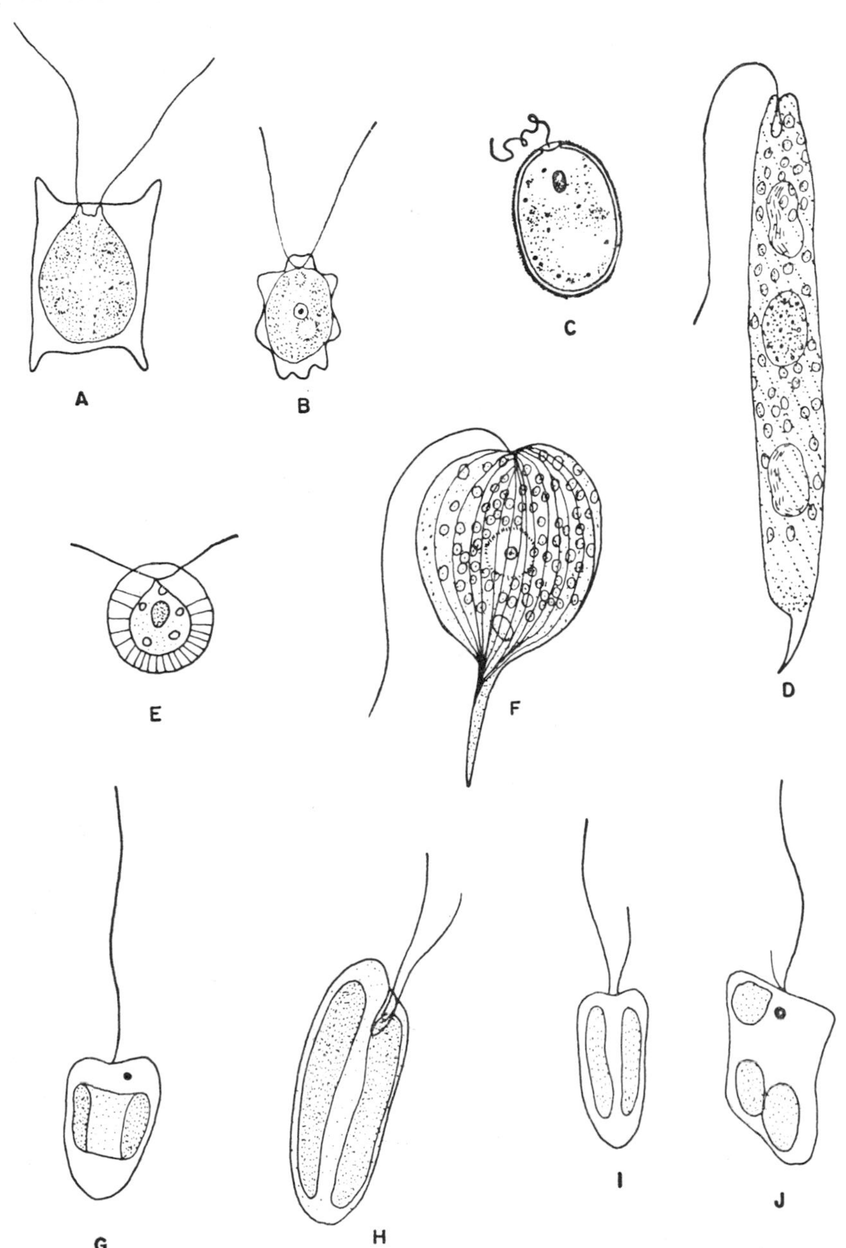

Plate 11. Pigmented flagellates: Single-celled (various phyla).

A—*Pteromonas*	(9–18 μ)	F—*Phacus*	(20–50 μ)
B—*Lobomonas*	(5–14 μ)	G—*Chromulina*	(4–10 μ)
C—*Trachelomonas*	(15–30 μ)	H—*Cryptomonas*	(6–12 μ)
D—*Euglena*	(10–25 μ)	I—*Ochromonas*	(7–14 μ)
E—*Haematococcus*	(40–45 μ)	J—*Chloramoeba*	(10–15 μ)

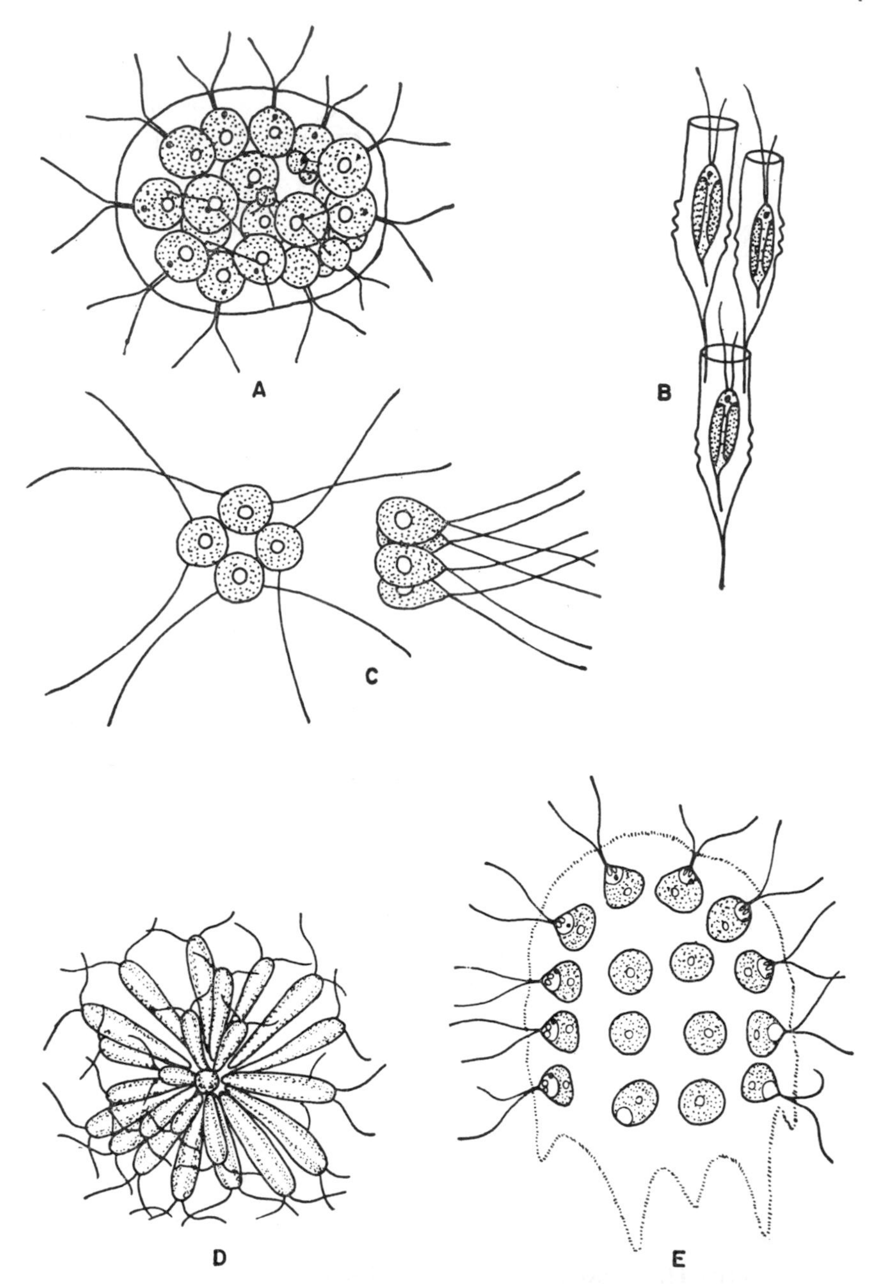

Plate 12. Pigmented flagellates: Colonial types (various phyla). Dimensions refer to individual cells unless otherwise specified.

A—*Pleodorina*	(8–10 μ)	D—*Synura*	(10–15 μ)
B—*Dinobryon*	(7–12 μ)	E—*Platydorina*	(66–70 μ, colony)
C—*Gonium*	(7–12 μ)		

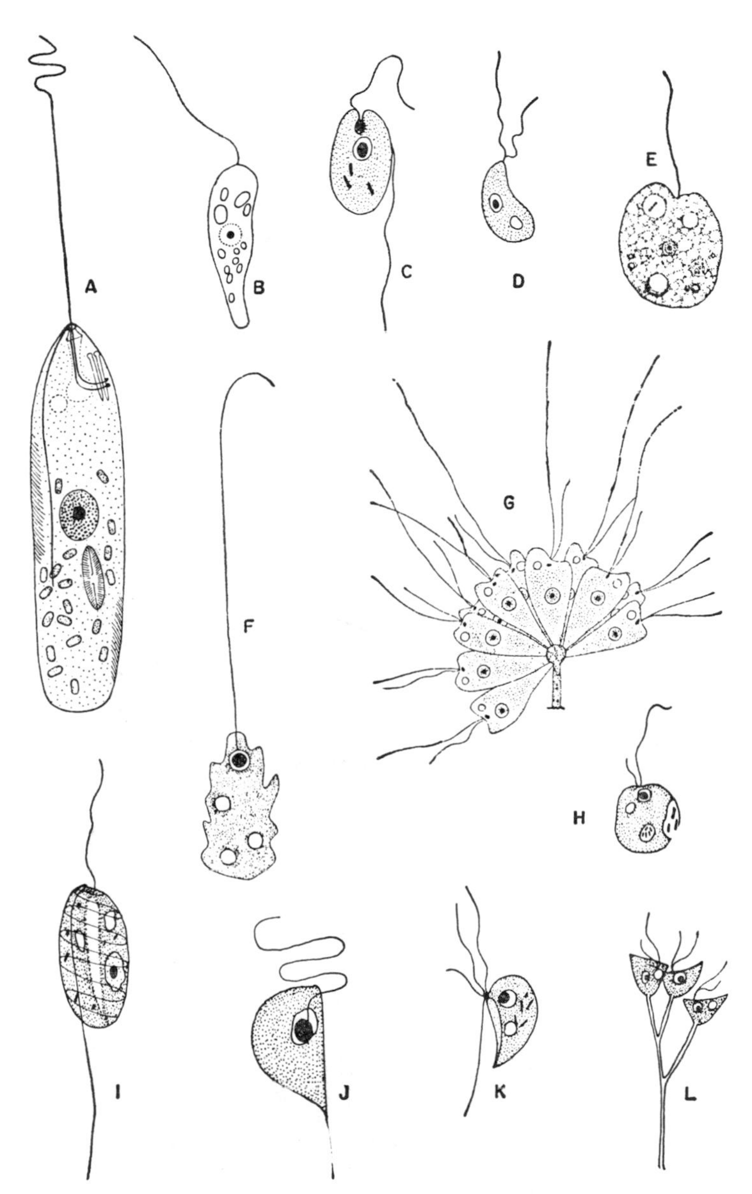

Plate 13. Nonpigmented flagellates (Phylum Protozoa).

A—*Peranema*	(40–70 μ)	G—*Anthophysa*	(5–6 μ)
B—*Astasia*	(40–50 μ)	H—*Monas*	(5–16 μ)
C—*Bodo*	(11–22 μ)	I—*Anisonema*	(14–60 μ)
D—*Dinomonas*	(15–16 μ)	J—*Cercomonas*	(10–36 μ)
E—*Oikomonas*	(5–20 μ)	K—*Tetramitus*	(11–30 μ)
F—*Mastigamoeba*	(28–200 μ)	L—*Dendromonas*	(8 μ)

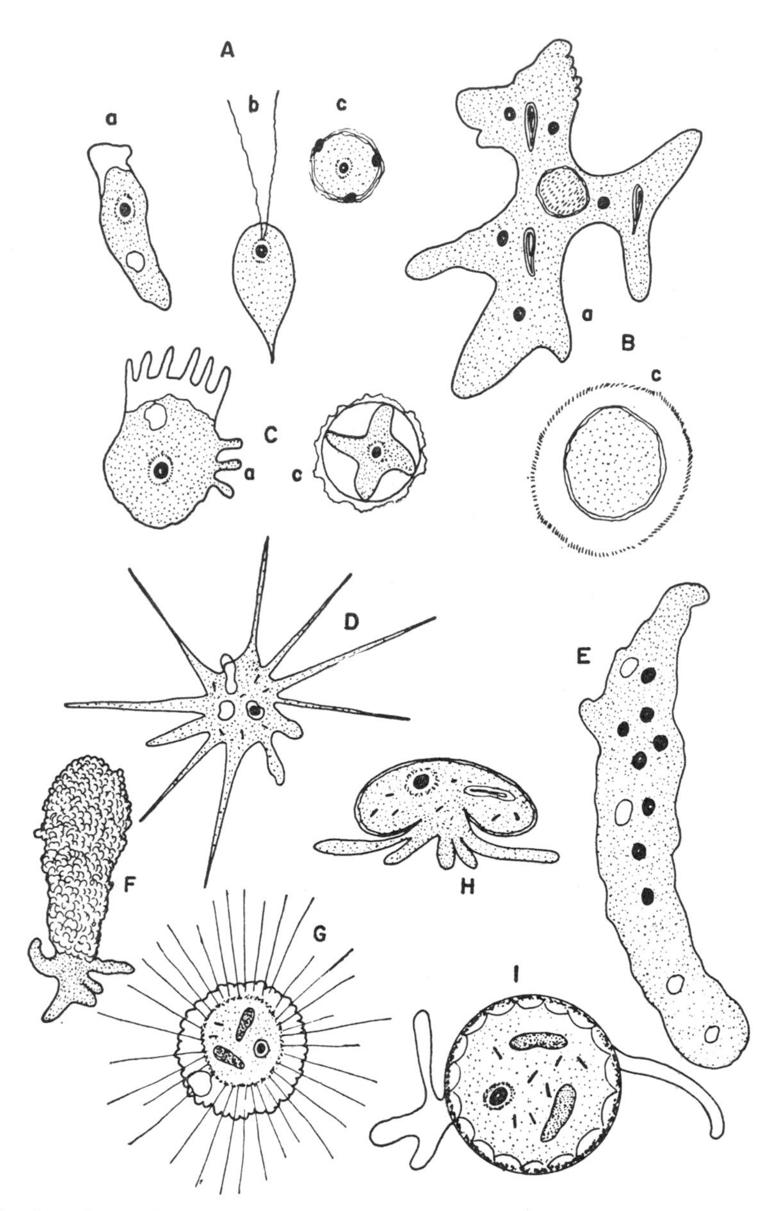

Plate 14. Amoebas (Phylum Protozoa). (a) Amoeboid stages, (b) flagellated stages, (c) cyst stages.

A—*Naegleria*	(10–36 μ)	E—*Pelomyxa*	(0.25–3 mm)
B—*Amoeba* sp.	(30–600 μ)	F—*Difflugia*	(40 μ)
C—*Acanthamoeba* (*Hartmannella*)	(15–25 μ)	G—*Actinophrys*	(25–50 μ)
D—*Amoeba radiosa*	(30–120 μ)	H—*Arcella* (side view)	(30–260 μ)
		I—*Arcella* (top view)	(30–260 μ)

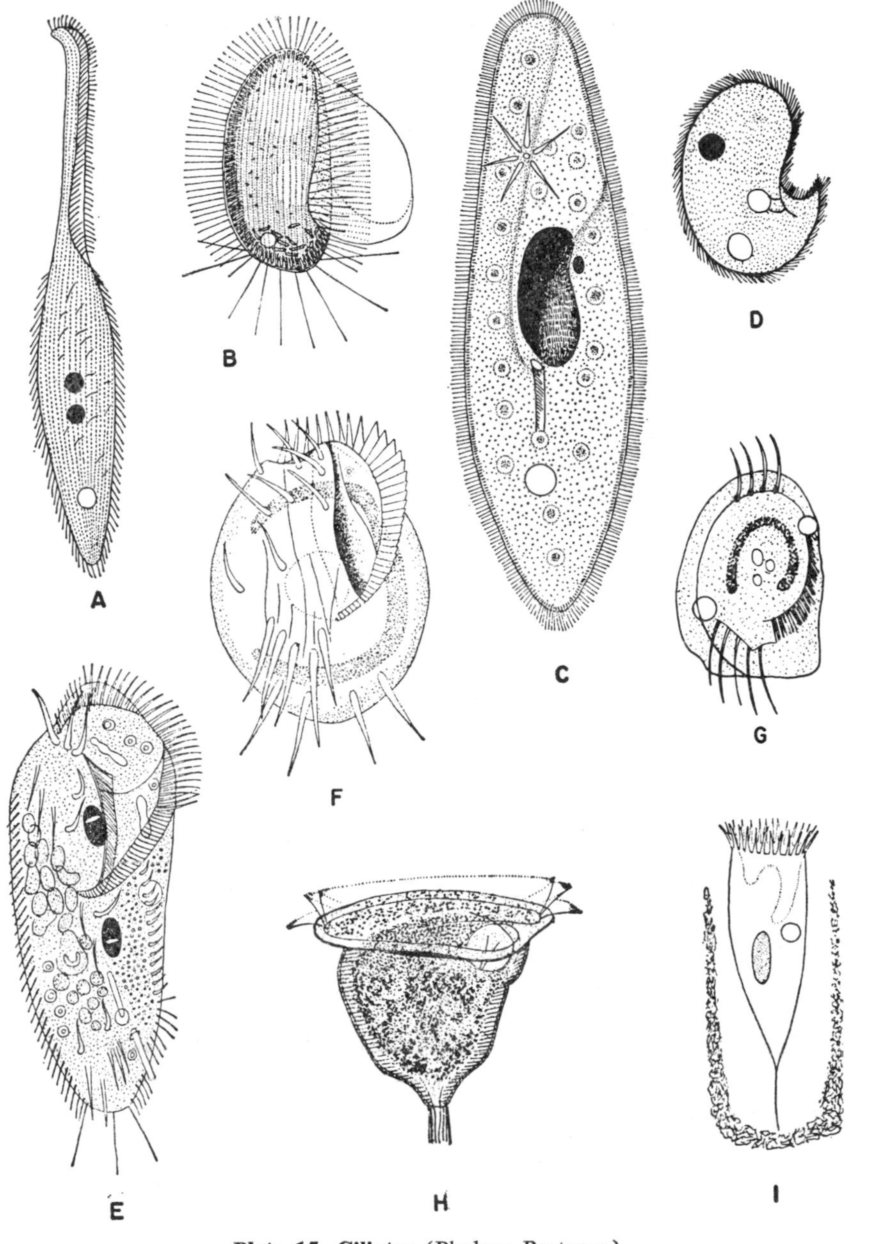

Plate 15. Ciliates (Phylum Protozoa).

A—*Lionotus*	(100 μ)	F—*Euplotes*	(70–195 μ)
B—*Pleuronema*	(38–120 μ)	G—*Aspidisca*	(30–50 μ)
C—*Paramoecium*	(50–330 μ)	H—*Vorticella*	(40–175 μ)
D—*Colpoda*	(12–110 μ)	I—*Tintinnidium*	(40–200 μ)
E—*Stylonychia*	(100–300 μ)		

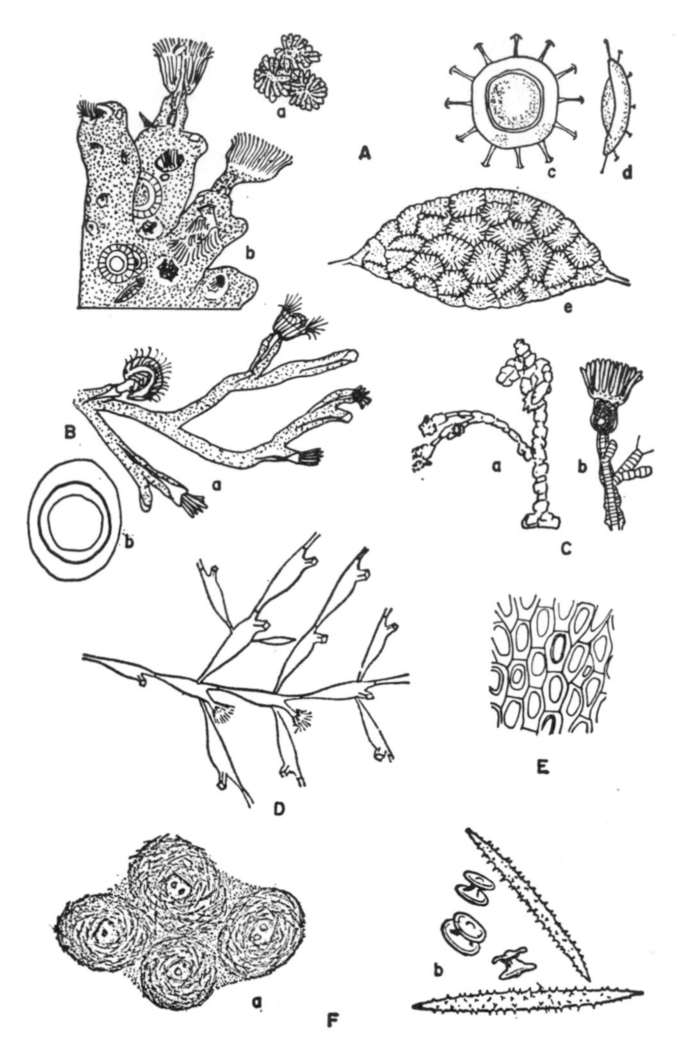

Plate 16. Sponges (Phylum Porifera) **and Bryozoans** (Phylum Bryozoa).

Bryozoa:

A—Jellyball, *Pectinatella*
- (a) Young colony (15 mm)
- (b) Section (highly magnified)
- (c) Statoblast (1 mm)
- (d) Statoblast (1 mm)
- (e) Colony on a plant stem (10 cm)

B—*Plumatella*
- (a) Colony (4 cm)
- (b) Statoblast (0.5 mm)

C—*Urnatella* (5 mm)
- (a) Colony (7 mm)
- (b) Individual zooid at tip of stalk (0.5 mm)

D—*Paludicella* (6 mm)

E—*Membranipora,* an encrusting marine form (individuals 1 mm, colonies unlimited)

Porifera:

F—*Trochospongilla*
- (a) Gemmules in a colony (1 mm)
- (b) Spicules (0.2 mm)

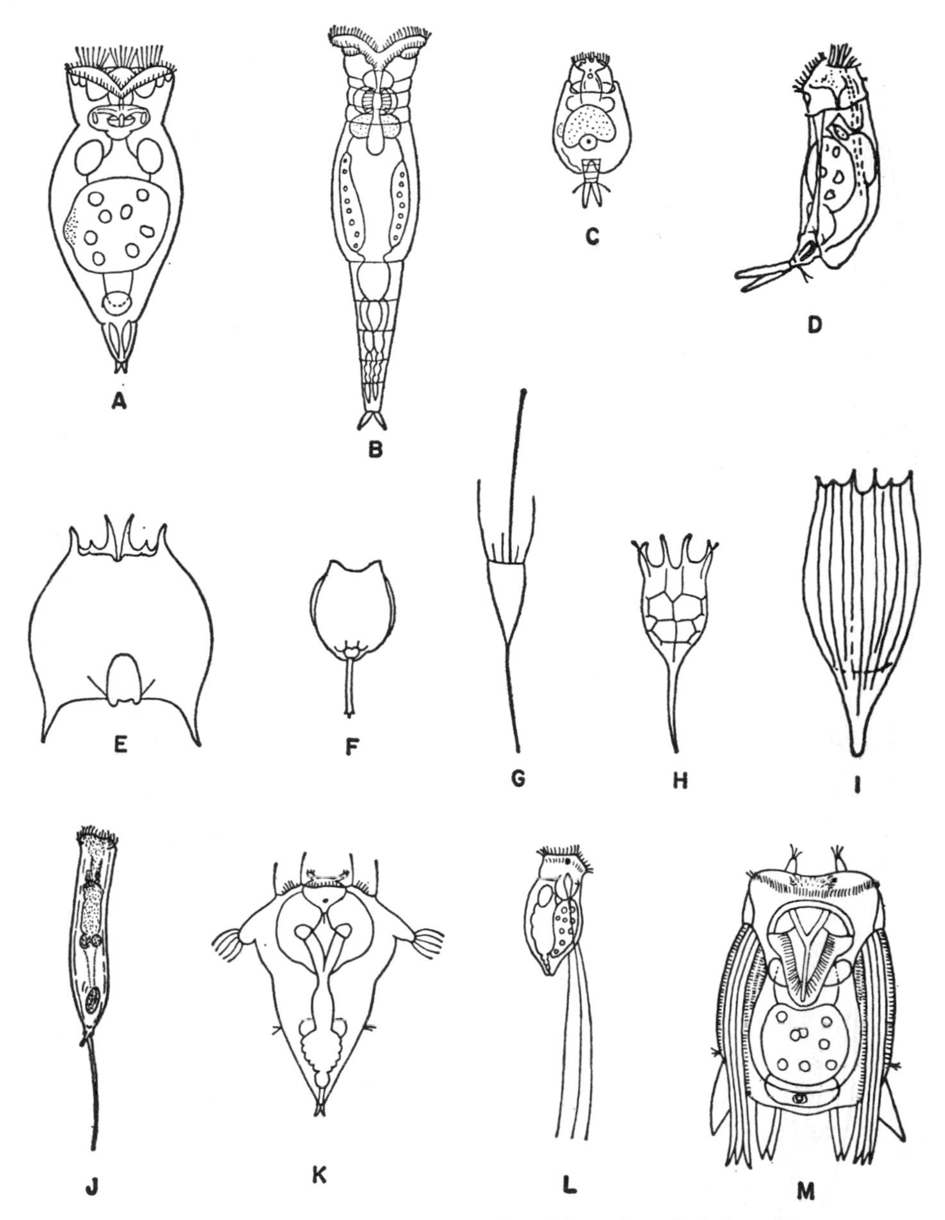

Plate 17. Rotifers (Phylum Rotatoria). Dimensions include spines.

A—*Epiphanes*	(600 μ)	H—*Keratella*	(200 μ)
B—*Philodina*	(400 μ)	I—*Notholca*	(200 μ)
C—*Euchlanis*	(250 μ)	J—*Trichocerca*	(600 μ)
D—*Proales*	(450 μ)	K—*Synchaeta*	(260 μ)
E—*Brachionus*	(200 μ)	L—*Filinia*	(150 μ)
F—*Monostyla*	(150 μ)	M—*Polyarthra*	(175 μ)
G—*Kellicottia*	(1 mm)		

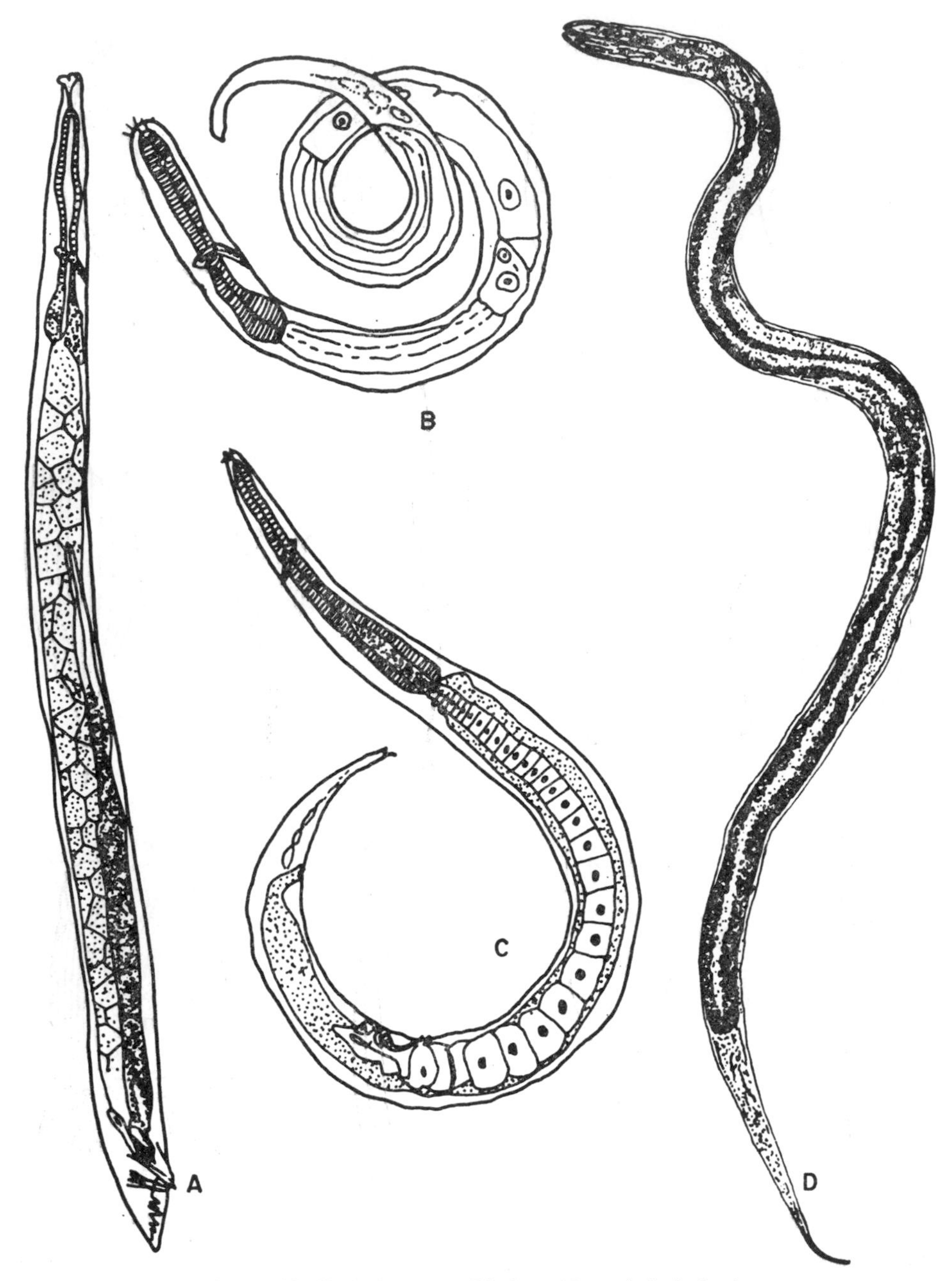

Plate 18. Roundworms (Phylum Nemathelminthes).

A—*Rhabditis* (male) (1.6–1.9 mm)
B—*Achromadora* (female) (0.3–0.7 mm)
C—*Monhystera* (female) (0.8–1.0 mm)
D—*Diplogasteroides* (female) (1.5–1.85 mm)

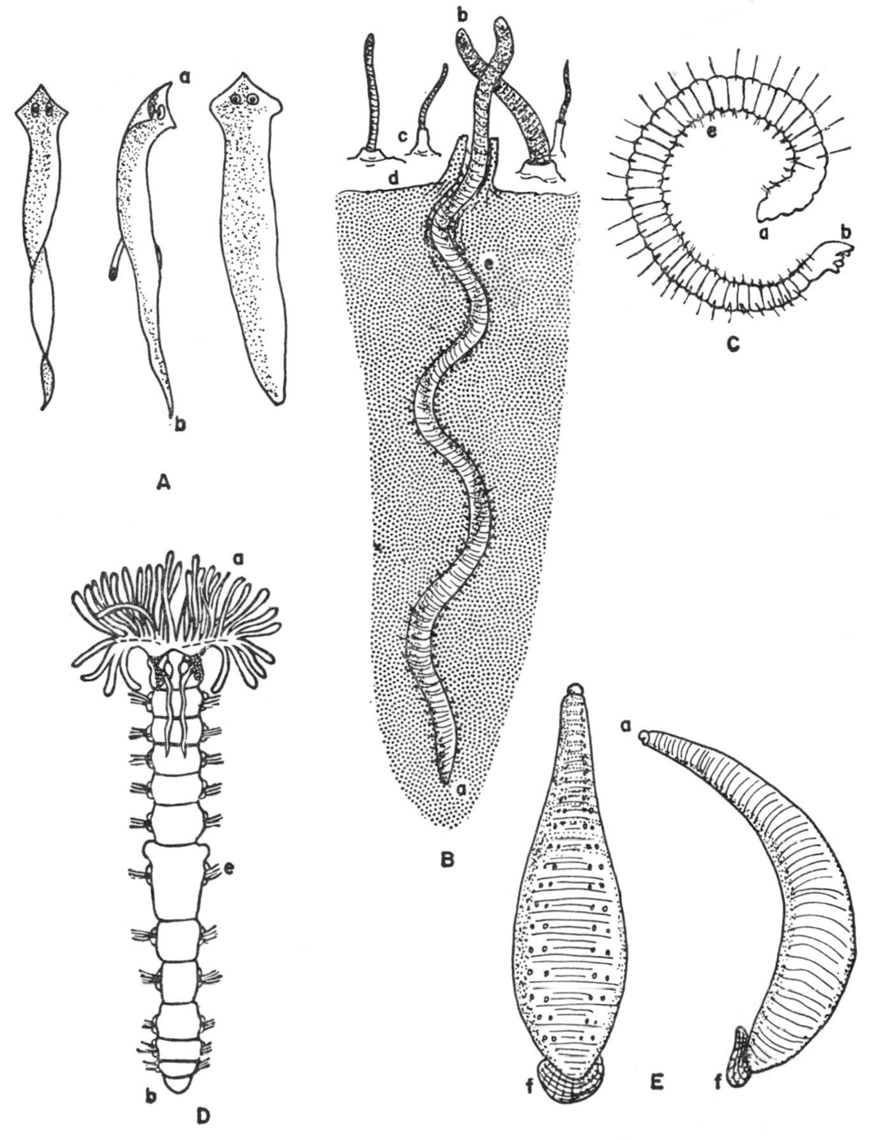

Plate 19. Flatworms (Phylum Platyhelminthes) **and segmented worms** (Phylum Annelida). (a) Anterior end, (b) posterior end, (c) tubes, (d) mud surface, (e) setae, (f) sucker disk.

Platyhelminthes:

A—*Planaria,* a free-living flatworm (5–13 mm)

Annelida:

B—*Tubifex,* a sludgeworm (25–50 mm)

C—*Dero,* a bristle worm (3–7 mm)

D—*Manayunkia,* a freshwater tube-building polychaet worm similar to certain common marine forms (5 mm)

E—Leech (50 mm)

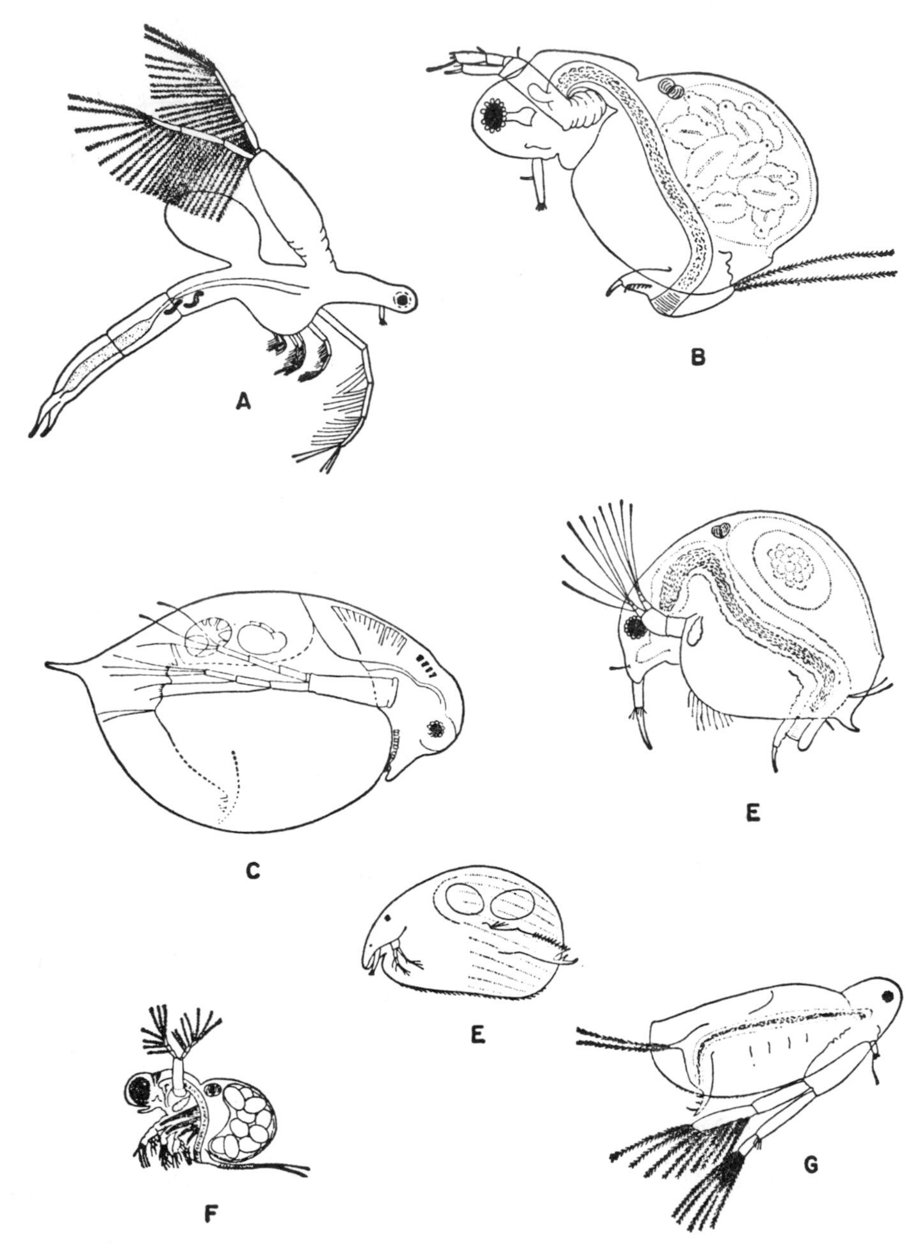

Plate 20. Crustaceans (Phylum Arthropoda, Class Crustacea): Types of cladocerans (Order Cladocera).

A—*Leptodora*	(9 mm)	E—*Bosmina*	(0.4 mm)
B—*Moina*	(1.5 mm)	F—*Polyphemus*	(1.5 mm)
C—*Daphnia*	(2 mm)	G—*Diaphanosoma*	(1.5 mm)
D—*Alona*	(0.4 mm)		

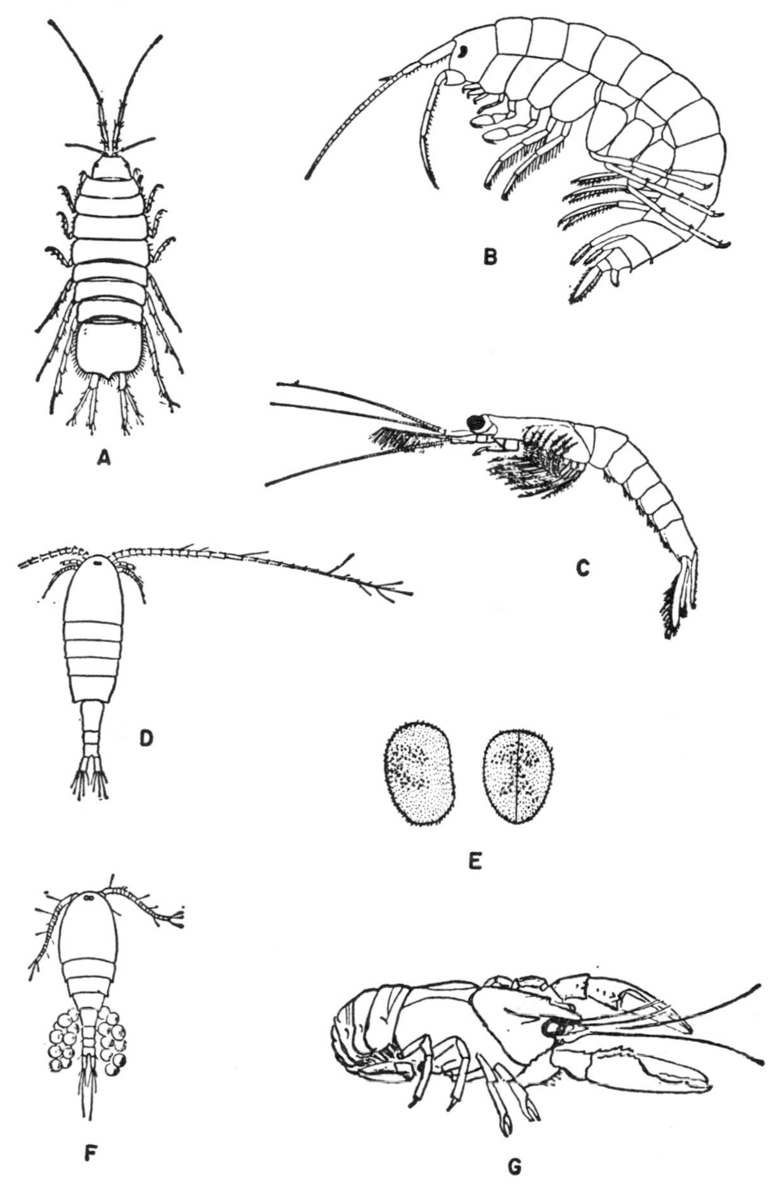

Plate 21. Crustaceans (Phylum Arthropoda, Class Crustacea): Selected common types.

A—Sowbug, *Asellus,* Order Isopoda (20 mm)
B—Scud, *Gammarus,* Order Amphipoda (15 mm)
C—Shrimp, *Mysis,* Order Decapoda (20 mm)
D—Copepod, *Diaptomus,* Order Copepoda (2 mm)
E—Ostracod, *Cypridopsis,* Order Ostracoda (1 mm)
F—Copepod, *Cyclops,* Order Copepoda (1 mm)
G—Crayfish, crawdad, *Cambarus,* Order Decapoda (150 cm)

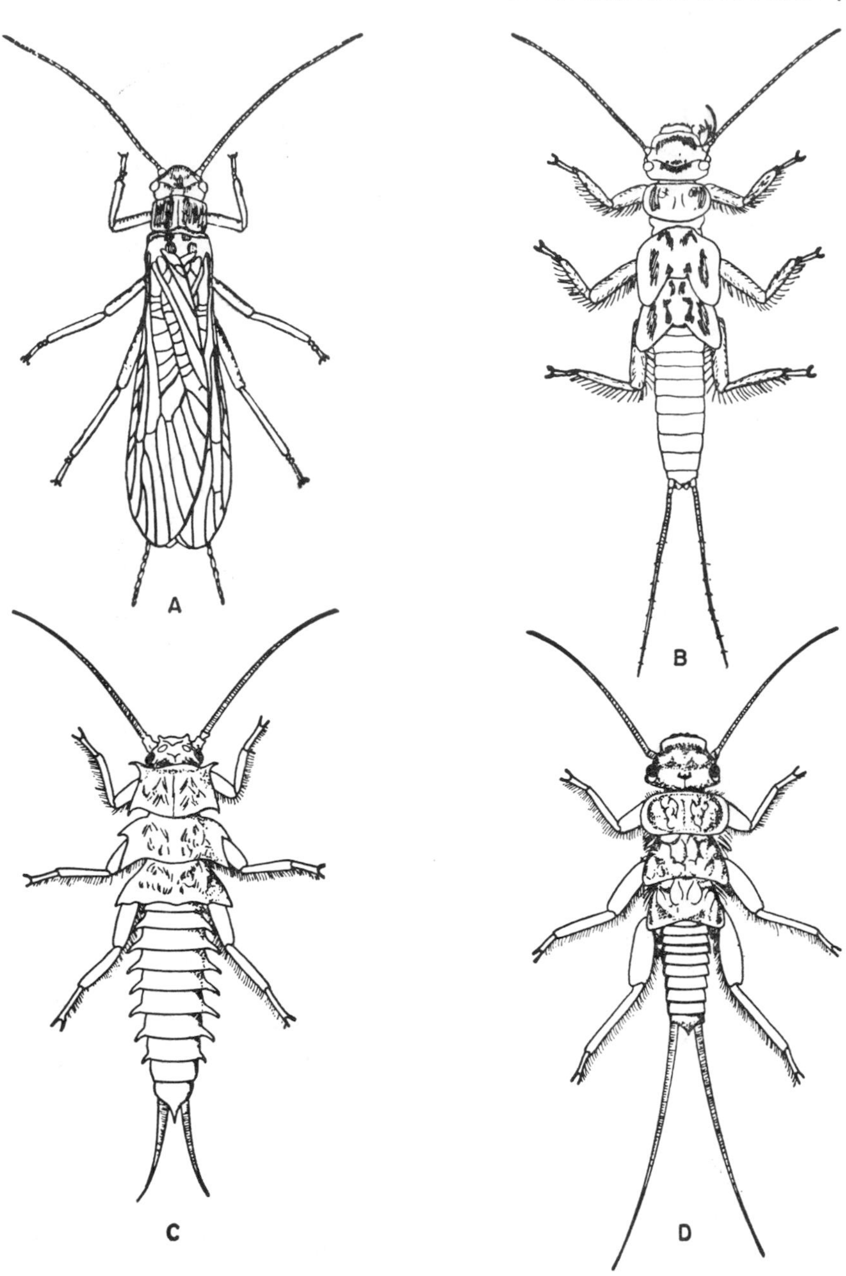

Plate 22. Stoneflies (Order Plecoptera).

A—Adult *Isoperla,* Isoperlidae (14–23 mm)
B—Nymph *Isoperla,* Isoperlidae (10–14 mm)
C—Nymph *Pteronarcys,* Pteronarcidae (10–40 mm)
D—Nymph *Acroneuria,* Perlidae (20–30 mm)

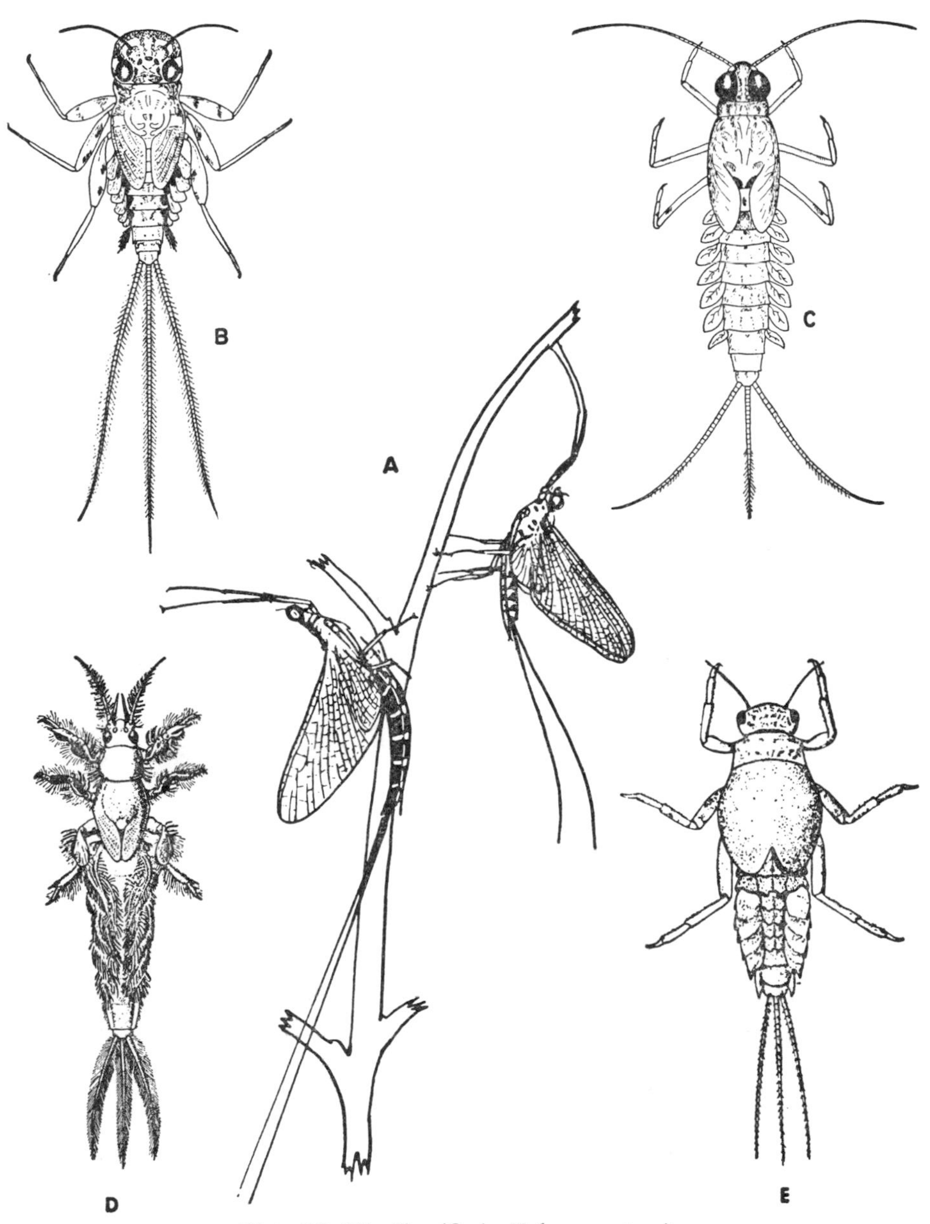

Plate 23. Mayflies (Order Ephemeroptera).

A—Adult mayfly, Heptageniidae (12–18 mm)
B—Nymph *Stenonema,* Heptageniidae (10–14 mm)
C—Nymph *Baetis,* Baetidae (7–14 mm)
D—Nymph *Hexagenia,* Ephemeridae (20–30 mm)
E—Nymph *Ephemerella,* Ephemerellidae (8–15 mm)

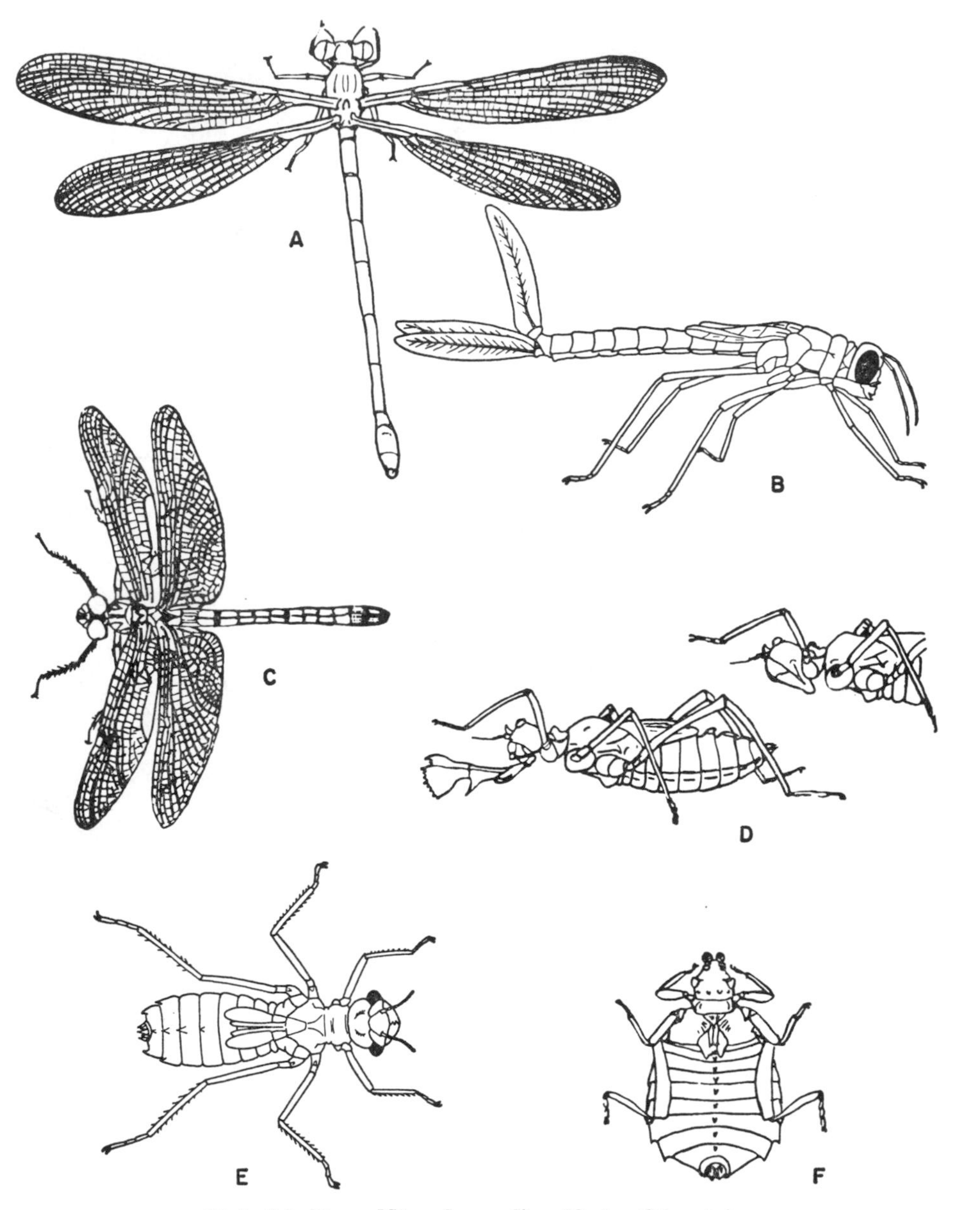

Plate 24: Damselflies, dragonflies (Order Odonata).

A—Adult damselfly (35–55 mm)
B—Damselfly nymph *Lestes,* Coenagrionidae (20–30 mm)
C—Adult dragonfly *Macromia,* Libellulidae (50–70 mm)
D—Dragonfly nymph *Macromia,* showing "mask" both extended and contracted, Libellulidae (15–45 mm)
E—Dragonfly nymph *Helocordulia* Libellulidae (15–45 mm)
F—Dragonfly nymph *Hagenius,* Gomphidae (15–20 mm)

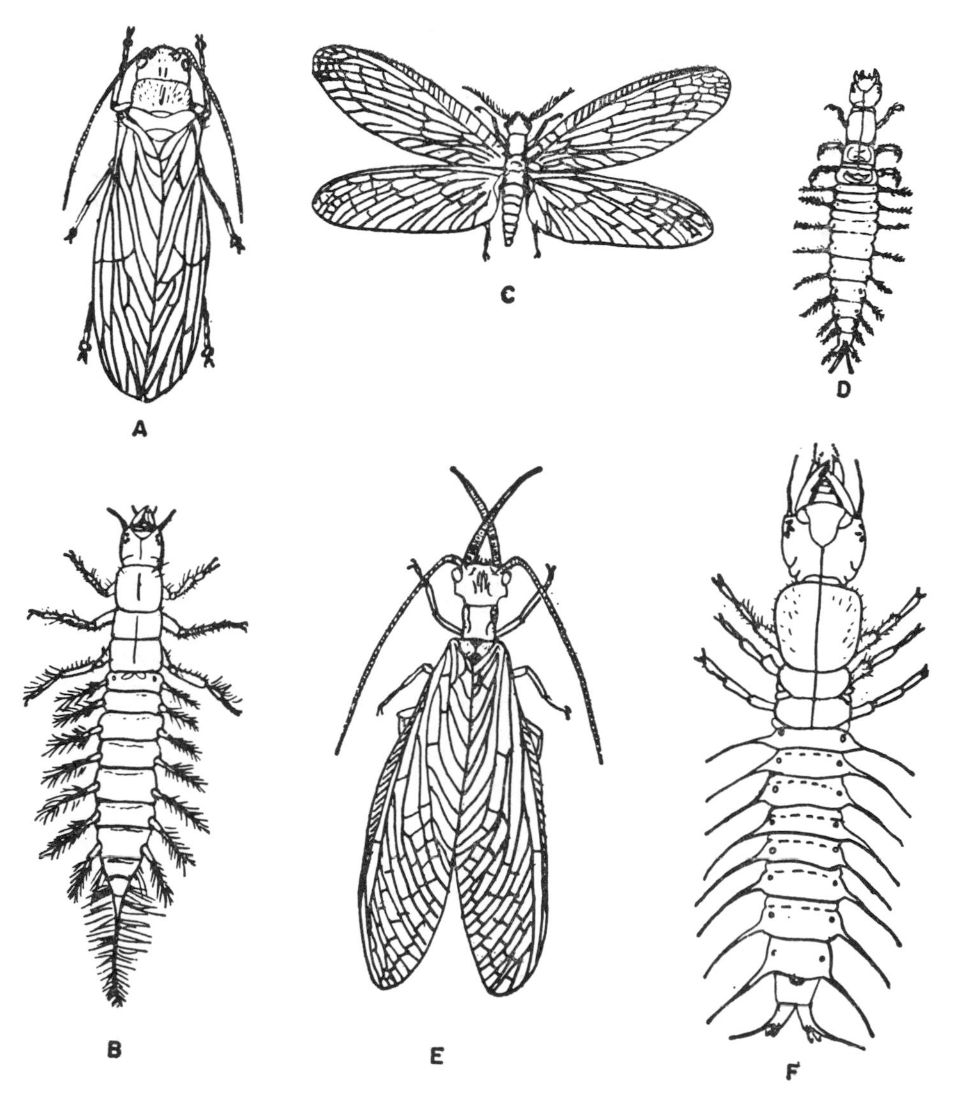

Plate 25. Hellgrammite and relatives.

A—Adult alderfly *Sialis,* Sialidae (9–15 mm)
B—Alderfly larva *Sialis,* Sialidae (15–30 mm)
C—Adult fishfly *Chauliodes,* Corydalidae (15–30 mm)
D—Fishfly larva *Chauliodes,* Corydalidae (20–40 mm)
E—Adult dobsonfly, *Corydalus* (25–70 mm)
F—Dobsonfly larva or hellgrammite, *Corydalus* (25–90 mm)

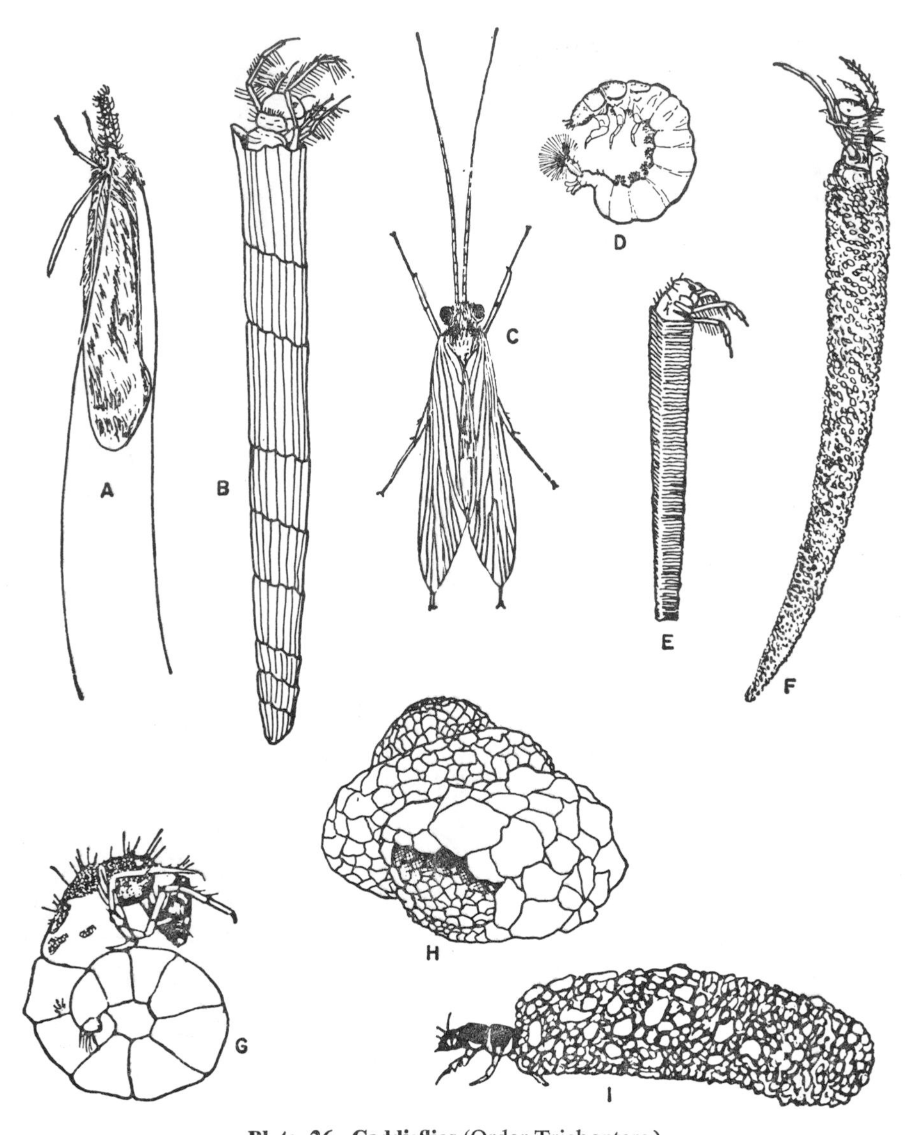

Plate 26. Caddisflies (Order Trichoptera).

A—Adult *Triaenodes,* Leptoceridae (10–20 mm)

B—Larva and case, *Triaenodes,* Leptoceridae (10–14 mm)

C—Adult *Hydropsyche,* Hydropsychidae (20–30 mm)

D—*Hydropsyche* larva, Hydropsychidae (20–30 mm)

E—Larva and case, *Brachycentrus,* Brachycentridae (12–16 mm)

F—Larva and case, *Leptocella,* Leptoceridae (14–18 mm)

G—*Helicopsyche* larva, Helicopsychidae (6–10 mm)

H—*Helicopsyche* case, Helicopsychidae (4–6 mm)

I—Larva and case, *Ochrotricha,* Hydroptilidae (4–6 mm)

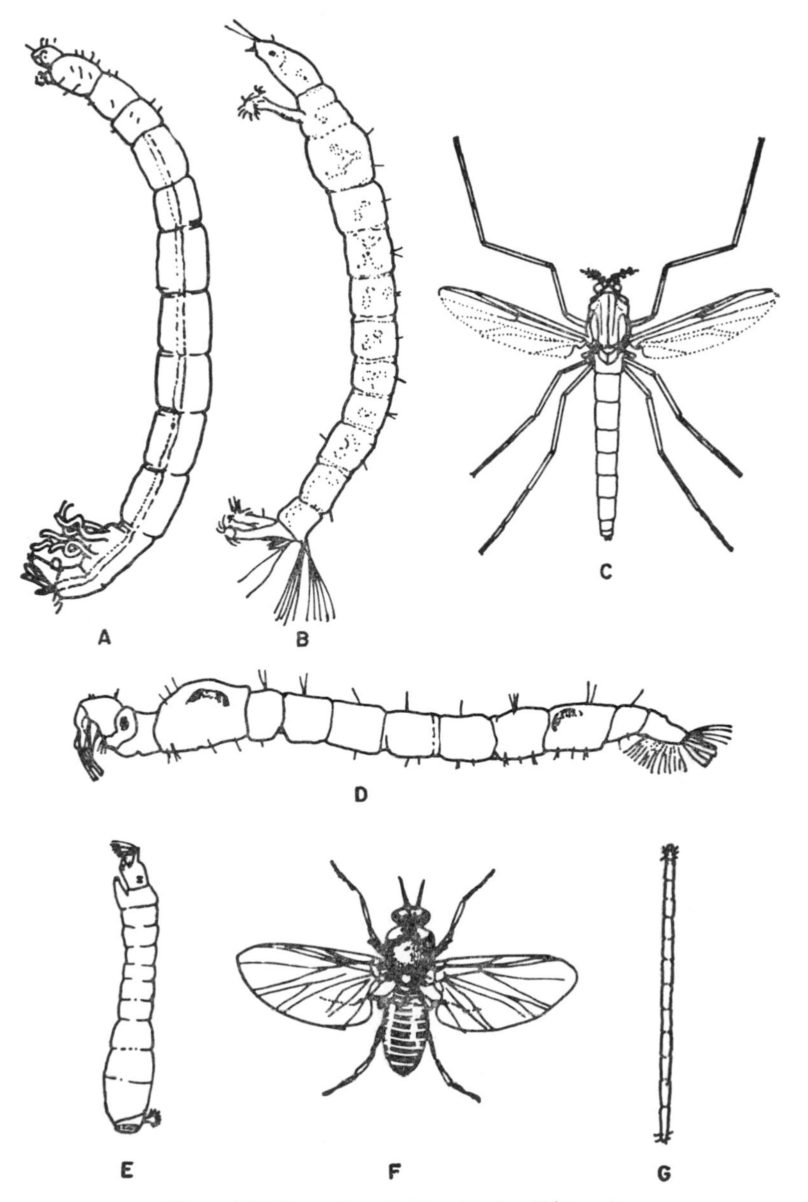

Plate 27. Two-winged flies (Order Diptera).

A—Larva midge *Chironomus,* Chironomidae (5–30 mm)
B—Larva midge *Ablabesmyia,* Chironomidae (5–10 mm)
C—Adult midge, Chironomidae (4–12 mm)
D—Larva phantom midge *Chaoborus,* Culicidae (8–12 mm)
E—Larva black fly *Simulium,* Simuliidae (3–8 mm)
F—Adult black fly *Simulium,* Simuliidae (2–6 mm)
G—Larva biting midge, Ceratopogonidae (3–12 mm)

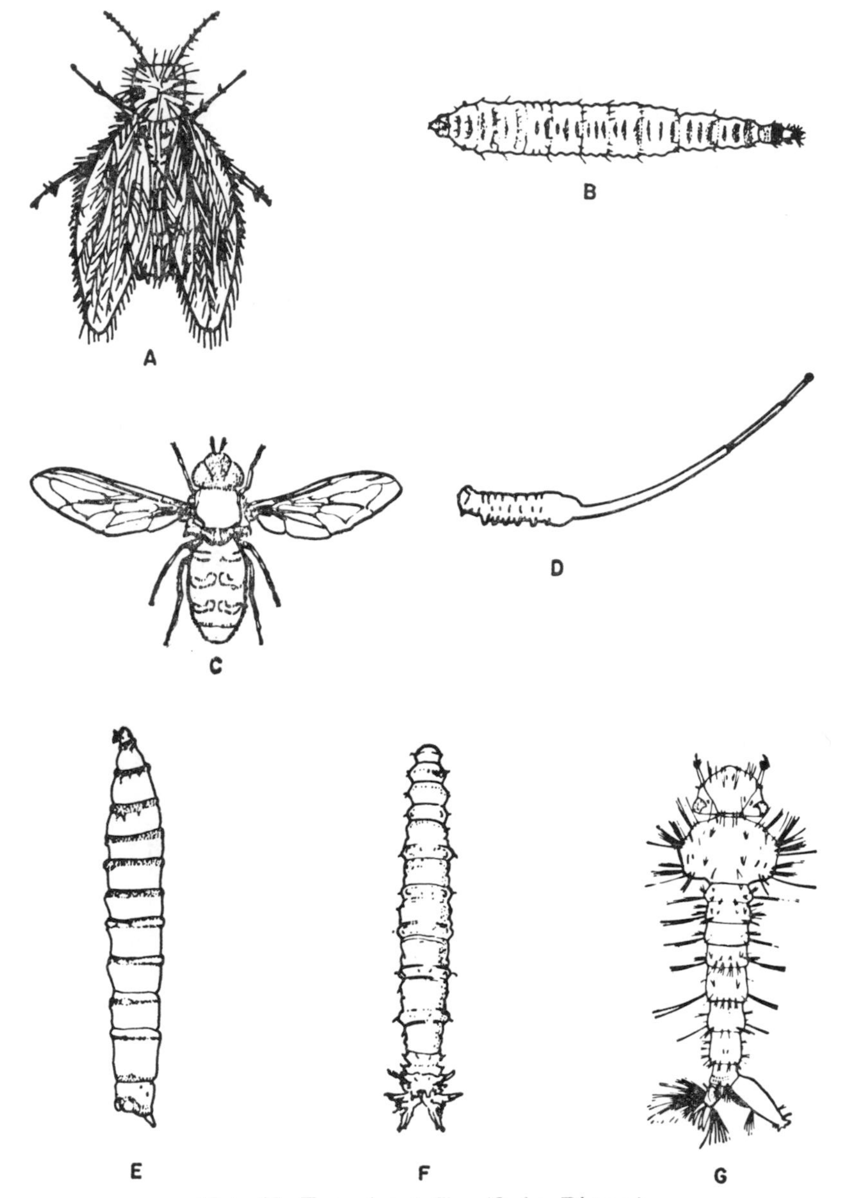

Plate 28. Two-winged flies (Order Diptera).

A—Adult sewage fly *Psychoda,* Psychodidae (2–5 mm)
B—Larva sewage fly *Psychoda,* Psychodidae (4–6 mm)
C—Adult drone fly, Syrphidae (10–15 mm)
D—Rat-tailed maggot *Eristalis,* Syrphidae (15–30 mm)
E—*Tabanus* larva, Tabanidae (30–40 mm)
F—Larva cranefly *Tipula,* Tipulidae (30–40 mm)
G—Larva mosquito *Aedes,* Culicidae (10–15 mm)

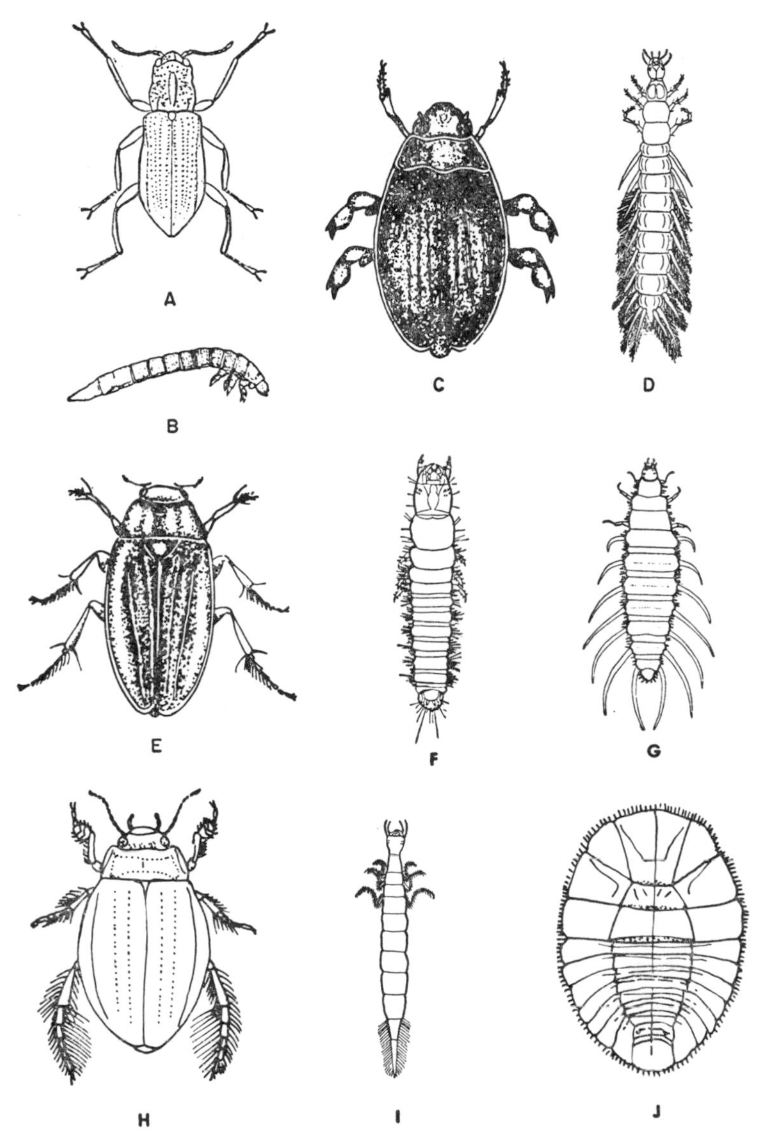

Plate 29. Beetles (Order Coleoptera).

A—Adult riffle beetle *Stenelmis*, Elmidae (2–5 mm)
B—Larva *Narpus*, Elmidae (4–10 mm)
C—Adult whirligig beetle *Dineutus*, Gyrinidae (7–15 mm)
D—Larva *Dineutus*, Gyrinidae (10–30 mm)
E—Adult water scavenger beetle *Hydrophilus*, Hydrophilidae (2–40 mm)
F—Larva *Berosus*, Hydrophilidae (5–20 mm)
G—Larva *Enochrus*, Hydrophilidae (10–25 mm)
H—Adult predacious diving beetle *Dytiscus*, Dytiscidae (2–40 mm)
I—Larva *Cybister*, Dytiscidae (10–25 mm)
J—Larva water penny *Psephenus*, Psephenidae (3–10 mm)

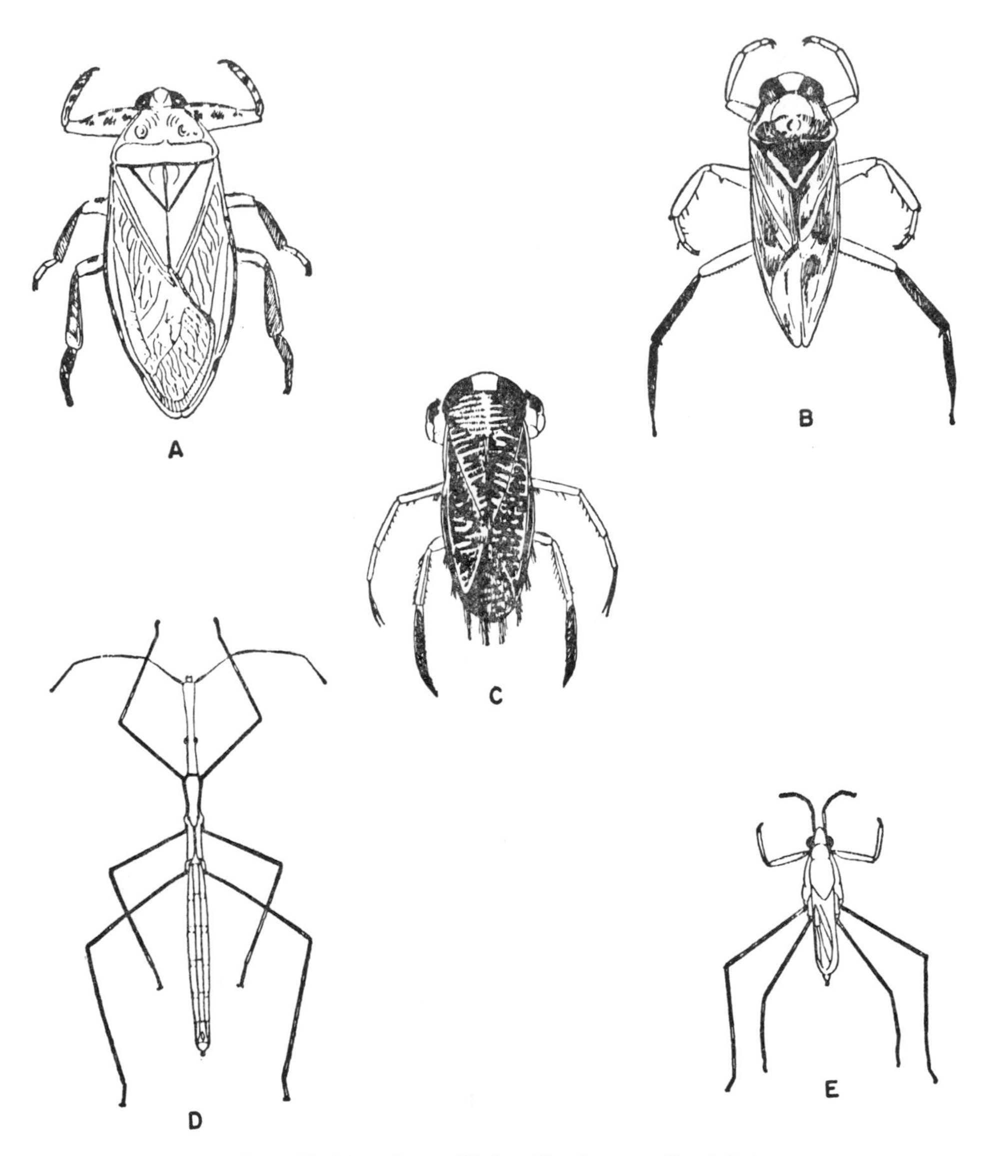

Plate 30. True bugs (Order Hemiptera, all adults).

A—Electric light bug, *Lethocerus,* Belostomidae (20–70 mm)
B—Backswimmer, *Notonecta,* Notonectidae (5–17 mm)
C—Water boatman *Sigara,* Corixidae (3–12 mm)
D—Marsh treader *Hydrometra,* Hydrometridae (8–11 mm)
E—Water strider *Gerris,* Gerridae (2–15 mm)

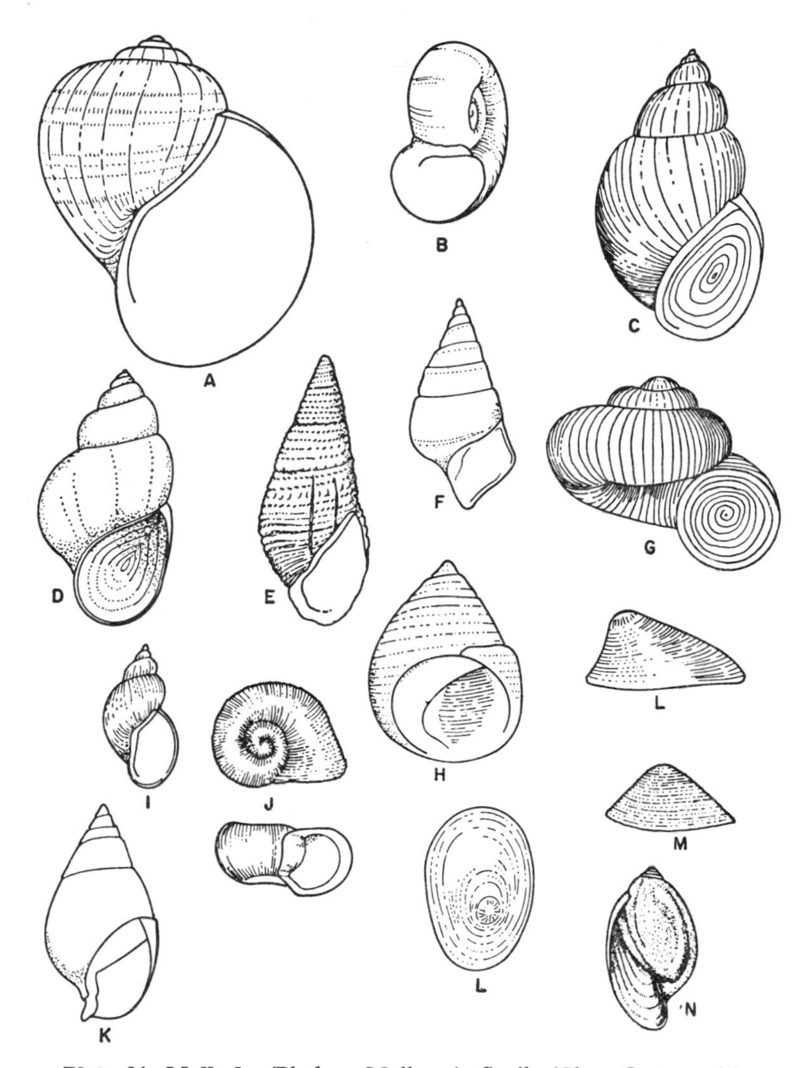

Plate 31. Mollusks (Phylum Mollusca): Snails (Class Gastropoda).

Gill-breathing families:

A—Apple snail *Pomacea,* Pilidae (5 cm)
B—*Marisa,* Pilidae (15 mm)
C—*Campeloma,* Viviparidae (4 cm)
D—Faucet snail *Bithynia,* Amnicolidae (2 cm)
E—*Tarebia,* Thiaridae (15 mm)
F—River snail *Pleurocera,* Pleuroceridae (3 cm)
G—*Valvata,* Valvatidae (1 cm)
H—Periwinkle *Littorina,* Littorinidae (marine, 2 cm)

Lung breathers:

I—Pond snail *Lymnaea,* Lymnaeidae (15 mm)
J—Orb snail *Helisoma,* Planorbidae (1 cm)
K—Mud snail *Nassa,* Nassidae (marine, 2 cm)
L—Limpet *Ferrissia,* Ancylidae (2 mm)
M—Limpet *Lanx,* Lancidae (10 mm)
N—Pouch snail *Physa,* Physidae (5 mm)

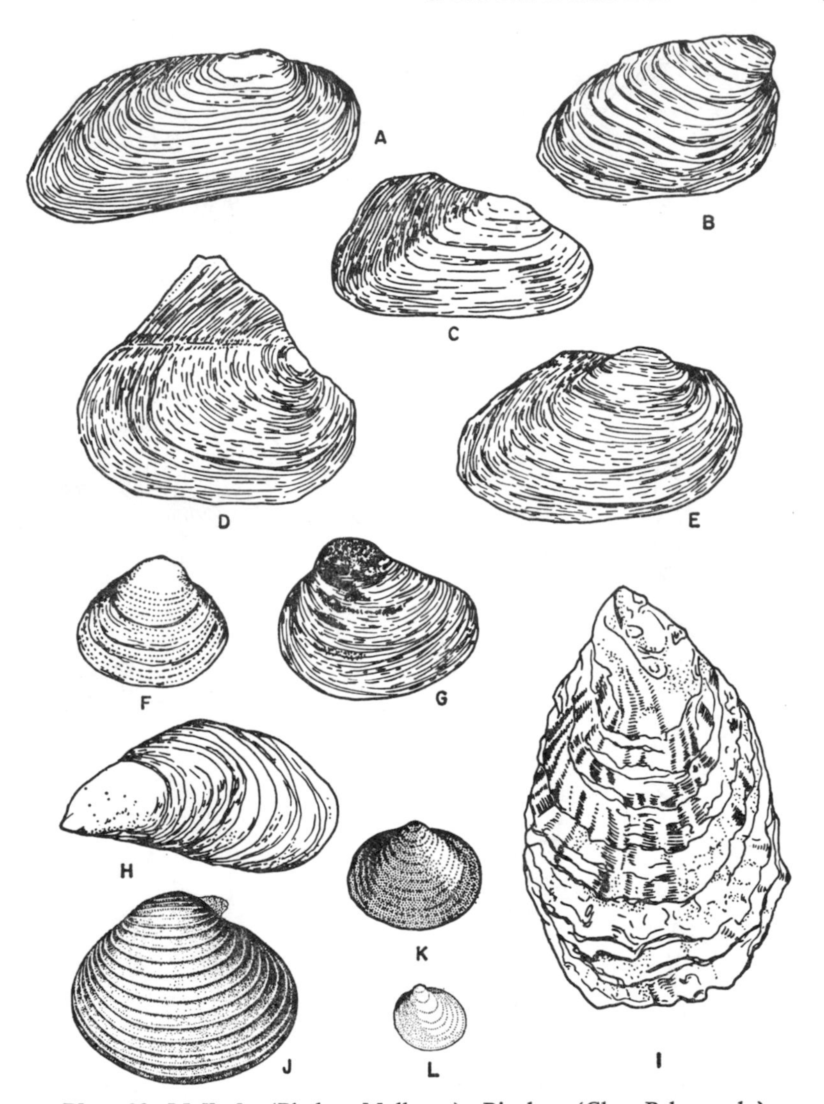

Plate 32. Mollusks (Phylum Mollusca): Bivalves (Class Pelecypoda)

A—Spectacle case *Margaritifera,* Margaritiferidae (10 cm)
B—Pearly mussel *Pleurobema,* Unionidae (10 cm)
C—Pearly mussel *Gonidea,* Unionidae (10 cm)
D—Winged lampshell *Proptera,* Lampsilinae (13 cm)
E—Papershell *Anodonta,* Anodontinae (14 cm)
F—Marsh clam *Polymesoda,* Corbiculidae (marine, 4 cm)
G—Rangia clam *Rangia,* Mactridae (marine, 5 cm)
H—Edible mussel *Mytilus,* Mytilidae (marine, 6 cm)
I—Oyster *Crassostrea,* Ostreidae (marine, 9 cm)
J—Asiatic clam *Corbicula,* Corbiculidae (4 cm)
K—Fingernail clam *Sphaerium,* Sphaeriidae (1 cm)
L—Peashell clam *Pisidium,* Sphaeriidae (5 mm)

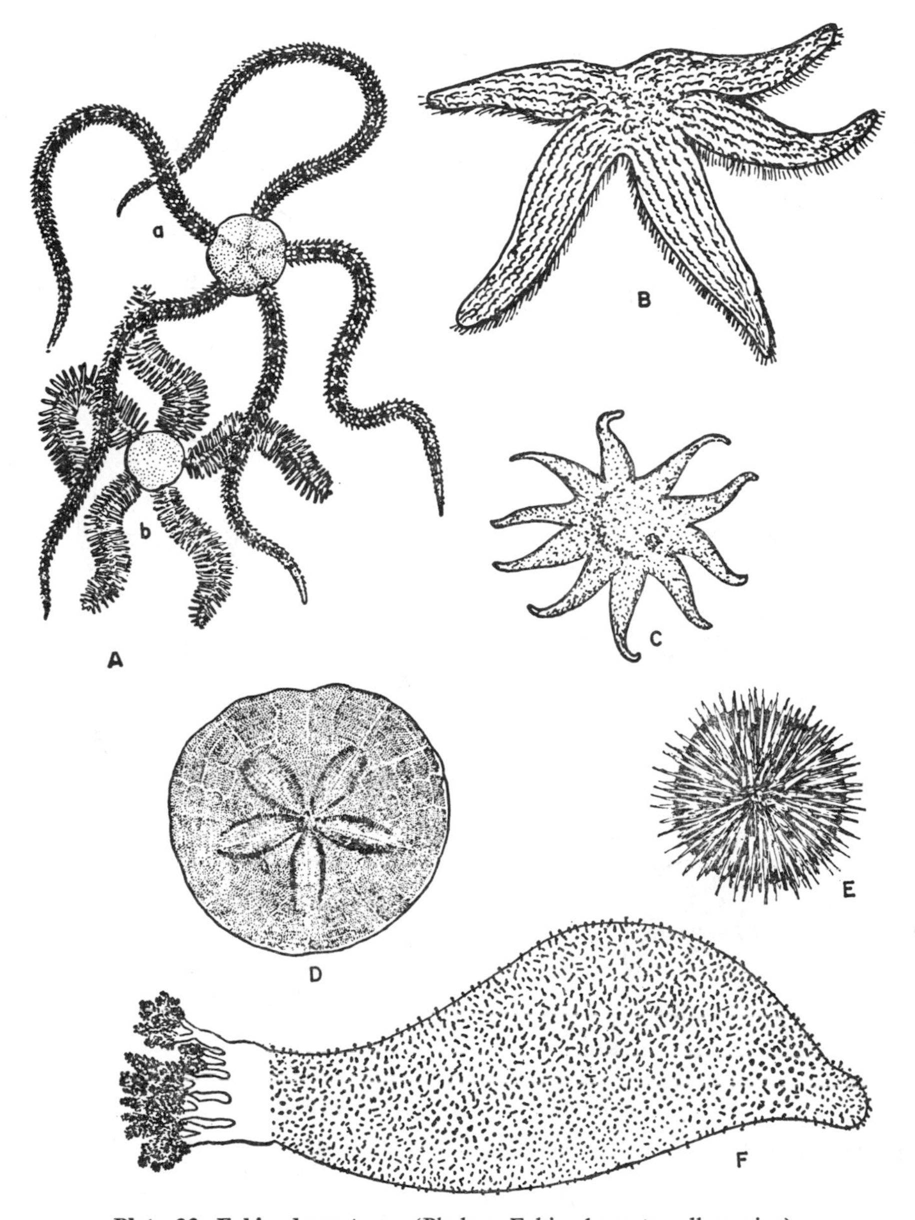

Plate 33. Echinoderm types (Phylum Echinodermata, all marine).

A—Brittle stars, Class Ophiuroidea:
(a) *Ophionereis* (15 cm)
(b) *Ophiothrix* (10 cm)

B—Five-armed starfish, Class Asteroidea: *Asterias* (15 cm)

C—Multi-armed starfish, Class Asteroidea: *Solaster* (40 cm)

D—Sand dollar, Class Echinoidea: *Echinarachnius* (7 cm)

E—Sea urchin, Class Echinoidea: *Strongylocentrotus* (6 cm)

F—Sea cucumber, Class Holothuroidea: *Thyone* (10 cm)

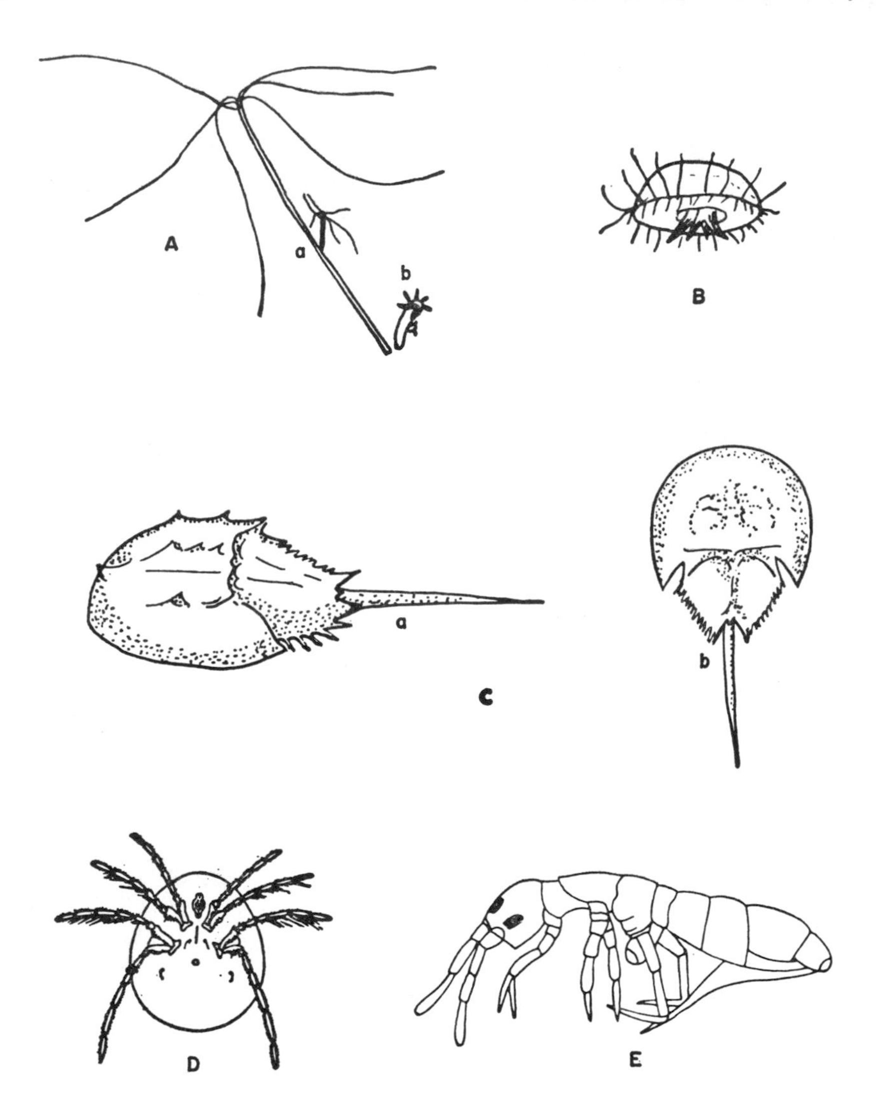

Plate 34. Miscellaneous invertebrates.

Freshwater coelenterates (Phylum Coelenterata):

A—*Hydra,* at (a) extended (2 cm) with bud, and at (b) contracted

B—Jellyfish (Medusa) stage of *Craspedacusta* (2 cm)

Arthropods (Phylum Arthropoda):

C—Horseshoe crab (Class Arachnoidea), marine: *Limulus* (30 cm); (a) shows side view and (b) top view.

D—Water mite (Class Arachnoidea): *Limnochares* (3 mm)

E—Springtail (Class Insecta, Order Collembola): *Orchesella* (2 mm)

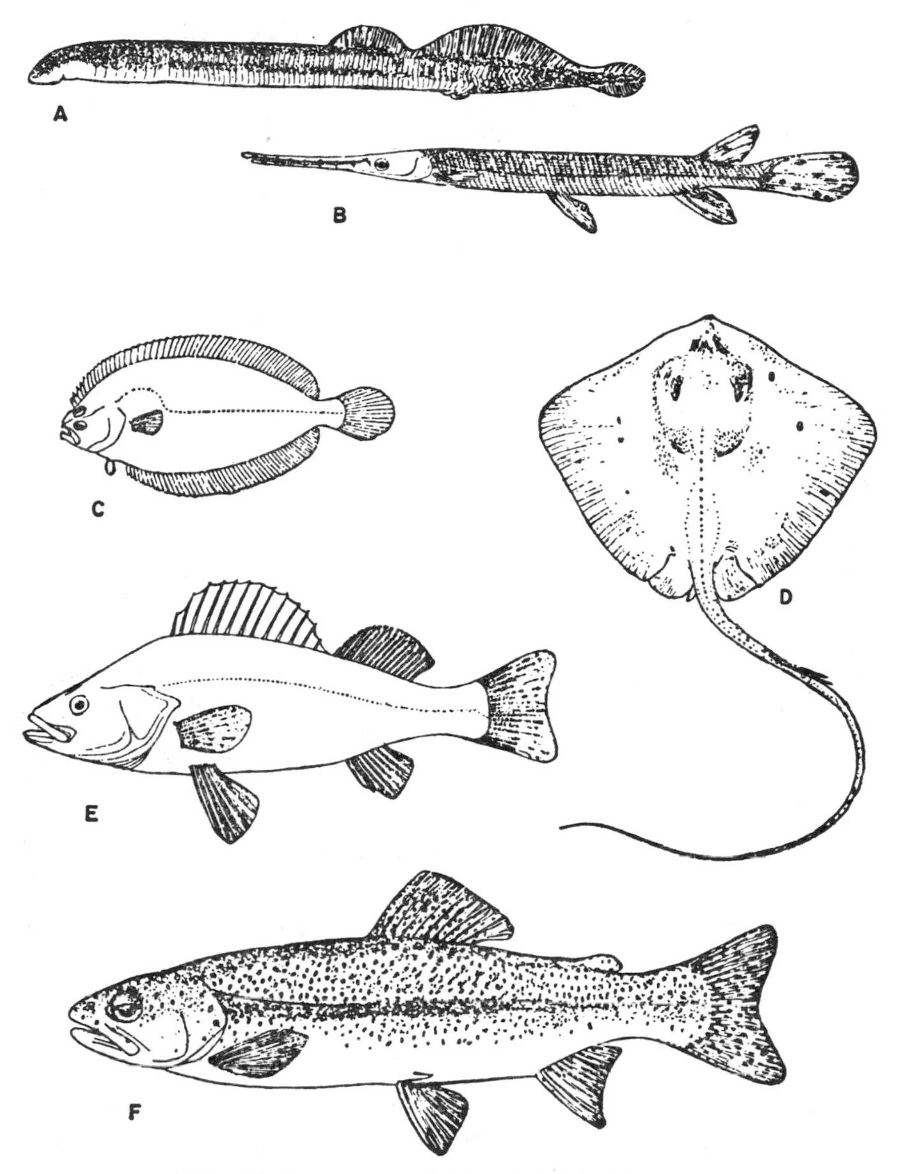

Plate 35. Some types of fishes (Phylum Chordata).

A—Jawless fish (Class Agnatha): lamprey, *Petromyzon* (750 cm)
B—Ganoid fish (Class Osteichthys, or Pisces): long-nosed gar, *Lepisosteus* (800 cm)
C—Flatfish (Class Osteichthys): flounder, *Paralichthys* (500 cm)
D—Cartilage fish (Class Chondrichthys): stingray, *Dasyatis* (2 m)
E—Spiny-rayed fish (Class Osteichthys): perch, *Perca* (30 cm)
F—Soft-rayed fish (Class Osteichthys): rainbow trout, *Salmo* (30 cm)

Plate 36. Types of amphibians (Phylum Chordata, Class Amphibia).

Frogs and toads (Order Salientia):

A—The "tadpole" larva (note the developing leg protruding from the body of the tadpole)

B—An adult frog, *Rana* (20 cm). Salientia with dry warty skins are usually called toads.

Salamanders (Order Caudata):

C—*Ambystoma* (20 cm). Adult is typically terrestrial.

D—*Ambystoma* larva is aquatic. Salamander larvae typically have gills.

E—Water dog or mud puppy, *Necturus* (to 60 cm). Larval gills are retained by the adult.

F—An adult aquatic salamander with a flat tail, *Diemictylus* (9 cm).

G—An aquatic salamander. The hind legs have been lost; *Siren* (1 m).

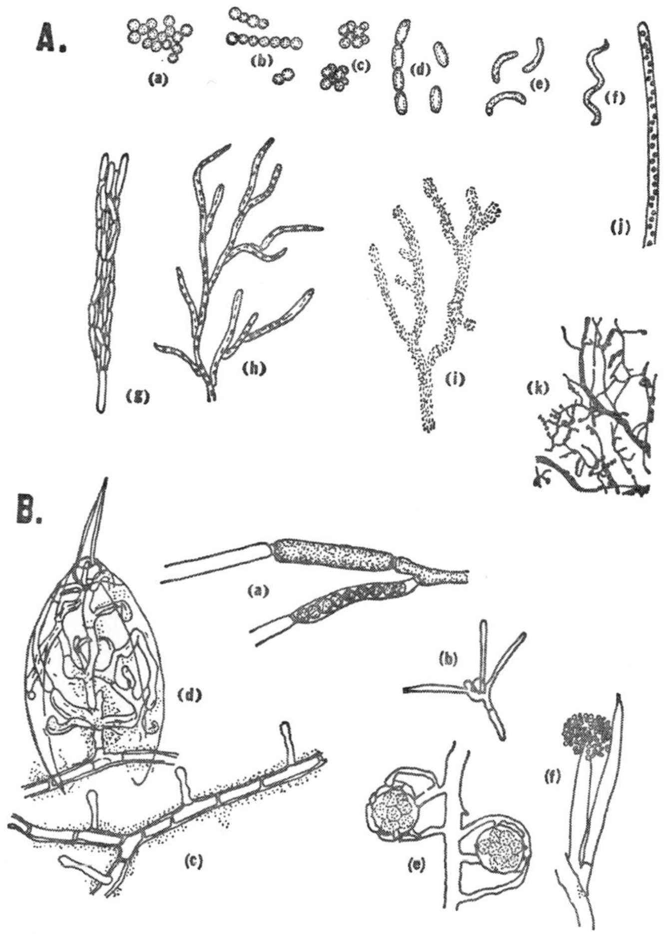

Plate 37. Bacteria and Fungi. (Diameter of most bacterial cells is less than 2 μ, though *Beggiatoa* may range up to 16 μ in diameter, and of indefinite length.)

A—Bacteria:

(Cellular forms and arrangements)

(a) micrococcus
(b) streptococcus
(c) sarcina
(d) bacillus
(e) vibrio
(f) spirillum

(Sewage organisms)

(g) *Sphaerotilus* ("sewage fungus") cells
(h) A *Sphaerotilus* growth form
(i) A growth form of *Zoogloea*
(j) *Beggiatoa* (sulfur bacterium)
(k) An actinomycete growth form from compost

B—Fungi:

(a) *Leptomitus,* showing zoospores and cellulin plugs (diameter 8.5–16 μ)
(b) *Tetracladium* (diameter 2.5–3.5 μ)
(c) *Zoophagus,* showing mycelial pegs
(d) *Zoophagus* with rotifer impaled on mycelial peg (diameter 3μ)
(e) *Achlya,* showing oospores
(f) *Achlya,* showing extruded encysted zoospores (Oogonia 50–60 μ, oospores 18.5–22 μ, encysted zoospores 3–5 μ)

606 D. Key for Identification of Freshwater Algae Common in Water Supplies and Polluted Waters (Color Plates A–F)

By C. Mervin Palmer

Beginning with 1a and 1b, choose one of the two contrasting statements and follow this procedure with the "a" and "b" statements of the number given at the end of the chosen statement. Continue until the name of the alga is given instead of another key number. (Where recent changes in names of algae have been made, the new name is given followed by the old name in parenthesis.)

	Refer to Couplet No.
1a. Plastid (separate color body) absent; complete protoplast pigmented; generally blue-green; iodine starch test * negative (blue-green algae)	4
1b. Plastid or plastids present; parts of protoplast free of some or all pigments; generally green, brown, red, etc., but not blue-green; iodine starch test * positive or negative	2
2a. Cell wall permanently rigid (never showing evidence of collapse), and with regular pattern of fine markings (striations, etc.); plastids brown to green; iodine starch test * negative; flagella absent; wall of two essentially similar halves, one placed over the other as a cover (diatoms)	29
2b. Cell wall, if present, capable of sagging, wrinkling, bulging or rigidity, depending on existing turgor pressure of cell protoplast; regular pattern of fine markings on wall generally absent; plastids green, red, brown, etc; iodine starch test * positive or negative; flagella present or absent; cell wall continuous and generally not of two parts	3
3a. Cell or colony motile; flagella present (often not readily visible); anterior and posterior ends of cell different from one another in contents and often in shape (flagellate algae)	51
3b. Nonmotile; true flagella absent; ends of cells often not differentiated (green algae and associated forms)	77

I. Blue-Green Algae

4a. Cells in filaments (or much elongated to form a thread)	5
4b. Cells not in (or as) filaments	23
5a. Heterocysts present	6
5b. Heterocysts absent	14
6a. Heterocyst located at one end of filament	7
6b. Heterocysts at various locations in filament	9
7a. Filaments radially arranged in a gelatinous bead	*Rivularia*
7b. Filaments isolated or irregularly grouped	8
8a. Filament gradually narrowed to one end	*Calothrix*
8b. Filament not gradually narrowed to one end	*Cylindrospermum*

---

* Add 1 drop of Lugol's (iodine) solution, diluted 1:1 with distilled water. In about 1 min, if positive, starch is stained blue and later black. Other structures (such as nucleus, plastids, cell wall) may also stain, but turn brown to yellow.

Key	Refer to Couplet No.
9a. Filament unbranched	10
9b. Filament with occasional (false) branches	13
10a. Crosswalls in filament much closer together than width of filament *Nodularia*	
10b. Crosswalls in filament at least as far apart as width of filament	11
11a. Filaments normally in tight parallel clusters; heterocysts and spores cylindric to long oval in shape . . . . *Aphanizomenon*	
11b. Filaments not in tight parallel clusters; heterocysts and spores often round to oval	12
12a. Filaments in a common gelatinous mass . . . . *Nostoc*	
12b. Filaments not in a common gelatinous mass . . . . *Anabaena*	
13a. False branches in pairs . . . . *Scytonema*	
13b. False branches, single . . . . *Tolypothrix*	
14a. Filament or elongated cell attached at one end, with one or more round cells (spores) at the other . . . . *Entophysalis (Chamaesiphon)*	
14b. Filament generally not attached at one end; no terminal spores present	15
15a. Filament with regular spiral form throughout	16
15b. Filament not spiral, or with spiral form limited to a portion of filament	17
16a. Filament septate . . . . *Arthrospira*	
16b. Filament nonseptate . . . . *Spirulina*	
17a. Filament very narrow, only 0.5–2.0 μ wide . . . . *Schizothrix*	
17b. Filament 3–95 μ wide	18
18a. Filaments loosely aggregated or not in clusters	19
18b. Filaments tightly aggregated and surrounded by a common gelatinous secretion that may be invisible	22
19a. Filament surrounded by wall-like sheath that frequently extends beyond the ends of the filament of cells; filament generally without movement	20
19b. Filament not surrounded by a wall-like sheath; filament may show movement	21
20a. Cells separated from one another by a space . . . . *Johannesbaptistia*	
20b. Cells in contact with adjacent cells . . . . *Lyngbya*	
21a. All filaments short, with less than 20 cells; one or both ends of filament sharply pointed . . . . *Raphidiopsis*	
21b. Filaments long, with more than 20 cells; filaments commonly without sharp-pointed ends . . . . *Oscillatoria*	
22a. Filaments arranged in a tight, essentially parallel bundle . . *Microcoleus*	
22b. Filaments arranged in irregular fashion, often forming a mat *Phormidium*	
23a. Cells in a regular pattern of parallel rows, forming a plate . . *Agmenellum (Merismopedia)*	
23b. Cells not regularly arranged to form a plate	24
24a. Cells regularly arranged near surface of a spherical gelatinous bead . .	25
24b. Gelatinous bead, if present, not spherical	26
25a. Cells ovate to heart-shaped, connected to center of bead by colorless stalks . . . . *Gomphosphaeria*	
25b. Cells round, without gelatinous stalks . *Gomphosphaeria* (*Coelosphaerium* type)	
26a. Cells cylindric-oval . . . . *Coccochloris (Aphanothece)*	
26b. Cells spherical	27
27a. Two or more distinct layers of gelatinous sheath around each cell or cell cluster . . . . *Anacystis (Gloeocapsa)*	
27b. Gelatinous sheath around cells not distinctly layered	28
28a. Cells isolated or in colonies of 2 to 32 cells . . . *Anacystis (Chroococcus)*	
28b. Cells in colonies composed of many cells . . . . . *Anacystis (Microcystis, Polycystis)*	

2. Diatoms

Refer to Couplet No.

29a. Front (valve) view circular in outline; markings radial in arrangement; cells may form a filament (centric diatoms) 30
29b. Front (valve) view elongate, not circular; transverse markings in one or two longitudinal rows; cells, if grouped, not forming a filament. (pennate diatoms) 32
30a. Cells in persistent filaments with valve faces in contact; therefore, cells commonly seen in side (girdle) view .... *Melosira*
30b. Cells isolated or in fragile filaments, often seen in front (valve) view.. 31
31a. Radial markings (striations), in valve view, extending from center to margin; short spines often present around margin (valve view) ..... *Stephanodiscus*
31b. Area of prominent radial markings, in valve view, limited to approximately outer half of circle, marginal spines generally absent .... *Cyclotella*
32a. Cell longitudinally symmetrical in valve view 33
32b. Cell longitudinally unsymmetrical (two sides unequal in shape), at least in valve view 49
33a. Raphe at or near the edge of the valve 34
33b. Raphe or pseudoraphe median or submedian 35
34a. Marginal, keeled raphe areas lie opposite one another on the two valves .... *Hantzschia*
34b. Marginal, keeled raphe areas lie diagonal to one another on the two valves .... *Nitzschia*
35a. Cell transversely symmetrical in valve view 36
35b. Cell transversely unsymmetrical (two ends unequal in shape or size), at least in valve view 44
36a. Cell round-oval in valve view, not more than twice as long as it is wide .... *Cocconeis*
36b. Cell elongate, more than twice as long as it is wide 37
37a. Cell flat (girdle face wide, valve face narrow) .... *Tabellaria*
37b. Girdle and valve faces about equal in width 38
38a. Cell with several markings (septa) extending without interruption across the valve face; no marginal line of pores present...... *Diatoma*
38b. Cross markings (striations or costae) on valve surface, interrupted by either longitudinal space (pseudoraphe), or line (raphe), or line of pores (carinal dots) 39
39a. Cells attached side by side to form a ribbon of several to many cells *Fragilaria*
39b. Cells isolated or in pairs 40
40a. Cell narrow, linear, often narrowed to both ends; true raphe absent *Synedra*
40b. Cell commonly "boat-shape" in valve view; true raphe present 41
41a. Cell longitudinally unsymmetrical in girdle view; sometimes with attachment stalk .... *Achnanthes*
41b. Cell symmetrical in girdle as well as valve view; generally not attached.... 42
42a. Area without striations extending as a transverse belt around middle of cell .... *Stauroneis*
42b. No continuous clear belt around middle of cell 43
43a. Cell with coarse transverse markings (costae), which appear as solid lines even under high magnification .... *Pinnularia*
43b. Cell with fine transverse markings (striae), which appear as lines of dots under high magnification .... *Navicula*
44a. Cells attached together at one end only to form radiating colony *Asterionella*
44b. Cell not forming a loose radiating colony 45

	Refer to Couplet No.
45a. Cells in fan-shaped colonies ... *Meridion*	
45b. Cells isolated or in pairs ...	46
46a. Prominent wall markings in addition to striations present just below lateral margins on valve surface of cell ... *Surirella*	
46b. Wall markings along sides of valve limited to striations ...	47
47a. Cell elongate, sides almost parallel except for terminal knobs ... *Asterionella*	
47b. Sides of cell converging toward one end ...	48
48a. Cells bent in girdle view ... *Rhoicosphenia*	
48b. Cells straight in girdle view ... *Gomphonema*	
49a. Valves with transverse septa or costae ... *Epithemia*	
49b. Valves with no transverse septa or costae ...	50
50a. Raphe located almost through center of valve ... *Cymbella*	
50b. Raphe excentric, near concave edge of valve ... *Amphora*	

3. Flagellate Algae

51a. Cell in a loose, rigid conical sac (lorica); isolated or in a branching colony ... *Dinobryon*	
51b. Case or sac, if present, not conical; colony, if present, not branching ...	52
52a. Cells isolated or in pairs ...	53
52b. Cells in a colony of four or more cells ...	71
53a. Prominent transverse groove encircles cell ...	54
53b. Cell without transverse groove ...	56
54a. Cell with prominent rigid projection, one forward and two or three on posterior end ... *Ceratium*	
54b. Cell without several rigid polar projections ...	55
55a. Portions above and below transverse groove about equal ... *Peridinium*	
55b. Front portion distinctly larger than posterior portion ... *Massartia*	
56a. Cell with long bristles extending from surface plates ... *Mallomonas*	
56b. Cell without bristles and surface plates ...	57
57a. Cell protoplast enclosed in loose rigid covering (lorica) ...	58
57b. Cell with tight membrane or wall but no loose rigid covering ...	60
58a. Lorica flattened; cell with two flagella ... *Phacotus*	
58b. Lorica not flattened; cell with one flagellum ...	59
59a. Lorica often opaque, generally dark brown to red; plastid green *Trachelomonas*	
59b. Lorica often transparent, colorless to light brown; plastid light brown *Chrysococcus*	
60a. Plastids brown to red to olive or blue-green ...	61
60b. Plastids grass green ...	64
61a. Plastids blue-green to blue ... *Chroomonas*	
61b. Plastids brown to red to olive green ...	62
62a. Plastid brown; one or two flagella ...	63
62b. Plastids red, red brown or olive green; two flagella ... *Rhodomonas*	
63a. Anterior end of cell oblique; two flagella ... *Cryptomonas*	
63b. Anterior end of cell rounded or pointed; one flagellum ... *Chromulina*	
64a. Cell with colorless rectangular wing ... *Pteromonas*	
64b. No wing extending from cell ...	65
65a. Cells flattened; margin rigid ... *Phacus*	
65b. Cell not flattened; margin rigid or flexible ...	66
66a. Pyrenoid present in the single plastid; no paramylon; margin not flexible; two or more flagella per cell ...	67
66b. Pyrenoid absent; paramylon present; several plastids per cell; margin flexible or rigid; one flagellum per cell ...	70

	Refer to Couplet No.
67a. Cells fusiform (tapering at each end) .... *Chlorogonium*	
67b. Cells not fusiform, generally almost spherical	68
68a. Plastids numerous .... *Vacuolaria*	
68b. Plastids few, commonly one	69
69a. Two flagella per cell .... *Chlamydomonas*	
69b. Four flagella per cell .... *Carteria*	
70a. Cell flexible in form; paramylon a capsule or disk; cell elongate. *Euglena*	
70b. Cell rigid in form; paramylon ring-shaped; cell almost spherical *Lepocinclis*	
71a. Plastids brown	72
71b. Plastids green	73
72a. Cells in contact with one another .... *Synura*	
72b. Cells separated from one another by space .... *Uroglenopsis*	
73a. Colony flat, one cell thick .... *Gonium*	
73b. Colony rounded, more than one cell thick	74
74a. Cells in contact with one another	75
74b. Cells separated from one another by space	76
75a. Cells radially arranged .... *Pandorina*	
75b. Cells all facing one direction .... *Pyrobotrys (Chlamydobotrys)*	
76a. Cells more than 400 per colony .... *Volvox*	
76b. Cells less than 75 per colony .... *Eudorina*	

4. Green Algae and Associated Forms

77a. Cells jointed together to form a net .... *Hydrodictyon*	
77b. Cells not forming a net	78
78a. Cells attached side by side to form a plate or ribbon one cell wide and thick; number of cells commonly two, four or eight ..... *Scenedesmus*	
78b. Cells not attached side by side	79
79a. Cells isolated or in nonfilamentous or nontubular thalli	80
79b. Cells in filaments or other tubular or threadlike thalli	111
80a. Cells isolated and narrowest at the center due to incomplete fissure (desmids)	81
80b. Cells isolated or in clusters but without central fissure	84
81a. Each half of cell with three spinelike or pointed knobular extensions *Staurastrum*	
81b. Cell margin with no such extensions	82
82a. Semicells with a median incision or depression	83
82b. Semicells with no median incision or depression .... *Cosmarium*	
83a. Margin with rounded lobes .... *Euastrum*	
83b. Margin with sharp-pointed teeth .... *Micrasterias*	
84a. Cells elongate	85
84b. Cells round to oval or angular	92
85a. Cell radiating from a central point .... *Actinastrum*	
85b. Cells isolated or in irregular clusters	86
86a. Cells with terminal spines .... *Schroederia*	
86b. Cells without terminal spines	87
87a. Cells with colorless attachment area at one end .... *Characium*	
87b. No attachment area at one end of cell	88
88a. Plastids two per cell; unpigmented area across center of cell. *Closterium*	
88b. Cell with plastid that continues across the center	89

		Refer to Couplet No.
89a.	Cell 5–10 times as long as it is broad	90
89b.	Cell 2–4 times as long as it is broad	91
90a.	Pyrenoid absent, or one per cell . . . *Ankistrodesmus*	
90b.	Pyrenoids several per cell . . . *Closteriopsis*	
91a.	Cells semicircular; cell ends pointed but with no terminal spines *Selenastrum*	
91b.	Cells arcuate but less than semicircular; cell ends pointed and each with a short spine . . . *Closteridium*	
92a.	Cells regularly arranged in a tight, flat colony . . . *Pediastrum*	
92b.	Cells not in a tight, flat regular colony	93
93a.	Cells angular	94
93b.	Cells round to oval	95
94a.	Two or more spines at each angle . . . *Polyedriopsis*	
94b.	Spines none or less than two at each angle . . . *Tetraedron*	
95a.	Cells with long sharp spines	96
95b.	Long sharp spines absent	99
96a.	Cells round	97
96b.	Cells oval	98
97a.	Cells isolated . . . *Golenkinia*	
97b.	Cells in colonies . . . *Micractinium*	
98a.	Each cell end has one spine . . . *Diacanthos*	
98b.	Each cell end has more than one spine . . . *Chodatella*	
99a.	Colony of definite regular form, round to oval	100
99b.	Colony, if present, not a definite oval or sphere; or cells may be isolated	104
100a.	Colony a tight sphere of cells	101
100b.	Colony a loose sphere of cells enclosed by a common membrane	102
101a.	Sphere solid, slightly irregular, no connecting processes between cells *Planktosphaeria*	
101b.	Sphere hollow, regular; short connecting processes between cells. *Coelastrum*	
102a.	Cells round	103
102b.	Cells oval . . . *Oocystis*	
103a.	Cells connected to center of colony by branching stalk . . . *Dictyosphaerium*	
103b.	No stalk connecting cells . . . *Sphaerocystis*	
104a.	Oval cells, enclosed in a somewhat spherical, often orange-colored matrix . . . *Botryococcus*	
104b.	Cells round, isolated or in colorless matrix	105
105a.	Adjoining cells with straight flat walls between their protoplasts	106
105b.	Adjoining cells with rounded walls between their protoplasts	107
106a.	Cells embedded in a common gelatinous matrix . . . *Palmella*	
106b.	No matrix or sheath outside of cell walls . . . *Phytoconis (Protococcus)*	
107a.	Cells loosely arranged in a large gelatinous matrix . . . *Tetraspora*	
107b.	Cells isolated or tightly grouped in a small colony	108
108a.	Cells located inside of protozoa . . . *Zoochlorella*	
108b.	Cells not inside of protozoa	109
109a.	Plastid filling ⅔ or less of cell	110
109b.	Plastid filling ¾ or more of cell . . . *Chlorococcum*	
110a.	Cell diameter 2 μ or less; reproduction by cell division . . *Nannochloris*	
110b.	Cell diameter 2.5 μ or more; reproduction by internal spores. *Chlorella*	
111a.	Cells attached end to end in an unbranched filament	112
111b.	Thallus branched, or more than one cell wide	119
112a.	Plastids in form of one or more marginal spiral ribbons . . . *Spirogyra*	
112b.	Plastids not in form of spiral ribbons	113

	Refer to Couplet No.
113a. Filaments, when breaking, separating through middle of cells............	114
113b. Filaments, when breaking, separating irregularly or at ends of cells........	115
114a. Starch test positive; cell margin straight; one plastid, granular *Microspora*	
114b. Starch test negative; cell margin slightly bulging; several plastids *Tribonema*	
115a. Marginal indentations between cells........................*Desmidium*	
115b. No marginal indentations between cells............................	116
116a. Plastids, two per cell ....*Zygnema*	
116b. Plastid, one per cell (sometimes appearing numerous)..............	117
117a. Some cells with walls having transverse wrinkles near one end; plastid an irregular net ....*Oedogonium*	
117b. No apical wrinkles in wall; plastid not porous.........................	118
118a. Plastid a flat or twisted axial ribbon...................*Mougeotia*	
118b. Plastid an arcuate marginal band.........................*Ulothrix*	
119a. Thallus a flat plate of cells..............................*Hildenbrandia*	
119b. Thallus otherwise	120
120a. Thallus a long tube without crosswalls..................*Vaucheria*	
120b. Thallus otherwise	121
121a. Thallus a leathery strand with regularly spaced swellings and a continuous surface membrane of cells...................................*Lemanea*	
121b. Thallus otherwise	122
122a. Filament unbranched ....*Schizomeris*	
122b. Filament branched	123
123a. Branches in whorls (clusters)	124
123b. Branches single or in pairs	126
124a. Thallus embedded in gelatinous matrix............*Batrachospermum*	
124b. Thallus not embedded in gelatinous matrix......................	125
125a. Main filament one cell thick.....................................*Nitella*	
125b. Main filament three cells thick..................................*Chara*	
126a. Most of filament surrounded by a layer of cells.......*Compsopogon*	
126b. Filament not surrounded by a layer of cells.....................	127
127a. End cell of branches with a rounded or blunt-pointed tip...............	128
127b. End cell of branches with a sharp-pointed tip.........................	130
128a. Plastids green; starch test positive................................	129
128b. Plastids red; starch test negative....................*Audouinella*	
129a. Some cells dense, swollen, dark green (spores); other cells light green, cylindric ....*Pithophora*	
129b. All cells essentially alike, light to medium green, cylindric....*Cladophora*	
130a. Filaments embedded in gelatinous matrix........................	131
130b. Filaments not embedded in gelatinous matrix..................	132
131a. Cells of main filament much wider than even the basal cells of branches *Draparnaldia*	
131b. No abrupt change in width of cells from main filament to branches *Chaetophora*	
132a. Branches very short, with no cross-walls.............*Rhizoclonium*	
132b. Branches long, with cross-walls..................................	133
133a. Branches ending in an abrupt spine having a bulbous base......*Bulbochaete*	
133b. Branches gradually reduced in width, ending in a long pointed cell, with or without color..*Stigeoclonium*	

606 E. Recent Changes in Names of Algae

Old Name	*New Name*
Aphanocapsa	Anacystis
Aphanothece	Coccochloris
Chamaesiphon	Entophysalis
Chantransia	Audouinella
Chlamydobotrys	Pyrobotrys
Chroococcus	Anacystis
Clathrocystis	Anacystis
Coelosphaerium	Gomphosphaeria
Encyonema	Cymbella
Gloeocapsa	Anacystis
Gloeothece	Coccochloris
Merismopedia	Agmenellum
Microcystis	Anacystis
Odontidium	Diatoma
Polycystis	Anacystis
Protococcus	Phytoconis
Sphaerella	Haematococcus
Synechococcus	Coccochloris

ALGAE COLOR PLATES

A through F

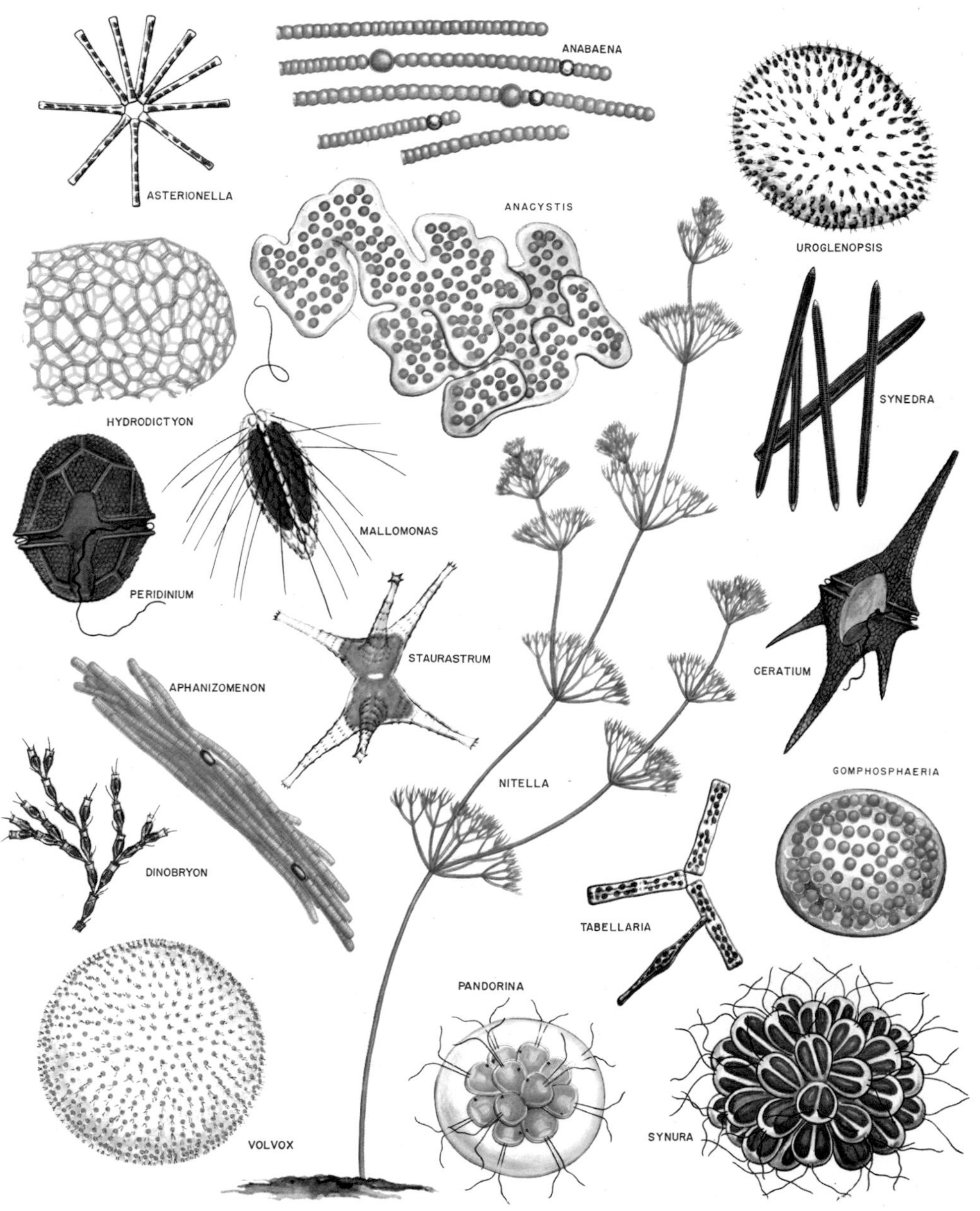

Plate A. Taste and odor algae

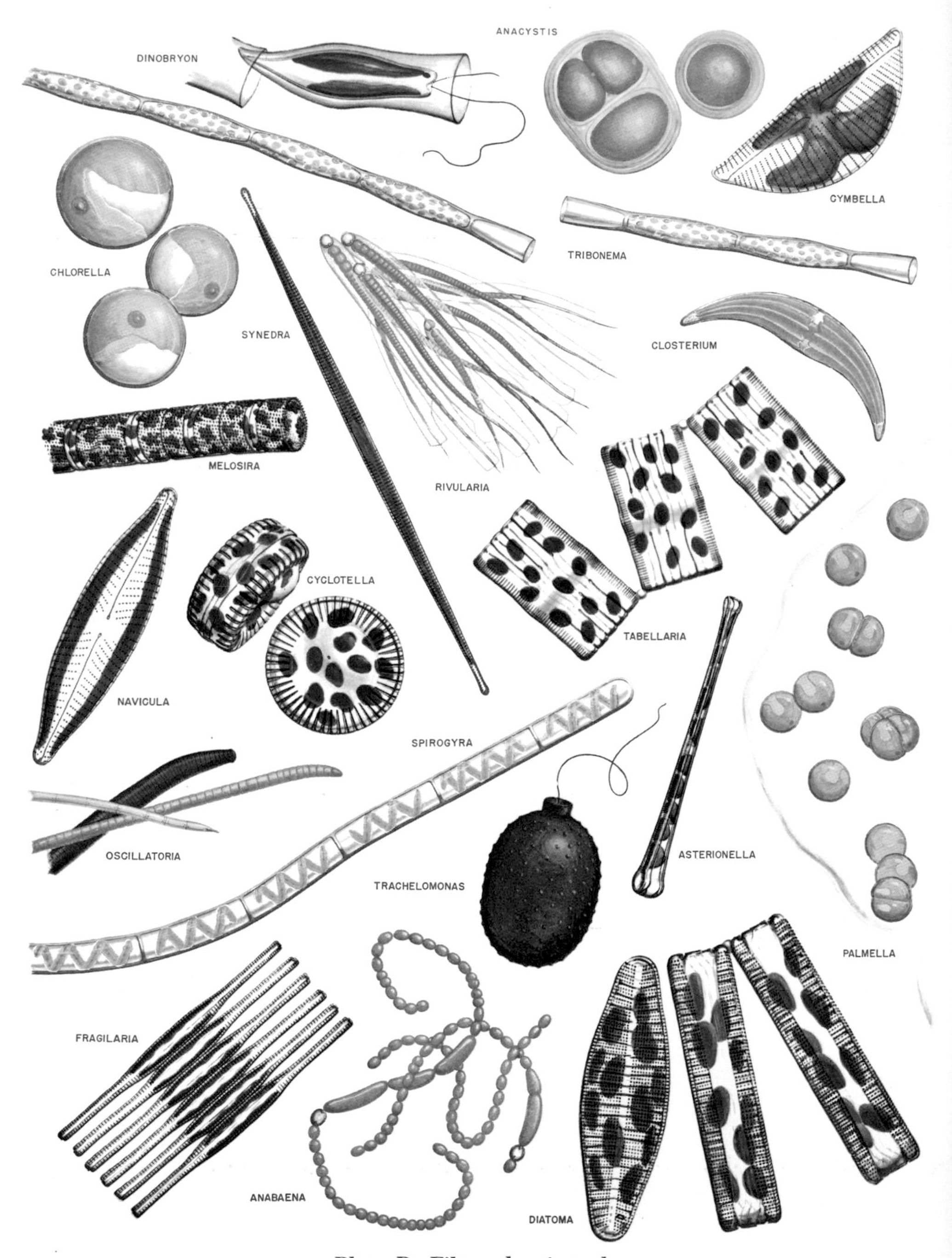

Plate B. Filter clogging algae

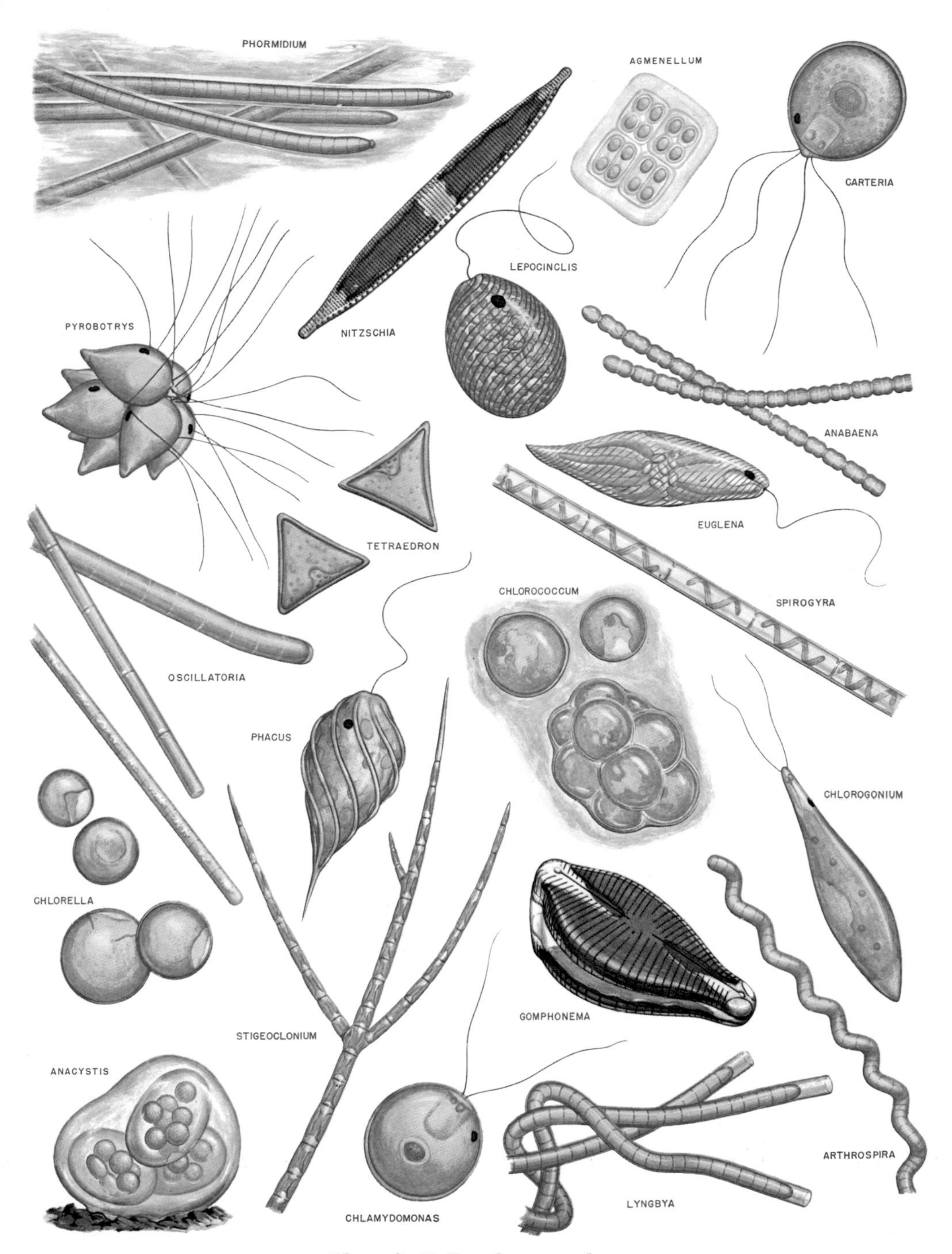

Plate C. Polluted water algae

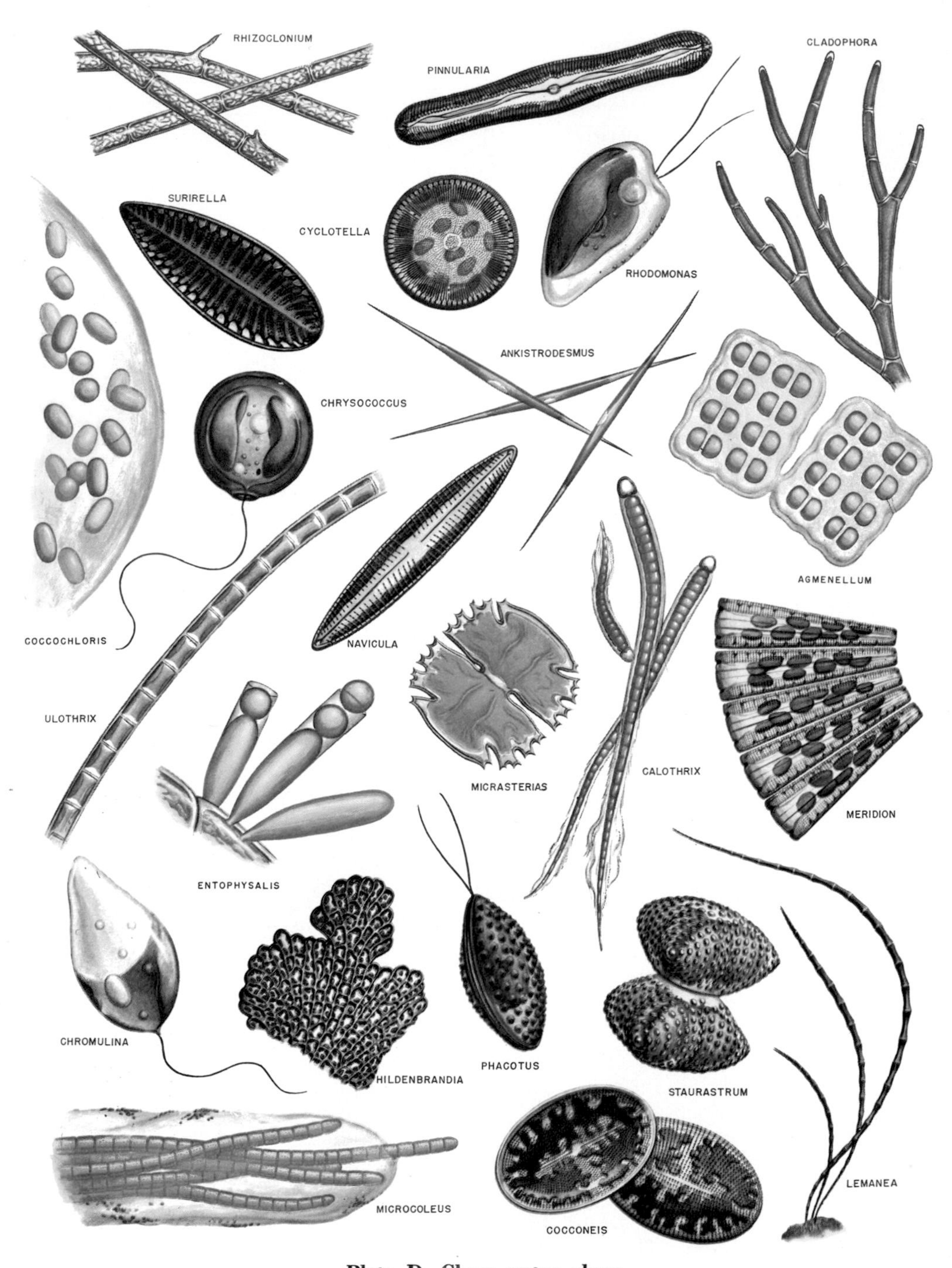

Plate D. Clean water algae

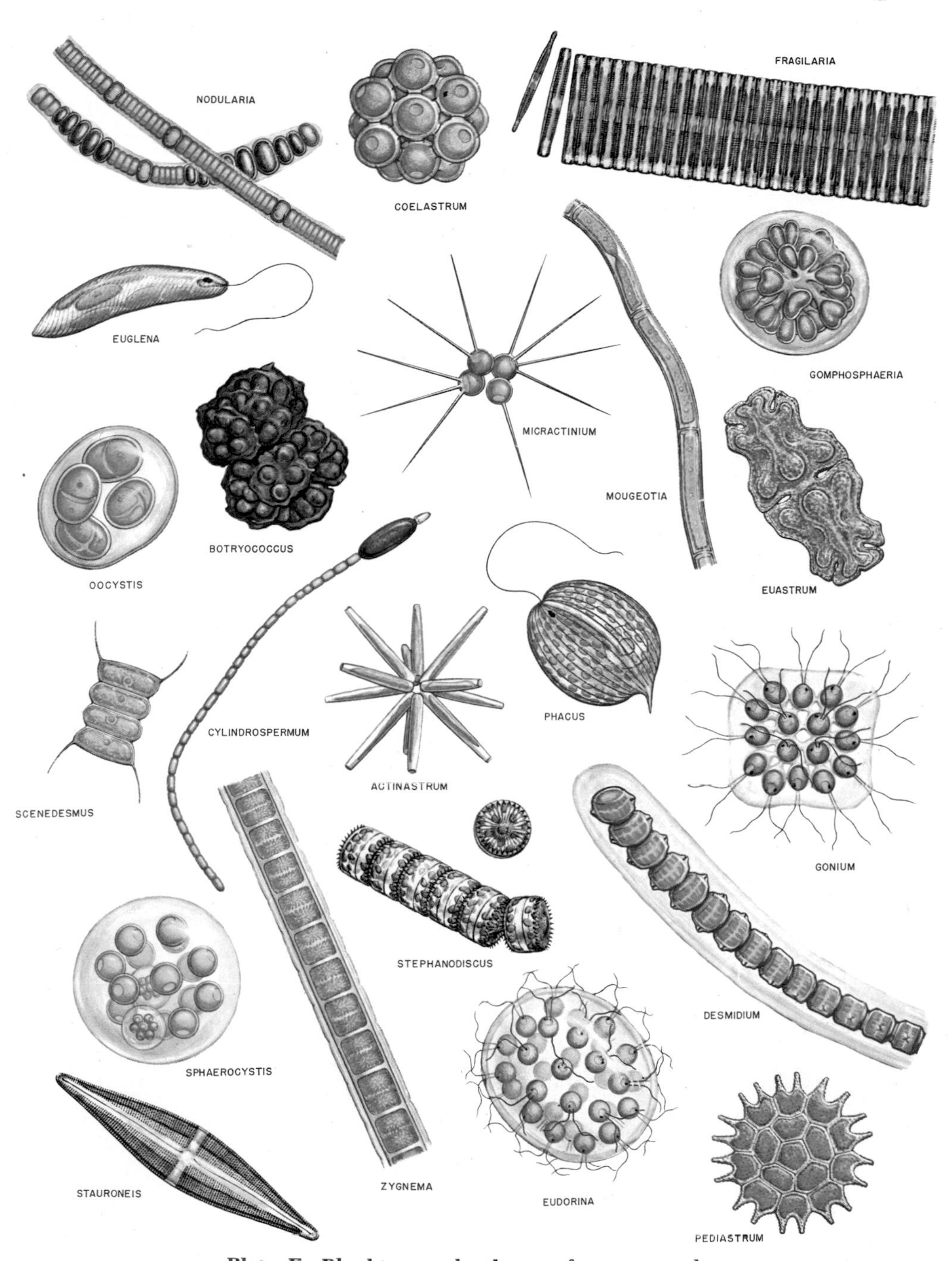

Plate E. Plankton and other surface water algae

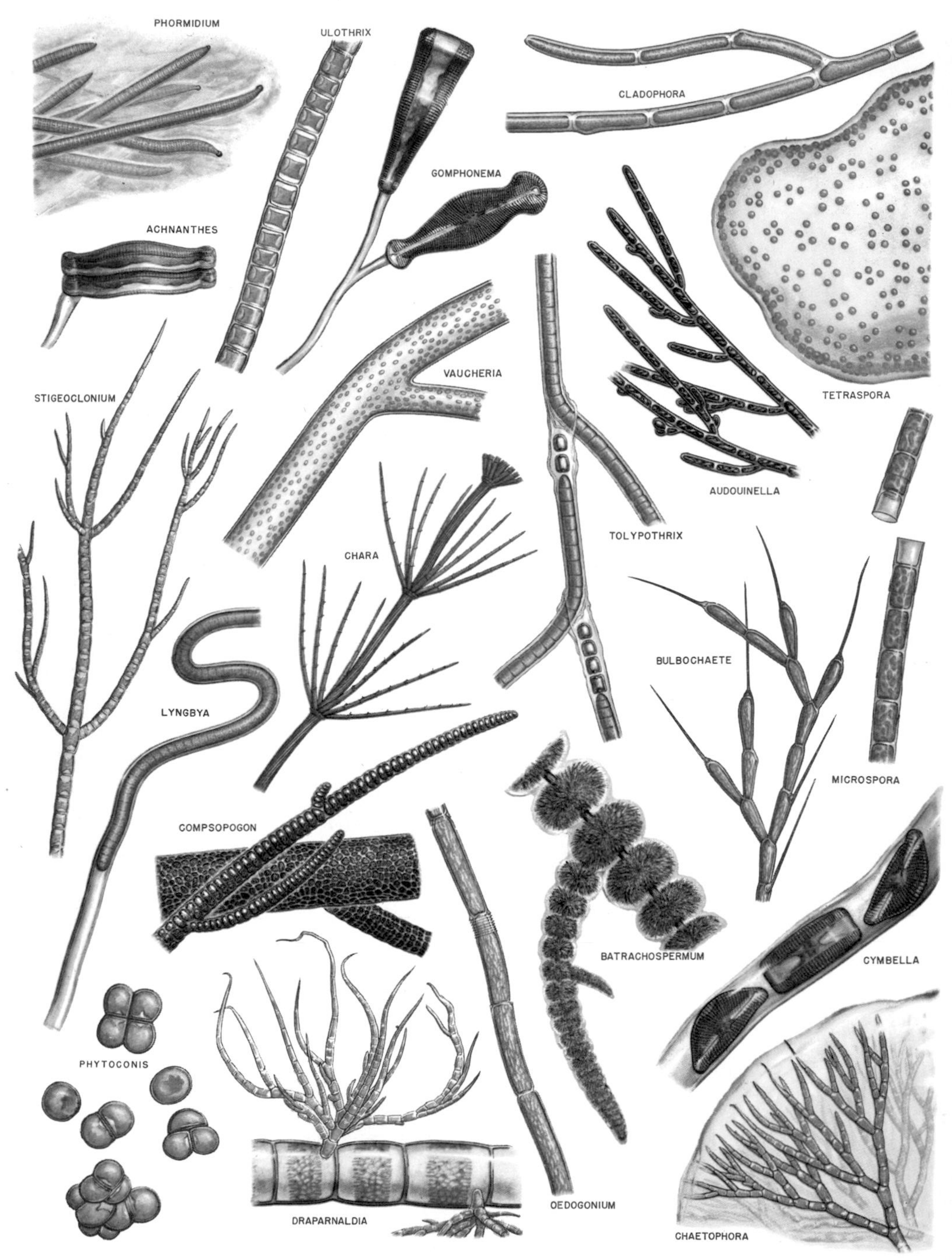

Plate F. Algae growing on reservoir walls

607 INDEX TO ILLUSTRATIONS

NOTE: Arabic numerals refer to black and white plate numbers, capital letters to color plates. See also "Recent Changes in Names of Algae," Section 606E preceding. Family names are not generally included.

608 SELECTED TAXONOMIC REFERENCES

1. General, Introductory

JAQUES, H. E. 1947. *Living Things: How To Know Them.* William C. Brown Co., Dubuque, Iowa.

MINER, R. W. 1950. *Field Book of Seashore Life.* G. P. Putnam's Sons, N. Y.

DAVIS, C. C. 1955. *The Marine and Fresh-Water Plankton.* Michigan State Univ. Press, East Lansing.

EDDY, S. & A. C. HODSON. 1961. *Taxonomic Keys to the Common Animals of the North Central States, Exclusive of the Parasite Worms, Insects, and Birds.* Burgess Pub. Co., Minneapolis, Minn.

HEDGPETH, J. & S. HINTON. 1961. *Common Seashore Life of Southern California.* Naturegraph Co., Healdsburg, Calif.

NEEDHAM, J. G. & P. R. NEEDHAM. 1962. *A Guide to the Study of Fresh-Water Biology* (5th ed.). Holden-Day Inc., San Francisco, Calif.

RICKETTS, E. F. & J. CALVIN. 1963. *Between Pacific Tides* (3d ed.). Revised by J. W. Hedgpeth. Stanford Univ. Press, Calif.

KLOTS, ELSIE B. 1966. *New Field Book of Freshwater Life.* G. P. Putnam's Sons, N. Y.

PIMENTEL, R. A. 1967. *Invertebrate Identification Manual.* Reinhold Pub. Corp., N. Y.

REID, G. K. 1967. *Pond Life. A Guide to Common Plants and Animals of North American Ponds and Lakes.* Golden Press, N. Y.

2. General, Advanced

PENNAK, R. W. 1953. *Fresh-Water Invertebrates of the United States.* The Ronald Press, N. Y.

EDMONDSON, W. T. Ed. 1959. *Ward and Whipple's Fresh Water Biology* (2nd ed.). John Wiley & Sons, N. Y.

BLAIR, W. F. *et al.* 1968. *Vertebrates of the United States.* McGraw-Hill, N. Y.

3. Algae, General

BRANDT, K. & C. APSTEIN. 1908. *Nordisches Plankton (Botanisher Teil).* Asher & Co., Amsterdam, reprinted in 1964.

SETCHELL, W. A. & N. L. GARDNER. 1919–1925. *The Marine Algae of the Pacific Coast of North America.* Univ. of California Publications in Botany No. 8 (Parts 1, 2, 3). J. Cramer, Weinheim, Germany. Reprinted in 1967.

DAWSON, E. Y. 1946. Marine algae of the Pacific Coast of North America. *Mem. Southern California Academy of Sciences* 3:2.

WHIPPLE, G. C. 1948. *The Microscopy of Drinking Water.* John Wiley & Sons, N. Y.

SMITH, G. M. 1950. *The Fresh-Water Algae of the United States.* McGraw-Hill, N. Y.

TIFFANY, L. H. & M. E. BRITTON. 1952. *The Algae of Illinois.* Univ. of Chicago Press, Chicago, Ill.

PRESCOTT, G. W. 1954. *How To Know the Fresh Water Algae.* Wm. C. Brown Co., Dubuque, Iowa.

FRITSCH, F. E. 1956. *The Structure and Reproduction of the Algae.* Vol. I: *Chlorophyceae, Xanthophyceae, Chrysophyceae, Bacillariophyceae, Cryptophyceae, Dinophyceae, Chloromonadineae, Euglenineae, and Colourless Flagellata.* Cambridge Univ. Press, Cambridge, England.

TAYLOR, W. R. 1957. *Marine Algae of the Northeastern Coast of North America* (2nd ed.). Univ. of Michigan Press, Ann Arbor.

PALMER, C. M. 1959. *Algae in Water Supplies.* USPHS Pub. No. 657, Washington, D. C.

GRIFFITH, R. E. 1961. "The Phytoplankton of Chesapeake Bay—An Illustrated Guide to the Genera." Chesapeake Biological Laboratory Contrib. No. 172.

PRESCOTT, G. W. 1962. *Algae of the Western Great Lakes Area* (rev. ed.). Wm. C. Brown Co., Dubuque, Iowa.

FRITSCH, F. E. 1965. *The Structure and Reproduction of the Algae.* Vol. II: *Phaeophyceae, Rhodophyceae, and Myxophyceae.* Cambridge Univ. Press, Cambridge, England.

ROUND, F. E. 1965. *The Biology of the Algae.* Edward Arnold, Ltd., London.

DAWSON, E. Y. 1966. *Marine Botany.* Holt, Rinehart & Winston, N. Y.

PRESCOTT, G. W. 1968. *The Algae: A Review.* Houghton Mifflin, Boston, Mass.

WOOD, R. D. & J. LUTES. 1968. *Guide to the Phytoplankton of Narragansett Bay, Rhode Island* (rev. ed.). Kingston Press, Kingston, R. I.

4. Blue-green Algae

GEITLER, L. 1930. "Cyanophyceae." In *Kryptogamenflora von Deutschland, Osterreich, und der Schweiz* (L. Rabenhorst, Ed.). Akad. Verlags., Leipsig. Reprinted in 1961.

HUBER-PESTALOZZI, G. 1938. "Blue-Green Algae, Bacteria and Aquatic Fungi." In *Die Binnengewasser*. Part 1: *Das Phytoplankton des Susswassers* (A. Thienemann, Ed.). E. Schweizerbart'sche Verlagsbuchhandlung, Stuttgart, Germany. Reprinted in 1962.

SMITH, G. W. 1950. *The Fresh-Water Algae of the United States*. McGraw-Hill, N. Y.

TIFFANY, L. H. & M. E. BRITTON. 1952. *The Algae of Illinois*. Univ. of Chicago Press, Chicago, Ill.

DROUET, F. & W. A. DAILY. 1956. Revision of the Coccoid Myxophyceae. *Butler Univ. Bot. Studies* XII.

DESIKACHARY, T. V. 1959. *Cyanophyta*. Indian Council on Agricultural Research, New Delhi.

GEITLER, L. 1960. "Schizophyzeen." In *Encyclopedia of Plant Anatomy* (W. Zimmermann and P. Ozeuda, Eds.). Gebruder Borntraeger, Berlin, Vol. 6, Part 1.

HUMM, H. J. 1962. *Key to the Genera of Marine Bluegreen Algae of Southeastern North America*. Virginia Fisheries Laboratory Special Science Report No. 28.

PRESCOTT, G. W. 1962. *Algae of the Western Great Lakes Area* (rev. ed.). Wm. C. Brown Co., Dubuque, Iowa.

WELCH, H. 1964. An Introduction to the Blue-Green Algae, with a Dichotomous Key to all the Genera. *Limnol. Soc. S. Africa News Letter* 1:25.

DROUET, F. 1968. Revision of the classification of the Oscillatoriaceae. *Philadelphia Academy of Natural Sciences Monogr. 15*.

5. Green Algae

COLLINS, F. S. 1909. *The Green Algae of North America*. Tufts College Studies. Scientific Series 2:79.

TIFFANY, L. H. 1937. "Oedogoniales, Oedogoniaceae." In *North American Flora* (New York Botanical Gardens) Hafner Pub. Co., N. Y. 11(1):1.

SMITH, G. M. 1950. *The Fresh-Water Algae of the United States*. McGraw-Hill, N. Y.

TRANSEAU, E. N. 1951. *The Zygnemataceae*. Ohio State Univ. Press, Columbus.

TIFFANY, L. H. & M. E. BRITTON. 1952. *The Algae of Illinois*. Univ. of Chicago Press, Chicago, Ill.

RANDHAWA, M. S. 1959. *Zygnemaceae*. Indian Council on Agricultural Research, New Delhi.

HIRN, K. E. 1960. *Monograph of the Oedogoniaceae*. Hafner Pub. Co., N. Y.

PAL, B. P., B. C. KUNDU, U. S. SUNDARALINGAM & G. S. VENKATARAMAN. 1962. *Charophyta*. Indian Council on Agricultural Research, New Delhi.

PRESCOTT, G. W. 1962. *Algae of the Western Great Lakes Area* (rev. ed.). Wm. C. Brown Co., Dubuque, Iowa.

ISLAM, A. K. M. 1963. A revision of the genus *Stigeoclonium*. *Nova Hedwigia* (Supplement) 10:1.

SODERSTROM, J. 1963. *Studies in Cladophora*. Almquist Pub. Co., Uppsala, Sweden.

VAN DER HOEK, C. 1963. *Revision of the European Species of Cladophora*. Brill Pub. Co., Leiden, Netherlands.

RAMANATHAN, K. R. 1964. *Ulotrichales*. Indian Council on Agricultural Research, New Delhi.

WOOD, R. D. & K. IMAHARI. 1964. *A Revision of the Characeae*. Vols. I, II. Monograph and Iconograph. J. Cramer Pub. Co., Weinheim, Germany.

6. Flagellates

KOFOID, C. A. & O. SWEZY. 1921. *The Free-Living Unarmored Dinoflagellata*. Univ. of California Press, Berkeley, Calif.

SKVORTZOW, B. V. 1925. The euglenoid genus *Trachelomonas* Ehr. Systematic review. *Proc. Sungari River Sta.* 1:1.

DEFLANDRE, G. 1926. *Monographie du genre Trachelomonas. Ehr.* Nemours: Impremerie André Lesot.

HUBER-PESTALOZZI, G. 1938. "Chrysophyceen. Farblose Flagellaten Heterokonten." In *Die Binnengewasser*. Vol. 16. *Das Phytoplankton des Susswassers*. Part 2 (A. Thienemann, Ed.). E.

Schweizerbart'sche Verlagsbuchhandlung, Stuttgart, Germany. Reprinted in 1962.

ALLEGRE, C. F. & T. L. JAHN. 1943. A survey of the Genus *Phacus* Dumardin. *Tr. Amer. Microscop. Soc.* 62:233.

GRAHAM, H. W. & N. BRONIKOVSKY. 1944. *The Genus Ceratium in the Pacific and North Atlantic Oceans.* Pub. No. 565, Carnegie Institute, Washington, D. C.

HUBER-PESTALOZZI, G. 1950. "Chryptophyceen, Chloromonadinen. Peridineen." In *Die Binnengewasser.* Vol. 16. *Das Phytoplankton des Susswassers.* Part 3 (A. Thienemann, Ed.). E. Schweizerbart'sche Verlagsbuchhandlung, Stuttgart, Germany. Reprinted in 1962.

SMITH, G. M. 1950. The *Fresh-Water Algae of the United States.* McGraw-Hill, N. Y.

TIFFANY, L. H. & M. E. BRITTON. 1952. *The Algae of Illinois.* Univ. of Chicago Press. Chicago, Ill.

GOJDICS, M. 1953. *The Genus Euglena.* Univ. of Wisconsin Press, Madison.

HUBER-PESTALOZZI, G. 1955. "Euglenophyceen." In *Die Binnengewasser.* Vol. 16. *Das Phytoplankton des Susswassers.* Part 4. (A. Thienemann, Ed.). E. Schweizerbart'sche Verlagsbuchhandlung, Stuttgart, Germany. Reprinted in 1962.

———. 1938. "Chlorophyceae; Ordnung Volvocales." In *Die Binnengewasser.* Vol. 16. Part 5: *Das Phytoplankton des Susswassers.* (A. Thienemann, Ed.). E. Schweizerbart'sche Verlagsbuchhandlung, Stuttgart, Germany. Reprinted in 1962.

PRESCOTT, C. W. 1962. *Algae of the Western Great Lakes Area* (rev. ed.). Wm. C. Brown Co., Dubuque, Iowa.

7. Diatoms

CLEVE, P. T. 1894–1896. *The Naviculoid Diatoms.* Asher & Co., Amsterdam. Reprinted in 1965.

VAN HEURCH, H. 1896. *A Treatise on the Diatomaceae.* Weldon & Wesley, Ltd., Herts, England. Reprinted in 1962.

BOYER, C. S. 1916. *The Diatomaceae of Philadelphia and Vicinity.* Reproduced in Xerox by University Microfilms, Ann Arbor, Mich.

ELMORE, C. J. 1922. *The Diatoms of Nebraska.* Univ. of Nebraska Series, Lincoln, 21(1–4).

BOYER, C. S. 1927. Synopsis of North American Diatomaceae. *Proc. Acad. Nat. Sci., Philadelphia,* Vol. 79.

GRAN, H. H. & E. C. ANGST. 1930. *Plankton Diatoms of Puget Sound.* Univ. of Washington, Seattle, Wash.

HUSTEDT, F. 1930. "The Diatoms." In *Kryptogamenflora von Deutschland, Osterreich und der Schweiz.* (L. Rabenhorst, Ed). Geest and Partig K-G, Leipzig, Germany, Parts 1, 2 and 3.

———. 1930. "Bacillariophyta." In *Die Susswasserflora Mitteleuropas* (A. Pascher, Ed.). Vol. 10. Reproduced in Xerox by University Microfilms, Ann Arbor, Mich.

HUBER-PESTALOZZI, G. 1942. "The Diatoms." In *Die Binnengewasser.* Part 1: *Das Phytoplankton des Susswassers* (A. Thienemann, Ed.). E. Schweizerbart'sche Verlagsbuchhandlung, Stuttgart, Germany. Reprinted in 1962.

CUPP, E. E. 1943. *The Marine Plankton Diatoms of the West Coast of North America.* Reproduced in Xerox by University Microfilms, Ann Arbor, Mich.

TIFFANY, L. H. & M. E. BRITTON. 1952. *The Algae of Illinois.* Univ. of Chicago Press, Chicago, Ill.

CLEVE-EULER, A. 1953. *The Diatoms of Sweden and Finland.* Almquest & Wiksells, Stockholm, Sweden.

HUSTEDT, F. 1955. Marine littoral diatoms, Beaufort, North Carolina. *Duke Univ. Marine Sta. Bull.* 6:5.

VAN DER WERFF, A. & H. HULS. 1957–1966. *Diatomenenflora van Nederlands,* Parts 1–8. Published by the author, De Hoef, Netherlands.

MULFORD, R. A. 1962. *Diatoms from Virginia Tidal Waters.* Virginia Institute of Marine Science Special Science Report No. 30.

HENDY, N. I. 1964. *An Introductory Account of the Smaller Algae of British Coastal Waters.* Part V: *Bacillariophyceae (Diatoms).* Fishery Invest. Series IV, Her Majesty's Stationery Office, London.

CHOLNOKY, B. J. 1966. *Diatomaceae,* Vol. I. Krebs, Weinheim, Germany.

PATRICK, R. & C. W. REIMER. 1966. *The Diatoms of the United States,* Vol. I, Philadelphia Academy of Natural Sciences Monogr. No. 13, Philadelphia, Pa.

WEBER, C. I. 1966. *A Guide to the Common Diatoms at Water Pollution Sur-*

veillance Stations. U.S. Dept. Interior, FWPCA, Cincinnati, Ohio.

8. Higher Plants, Introductory

EYLES, D. E. & J. L. ROBERTSON. 1963. Guide and key to the aquatic plants of the southeastern United States. U.S. Fish & Wildlife Service Circular 158.

HOTCHKISS, NEIL. 1967. *Underwater and Floating-Leaved Plants of the United States and Canada.* U.S. Fish & Wildlife Service Resource Pub. No. 44.

WELDON, L. W. 1969. *Common Aquatic Weeds.* U.S. Dept. Agriculture Agr. Handbook No. 352.

9. Higher Plants, Advanced

MUENSCHER, W. C. 1944. *Aquatic Plants of the United States.* Comstock Pub. Co., Ithaca, N. Y.

OGDEN, E. C. 1953. Key to the North American species of *Potamogeton. Circ. N. Y. State Mus.* 31:1.

FASSETT, N. C. 1960. *A Manual of Aquatic Plants* (with a revision appendix by E. C. Ogden). Univ. of Wisconsin Press, Madison.

SCULTHORPE, C. D. 1967. *The Biology of Aquatic Vascular Plants.* St. Martin's Press, N. Y.

10. General Invertebrates, Introductory

BUCHSBAUM, R. M. & L. J. MILNE. 1960. *The Lower Animals, Living Invertebrates of the World.* Chanticleer Press, Garden City, N. Y.

HICKMAN, C. P. 1967. *Biology of the Invertebrates.* C. V. Mosby, St. Louis, Mo.

11. General Invertebrates, Advanced

PRATT, H. S. 1951. *A Manual of the Common Invertebrate Animals Exclusive of Insects.* The Blakiston Co., Philadelphia, Pa.

PENNAK, R. W. 1953. *Fresh-Water Invertebrates of the United States.* The Ronald Press Co., N. Y.

LIGHT, S. F., R. I. SMITH, F. A. PITELKA, D. P. ABBOTT & F. M. WEESNER. 1961. *Intertidal Invertebrates of the Central California Coast.* Univ. of California Press, Berkeley.

12. Protozoa

JAHN, T. L. & F. F. JAHN. 1949. *How To Know the Protozoa.* Wm. C. Brown Co., Dubuque, Iowa.

KUDO, R. 1950. *Protozoology.* Charles C Thomas, Springfield, Ill.

CORLISS, J. O. 1961. *Ciliated Protozoa: Characterization, Classification, and Guide to the Literature.* Pergamon Press, N. Y.

CALAWAY, W. T. & J. B. LACKEY. 1962. *Waste Treatment Protozoa, Flagellata.* Univ. of Florida, Florida Eng. Series No. 3.

13. Sponges and Bryozoa

DELAUBENFELS, M. W. 1953. *Guide to the Sponges of Eastern North America.* Univ. of Miami, Coral Gables, Fla.

ROGICK, MARY DORA. 1960. Ectoprocta. *McGraw-Hill Encyc. Sci. Tech.* 5:7.

———. 1960. Bryozoa. *McGraw-Hill Encyc. Sci. Tech.* 2:354.

BUSHNELL, J. H., JR. 1965. On the taxonomy and distribution of the freshwater Ectoprocta in Michigan (Parts I–III). *Tr. Amer. Microscop. Soc.* 84:231; 339; 529.

PENNEY, J. T. & A. A. RACEK. 1968. *Comprehensive Revision of a Worldwide Collection of Freshwater Sponges. (Porifera: Spongillidae).* USNM Bull. 272.

14. Rotifers

VOIGT, MAX. 1957. *Rotataria—Die Radertiere. Mitteleuropas.* Borntraeger, Berlin, Vols. I and II.

DONNER, JOSEF. 1966. *Rotifers.* Warne, London & N. Y.

15. Roundworms (Nemathelminthes)

CHITWOOD, B. G. 1951. North American marine nematodes. *Texas J. Sci.* 3:617.

GOODEY, T. 1963. *Soil and Freshwater Nematodes* (revised by J. B. Goodey). John Wiley & Sons, N. Y.

WIESER, W. & B. E. HOPPER. 1967. Marine nematodes of the East Coast of North America. 1. *Florida Bull. Mus. Comp. Zool.* 135:239.

16. Segmented Worms (Annelids)

SPERBER, CHRISTINA. 1948. *A Taxonomical Study of the Naididae.* Zool. Bidrag Fran Uppsala, Sweden. Band. 28.

BRINKHURST, R. O. 1964–1966. Studies on the North American aquatic Oligochaeta: I. Naididae and Opistocystidae; II Tubificidae; III Lumbriculidae and Additional Notes and Records of other Families. *Proc. Acad. Nat. Sci. Philadelphia* 116:195; 117:117; 118:1.

———. 1966. Detection and assessment of water pollution using oligochaete worms. *Water & Sewage Works* 113:398, 438, Parts I and II.

17. Flatworms (Platyhelminthes)

EDMONDSON, W. T., Ed. 1959. *Ward and Whipple's Fresh Water Biology* (2nd ed.). John Wiley & Sons, N. Y.

18. Crustaceans

HOBBS, H. H., JR. 1942. The crayfishes of Florida. *Univ. Florida Pub. Biol. Sci. Series* 3:1.

HUBRICHT, LESLIE & J. G. MACKIN. 1949. The freshwater isopods of the genus *Lirceus* (Asellota, Asellidae). *Amer. Mid. Nat.* 42:334.

BOUSFIELD, E. L. 1958. Freshwater amphipod crustaceans of glaciated North America. *Can. Field Nat.* 72:55.

WATERMAN, T. H. 1960. *The Physiology of Crustacea.* Vol. I. *Metabolism and Growth.* Academic Press, N. Y.

19. Insects, General and Introductory

LUTZ, P. E. 1927. *Field Book of Insects.* G. P. Putnam's Sons, N. Y.

CHU, H. F. 1949. *How To Know the Immature Insects.* Wm. C. Brown Co., Dubuque, Iowa.

USINGER, R. L. 1956. *Aquatic Insects of California, with Keys to North American Genera and California Species.* Univ. of California Press, Berkeley.

20. Stoneflies (Plecoptera)

NEEDHAM, J. G. & P. W. CLAASEN. 1925. *A Monograph of the Plecoptera or Stoneflies of America North of Mexico,* Vol. 2. Thomas Say Foundation, Lafayette, Ind.

FRISON, T. H. 1935. The stoneflies, or Plecoptera, of Illinois. *Bull. Illinois Nat. Hist. Survey* 20:281.

———. 1942. Studies of North American Plecoptera, with special reference to the fauna of Illinois. *Bull. Illinois Nat. Hist. Survey* 22:235.

JEWETT, S. G. 1960. The stoneflies (Plecoptera) of California. *Bull. Calif. Insect Survey* 6:125.

21. Mayflies (Ephemeroptera)

NEEDHAM, J. G., J. R. TRAVER & Y. HSU. 1935. *The Biology of Mayflies.* Comstock Pub. Co., Ithaca, N. Y.

BERNER, L. 1950. *The Mayflies of Florida.* Univ. of Florida Press, Gainesville.

BURKS, B. D. 1953. The mayflies, or Ephemeroptera, of Illinois. *Bull. Illinois Nat. Hist. Survey* 26:1.

BERNER, L. 1959. A tabular summary of the biology of North American mayfly nymphs (Ephemeroptera). *Bull. Florida State Mus.* (Gainesville) 4:1.

EDMONDS, G. F., R. K. ALLEN & W. L. PETERS. 1963. An annotated key to the nymphs of the families and subfamilies of mayflies (Ephemeroptera). *Univ. Utah Biol. Series* 13:1.

22. Dragonflies and Damselflies (Odonata)

NEEDHAM, J. G. & M. J. WESTFALL, JR. 1955. *A Manual of the Dragonflies of North America, Including the Greater Antilles and the Provinces of the Mexican Border.* Univ. of California Press, Berkeley.

WALKER, E. M. 1958. *The Odonata of Canada and Alaska,* Vols. I and II. Univ. of Toronto Press, Toronto, Canada.

23. Hellgrammites and Relatives

PENNAK, R. W. 1953. *Fresh-water Invertebrates of the United States.* The Ronald Press, N. Y.

EDMONDSON, W. T., Ed. 1959. *Ward and Whipple's Fresh Water Biology* (2nd ed.). John Wiley & Sons, N. Y.

24. Caddisflies (Trichoptera)

ROSS, H. H. 1944. The caddis flies, or Trichoptera, of Illinois. *Bull. Illinois Nat. Hist. Survey* 23:1.

FLINT, O. S., JR. 1962. Taxonomy and biology of nearctic limnephilid larvae (Trichoptera), with special reference to species found in eastern United States. *Entomol. Amer.* 40:1.

25. Two-Winged Flies (Diptera)

JOHANNSEN, O. A. 1933, 1935, 1936, 1937. Memoirs of the Cornell University Agricultural Experiment Station. Parts I–IV. (Part V by L. C. Thomsen.) Reproduced in 1969 by *Ent. Reprint Specialists,* East Lansing, Mich.

ROBACK, S. S. 1957. *The Immature Tendipedids of the Philadelphia Area.* Philadelphia Academy of Natural Sciences Monogr. No. 9.

BECK, W. M., JR. & ELISABETH C. BECK. 1966. Chironomidae (Diptera) of Florida. I: Pentaneurini (Tanypodinae). *Bull. Florida State Mus.* 10:305.

MASON, W. T. 1968. *An Introduction to the Identification of Chironomid Larvae.* Federal Water Pollution Control Administration, Washington, D. C.

SNODDY, E. L. 1969. Simuliidae of Alabama. *Alabama Agr. Exp. Sta. Bull.* 390.

26. Beetles (Coleoptera)

JAQUES, H. E. 1951. *How To Know the Beetles.* Wm. C. Brown, Dubuque, Iowa.

YOUNG, F. N. 1954. *Water Beetles of Florida.* Univ. of Florida Press, Gainesville.

DILLON, E. S. & L. S. DILLON. 1961. *Manual of Common Beetles of Eastern North America.* Harper and Row, N. Y.

27. True Bugs (Hemiptera)

PENNAK, R. W. 1953. *Fresh-Water Invertebrates of the United States.* The Ronald Press, N. Y.

EDMONDSON, W. T., Ed. 1959. *Ward and Whipple's Fresh Water Biology* (2nd ed.). John Wiley & Sons, N. Y.

28. Mollusks, General and Introductory

PENNAK, R. W. 1953. *Fresh-Water Invertebrates of the United States.* The Ronald Press, N. Y.

EDMONDSON, W. T., Ed. 1959. *Ward and Whipple's Fresh Water Biology* (2nd ed.). John Wiley & Sons, N. Y.

29. Snails (Gastropoda)

BAKER, F. C. 1928. The fresh-water mollusca of Wisconsin. Part I. Gastropoda. *Wisconsin Geol. Nat. Hist. Survey Bull.* No. 70.

KEEN, A. M. & J. C. PEARSON. 1952. *Illustrated Key to West North American Gastropod Genera.* Stanford Univ. Press, Stanford, Calif.

WALTER, HAROLD J. & J. B. BURCH. 1957. Key to the Genera of Freshwater Gastropods (Snails and Limpets) Occurring in Michigan. Museum of Zoology, Univ. of Michigan Circular No. 3.

LEONARD, A. B. 1959. *Handbook of Gastropods in Kansas.* Univ. of Kansas Museum of Natural History Misc. Pub. No. 20.

LAROCQUE, AURELE. 1968. Pleistocene mollusca of Ohio. *Ohio Geol. Survey Bull.* 62:357.

30. Bivalves (Pelecypoda)

WALKER, B. 1918. *A Synopsis of the Classification of Freshwater Mollusca of North America, North of Mexico, and a Catalogue of the More Recently Described Species, with notes.* Museum of Zoology, Univ. of Michigan Misc. Pub. No. 6.

BAKER, F. C. 1928. The fresh-water mollusca of Wisconsin. Part II. Pelecypoda. *Wisconsin Geol. Nat. Hist. Survey Bull.* No. 70.

KEEN, A. M. & D. FRIZZELL. 1946. *Illustrated Key to West North American Pelecepod Genera.* Stanford Univ. Press, Stanford, Calif.

MURRAY, H. D. & A. B. LEONARD. 1962. *Handbook of Unionid Mussels in Kansas.* Univ. of Kansas Museum of Natural History Misc. Pub. No. 28.

HERRINGTON, H. B. 1962. *A Revision of the Sphaeriidae of North America (Mollusca: Pelecypoda).* Univ. of Michigan Museum of Zoology Misc. Pub. No. 118.

NEEL, J. K. & W. R. ALLEN. 1963. The mussel fauna of the Upper Cumberland Basin before its impoundment. *Malacologia* 1:427.

HEARD, W. H. & J. BURCH. 1966. *Keys to the Genera of Freshwater Pelecypods of*

Michigan. Museum of Zoology, Univ. of Michigan Circular No. 4.

LaRocque, Aurele. 1967. Pleistocene mollusca of Ohio. *Ohio Geol. Survey Bull.* No. 62.

31. Echinoderms

Miner, R. W. 1950. *Field Book of Seashore Life.* G. P. Putnam's Sons, N. Y.

Harvey, E. B. 1956. *The American Arbacia and Other Sea Urchins.* Princeton Univ. Press, Princeton, N. J.

32. Fishes

Walford, L. A. 1937. *Marine Game Fishes of the Pacific Coast from Alaska to the Equator.* Univ. of California Press, Berkeley.

Breder, C. M. 1948. *Fieldbook of Marine Fishes.* G. P. Putnam's Sons, N. Y.

Eddy, Samuel. 1957. *How To Know the Freshwater Fishes.* Wm. C. Brown Co., Dubuque, Iowa.

Trautman, M. B. 1957. *The Fishes of Ohio.* Ohio State Univ. Press, Columbus.

Bailey, R. M., *et al.* 1960. A list of common and scientific names of fishes from the United States and Canada. *American Fisheries Society Special Pub.* No. 2.

Perlmutter, A. 1961. *Guide to Marine Fishes.* New York Univ. Press, N. Y.

Hubbs, C. L. & K. F. Lagler. 1964. *Fishes of the Great Lakes Region.* Univ. of Michigan Press, Ann Arbor.

Cross, F. B. 1967. *Handbook of Fishes of Kansas.* Univ. of Kansas Museum of Natural History, Lawrence, Kans.

Blair, W. F. & G. A. Moore. 1968. "Fishes." In *Vertebrates of the United States* (2d ed.). McGraw-Hill, N. Y.

33. Amphibians

Bishop, S. C. 1943. *Handbook of Salamanders.* Comstock Pub. Co., Ithaca, N. Y.

Conant, Roger. 1958. *Field Guide to the Reptiles and Amphibians of Eastern North America.* Houghton-Mifflin, N. Y.

Brandon, R. A. 1961. A comparison of the larvae of five Northeastern species of *Ambystoma* (Amphibia, Caudata). *Copeia* 4:377.

———. 1964. An annotated and illustrated key to multistage larvae of Ohio salamanders. *Ohio J. Sci.* 64:252.

Blair, W. F. *et al.* 1968. *Vertebrates of the United States.* McGraw-Hill, N. Y.

34. Bacteria and Fungi

Breed, R. S., E. G. D. Murray & N. R. Smith. 1957. *Bergey's Manual of Determinative Bacteriology* (7th ed.). Williams & Wilkins, Baltimore, Md.

Cooke, W. B. 1963. *A Laboratory Guide to Fungi in Polluted Waters.* USPHS, Cincinnati, Ohio.

Johnson, T. W., Jr. 1968. "Saprobic Marine Fungi." In *The Fungi,* Vol. III. (G. C. Ainsworth & A. S. Sussman, Eds.). Academic Press, N. Y.

INDEX

B

C

E

F

G

K

L

N

O

P

Q

R

S

U

V

W

X

Y

Z

ABBREVIATIONS

The following symbols and abbreviations are employed throughout this manual:

Abbreviation	*Referent*
A or amp	ampere(s)
Å	angstrom(s); 10^{-7} mm
a.c.	alternating current
ACS	American Chemical Society
AJPH	American Journal of Public Health
APHA	American Public Health Association
ASTM	American Society for Testing and Materials
AWWA	American Water Works Association
BOD	biochemical oxygen demand
C	degree(s) Centigrade
c	count(s)
cc	cubic centimeter(s)
CAE	carbon alcohol extract
CCE	carbon chloroform extract
cfs	cubic feet per second
Ci	curie(s)
CIE	International Commission on Illumination
cm	centimeter(s)
COD	chemical oxygen demand
Col.	column(s)
conc	concentrated
cpm	counts per minute
cps	centipoises or counts per second
cu ft	cubic foot (feet)
d.c.	direct current
DO	dissolved oxygen
dpm	disintegration(s) per minute
EDTA	ethylenediamine tetraacetic acid (or its salts)
F	degree(s) Fahrenheit
ft	foot (feet)
fps	feet per second
g	gram(s)
gal	gallon(s)
gph	gallons per hour
gpm	gallons per minute
hr	hour(s)
I	electrical current
I.D.	inside diameter
IDOD	immediate dissolved oxygen demand
in.	inch(es)
JAWWA	Journal of the American Water Works Association
JWPCF	Journal of the Water Pollution Control Federation
K	degree(s) Kelvin
KeV	kiloelectron volt(s)
l	liter(s)
LAS	linear alkylate sulfonate
lb	pound(s)
LC	lethal concentration
LD	lethal dose
μ	micron(s)
μA	microampere(s)
μCi	microcurie(s)
μg	microgram(s)
μl	microliter(s)
μmho	micromho(s)
μS	microSiemen(s)
m	meter(s)
M	molar
me	milliequivalent(s)